List of Elements with Their Symbols and Atomic Weights

Element	Symbol	Atomic Number	Atomic Weight
Actinium	Ac	89	227.03[a]
Aluminum	Al	13	26.981538
Americium	Am	95	243.06[a]
Antimony	Sb	51	121.760
Argon	Ar	18	39.948
Arsenic	As	33	74.92160
Astatine	At	85	209.99[a]
Barium	Ba	56	137.327
Berkelium	Bk	97	247.07[a]
Beryllium	Be	4	9.012182
Bismuth	Bi	83	208.98038
Bohrium	Bh	107	264.12[a]
Boron	B	5	10.811
Bromine	Br	35	79.904
Cadmium	Cd	48	112.411
Calcium	Ca	20	40.078
Californium	Cf	98	251.08[a]
Carbon	C	6	12.0107
Cerium	Ce	58	140.116
Cesium	Cs	55	132.90545
Chlorine	Cl	17	35.453
Chromium	Cr	24	51.9961
Cobalt	Co	27	58.933200
Copernicium	Cn	112	285
Copper	Cu	29	63.546
Curium	Cm	96	247.07[a]
Darmstadtium	Ds	110	281.15[a]
Dubnium	Db	105	262.11[a]
Dysprosium	Dy	66	162.50
Einsteinium	Es	99	252.08[a]
Erbium	Er	68	167.259
Europium	Eu	63	151.964
Fermium	Fm	100	257.10[a]
Fluorine	F	9	18.9984032
Francium	Fr	87	223.02[a]
Gadolinium	Gd	64	157.25
Gallium	Ga	31	69.723
Germanium	Ge	32	72.64
Gold	Au	79	196.96655

Element	Symbol	Atomic Number	Atomic Weight
Hafnium	Hf	72	178.49
Hassium	Hs	108	269.13[a]
Helium	He	2	4.002602[a]
Holmium	Ho	67	164.93032
Hydrogen	H	1	1.00794
Indium	In	49	114.818
Iodine	I	53	126.90447
Iridium	Ir	77	192.217
Iron	Fe	26	55.845
Krypton	Kr	36	83.80
Lanthanum	La	57	138.9055
Lawrencium	Lr	103	262.11[a]
Lead	Pb	82	207.2
Lithium	Li	3	6.941
Lutetium	Lu	71	174.967
Magnesium	Mg	12	24.3050
Manganese	Mn	25	54.938049
Meitnerium	Mt	109	268.14[a]
Mendelevium	Md	101	258.10[a]
Mercury	Hg	80	200.59
Molybdenum	Mo	42	95.94
Neodymium	Nd	60	144.24
Neon	Ne	10	20.1797
Neptunium	Np	93	237.05[a]
Nickel	Ni	28	58.6934
Niobium	Nb	41	92.90638
Nitrogen	N	7	14.0067
Nobelium	No	102	259.10[a]
Osmium	Os	76	190.23
Oxygen	O	8	15.9994
Palladium	Pd	46	106.42
Phosphorus	P	15	30.973761
Platinum	Pt	78	195.078
Plutonium	Pu	94	244.06[a]
Polonium	Po	84	208.98[a]
Potassium	K	19	39.0983
Praseodymium	Pr	59	140.90765
Promethium	Pm	61	145[a]
Protactinium	Pa	91	231.03588
Radium	Ra	88	226.03[a]

Element	Symbol	Atomic Number	Atomic Weight
Radon	Rn	86	222.02[a]
Rhenium	Re	75	186.207[a]
Rhodium	Rh	45	102.90550
Roentgenium	Rg	111	272.15[a]
Rubidium	Rb	37	85.4678
Ruthenium	Ru	44	101.07
Rutherfordium	Rf	104	261.11[a]
Samarium	Sm	62	150.36
Scandium	Sc	21	44.955910
Seaborgium	Sg	106	266[a]
Selenium	Se	34	78.96
Silicon	Si	14	28.0855
Silver	Ag	47	107.8682
Sodium	Na	11	22.989770
Strontium	Sr	38	87.62
Sulfur	S	16	32.065
Tantalum	Ta	73	180.9479
Technetium	Tc	43	98[a]
Tellurium	Te	52	127.60
Terbium	Tb	65	158.92534
Thallium	Tl	81	204.3833
Thorium	Th	90	232.0381
Thulium	Tm	69	168.93421
Tin	Sn	50	118.710
Titanium	Ti	22	47.867
Tungsten	W	74	183.84
Uranium	U	92	238.02891
Vanadium	V	23	50.9415
Xenon	Xe	54	131.293
Ytterbium	Yb	70	173.04
Yttrium	Y	39	88.90585
Zinc	Zn	30	65.39
Zirconium	Zr	40	91.224
*	[b]	113	284[a]
*	[b]	114	289[a]
*	[b]	115	288[a]
*	[b]	116	292[a]
*	[b]	117	294[a]
*	[b]	118	294[a]

[a]Mass of longest-lived or most important isotope.
[b]The names of elements 113 and above have not yet been decided.

Chemistry
Volume 1

Third Custom Edition for University of North Carolina Wilmington

Taken from:
Chemistry: The Central Science, Twelfth Edition
by Theodore L. Brown, H. Eugene LeMay, Jr., Bruce E. Bursten,
Catherine J. Murphy, and Patrick M. Woodward

A Short Guide to Writing About Chemistry
by Holly B. Davis, Julia F. Tyson, and Jan A. Pechenik

Pearson Learning Solutions, 501 Boylston Street, Suite 900, Boston, MA 02116
A Pearson Education Company
www.pearsoned.com

Printed in the United States of America

1 2 3 4 5 6 7 8 9 10 V363 17 16 15 14 13

000200010271788931

CW

ISBN 10: 1-269-42228-6
ISBN 13: 978-1-269-42228-4

To our students,
whose enthusiasm and curiosity
have often inspired us,
and whose questions and suggestions
have sometimes taught us.

BRIEF CONTENTS

Taken from: *Chemistry: The Central Science*, Twelfth Edition
by Theodore L. Brown, H. Eugene LeMay, Jr., Bruce E. Bursten,
Catherine J. Murphy, and Patrick M. Woodward

Taken from: *A Short Guide to Writing About Chemistry*
by Holly B. Davis, Julia F. Tyson, and Jan A. Pechenik

CONTENTS

3 STOICHIOMETRY: CALCULATIONS WITH CHEMICAL FORMULAS AND EQUATIONS 76

4 REACTIONS IN AQUEOUS SOLUTION 114

5 THERMOCHEMISTRY 158

6 ELECTRONIC STRUCTURE OF ATOMS 206

7 PERIODIC PROPERTIES OF THE ELEMENTS 248

8 BASIC CONCEPTS OF CHEMICAL BONDING   288

9 MOLECULAR GEOMETRY AND BONDING THEORIES 330

11 LIQUIDS AND INTERMOLECULAR FORCES 424

Appendices

Taken from: *A Short Guide to Writing About Chemistry* by Holly B. Davis, Julia F. Tyson, and Jan A. Pechenik

7 WRITING LABORATORY REPORTS 111

CHEMICAL APPLICATIONS AND ESSAYS

PREFACE

TO THE INSTRUCTOR

Philosophy

The cover of this new edition of *Chemistry: The Central Science* features a striking illustration of the structure of graphene, a recently discovered form of carbon. As we began preparing the previous edition in 2006, single-layer graphene was virtually unknown. The extraordinary properties of graphene, and its promise for future applications, has already resulted in a Nobel Prize. An understanding of the structure and many of the properties of graphene is well within the reach of an undergraduate student of general chemistry. Through such examples, it is possible to demonstrate in a general chemistry course that chemistry is a dynamic science in continuous development. New research leads to new applications of chemistry in other fields of science and in technology. In addition, environmental and economic concerns bring about changes in the place of chemistry in society. Our textbook reflects this dynamic, changing character. We hope that it also conveys the excitement that scientists experience in making new discoveries that contribute to our understanding of the physical world.

New ideas about how to teach chemistry are constantly being developed, and many of them are reflected in how our textbook is organized and in the ways in which topics are presented. This edition incorporates a number of new methodologies to assist students, including use of the Internet, computer-based classroom tools, Web-based tools, particularly MasteringChemistry®, and more effective means of testing.

As authors, we want this text to be a central, indispensable learning tool for students. It can be carried everywhere and used at any time. It is the one place students can go to obtain the information needed for learning, skill development, reference, and test preparation. At the same time, the text provides the background in modern chemistry that students need to serve their professional interests and, as appropriate, to prepare for more advanced chemistry courses.

If the text is to be effective in supporting your role as teacher, it must be addressed to the students. We have done our best to keep our writing clear and interesting and the book attractive and well illustrated. The book has numerous in-text study aids for students, including carefully placed descriptions of problem-solving strategies. Together we have logged many years of teaching experience. We hope this is evident in our pacing, choice of examples, and the kinds of study aids and motivational tools we have employed. Because we believe that students are more enthusiastic about learning chemistry when they see its importance to their own goals and interests, we have highlighted many important applications of chemistry in everyday life. We hope you make use of this material.

A textbook is only as useful to students as the instructor permits it to be. This book is replete with features that can help students learn and that can guide them as they acquire both conceptual understanding and problem-solving skills. But the text and all the supplementary materials provided to support its use must work in concert with you, the instructor. There is a great deal for the students to use here, too much for all of it to be absorbed by any one student. You will be the guide to the best use of the book. Only with your active help will the students be able to utilize most effectively all that the text and its supplements offer. Students care about grades, of course, and with encouragement they will also become interested in the subject matter and care about learning. Please consider emphasizing features of the book that can enhance student appreciation of chemistry, such as the ***Chemistry Put to Work*** and ***Chemistry and Life*** boxes that show how chemistry impacts modern life and its relationship to health and life processes. Learn to use, and urge students to use, the rich Internet resources available. Emphasize conceptual understanding and place less emphasis on simple manipulative, algorithmic problem solving.

What's New in This Edition?

A great many changes have been made in producing this twelfth edition. The entire art program for the text has been reworked, and new features connected with the art have been introduced.

- Nearly every figure in the book has undergone some modification, and hundreds of figures have been entirely redone.
- A systematic effort has been made to move information that was contained in figure captions directly into the figures.
- Explanatory labels have been employed extensively in figures to guide the student in understanding the art.
- In several important places, art has been modified to convey the notion of progression in time, as in a reaction. See, for instance, Figures 4.4 and 14.27.
- New designs have been employed to more closely integrate photographic materials into figures that convey chemical principles, as in Figure 2.21.
- A new feature called **Go Figure** has been added to about 40% of the figures. This feature asks the student a question that can be answered by examining the figure. It tests whether the student has in fact examined the figure and understands its primary message. Answers to the **Go Figure** questions are provided in the back of the text.
- New end-of-chapter exercises have been added, and many of those carried over from the eleventh edition have been significantly revised. Results from analysis of student responses to MasteringChemistry, the online homework program connected with the text, have been used to eliminate questions that did not appear to be functioning well and to assess the degree to which instructors have used the end-of-chapter materials. On the basis of these analyses, many exercises have been revised or eliminated.
- Chapter introductions have been redesigned to enhance the student's exposure to the aims of the chapter and its contents.
- The presentation of hybrid orbitals in Chapter 9 and elsewhere has been rewritten to limit the treatment to s and p orbitals, based on theoretical work indicating that d orbital participation in hybridization is not significant.
- The treatment of condensed phases, liquids and solids, has been reorganized into two chapters that contain much new material. Chapter 11 deals with liquids and intermolecular forces, while Chapter 12 deals with solids, starting from the basics of crystal structures and covering a broad range of materials (including metals, semiconductors, polymers, and nanomaterials) in a cohesive manner.
- Chapter 18 on the Chemistry of the Environment has been substantially revised to focus on how human activities affect Earth's atmosphere and water, and to enlarge the coverage of the green chemistry initiative.
- The treatment of metals, Chapter 23 of the eleventh edition, has been reorganized and augmented. Structure and bonding in metals and alloys are now covered in Chapter 12 (Solids and Modern Materials), and other parts of Chapter 23 have been combined with material from Chapter 24 of the eleventh edition to form a new chapter, Transition Metals and Coordination Chemistry. Material covering occurrences and production of metals that was not widely used by instructors has been eliminated.

Throughout the text, the writing has been improved by enhancing the clarity and flow of ideas while achieving an economy of words. Thus, despite the addition of new features, the length of the text has not changed significantly.

Organization and Contents

The first five chapters give a largely macroscopic, phenomenological view of chemistry. The basic concepts introduced—such as nomenclature, stoichiometry, and thermochemistry—provide necessary background for many of the laboratory experiments usually performed in general chemistry. We believe that an early introduction to thermochemistry is desirable because so much of our understanding of chemical processes is based on considerations of energy changes. Thermochemistry is also important when we come to a discussion of bond enthalpies. We believe we have produced an effective, balanced approach to teaching thermodynamics in general chemistry, as well as providing students with an introduction to some of the global issues involving energy production and consumption. It is no easy matter to walk the narrow pathway between—on the one hand—trying to teach too much at too high a level and—on the other hand—resorting to oversimplifications. As with the book as a whole, the emphasis has been on imparting *conceptual* understanding, as opposed to presenting equations into which students are supposed to plug numbers.

The next four chapters (Chapters 6–9) deal with electronic structure and bonding. We have largely retained our presentation of atomic orbitals. For more advanced students, *Closer Look* boxes in Chapters 6 and 9 deal with radial probability functions and the phases of orbitals. Our approach of placing this latter discussion in a Closer Look box in Chapter 9 enables those who wish to cover this topic to do so, while others may wish to bypass it. In treating this topic and others in Chapters 7 and 9 we have materially enhanced the accompanying figures to more effectively bring home their central messages.

The focus of the text then changes (Chapters 10–13) to the next level of the organization of matter, examining the states of matter. Chapters 10 and 11 deal with gases, liquids, and intermolecular forces, much as in earlier editions. Chapter 12, however, is now devoted to solids, presenting an enlarged and more contemporary view of the solid state as well as of modern materials. This change is appropriate, given the ever-increasing importance of solid-state materials in solar energy, illumination, and electronics. Chapter 12 provides an opportunity to show how abstract chemical bonding concepts impact real-world applications. The modular organization of the chapter allows you to tailor your coverage to focus on materials (semiconductors, polymers, nanomaterials, and so forth) that are most relevant to your students and your own interests. Chapter 13 treats the formation and properties of solutions in much the same manner as the previous edition.

The next several chapters examine the factors that determine the speed and extent of chemical reactions: kinetics (Chapter 14), equilibria (Chapters 15–17), thermodynamics (Chapter 19), and electrochemistry (Chapter 20). Also in this section is a chapter on environmental chemistry (Chapter 18), in which the concepts developed in preceding chapters are applied to a discussion of the atmosphere and hydrosphere. This chapter has been revised to focus more sharply on the impacts of human activities on Earth's water and atmosphere and on green chemistry.

After a discussion of nuclear chemistry (Chapter 21), the book ends with three survey chapters. Chapter 22, on nonmetals, has been consolidated slightly from the eleventh edition. Chapter 23 now deals with the chemistry of transition metals, including coordination compounds, and the last chapter deals with the chemistry of organic compounds and elementary biochemical themes. These final four chapters are developed in a parallel fashion and can be treated in any order.

Our chapter sequence provides a fairly standard organization, but we recognize that not everyone teaches all the topics in just the order we have chosen. We have therefore made sure that instructors can make common changes in teaching sequence with no loss in student comprehension. In particular, many instructors prefer to introduce gases (Chapter 10) after stoichiometry (Chapter 3) rather than with states of matter. The chapter on gases has been written to permit this change with *no* disruption in the flow of material. It is also possible to treat balancing redox equations (Sections 20.1 and 20.2) earlier, after the introduction of redox reactions in Section 4.4. Finally, some instructors like to cover organic chemistry (Chapter 24) right after bonding (Chapters 8 and 9). This, too, is a largely seamless move.

We have brought students into greater contact with descriptive organic and inorganic chemistry by integrating examples throughout the text. You will find pertinent and relevant examples of "real" chemistry woven into all the chapters to illustrate principles and applications. Some chapters, of course, more directly address the "descriptive" properties of elements and their compounds, especially Chapters 4, 7, 11, 18, and 22–24. We also incorporate descriptive organic and inorganic chemistry in the end-of-chapter exercises.

Changes in This Edition

The **What's New in This Edition** on page xxvii details changes made throughout the new edition. Beyond a mere listing, however, it is worth dwelling on the general goals we set in formulating the twelfth edition. *Chemistry: The Central Science* has traditionally been valued for its clarity of writing, its scientific accuracy and currency, its strong end-of-chapter exercises, and its consistency in level of coverage. In making changes, we have made sure not to compromise these characteristics, and we have also continued to employ an open, clean design in the layout of the book.

The major systemic change in the new edition involves the art program. It is widely recognized that contemporary students rely more on visual learning materials than in the past, yet for the most part textbook art has not evolved greatly in response other than a greater use of molecular art. In this edition, with the help of a strong editorial development team, we have redone a large portion of the figures with the aim of increasing their power as teaching tools. What can we do to encourage students to study a figure, and how can we help them learn from it? The first step has been to incorporate elements that direct attention to the figure's major features. The flow from one important aspect to the next, particularly involving processes occurring over time, has been emphasized through new layouts and through the use of both visual and textual cues, as in Figures 2.15, 4.3, 4.9, and 14.17. Our aim is to draw the student into a more careful and thoughtful viewing through extensive use of explanatory labels and other devices. A new feature called **Go Figure**, analogous to the **Give It Some Thought** exercises we pioneered in the tenth edition, directs attention to the art and provides an opportunity for students to judge whether they have really absorbed the content of the figure. We have also found new and more effective ways to show trends and relationships in figures involving presentations of data, as in Figures 7.6, 8.8, and 8.15.

We have continued to use the **What's Ahead** overview at the opening of each chapter, introduced in the ninth edition. *Concept links* (∞) continue to provide easy-to-see cross-references to pertinent material covered earlier in the text. The essays titled *Strategies in Chemistry*, which provide advice to students on problem solving and "thinking like a chemist," continue to be an important feature. The **Give It Some Thought** exercises that we introduced in the tenth edition have proved to be very popular, and we have continued to refine their use. These informal, sharply focused questions give students opportunities to test whether they are "getting it" as they read along.

We have continued to emphasize conceptual exercises in the end-of-chapter exercise materials. The **Visualizing Concepts** exercise category has been continued in this edition. These exercises are designed to facilitate concept understanding through use of models, graphs, and other visual materials. They precede the regular end-of-chapter exercises and are identified in each case with the relevant chapter section number. The **Integrative Exercises**, which give students the opportunity to solve problems that integrate concepts from the present chapter with those of previous chapters, have been continued. The importance of integrative problem solving is highlighted by the **Sample Integrative Exercise** that ends each chapter beginning with Chapter 4. In general, we have included more conceptual end-of-chapter exercises and have made sure that there is a good representation of somewhat more difficult exercises to provide a better mix in terms of topic and level of difficulty. The results from student use of MasteringChemistry have enabled us to more reliably evaluate the effectiveness of our end-of-chapter exercises and make changes accordingly.

New essays in our well-received *Chemistry Put to Work* and *Chemistry and Life* series emphasize world events, scientific discoveries, and medical breakthroughs that have occurred since publication of the eleventh edition. We maintain our focus on the positive aspects of chemistry without neglecting the problems that can arise in an increasingly technological world. Our goal is to help students appreciate the real-world perspective of chemistry and the ways in which chemistry affects their lives.

TO THE STUDENT

Chemistry: The Central Science, **Twelfth Edition,** has been written to introduce you to modern chemistry. As authors, we have, in effect, been engaged by your instructor to help you learn chemistry. Based on the comments of students and instructors who have used this book in its previous editions, we believe that we have done that job well. Of course, we expect the text to continue to evolve through future editions. We invite you to write to tell us what you like about the book so that we will know where we have helped you most. Also, we would like to learn of any shortcomings so that we might further improve the book in subsequent editions. Our addresses are given at the end of the Preface.

Advice for Learning and Studying Chemistry

Learning chemistry requires both the assimilation of many concepts and the development of analytical skills. In this text we have provided you with numerous tools to help you succeed in both tasks. If you are going to succeed in your chemistry course, you will have to develop good study habits. Science courses, and chemistry in particular, make different demands on your learning skills than do other types of courses. We offer the following tips for success in your study of chemistry:

Don't fall behind! As the course moves along, new topics will build on material already presented. If you don't keep up in your reading and problem solving, you will find it much harder to follow the lectures and discussions on current topics. Experienced teachers know that students who read the relevant sections of the text *before* coming to a class learn more from the class and retain greater recall. "Cramming" just before an exam has been shown to be an ineffective way to study any subject, chemistry included. So now you know. How important to you in this competitive world is a good grade in chemistry?

Focus your study. The amount of information you will be expected to learn can sometimes seem overwhelming. It is essential to recognize those concepts and skills that are particularly important. Pay attention to what your instructor is emphasizing. As you work through the **Sample Exercises** and homework assignments, try to see what general principles and skills they employ. Use the **What's Ahead** feature at the beginning of each chapter to help orient yourself to what is important in each chapter. A single reading of a chapter will simply not be enough for successful learning of chapter concepts and problem-solving skills. You will need to go over assigned materials more than once. Don't skip the **Give It Some Thought** and **Go Figure** features, **Sample Exercises**, and **Practice Exercises**. They are your guides to whether you are learning the material. The **Key Skills** and **Key Equations** at the end of the chapter should help you focus your study.

Keep good lecture notes. Your lecture notes will provide you with a clear and concise record of what your instructor regards as the most important material to learn. Using your lecture notes in conjunction with this text is the best way to determine which material to study.

Skim topics in the text before they are covered in lecture. Reviewing a topic before lecture will make it easier for you to take good notes. First read the **What's Ahead** points and the end-of-chapter **Summary**; then quickly read through the chapter, skipping Sample Exercises and supplemental sections. Paying attention to the titles of sections and subsections gives you a feeling for the scope of topics. Try to avoid thinking that you must learn and understand everything right away.

After lecture, carefully read the topics covered in class. As you read, pay attention to the concepts presented and to the application of these concepts in the Sample

Exercises. Once you think you understand a Sample Exercise, test your understanding by working the accompanying Practice Exercise.

Learn the language of chemistry. As you study chemistry, you will encounter many new words. It is important to pay attention to these words and to know their meanings or the entities to which they refer. Knowing how to identify chemical substances from their names is an important skill; it can help you avoid painful mistakes on examinations. For example, "chlorine" and "chloride" refer to very different things.

Attempt the assigned end-of-chapter exercises. Working the exercises selected by your instructor provides necessary practice in recalling and using the essential ideas of the chapter. You cannot learn merely by observing; you must be a participant. In particular, try to resist checking the *Student-Solutions Manual* (if you have one) until you have made a sincere effort to solve the exercise yourself. If you get stuck on an exercise, however, get help from your instructor, your teaching assistant, or another student. Spending more than 20 minutes on a single exercise is rarely effective unless you know that it is particularly challenging.

Use online resources. Some things are more easily learned by discovery, and others are best shown in three dimensions. If your instructor has included MasteringChemistry with your book, take advantage of the unique tools it provides to get the most out of your time in chemistry.

The bottom line is to work hard, study effectively, and use the tools available to you, including this textbook. We want to help you learn more about the world of chemistry and why chemistry is the central science. If you really learn chemistry, you can be the life of the party, impress your friends and parents, and . . . well, also pass the course with a good grade.

ACKNOWLEDGMENTS

The production of a textbook is a team effort requiring the involvement of many people besides the authors who contributed hard work and talent to bring this edition to life. Although their names don't appear on the cover of the book, their creativity, time, and support have been instrumental in all stages of its development and production.

Each of us has benefited greatly from discussions with colleagues and from correspondence with instructors and students both here and abroad. Colleagues have also helped immensely by reviewing our materials, sharing their insights, and providing suggestions for improvements. On this edition we were particularly blessed with an exceptional group of accuracy checkers who read through our materials looking for both technical inaccuracies and typographical errors.

Twelfth Edition Reviewers

Rebecca Barlag	Ohio University
Hafed, Bascal	University of Findlay
Donald Bellew	University of New Mexico
Elzbieta Cook	Louisiana State University
Robert Dunn	University of Kansas
Michael Hay	Pennsylvania State University
Carl Hoeger	University of California at San Diego
Kathryn Rowberg	Purdue University at Calumet
Lewis Silverman	University of Missouri at Columbia
Clyde Webster	University of California at Riverside
Troy Wood	University of Buffalo

Twelfth Edition Accuracy Reviewers

Rebecca Barlag	Ohio University
Kelly Beefus	Anoka-Ramsey Community College
Louis J. Kirschenbaum	University of Rhode Island
Barbara Mowery	York College
Maria Vogt	Bloomfield College

Twelth Edition Focus Group Participants

Robert Carter	University of Massachusetts at Boston Harbor
Tom Clayton	Knox College
Elzbieta Cook	Louisiana State University
Debra Feakes	Texas State University at San Marcos
Robert Gellert	Glendale Community College
John Gorden	Auburn University
Thomas J. Greenbowe	Iowa State University
Kingston Jesudoss	Iowa State University
Daniela Kohen	Carleton University
Sergiy Kryatov	Tufts University
Jeff McVey	Texas State University at San Marcos
Michael Seymour	Hope College
Matthew Stoltzfus	The Ohio State University

MasteringChemistry® Summit Participants

Phil Bennett	Santa Fe Community College
Jo Blackburn	Richland College
John Bookstaver	St. Charles Community College
David Carter	Angelo State University
Doug Cody	Nassau Community College
Tom Dowd	Harper College
Palmer Graves	Florida International University
Margie Haak	Oregon State University
Brad Herrick	Colorado School of Mines
Jeff Jenson	University of Findlay
Jeff McVey	Texas State University at San Marcos
Gary Michels	Creighton University
Bob Pribush	Butler University
Al Rives	Wake Forest University
Joel Russell	Oakland University
Greg Szulczewski	University of Alabama, Tuscaloosa
Matt Tarr	University of New Orleans
Dennis Taylor	Clemson University
Harold Trimm	Broome Community College
Emanuel Waddell	University of Alabama, Huntsville
Kurt Winkelmann	Florida Institute of Technology
Klaus Woelk	University of Missouri, Rolla
Steve Wood	Brigham Young University

Reviewers of Previous Editions of *Chemistry: The Central Science*

S.K. Airee	University of Tennessee
John J. Alexander	University of Cincinnati
Robert Allendoerfer	SUNY Buffalo
Patricia Amateis	Virginia Polytechnic Institute and State University
Sandra Anderson	University of Wisconsin
John Arnold	University of California
Socorro Arteaga	El Paso Community College
Margaret Asirvatham	University of Colorado
Todd L. Austell	University of North Carolina, Chapel Hill
Melita Balch	University of Illinois at Chicago
Rosemary Bartoszek-Loza	The Ohio State University
Boyd Beck	Snow College
Amy Beilstein	Centre College
Victor Berner	New Mexico Junior College
Narayan Bhat	University of Texas, Pan American
Merrill Blackman	United States Military Academy
Salah M. Blaih	Kent State University
James A. Bciani	SUNY Geneseo
Leon Borowski	Diablo Valley College
Simon Bott	University of Houston
Kevin L. Bray	Washington State University
Daeg Scott Brenner	Clark University
Gregory Alan Brewer	Catholic University of America
Karen Brewer	Virginia Polytechnic Institute and State University
Edward Brown	Lee University
Gary Buckley	Cameron University
Carmela Byrnes	Texas A&M University
B. Edward Cain	Rochester Institute of Technology

Kim Calvo	University of Akron
Donald L. Campbell	University of Wisconsin
Gene O. Carlisle	Texas A&M University
Elaine Carter	Los Angeles City College
Robert Carter	University of Massachusetts
Ann Cartwright	San Jacinto Central College
David L. Cedeño	Illinois State University
Dana Chatellier	University of Delaware
Stanton Ching	Connecticut College
Paul Chirik	Cornell University
William Cleaver	University of Vermont
Beverly Clement	Blinn College
Robert D. Cloney	Fordham University
John Collins	Broward Community College
Edward Werner Cook	Tunxis Community Technical College
Elzbieta Cook	Louisiana State University
Enriqueta Cortez	South Texas College
Thomas Edgar Crumm	Indiana University of Pennsylvania
Dwaine Davis	Forsyth Tech Community College
Ramón López de la Vega	Florida International University
Nancy De Luca	University of Massachusetts, Lowell North Campus
Angel de Dios	Georgetown University
John M. DeKorte	Glendale Community College
Daniel Domin	Tennessee State University
James Donaldson	University of Toronto
Bill Donovan	University of Akron
Stephen Drucker	University of Wisconsin-Eau Claire
Ronald Duchovic	Indiana University-Purdue University at Fort Wayne
David Easter	Southwest Texas State University
Joseph Ellison	United States Military Academy
George O. Evans II	East Carolina University
James M. Farrar	University of Rochester
Gregory M. Ferrence	Illinois State University
Clark L. Fields	University of Northern Colorado
Jennifer Firestine	Lindenwood University
Jan M. Fleischner	College of New Jersey
Paul A. Flowers	University of North Carolina at Pembroke
Michelle Fossum	Laney College
Roger Frampton	Tidewater Community College
Joe Franek	University of Minnesota
David Frank	California State University
Cheryl B. Frech	University of Central Oklahoma
Ewa Fredette	Moraine Valley College
Kenneth A. French	Blinn College
Karen Frindell	Santa Rosa Junior College
John I. Gelder	Oklahoma State University
Paul Gilletti	Mesa Community College
Peter Gold	Pennsylvania State University
Eric Goll	Brookdale Community College
James Gordon	Central Methodist College
Thomas J. Greenbowe	Iowa State University
Michael Greenlief	University of Missouri
Eric P. Grimsrud	Montana State University
John Hagadorn	University of Colorado
Randy Hall	Louisiana State University
John M. Halpin	New York University
Marie Hankins	University of Southern Indiana
Robert M. Hanson	St. Olaf College
Daniel Haworth	Marquette University
Inna Hefley	Blinn College
David Henderson	Trinity College
Paul Higgs	Barry University
Carl A. Hoeger	University of California, San Diego
Gary G. Hoffman	Florida International University
Deborah Hokien	Marywood University
Robin Horner	Fayetteville Tech Community College
Roger K. House	Moraine Valley College
Michael O. Hurst	Georgia Southern University
William Jensen	South Dakota State University
Janet Johannessen	County College of Morris
Milton D. Johnston, Jr.	University of South Florida
Andrew Jones	Southern Alberta Institute of Technology
Booker Juma	Fayetteville State University
Ismail Kady	East Tennessee State University
Siam Kahmis	University of Pittsburgh
Steven Keller	University of Missouri
John W. Kenney	Eastern New Mexico University
Neil Kestner	Louisiana State University
Leslie Kinsland	University of Louisiana
Louis J. Kirschenbaum	University of Rhode Island
Donald Kleinfelter	University of Tennessee, Knoxville
David Kort	George Mason University
George P. Kreishman	University of Cincinnati
Paul Kreiss	Anne Arundel Community College
Manickham Krishnamurthy	Howard University
Brian D. Kybett	University of Regina
William R. Lammela	Nazareth College
John T. Landrum	Florida International University
Richard Langley	Stephen F. Austin State University
N. Dale Ledford	University of South Alabama
Ernestine Lee	Utah State University
David Lehmpuhl	University of Southern Colorado
Robley J. Light	Florida State University
Donald E. Linn, Jr.	Indiana University-Purdue University Indianapolis
David Lippmann	Southwest Texas State
Patrick Lloyd	Kingsborough Community College
Encarnacion Lopez	Miami Dade College, Wolfson
Arthur Low	Tarleton State University
Gary L. Lyon	Louisiana State University
Preston J. MacDougall	Middle Tennessee State University
Jeffrey Madura	Duquesne University
Larry Manno	Triton College
Asoka Marasinghe	Moorhead State University
Earl L. Mark	ITT Technical Institute
Pamela Marks	Arizona State University
Albert H. Martin	Moravian College
Przemyslaw Maslak	Pennsylvania State University
Hilary L. Maybaum	ThinkQuest, Inc.
Armin Mayr	El Paso Community College
Marcus T. McEllistrem	University of Wisconsin
Craig McLauchlan	Illinois State University
William A. Meena	Valley College
Joseph Mercla	Virginia Polytechnic Institute and State University
Stephen Mezyk	California State University
Eric Miller	San Juan College
Gordon Miller	Iowa State University
Shelley Minteer	Saint Louis University
Massoud (Matt) Miri	Rochester Institute of Technology
Mohammad Moharerrzadeh	Bowie State University
Tracy Morkin	Emory University
Barbara Mowery	Yorktown, VA
Kathleen E. Murphy	Daemen College
Kathy Nabona	Austin Community College
Robert Nelson	Georgia Southern University
Al Nichols	Jacksonville State University

Ross Nord	Eastern Michigan University
Jessica Orvis	Georgia Southern University
Mark Ott	Jackson Community College
Jason Overby	College of Charleston
Robert H. Paine	Rochester Institute of Technology
Robert T. Paine	University of New Mexico
Sandra Patrick	Malaspina University College
Mary Jane Patterson	Brazosport College
Tammi Pavelec	Lindenwood University
Albert Payton	Broward Community College
Christopher J. Peeples	University of Tulsa
Kim Percell	Cape Fear Community College
Gita Perkins	Estrella Mountain Community College
Richard Perkins	University of Louisiana
Nancy Peterson	North Central College
Robert C. Pfaff	Saint Joseph's College
John Pfeffer	Highline Community College
Lou Pignolet	University of Minnesota
Bernard Powell	University of Texas
Jeffrey A. Rahn	Eastern Washington University
Steve Rathbone	Blinn College
Scott Reeve	Arkansas State University
John Reissner	University of North Carolina
Helen Richter	University of Akron
Thomas Ridgway	University of Cincinnati
Mark G. Rockley	Oklahoma State University
Lenore Rodicio	Miami Dade College
Amy L. Rogers	College of Charleston
Jimmy R. Rogers	University of Texas at Arlington
Steven Rowley	Middlesex Community College
James E. Russo	Whitman College
Theodore Sakano	Rockland Community College
Michael J. Sanger	University of Northern Iowa
Jerry L. Sarquis	Miami University
James P. Schneider	Portland Community College
Mark Schraf	West Virginia University
Gray Scrimgeour	University of Toronto
Paula Secondo	Western Connecticut State University
Kathy Thrush Shaginaw	Villanova University
Susan M. Shih	College of DuPage
David Shinn	University of Hawaii at Hilo
Vince Sollimo	Burlington Community College
David Soriano	University of Pittsburgh-Bradford
Eugene Stevers	Binghamton University
James Symes	Cosumnes River College
Iwao Teraoka	Polytechnic University
Kathy Thrush	Villanova University
Domenic J. Tiani	University of North Carolina, Chapel Hill
Edmund Tisko	University of Nebraska at Omaha
Richard S. Treptow	Chicago State University
Michael Tubergen	Kent State University
Claudia Turro	The Ohio State University
James Tyrell	Southern Illinois University
Michael J. Van Stipdonk	Wichita State University
Philip Verhalen	Panola College
Ann Verner	University of Toronto at Scarborough
Edward Vickner	Gloucester County Community College
John Vincent	University of Alabama
Maria Vogt	Bloomfield College
Tony Wallner	Barry University
Lichang Wang	Southern Illinois University
Thomas R. Webb	Auburn University
Karen Weichelman	University of Louisiana-Lafayette
Paul G. Wenthold	Purdue University
Laurence Werbelow	New Mexico Institute of Mining and Technology
Wayne Wesolowski	University Of Arizona
Sarah West	University of Notre Dame
Linda M. Wilkes	University at Southern Colorado
Charles A. Wilkie	Marquette University
Darren L. Williams	West Texas A&M University
Troy Wood	SUNY Buffalo
Thao Yang	University of Wisconsin
David Zax	Cornell University
Dr. Susan M. Zirpoli	Slippery Rock University

We would also like to express our gratitude to our many team members at Pearson Prentice Hall whose hard work, imagination, and commitment have contributed so greatly to the final form of this edition: Nicole Folchetti, our former Editor in Chief, brought energy and imagination not only to this edition but to earlier ones as well; Terry Haugen, our Chemistry Editor, for many fresh ideas and his unflagging enthusiasm, continuous encouragement, and support; Jennifer Hart, our Project Editor, who very effectively coordinated the scheduling and tracked the multidimensional deadlines that come with a project of this magnitude; Erin Gardner, our marketing manager, for her energy, enthusiam, and creative promotion of our text; Irene Nunes, our Development Editor, whose diligence and careful attention to detail were invaluable to this revision, especially in keeping us on task in terms of consistency and student understanding; Donna Mulder, our Copy Editor, for her keen eye; Greg Gambino, our Art Developmental Editor, who managed the complex task of bringing our sketches into final form and who contributed so many great ideas to the new art program; Shari Toron, our Project Manager, who managed the complex responsibilities of bringing the design, photos, artwork, and writing together with efficiency and good cheer. The Pearson Prentice Hall team is a first-class operation.

There are many others who also deserve special recognition, including the following: Eric Schrader, our photo researcher, who was so effective in finding photos to bring chemistry to life for students, and Roxy Wilson (University of Illinois), who so ably coordinated the difficult job of working out solutions to the end-of-chapter exercises. We thank Dr. Jannik C. Meyer of the University of Ulm, Germany, for providing us with a high resolution image of graphene used in the cover design.

Finally, we wish to thank our families and friends for their love, support, encouragement, and patience as we brought this twelfth edition to completion.

Theodore L. Brown
Department of Chemistry
University of Illinois
at Urbana-Champaign
Urbana, IL 61801
tlbrown@illinois.edu
or tlbrown1@earthlink.net

H. Eugene LeMay, Jr.
Department of Chemistry
University of Nevada
Reno, NV 89557
lemay@unr.edu

Bruce E. Bursten
College of Arts and Sciences
University of Tennessee
Knoxville, TN 37996
bbursten@utk.edu

Catherine J. Murphy
Department of Chemistry
University of Illinois
at Urbana-Champaign
Urbana, IL 61801
murphycj@illinois.edu.

Patrick M. Woodward
Department of Chemistry
The Ohio State University
Columbus, OH 43210
woodward@chemistry.
ohio-state.edu

LIST OF RESOURCES

For Students

MasteringChemistry®
(http://www.masteringchemistry.com)

MasteringChemistry is the most effective, widely used online tutorial, homework and assessment system for chemistry. It helps instructors maximize class time with customizable, easy-to-assign, and automatically graded assessments that motivate students to learn outside of class and arrive prepared for lecture. These assessments can easily be customized and personalized by instructors to suit their individual teaching style. The powerful gradebook provides unique insight into student and class performance even before the first test. As a result, instructors can spend class time where students need it most.

Pearson eText The integration of Pearson eText within MasteringChemistry gives students with eTexts easy access to the electronic text when they are logged into Mastering Chemistry. Pearson eText pages look exactly like the printed text, offering powerful new functionality for students and instructors. Users can create notes, highlight text in different colors, create bookmarks, zoom, view in single-page or two-page view, and more.

Student's Guide (0-321-70458-4) Prepared by James C. Hill of California State University. This book assists students through the text material with chapter overviews, learning objectives, a review of key terms, as well as self-tests with answers and explanations. This edition also features MCAT practice questions.

Solutions to Red Exercises (0-321-70548-3) Prepared by Roxy Wilson of the University of Illinois, Urbana-Champaign. Full solutions to all the red-numbered exercises in the text are provided. (Short answers to red exercises are found in the appendix of the text.)

Solutions to Black Exercises (0-321-70501-7) Prepared by Roxy Wilson of the University of Illinois, Urbana-Champaign. Full solutions to all the black-numbered exercises in the text are provided.

Laboratory Experiments (0-321-70502-5) Prepared by John H. Nelson and Kenneth C. Kemp, both of the University of Nevada, with contributions by Matthew Stoltzfus of The Ohio State University. This manual contains 43 finely tuned experiments chosen to introduce students to basic lab techniques and to illustrate core chemical principles. This new edition has been revised to correlate more tightly with the text and now includes GIST questions and section references to the text. You can also customize these labs through Catalyst, our custom database program. For more information, visit *http://www.pearsoncustom.com/custom-library/*

For Instructors

Solutions to Exercises (0-321-70500-9) Prepared by Roxy Wilson of the University of Illinois, Urbana-Champaign. This manual contains all end-of-chapter exercises in the text. With an instructor's permission, this manual may be made available to students.

Instructor's Resource Center on CD-DVD (0-321-70503-3) This resource provides an integrated collection of resources to help instructors make efficient and effective use of their time. This DVD features all artwork from the text, including figures and tables in PDF format for high-resolution printing. as well as four prebuilt PowerPoint™ presentations. The first presentation contains the images embedded within PowerPoint slides. The second includes a complete lecture outline that is modifiable by the user. The final two presentations contain worked "in-chapter" sample exercises and questions to be used with Classroom Response Systems. This DVD also contains movies, animations, and electronic files of the Instructor's Resource Manual, as well as the Test Item File.

Printed Testbank (0-321-70497-5) Prepared by Joseph P. Laurino of the University of Tampa. The Test Item File now provides a selection of more than 4000 test questions with 300 new questions in the twelfth edition and 200 additional algorithmic questions.

Instructor's Resource Manual (0-321-70499-1) Prepared by Linda Brunauer of Santa Clara University and Elzbieta Cook of Louisiana State University. Organized by chapter, this manual offers detailed lecture outlines and complete descriptions of all available lecture demonstrations, interactive media assets, common student misconceptions, and more.

Transparencies (0-321-70498-3) Approximately 275 full-color transparencies put principles into visual perspective and save you time when preparing lectures.

Annotated Instructor's Edition to Laboratory Experiments (0-321-71197-1) Prepared by John H. Nelson and Kenneth C. Kemp, both of the University of Nevada, with contributions by Matthew Stoltzfus of The Ohio State University. This AIE combines the full student lab manual with appendices covering the proper disposal of chemical waste, safety instructions for the lab, descriptions of standard lab equipment, answers to questions, and more.

WebCT Test Item File (IRC download only)
978-0-321-70506-8 / 0-321-70506-8

Blackboard Test Item File (IRC download only)
978-0-321-70507-5 / 0-321-70507-6

THEODORE L. BROWN received his Ph.D. from Michigan State University in 1956. Since then, he has been a member of the faculty of the University of Illinois, Urbana-Champaign, where he is now Professor of Chemistry, Emeritus. He served as Vice Chancellor for Research, and Dean of The Graduate College, from 1980 to 1986, and as Founding Director of the Arnold and Mabel Beckman Institute for Advanced Science and Technology from 1987 to 1993. Professor Brown has been an Alfred P. Sloan Foundation Research Fellow and has been awarded a Guggenheim Fellowship. In 1972 he was awarded the American Chemical Society Award for Research in Inorganic Chemistry and received the American Chemical Society Award for Distinguished Service in the Advancement of Inorganic Chemistry in 1993. He has been elected a Fellow of the American Association for the Advancement of Science, the American Academy of Arts and Sciences, and the American Chemical Society.

H. EUGENE LEMAY, JR., received his B.S. degree in Chemistry from Pacific Lutheran University (Washington) and his Ph.D. in Chemistry in 1966 from the University of Illinois, Urbana-Champaign. He then joined the faculty of the University of Nevada, Reno, where he is currently Professor of Chemistry, Emeritus. He has enjoyed Visiting Professorships at the University of North Carolina at Chapel Hill, at the University College of Wales in Great Britain, and at the University of California, Los Angeles. Professor LeMay is a popular and effective teacher, who has taught thousands of students during more than 40 years of university teaching. Known for the clarity of his lectures and his sense of humor, he has received several teaching awards, including the University Distinguished Teacher of the Year Award (1991) and the first Regents' Teaching Award given by the State of Nevada Board of Regents (1997).

BRUCE E. BURSTEN received his Ph.D. in Chemistry from the University of Wisconsin in 1978. After two years as a National Science Foundation Postdoctoral Fellow at Texas A&M University, he joined the faculty of The Ohio State University, where he rose to the rank of Distinguished University Professor. In 2005, he moved to the University of Tennessee, Knoxville, as Distinguished Professor of Chemistry and Dean of the College of Arts and Sciences. Professor Bursten has been a Camille and Henry Dreyfus Foundation Teacher-Scholar and an Alfred P. Sloan Foundation Research Fellow, and he is a Fellow of both the American Association for the Advancement of Science and the American Chemical Society. At Ohio State he has received the University Distinguished Teaching Award in 1982 and 1996, the Arts and Sciences Student Council Outstanding Teaching Award in 1984, and the University Distinguished Scholar Award in 1990. He received the Spiers Memorial Prize and Medal of the Royal Society of Chemistry in 2003, and the Morley Medal of the Cleveland Section of the American Chemical Society in 2005. He was President of the American Chemical Society for 2008. In addition to his teaching and service activities, Professor Bursten's research program focuses on compounds of the transition-metal and actinide elements.

CATHERINE J. MURPHY received two B.S. degrees, one in Chemistry and one in Biochemistry, from the University of Illinois, Urbana-Champaign, in 1986. She received her Ph.D. in Chemistry from the University of Wisconsin in 1990. She was a National Science Foundation and National Institutes of Health Postdoctoral Fellow at the California Institute of Technology from 1990 to 1993. In 1993, she joined the faculty of the University of South Carolina, Columbia, becoming the Guy F. Lipscomb Professor of Chemistry in 2003. In 2009 she moved to the University of Illinois, Urbana-Champaign, as the Peter C. and Gretchen Miller Markunas Professor of Chemistry. Professor Murphy has been honored for both research and teaching as a Camille Dreyfus Teacher-Scholar, an Alfred P. Sloan Foundation Research Fellow, a Cottrell Scholar of the Research Corporation, a National Science Foundation CAREER Award winner, and a subsequent NSF Award for Special Creativity. She has also received a USC Mortar Board Excellence in Teaching Award, the USC Golden Key Faculty Award for Creative Integration of Research and Undergraduate Teaching, the USC Michael J. Mungo Undergraduate Teaching Award, and the USC Outstanding Undergraduate Research Mentor Award. Since 2006, Professor Murphy has served as a Senior Editor for the Journal of Physical Chemistry. In 2008 she was elected a Fellow of the American Association for the Advancement of Science. Professor Murphy's research program focuses on the synthesis and optical properties of inorganic nanomaterials, and on the local structure and dynamics of the DNA double helix.

PATRICK M. WOODWARD received B.S. degrees in both Chemistry and Engineering from Idaho State University in 1991. He received a M.S. degree in Materials Science and a Ph.D. in Chemistry from Oregon State University in 1996. He spent two years as a postdoctoral researcher in the Department of Physics at Brookhaven National Laboratory. In 1998, he joined the faculty of the Chemistry Department at The Ohio State University where he currently holds the rank of Professor. He has enjoyed visiting professorships at the University of Bordeaux in France and the University of Sydney in Australia. Professor Woodward has been an Alfred P. Sloan Foundation Research Fellow and a National Science Foundation CAREER Award winner. He currently serves as an Associate Editor to the Journal of Solid State Chemistry and as the director of the Ohio REEL program, an NSF-funded center that works to bring authentic research experiments into the laboratories of first- and second-year chemistry classes in 15 colleges and universities across the state of Ohio. Professor Woodward's research program focuses on understanding the links between bonding, structure, and properties of solid-state inorganic functional materials.

A GUIDE TO USING THIS TEXT

■ *Chemistry: The Central Science* has been the leader in general chemistry for decades. Now, its unrivaled problems, scientific accuracy, and clarity have been upheld and are woven seamlessly with each new feature. The **Twelfth Edition** is this text's most ambitious revision to date; every word and piece of art has been scrutinized for effectiveness by all five authors, and many revisions are based on student performance data gathered through MasteringChemistry.®

Visualizing concepts makes chemistry accessible

Chemistry is by nature an abstract subject. First, it relies on a symbolic language based on chemical formulas and equations. Second, it is based on the behavior of atoms and molecules—particles far too small to see. By presenting chemistry visually, the authors help you to "see" the chemistry you need to learn and increase your success in the course.

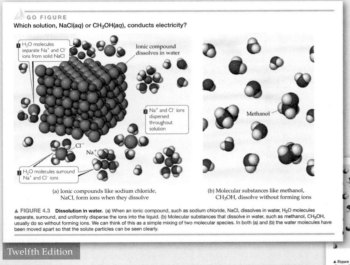

Twelfth Edition

Molecular Illustrations

Molecular Illustrations are computer-generated renditions of molecules and materials that represent matter visually at the atomic level. These drawings help you visualize molecules in three dimensions, and enhance your understanding of molecular architecture.

Eleventh Edition

Twelfth Edition

Multi-Focus Graphics

To help you develop a more complete understanding of the topic presented, **Multi-Focus Graphics** provide macroscopic, microscopic, and symbolic perspectives to portray various chemical concepts. The Twelfth Edition adds to these graphics an intermediate process that shows you where chemistry is occurring in problem solving.

▲ Figure 4.1 **Limestone cave.** When CO_2 dissolves in water, the resulting solution is slightly acidic. Limestone caves are formed by the dissolving action of this acidic solution acting on $CaCO_3$ in the limestone.

Eleventh Edition

xxviii

▲ FIGURE 4.13 **Reaction of magnesium metal with hydrochloric acid.** The metal is readily oxidized by the acid, producing hydrogen gas, $H_2(g)$, and $MgCl_2(aq)$.

Labels within figure:
H^+ Cl^- Mg $Mg(s)$ is oxidized (loses electrons) $H^+(aq)$ is reduced (gains electrons) H_2 Mg^{2+}

Reactants   *Products*
$2 HCl(aq) + Mg(s)$ ⟶ $H_2(g) + MgCl_2(aq)$
Oxidation number $+1 \; -1$ 0 0 $+2 \; -1$

Macro to Micro Art

These illustrations offer three parts: a macroscopic image (what you can see with your eyes); a molecular image (what the molecules are doing); and a symbolic representation (how chemists represent the process with symbols and equations).

A new intermediate step has been added, showing where chemistry occurs in the problem-solving process.

A focus on relevance makes chemistry meaningful

Chemistry occurs all around us, throughout every day. Recognizing the importance of chemistry in your daily life can improve your understanding of chemical concepts.

CHEMISTRY PUT TO WORK

Antacids

Your stomach secretes acids to help digest foods. These acids, which include hydrochloric acid, contain about 0.1 mol of H^+ per liter of solution. The stomach and digestive tract are normally protected from the corrosive effects of stomach acid by a mucosal lining. Holes can develop in this lining, however, allowing the acid to attack the underlying tissue, causing painful damage. These holes, known as ulcers, can be caused by the secretion of excess acids or by a weakness in the digestive lining. Studies indicate, however, that many ulcers are caused by bacterial infection. Between 10 and 20% of Americans suffer from ulcers at some point in their lives. Many others experience occasional indigestion or heartburn due to digestive acids entering the esophagus.

We can address the problem of excess stomach acid in two ways: (1) removing the excess acid or (2) decreasing the production of acid. Substances that remove excess acid are called *antacids*, whereas those that decrease acid production are called *acid inhibitors*. ◄ FIGURE 4.10 shows several common over-the-counter antacids, which usually contain hydroxide, carbonate, or bicarbonate ions (▼ TABLE 4.4). Antiulcer drugs, such as Tagamet® and Zantac®, are acid inhibitors. They act on acid-producing cells in the lining of the stomach. Formulations that control acid in this way are now available as over-the-counter drugs.

RELATED EXERCISE: 4.95

▲ FIGURE 4.10 **Antacids.** These products all serve as acid-neutralizing agents in the stomach.

TABLE 4.4 ∙ Some Common Antacids

Commercial Name	Acid-Neutralizing Agents
Alka-Seltzer®	$NaHCO_3$
Amphojel®	$Al(OH)_3$
Di-Gel®	$Mg(OH)_2$ and $CaCO_3$
Milk of Magnesia	$Mg(OH)_2$
Maalox®	$Mg(OH)_2$ and $Al(OH)_3$
Mylanta®	$Mg(OH)_2$ and $Al(OH)_3$
Rolaids®	$NaAl(OH)_2CO_3$
Tums®	$CaCO_3$

Chemistry Put to Work and **Chemistry and Life**
Chemistry's connection to world events, scientific discoveries, and medical breakthroughs are showcased in **Chemistry and Life** and **Chemistry Put to Work** features throughout the text.

CHEMISTRY AND LIFE

DRINKING TOO MUCH WATER CAN KILL YOU

For a long time dehydration was considered a potential danger for people engaged in extended vigorous activity. Thus, athletes were encouraged to drink lots of water while engaged in active sport. The trend toward extensive hydration has spread throughout society, so that today many people carry water bottles everywhere and dutifully keep well hydrated.

In some circumstances, however, drinking too much water is a greater danger than not drinking enough. Excess water consumption can lead to *hyponatremia*, a condition in which the concentration of sodium ion in the blood is too low. In the past decade at least four marathon runners have died from hyponatremia-related trauma, and dozens more have become seriously ill. For example, a first-time marathoner named Hillary Bellamy, running in the Marine Corps marathon in 2003, collapsed near mile 22 and died the next day. One physician who treated her said that she died from hyponatremia-induced brain swelling, the result of drinking too much water before and during the race.

The normal blood sodium level is 135 to 145 mM *(millimolar)*. When that level drops to 125 mM, dizziness and confusion set in. A concentration below 120 mM can be critical. Dangerously low levels can occur in any active athlete who is sweating out salt (NaCl) at the same time that excessive amounts of NaCl-free water are being drunk to compensate for water loss. The condition affects women more than men because of differences in body composition and patterns of metabolism. Drinking a sport drink that contains some electrolytes helps to prevent hyponatremia.

RELATED EXERCISES: 4.63, 4.64

CONCEPTUAL UNDERSTANDING BRINGS CHEMISTRY TO LIFE

The authors help you achieve a deeper understanding of concepts through a variety of learning aids, including **Give it Some Thought** and **NEW! Go Figure** questions.

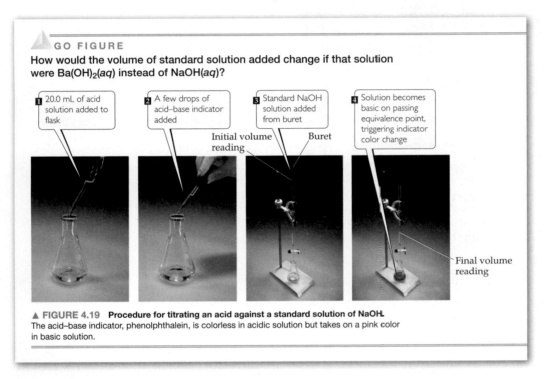

▲ GO FIGURE

How would the volume of standard solution added change if that solution were Ba(OH)₂(*aq*) instead of NaOH(*aq*)?

1 20.0 mL of acid solution added to flask

2 A few drops of acid–base indicator added

3 Standard NaOH solution added from buret

4 Solution becomes basic on passing equivalence point, triggering indicator color change

Initial volume reading   Buret

Final volume reading

▲ FIGURE 4.19   **Procedure for titrating an acid against a standard solution of NaOH.** The acid–base indicator, phenolphthalein, is colorless in acidic solution but takes on a pink color in basic solution.

NEW! Go Figure questions
Go Figure questions encourage you to stop and analyze the artwork in the text, for conceptual understanding. "Voice Balloons" in selected figures help you break down and understand the components of the image. These questions are also available in MasteringChemistry.

▲ GIVE IT SOME THOUGHT
What is the principal reason we must consider the uncertainty principle when discussing electrons and other subatomic particles but not when discussing our macroscopic world?

Give It Some Thought (GIST) questions
These informal, sharply focused exercises give you opportunities to test whether you are "getting it" as you read along. We've increased the number of GIST questions in the Twelfth Edition.

PROBLEM-SOLVING SKILLS HELP YOU SUCCEED IN YOUR COURSE

A consistent problem-solving process is incorporated throughout, so you'll always know where to go when solving problems.

Analyze/Plan/Solve/Check

This four-step problem-solving method helps you understand what you are being asked to solve, to plan how you will solve each problem, to work your way through the solution, and to check your answers. This method is introduced in Chapter 3 and reinforced throughout the book.

Dual-Column Problem-Solving Strategies

Found in Selected Sample Exercises, these strategies explain the thought process involved in each step of a mathematical calculation using a unique layout for clarity. They help you develop a conceptual understanding of those calculations.

SAMPLE EXERCISE 5.6   Measuring ΔH Using a Coffee-Cup Calorimeter

When a student mixes 50 mL of 1.0 M HCl and 50 mL of 1.0 M NaOH in a coffee-cup calorimeter, the temperature of the resultant solution increases from 21.0 °C to 27.5 °C. Calculate the enthalpy change for the reaction in kJ/mol HCl, assuming that the calorimeter loses only a negligible quantity of heat, that the total volume of the solution is 100 mL, that its density is 1.0 g/mL, and that its specific heat is 4.18 J/g-K.

SOLUTION

Analyze Mixing solutions of HCl and NaOH results in an acid–base reaction:

$$HCl(aq) + NaOH(aq) \longrightarrow H_2O(l) + NaCl(aq)$$

We need to calculate the heat produced per mole of HCl, given the temperature increase of the solution, the number of moles of HCl and NaOH involved, and the density and specific heat of the solution.

Plan The total heat produced can be calculated using Equation 5.23. The number of moles of HCl consumed in the reaction must be calculated from the volume and molarity of this substance, and this amount is then used to determine the heat produced per mol HCl.

Solve

Because the total volume of the solution is 100 mL, its mass is

$$(100 \text{ mL})(1.0 \text{ g/mL}) = 100 \text{ g}$$

The temperature change is

$$\Delta T = 27.5 \text{ °C} - 21.0 \text{ °C} = 6.5 \text{ °C} = 6.5 \text{ K}$$

Using Equation 5.23, we have

$$q_{rxn} = -C_s \times m \times \Delta T$$
$$= -(4.18 \text{ J/g-K})(100 \text{ g})(6.5 \text{ K}) = -2.7 \times 10^3 \text{ J} = -2.7 \text{ kJ}$$

Because the process occurs at constant pressure,

$$\Delta H = q_P = -2.7 \text{ kJ}$$

To express the enthalpy change on a molar basis, we use the fact that the number of moles of HCl is given by the product of the volume (50 mL = 0.050 L) and concentration (1.0 M = 1.0 mol/L) of the HCl solution:

$$(0.050 \text{ L})(1.0 \text{ mol/L}) = 0.050 \text{ mol}$$

Thus, the enthalpy change per mole of HCl is

$$\Delta H = -2.7 \text{ kJ}/0.050 \text{ mol} = -54 \text{ kJ/mol}$$

Check ΔH is negative (exothermic), which is expected for the reaction of an acid with a base and evidenced by the fact that the reaction causes the temperature of the solution to increase. The magnitude of the molar enthalpy change seems reasonable.

PRACTICE EXERCISE

When 50.0 mL of 0.100 M AgNO$_3$ and 50.0 mL of 0.100 M HCl are mixed in a constant-pressure calorimeter, the temperature of the mixture increases from 22.30 °C to 23.11 °C. The temperature increase is caused by the following reaction:

$$AgNO_3(aq) + HCl(aq) \longrightarrow AgCl(s) + HNO_3(aq)$$

Calculate ΔH for this reaction in kJ/mol AgNO$_3$, assuming that the combined solution has a mass of 100.0 g and a specific heat of 4.18 J/g °C.
Answer: $-68,000$ J/mol $= -68$ kJ/mol

STRATEGIES IN CHEMISTRY

PROBLEM SOLVING

Practice is the key to success in solving problems. As you practice, you can improve your skills by following these steps:

Step 1: Analyze the problem. Read the problem carefully. What does it say? Draw a picture or diagram that will help you to visualize the problem. Write down both the data you are given and the quantity you need to obtain (the unknown).

Step 2: Develop a plan for solving the problem. Consider a possible path between the given information and the unknown. What principles or equations relate the known data to the unknown?

Recognize that some data may not be given explicitly in the problem; you may be expected to know certain quantities (such as Avogadro's number) or look them up in tables (such as atomic weights). Recognize also that your plan may involve either a single step or a series of steps with intermediate answers.

Step 3: Solve the problem. Use the known information and suitable equations or relationships to solve for the unknown. Dimensional analysis ∞∞ (Section 1.6) is a useful tool for solving a great number of problems. Be careful with significant figures, signs, and units.

Step 4: Check the solution. Read the problem again to make sure you have found all the solutions asked for in the problem. Does your answer make sense? That is, is the answer outrageously large or small or is it in the ballpark? Finally, are the units and significant figures correct?

Strategies in Chemistry

Strategies in Chemistry teach ways to analyze information and organize thoughts, helping to improve your problem-solving and critical-thinking abilities.

UPDATED END-OF-CHAPTER MATERIALS BOOST YOUR COMPREHENSION

Unique to the Twelfth Edition, the end-of-chapter materials have been updated and streamlined based on student performance data gathered through MasteringChemistry. Only content that has proven to increase student comprehension of fundamental concepts has been retained.

CHAPTER SUMMARY AND KEY TERMS

INTRODUCTION AND SECTION 3.1 The study of the quantitative relationships between chemical formulas and chemical equations is known as **stoichiometry**. One of the important concepts of stoichiometry is the law of conservation of mass, which states that the total mass of the products of a chemical reaction is the same as the total mass of the reactants. The same numbers of atoms of each type are present before and after a chemical reaction. A balanced **chemical equation** shows equal numbers of atoms of each element on each side of the equation. Equations are balanced by placing coefficients in front of the chemical formulas for the **reactants** and **products** of a reaction, *not* by changing the subscripts in chemical formulas.

SECTION 3.2 Among the reaction types described in this chapter are (1) **combination reactions**, in which two reactants combine to form one product; (2) **decomposition reactions**, in which a single reactant forms two or more products; and (3) **combustion reactions** in oxygen, in which a hydrocarbon or related compound reacts with O_2 to form CO_2 and H_2O.

SECTION 3.3 Much quantitative information can be determined from chemical formulas and balanced chemical equations by using atomic weights. The **formula weight** of a compound equals the sum of the atomic weights of the atoms in its formula. If the formula is a molecular formula, the formula weight is also called the **molecular weight**. Atomic weights and formula weights can be used to determine the elemental composition of a compound.

SECTION 3.4 A mole of any substance is **Avogadro's number** (6.02×10^{23}) of formula units of that substance. The mass of a **mole** of atoms, molecules, or ions (the **molar mass**) equals the formula weight of that material expressed in grams. The mass of one molecule of H_2O, for example, is 18 amu, so the mass of 1 mol of H_2O is 18 g. That is, the molar mass of H_2O is 18 g/mol.

SECTION 3.5 The empirical formula of any substance can be determined from its percent composition by calculating the relative number of moles of each atom in 100 g of the substance. If the substance is molecular in nature, its molecular formula can be determined from the empirical formula if the molecular weight is also known.

SECTIONS 3.6 AND 3.7 The mole concept can be used to calculate the relative quantities of reactants and products in chemical reactions. The coefficients in a balanced equation give the relative numbers of moles of the reactants and products. To calculate the number of grams of a product from the number of grams of a reactant, first convert grams of reactant to moles of reactant. Then use the coefficients in the balanced equation to convert the number of moles of reactant to moles of product. Finally, convert moles of product to grams of product.

A **limiting reactant** is completely consumed in a reaction. When it is used up, the reaction stops, thus limiting the quantities of products formed. The **theoretical yield** of a reaction is the quantity of product calculated to form when all of the limiting reactant reacts. The actual yield of a reaction is always less than the theoretical yield. The **percent yield** compares the actual and theoretical yields.

Summary with Key Terms
These list all of the chapter's boldfaced items, organized by section in order of appearance, with page references. Definitions are found in the Glossary.

KEY EQUATIONS

- $E_{el} = \dfrac{\kappa Q_1 Q_2}{d}$ [8.4]   The potential energy of two interacting charges

- $\mu = Qr$ [8.11]   The dipole moment of two charges of equal magnitude but opposite sign, separated by a distance r

- $\Delta H_{rxn} = \Sigma(\text{bond enthalpies of bonds broken}) - \Sigma(\text{bond enthalpies of bonds formed})$ [8.12]   The enthalpy change as a function of bond enthalpies for reactions involving gas-phase molecules

Key Equations
The **Key Equations** section lists each of the key equations and important quantitative relationships from the chapter.

KEY SKILLS

- Write Lewis symbols for atoms and ions. (Section 8.1)
- Understand lattice energy and be able to arrange compounds in order of increasing lattice energy based on the charges and sizes of the ions involved. (Section 8.2)
- Use atomic electron configurations and the octet rule to write Lewis structures for molecules to determine their electron distribution. (Section 8.3)
- Use electronegativity differences to identify nonpolar covalent, polar covalent, and ionic bonds. (Section 8.4)
- Calculate charge separation in diatomic molecules based on the experimentally measured dipole moment and bond distance. (Section 8.4)
- Calculate formal charges from Lewis structures and use those formal charges to identify the dominant Lewis structure for a molecule or ion. (Section 8.5)
- Recognize molecules where resonance structures are needed to describe the bonding. (Section 8.6)
- Recognize exceptions to the octet rule and draw accurate Lewis structures even when the octet rule is not obeyed. (Section 8.7)
- Understand the relationship between bond type (single, double, and triple), bond strength (or enthalpy), and bond length. (Section 8.8)
- Use bond enthalpies to estimate enthalpy changes for reactions involving gas-phase reactants and products. (Section 8.8)

Key Skills
The **Key Skills** section in each chapter lists the fundamental concepts you should comprehend.

VISUALIZING CONCEPTS

4.1 Which of the following schematic drawings best describes a solution of Li_2SO_4 in water (water molecules not shown for simplicity)? [Section 4.1]

    (a)   (b)   (c)

4.2 Aqueous solutions of three different substances, AX, AY, and AZ, are represented by the three accompanying diagrams. Identify each substance as a strong electrolyte, weak electrolyte, or nonelectrolyte. [Section 4.1]

  AX   AY   AZ

    (a)   (b)   (c)

4.3 Use the molecular representations shown here to classify each compound as either a nonelectrolyte, a weak electrolyte, or a strong electrolyte. [Sections 4.1 and 4.3]

    (a)   (b)   (c)

See inside back cover for element color scheme.

4.4 A 0.1 *M* solution of acetic acid, CH_3COOH, causes the light-bulb in the apparatus of Figure 4.2 to glow about as brightly as a 0.001 *M* solution of HBr. How do you account for this fact? [Section 4.1]

4.5 You are presented with a white solid and told that due to careless labeling it is not clear if the substance is barium chloride, lead chloride, or zinc chloride. When you transfer the solid to a beaker and add water, the solid dissolves to give a clear solution. Next a $Na_2SO_4(aq)$ solution is added and a white precipitate forms. What is the identity of the unknown white solid? [Section 4.2]

4.6 We have seen that ions in aqueous solution are stabilized by the attractions between the ions and the water molecules. Why then do some pairs of ions in solution form precipitates? [Section 4.2]

4.7 Which of the following ions will *always* be a spectator ion in a precipitation reaction? (a) Cl^-, (b) NO_3^-, (c) NH_4^+, (d) S^{2-}, (e) SO_4^{2-}. Explain briefly. [Section 4.2]

4.8 The labels have fallen off three bottles containing powdered samples of metals; one contains zinc, one lead, and the other platinum. You have three solutions at your disposal: 1 *M* sodium nitrate, 1 *M* nitric acid, and 1 *M* nickel nitrate. How could you use these solutions to determine the identities of each metal powder? [Section 4.4]

4.9 Explain how a redox reaction involves electrons in the same way that a neutralization reaction involves protons. [Sections 4.3 and 4.4]

4.10 If you want to double the concentration of a solution, how could you do it? [Section 4.5]

EXERCISES

VISUALIZING CONCEPTS

8.1 For each of these Lewis symbols, indicate the group in the periodic table in which the element X belongs: [Section 8.1]

(a) $\cdot\dot{X}\cdot$ (b) $\cdot X\cdot$ (c) $:\dot{X}\cdot$

8.2 Illustrated are four ions—A, B, X, and Y— showing their relative ionic radii. The ions shown in red carry positive charges: a

  +2   +1   −1   −2

  A   B   X   Y

INTEGRATIVE EXERCISES

6.97 Microwave ovens use microwave radiation to heat food. The energy of the microwaves is absorbed by water molecules in food and then transferred to other components of the food. (a) Suppose that the microwave radiation has a wavelength of 11.2 cm. How many photons are required to heat 200 mL of coffee from 23 °C to 60 °C? (b) Suppose the microwave's power is 900 W (1 Watt = 1 joule-second). How long would you have to heat the coffee in part (a)?

6.98 The stratospheric ozone (O_3) layer helps to protect us from harmful ultraviolet radiation. It does so by absorbing ultraviolet light and falling apart into an O_2 molecule and an oxygen atom, a process known as photodissociation.

$$O_3(g) \longrightarrow O_2(g) + O(g)$$

Use the data in Appendix C to calculate the enthalpy change for this reaction. What is the maximum wavelength a photon can have if it is to possess sufficient energy to cause this dissociation? In what portion of the spectrum does this wavelength occur?

ADDITIONAL EXERCISES

6.75 Consider the two waves shown here, which we will consider to represent two electromagnetic radiations:
(a) What is the wavelength of wave A? Of wave B?
(b) What is the frequency of wave A? Of wave B?
(c) Identify the regions of the electromagnetic spectrum to which waves A and B belong.

       1.6×10^{-7} m

[4.114] The newest US standard for arsenate in drinking water, mandated by the Safe Drinking Water Act, required that by January 2006, public water supplies must contain no greater than 10 parts per billion (ppb) arsenic. If this arsenic is present as arsenate, AsO_4^{3-}, what mass of sodium arsenate would be present in a 1.00-L sample of drinking water that just meets the standard? Parts per billion is defined on a mass basis as

$$ppb = \frac{g\ solute}{g\ solution} \times 10^9.$$

Visualizing Concepts

Visualizing Concepts exercises begin the end-of-chapter exercises and ask you to consider concepts through the use of models, graphs, and other visual materials. These help you develop a conceptual understanding of the key ideas in the chapter. Additional conceptual exercises are found among the end-of-chapter exercises.

Exercises

End-of-Chapter Exercises are grouped by topic and presented in matched pairs based on data gathered from MasteringChemistry, giving you multiple opportunities to test each concept.

Integrative Exercises

Included among the exercises at the end of Chapters 3-24, **Integrative Exercises** connect concepts for the current chapter with those from previous chapters. These help you gain a deeper understanding of how chemistry fits together and serve as an overall review of key concepts.

Bracketed Challenge Problems

The Bracketed Challenge Problems have been revised for the Twelfth Edition, based on student performance data gathered through MasteringChemistry reflecting the difficulty of the problem.

Additional Exercises

Additional Exercises follow the paired exercises and are not categorized, because many of these exercises draw on multiple concepts from within the chapter.

Mastering**CHEMISTRY**®

MasteringChemistry is the most effective, widely used online tutorial, homework and assessment system for chemistry. It helps instructors maximize class time with customizable, easy-to-assign, and automatically graded assessments that motivate students to learn outside of class and arrive prepared for lecture. These assessments can easily be customized and personalized by instructors to suit their individual teaching style. To learn more, visit **www.masteringchemistry.com**

Student Tutorials

MasteringChemistry is the only system to provide instantaneous feedback specific to the most-common wrong answers. Students can submit an answer and receive immediate, error-specific feedback. Simpler sub-problems—"hints"—are provided upon request.

Gradebook

MasteringChemistry is the only system to capture the step-by-step work of each student in class, including wrong answers submitted, hints requested, and time taken on every step. This data powers an unprecedented gradebook.

Student Performance Snapshot

This screen provides your favorite weekly diagnostics. With a single click, charts summarize the most difficult problems, vulnerable students, grade distribution, and even score improvement over the course.

EXTEND LEARNING
BEYOND THE CLASSROOM

Pearson eText

The eText gives students access to the text whenever and wherever they can access the Internet. The eText pages look exactly like the printed text, and include powerful interactive and customization features.

Students can:

- Create notes, highlight text in different colors, create book marks, zoom, click hyperlinked words and phrases to view definitions, and view in single-page or two-page format.

- Link directly to associated media files, enabling them to view an animation as they read the text.

- Perform a full-text search and save or export notes.

Instructors can share their notes and highlights with students, and can also hide chapters that they do not want students to read.

NEW! Visualizations

These new tutorials enable you to make connections between real-life phenomena and the underlying chemistry that explains such phenomena. The tutorials increase your understanding of chemistry and clearly illustrate cause-and-effect relationships.

NEW! Reading Quizzes

Chapter-specific quizzes and activities focus on important, hard-to-grasp chemistry concepts.

WHAT'S AHEAD

HUBBLE SPACE TELESCOPE IMAGE of the Omega Nebula, a 15-light-year-wide expanding remnant of a star's supernova explosion. The orange filaments are the tattered remains of the star and consist mostly of hydrogen, the simplest and most plentiful element in the universe. Hydrogen occurs as molecules in cool regions of the nebula, as atoms in hotter regions, and as ions in the hottest regions. The processes that occur within stars are responsible for creating other chemical elements from hydrogen.

INTRODUCTION: MATTER AND MEASUREMENT

HAVE YOU EVER WONDERED why the stars shine? Or why leaves change color in the fall or how a battery generates electricity? Have you ever wondered why keeping foods cold slows their spoilage and how our bodies use food to maintain life? Chemistry answers these questions as well as countless others.

Chemistry is the study of matter and the changes that matter undergoes. One of the joys of learning chemistry is seeing how chemical principles operate in all aspects of our lives, from everyday activities like cooking dinner to more complex processes like the development of drugs to cure cancer. Chemical principles also operate in the far reaches of our galaxy (chapter-opening photograph) as well as within and around us.

This first chapter provides an overview of what chemistry is about and what chemists do. The preceding "What's Ahead" list gives an overview of the chapter organization and of some of the ideas we will consider. As you study, keep in mind that the chemical facts and concepts you are asked to learn are not ends in themselves; they are tools to help you better understand the world around you.

1.1 | THE STUDY OF CHEMISTRY

Before traveling to an unfamiliar city, you might look at a map to get some sense of where you are heading. Because chemistry may be unfamiliar to you, it's useful to get a general idea of what lies ahead before you embark on your journey. In fact, you might even ask why you are taking the trip.

The Atomic and Molecular Perspective of Chemistry

Chemistry is the study of the properties and behavior of matter. **Matter** is the physical material of the universe; it is anything that has mass and occupies space. A **property** is any characteristic that allows us to recognize a particular type of matter and to distinguish it from other types. This book, your body, the air you are breathing, and the clothes you are wearing are all samples of matter. Countless experiments have shown that the tremendous variety of matter in our world is due to combinations of only about 100 substances called **elements**. As we proceed through this text, we will seek to relate the properties of matter to its composition, that is, to the particular elements it contains.

Chemistry also provides a background for understanding the properties of matter in terms of **atoms**, the almost infinitesimally small building blocks of matter. Each element is composed of a unique kind of atom. We will see that the properties of matter relate to both the kinds of atoms the matter contains (*composition*) and to the arrangements of these atoms (*structure*).

In **molecules**, two or more atoms are joined together in specific shapes. Throughout this text you will see molecules represented using colored spheres to show how the atoms are connected (▼ **FIGURE 1.1**). The color provides a convenient way to distinguish between atoms of different elements. For example, notice that the molecules of ethanol and ethylene glycol in Figure 1.1 have different compositions and structures. Ethanol contains one oxygen atom, depicted by one red sphere. In contrast, ethylene glycol contains two oxygen atoms.

Even apparently minor differences in the composition or structure of molecules can cause profound differences in properties. Ethanol, for example, is the alcohol in

GO FIGURE

How many carbon atoms are in one aspirin molecule?

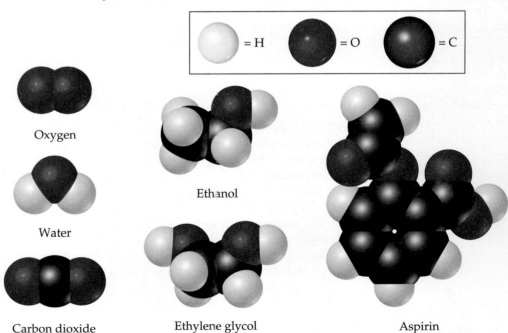

Oxygen

Water

Carbon dioxide

Ethanol

Ethylene glycol

Aspirin

▲ **FIGURE 1.1 Molecular models.** The white, black, and red spheres represent atoms of hydrogen, carbon, and oxygen, respectively.

beverages such as beer and wine, whereas ethylene glycol is a viscous liquid used as automobile antifreeze. The properties of these two substances differ in many ways, as do their biological activities. Ethanol is consumed throughout the world, but you should *never* consume ethylene glycol because it is highly toxic. One of the challenges chemists undertake is to alter the composition or structure of molecules in a controlled way, creating new substances with different properties.

Every change in the observable world—from boiling water to the changes that occur as our bodies combat invading viruses—has its basis in the world of atoms and molecules. Thus, as we proceed with our study of chemistry, we will find ourselves thinking in two realms: the *macroscopic* realm of ordinary-sized objects (*macro* = large) and the *submicroscopic* realm of atoms and molecules. We make our observations in the macroscopic world, but in order to understand that world, we must visualize how atoms and molecules behave at the submicroscopic level. Chemistry is the science that seeks to understand the properties and behavior of matter by studying the properties and behavior of atoms and molecules.

 GIVE IT SOME THOUGHT

    a. Approximately how many elements are there?
    b. What submicroscopic particles are the building blocks of matter?

Why Study Chemistry?

Chemistry greatly impacts our daily lives. Indeed, chemistry lies near the heart of many matters of public concern: improvement of health care, conservation of natural resources, protection of the environment, and provision of our daily needs for food, clothing, and shelter. Using chemistry, we have discovered pharmaceutical chemicals that enhance health and prolong lives. We have increased food production through the use of fertilizers and pesticides, and we have developed plastics and other materials used in almost every facet of our lives, from electronics to sporting equipment to building construction. Unfortunately, some chemicals can harm our health or the environment. As educated citizens and consumers, it is in our best interest to understand the profound effects, both positive and negative, that chemicals have on our lives and to strike an informed balance about their uses.

Most of you are studying chemistry, however, not merely to satisfy your curiosity or to become more informed consumers or citizens but also because it is an essential part of your curriculum. Your major might be chemistry, but it could be biology, engineering, pharmacy, agriculture, geology, or some other field. Why do so many subjects share an essential tie to chemistry? The answer is that chemistry is the *central science,* central to a fundamental understanding of other sciences and technologies. For example, our interactions with the material world raise basic questions about the materials around us. What are their compositions and properties? How do they interact with us and with our environment? How, why, and when do materials undergo change? These questions are important whether the material is part of a solar cell, a pigment used by a Renaissance painter, or a living creature (▼ FIGURE 1.2).

(a)

(b)

(c)

◀ FIGURE 1.2
Chemistry helps us understand the world around us.
(a) Solar cells are made of silicon. (b) A Renaissance painting, *Young Girl Reading,* by Vittore Carpaccio (1472–1526), uses pigments that keep their color for years. (c) The light from this firefly is the result of a chemical reaction within the animal.

By studying chemistry, you will learn to use the powerful language and ideas that have evolved to describe and enhance our understanding of matter. Furthermore, an understanding of chemistry provides powerful insights into other areas of modern science, technology, and engineering.

CHEMISTRY PUT TO WORK

Chemistry and the Chemical Industry

Chemistry is all around us. Many people are familiar with household chemicals such as those shown in ▶ FIGURE 1.3, but few realize the size and importance of the chemical industry. Worldwide sales of chemicals and related products manufactured in the United States total approximately $550 billion annually. The chemical industry employs more than 10% of all scientists and engineers and is a major contributor to the US economy.

Vast amounts of chemicals are produced each year and serve as raw materials for a variety of uses, including the manufacture and processing of metals, plastics, fertilizers, pharmaceuticals, fuels, paints, adhesives, pesticides, synthetic fibers, and microprocessor chips. ▼ TABLE 1.1 lists the top eight chemicals produced in the United States.

Who are chemists, and what do they do? People who have degrees in chemistry hold a variety of positions in industry, government, and academia. Those in industry work as laboratory chemists, developing new products (research and development), analyzing materials (quality control), or assisting customers in using products (sales and service). Those with more experience or training may work as managers or company directors. Chemists are important members of the scientific workforce in government (the National Institutes of Health, Department of Energy, and Environmental Protection Agency all employ chemists) and at universities. A chemistry degree is also good preparation for careers in teaching, medicine, biomedical research, information science, environmental work, technical sales, work with government regulatory agencies, and patent law.

Fundamentally, chemists do three things: (1) make new types of matter: materials, substances, or combinations of substances with

▶ FIGURE 1.3
Common household chemicals.

desired properties; (2) measure the properties of matter; and (3) develop models that explain and/or predict the properties of matter. One chemist, for example, may spend years working in the laboratory to discover new drugs. Another may concentrate on the development of new instrumentation to measure properties of matter at the atomic level. Other chemists may use existing materials and methods to understand how pollutants are transported in the environment or how drugs are processed in the body. Yet another chemist will develop theory, write computer code, or run computer simulations to understand how molecules move and react on very fast time scales. The collective chemical enterprise is a rich mix of all of these activities.

TABLE 1.1 • The Top Eight Chemicals Produced by the US Chemical Industry in 2008[a]

Rank	Chemical	Formula	2008 Production (Billions of Pounds)	Principal End Uses
1	Sulfuric acid	H_2SO_4	71	Fertilizers, chemical manufacturing
2	Ethylene	C_2H_4	50	Plastics, antifreeze
3	Lime	CaO	44	Paper, cement, steel
4	Propylene	C_3H_6	33	Plastics
5	Ammonia	NH_3	21	Fertilizers
6	Chlorine	Cl_2	21	Bleaches, plastics, water purification
7	Phosphoric acid	H_3PO_4	20	Fertilizers
8	Sodium hydroxide	$NaOH$	16	Aluminum production, soap

[a]Most data from *Chemical and Engineering News,* July 6, 2009, pp. 53, 56. Data on lime from U.S. Geological Survey.

1.2 | CLASSIFICATIONS OF MATTER

Let's begin our study of chemistry by examining some fundamental ways in which matter is classified. Two principal ways of classifying matter are according to physical state (gas, liquid, or solid) and according to composition (element, compound, or mixture).

States of Matter

A sample of matter can be a gas, a liquid, or a solid. These three forms, called the **states of matter**, differ in some of their observable properties. A **gas** (also known as *vapor*) has no fixed volume or shape; rather, it conforms to the volume and shape of its container. A gas can be compressed to occupy a smaller volume, or it can expand to occupy a larger one. A **liquid** has a distinct volume independent of its container but has no specific shape. It assumes the shape of the portion of the container it occupies. A **solid** has both a definite shape and a definite volume. Neither liquids nor solids can be compressed to any appreciable extent.

The properties of the states of matter can be understood on the molecular level (▶ FIGURE 1.4). In a gas the molecules are far apart and moving at high speeds, colliding repeatedly with one another and with the walls of the container. Compressing a gas decreases the amount of space between molecules and increases the frequency of collisions between molecules but does not alter the size or shape of the molecules. In a liquid the molecules are packed closely together but still move rapidly. The rapid movement allows the molecules to slide over one another; thus, a liquid pours easily. In a solid the molecules are held tightly together, usually in definite arrangements in which the molecules can wiggle only slightly in their otherwise fixed positions. Thus, the distances between molecules are similar in the liquid and solid states, but the two states differ in how free the molecules are to move around. Changes in temperature and/or pressure can lead to conversion from one state of matter to another, illustrated by such familiar processes as ice melting or water vapor condensing.

Pure Substances

Most forms of matter we encounter—the air we breathe (a gas), the gasoline we burn in our cars (a liquid), and the sidewalk we walk on (a solid)—are not chemically pure. We can, however, separate these forms of matter into pure substances. A **pure substance** (usually referred to simply as a *substance*) is matter that has distinct properties and a composition that does not vary from sample to sample. Water and table salt (sodium chloride), the primary components of seawater, are examples of pure substances.

All substances are either elements or compounds. **Elements** are substances that cannot be decomposed into simpler substances. On the molecular level, each element is composed of only one kind of atom [▶ FIGURE 1.5(a and b)]. **Compounds** are substances composed of two or more elements; they contain two or more kinds of atoms [Figure 1.5(c)]. Water, for example, is a compound composed of two elements: hydrogen and oxygen. Figure 1.5(d) shows a mixture of substances. **Mixtures** are combinations of two or more substances in which each substance retains its chemical identity.

Elements

Currently, 118 elements are known, though they vary widely in abundance. For example, only five elements—oxygen, silicon, aluminum, iron, and calcium—account for over 90% of Earth's crust (including oceans and atmosphere) and only three—oxygen,

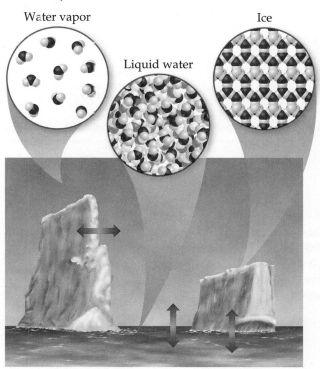

GO FIGURE

In which form of water are the water molecules farthest apart?

Water vapor   Liquid water   Ice

▲ **FIGURE 1.4   The three physical states of water—water vapor, liquid water, and ice.** We see the liquid and solid states but cannot see the gas (vapor) state. When we look at steam or clouds, we see tiny droplets of liquid water dispersed in the atmosphere. The red arrows show that the three states of matter interconvert.

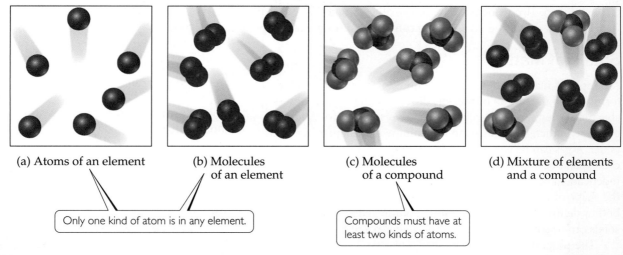

How do the molecules of a compound differ from the molecules of an element?

(a) Atoms of an element

(b) Molecules of an element

(c) Molecules of a compound

(d) Mixture of elements and a compound

Only one kind of atom is in any element.

Compounds must have at least two kinds of atoms.

▲ FIGURE 1.5 Molecular comparison of elements, compounds, and mixtures.

Can you name two significant differences between the elemental composition of Earth's crust and the elemental composition of the human body?

Aluminum 7.5%

Iron 4.7%

Other 9.2%

Calcium 3.4%

Silicon 25.7%

Oxygen 49.5%

Earth's crust

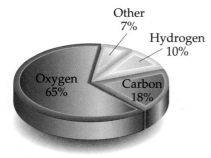

Other 7%

Hydrogen 10%

Oxygen 65%

Carbon 18%

Human body

▲ FIGURE 1.6 **Relative abundances of elements.** Elements in percent by mass in Earth's crust (including oceans and atmosphere) and the human body.

carbon, and hydrogen—account for over 90% of the mass of the human body (◄ FIGURE 1.6).

▼ TABLE 1.2 lists some common elements, along with the chemical *symbols* used to denote them. The symbol for each element consists of one or two letters, with the first letter capitalized. These symbols are derived mostly from the English names of the elements, but sometimes they are derived from a foreign name instead (last column in Table 1.2). You will need to know these symbols and learn others as we encounter them in the text.

All of the known elements and their symbols are listed on the front inside cover of this text in a table known as the *periodic table*. In the periodic table the elements are arranged in columns so that closely related elements are grouped together. We describe the periodic table in more detail in Section 2.5 and consider the periodically repeating properties of the elements in Chapter 7.

Compounds

Most elements can interact with other elements to form compounds. For example, when hydrogen gas burns in oxygen gas, the elements hydrogen and oxygen combine to form the compound water. Conversely, water can be decomposed into its elements by passing an electrical current through it (► FIGURE 1.7). Pure water, regardless of its source, consists of 11% hydrogen and 89% oxygen by mass. This

TABLE 1.2 • Some Common Elements and Their Symbols					
Carbon	C	Aluminum	Al	Copper	Cu (from *cuprum*)
Fluorine	F	Bromine	Br	Iron	Fe (from *ferrum*)
Hydrogen	H	Calcium	Ca	Lead	Pb (from *plumbum*)
Iodine	I	Chlorine	Cl	Mercury	Hg (from *hydrargyrum*)
Nitrogen	N	Helium	He	Potassium	K (from *kalium*)
Oxygen	O	Lithium	Li	Silver	Ag (from *argentum*)
Phosphorus	P	Magnesium	Mg	Sodium	Na (from *natrium*)
Sulfur	S	Silicon	Si	Tin	Sn (from *stannum*)

What is the connection between the relative gas volumes collected in the two tubes and the relative number of gas molecules in the tubes?

Oxygen gas, O_2

Water, H_2O

Hydrogen gas, H_2

◀ **FIGURE 1.7**
Electrolysis of water.
Water decomposes into its
component elements,
hydrogen and oxygen, when
an electrical current is
passed through it. The
volume of hydrogen,
collected in the right test
tube, is twice the volume of
oxygen.

macroscopic composition corresponds to the molecular composition, which consists of
two hydrogen atoms combined with one oxygen atom:

| Hydrogen atom | Oxygen atom | Water molecule |
| (written H) | (written O) | (written H_2O) |

The elements hydrogen and oxygen themselves exist naturally as diatomic (two-
atom) molecules:

Oxygen molecule   (written O_2)

Hydrogen molecule   (written H_2)

As seen in ▼ **TABLE 1.3**, the properties of water bear no resemblance to the
properties of its component elements. Hydrogen, oxygen, and water are each a unique
substance, a consequence of the uniqueness of their respective molecules.

TABLE 1.3 • Comparison of Water, Hydrogen, and Oxygen

	Water	Hydrogen	Oxygen
State[a]	Liquid	Gas	Gas
Normal boiling point	100 °C	−253 °C	−183 °C
Density[a]	1000 g/L	0.084 g/L	1.33 g/L
Flammable	No	Yes	No

[a]At room temperature and atmospheric pressure.

The observation that the elemental composition of a compound is always the same is known as the **law of constant composition** (or the **law of definite proportions**). French chemist Joseph Louis Proust (1754–1826) first stated the law in about 1800. Although this law has been known for 200 years, the belief persists among some people that a fundamental difference exists between compounds prepared in the laboratory and the corresponding compounds found in nature. However, a pure compound has the same composition and properties regardless of its source. Both chemists and nature must use the same elements and operate under the same natural laws. When two materials differ in composition or properties, either they are composed of different compounds or they differ in purity.

 GIVE IT SOME THOUGHT

Hydrogen, oxygen, and water are all composed of molecules. What is it about a molecule of water that makes it a compound, whereas hydrogen and oxygen are elements?

Mixtures

Most of the matter we encounter consists of mixtures of different substances. Each substance in a mixture retains its chemical identity and properties. In contrast to a pure substance, which by definition has a fixed composition, the composition of a mixture can vary. A cup of sweetened coffee, for example, can contain either a little sugar or a lot. The substances making up a mixture are called *components* of the mixture.

Some mixtures do not have the same composition, properties, and appearance throughout. Rocks and wood, for example, vary in texture and appearance in any typical sample. Such mixtures are *heterogeneous* [▼ FIGURE 1.8(a)]. Mixtures that are uniform throughout are *homogeneous*. Air is a homogeneous mixture of nitrogen, oxygen, and smaller amounts of other gases. The nitrogen in air has all the properties of pure nitrogen because both the pure substance and the mixture contain the same nitrogen molecules. Salt, sugar, and many other substances dissolve in water to form homogeneous mixtures [Figure 1.8(b)]. Homogeneous mixtures are also called **solutions**. Although the term *solution* conjures an image of a liquid, solutions can be solids, liquids, or gases.

▶ FIGURE 1.9 summarizes the classification of matter into elements, compounds, and mixtures.

(a)   (b)

▲ **FIGURE 1.8   Mixtures.** (a) Many common materials, including rocks, are heterogeneous mixtures. This photograph of granite shows a heterogeneous mixture of silicon dioxide and other metal oxides. (b) Homogeneous mixtures are called solutions. Many substances, including the blue solid shown here [copper(II) sulfate], dissolve in water to form solutions.

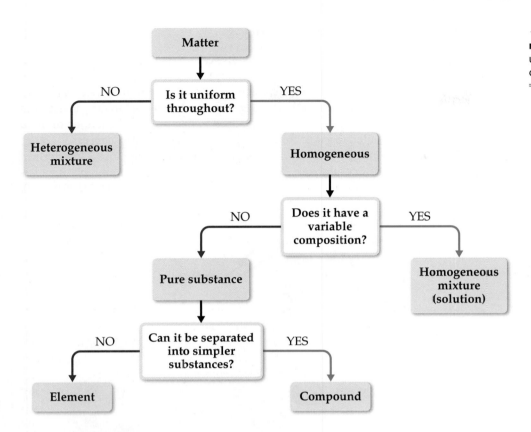

◄ **FIGURE 1.9   Classification of matter.** All pure matter is classified ultimately as either an element or a compound.

| **SAMPLE EXERCISE 1.1** | **Distinguishing among Elements, Compounds, and Mixtures** |

"White gold" contains gold and a "white" metal, such as palladium. Two samples of white gold differ in the relative amounts of gold and palladium they contain. Both samples are uniform in composition throughout. Use Figure 1.9 to classify white gold.

SOLUTION

Because the material is uniform throughout, it is homogeneous. Because its composition differs for the two samples, it cannot be a compound. Instead, it must be a homogeneous mixture.

PRACTICE EXERCISE

Aspirin is composed of 60.0% carbon, 4.5% hydrogen, and 35.5% oxygen by mass, regardless of its source. Use Figure 1.9 to classify aspirin.

Answer: It is a compound because it has constant composition and can be separated into several elements.

1.3 | PROPERTIES OF MATTER

Every substance has unique properties. For example, the properties listed in Table 1.3 allow us to distinguish hydrogen, oxygen, and water from one another. The properties of matter can be categorized as physical or chemical. **Physical properties** can be observed without changing the identity and composition of the substance. These properties include color, odor, density, melting point, boiling point, and hardness. **Chemical properties** describe the way a substance may change, or *react,* to form other substances. A common chemical property is flammability, the ability of a substance to burn in the presence of oxygen.

Some properties, such as temperature and melting point, are **intensive properties**. They do not depend on the amount of sample being examined and are particularly useful in chemistry because many intensive properties can be used to *identify* substances. **Extensive properties** depend on the amount of sample, with two examples being mass and volume. Extensive properties relate to the *amount* of substance present.

Physical and Chemical Changes

The changes substances undergo are either physical or chemical. During a **physical change**, a substance changes its physical appearance but not its composition. (That is, it is the same substance before and after the change.) The evaporation of water is a physical change. When water evaporates, it changes from the liquid state to the gas state, but it is still composed of water molecules, as depicted in Figure 1.4. All **changes of state** (for example, from liquid to gas or from liquid to solid) are physical changes.

In a **chemical change** (also called a **chemical reaction**), a substance is transformed into a chemically different substance. When hydrogen burns in air, for example, it undergoes a chemical change because it combines with oxygen to form water (▼ FIGURE 1.10).

► FIGURE 1.10 **A chemical reaction.**

H_2 O_2 Burn H_2O

Chemical changes can be dramatic. In the account that follows, Ira Remsen, author of a popular chemistry text published in 1901, describes his first experiences with chemical reactions. The chemical reaction that he observed is shown in ▼ FIGURE 1.11.

▲ FIGURE 1.11 **The chemical reaction between a copper penny and nitric acid.** The dissolved copper produces the blue-green solution; the reddish brown gas produced is nitrogen dioxide.

While reading a textbook of chemistry, I came upon the statement "nitric acid acts upon copper," and I determined to see what this meant. Having located some nitric acid, I had only to learn what the words "act upon" meant. In the interest of knowledge I was even willing to sacrifice one of the few copper cents then in my possession. I put one of them on the table, opened a bottle labeled "nitric acid," poured some of the liquid on the copper, and prepared to make an observation. But what was this wonderful thing which I beheld? The cent was already changed, and it was no small change either. A greenish-blue liquid foamed and fumed over the cent and over the table. The air became colored dark red. How could I stop this? I tried by picking the cent up and throwing it out the window. I learned another fact: nitric acid acts upon fingers. The pain led to another unpremeditated experiment. I drew my fingers across my trousers and discovered nitric acid acts upon trousers. That was the most impressive experiment I have ever performed. I tell of it even now with interest. It was a revelation to me. Plainly the only way to learn about such remarkable kinds of action is to see the results, to experiment, to work in the laboratory.

◢ GIVE IT SOME THOUGHT

Which of these changes are physical and which are chemical? Explain.
a. Plants make sugar from carbon dioxide and water.
b. Water vapor in the air forms frost.
c. A goldsmith melts a nugget of gold and pulls it
   into a wire.

Separation of Mixtures

We can separate a mixture into its components by taking advantage of differences in their properties. For example, a heterogeneous mixture of iron filings and gold filings could be sorted by color into iron and gold. A less tedious approach would be to use a magnet to attract the iron filings, leaving the gold ones behind. We can also take advantage of an important chemical difference between these two metals: Many acids dissolve iron but not gold. Thus, if we put our mixture into an appropriate acid, the acid would dissolve the iron and the solid gold would be left behind. The two could then be separated by *filtration* (▼ FIGURE 1.12). We would have to use other chemical reactions, which we will learn about later, to transform the dissolved iron back into metal.

An important method of separating the components of a homogeneous mixture is *distillation,* a process that depends on the different abilities of substances to form gases.

▲ FIGURE 1.12   **Separation by filtration.** A mixture of a solid and a liquid is poured through filter paper. The liquid passes through the paper while the solid remains on the paper.

For example, if we boil a solution of salt and water, the water evaporates, forming a gas, and the salt is left behind. The gaseous water can be converted back to a liquid on the walls of a condenser, as shown in ▼ FIGURE 1.13.

1 Boiling the solution vaporizes the water

2 Water is condensed, then collected in the receiving flask

Salt water

Condenser

Cold water out

Cold water in

3 After water has boiled away, pure sodium chloride remains

Pure water in receiving flask

► FIGURE 1.13 **Distillation.** Apparatus for separating a sodium chloride solution (salt water) into its components.

The differing abilities of substances to adhere to the surfaces of solids can also be used to separate mixtures. This ability is the basis of *chromatography* (literally, "the writing of colors"), a technique shown in ▼ FIGURE 1.14.

▲ FIGURE 1.14 **Separation of ink into components by paper chromatography.**

1.4 | UNITS OF MEASUREMENT

Many properties of matter are *quantitative,* that is, associated with numbers. When a number represents a measured quantity, the units of that quantity must be specified. To say that the length of a pencil is 17.5 is meaningless. Expressing the number with its units, 17.5 centimeters (cm), properly specifies the length. The units used for scientific measurements are those of the **metric system**.

The metric system, developed in France during the late eighteenth century, is used as the system of measurement in most countries. The United States has traditionally used the English system, although use of the metric system has become more common (◄ FIGURE 1.15).

► FIGURE 1.15 **Metric units.** Metric measurements are increasingly common in the United States, as exemplified by the volume printed on this soda can in both English units (fluid ounces, fl oz) and metric units (milliliters, mL).

A CLOSER LOOK

THE SCIENTIFIC METHOD

Although two scientists rarely approach the same problem in exactly the same way, they use guidelines for the practice of science known as the **scientific method**. As ▶ FIGURE 1.16 shows, we begin by collecting information, or *data,* by observation and experiment. The ultimate goal, however, is not collecting data but rather finding a pattern or sense of order in our observations and understanding the origin of this order.

As we gather more data, we may see patterns that lead us to a *tentative explanation,* or **hypothesis,** that guides us in planning further experiments. A key feature of a good hypothesis is that it proposes a mechanism that underlies our observations and can be used to make predictions about new experiments. If a hypothesis is sufficiently general and repeatedly effective in predicting results of future experiments, it is called a theory. A **theory** *is an explanation of the general causes of certain phenomena, with considerable evidence or facts to support it.* For example, Einstein's theory of relativity was a revolutionary way of thinking about space and time. It was more than just a hypothesis because it could be used to make predictions that could be tested experimentally. The results of these experiments were generally in agreement with Einstein's predictions and were not explainable by earlier theories.

In spite of the landmark achievements of Einstein's theory, scientists can never say the theory is "proven." A theory that has excellent predictive power today may not work as well in the future as more data and improved scientific equipment are developed. Thus, science is always a work in progress.

Eventually, we may be able to tie together a great number of observations in a **scientific law**, which is *a concise verbal statement or mathematical equation that summarizes a broad variety of observations and experiences.* We tend to think of scientific laws as the basic rules under which nature operates. However, it is not so much that matter obeys these laws, but rather that these laws describe the behavior of matter. As we proceed through this text, we will rarely have the opportunity to discuss the doubts, conflicts, clashes of personalities, and revolutions of perception that have led to our present scientific ideas. You need to be aware that just because we can spell out the results of science so concisely and neatly in textbooks does not mean scientific progress is smooth, certain, and predictable. Some of the ideas we present in this text took centuries to develop and involved many scientists. We gain our view of the natural world by standing on the shoulders of the scientists who came before us. Take advantage of this view. As you study, exercise your imagination. Don't be afraid to ask daring questions when they occur to you. You may be fascinated by what you discover!

RELATED EXERCISE: 1.58

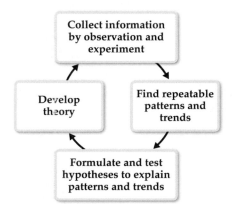

▲ FIGURE 1.16 **The scientific method.** This general approach to solving problems involves making observations, confirming that they are reproducible, seeking patterns in the observations, formulating hypotheses to explain the observations, and testing these hypotheses by further experiments. Hypotheses that withstand such tests and prove themselves useful in explaining and predicting behavior become known as theories.

SI Units

In 1960 an international agreement was reached specifying a particular choice of metric units for use in scientific measurements. These preferred units are called **SI units**, after the French *Système International d'Unités.* This system has seven *base units* from which all other units are derived (▼ TABLE 1.4). In this chapter we will consider the base units for length, mass, and temperature.

TABLE 1.4 • SI Base Units

Physical Quantity	Name of Unit	Abbreviation
Mass	Kilogram	kg
Length	Meter	m
Time	Second	s or sec
Temperature	Kelvin	K
Amount of substance	Mole	mol
Electric current	Ampere	A or amp
Luminous intensity	Candela	cd

TABLE 1.5 • Prefixes Used in the Metric System and with SI Units			
Prefix	**Abbreviation**	**Meaning**	**Example**
Peta	P	10^{15}	1 petawatt (PW) $= 1 \times 10^{15}$ watts[a]
Tera	T	10^{12}	1 terawatt (TW) $= 1 \times 10^{12}$ watts
Giga	G	10^{9}	1 gigawatt (GW) $= 1 \times 10^{9}$ watts
Mega	M	10^{6}	1 megawatt (MW) $= 1 \times 10^{6}$ watts
Kilo	k	10^{3}	1 kilowatt (kW) $= 1 \times 10^{3}$ watts
Deci	d	10^{-1}	1 deciwatt (dW) $= 1 \times 10^{-1}$ watt
Centi	c	10^{-2}	1 centiwatt (cW) $= 1 \times 10^{-2}$ watt
Milli	m	10^{-3}	1 milliwatt (mW) $= 1 \times 10^{-3}$ watt
Micro	μ[b]	10^{-6}	1 microwatt (μW) $= 1 \times 10^{-6}$ watt
Nano	n	10^{-9}	1 nanowatt (nW) $= 1 \times 10^{-9}$ watt
Pico	p	10^{-12}	1 picowatt (pW) $= 1 \times 10^{-12}$ watt
Femto	f	10^{-15}	1 femtowatt (fW) $= 1 \times 10^{-15}$ watt
Atto	a	10^{-18}	1 attowatt (aW) $= 1 \times 10^{-18}$ watt
Zepto	z	10^{-21}	1 zeptowatt (zW) $= 1 \times 10^{-21}$ watt

[a]The watt (W) is the SI unit of power, which is the rate at which energy is either generated or consumed. The SI unit of energy is the joule (J); $1 \text{ J} = 1 \text{ kg} \cdot \text{m}^2/\text{s}^2$ and $1 \text{ W} = 1 \text{ J/s}$.
[b]Greek letter mu, pronounced "mew."

With SI units, prefixes are used to indicate decimal fractions or multiples of various units. For example, the prefix *milli-* represents a 10^{-3} fraction, one-thousandth, of a unit: A milligram (mg) is 10^{-3} gram (g), a millimeter (mm) is 10^{-3} meter (m), and so forth. ▲ TABLE 1.5 presents the prefixes commonly encountered in chemistry. In using SI units and in working problems throughout this text, you must be comfortable using exponential notation. If you are unfamiliar with exponential notation or want to review it, refer to Appendix A.1.

Although non–SI units are being phased out, some are still commonly used by scientists. Whenever we first encounter a non–SI unit in the text, the SI unit will also be given. The relations between the non–SI and SI units we will use most frequently in this text appear on the back inside cover. We will discuss how to convert from one to the other in Section 1.6.

 GIVE IT SOME THOUGHT

Which quantity is the smallest: 1 mg, 1 μg, or 1 pg?

Length and Mass

The SI base unit of *length* is the meter, a distance slightly longer than a yard. **Mass*** is a measure of the amount of material in an object. The SI base unit of mass is the kilogram (kg), which is equal to about 2.2 pounds (lb). This base unit is unusual because it uses a prefix, *kilo-*, instead of the word *gram* alone. We obtain other units for mass by adding prefixes to the word *gram*.

SAMPLE EXERCISE 1.2 Using SI Prefixes

What is the name of the unit that equals (a) 10^{-9} gram, (b) 10^{-6} second, (c) 10^{-3} meter?

SOLUTION

We can find the prefix related to each power of ten in Table 1.5: (a) nanogram, ng, (b) microsecond, μs, (c) millimeter, mm.

*Mass and weight are often incorrectly thought to be the same. The weight of an object is the force that is exerted on its mass by gravity. In space, where gravitational forces are very weak, an astronaut can be weightless, but he or she cannot be massless. The astronaut's mass in space is the same as it is on Earth.

Temperature

Temperature, a measure of the hotness or coldness of an object, is a physical property that determines the direction of heat flow. Heat always flows spontaneously from a substance at higher temperature to one at lower temperature. Thus, we feel the influx of heat when we touch a hot object, and we know that the object is at a higher temperature than our hand.

The temperature scales commonly employed in science are the Celsius and Kelvin scales. The **Celsius scale** was originally based on the assignment of 0 °C to the freezing point of water and 100 °C to its boiling point at sea level (▼ **FIGURE 1.17**).

The **Kelvin scale** is the SI temperature scale, and the SI unit of temperature is the *kelvin* (K). Zero on the Kelvin scale is the lowest attainable temperature, −273.15 °C, referred to as *absolute zero*. The Celsius and Kelvin scales have equal-sized units—that is, a kelvin is the same size as a degree Celsius. Thus, the Kelvin and Celsius scales are related according to

$$K = °C + 273.15 \qquad\qquad [1.1]$$

The freezing point of water, 0 °C, is 273.15 K (Figure 1.17). Notice that we do not use a degree sign (°) with temperatures on the Kelvin scale.

The common temperature scale in the United States is the *Fahrenheit scale,* which is not generally used in science. Water freezes at 32 °F and boils at 212 °F. The Fahrenheit and Celsius scales are related according to

$$°C = \frac{5}{9}(°F - 32) \quad \text{or} \quad °F = \frac{9}{5}(°C) + 32 \qquad\qquad [1.2]$$

◢ GO FIGURE

True or false: The "size" of a degree on the Celsius scale is the same as the "size" of a degree on the Kelvin scale.

373 K	100 °C	212 °F	Water boils
310 K	37.0 °C	98.6 °F	Normal body temperature
273 K	0 °C	32 °F	Water freezes
Kelvin scale	Celsius scale	Fahrenheit scale	

100 degree-intervals   100 degree-intervals   180 degree-intervals

◀ **FIGURE 1.17 Comparison of the Kelvin, Celsius, and Fahrenheit temperature scales.**

⚠ **GO FIGURE**

How many 1-L bottles are required to contain 1 m³ of liquid?

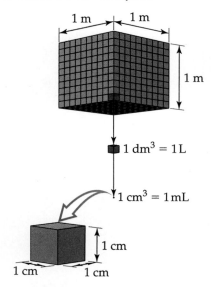

▲ **FIGURE 1.18**   **Volume relationships.** The volume occupied by a cube 1 m on each edge is one cubic meter, 1 m³. Each cubic meter contains 1000 dm³. One liter is the same volume as one cubic decimeter, 1 L = 1 dm³. Each cubic decimeter contains 1000 cubic centimeters, 1 dm³ = 1000 cm³. One cubic centimeter equals one milliliter, 1 cm³ = 1 mL.

SAMPLE EXERCISE 1.3   **Converting Units of Temperature**

A weather forecaster predicts the temperature will reach 31 °C. What is this temperature (a) in K, (b) in °F?

SOLUTION

(a) Using Equation 1.1, we have K = 31 + 273 = 304 K.

(b) Using Equation 1.2, we have $°F = \frac{9}{5}(31) + 32 = 56 + 32 = 88 \ °F$.

PRACTICE EXERCISE

Ethylene glycol, the major ingredient in antifreeze, freezes at −11.5 °C. What is the freezing point in (a) K, (b) °F?

Answers: (a) 261.7 K, (b) 11.3 °F

Derived SI Units

The SI base units are used to obtain *derived units*. To do so, we use the defining equation for the quantity, substituting the appropriate base units. For example, speed is defined as the ratio of distance traveled to elapsed time. Thus, the SI unit for speed—m/s, read "meters per second"—is a derived unit, the SI unit for distance (length), m, divided by the SI unit for time, s. Two common derived units in chemistry are those for volume and density.

Volume

The *volume* of a cube is its length cubed, (length)³. Thus, the derived SI unit of volume is the SI unit of length, m, raised to the third power. The cubic meter, m³, is the volume of a cube that is 1 m on each edge (◀ **FIGURE 1.18**). Smaller units, such as cubic centimeters, cm³ (sometimes written cc), are frequently used in chemistry. Another volume unit used in chemistry is the *liter* (L), which equals a cubic decimeter, dm³, and is slightly larger than a quart. (The liter is the first metric unit we have encountered that is *not* an SI unit.) There are 1000 milliliters (mL) in a liter, and 1 mL is the same volume as 1 cm³: 1 mL = 1 cm³. The devices used most frequently in chemistry to measure volume are illustrated in ▼ **FIGURE 1.19**.

These deliver **variable** volumes   Pipet **delivers** a **specific** volume   Volumetric flask **contains** a specific volume

▲ **FIGURE 1.19**   **Common volumetric glassware.**

Syringes, burets, and pipets deliver amounts of liquids with more precision than graduated cylinders. Volumetric flasks are used to contain specific volumes of liquid.

 GIVE IT SOME THOUGHT

Which of the following quantities represents volume measurements: $15\,m^2$; $2.5 \times 10^2\ m^3$; 5.77 L/s? How do you know?

Density

Density is defined as the amount of mass in a unit volume of a substance:

$$\text{Density} = \frac{\text{mass}}{\text{volume}} \qquad [1.3]$$

The densities of solids and liquids are commonly expressed in either grams per cubic centimeter (g/cm^3) or grams per milliliter (g/mL). The densities of some common substances are listed in ▶ TABLE 1.6. It is no coincidence that the density of water is 1.00 g/mL; the gram was originally defined as the mass of 1 mL of water at a specific temperature. Because most substances change volume when they are heated or cooled, densities are temperature dependent, and so temperature should be specified when reporting densities. If no temperature is reported, we assume 25 °C, close to normal room temperature.

The terms *density* and *weight* are sometimes confused. A person who says that iron weighs more than air generally means that iron has a higher density than air—1 kg of air has the same mass as 1 kg of iron, but the iron occupies a smaller volume, thereby giving it a higher density. If we combine two liquids that do not mix, the less dense liquid will float on the denser liquid.

TABLE 1.6 • Densities of Selected Substances at 25 °C

Substance	Density (g/cm^3)
Air	0.001
Balsa wood	0.16
Ethanol	0.79
Water	1.00
Ethylene glycol	1.09
Table sugar	1.59
Table salt	2.16
Iron	7.9
Gold	19.32

SAMPLE EXERCISE 1.4 Determining Density and Using Density to Determine Volume or Mass

(a) Calculate the density of mercury if 1.00×10^2 g occupies a volume of $7.36\ cm^3$.
(b) Calculate the volume of 65.0 g of liquid methanol (wood alcohol) if its density is 0.791 g/mL.
(c) What is the mass in grams of a cube of gold (density = $19.32\ g/cm^3$) if the length of the cube is 2.00 cm?

SOLUTION

(a) We are given mass and volume, so Equation 1.3 yields

$$\text{Density} = \frac{\text{mass}}{\text{volume}} = \frac{1.00 \times 10^2\ g}{7.36\ cm^3} = 13.6\ g/cm^3$$

(b) Solving Equation 1.3 for volume and then using the given mass and density gives

$$\text{Volume} = \frac{\text{mass}}{\text{density}} = \frac{65.0\ g}{0.791\ g/mL} = 82.2\ mL$$

(c) We can calculate the mass from the volume of the cube and its density. The volume of a cube is given by its length cubed:

$$\text{Volume} = (2.00\ cm)^3 = (2.00)^3\ cm^3 = 8.00\ cm^3$$

Solving Equation 1.3 for mass and substituting the volume and density of the cube, we have

$$\text{Mass} = \text{volume} \times \text{density} = (8.00\ cm^3)(19.32\ g/cm^3) = 155\ g$$

PRACTICE EXERCISE

(a) Calculate the density of a 374.5-g sample of copper if it has a volume of $41.8\ cm^3$. (b) A student needs 15.0 g of ethanol for an experiment. If the density of ethanol is 0.789 g/mL, how many milliliters of ethanol are needed? (c) What is the mass, in grams, of 25.0 mL of mercury (density = 13.6 g/mL)?

Answers: (a) $8.96\ g/cm^3$, (b) 19.0 mL, (c) 340 g

CHEMISTRY PUT TO WORK

Chemistry in the News

Because chemistry is so central to our lives, reports on matters of chemical significance appear in the news nearly every day. Some reports tell of breakthroughs in the development of new pharmaceuticals, materials, and processes. Others deal with energy, environmental, and public safety issues. As you study chemistry, you will develop the skills to better understand the importance of chemistry in your life. Here are summaries of a few recent stories in which chemistry plays a role.

Biofuels Reality Check

With the Energy Policy Act of 2005, the US Congress gave a big push to fuels derived from biomass (plants or algae) as a renewable alternative to gasoline. The 2005 act was followed by the Energy Independence and Security Act of 2007, which required that 9.0 billion gallons of renewable fuel be used in gasoline in 2008, 11.1 billion gallons in 2009, and 36 billion gallons by 2022. The United States currently consumes about 140 billion gallons of gasoline per year.

Ethanol derived from corn currently dominates the alternatives, with 40% of all gasoline now containing some ethanol. A blend of 10% ethanol and 90% gasoline, called E10, is the most common blend because it can be used in virtually all vehicles. Blends of 85% ethanol and 15% gasoline, called E85, are also available but can be used only with specially modified engines (▶ FIGURE 1.20).

However, using a food crop to produce transportation fuel may not be the best long-term solution for the energy problem. In 2006, researchers at the University of Minnesota calculated that "even dedicating all US corn and soybean production to biofuels would meet only 12% of gasoline and 6% of diesel demand." The conversion of a much wider range of plant material, using a much greater fraction of available plant matter, into fuels will be necessary to improve these numbers substantially. Because the most abundant plant material, cellulose, does not readily convert to ethanol, a great deal of research will be needed to solve this challenging problem. Meanwhile, it is worth reflecting that a 3% improvement in vehicle fuel efficiency would displace more gasoline use than the entire 2006 US ethanol production. An alternative to ethanol relies on coaxing microorganisms to produce molecules that can be used as fuel. In 2009, ExxonMobil

◀ FIGURE 1.20 A gasoline pump that dispenses E85, a mixture of 85% ethanol and 15% gasoline.

Research and Engineering Company partnered with a start-up company, Synthetic Genomics, to find strains of photosynthetic algae that will efficiently produce oils and hydrocarbons from sunlight and carbon dioxide.

Advances in Solar Energy

In the 1970s, at the height of the oil crisis, there was a burst of research on renewable energy, including solar energy. After the oil crisis passed and gasoline was once again cheap and readily available, solar energy research was less of a priority. With the more recent increase in gasoline prices and a greater realization that the burning of fossil fuels contributes to global warming, solar energy research is again in vogue. The amount of solar radiation reaching Earth every day is enormous, and if we could harness it efficiently, our energy needs could be easily met. Solar panels like those shown in Figure 1.2a are about 10% efficient in converting light directly into electricity. However, storage of solar energy remains a vigorous area of research:

1.5 | UNCERTAINTY IN MEASUREMENT

Two kinds of numbers are encountered in scientific work: *exact numbers* (those whose values are known exactly) and *inexact numbers* (those whose values have some uncertainty). Most of the exact numbers we will encounter in this book have defined values. For example, there are exactly 12 eggs in a dozen, exactly 1000 g in a kilogram, and exactly 2.54 cm in an inch. The number 1 in any conversion factor, such as $1\,m = 100\,cm$ or $1\,kg = 2.2046\,lb$, is an exact number. Exact numbers can also result from counting objects. For example, we can count the exact number of marbles in a jar or the exact number of people in a classroom.

Numbers obtained by measurement are always *inexact*. The equipment used to measure quantities always has inherent limitations (equipment errors), and there are differences in how different people make the same measurement (human errors). Suppose ten students with ten balances are to determine the mass of the same dime. The ten

How can we capture solar energy for use when the Sun is not shining? One potential answer is to store the energy in chemical bonds. One promising new material, first reported in 2008, is a cobalt-containing compound that can convert water into oxygen with sunlight. Hydrogen can also be generated in sunlight from water but using a different compound to facilitate the reaction. Electricity can then be produced by combining the hydrogen and oxygen in a fuel cell.

Important Antibiotic Modified to Combat Bacterial Resistance

Vancomycin is an antibiotic of last resort—used only when other antibacterial agents are ineffective. Some bacteria have developed resistance to vancomycin, causing researchers to modify the molecular structure of the substance to make it more effective in killing bacteria. This approach was based on the knowledge that vancomycin works by binding to a protein that is essential to forming bacterial cell walls. Researchers have synthesized a vancomycin analog in which a CO group has been converted to a CH_2 group (▼ FIGURE 1.21). This modification increases the compound's binding affinity in the cell walls of vancomycin-resistant bacteria, making the analog 100 times more active than vancomycin against vancomycin-resistant bacteria.

Replacing the Lightbulb through Chemistry

If you want to save the world from global warming, you can start by replacing incandescent lightbulbs. In 2001 approximately 22% of all electricity generated in the United States was used for lighting. This surprisingly high number is due in part to the fact that incandescent lights convert only 5% of the energy supplied to them into visible light and last only 1000 hours on average. Compact fluorescent lamps are more efficient (20% of their output energy is converted into visible light) and last longer (up to 15,000 hours), but they contain mercury, which is toxic and creates disposal problems. A promising replacement bulb is the light-emitting diode (LED). Red LEDs were first made in 1962. As a result of subsequent increases in efficiency and development of other colors, LEDs are now used in traffic lights, car taillights, and a host of electronics applications. These "solid state" devices do not contain mercury, can achieve efficiencies as high as 50%, and hold the promise of longer lifetimes (red LEDs last up to 100,000 hours). With advances in research and development, costs are coming down to the point that some small cities are replacing their streetlights with white LEDs (▼ FIGURE 1.22).

▲ **FIGURE 1.22   LED lighting.** Ann Arbor, Michigan, has replaced incandescent streetlights with white LEDs. The city estimates the change will save $100,000 per year and reduce annual greenhouse gas emissions by 267 tons.

▲ **FIGURE 1.21   Comparing CO and CH₂ groups.** The molecule on the left contains a CO group, and the one on the right contains a CH_2 group. This subtle difference is similar to how the structure of the much more complex vancomycin molecule was modified.

measurements will probably vary slightly for various reasons. The balances might be calibrated slightly differently, and there might be differences in how each student reads the mass from the balance. Remember: *Uncertainties always exist in measured quantities.*

 GIVE IT SOME THOUGHT

Which of the following is an inexact quantity:
a. the number of people in your chemistry class,
b. the mass of a penny,
c. the number of grams in a kilogram?

Precision and Accuracy

The terms *precision* and *accuracy* are often used in discussing the uncertainties of measured values. **Precision** is a measure of how closely individual measurements agree with one another. **Accuracy** refers to how closely individual measurements agree with the

GO FIGURE

How would the darts be positioned on the target for the case of "good accuracy, poor precision"?

Good accuracy
Good precision

Poor accuracy
Good precision

Poor accuracy
Poor precision

▲ FIGURE 1.23 **Precision and accuracy.**

correct, or "true," value. The dart analogy in ◄ FIGURE 1.23 illustrates the difference between these two concepts.

In the laboratory we often perform several "trials" of an experiment and average the results. The precision of the measurements is often expressed in terms of the *standard deviation* (Appendix A.5), which reflects how much the individual measurements differ from the average. We gain confidence in our measurements if we obtain nearly the same value each time—that is, the standard deviation is small. Figure 1.23 reminds us, however, that precise measurements can be inaccurate. For example, if a very sensitive balance is poorly calibrated, the masses we measure will be consistently either high or low. They will be inaccurate even if they are precise.

Significant Figures

Suppose you determine the mass of a dime on a balance capable of measuring to the nearest 0.0001 g. You could report the mass as 2.2405 ± 0.0001 g. The ± notation (read "plus or minus") expresses the magnitude of the uncertainty of your measurement. In much scientific work we drop the ± notation with the understanding that *there is always some uncertainty in the last digit reported for any measured quantity.*

▼ FIGURE 1.24 shows a thermometer with its liquid column between two scale marks. We can read the certain digits from the scale and estimate the uncertain one. Seeing that the liquid is between the 25 °C and 30 °C marks, we estimate the temperature to be 27 °C, being uncertain of the second digit of our measurement.

All digits of a measured quantity, including the uncertain one, are called **significant figures**. A measured mass reported as 2.2 g has two significant figures, whereas one reported as 2.2405 g has five significant figures. The greater the number of significant figures, the greater the certainty implied for the measurement.

SAMPLE EXERCISE 1.5 | **Relating Significant Figures to the Uncertainty of a Measurement**

What difference exists between the measured values 4.0 g and 4.00 g?

SOLUTION

The value 4.0 has two significant figures, whereas 4.00 has three. This difference implies that the 4.0 has more uncertainty. A mass reported as 4.0 g indicates that the uncertainty is in the first decimal place. Thus, the mass might be anything between 3.9 and 4.1 g, which we can represent as 4.0 ± 0.1 g. A mass reported as 4.00 g indicates that the uncertainty is in the second decimal place. Thus, the mass might be anything between 3.99 and 4.01 g, which we can represent as 4.00 ± 0.01 g. (Without further information, we cannot be sure whether the difference in uncertainties of the two measurements reflects the precision or the accuracy of the measurement.)

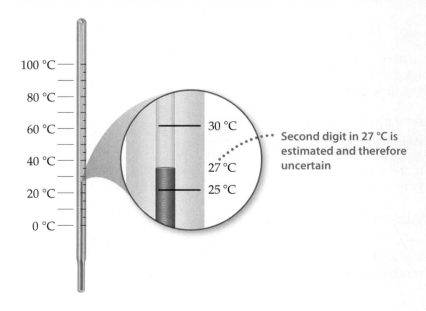

► FIGURE 1.24 **Uncertainty and significant figures in a measurement.**

PRACTICE EXERCISE

A sample that has a mass of about 25 g is placed on a balance that has a precision of $\pm\ 0.001$ g. How many significant figures should be reported for this measurement?

Answer: five, as in the measurement 24.995 g, the uncertainty being in the third decimal place

To determine the number of significant figures in a reported measurement, read the number from left to right, counting the digits starting with the first digit that is not zero. *In any measurement that is properly reported, all nonzero digits are significant.* Because zeros can be used either as part of the measured value or merely to locate the decimal point, they may or may not be significant:

1. Zeros *between* nonzero digits are always significant—1005 kg (four significant figures); 7.03 cm (three significant figures).

2. Zeros *at the beginning* of a number are never significant; they merely indicate the position of the decimal point—0.02 g (one significant figure); 0.0026 cm (two significant figures).

3. Zeros *at the end* of a number are significant if the number contains a decimal point—0.0200 g (three significant figures); 3.0 cm (two significant figures).

A problem arises when a number ends with zeros but contains no decimal point. In such cases, it is normally assumed that the zeros are not significant. Exponential notation (Appendix A.1) can be used to indicate whether end zeros are significant. For example, a mass of 10,300 g can be written to show three, four, or five significant figures depending on how the measurement is obtained:

"MY GOODNESS, IT'S 12:15:0936420175! TIME FOR LUNCH."

1.03×10^4 g	(three significant figures)
1.030×10^4 g	(four significant figures)
1.0300×10^4 g	(five significant figures)

In these numbers all the zeros to the right of the decimal point are significant (rules 1 and 3). (The exponential term 10^4 does not add to the number of significant figures.)

SAMPLE EXERCISE 1.6 **Determining the Number of Significant Figures in a Measurement**

How many significant figures are in each of the following numbers (assume that each number is a measured quantity): (a) 4.003, (b) 6.023×10^{23}, (c) 5000?

SOLUTION

(a) Four; the zeros are significant figures. (b) Four; the exponential term does not add to the number of significant figures. (c) One; we assume that the zeros are not significant when there is no decimal point shown. If the number has more significant figures, a decimal point should be employed or the number written in exponential notation. Thus, 5000. has four significant figures, whereas 5.00×10^3 has three.

PRACTICE EXERCISE

How many significant figures are in each of the following measurements: (a) 3.549 g, (b) 2.3×10^4 cm, (c) 0.00134 m^3?

Answers: (a) four, (b) two, (c) three

Significant Figures in Calculations

When carrying measured quantities through calculations, *the least certain measurement limits the certainty of the calculated quantity and thereby determines the number of significant figures in the final answer.* The final answer should be reported with only one uncertain digit. To keep track of significant figures in calculations, we will make frequent use of two rules, one for addition and subtraction, and another for multiplication and division.

1. *For addition and subtraction,* the result has the same number of decimal places as the measurement with the fewest decimal places. When the result contains more than the correct number of significant figures, it must be rounded off. Consider the following example in which the uncertain digits appear in color:

This number limits	20.42	← two decimal places
the number of significant	1.322	← three decimal places
figures in the result →	83.1	← one decimal place
	104.842	← round off to one decimal place (104.8)

We report the result as 104.8 because 83.1 has only one decimal place.

2. *For multiplication and division,* the result contains the same number of significant figures as the measurement with the fewest significant figures. When the result contains more than the correct number of significant figures, it must be rounded off. For example, the area of a rectangle whose measured edge lengths are 6.221 cm and 5.2 cm should be reported as 32 cm^2 even though a calculator shows the product to have more digits:

$$\text{Area} = (6.221 \, \text{cm})(5.2 \, \text{cm}) = 32.3492 \, \text{cm}^2 \Rightarrow \text{round off to } 32 \, \text{cm}^2$$

because 5.2 has two significant figures.

Notice that for addition and subtraction, decimal places are counted in determining how many digits to report in an answer, whereas for multiplication and division, significant figures are counted in determining how many digits to report.

In determining the final answer for a calculated quantity, *exact numbers* are assumed to have an infinite number of significant figures. Thus, when we say, "There are 12 inches in 1 foot," the number 12 is exact, and we need not worry about the number of significant figures in it.

In *rounding off numbers,* look at the leftmost digit to be removed:

- If the leftmost digit removed is less than 5, the preceding number is left unchanged. Thus, rounding 7.248 to two significant figures gives 7.2.
- If the leftmost digit removed is 5 or greater, the preceding number is increased by 1. Rounding 4.735 to three significant figures gives 4.74, and rounding 2.376 to two significant figures gives 2.4.*

SAMPLE EXERCISE 1.7 | **Determining the Number of Significant Figures in a Calculated Quantity**

The width, length, and height of a small box are 15.5 cm, 27.3 cm, and 5.4 cm, respectively. Calculate the volume of the box, using the correct number of significant figures in your answer.

SOLUTION

In reporting the volume, we can show only as many significant figures as given in the dimension with the fewest significant figures, that for the height (two significant figures):

$$\text{Volume} = \text{width} \times \text{length} \times \text{height}$$
$$= (15.5 \, \text{cm})(27.3 \, \text{cm})(5.4 \, \text{cm}) = 2285.01 \, \text{cm}^3 \Rightarrow 2.3 \times 10^3 \, \text{cm}^3$$

A calculator used for this calculation shows 2285.01, which we must round off to two significant figures. Because the resulting number is 2300, it is best reported in exponential notation, 2.3×10^3, to clearly indicate two significant figures.

---

*Your instructor may want you to use a slight variation on the rule when the leftmost digit to be removed is exactly 5, with no following digits or only zeros following. One common practice is to round up to the next higher number if that number will be even and down to the next lower number otherwise. Thus, 4.7350 would be rounded to 4.74, and 4.7450 would also be rounded to 4.74.

PRACTICE EXERCISE

It takes 10.5 s for a sprinter to run 100.00 m. Calculate her average speed in meters per second, and express the result to the correct number of significant figures.

Answer: 9.52 m/s (three significant figures)

| **SAMPLE EXERCISE 1.8** | Determining the Number of Significant Figures in a Calculated Quantity |

A gas at 25 °C fills a container whose volume is 1.05×10^3 cm^3. The container plus gas has a mass of 837.6 g. The container, when emptied of all gas, has a mass of 836.2 g. What is the density of the gas at 25 °C?

SOLUTION

To calculate the density, we must know both the mass and the volume of the gas. The mass of the gas is just the difference in the masses of the full and empty container:

$$(837.6 - 836.2)\ g = 1.4\ g$$

In subtracting numbers, we determine the number of significant figures in our result by counting decimal places in each quantity. In this case each quantity has one decimal place. Thus, the mass of the gas, 1.4 g, has one decimal place.

Using the volume given in the question, 1.05×10^3 cm^3, and the definition of density, we have

$$\text{Density} = \frac{\text{mass}}{\text{volume}} = \frac{1.4\ g}{1.05 \times 10^3\ cm^3}$$

$$= 1.3 \times 10^{-3}\ g/cm^3 = 0.0013\ g/cm^3$$

In dividing numbers, we determine the number of significant figures in our result by counting the number of significant figures in each quantity. There are two significant figures in our answer, corresponding to the smaller number of significant figures in the two numbers that form the ratio. Notice that in this example, following the rules for determining significant figures gives an answer containing only two significant figures, even though each of the measured quantities contained at least three significant figures.

PRACTICE EXERCISE

To how many significant figures should the mass of the container be measured (with and without the gas) in Sample Exercise 1.8 for the density to be calculated to three significant figures?

Answer: five (For the difference in the two masses to have three significant figures, there must be two decimal places in the masses of the filled and empty containers. Therefore, each mass must be measured to five significant figures.)

When a calculation involves two or more steps and you write answers for intermediate steps, retain at least one nonsignificant digit for the intermediate answers. This procedure ensures that small errors from rounding at each step do not combine to affect the final result. When using a calculator, you may enter the numbers one after another, rounding only the final answer. Accumulated rounding-off errors may account for small differences among results you obtain and answers given in the text for numerical problems.

1.6 | DIMENSIONAL ANALYSIS

Throughout the text we use **dimensional analysis** in solving problems. In this approach, units are multiplied together, divided into each other, or "canceled." Using dimensional analysis helps ensure that solutions to problems yield the proper units. Moreover, it provides a systematic way of solving many numerical problems and of checking solutions for possible errors.

The key to using dimensional analysis is the correct use of conversion factors to change one unit into another. A **conversion factor** is a fraction whose numerator and denominator are the same quantity expressed in different units. For example, 2.54 cm and 1 in. are the same length, 2.54 cm = 1 in. This relationship allows us to write two conversion factors:

$$\frac{2.54\ cm}{1\ in.} \quad \text{and} \quad \frac{1\ in.}{2.54\ cm}$$

We use the first factor to convert inches to centimeters. For example, the length in centimeters of an object that is 8.50 in. long is

$$\text{Number of centimeters} = (8.50 \; \cancel{\text{in.}}) \; \underbrace{\frac{2.54 \; cm}{1 \; \cancel{\text{in.}}}}_{} = 21.6 \; cm$$

Desired unit
Given unit

The unit inches in the denominator of the conversion factor cancels the unit inches in the given data (8.50 *inches*). The unit centimeters in the numerator of the conversion factor becomes the unit of the final answer. Because the numerator and denominator of a conversion factor are equal, multiplying any quantity by a conversion factor is equivalent to multiplying by the number 1 and so does not change the intrinsic value of the quantity. The length 8.50 in. is the same as the length 21.6 cm.

In general, we begin any conversion by examining the units of the given data and the units we desire. We then ask ourselves what conversion factors we have available to take us from the units of the given quantity to those of the desired one. When we multiply a quantity by a conversion factor, the units multiply and divide as follows:

$$\cancel{\text{Given unit}} \times \frac{\text{desired unit}}{\cancel{\text{given unit}}} = \text{desired unit}$$

If the desired units are not obtained in a calculation, an error must have been made somewhere. Careful inspection of units often reveals the source of the error.

SAMPLE EXERCISE 1.9   Converting Units

If a woman has a mass of 115 lb, what is her mass in grams? (Use the relationships between units given on the back inside cover of the text.)

SOLUTION

Because we want to change from pounds to grams, we look for a relationship between these units of mass. From the back inside cover we have 1 lb = 453.6 g. To cancel pounds and leave grams, we write the conversion factor with grams in the numerator and pounds in the denominator:

$$\text{Mass in grams} = (115 \; \cancel{\text{lb}}) \left(\frac{453.6 \; g}{1 \; \cancel{\text{lb}}} \right) = 5.22 \times 10^4 \; g$$

The answer can be given to only three significant figures, the number of significant figures in 115 lb. The process we have used is diagrammed in the margin.

PRACTICE EXERCISE

By using a conversion factor from the back inside cover, determine the length in kilometers of a 500.0-mi automobile race.
Answer: 804.7 km

Given: **lb**

Use $\dfrac{453.6 \; g}{1 \; lb}$

Find: **g**

STRATEGIES IN CHEMISTRY

ESTIMATING ANSWERS

A friend once remarked cynically that calculators let you get the wrong answer more quickly. He was implying that unless you have the correct strategy for solving a problem and have punched in the correct numbers, the answer will be incorrect. If you learn to *estimate* answers, however, you will be able to check whether the answers to your calculations are reasonable.

The idea is to make a rough calculation using numbers that are rounded off in such a way that the arithmetic can be done without a calculator. This approach is often referred to as making a "ballpark" estimate, meaning that although it does not give an exact answer, it gives one that is roughly the right size. By using dimensional analysis and by estimating answers, we can readily check the reasonableness of our answers to calculations.

⚠ **GIVE IT SOME THOUGHT**

How do we determine how many digits to use in conversion factors, such as the one between pounds and grams in Sample Exercise 1.9?

Using Two or More Conversion Factors

It is often necessary to use several conversion factors in solving a problem. As an example, let's convert the length of an 8.00-m rod to inches. The table on the back inside cover does not give the relationship between meters and inches. It *does,* however, give the relationship between centimeters and inches (1 in. = 2.54 cm). From our knowledge of SI prefixes, we know that $1\,cm = 10^{-2}$ m. Thus, we can convert step by step, first from meters to centimeters and then from centimeters to inches:

Combining the given quantity (8.00 m) and the two conversion factors, we have

$$\text{Number of inches} = (8.00\,\cancel{m})\left(\frac{1\,\cancel{cm}}{10^{-2}\,\cancel{m}}\right)\left(\frac{1\,in.}{2.54\,\cancel{cm}}\right) = 315\,in.$$

The first conversion factor is used to cancel meters and convert the length to centimeters. Thus, meters are written in the denominator and centimeters in the numerator. The second conversion factor is used to cancel centimeters and convert the length to inches, so it has centimeters in the denominator and inches, the desired unit, in the numerator.

Note that you could have used 100 cm = 1 m as a conversion factor as well in the second parentheses. As long as you follow your units and cancel them properly to obtain the desired units, you are likely to be successful in your calculations.

SAMPLE EXERCISE 1.10   **Converting Units Using Two or More Conversion Factors**

The average speed of a nitrogen molecule in air at 25 °C is 515 m/s. Convert this speed to miles per hour.

SOLUTION

To go from the given units, m/s, to the desired units, mi/hr, we must convert meters to miles and seconds to hours. From our knowledge of SI prefixes we know that $1\,km = 10^3$ m. From the relationships given on the back inside cover of the book, we find that 1 mi = 1.6093 km.

Thus, we can convert m to km and then convert km to mi. From our knowledge of time we know that 60 s = 1 min and 60 min = 1 hr. Thus, we can convert s to min and then convert min to hr. The overall process is

Applying first the conversions for distance and then those for time, we can set up one long equation in which unwanted units are canceled:

$$\text{Speed in mi/hr} = \left(515\,\frac{\cancel{m}}{\cancel{s}}\right)\left(\frac{1\,\cancel{km}}{10^3\,\cancel{m}}\right)\left(\frac{1\,mi}{1.6093\,\cancel{km}}\right)\left(\frac{60\,\cancel{s}}{1\,\cancel{min}}\right)\left(\frac{60\,\cancel{min}}{1\,hr}\right)$$

$$= 1.15 \times 10^3\ mi/hr$$

Our answer has the desired units. We can check our calculation, using the estimating procedure described in the "Strategies in Chemistry" box. The given speed is about $500\,\text{m/s}$. Dividing by 1000 converts m to km, giving $0.5\,\text{km/s}$. Because 1 mi is about 1.6 km, this speed corresponds to $0.5/1.6 = 0.3\,\text{mi/s}$. Multiplying by 60 gives about $0.3 \times 60 = 20\,\text{mi/min}$. Multiplying again by 60 gives $20 \times 60 = 1200\,\text{mi/hr}$. The approximate solution (about $1200\,\text{mi/hr}$) and the detailed solution ($1150\,\text{mi/hr}$) are reasonably close. The answer to the detailed solution has three significant figures, corresponding to the number of significant figures in the given speed in m/s.

PRACTICE EXERCISE

A car travels 28 mi per gallon of gasoline. How many kilometers per liter will it go?

Answer: $12\,\text{km/L}$

Conversions Involving Volume

The conversion factors previously noted convert from one unit of a given measure to another unit of the same measure, such as from length to length. We also have conversion factors that convert from one measure to a different one. The density of a substance, for example, can be treated as a conversion factor between mass and volume. Suppose we want to know the mass in grams of 2 cubic inches ($2.00\,\text{in.}^3$) of gold, which has a density of $19.3\,\text{g/cm}^3$. The density gives us the conversion factor:

$$\frac{19.3\text{ g}}{1\text{ cm}^3} \quad \text{and} \quad \frac{1\text{ cm}^3}{19.3\text{ g}}$$

Because we want a mass in grams, we use the first factor, which has mass in grams in the numerator. To use this factor, however, we must first convert cubic inches to cubic centimeters. The relationship between in.^3 and cm^3 is not given on the back inside cover, but the relationship between inches and centimeters is given: $1\,\text{in.} = 2.54\,\text{cm}$ (exactly). Cubing both sides of this equation gives $(1\,\text{in.})^3 = (2.54\,\text{cm})^3$, from which we write the desired conversion factor:

$$\frac{(2.54\text{ cm})^3}{(1\text{ in.})^3} = \frac{(2.54)^3\text{ cm}^3}{(1)^3\text{ in.}^3} = \frac{16.39\text{ cm}^3}{1\text{ in.}^3}$$

Notice that both the numbers and the units are cubed. Also, because 2.54 is an exact number, we can retain as many digits of $(2.54)^3$ as we need. We have used four, one more than the number of digits in the density ($19.3\,\text{g/cm}^3$). Applying our conversion factors, we can now solve the problem:

$$\text{Mass in grams} = (2.00\ \cancel{\text{in.}^3})\left(\frac{16.39\ \cancel{\text{cm}^3}}{1\ \cancel{\text{in.}^3}}\right)\left(\frac{19.3\text{ g}}{1\ \cancel{\text{cm}^3}}\right) = 633\text{ g}$$

The procedure is diagrammed here. The final answer is reported to three significant figures, the same number of significant figures as in $2.00\,\text{in.}^3$ and $19.3\,\text{g}$.

SAMPLE EXERCISE 1.11   **Converting Volume Units**

Earth's oceans contain approximately $1.36 \times 10^9\,\text{km}^3$ of water. Calculate the volume in liters.

SOLUTION

From the back inside cover, we find $1\,\text{L} = 10^{-3}\,\text{m}^3$, but there is no relationship listed involving km^3. From our knowledge of SI prefixes, however, we know $1\,\text{km} = 10^3\,\text{m}$ and we can use this relationship between lengths to write the desired conversion factor between volumes:

$$\left(\frac{10^3\text{ m}}{1\text{ km}}\right)^3 = \frac{10^9\text{ m}^3}{1\text{ km}^3}$$

Thus, converting from km^3 to m^3 to L, we have

$$\text{Volume in liters} = (1.36 \times 10^9 \text{ km}^3)\left(\frac{10^9 \text{ m}^3}{1 \text{ km}^3}\right)\left(\frac{1 \text{ L}}{10^{-3} \text{ m}^3}\right) = 1.36 \times 10^{21} \text{ L}$$

PRACTICE EXERCISE

If the volume of an object is reported as 5.0 ft^3, what is the volume in cubic meters?
Answer: 0.14 m^3

STRATEGIES IN CHEMISTRY

THE IMPORTANCE OF PRACTICE

If you have ever played a musical instrument or participated in athletics, you know that the keys to success are practice and discipline. You cannot learn to play a piano merely by listening to music, and you cannot learn how to play basketball merely by watching games on television. Likewise, you cannot learn chemistry by merely watching your instructor do it. Simply reading this book, listening to lectures, or reviewing notes will not usually be sufficient when exam time comes around. Your task is not only to understand how someone else does chemistry but also to be able to do it yourself. That takes practice on a regular basis, and anything that you have to do on a regular basis requires self-discipline until it becomes a habit.

Throughout the book, we have provided sample exercises in which the solutions are shown in detail. A practice exercise, for which only the answer is given, accompanies each sample exercise. It is important that you use these exercises as learning aids. End-of-chapter exercises provide additional questions to help you understand the material in the chapter. A review of basic mathematics is given in Appendix A.

The practice exercises in this text and the homework assignments given by your instructor provide the minimal practice that you will need to succeed in your chemistry course. Only by working all the assigned problems will you face the full range of difficulty and coverage that your instructor expects you to master for exams. There is no substitute for a determined and perhaps lengthy effort to work problems on your own. If you are stuck on a problem, however, ask for help from your instructor, a teaching assistant, a tutor, or a fellow student. Spending an inordinate amount of time on a single exercise is rarely effective unless you know that it is particularly challenging and requires extensive thought and effort.

SAMPLE EXERCISE 1.12   Conversions Involving Density

What is the mass in grams of 1.00 gal of water? The density of water is 1.00 g/mL.

SOLUTION

Before we begin solving this exercise, we note the following:

1. We are given 1.00 gal of water (the known, or given, quantity) and asked to calculate its mass in grams (the unknown).

2. We have the following conversion factors either given, commonly known, or available on the back inside cover of the text:

$$\frac{1.00 \text{ g water}}{1 \text{ mL water}} \qquad \frac{1 \text{ L}}{1000 \text{ mL}} \qquad \frac{1 \text{ L}}{1.057 \text{ qt}} \qquad \frac{1 \text{ gal}}{4 \text{ qt}}$$

The first of these conversion factors must be used as written (with grams in the numerator) to give the desired result, whereas the last conversion factor must be inverted in order to cancel gallons:

$$\text{Mass in grams} = (1.00 \text{ gal})\left(\frac{4 \text{ qt}}{1 \text{ gal}}\right)\left(\frac{1 \text{ L}}{1.057 \text{ qt}}\right)\left(\frac{1000 \text{ mL}}{1 \text{ L}}\right)\left(\frac{1.00 \text{ g}}{1 \text{ mL}}\right)$$

$$= 3.78 \times 10^3 \text{ g water}$$

The unit of our final answer is appropriate, and we've taken care of our significant figures. We can further check our calculation by estimating. We can round 1.057 off to 1. Then focusing on the numbers that do not equal 1 gives $4 \times 1000 = 4000$ g, in agreement with the detailed calculation.

You should also use common sense to assess the reasonableness of your answer. In this case we know that most people can lift a gallon of milk with one hand, although it would be tiring to carry it around all day. Milk is mostly water and will have a density not too different from that of water. Therefore, we might estimate that a gallon of water has mass that is more than 5 lb but less than 50 lb. The mass we have calculated, 3.78 kg $\times$ 2.2 lb/kg = 8.3 lb, is thus reasonable as an order-of-magnitude estimate.

PRACTICE EXERCISE
The density of benzene is 0.879 g/mL. Calculate the mass in grams of 1.00 qt of benzene.

Answer: 832 g

STRATEGIES IN CHEMISTRY

THE FEATURES OF THIS BOOK

To help you understand chemistry, this book includes features that help you organize your thoughts. At the beginning of each chapter, "What's Ahead," which outlines the chapter by section, will prepare you for the material in the chapter. At the end of each chapter, the Summary, Key Terms, Key Skills, and Key Equations will help you remember what you have learned and prepare you for quizzes and exams.

During the course of the chapter, there are "speed bumps" to prompt you to think about what you have just read. The "Give It Some Thought" features are embedded in the text after a key concept; the "Go Figure" features are associated with artwork and ask you to interpret a concept visually. Sample Exercises, with worked-out solutions and answers, and Practice Exercises, which provide only the answer, test your problem-solving skills in chemistry.

At the end of each chapter is a series of exercises, again to test your problem-solving skills in chemistry. Your instructor will very likely assign some of these end-of-chapter exercises as homework. The first few exercises called "Visualizing Concepts" are meant to test how well you understand a concept without plugging a lot of numbers into a formula. The other exercises are divided into sections that reflect the order of the material in the chapter. These exercises are grouped in pairs, with the answers given in the back of the book to the odd-numbered exercises, as indicated by the red exercise numbers. An exercise with a [bracket] around its number means that it is more challenging. Additional Exercises appear after the regular exercises; the chapter sections that they cover are not identified, and they are not paired. Integrative Exercises, which start appearing in Chapter 3, are problems that require skills learned in previous chapters.

Throughout the book you will occasionally find little blue link [∞] symbols. These "concept links" tell you in which section of the book this concept is first discussed in case you wish to turn to that section and review it.

Throughout the book boxed essays highlight the importance of chemistry to our everyday lives. The "Chemistry and Life" boxes focus on biological and environmental aspects of chemistry. The "Chemistry Put to Work" boxes illustrate the large industrial role chemistry plays in modern society. "Strategies in Chemistry" boxes, like this one, are meant to help you think about the material you are learning. Finally, boxes entitled "A Closer Look" provide in-depth coverage of a key chemical concept.

Many chemical databases are available, usually through your school. The *CRC Handbook of Chemistry and Physics* is the standard reference for many types of data and is available in libraries. The *Merck Index* is a standard reference for the properties of many small organic compounds, especially ones of biological interest. WebElements (http://www.webelements.com) is a good Web site for looking up the properties of the elements.

CHAPTER SUMMARY AND KEY TERMS

INTRODUCTION AND SECTION 1.1   **Chemistry** is the study of the composition, structure, properties, and changes of **matter**. The composition of matter relates to the kinds of **elements** it contains. The structure of matter relates to the ways the **atoms** of these elements are arranged. A **property** is any characteristic that gives a sample of matter its unique identity. A **molecule** is an entity composed of two or more atoms with the atoms attached to one another in a specific way.

SECTION 1.2   Matter exists in three physical states, **gas, liquid**, and **solid**, which are known as the **states of matter**. There are two kinds of **pure substances: elements** and **compounds**. Each element has a single kind of atom and is represented by a chemical symbol consisting of

one or two letters, with the first letter capitalized. Compounds are composed of two or more elements joined chemically. The **law of constant composition**, also called the **law of definite proportions**, states that the elemental composition of a pure compound is always the same. Most matter consists of a mixture of substances. **Mixtures** have variable compositions and can be either homogeneous or heterogeneous; homogeneous mixtures are called **solutions**.

SECTION 1.3   Each substance has a unique set of **physical properties** and **chemical properties** that can be used to identify it. During a **physical change**, matter does not change its composition. **Changes of state** are physical changes. In a **chemical change** (**chemical**

reaction) a substance is transformed into a chemically different substance. **Intensive properties** are independent of the amount of matter examined and are used to identify substances. **Extensive properties** relate to the amount of substance present. Differences in physical and chemical properties are used to separate substances.

The **scientific method** is a dynamic process used to answer questions about our physical world. Observations and experiments lead to **scientific laws**, general rules that summarize how nature behaves. Observations also lead to tentative explanations or **hypotheses**. As a hypothesis is tested and refined, a **theory** may be developed that can predict the results of future observations and experiments.

SECTION 1.4 Measurements in chemistry are made using the **metric system**. Special emphasis is placed on **SI units**, which are based on the meter, the kilogram, and the second as the basic units of length, **mass**, and time, respectively. SI units use prefixes to indicate fractions or multiples of base units. The SI temperature scale is the **Kelvin scale**, although the **Celsius scale** is frequently used as well. **Density** is an important property that equals mass divided by volume.

SECTION 1.5 All measured quantities are inexact to some extent. The **precision** of a measurement indicates how closely different measurements of a quantity agree with one another. The **accuracy** of a measurement indicates how well a measurement agrees with the accepted or "true" value. The **significant figures** in a measured quantity include one estimated digit, the last digit of the measurement. The significant figures indicate the extent of the uncertainty of the measurement. Certain rules must be followed so that a calculation involving measured quantities is reported with the appropriate number of significant figures.

SECTION 1.6 In the **dimensional analysis** approach to problem solving, we keep track of units as we carry measurements through calculations. The units are multiplied together, divided into each other, or canceled like algebraic quantities. Obtaining the proper units for the final result is an important means of checking the method of calculation. When converting units and when carrying out several other types of problems, **conversion factors** can be used. These factors are ratios constructed from valid relations between equivalent quantities.

KEY SKILLS

- Distinguish among elements, compounds, and mixtures. (Section 1.2)
- Memorize symbols of common elements. (Section 1.2)
- Memorize common metric prefixes. (Section 1.4)
- Use significant figures, scientific notation, and SI units in calculations. (Section 1.5)
- Use dimensional analysis in calculations. (Section 1.6)

KEY EQUATIONS

- $K = °C + 273.15$ [1.1] Converting between Celsius (°C) and Kelvin (K) temperature scales
- $°C = \dfrac{5}{9}(°F - 32)$ or $°F = \dfrac{9}{5}(°C) + 32$ [1.2] Converting between Celsius (°C) and Fahrenheit (°F) temperature scales
- $\text{Density} = \dfrac{\text{mass}}{\text{volume}}$ [1.3] Definition of density

EXERCISES

VISUALIZING CONCEPTS

1.1 Which of the following figures represents (**a**) a pure element, (**b**) a mixture of two elements, (**c**) a pure compound, (**d**) a mixture of an element and a compound? (More than one picture might fit each description.) [Section 1.2]

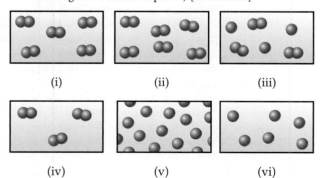

(i)   (ii)   (iii)

(iv)   (v)   (vi)

1.2 Does the following diagram represent a chemical or physical change? How do you know? [Section 1.3]

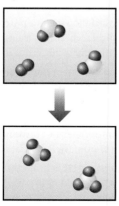

1.3 Describe the separation method(s) involved in brewing a cup of coffee. [Section 1.3]

1.4 Identify each of the following as measurements of length, area, volume, mass, density, time, or temperature: (a) 25 ps, (b) 374.2 mg, (c) 77 K, (d) 100,000 km^2, (e) 1.06 μm, (f) 16 nm^2, (g) −78 °C, (h) 2.56 g/cm^3, (i) 28 cm^3. [Section 1.4]

1.5 (a) Three spheres of equal size are composed of aluminum (density = 2.70 g/cm^3), silver (density = 10.49 g/cm^3), and nickel (density = 8.90 g/cm^3). List the spheres from lightest to heaviest. (b) Three cubes of equal mass are composed of gold (density = 19.32 g/cm^3), platinum (density = 21.45 g/cm^3), and lead (density = 11.35 g/cm^3). List the cubes from smallest to largest. [Section 1.4]

1.6 The following dartboards illustrate the types of errors often seen when one measurement is repeated several times. The bull's-eye represents the "true value," and the darts represent the experimental measurements. Which board best represents each of the following scenarios: (a) measurements both accurate and precise, (b) measurements precise but inaccurate, (c) measurements imprecise but yielding an accurate average? [Section 1.5]

(i)   (ii)   (iii)

1.7 (a) What is the length of the pencil in the following figure if the ruler reads in centimeters? How many significant figures are there in this measurement? (b) An automobile speedometer with circular scales reading both miles per hour and kilometers per hour is shown. What speed is indicated, in both units? How many significant figures are in the measurements? [Section 1.5]

1.8 (a) How many significant figures should be reported for the volume of the metal bar shown here? (b) If the mass of the bar is 104.72 g, how many significant figures should be reported when its density is determined using the calculated volume? [Section 1.5]

1.9 When you convert units, how do you decide which part of the conversion factor is in the numerator and which is in the denominator? [Section 1.6]

1.10 Show the steps to convert the speed of sound, 344 meters per second, into miles per hour. [Section 1.6]

CLASSIFICATION AND PROPERTIES OF MATTER (sections 1.2 and 1.3)

1.11 Classify each of the following as a pure substance or a mixture. If a mixture, indicate whether it is homogeneous or heterogeneous: (a) rice pudding, (b) seawater, (c) magnesium, (d) crushed ice.

1.12 Classify each of the following as a pure substance or a mixture. If a mixture, indicate whether it is homogeneous or heterogeneous: (a) air, (b) tomato juice, (c) iodine crystals, (d) sand.

1.13 Give the chemical symbol or name for the following elements, as appropriate: (a) sulfur, (b) gold, (c) potassium, (d) chlorine, (e) copper, (f) U, (g) Ni, (h) Na, (i) Al, (j) Si.

1.14 Give the chemical symbol or name for each of the following elements, as appropriate: (a) carbon, (b) nitrogen, (c) titanium, (d) zinc, (e) iron, (f) P, (g) Ca, (h) He, (i) Pb, (j) Ag.

1.15 A solid white substance A is heated strongly in the absence of air. It decomposes to form a new white substance B and a gas C. The gas has exactly the same properties as the product obtained when carbon is burned in an excess of oxygen. Based on these observations, can we determine whether solids A and B and gas C are elements or compounds? Explain your conclusions for each substance.

1.16 You are hiking in the mountains and find a shiny gold nugget. It might be the element gold, or it might be "fool's gold," which is a nickname for iron pyrite, FeS$_2$. What kinds of experiments could be done to determine if the shiny nugget is really gold?

1.17 In the process of attempting to characterize a substance, a chemist makes the following observations: The substance is a silvery white, lustrous metal. It melts at 649 °C and boils at 1105 °C. Its density at 20 °C is 1.738 g/cm^3. The substance burns in air, producing an intense white light. It reacts with chlorine to give a brittle white solid. The substance can be pounded into thin sheets or drawn into wires. It is a good conductor of electricity. Which of these characteristics are physical properties, and which are chemical properties?

1.18 Read the following description of the element zinc and indicate which are physical properties and which are chemical properties. Zinc is a silver-gray–colored metal that melts at 420 °C. When zinc granules are added to dilute sulfuric acid, hydrogen is given off and the metal dissolves. Zinc has a hardness on the Mohs scale of 2.5 and a density of 7.13 g/cm³ at 25 °C. It reacts slowly with oxygen gas at elevated temperatures to form zinc oxide, ZnO.

1.19 Label each of the following as either a physical process or a chemical process: (a) rusting of a metal can, (b) boiling a cup of water, (c) pulverizing an aspirin, (d) digesting a candy bar, (e) exploding of nitroglycerin.

1.20 A match is lit and held under a cold piece of metal. The following observations are made: (a) The match burns. (b) The metal gets warmer. (c) Water condenses on the metal. (d) Soot (carbon) is deposited on the metal. Which of these occurrences are due to physical changes, and which are due to chemical changes?

1.21 Suggest a method of separating each of the following mixtures into two components: (a) sugar and sand, (b) oil and vinegar.

1.22 Three beakers contain clear, colorless liquids. One beaker contains pure water, another contains salt water, and another contains sugar water. How can you tell which beaker is which? (No tasting allowed!)

UNITS AND MEASUREMENT (section 1.4)

1.23 What exponential notation do the following abbreviations represent: (a) d, (b) c, (c) f, (d) μ, (e) M, (f) k, (g) n, (h) m, (i) p?

1.24 Use appropriate metric prefixes to write the following measurements without use of exponents: (a) 2.3×10^{-10} L, (b) 4.7×10^{-6} g, (c) 1.85×10^{-12} m, (d) 16.7×10^{6} s; (e) 15.7×10^{3} g, (f) 1.34×10^{-3} m, (g) 1.84×10^{2} cm.

1.25 Make the following conversions: (a) 72 °F to °C, (b) 216.7 °C to °F, (c) 233 °C to K, (d) 315 K to °F, (e) 2500 °F to K, (f) 0 K to °F.

1.26 (a) The temperature on a warm summer day is 87 °F. What is the temperature in °C? (b) Many scientific data are reported at 25 °C. What is this temperature in kelvins and in degrees Fahrenheit? (c) Suppose that a recipe calls for an oven temperature of 400 °F. Convert this temperature to degrees Celsius and to kelvins. (d) Liquid nitrogen boils at 77 K. Convert this temperature to degrees Fahrenheit and to degrees Celsius.

1.27 (a) A sample of tetrachloroethylene, a liquid used in dry cleaning that is being phased out because of its potential to cause cancer, has a mass of 40.55 g and a volume of 25.0 mL at 25 °C. What is its density at this temperature? Will tetrachloroethylene float on water? (Materials that are less dense than water will float.) (b) Carbon dioxide (CO_2) is a gas at room temperature and pressure. However, carbon dioxide can be put under pressure to become a "supercritical fluid" that is a much safer dry-cleaning agent than tetrachloroethylene. At a certain pressure, the density of supercritical CO_2 is 0.469 g/cm³. What is the mass of a 25.0-mL sample of supercritical CO_2 at this pressure?

1.28 (a) A cube of osmium metal 1.500 cm on a side has a mass of 76.31 g at 25 °C. What is its density in g/cm³ at this temperature? (b) The density of titanium metal is 4.51 g/cm³ at 25 °C. What mass of titanium displaces 125.0 mL of water at 25 °C? (c) The density of benzene at 15 °C is 0.8787 g/mL. Calculate the mass of 0.1500 L of benzene at this temperature.

1.29 (a) To identify a liquid substance, a student determined its density. Using a graduated cylinder, she measured out a 45-mL sample of the substance. She then measured the mass of the sample, finding that it weighed 38.5 g. She knew that the substance had to be either isopropyl alcohol (density 0.785 g/mL) or toluene (density 0.866/mL). What are the calculated density and the probable identity of the substance? (b) An experiment requires 45.0 g of ethylene glycol, a liquid whose density is 1.114 g/mL. Rather than weigh the sample on a balance, a chemist chooses to dispense the liquid using a graduated cylinder. What volume of the liquid should he use? (c) A cubic piece of metal measures 5.00 cm on each edge. If the metal is nickel, whose density is 8.90 g/cm³, what is the mass of the cube?

1.30 (a) After the label fell off a bottle containing a clear liquid believed to be benzene, a chemist measured the density of the liquid to verify its identity. A 25.0-mL portion of the liquid had a mass of 21.95 g. A chemistry handbook lists the density of benzene at 15 °C as 0.8787 g/mL. Is the calculated density in agreement with the tabulated value? (b) An experiment requires 15.0 g of cyclohexane, whose density at 25 °C is 0.7781 g/mL. What volume of cyclohexane should be used? (c) A spherical ball of lead has a diameter of 5.0 cm. What is the mass of the sphere if lead has a density of 11.34 g/cm³? (The volume of a sphere is $(4/3)\pi r^3$ where r is the radius.)

1.31 In the year 2007, an estimated amount of 31 billion tons of carbon dioxide (CO_2) was emitted worldwide due to fossil fuel combustion and cement production. Express this mass of CO_2 in grams without exponential notation, using an appropriate metric prefix.

1.32 Silicon for computer chips is grown in large cylinders called "boules" that are 300 mm in diameter and 2 m in height. The density of silicon is 2.33 g/cm³. Silicon wafers for making integrated circuits are sliced from a 2.0 m boule and are typically 0.75 mm thick and 300 mm in diameter. (a) How many wafers can be cut from a single boule? (b) What is the mass of a silicon wafer? (The volume of a cylinder is given by $\pi r^2 h$, where r is the radius and h is its height.)

UNCERTAINTY IN MEASUREMENT (section 1.5)

1.33 Indicate which of the following are exact numbers: (a) the mass of a piece of paper, (b) the volume of a cup of coffee, (c) the number of inches in a mile, (d) the number of ounces in a pound, (e) the number of microseconds in a week, (f) the number of pages in this book.

1.34 Indicate which of the following are exact numbers: (a) the mass of a 32-oz can of coffee, (b) the number of students in your chemistry class, (c) the temperature of the surface of the sun, (d) the mass of a postage stamp, (e) the number of milliliters in a cubic meter of water, (f) the average height of students in your school.

1.35 What is the number of significant figures in each of the following measured quantities? (a) 601 kg, (b) 0.054 s, (c) 6.3050 cm, (d) 0.0105 L, (e) 7.0500×10^{-3} m^3, (f) 400 g.

1.36 Indicate the number of significant figures in each of the following measured quantities: (a) 3.774 km, (b) 205 m^2, (c) 1.700 cm, (d) 350.00 K, (e) 307.080 g, (f) 1.3×10^3 m/s.

1.37 Round each of the following numbers to four significant figures, and express the result in standard exponential notation: (a) 102.53070, (b) 656,980, (c) 0.008543210, (d) 0.000257870, (e) −0.0357202.

1.38 (a) The diameter of Earth at the equator is 7926.381 mi. Round this number to three significant figures, and express it in standard exponential notation. (b) The circumference of Earth through the poles is 40,008 km. Round this number to four significant figures, and express it in standard exponential notation.

1.39 Carry out the following operations, and express the answers with the appropriate number of significant figures.
(a) $14.3505 + 2.65$
(b) $952.7 - 140.7389$
(c) $(3.29 \times 10^4)(0.2501)$
(d) $0.0588/0.677$

1.40 Carry out the following operations, and express the answer with the appropriate number of significant figures.
(a) $320.5 - (6104.5/2.3)$
(b) $[(285.3 \times 10^5) - (1.200 \times 10^3)] \times 2.8954$
(c) $(0.0045 \times 20,000.0) + (2813 \times 12)$
(d) $863 \times [1255 - (3.45 \times 108)]$

1.41 You weigh an object on a balance and read the mass in grams according to the picture. How many significant figures are in this measurement?

1.42 You have a graduated cylinder that contains a liquid (see photograph). Write the volume of the liquid, in milliliters, using the proper number of significant figures.

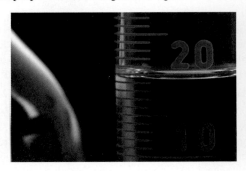

DIMENSIONAL ANALYSIS (section 1.6)

1.43 Using your knowledge of metric units, English units, and the information on the back inside cover, write down the conversion factors needed to convert (a) mm to nm, (b) mg to kg, (c) km to ft, (d) in.^{3} to cm^3.

1.44 Using your knowledge of metric units, English units, and the information on the back inside cover, write down the conversion factors needed to convert (a) μm to mm, (b) ms to ns, (c) mi to km, (d) ft^3 to L.

1.45 (a) A bumblebee flies with a ground speed of 15.2 m/s. Calculate its speed in km/h. (b) The lung capacity of the blue whale is 5.0×10^3 L. Convert this volume into gallons. (c) The Statue of Liberty is 151 ft tall. Calculate its height in meters. (d) Bamboo can grow up to 60.0 cm/day. Convert this growth rate into inches per hour.

1.46 (a) The speed of light in a vacuum is 2.998×10^8 m/s. Calculate its speed in miles per hour. (b) The Sears Tower in Chicago is 1454 ft tall. Calculate its height in meters. (c) The Vehicle Assembly Building at the Kennedy Space Center in Florida has a volume of 3,666,500 m^3. Convert this volume to liters and express the result in standard exponential notation. (d) An individual suffering from a high cholesterol level in her blood has 242 mg of cholesterol per 100 mL of blood. If the total blood volume of the individual is 5.2 L, how many grams of total blood cholesterol does the individual's body contain?

1.47 Perform the following conversions: (a) 5.00 days to s, (b) 0.0550 mi to m, (c) \$1.89/gal to dollars per liter, (d) 0.510 in./ms to km/hr, (e) 22.50 gal/min to L/s, (f) 0.02500 ft^3 to cm^3.

1.48 Carry out the following conversions: (a) 0.105 in. to mm, (b) 0.650 qt to mL, (c) 8.75 μm/s to km/hr, (d) 1.955 m^3 to yd^3, (e) \$3.99/lb to dollars per kg, (f) 8.75 lb/ft^3 to g/mL.

1.49 (a) How many liters of wine can be held in a wine barrel whose capacity is 31 gal? (b) The recommended adult dose of Elixophyllin®, a drug used to treat asthma, is 6 mg/kg of body mass. Calculate the dose in milligrams for a 185-lb person. (c) If an automobile is able to travel 400 km on 47.3 L of gasoline, what is the gas mileage in miles per gallon? (d) A pound of coffee beans yields 50 cups of coffee (4 cups = 1 qt). How many milliliters of coffee can be obtained from 1 g of coffee beans?

1.50 (a) If an electric car is capable of going 225 km on a single charge, how many charges will it need to travel from Seattle, Washington, to San Diego, California, a distance of 1257 mi, assuming that the trip begins with a full charge? (b) If a migrating loon flies at an average speed of 14 m/s, what is its average speed in mi/hr? (c) What is the engine piston displacement in liters of an engine whose displacement is listed as 450 in.^{3}? (d) In March 1989 the *Exxon Valdez* ran aground and spilled 240,000 barrels of crude petroleum off the coast of Alaska. One barrel of petroleum is equal to 42 gal. How many liters of petroleum were spilled?

1.51 The density of air at ordinary atmospheric pressure and 25 °C is 1.19 g/L. What is the mass, in kilograms, of the air in a room that measures 14.5 ft × 16.5 ft × 8.0 ft?

1.52 The concentration of carbon monoxide in an urban apartment is 48 μg/m^3. What mass of carbon monoxide in grams is present in a room measuring 11.0 ft × 11.5 ft × 20.5 ft?

1.53 By using estimation techniques, arrange these items in order from shortest to longest: a 57-cm length of string, a 14-in.-long shoe, and a 1.1-m length of pipe.

1.54 By using estimation techniques, determine which of the following is the heaviest and which is the lightest: a 5-lb bag of potatoes, a 5-kg bag of sugar, or 1 gal of water (density = 1.0 g/mL).

1.55 Gold can be hammered into extremely thin sheets called gold leaf. An architect wants to cover a 100 ft × 82 ft ceiling with gold leaf that is five-millionths of an inch thick. The density of gold is 19.32 g/cm^3, and gold costs $953 per troy ounce (1 troy ounce = 31.1034768 g). How much will it cost the architect to buy the necessary gold?

1.56 A copper refinery produces a copper ingot weighing 150 lb. If the copper is drawn into wire whose diameter is 7.50 mm, how many feet of copper can be obtained from the ingot? The density of copper is 8.94 g/cm^3. (Assume that the wire is a cylinder whose volume $V = \pi r^2 h$, where r is its radius and h is its height or length.)

ADDITIONAL EXERCISES

1.57 (a) Classify each of the following as a pure substance, a solution, or a heterogeneous mixture: a gold coin, a cup of coffee, a wood plank. (b) What ambiguities are there in answering part (a) from the descriptions given?

1.58 (a) What is the difference between a hypothesis and a theory? (b) Explain the difference between a theory and a scientific law. Which addresses how matter behaves, and which addresses why it behaves that way?

1.59 A sample of ascorbic acid (vitamin C) is synthesized in the laboratory. It contains 1.50 g of carbon and 2.00 g of oxygen. Another sample of ascorbic acid isolated from citrus fruits contains 6.35 g of carbon. How many grams of oxygen does it contain? Which law are you assuming in answering this question?

1.60 Two students determine the percentage of lead in a sample as a laboratory exercise. The true percentage is 22.52%. The students' results for three determinations are as follows:
1. 22.52, 22.48, 22.54
2. 22.64, 22.58, 22.62

(a) Calculate the average percentage for each set of data, and state which set is the more accurate based on the average. (b) Precision can be judged by examining the average of the deviations from the average value for that data set. (Calculate the average value for each data set; then calculate the average value of the absolute deviations of each measurement from the average.) Which set is more precise?

1.61 Is the use of significant figures in each of the following statements appropriate? Why or why not? (a) Apple sold 22,727,000 iPods during the last three months of 2008. (b) New York City receives 49.7 inches of rain, on average, per year. (c) In the United States, 0.621% of the population has the surname Brown. (d) You calculate your grade point average to be 3.87562.

1.62 What type of quantity (for example, length, volume, density) do the following units indicate: (a) mL, (b) cm^2, (c) mm^3, (d) mg/L, (e) ps, (f) nm, (g) K?

1.63 Give the derived SI units for each of the following quantities in base SI units: (a) acceleration = distance/time^2, (b) force = mass × acceleration, (c) work = force × distance, (d) pressure = force/area, (e) power = work/time, (f) velocity = distance/time, (g) energy = mass × (velocity)^2.

1.64 The distance from Earth to the Moon is approximately 240,000 mi. (a) What is this distance in meters? (b) The peregrine falcon has been measured as traveling up to 350 km/hr in a dive. If this falcon could fly to the Moon at this speed, how many seconds would it take? (c) The speed of light is 3.00×10^8 m/s. How long does it take for light to travel from Earth to the Moon and back again? (d) Earth travels around the Sun at an average speed of 29.783 km/s. Convert this speed to miles per hour.

1.65 The US quarter has a mass of 5.67 g and is approximately 1.55 mm thick. (a) How many quarters would have to be stacked to reach 575 ft, the height of the Washington Monument? (b) How much would this stack weigh? (c) How much money would this stack contain? (d) The US National Debt Clock showed the outstanding public debt to be $11,687,233,914,811.11 on August 19, 2009. How many stacks like the one described would be necessary to pay off this debt?

1.66 In the United States, water used for irrigation is measured in acre-feet. An acre-foot of water covers an acre to a depth of exactly 1 ft. An acre is 4840 yd^2. An acre-foot is enough water to supply two typical households for 1.00 yr. (a) If desalinated water costs $1950 per acre-foot, how much does desalinated water cost per liter? (b) How much would it cost one household per day if it were the only source of water?

1.67 Suppose you decide to define your own temperature scale using the freezing point (13 °C) and boiling point (360 °C) of oleic acid, the main component of olive oil. If you set the freezing point of oleic acid as 0 °O and the boiling point as 100 °O, what is the freezing point of water on this new scale?

1.68 The liquid substances mercury (density = 13.6 g/mL), water (1.00 g/mL), and cyclohexane (0.778 g/mL) do not form a solution when mixed but separate in distinct layers. Sketch how the liquids would position themselves in a test tube.

1.69 Two spheres of equal volume are placed on the scales as shown. Which one is more dense?

1.70 Water has a density of 0.997 g/cm^3 at 25 °C; ice has a density of 0.917 g/cm^3 at −10 °C. **(a)** If a soft-drink bottle whose volume is 1.50 L is completely filled with water and then frozen to −10 °C, what volume does the ice occupy? **(b)** Can the ice be contained within the bottle?

1.71 A 32.65-g sample of a solid is placed in a flask. Toluene, in which the solid is insoluble, is added to the flask so that the total volume of solid and liquid together is 50.00 mL. The solid and toluene together weigh 58.58 g. The density of toluene at the temperature of the experiment is 0.864 g/mL. What is the density of the solid?

1.72 A thief plans to steal a gold sphere with a radius of 28.9 cm from a museum. If the gold has a density of 19.3 g/cm^3, what is the mass of the sphere in pounds? [The volume of a sphere is $V = (4/3)\pi r^3$.] Is the thief likely to be able to walk off with the gold sphere unassisted?

1.73 Automobile batteries contain sulfuric acid, which is commonly referred to as "battery acid." Calculate the number of grams of sulfuric acid in 1.00 gallon of battery acid if the solution has a density of 1.28 g/mL and is 38.1% sulfuric acid by mass.

1.74 A 40-lb container of peat moss measures 14 × 20 × 30 in. A 40-lb container of topsoil has a volume of 1.9 gal. **(a)** Calculate the average densities of peat moss and topsoil in units of g/cm^3. Would it be correct to say that peat moss is "lighter" than topsoil? Explain. **(b)** How many bags of peat moss are needed to cover an area measuring 15.0 ft × 20.0 ft to a depth of 3.0 in.?

1.75 A package of aluminum foil contains 50 ft^2 of foil, which weighs approximately 8.0 oz. Aluminum has a density of 2.70 g/cm^3. What is the approximate thickness of the foil in millimeters?

1.76 The total power used by humans worldwide is approximately 15 TW (terawatts). Sunlight striking Earth provides 1.336 kW per square meter (assuming no clouds). The surface area of Earth is approximately 197,000,000 square miles. How much of Earth's surface would we need to cover with solar energy collectors to power the planet for use by all humans? Assume that the solar energy collectors can only convert 10% of the available sunlight into useful power.

1.77 A 15.0-cm long cylindrical glass tube, sealed at one end, is filled with ethanol. The mass of ethanol needed to fill the tube is found to be 11.86 g. The density of ethanol is 0.789 g/mL. Calculate the inner diameter of the tube in centimeters.

1.78 Gold is alloyed (mixed) with other metals to increase its hardness in making jewelry. **(a)** Consider a piece of gold jewelry that weighs 9.85 g and has a volume of 0.675 cm^3. The jewelry contains only gold and silver, which have densities of 19.3 g/cm^3 and 10.5 g/cm^3, respectively. If the total volume of the jewelry is the sum of the volumes of the gold and silver that it contains, calculate the percentage of gold (by mass) in the jewelry. **(b)** The relative amount of gold in an alloy is commonly expressed in units of carats. Pure gold is 24 carat, and the percentage of gold in an alloy is given as a percentage of this value. For example, an alloy that is 50% gold is 12 carat. State the purity of the gold jewelry in carats.

1.79 Chromatography (Figure 1.14) is a simple but reliable method for separating a mixture into its constituent substances. You have a mixture of two vegetable dyes, one red and one blue, that you are trying to separate. You try two different chromatography procedures and achieve the separations shown in the figure. Which procedure worked better? Can you suggest a method to quantify how good or poor the separation was?

1.80 You are assigned the task of separating a desired granular material with a density of 3.62 g/cm^3 from an undesired granular material that has a density of 2.04 g/cm^3. You want to do this by shaking the mixture in a liquid in which the heavier material will fall to the bottom and the lighter material will float. A solid will float on any liquid that is more dense. Using the Internet or a handbook of chemistry, find the densities of the following substances: carbon tetrachloride, hexane, benzene, and diiodomethane. Which of these liquids will serve your purpose, assuming no chemical interaction between the liquid and the solids?

1.81 In 2009, a team from Northwestern University and Western Washington University reported the preparation of a new "spongy" material composed of nickel, molybdenum, and sulfur that excels at removing mercury from water. The density of this new material is 0.20 g/cm^3, and its surface area is 1242 m^2 per gram of material. **(a)** Calculate the volume of a 10.0-mg sample of this material. **(b)** Calculate the surface area for a 10.0-mg sample of this material. **(c)** A 10.0-mL sample of contaminated water had 7.748 mg of mercury in it. After treatment with 10.0 mg of the new spongy material, 0.001 mg of mercury remained in the contaminated water. What percentage of the mercury was removed from the water? **(d)** What is the final mass of the spongy material after the exposure to mercury?

1.82 The concepts of accuracy and precision are not always easy to grasp. Here are two sets of studies: **(a)** The mass of a secondary weight standard is determined by weighing it on a very precise balance under carefully controlled laboratory conditions. The average of 18 different weight measurements is taken as the weight of the standard. **(b)** A group of 10,000 males between the ages of 50 and 55 is surveyed to ascertain a relationship between calorie intake and blood cholesterol level. The survey questionnaire is quite detailed, asking the respondents about what they eat, smoke, drink, and so on. The results are reported as showing that for men of comparable lifestyles, there is a 40% chance of the blood cholesterol level being above 230 mg/dL for those who consume more than 40 calories per gram of body weight per day, as compared with those who consume fewer than 30 calories per gram of body weight per day.

Discuss and compare these two studies in terms of the precision and accuracy of the result in each case. How do the two studies differ in ways that affect the accuracy and precision of the results? What makes for high precision and accuracy in any given study? In each of these studies, what factors might not be controlled that could affect the accuracy and precision? What steps can be taken generally to attain higher precision and accuracy?

WHAT'S AHEAD

A COLLECTION OF UNCUT DIAMONDS.
Diamond is one of the crystalline forms of carbon. Pure diamonds are clear and colorless. Small levels of impurities or defects cause diamond to have color—nitrogen produces yellow, whereas boron produces blue.

2

ATOMS, MOLECULES, AND IONS

LOOK AROUND AT THE GREAT variety of colors, textures, and other properties in the materials that surround you—the colors in a garden, the texture of the fabric in your clothes, the solubility of sugar in a cup of coffee, or the transparency and beauty of a diamond. The materials in our world exhibit a striking and

seemingly infinite variety of properties, but how do we understand and explain them? What makes diamonds transparent and hard, whereas table salt is brittle and dissolves in water? Why does paper burn, and why does water quench fires? The structure and behavior of atoms are key to understanding both the physical and chemical properties of matter.

Although the materials in our world vary greatly in their properties, everything is formed from only about 100 elements and, therefore, from only about 100 chemically different kinds of atoms. In a sense, the atoms are like the 26 letters of the English alphabet that join in different combinations to form the immense number of words in our language. But what rules govern the ways in which atoms combine? How do the properties of a substance relate to the kinds of atoms it contains? Indeed, what is an atom like, and what makes the atoms of one element different from those of another?

In this chapter we examine the basic structure of atoms and discuss the formation of molecules and ions, thereby providing a foundation for exploring chemistry more deeply in later chapters.

2.1 | THE ATOMIC THEORY OF MATTER

Philosophers from the earliest times speculated about the nature of the fundamental "stuff" from which the world is made. Democritus (460–370 BC) and other early Greek philosophers described the material world as made up of tiny indivisible particles they called *atomos,* meaning "indivisible or uncuttable." Later, however, Plato and Aristotle formulated the notion that there can be no ultimately indivisible particles, and the "atomic" view of matter faded for many centuries during which Aristotelean philosophy dominated Western culture.

The notion of **atoms** reemerged in Europe during the seventeenth century. As chemists learned to measure the amounts of elements that reacted with one another to form new substances, the ground was laid for an atomic theory that linked the idea of elements with the idea of atoms. That theory came from the work of John Dalton during the period from 1803 to 1807. Dalton's atomic theory was based on the four postulates given in ▼ FIGURE 2.1.

Dalton's theory explains several laws of chemical combination that were known during his time, including the *law of constant composition* ∞ (Section 1.2),* based on postulate 4:

In a given compound, the relative numbers and kinds of atoms are constant.

It also explains the *law of conservation of mass,* based on postulate 3:

The total mass of materials present after a chemical reaction is the same as the total mass present before the reaction.

A good theory explains known facts and predicts new ones. Dalton used his theory to deduce the *law of multiple proportions*:

If two elements A and B combine to form more than one compound, the masses of B that can combine with a given mass of A are in the ratio of small whole numbers.

Dalton's Atomic Theory

1. Each element is composed of extremely small particles called atoms.

An atom of the element oxygen   An atom of the element nitrogen

2. All atoms of a given element are identical, but the atoms of one element are different from the atoms of all other elements.

Oxygen   Nitrogen

3. Atoms of one element cannot be changed into atoms of a different element by chemical reactions; atoms are neither created nor destroyed in chemical reactions.

Oxygen ⊘→ Nitrogen

4. Compounds are formed when atoms of more than one element combine; a given compound always has the same relative number and kind of atoms.

N + O ⟶ NO

Elements   Compound

▶ FIGURE 2.1 **Dalton's atomic theory.** John Dalton (1766–1844), the son of a poor English weaver, began teaching at age 12. He spent most of his years in Manchester, where he taught both grammar school and college. His lifelong interest in meteorology led him to study gases, then chemistry, and eventually atomic theory. Despite his humble beginnings, Dalton gained a strong scientific reputation during his lifetime.

*The short chainlike symbol that precedes the section reference indicates a link to ideas presented earlier in the text.

We can illustrate this law by considering water and hydrogen peroxide, both of which consist of the elements hydrogen and oxygen. In forming water, 8.0 g of oxygen combine with 1.0 g of hydrogen. In forming hydrogen peroxide, 16.0 g of oxygen combine with 1.0 g of hydrogen. Thus, the ratio of the mass of oxygen per gram of hydrogen in the two compounds is 2:1. Using Dalton's atomic theory, we conclude that hydrogen peroxide contains twice as many atoms of oxygen per hydrogen atom as does water.

 GIVE IT SOME THOUGHT

Compound A contains 1.333 g of oxygen per gram of carbon, whereas compound B contains 2.666 g of oxygen per gram of carbon.
a. What chemical law do these data illustrate?
b. If compound A has an equal number of oxygen and carbon atoms, what can we conclude about the composition of compound B?

2.2 | THE DISCOVERY OF ATOMIC STRUCTURE

Dalton based his conclusions about atoms on chemical observations made in the laboratory. Neither he nor those who followed him during the century after his work was published had any direct evidence for the existence of atoms. Today, however, we can measure the properties of individual atoms and even provide images of them (▶ FIGURE 2.2).

As scientists developed methods for probing the nature of matter, the supposedly indivisible atom began to show signs of a more complex structure, and today we know that the atom is composed of **subatomic particles**. Before we summarize the current model, we briefly consider a few of the landmark discoveries that led to that model. We will see that the atom is composed in part of electrically charged particles, some with a positive charge and some with a negative charge. As we discuss the development of our current model of the atom, keep in mind this fact: *Particles with the same charge repel one another, whereas particles with unlike charges attract one another.*

Cathode Rays and Electrons

During the mid-1800s, scientists began to study electrical discharge through a glass tube pumped almost empty of air (▼ FIGURE 2.3). When a high voltage was applied to the electrodes in the tube, radiation was produced between the electrodes. This radiation, called **cathode rays**, originated at the negative electrode and traveled to the positive electrode. Although the rays could not be seen, their presence was detected because they cause certain materials to *fluoresce*, or to give off light.

▲ FIGURE 2.2   **An image of the surface of silicon.** The image was obtained by a technique called scanning tunneling microscopy. The color was added to the image by computer to help distinguish its features. Each purple sphere is a silicon atom.

 GO FIGURE

How do we know that the cathode rays travel from cathode to anode?

(a) Electrons move from the cathode (negative electrode) to the anode (positive electrode). The tube contains a glass screen (set diagonally to the electron beam) that fluoresces, showing the path of the cathode rays.

(b) The rays are deflected by a magnet.

◀ FIGURE 2.3   **Cathode-ray tube.**

If no magnetic field were applied, would you expect the electron beam to be deflected upward or downward by the electric field?

► **FIGURE 2.4 Cathode-ray tube with perpendicular magnetic and electric fields.** The cathode rays (electrons) originate at the cathode and are accelerated toward the anode, which has a hole in its center. A narrow beam of electrons passes through the hole and travels to the fluorescent screen. The strengths of the electric and magnetic fields are adjusted so their effects cancel each other allowing the beam to travel a straight path.

Experiments showed that cathode rays are deflected by electric or magnetic fields in a way consistent with their being a stream of negative electrical charge. The British scientist J. J. Thomson (1856–1940) observed that cathode rays are the same regardless of the identity of the cathode material. In a paper published in 1897, Thomson described cathode rays as streams of negatively charged particles. His paper is generally accepted as the "discovery" of what became known as the *electron*.

Thomson constructed a cathode-ray tube having a hole in the anode through which a beam of electrons passed. Electrically charged plates and a magnet were positioned perpendicular to the electron beam, and a fluorescent screen was located at one end (▲ **FIGURE 2.4**). The electric field deflected the rays in one direction, and the magnetic field deflected them in the opposite direction. Thomson adjusted the strengths of the fields so that the effects balanced each other, allowing the electrons to travel in a straight path to the screen. Knowing the strengths that resulted in the straight path made it possible to calculate a value of 1.76×10^8 coulombs per gram for the ratio of the electron's electrical charge to its mass.*

Once the charge-to-mass ratio of the electron was known, measuring either quantity allowed scientists to calculate the other. In 1909, Robert Millikan (1868–1953) of the University of Chicago succeeded in measuring the charge of an electron by performing the experiment described in ◄ **FIGURE 2.5**. He then calculated the mass of the electron by using his experimental value for the charge, 1.602×10^{-19} C, and Thomson's charge-to-mass ratio, 1.76×10^8 C/g:

▲ **FIGURE 2.5 Millikan's oil-drop experiment used to measure the charge of the electron.** Small drops of oil were allowed to fall between electrically charged plates. The drops picked up extra electrons as a result of irradiation by X-rays and so became negatively charged. Millikan measured how varying the voltage between the plates affected the rate of fall. From these data he calculated the negative charge on the drops. Because the charge on any drop was always some integral multiple of 1.602×10^{-19} C, Millikan deduced this value to be the charge of a single electron.

$$\text{Electron mass} = \frac{1.602 \times 10^{-19}\ \text{C}}{1.76 \times 10^8\ \text{C/g}} = 9.10 \times 10^{-28}\ \text{g}$$

*The coulomb (C) is the SI unit for electrical charge.

This result agrees well with the currently accepted value for the electron mass, 9.10938×10^{-28} g. This mass is about 2000 times smaller than that of hydrogen, the lightest atom.

Radioactivity

In 1896 the French scientist Henri Becquerel (1852–1908) discovered that a compound of uranium spontaneously emits high-energy radiation. This spontaneous emission of radiation is called **radioactivity**. At Becquerel's suggestion, Marie Curie (▶ **FIGURE 2.6**) and her husband, Pierre, began experiments to isolate the radioactive components of the compound.

Further study of radioactivity, principally by the British scientist Ernest Rutherford (▶ **FIGURE 2.7**), revealed three types of radiation: alpha (α), beta (β), and gamma (γ). The paths of α and β radiation are bent by an electric field, although in opposite directions; γ radiation is unaffected by the field (▼ **FIGURE 2.8**).

Rutherford showed that α and β rays consist of fast-moving particles. In fact, β particles are high-speed electrons and can be considered the radioactive equivalent of cathode rays. They are attracted to a positively charged plate. The α particles have a positive charge and are attracted to a negative plate. In units of the charge of the electron, β particles have a charge of $1-$ and α particles a charge of $2+$. Each α particle has a mass about 7400 times that of an electron. Gamma radiation is high-energy radiation similar to X-rays; it does not consist of particles and carries no charge.

The Nuclear Model of the Atom

With growing evidence that the atom is composed of smaller particles, attention was given to how the particles fit together. During the early 1900s, Thomson reasoned that because electrons contribute only a very small fraction of an atom's mass they probably were responsible for an equally small fraction of the atom's size. He proposed that the atom consisted of a uniform positive sphere of matter in which the electrons were embedded like raisins in a pudding or seeds in a watermelon (▶ **FIGURE 2.9**). This *plum-pudding model*, named after a traditional English dessert, was very short-lived.

In 1910, Rutherford was studying the angles at which α particles were deflected, or *scattered,* as they passed through a thin sheet of gold foil (▶ **FIGURE 2.10**). He discovered that almost all the particles passed directly through the foil without deflection, with a few particles deflected about 1 degree, consistent with Thomson's plum-pudding model. For the sake of completeness, Rutherford suggested that Ernest Marsden, an undergraduate student working in the laboratory, look for scattering at large angles. To everyone's surprise, a small amount of scattering was observed at large angles, with some particles scattered back in the direction from which they had come. The explanation for these results was not immediately obvious, but they were clearly inconsistent with Thomson's plum-pudding model.

▲ **FIGURE 2.6 Marie Sklodowska Curie (1867–1934).** When Marie Curie presented her doctoral thesis, it was described as the greatest single contribution of any doctoral thesis in the history of science. In 1903 Henri Becquerel, Maire Curie, and her husband, Pierre, were jointly awarded the Nobel Prize in Physics for their pioneering work on radioactivity (a term she introduced). In 1911 Marie Curie won a second Nobel Prize, this time in chemistry for her discovery of the elements polonium and radium.

▲ **FIGURE 2.7 Ernest Rutherford (1871–1937).** In 1895, Rutherford was awarded a position at Cambridge University in England, where he worked with J. J. Thomson. In 1898 he moved to McGill University in Montreal, where he did the research on radioactivity that led to his 1908 Nobel Prize in Chemistry. In 1907 Rutherford returned to England as a faculty member at Manchester University, where in 1910 he performed his famous α-particle scattering experiments. In 1992 his native New Zealand honored him by putting his likeness on their $100 currency note.

⚠ **GO FIGURE**

Which of the three kinds of radiation shown consists of electrons? Why are these rays deflected to a greater extent than the others?

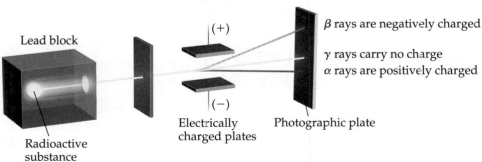

β rays are negatively charged

γ rays carry no charge

α rays are positively charged

Lead block

(+)

(−)

Radioactive substance

Electrically charged plates

Photographic plate

▲ **FIGURE 2.8 Behavior of alpha (α), beta (β), and gamma (γ) rays in an electric field.**

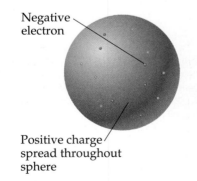

Negative electron

Positive charge spread throughout sphere

▲ **FIGURE 2.9 J. J. Thomson's plum-pudding model of the atom.** Ernest Rutherford proved this model wrong.

GO FIGURE

What is the charge on the particles that form the beam?

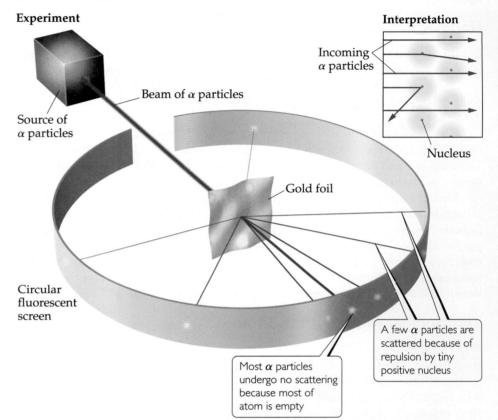

Experiment

Source of
α particles

Beam of α particles

Circular
fluorescent
screen

Gold foil

Interpretation

Incoming
α particles

Nucleus

Most α particles
undergo no scattering
because most of
atom is empty

A few α particles are
scattered because of
repulsion by tiny
positive nucleus

▶ **FIGURE 2.10 Rutherford's α-scattering experiment.** When α particles pass through a gold foil, most pass through undeflected but some are scattered, a few at very large angles. According to the plum-pudding model of the atom, the particles should experience only very minor deflections. The nuclear model of the atom explains why a few α particles are deflected at large angles. For clarity, the nuclear atom is shown here as a colored sphere, but most of the space around the nucleus is empty except for the tiny electrons moving around.

Rutherford explained the results by postulating the **nuclear model** of the atom, a model in which most of the mass of each gold atom and all of its positive charge reside in a very small, extremely dense region that he called the **nucleus**. He postulated further that most of the volume of an atom is empty space in which electrons move around the nucleus. In the α-scattering experiment, most of the particles passed through the foil unscattered because they did not encounter the minute nucleus of any gold. Occasionally, however, an α particle came close to a gold nucleus. The repulsion between the highly positive charge of the gold nucleus and the positive charge of the α particle was then strong enough to deflect the particle, as shown in Figure 2.10.

Subsequent experiments led to the discovery of positive particles (*protons*) and neutral particles (*neutrons*) in the nucleus. Protons were discovered in 1919 by Rutherford and neutrons in 1932 by British scientist James Chadwick (1891–1972). Thus, the atom is composed of electrons, protons, and neutrons.

▲ **GIVE IT SOME THOUGHT**

What happens to most of the α particles that strike the gold foil in Rutherford's experiment? Why do they behave that way?

2.3 | THE MODERN VIEW OF ATOMIC STRUCTURE

Since Rutherford's time, as physicists have learned more and more about atomic nuclei, the list of particles that make up nuclei has grown and continues to increase. As chemists, however, we can take a simple view of the atom because only three subatomic particles—the **proton**, **neutron**, and **electron**—have a bearing on chemical behavior.

As noted earlier, the charge of an electron is -1.602×10^{-19} C. That of a proton is equal in magnitude, $+1.602 \times 10^{-19}$ C. The quantity 1.602×10^{-19} C is called the

electronic charge. For convenience, the charges of atomic and subatomic particles are usually expressed as multiples of this charge rather than in coulombs. Thus, the charge of the electron is 1− and that of the proton is 1+. Neutrons are electrically neutral (which is how they received their name). *Every atom has an equal number of electrons and protons, so atoms have no net electrical charge.*

Protons and neutrons reside in the tiny nucleus of the atom. The vast majority of an atom's volume is the space in which the electrons reside (▶ **FIGURE 2.11**). The electrons are attracted to the protons in the nucleus by the electrostatic force that exists between particles of opposite electrical charge. In later chapters we will see that the strength of the attractive forces between electrons and nuclei can be used to explain many of the differences among different elements.

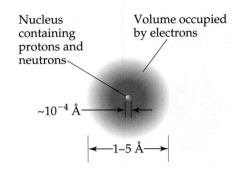

▲ **FIGURE 2.11** **The structure of the atom.** A cloud of rapidly moving electrons occupies most of the volume of the atom. The nucleus occupies a tiny region at the center of the atom and is composed of the protons and neutrons. The nucleus contains virtually all the mass of the atom.

GIVE IT SOME THOUGHT

a. If an atom has 15 protons, how many electrons does it have?
b. Where do the protons reside in an atom?

Atoms have extremely small masses. The mass of the heaviest known atom, for example, is approximately 4×10^{-22} g. Because it would be cumbersome to express such small masses in grams, we use the **atomic mass unit** (amu),* where 1 amu = 1.66054×10^{-24} g. A proton has a mass of 1.0073 amu, a neutron 1.0087 amu, and an electron 5.486×10^{-4} amu (▼ **TABLE 2.1**). Because it takes 1836 electrons to equal the mass of one proton or one neutron, the nucleus contains most of the mass of an atom.

Most atoms have diameters between 1×10^{-10} m and 5×10^{-10} m. A convenient non–SI unit of length used for atomic dimensions is the **angstrom** (Å), where $1 \text{ Å} = 1 \times 10^{-10}$ m. Thus, atoms have diameters of approximately 1−5 Å. The diameter of a chlorine atom, for example, is 200 pm, or 2.0 Å.

SAMPLE EXERCISE 2.1 | **Atomic Size**

The diameter of a US dime is 17.9 mm, and the diameter of a silver atom is 2.88 Å. How many silver atoms could be arranged side by side across the diameter of a dime?

SOLUTION

The unknown is the number of silver (Ag) atoms. Using the relationship 1 Ag atom = 2.88 Å as a conversion factor relating number of atoms and distance, we start with the diameter of the dime, first converting this distance into angstroms and then using the diameter of the Ag atom to convert distance to number of Ag atoms:

$$\text{Ag atoms} = (17.9 \text{ mm})\left(\frac{10^{-3} \text{ m}}{1 \text{ mm}}\right)\left(\frac{1 \text{ Å}}{10^{-10} \text{ m}}\right)\left(\frac{1 \text{ Ag atom}}{2.88 \text{ Å}}\right) = 6.22 \times 10^7 \text{ Ag atoms}$$

That is, 62.2 million silver atoms could sit side by side across a dime!

PRACTICE EXERCISE

The diameter of a carbon atom is 1.54 Å. **(a)** Express this diameter in picometers. **(b)** How many carbon atoms could be aligned side by side across the width of a pencil line that is 0.20 mm wide?

Answers: **(a)** 154 pm, **(b)** 1.3×10^6 C atoms

The diameter of an atomic nucleus is approximately 10^{-4} Å, only a small fraction of the diameter of the atom as a whole. You can appreciate the relative sizes of the atom and its nucleus by imagining that if the hydrogen atom were as large as a football stadium,

---

TABLE 2.1 • **Comparison of the Proton, Neutron, and Electron**

Particle	Charge	Mass (amu)
Proton	Positive (1+)	1.0073
Neutron	None (neutral)	1.0087
Electron	Negative (1−)	5.486×10^{-4}

---

*The SI abbreviation for the atomic mass unit is u. We will use the more common abbreviation amu.

A CLOSER LOOK

BASIC FORCES

Four basic forces are known in nature: (1) gravitational, (2) electromagnetic, (3) strong nuclear, and (4) weak nuclear. *Gravitational forces* are attractive forces that act between all objects in proportion to their masses. Gravitational forces between atoms or between subatomic particles are so small that they are of no chemical significance.

Electromagnetic forces are attractive or repulsive forces that act between either electrically charged or magnetic objects. Electric forces are important in understanding the chemical behavior of atoms. The magnitude of the electric force between two charged particles is given by *Coulomb's law*: $F = kQ_1Q_2/d^2$, where Q_1 and Q_2 are the magnitudes of the charges on the two particles, d is the distance between their centers, and k is a constant determined by the units for Q and d. A negative value for the force indicates attraction, whereas a positive value indicates repulsion.

All nuclei except those of hydrogen atoms contain two or more protons. Because like charges repel, electrical repulsion would cause the protons to fly apart if the *strong nuclear force* did not keep them together. This force acts between subatomic particles, as in the nucleus. At this distance, the attractive strong nuclear force is stronger than the positive–positive repulsive electric force and holds the nucleus together.

The *weak nuclear force* is weaker than the electric force but stronger than the gravitational force. We are aware of its existence only because it shows itself in certain types of radioactivity.

RELATED EXERCISE: 2.88

---

the nucleus would be the size of a small marble. Because the tiny nucleus carries most of the mass of the atom in such a small volume, it has an incredibly high density—on the order of 10^{13}–10^{14} g/cm³. A matchbox full of material of such density would weigh over 2.5 billion tons!

An illustration of the atom that incorporates the features we have just discussed is shown in Figure 2.11. The electrons play the major role in chemical reactions. The significance of representing the region containing the electrons as an indistinct cloud will become clear in later chapters when we consider the energies and spatial arrangements of the electrons.

Atomic Numbers, Mass Numbers, and Isotopes

What makes an atom of one element different from an atom of another element is that the atoms of each element have a *characteristic number of protons*. Indeed, the number of protons in an atom of any particular element is called that element's **atomic number**. Because an atom has no net electrical charge, the number of electrons it contains must equal the number of protons. All atoms of carbon, for example, have six protons and six electrons, whereas all atoms of oxygen have eight protons and eight electrons. Thus, carbon has atomic number 6, and oxygen has atomic number 8. The atomic number of each element is listed with the name and symbol of the element on the inside front cover of the text.

Atoms of a given element can differ in the number of neutrons they contain and, consequently, in mass. For example, most atoms of carbon have six neutrons, although some have more and some have less. The symbol $^{12}_{6}\text{C}$ (read "carbon twelve," carbon-12) represents the carbon atom containing six protons and six neutrons. The atomic number is shown by the subscript; the superscript, called the **mass number**, is the number of protons plus neutrons in the atom:

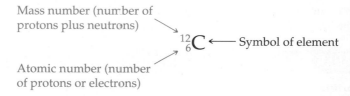

Because all atoms of a given element have the same atomic number, the subscript is redundant and is often omitted. Thus, the symbol for carbon-12 can be represented simply as ^{12}C. As one more example of this notation, carbon atoms that contain six protons and eight neutrons have mass number 14, are represented as $^{14}_{6}\text{C}$ or ^{14}C, and are referred to as carbon-14.

TABLE 2.2 • Some Isotopes of Carbon*			
Symbol	Number of Protons	Number of Electrons	Number of Neutrons
^{11}C	6	6	5
^{12}C	6	6	6
^{13}C	6	6	7
^{14}C	6	6	8

*Almost 99% of the carbon found in nature is ^{12}C.

Atoms with identical atomic numbers but different mass numbers (that is, same number of protons but different numbers of neutrons) are called **isotopes** of one another. Several isotopes of carbon are listed in ▲ TABLE 2.2. We will generally use the notation with superscripts only when referring to a particular isotope of an element.

SAMPLE EXERCISE 2.2 Determining the Number of Subatomic Particles in Atoms

How many protons, neutrons, and electrons are in (a) an atom of ^{197}Au, (b) an atom of strontium-90?

SOLUTION

(a) The superscript 197 is the mass number (protons + neutrons). According to the list of elements given on the inside front cover, gold has atomic number 79. Consequently, an atom of ^{197}Au has 79 protons, 79 electrons, and $197 - 79 = 118$ neutrons. (b) The atomic number of strontium (listed on inside front cover) is 38. Thus, all atoms of this element have 38 protons and 38 electrons. The strontium-90 isotope has $90 - 38 = 52$ neutrons.

PRACTICE EXERCISE

How many protons, neutrons, and electrons are in (a) a ^{138}Ba atom, (b) an atom of phosphorus-31?
Answer: (a) 56 protons, 56 electrons, and 82 neutrons, (b) 15 protons, 15 electrons, and 16 neutrons

---

SAMPLE EXERCISE 2.3 Writing Symbols for Atoms

Magnesium has three isotopes with mass numbers 24, 25, and 26. (a) Write the complete chemical symbol (superscript and subscript) for each. (b) How many neutrons are in an atom of each isotope?

SOLUTION

(a) Magnesium has atomic number 12, so all atoms of magnesium contain 12 protons and 12 electrons. The three isotopes are therefore represented by $^{24}_{12}Mg$, $^{25}_{12}Mg$, and $^{26}_{12}Mg$. (b) The number of neutrons in each isotope is the mass number minus the number of protons. The numbers of neutrons in an atom of each isotope are therefore 12, 13, and 14, respectively.

PRACTICE EXERCISE

Give the complete chemical symbol for the atom that contains 82 protons, 82 electrons, and 126 neutrons.
Answer: $^{208}_{82}Pb$

2.4 | ATOMIC WEIGHTS

Atoms are small pieces of matter, so they have mass. In this section we discuss the mass scale used for atoms and introduce the concept of *atomic weights*.

The Atomic Mass Scale

Scientists of the nineteenth century were aware that atoms of different elements have different masses. They found, for example, that each 100.0 g of water contains 11.1 g of hydrogen and 88.9 g of oxygen. Thus, water contains $88.9/11.1 = 8$ times as much oxygen, by mass, as hydrogen. Once scientists understood that water contains two hydrogen atoms for each oxygen atom, they concluded that an oxygen atom must have $2 \times 8 = 16$ times as much mass as a hydrogen atom. Hydrogen, the lightest atom, was arbitrarily assigned a relative mass of 1 (no units). Atomic masses of other elements were at first determined relative to this value. Thus, oxygen was assigned an atomic mass of 16.

Today we can determine the masses of individual atoms with a high degree of accuracy. For example, we know that the ^1H atom has a mass of 1.6735×10^{-24} g and the ^{16}O atom has a mass of 2.6560×10^{-23} g. As we noted in Section 2.3, it is convenient to use the *atomic mass unit* (amu) when dealing with these extremely small masses:

$$1 \text{ amu} = 1.66054 \times 10^{-24} \text{ g and } 1 \text{ g} = 6.02214 \times 10^{23} \text{ amu}$$

The atomic mass unit is presently defined by assigning a mass of exactly 12 amu to an atom of the ^{12}C isotope of carbon. In these units, an ^1H atom has a mass of 1.0078 amu and an ^{16}O atom has a mass of 15.9949 amu.

Atomic Weight

Most elements occur in nature as mixtures of isotopes. We can determine the *average atomic mass* of an element, usually called the element's **atomic weight**, by using the masses of its isotopes and their relative abundances:

$$\text{Atomic weight} = \sum [(\text{isotope mass}) \times (\text{fractional isotope abundance})]$$

over all isotopes of the element   [2.1]

Naturally occurring carbon, for example, is composed of 98.93% ^{12}C and 1.07% ^{13}C. The masses of these isotopes are 12 amu (exactly) and 13.00335 amu, respectively, making the atomic weight of carbon

$$(0.9893)(12 \text{ amu}) + (0.0107)(13.00335 \text{ amu}) = 12.01 \text{ amu}$$

The atomic weights of the elements are listed in both the periodic table and the table of elements inside the front cover of this text.

 GIVE IT SOME THOUGHT

A particular atom of chromium has a mass of 52.94 amu, whereas the atomic weight of chromium is 51.99 amu. Explain the difference in the two masses.

SAMPLE EXERCISE 2.4 **Calculating the Atomic Weight of an Element from Isotopic Abundances**

Naturally occurring chlorine is 75.78% ^{35}Cl (atomic mass 34.969 amu) and 24.22% ^{37}Cl (atomic mass 36.966 amu). Calculate the atomic weight of chlorine.

SOLUTION

We can calculate the atomic weight by multiplying the abundance of each isotope by its atomic mass and summing these products. Because 75.78% = 0.7578 and 24.22% = 0.2422, we have

$$\text{Atomic weight} = (0.7578)(34.969 \text{ amu}) + (0.2422)(36.966 \text{ amu})$$
$$= 26.50 \text{ amu} + 8.953 \text{ amu}$$
$$= 35.45 \text{ amu}$$

This answer makes sense: The atomic weight, which is actually the average atomic mass, is between the masses of the two isotopes and is closer to the value of ^{35}Cl, the more abundant isotope.

PRACTICE EXERCISE

Three isotopes of silicon occur in nature: ^{28}Si (92.23%), atomic mass 27.97693 amu; ^{29}Si (4.68%), atomic mass 28.97649 amu; and ^{30}Si (3.09%), atomic mass 29.97377 amu. Calculate the atomic weight of silicon.
Answer: 28.09 amu

A CLOSER LOOK

THE MASS SPECTROMETER

The most accurate means for determining atomic weights is provided by the **mass spectrometer** (▼ FIGURE 2.12). A gaseous sample is introduced at *A* and bombarded by a stream of high-energy electrons at *B*. Collisions between the electrons and the atoms or molecules of the gas produce positively charged particles that are then accelerated toward a negatively charged grid (*C*). After the particles pass through the grid, they encounter two slits that allow only a narrow beam of particles to pass. This beam then passes between the poles of a magnet, which deflects the particles into a curved path. For particles with the same charge, the extent of deflection depends on mass—the more massive the particle, the less the deflection. The particles are thereby separated according to their masses. By changing the strength of the magnetic field or the accelerating voltage on the grid, charged particles of various masses can be selected to enter the detector.

A graph of the intensity of the detector signal versus particle atomic mass is called a *mass spectrum* (▼ FIGURE 2.13). Analysis of a mass spectrum gives both the masses of the charged particles reaching the detector and their relative abundances, which are obtained from the signal intensities. Knowing the atomic mass and the abundance of each isotope allows us to calculate the atomic weight of an element, as shown in Sample Exercise 2.4.

Mass spectrometers are used extensively today to identify chemical compounds and analyze mixtures of substances. Any molecule that loses electrons can fall apart, forming an array of positively charged fragments. The mass spectrometer measures the masses of these fragments, producing a chemical "fingerprint" of the molecule and providing clues about how the atoms were connected in the original molecule. Thus, a chemist might use this technique to determine the molecular structure of a newly synthesized compound or to identify a pollutant in the environment.

RELATED EXERCISES: 2.33, 2.34, 2.35(b), 2.36, 2.92, and 2.93

▲ FIGURE 2.12   **A mass spectrometer.** Cl atoms are introduced at *A* and are ionized to form Cl⁺ ions, which are then directed through a magnetic field. The paths of the ions of the two Cl isotopes diverge as they pass through the field.

▲ FIGURE 2.13   **Mass spectrum of atomic chlorine.** The fractional abundances of the isotopes ^{35}Cl and ^{37}Cl are indicated by the relative signal intensities of the beams reaching the detector of the mass spectrometer.

2.5 | THE PERIODIC TABLE

As the list of known elements expanded during the early 1800s, attempts were made to find patterns in chemical behavior. These efforts culminated in the development of the periodic table in 1869. We will have much to say about the periodic table in later chapters, but it is so important and useful that you should become acquainted with it now. You will quickly learn that *the periodic table is the most significant tool that chemists use for organizing and remembering chemical facts.*

Many elements show strong similarities to one another. The elements lithium (Li), sodium (Na), and potassium (K) are all soft, very reactive metals, for example. The elements helium (He), neon (Ne), and argon (Ar) are all very nonreactive gases. If the elements are arranged in order of increasing atomic number, their chemical and physical properties show a repeating, or *periodic,* pattern. For example, each of the soft, reactive metals—lithium, sodium, and potassium—comes immediately after one of the nonreactive gases—helium, neon, and argon—as shown in ▶ FIGURE 2.14.

◢ **GO FIGURE**

If F is a reactive nonmetal, which other element or elements shown here do you expect to also be a reactive nonmetal?

▶ **FIGURE 2.14 Arranging elements by atomic number reveals a periodic pattern of properties.** This pattern is the basis of the periodic table.

The arrangement of elements in order of increasing atomic number, with elements having similar properties placed in vertical columns, is known as the **periodic table** (▼ **FIGURE 2.15**). The table shows the atomic number and atomic symbol for each element, and the atomic weight is often given as well, as in this typical entry for potassium:

You may notice slight variations in periodic tables from one book to another or between those in the lecture hall and in the text. These are simply matters of style, or they might concern the particular information included. There are no fundamental differences.

Periods - horizontal rows

Groups - vertical columns containing elements with similar properties

1A 1																	8A 18
1 **H**	2A 2	**Elements** arranged in order of increasing atomic number			**Steplike line divides** metals from nonmetals							3A 13	4A 14	5A 15	6A 16	7A 17	**2** **He**
3 **Li**	**4** **Be**											**5** **B**	**6** **C**	**7** **N**	**8** **O**	**9** **F**	**10** **Ne**
11 **Na**	**12** **Mg**	3B 3	4B 4	5B 5	6B 6	7B 7	8B 8	9	10	1B 11	2B 12	**13** **Al**	**14** **Si**	**15** **P**	**16** **S**	**17** **Cl**	**18** **Ar**
19 **K**	**20** **Ca**	**21** **Sc**	**22** **Ti**	**23** **V**	**24** **Cr**	**25** **Mn**	**26** **Fe**	**27** **Co**	**28** **Ni**	**29** **Cu**	**30** **Zn**	**31** **Ga**	**32** **Ge**	**33** **As**	**34** **Se**	**35** **Br**	**36** **Kr**
37 **Rb**	**38** **Sr**	**39** **Y**	**40** **Zr**	**41** **Nb**	**42** **Mo**	**43** **Tc**	**44** **Ru**	**45** **Rh**	**46** **Pd**	**47** **Ag**	**48** **Cd**	**49** **In**	**50** **Sn**	**51** **Sb**	**52** **Te**	**53** **I**	**54** **Xe**
55 **Cs**	**56** **Ba**	**71** **Lu**	**72** **Hf**	**73** **Ta**	**74** **W**	**75** **Re**	**76** **Os**	**77** **Ir**	**78** **Pt**	**79** **Au**	**80** **Hg**	**81** **Tl**	**82** **Pb**	**83** **Bi**	**84** **Po**	**85** **At**	**86** **Rn**
87 **Fr**	**88** **Ra**	**103** **Lr**	**104** **Rf**	**105** **Db**	**106** **Sg**	**107** **Bh**	**108** **Hs**	**109** **Mt**	**110** **Ds**	**111** **Rg**	**112** **Cn**	113	114	115	116	117	118

☐ Metals
☐ Metalloids
☐ Nonmetals

57 **La**	**58** **Ce**	**59** **Pr**	**60** **Nd**	**61** **Pm**	**62** **Sm**	**63** **Eu**	**64** **Gd**	**65** **Tb**	**66** **Dy**	**67** **Ho**	**68** **Er**	**69** **Tm**	**70** **Yb**
89 **Ac**	**90** **Th**	**91** **Pa**	**92** **U**	**93** **Np**	**94** **Pu**	**95** **Am**	**96** **Cm**	**97** **Bk**	**98** **Cf**	**99** **Es**	**100** **Fm**	**101** **Md**	**102** **No**

▲ **FIGURE 2.15 Periodic table of the elements.**

The horizontal rows of the periodic table are called **periods**. The first period consists of only two elements, hydrogen (H) and helium (He). The second and third periods consist of eight elements each. The fourth and fifth periods contain 18 elements. The sixth period has 32 elements, but for it to fit on a page, 14 of these elements (atomic numbers 57–70) appear at the bottom of the table. The seventh period is incomplete, but it also has 14 of its members placed in a row at the bottom of the table.

The vertical columns are **groups**. The way in which the groups are labeled is somewhat arbitrary. Three labeling schemes are in common use, two of which are shown in Figure 2.15. The top set of labels, which have A and B designations, is widely used in North America. Roman numerals, rather than Arabic ones, are often employed in this scheme. Group 7A, for example, is often labeled VIIA. Europeans use a similar convention that numbers the columns from 1A through 8A and then from 1B through 8B, thereby giving the label 7B (or VIIB) instead of 7A to the group headed by fluorine (F). In an effort to eliminate this confusion, the International Union of Pure and Applied Chemistry (IUPAC) has proposed a convention that numbers the groups from 1 through 18 with no A or B designations, as shown in Figure 2.15. We will use the traditional North American convention with Arabic numerals and the letters A and B.

Elements in a group often exhibit similarities in physical and chemical properties. For example, the "coinage metals"—copper (Cu), silver (Ag), and gold (Au)—belong to group 1B. These elements are less reactive than most metals, which is why they are used throughout the world to make coins. Many other groups in the periodic table also have names, listed in ▼ TABLE 2.3.

We will learn in Chapters 6 and 7 that elements in a group have similar properties because they have the same arrangement of electrons at the periphery of their atoms. However, we need not wait until then to make good use of the periodic table; after all, chemists who knew nothing about electrons developed the table! We can use the table, as they intended, to correlate behaviors of elements and to help us remember many facts. The color code of Figure 2.15 shows that, except for hydrogen, all the elements on the left and in the middle of the table are **metallic elements**, or **metals**. All the metallic elements share characteristic properties, such as luster and high electrical and heat conductivity, and all of them except mercury (Hg) are solid at room temperature. The metals are separated from the **nonmetallic elements**, or **nonmetals**, by a stepped line that runs from boron (B) to astatine (At). (Note that hydrogen, although on the left side of the table, is a nonmetal.) At room temperature some of the nonmetals are gaseous, some are solid, and one is liquid. Nonmetals generally differ from the metals in appearance (▶ FIGURE 2.16) and in other physical properties. Many of the elements that lie along the line that separates metals from nonmetals have properties that fall between those of metals and those of nonmetals. These elements are often referred to as **metalloids**.

GIVE IT SOME THOUGHT

Chlorine is a halogen (Table 2.3). Locate this element in the periodic table.
a. What is its symbol?
b. In which period and in which group is the element located?
c. What is its atomic number?
d. Is it a metal or nonmetal?

▲ FIGURE 2.16 **Examples of metals (top) and nonmetals (bottom).**

TABLE 2.3 • Names of Some Groups in the Periodic Table		
Group	**Name**	**Elements**
1A	Alkali metals	Li, Na, K, Rb, Cs, Fr
2A	Alkaline earth metals	Be, Mg, Ca, Sr, Ba, Ra
6A	Chalcogens	O, S, Se, Te, Po
7A	Halogens	F, Cl, Br, I, At
8A	Noble gases (or rare gases)	He, Ne, Ar, Kr, Xe, Rn

A CLOSER LOOK

GLENN SEABORG AND SEABORGIUM

Prior to 1940 the periodic table ended at uranium, element number 92. Since that time, no scientist has had a greater effect on the periodic table than Glenn Seaborg (▶ FIGURE 2.17). In 1940 Seaborg, Edwin McMillan, and coworkers at the University of California, Berkeley, succeeded in isolating plutonium (Pu) as a product of the reaction between uranium and neutrons. We will talk about reactions of this type, called *nuclear reactions,* in Chapter 21.

Between 1944 and 1958, Seaborg and his coworkers also identified various products of nuclear reactions as being the elements having atomic numbers 95 through 102. All these elements are radioactive and are not found in nature; they can be synthesized only via nuclear reactions. For their efforts in identifying the elements beyond uranium (the *transuranium* elements), McMillan and Seaborg shared the 1951 Nobel Prize in Chemistry.

From 1961 to 1971, Seaborg served as the chairman of the US Atomic Energy Commission (now the Department of Energy). In this position he had an important role in establishing international treaties to limit the testing of nuclear weapons. Upon his return to Berkeley, he was part of the team that in 1974 first identified element number 106. In 1994, to honor Seaborg's many contributions to the discovery of new elements, the American Chemical Society proposed that element number 106 be named seaborgium (Sg). After several years of controversy about whether an element should be named

◀ FIGURE 2.17 **Glenn Seaborg (1912–1999).** Seaborg at Berkeley in 1941 measuring radiation produced by plutonium.

after a living person, the IUPAC officially adopted the name in 1997. Seaborg became the first person to have an element named after him while he was alive.

RELATED EXERCISE: 2.95

SAMPLE EXERCISE 2.5 **Using the Periodic Table**

Which two of these elements would you expect to show the greatest similarity in chemical and physical properties: B, Ca, F, He, Mg, P?

SOLUTION

Elements in the same group of the periodic table are most likely to exhibit similar properties. We therefore expect Ca and Mg to be most alike because they are in the same group (2A, the alkaline earth metals).

PRACTICE EXERCISE

Locate Na (sodium) and Br (bromine) in the periodic table. Give the atomic number of each and classify each as metal, metalloid, or nonmetal.

Answer: Na, atomic number 11, is a metal; Br, atomic number 35, is a nonmetal.

2.6 | MOLECULES AND MOLECULAR COMPOUNDS

Even though the atom is the smallest representative sample of an element, only the noble-gas elements are normally found in nature as isolated atoms. Most matter is composed of molecules or ions. We examine molecules here and ions in Section 2.7.

Molecules and Chemical Formulas

Several elements are found in nature in molecular form—two or more of the same type of atom bound together. For example, most of the oxygen in air consists of molecules that contain two oxygen atoms. As we saw in Section 1.2, we represent this molecular oxygen by the **chemical formula** O_2 (read "oh two"). The subscript tells us that two oxygen atoms are present in each molecule. A molecule made up of two atoms is called a **diatomic molecule**.

Oxygen also exists in another molecular form known as *ozone*. Molecules of ozone consist of three oxygen atoms, making the chemical formula O_3. Even though "normal" oxygen (O_2) and ozone (O_3) are both composed only of oxygen atoms, they exhibit very different chemical and physical properties. For example, O_2 is essential for life, but O_3 is toxic; O_2 is odorless, whereas O_3 has a sharp, pungent smell.

The elements that normally occur as diatomic molecules are hydrogen, oxygen, nitrogen, and the halogens (H_2, O_2, N_2, F_2, Cl_2, Br_2, and I_2). Except for hydrogen, these diatomic elements are clustered on the right side of the periodic table.

Compounds composed of molecules contain more than one type of atom and are called **molecular compounds**. A molecule of the compound methane, for example, consists of one carbon atom and four hydrogen atoms and is therefore represented by the chemical formula CH_4. Lack of a subscript on the C indicates one atom of C per methane molecule. Several common molecules of both elements and compounds are shown in ▶ **FIGURE 2.18**. Notice how the composition of each substance is given by its chemical formula. Notice also that these substances are composed only of nonmetallic elements. *Most molecular substances we will encounter contain only nonmetals.*

Molecular and Empirical Formulas

Chemical formulas that indicate the actual numbers of atoms in a molecule are called **molecular formulas**. (The formulas in Figure 2.18 are molecular formulas.) Chemical formulas that give only the relative number of atoms of each type in a molecule are called **empirical formulas**. The subscripts in an empirical formula are always the smallest possible whole-number ratios. The molecular formula for hydrogen peroxide is H_2O_2, for example, whereas its empirical formula is HO. The molecular formula for ethylene is C_2H_4, and its empirical formula is CH_2. For many substances, the molecular formula and the empirical formula are identical, as in the case of water, H_2O.

Whenever we know the molecular formula of a compound, we can determine its empirical formula. The converse is not true, however. If we know the empirical formula of a substance, we cannot determine its molecular formula unless we have more information. So why do chemists bother with empirical formulas? As we will see in Chapter 3, certain common methods of analyzing substances lead to the empirical formula only. Once the empirical formula is known, additional experiments can give the information needed to convert the empirical formula to the molecular one. In addition, there are substances that do not exist as isolated molecules. For these substances, we must rely on empirical formulas.

Hydrogen, H_2

Oxygen, O_2

Water, H_2O

Hydrogen peroxide, H_2O_2

Carbon monoxide, CO

Carbon dioxide, CO_2

Methane, CH_4

Ethylene, C_2H_4

▲ **FIGURE 2.18   Molecular models.** Notice how the chemical formulas of these simple molecules correspond to their compositions.

SAMPLE EXERCISE 2.6	**Relating Empirical and Molecular Formulas**

Write the empirical formulas for **(a)** glucose, a substance also known as either blood sugar or dextrose, molecular formula $C_6H_{12}O_6$; **(b)** nitrous oxide, a substance used as an anesthetic and commonly called laughing gas, molecular formula N_2O.

SOLUTION

(a) The subscripts of an empirical formula are the smallest whole-number ratios. The smallest ratios are obtained by dividing each subscript by the largest common factor, in this case 6. The resultant empirical formula for glucose is CH_2O.

(b) Because the subscripts in N_2O are already the lowest integral numbers, the empirical formula for nitrous oxide is the same as its molecular formula, N_2O.

PRACTICE EXERCISE

Give the empirical formula for *diborane*, whose molecular formula is B_2H_6.
Answer: BH_3

What advantage does a ball-and-stick model have over a space-filling model?

CH_4

Molecular formula

Structural formula

Dashed wedge is bond behind page

Solid line is bond in plane of page

Wedge is bond out of page

Perspective drawing

Ball-and-stick model

Space-filling model

▲ **FIGURE 2.19** **Different representations of the methane (CH_4) molecule.** Structural formulas, perspective drawings, ball-and-stick models, and space-filling models correspond to the molecular formula, and each helps us visualize the ways atoms are attached to each other.

Picturing Molecules

The molecular formula of a substance summarizes the composition of the substance but does not show how the atoms are joined together in the molecule. A **structural formula** shows which atoms are attached to which, as in the following examples:

Water   Hydrogen peroxide   Methane

The atoms are represented by their chemical symbols, and lines are used to represent the bonds that hold the atoms together.

A structural formula usually does not depict the actual geometry of the molecule, that is, the actual angles at which atoms are joined together. A structural formula can be written as a *perspective drawing* (◄ **FIGURE 2.19**), however, to give some sense of three-dimensional shape.

Scientists also rely on various models to help visualize molecules. *Ball-and-stick models* show atoms as spheres and bonds as sticks. This type of model has the advantage of accurately representing the angles at which the atoms are attached to one another in the molecule (Figure 2.19). Sometimes the chemical symbols of the elements are superimposed on the balls, but often the atoms are identified simply by color.

A *space-filling model* depicts what the molecule would look like if the atoms were scaled up in size (Figure 2.19). These models show the relative sizes of the atoms, but the angles between atoms, which help define their molecular geometry, are often more difficult to see than in ball-and-stick models. As in ball-and-stick models, the identities of the atoms are indicated by color, but they may also be labeled with the element's symbol.

GIVE IT SOME THOUGHT

The structural formula for ethane is

a. What is the molecular formula for ethane?
b. What is its empirical formula?
c. Which kind of molecular model would most clearly show the angles between atoms?

2.7 | IONS AND IONIC COMPOUNDS

The nucleus of an atom is unchanged by chemical processes, but some atoms can readily gain or lose electrons. If electrons are removed from or added to an atom, a charged particle called an **ion** is formed. An ion with a positive charge is a **cation** (pronounced CAT-ion); a negatively charged ion is an **anion** (AN-ion).

To see how ions form, consider the sodium atom, which has 11 protons and 11 electrons. This atom easily loses one electron. The resulting cation has 11 protons and 10 electrons, which means it has a net charge of 1+.

$11p^+$ $11e^-$ $11p^+$ $10e^-$

Loses an electron

Na atom Na^+ ion

The net charge on an ion is represented by a superscript. The superscripts $+$, $2+$, and $3+$, for instance, mean a net charge resulting from the *loss* of one, two, and three electrons, respectively. The superscripts $-$, $2-$, and $3-$ represent net charges resulting from the *gain* of one, two, and three electrons, respectively. Chlorine, with 17 protons and 17 electrons, for example, can gain an electron in chemical reactions, producing the Cl^- ion:

Cl atom	Cl^- ion

In general, metal atoms tend to lose electrons to form cations and nonmetal atoms tend to gain electrons to form anions. Thus, ionic compounds tend to be composed of metals bonded with nonmetals, as in NaCl.

SAMPLE EXERCISE 2.7   **Writing Chemical Symbols for Ions**

Give the chemical symbol, including superscript indicating mass number, for **(a)** the ion with 22 protons, 26 neutrons, and 19 electrons; **(b)** the ion of sulfur that has 16 neutrons and 18 electrons.

SOLUTION

(a) The number of protons is the atomic number of the element. A periodic table or list of elements tells us that the element with atomic number 22 is titanium (Ti). The mass number (protons plus neutrons) of this isotope of titanium is $22 + 26 = 48$. Because the ion has three more protons than electrons, it has a net charge of $3+$: $^{48}Ti^{3+}$.

(b) The periodic table tells us that sulfur (S) has an atomic number of 16. Thus, each atom or ion of sulfur contains 16 protons. We are told that the ion also has 16 neutrons, meaning the mass number is $16 + 16 = 32$. Because the ion has 16 protons and 18 electrons, its net charge is $2-$ and the ion symbol is $^{32}S^{2-}$.

In general, we will focus on the net charges of ions and ignore their mass numbers unless the circumstances dictate that we specify a certain isotope.

PRACTICE EXERCISE

How many protons, neutrons, and electrons does the $^{79}Se^{2-}$ ion possess?

Answer: 34 protons, 45 neutrons, and 36 electrons

In addition to simple ions such as Na^+ and Cl^-, there are **polyatomic ions**, such as NH_4^+ (ammonium ion) and SO_4^{2-} (sulfate ion). These latter ions consist of atoms joined as in a molecule, but they have a net positive or negative charge. We consider polyatomic ions in Section 2.8.

It is important to realize that the chemical properties of ions are very different from the chemical properties of the atoms from which the ions are derived. Although a given atom and its ion may be essentially the same (plus or minus a few electrons), the behavior of the ion is very different from that of its associated atom.

Predicting Ionic Charges

Many atoms gain or lose electrons to end up with the same number of electrons as the noble gas closest to them in the periodic table. Noble-gas elements are chemically non-reactive and form very few compounds. We might deduce that this is because their electron arrangements are very stable. Nearby elements can obtain these same stable arrangements by losing or gaining electrons. For example, the loss of one electron from an atom of sodium leaves it with the same number of electrons as in a neon atom (10). Similarly, when chlorine gains an electron, it ends up with 18, the same number of electrons as in argon. We will use this simple observation to explain the formation of ions until Chapter 8, where we discuss chemical bonding.

SAMPLE EXERCISE 2.8 Predicting Ionic Charge

Predict the charge expected for the most stable ion of barium and the most stable ion of oxygen.

SOLUTION

We will assume that these elements form ions that have the same number of electrons as the nearest noble-gas atom. From the periodic table, we see that barium has atomic number 56. The nearest noble gas is xenon, atomic number 54. Barium can attain a stable arrangement of 54 electrons by losing two electrons, forming the Ba^{2+} cation.

Oxygen has atomic number 8. The nearest noble gas is neon, atomic number 10. Oxygen can attain this stable electron arrangement by gaining two electrons, forming the O^{2-} anion.

PRACTICE EXERCISE

Predict the charge expected for the most stable ion of (a) aluminum and (b) fluorine.

Answer: (a) 3+, (b) 1−

The periodic table is very useful for remembering ionic charges, especially those of elements on the left and right sides of the table. As ▼ **FIGURE 2.20** shows, the charges of these ions relate in a simple way to their positions in the table: The group 1A elements (alkali metals) form 1+ ions, the group 2A elements (alkaline earths) form 2+ ions, the group 7A elements (halogens) form 1− ions, and the group 6A elements form 2− ions. (Many of the other groups do not lend themselves to such simple rules.)

Ionic Compounds

A great deal of chemical activity involves the transfer of electrons from one substance to another. ▶ **FIGURE 2.21** shows that when elemental sodium is allowed to react with elemental chlorine, an electron transfers from a sodium atom to a chlorine atom, forming a Na^+ ion and a Cl^- ion. Because objects of opposite charge attract, the Na^+ and the Cl^- ions bind together to form the compound sodium chloride (NaCl). Sodium chloride, which we know better as common table salt, is an example of an **ionic compound**, a compound made up of cations and anions.

We can often tell whether a compound is ionic (consisting of ions) or molecular (consisting of molecules) from its composition. In general, cations are metal ions and anions are nonmetal ions. Consequently, *ionic compounds are generally combinations of metals and nonmetals,* as in NaCl. In contrast, *molecular compounds are generally composed of nonmetals only,* as in H_2O.

▲ **GO FIGURE**

The most common ions for silver, zinc, and scandium are Ag^+, Zn^{2+}, and Sc^{3+}. Locate the boxes in which you would place these ions in this table. Which of these ions have the same number of electrons as a noble-gas element?

▶ **FIGURE 2.20** **Predictable charges of some common ions.** Notice that the red stepped line that divides metals from nonmetals also separates cations from anions. Hydrogen forms both 1+ and 1− ions.

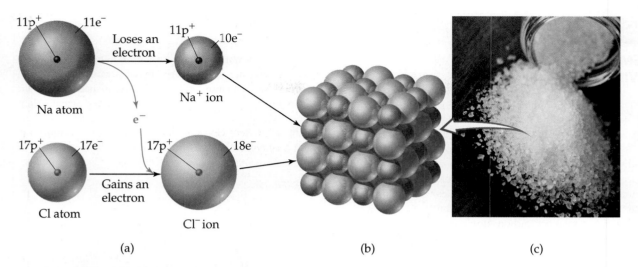

▲ **FIGURE 2.21** **Formation of an ionic compound.** (a) The transfer of an electron from a Na atom to a Cl atom leads to the formation of a Na^+ ion and a Cl^- ion. (b) Arrangement of these ions in solid sodium chloride, NaCl. (c) A sample of sodium chloride crystals.

SAMPLE EXERCISE 2.9   **Identifying Ionic and Molecular Compounds**

Which of these compounds would you expect to be ionic: N_2O, Na_2O, $CaCl_2$, SF_4?

SOLUTION

We predict that Na_2O and $CaCl_2$ are ionic compounds because they are composed of a metal combined with a nonmetal. We predict (correctly) that N_2O and SF_4 are molecular compounds because they are composed entirely of nonmetals.

PRACTICE EXERCISE

Which of these compounds are molecular: CBr_4, FeS, P_4O_6, PbF_2?
Answer: CBr_4 and P_4O_6

The ions in ionic compounds are arranged in three-dimensional structures, as Figure 2.21(b) shows for NaCl. Because there is no discrete "molecule" of NaCl, we are able to write only an empirical formula for this substance. This is true for most other ionic compounds.

We can write the empirical formula for an ionic compound if we know the charges of the ions. This is true because chemical compounds are always electrically neutral. Consequently, the ions in an ionic compound always occur in such a ratio that the total positive charge equals the total negative charge. Thus, there is one Na^+ to one Cl^- (giving NaCl), one Ba^{2+} to two Cl^- (giving $BaCl_2$), and so forth.

As you consider these and other examples, you will see that if the charges on the cation and anion are equal, the subscript on each ion is 1. If the charges are not equal, the charge on one ion (without its sign) will become the subscript on the other ion. For example, the ionic compound formed from Mg (which forms Mg^{2+} ions) and N (which forms N^{3-} ions) is Mg_3N_2:

$$Mg^{\textcircled{2}+} \times N^{\textcircled{3}-} \longrightarrow Mg_3N_2$$

⚠ GIVE IT SOME THOUGHT

Why don't we write the formula for the compound formed by Ca^{2+} and O^{2-} as Ca_2O_2?

CHEMISTRY AND LIFE

ELEMENTS REQUIRED BY LIVING ORGANISMS

The colored regions of ▶ FIGURE 2.22 shows the elements essential to life. More than 97% of the mass of most organisms is made up of just six of these elements—oxygen, carbon, hydrogen, nitrogen, phosphorus, and sulfur. Water is the most common compound in living organisms, accounting for at least 70% of the mass of most cells. In the solid components of cells, carbon is the most prevalent element by mass. Carbon atoms are found in a vast variety of organic molecules, bonded either to other carbon atoms or to atoms of other elements. All proteins, for example, contain the group

$$-N-C- $$

which occurs repeatedly in the molecules. (R is either an H atom or a combination of atoms, such as CH_3.)

In addition, 23 more elements have been found in various living organisms. Five are ions required by all organisms: Ca^{2+}, Cl^-, Mg^{2+}, K^+, and Na^+. Calcium ions, for example, are necessary for the formation of bone and transmission of nervous system signals. Many other elements are needed in only very small quantities and consequently are called *trace* elements. For example, trace quantities of copper are required in the diet of humans to aid in the synthesis of hemoglobin.

RELATED EXERCISE: 2.96

▲ FIGURE 2.22 **Elements essential to life.**

STRATEGIES IN CHEMISTRY

PATTERN RECOGNITION

Someone once said that drinking at the fountain of knowledge in a chemistry course is like drinking from a fire hydrant. Indeed, the pace can sometimes seem brisk. More to the point, however, we can drown in the facts if we do not see the general patterns. The value of recognizing patterns and learning rules and generalizations is that they free us from having to learn (or trying to memorize) many individual facts. The patterns, rules, and generalizations tie ideas together so that we do not get lost in the details.

Many students struggle with chemistry because they do not see how different topics relate to one another so they treat every idea and problem as being unique instead of as an example or application of a general rule, procedure, or relationship. You can avoid this pitfall by remembering the following.

Notice the structure of the topic you are studying. Pay attention to trends and rules given to summarize a large body of information. Notice, for example, how atomic structure helps us understand the existence of isotopes (as Table 2.2 shows) and how the periodic table helps us remember ionic charges (as Figure 2.20 shows).

You may surprise yourself by observing patterns that are not explicitly spelled out yet. Perhaps you have noticed certain trends in chemical formulas, for instance. Moving across the periodic table from element 11 (Na), we find that the elements form compounds with F having the following compositions: NaF, MgF_2, and AlF_3. Does this trend continue? Do SiF_4, PF_5, and SF_6 exist? Indeed they do. If you have noticed trends like this from the scraps of information you have seen so far, then you are ahead of the game and have prepared yourself for some topics we will address in later chapters.

SAMPLE EXERCISE 2.10 | **Using Ionic Charge to Write Empirical Formulas for Ionic Compounds**

Write the empirical formula of the compound formed by (a) Al^{3+} and Cl^- ions, (b) Al^{3+} and O^{2-} ions, (c) Mg^{2+} and NO_3^- ions.

SOLUTION

(a) Three Cl^- ions are required to balance the charge of one Al^{3+} ion, making the formula $AlCl_3$.

(b) Two Al^{3+} ions are required to balance the charge of three O^{2-} ions. That is, the total positive charge is $6+$, and the total negative charge is $6-$. The formula is Al_2O_3.

(c) Two NO_3^- ions are needed to balance the charge of one Mg^{2+}, yielding $Mg(NO_3)_2$. Note that the formula for the polyatomic ion, NO_3^-, must be enclosed in parentheses so that it is clear that the subscript 2 applies to all the atoms of that ion.

PRACTICE EXERCISE
Write the empirical formula for the compound formed by **(a)** Na^+ and PO_4^{3-}, **(b)** Zn^{2+} and SO_4^{2-}, **(c)** Fe^{3+} and CO_3^{2-}.
Answers: **(a)** Na_3PO_4, **(b)** $ZnSO_4$, **(c)** $Fe_2(CO_3)_3$

2.8 | NAMING INORGANIC COMPOUNDS

The names and chemical formulas of compounds are essential vocabulary in chemistry. The system used in naming substances is called **chemical nomenclature**, from the Latin words *nomen* (name) and *calare* (to call).

There are more than 50 million known chemical substances. Naming them all would be a hopelessly complicated task if each had a name independent of all others. Many important substances that have been known for a long time, such as water (H_2O) and ammonia (NH_3), do have traditional names (called *common names*). For most substances, however, we rely on a set of rules that leads to an informative and unique name for each substance, a name based on the composition of the substance.

The rules for chemical nomenclature are based on the division of substances into categories. The major division is between organic and inorganic compounds. *Organic compounds* contain carbon and hydrogen, often in combination with oxygen, nitrogen, or other elements. All others are *inorganic compounds*. Early chemists associated organic compounds with plants and animals and inorganic compounds with the nonliving portion of our world. Although this distinction is no longer pertinent, the classification between organic and inorganic compounds continues to be useful. In this section we consider the basic rules for naming three categories of inorganic compounds: ionic compounds, molecular compounds, and acids.

Names and Formulas of Ionic Compounds

Recall from Section 2.7 that ionic compounds usually consist of metal ions combined with nonmetal ions. The metals form the cations, and the nonmetals form the anions.

1. Cations

    a. *Cations formed from metal atoms have the same name as the metal:*

Na^+ sodium ion	Zn^{2+} zinc ion	Al^{3+} aluminum ion

    b. *If a metal can form cations with different charges, the positive charge is indicated by a Roman numeral in parentheses following the name of the metal:*

Fe^{2+} iron(II) ion	Cu^+ copper(I) ion
Fe^{3+} iron(III) ion	Cu^{2+} copper(II) ion

    Ions of the same element that have different charges have different properties, such as different colors (▶ **FIGURE 2.23**).

    Most metals that form cations with different charges are *transition metals,* elements that occur in the middle of the periodic table, from group 3B to group 2B. The metals that form only one cation (only one possible charge) are those of group 1A and group 2A, as well as Al^{3+} (group 3A) and two transition-metal ions: Ag^+ (group 1B) and Zn^{2+} (group 2B). Charges are not expressed when naming these ions. However, if there is any doubt in your mind whether a metal forms more than one cation, use a Roman numeral to indicate the charge. It is never wrong to do so, even though it may be unnecessary.

▲ **FIGURE 2.23 Different ions of the same element have different properties.** Both substances shown are compounds of iron. The substance on the left is Fe_3O_4, which contains Fe^{2+} and Fe^{3+} ions. The substance on the right is Fe_2O_3, which contains Fe^{3+} ions.

An older method still widely used for distinguishing between differently charged ions of a metal uses the endings *-ous* and *-ic* added to the root of the element's Latin name:

Fe^{2+}	ferrous ion	Cu^+	cuprous ion
Fe^{3+}	ferric ion	Cu^{2+}	cupric ion

Although we will only rarely use these older names in this text, you might encounter them elsewhere.

c. *Cations formed from nonmetal atoms have names that end in* -ium:

NH_4^+	ammonium ion	H_3O^+	hydronium ion

These two ions are the only ions of this kind that we will encounter frequently in the text.

The names and formulas of some common cations are shown in ▼ **TABLE 2.4** and on the back inside cover of the text. The ions on the left side in Table 2.4 are the monatomic ions that do not have more than one possible charge. Those on the right side are either polyatomic cations or cations with more than one possible charge. The Hg_2^{2+} ion is unusual because, even though it is a metal ion, it is not monatomic. It is called the mercury(I) ion because it can be thought of as two Hg^+ ions bound together. The cations that you will encounter most frequently are shown in boldface. You should learn these cations first.

▲ GIVE IT SOME THOUGHT

a. Why is CrO named using a Roman numeral, chromium(II) oxide, whereas CaO is named without a Roman numeral, calcium oxide?

b. What does the *-ium* ending on the name ammonium ion tell you about the composition of the ion?

TABLE 2.4 • Common Cations*

Charge	Formula	Name	Formula	Name
1+	**H^+**	**hydrogen ion**	**NH_4^+**	**ammonium ion**
	Li^+	lithium ion	Cu^+	copper(I) or cuprous ion
	Na^+	**sodium ion**		
	K^+	**potassium ion**		
	Cs^+	cesium ion		
	Ag^+	**silver ion**		
2+	**Mg^{2+}**	**magnesium ion**	Co^{2+}	cobalt(II) or cobaltous ion
	Ca^{2+}	**calcium ion**	**Cu^{2+}**	**copper(II) or cupric ion**
	Sr^{2+}	strontium ion	**Fe^{2+}**	**iron(II) or ferrous ion**
	Ba^{2+}	barium ion	Mn^{2+}	manganese(II) or manganous ion
	Zn^{2+}	**zinc ion**	Hg_2^{2+}	mercury(I) or mercurous ion
	Cd^{2+}	cadmium ion	**Hg^{2+}**	**mercury(II) or mercuric ion**
			Ni^{2+}	nickel(II) or nickelous ion
			Pb^{2+}	**lead(II) or plumbous ion**
			Sn^{2+}	tin(II) or stannous ion
3+	**Al^{3+}**	**aluminum ion**	Cr^{3+}	chromium(III) or chromic ion
			Fe^{3+}	**iron(III) or ferric ion**

*The ions we use most often in this course are in boldface. Learn them first.

2. Anions

   a. *The names of monatomic anions are formed by replacing the ending of the name of the element with* -ide:

      H^- hydride ion O^{2-} oxide ion N^{3-} nitride ion

   A few polyatomic anions also have names ending in *-ide*:

      OH^- hydroxide ion CN^- cyanide ion O_2^{2-} peroxide ion

   b. *Polyatomic anions containing oxygen have names ending in either* -ate *or* -ite *and are called* **oxyanions**. The *-ate* is used for the most common or representative oxyanion of an element, and *-ite* is used for an oxyanion that has the same charge but one O atom fewer:

      NO_3^- nitrate ion SO_4^{2-} sulfate ion
      NO_2^- nitrite ion SO_3^{2-} sulfite ion

     Prefixes are used when the series of oxyanions of an element extends to four members, as with the halogens. The prefix *per-* indicates one more O atom than the oxyanion ending in *-ate*; *hypo-* indicates one O atom fewer than the oxyanion ending in *-ite*:

      ClO_4^- perchlorate ion (one more O atom than chlorate)
      ClO_3^- **chlorate ion**
      ClO_2^- chlorite ion (one O atom fewer than chlorate)
      ClO^- hypochlorite ion (one O atom fewer than chlorite)

     These rules are summarized in ▼ **FIGURE 2.24**.

 GIVE IT SOME THOUGHT

What information is conveyed by the endings *-ide, -ate,* and *-ite* in the name of an anion?

    ▶ **FIGURE 2.25** can help you remember the charge and number of oxygen atoms in the various oxyanions. Notice that C and N, both period 2 elements, have only three O atoms each, whereas the period 3 elements P, S, and Cl have four O atoms each. Beginning at the lower right in Figure 2.25, note that ionic charge increases from right to left, from $1-$ for ClO_4^- to $3-$ for PO_4^{3-}. In the second period the charges also increase from right to left, from $1-$ for NO_3^- to $2-$ for CO_3^{2-}. Notice also that although each of the anions in Figure 2.25 ends in *-ate*, the ClO_4^- ion also has a *per-* prefix.

△ **GO FIGURE**

Name the anion obtained by removing one oxygen atom from the perbromate ion, BrO_4^-.

Simple anion: _____ide (chloride, Cl^-)

Oxyanions:

per_____ate (perchlorate, ClO_4^-) —+O atom→ _____ate (chlorate, ClO_3^-) (Common or representative oxyanion) —−O atom→ _____ite (chlorite, ClO_2^-) —−O atom→ hypo____ite (hypochlorite, ClO^-)

▲ **FIGURE 2.24   Procedure for naming anions.** The first part of the element's name, such as "chlor" for chlorine or "sulf" for sulfur, goes in the blank.

Maximum of 3 O atoms in period 2.

Maximum of 4 O atoms in period 3.

Charges increase right to left.

	Group 4A	Group 5A	Group 6A	Group 7A
Period 2	CO_3^{2-} **Carbonate ion**	NO_3^- **Nitrate ion**		
Period 3		PO_4^{3-} **Phosphate ion**	SO_4^{2-} **Sulfate ion**	ClO_4^- **Perchlorate ion**

▲ FIGURE 2.25 **Common oxyanions.** The composition and charges of common oxyanions are related to their location in the periodic table.

⚠ **GIVE IT SOME THOUGHT**

Predict the formulas for the borate ion and silicate ion, assuming they contain a single B and Si atom, respectively, and follow the trends shown in Figure 2.25.

SAMPLE EXERCISE 2.11   **Determining the Formula of an Oxyanion from Its Name**

Based on the formula for the sulfate ion, predict the formula for (**a**) the selenate ion and (**b**) the selenite ion. (Sulfur and selenium are both in group 6A and form analogous oxyanions.)

SOLUTION

(**a**) The sulfate ion is SO_4^{2-}. The analogous selenate ion is therefore SeO_4^{2-}.
(**b**) The ending -*ite* indicates an oxyanion with the same charge but one O atom fewer than the corresponding oxyanion that ends in -*ate*. Thus, the formula for the selenite ion is SeO_3^{2-}.

PRACTICE EXERCISE

The formula for the bromate ion is analogous to that for the chlorate ion. Write the formula for the hypobromite and bromite ions.
Answer: BrO^- and BrO_2^-

---

c. *Anions derived by adding H^+ to an oxyanion are named by adding as a prefix the word* hydrogen *or* dihydrogen, *as appropriate:*

CO_3^{2-}	carbonate ion	PO_4^{3-}	phosphate ion
HCO_3^-	hydrogen carbonate ion	$H_2PO_4^-$	dihydrogen phosphate ion

Notice that each H^+ added reduces the negative charge of the parent anion by one. An older method for naming some of these ions uses the prefix *bi*-. Thus, the HCO_3^- ion is commonly called the bicarbonate ion, and HSO_4^- is sometimes called the bisulfate ion.

The names and formulas of the common anions are listed in ▶ **TABLE 2.5** and on the back inside cover of the text. Those anions whose names end in -*ide* are listed on the left portion of Table 2.5, and those whose names end in -*ate* are listed on the right. The most common of these ions are shown in boldface. You should learn names and formulas of these anions first. The formulas of the ions whose names end with -*ite* can be derived from those ending in -*ate* by removing an O atom. Notice the location of the monatomic ions in the periodic table. Those of group 7A always have a 1− charge (F^-, Cl^-, Br^-, and I^-), and those of group 6A have a 2− charge (O^{2-} and S^{2-}).

3. Ionic Compounds

Names of ionic compounds consist of the cation name followed by the anion name:

$CaCl_2$	calcium chloride
$Al(NO_3)_3$	aluminum nitrate
$Cu(ClO_4)_2$	copper(II) perchlorate (or cupric perchlorate)

In the chemical formulas for aluminum nitrate and copper(II) perchlorate, parentheses followed by the appropriate subscript are used because the compounds contain two or more polyatomic ions.

SAMPLE EXERCISE 2.12 | Determining the Names of Ionic Compounds from Their Formulas

Name the ionic compounds (**a**) K_2SO_4, (**b**) $Ba(OH)_2$, (**c**) $FeCl_3$.

SOLUTION

In naming ionic compounds, it is important to recognize polyatomic ions and to determine the charge of cations with variable charge.

(**a**) The cation is K^+, the potassium ion, and the anion is SO_4^{2-}, the sulfate ion, making the name potassium sulfate. (If you thought the compound contained S^{2-} and O^{2-} ions, you failed to recognize the polyatomic sulfate ion.)

(**b**) The cation is Ba^{2+}, the barium ion, and the anion is OH^-, the hydroxide ion: barium hydroxide.

(**c**) You must determine the charge of Fe in this compound because an iron atom can form more than one cation. Because the compound contains three chloride ions, Cl^-, the cation must be Fe^{3+}, the iron(III), or ferric, ion. Thus, the compound is iron(III) chloride or ferric chloride.

PRACTICE EXERCISE

Name the ionic compounds (**a**) NH_4Br, (**b**) Cr_2O_3, (**c**) $Co(NO_3)_2$.

Answers: (**a**) ammonium bromide, (**b**) chromium(III) oxide, (**c**) cobalt(II) nitrate

TABLE 2.5 • Common Anions*

Charge	Formula	Name	Formula	Name
1−	H^-	hydride ion	CH_3COO^- (or $C_2H_3O_2^-$)	**acetate ion**
	F^-	**fluoride ion**	ClO_3^-	chlorate ion
	Cl^-	**chloride ion**	ClO_4^-	**perchlorate ion**
	Br^-	**bromide ion**	NO_3^-	**nitrate ion**
	I^-	**iodide ion**	MnO_4^-	permanganate ion
	CN^-	cyanide ion		
	OH^-	**hydroxide ion**		
2−	O^{2-}	**oxide ion**	CO_3^{2-}	**carbonate ion**
	O_2^{2-}	peroxide ion	CrO_4^{2-}	chromate ion
	S^{2-}	**sulfide ion**	$Cr_2O_7^{2-}$	dichromate ion
			SO_4^{2-}	**sulfate ion**
3−	N^{3-}	nitride ion	PO_4^{3-}	**phosphate ion**

*The ions we use most often are in boldface. Learn them first.

SAMPLE EXERCISE 2.13 | Determining the Formulas of Ionic Compounds from Their Names

Write the chemical formulas for (**a**) potassium sulfide, (**b**) calcium hydrogen carbonate, (**c**) nickel(II) perchlorate.

SOLUTION

In going from the name of an ionic compound to its chemical formula, you must know the charges of the ions to determine the subscripts.

(**a**) The potassium ion is K^+, and the sulfide ion is S^{2-}. Because ionic compounds are electrically neutral, two K^+ ions are required to balance the charge of one S^{2-} ion, giving K_2S for the empirical formula.

(b) The calcium ion is Ca^{2+}. The carbonate ion is CO_3^{2-}, so the hydrogen carbonate ion is HCO_3^-. Two HCO_3^- ions are needed to balance the positive charge of Ca^{2+}, giving $Ca(HCO_3)_2$.

(c) The nickel(II) ion is Ni^{2+}. The perchlorate ion is ClO_4^-. Two ClO_4^- ions are required to balance the charge on one Ni^{2+} ion, giving $Ni(ClO_4)_2$.

PRACTICE EXERCISE
Give the chemical formulas for **(a)** magnesium sulfate, **(b)** silver sulfide, **(c)** lead(II) nitrate.
Answers: **(a)** $MgSO_4$, **(b)** Ag_2S, **(c)** $Pb(NO_3)_2$

Names and Formulas of Acids

Acids are an important class of hydrogen-containing compounds, and they are named in a special way. For our present purposes, an *acid* is a substance whose molecules yield hydrogen ions (H^+) when dissolved in water. When we encounter the chemical formula for an acid at this stage of the course, it will be written with H as the first element, as in HCl and H_2SO_4.

An acid is composed of an anion connected to enough H^+ ions to neutralize, or balance, the anion's charge. Thus, the SO_4^{2-} ion requires two H^+ ions, forming H_2SO_4. The name of an acid is related to the name of its anion, as summarized in ▼ FIGURE 2.26.

1. *Acids containing anions whose names end in* -ide *are named by changing the* -ide *ending to* -ic, *adding the prefix* hydro- *to this anion name, and then following with the word* acid:

Anion	Corresponding Acid
Cl^- (chloride)	HCl (hydrochloric acid)
S^{2-} (sulfide)	H_2S (hydrosulfuric acid)

2. *Acids containing anions whose names end in* -ate *or* -ite *are named by changing* -ate *to* -ic *and* -ite *to* -ous *and then adding the word* acid. Prefixes in the anion name are retained in the name of the acid:

Anion		Corresponding Acid	
ClO_4^-	(perchlorate)	$HClO_4$	(perchloric acid)
ClO_3^-	(chlorate)	$HClO_3$	(chloric acid)
ClO_2^-	(chlorite)	$HClO_2$	(chlorous acid)
ClO^-	(hypochlorite)	HClO	(hypochlorous acid)

▶ **FIGURE 2.26 How anion names and acid names relate.** The prefixes *per-* and *hypo-* are retained in going from the anion to the acid.

GIVE IT SOME THOUGHT

Name the acid obtained by adding H^+ to the iodate ion, IO_3^-.

SAMPLE EXERCISE 2.14 | **Relating the Names and Formulas of Acids**

Name the acids **(a)** HCN, **(b)** HNO_3, **(c)** H_2SO_4, **(d)** H_2SO_3.

SOLUTION

(a) The anion from which this acid is derived is CN^-, the cyanide ion. Because this ion has an *-ide* ending, the acid is given a *hydro-* prefix and an *-ic* ending: hydrocyanic acid. Only water solutions of HCN are referred to as hydrocyanic acid. The pure compound, which is a gas under normal conditions, is called hydrogen cyanide. Both hydrocyanic acid and hydrogen cyanide are *extremely* toxic.

(b) Because NO_3^- is the nitrate ion, HNO_3 is called nitric acid (the *-ate* ending of the anion is replaced with an *-ic* ending in naming the acid).

(c) Because SO_4^{2-} is the sulfate ion, H_2SO_4 is called sulfuric acid.

(d) Because SO_3^{2-} is the sulfite ion, H_2SO_3 is sulfurous acid (the *-ite* ending of the anion is replaced with an *-ous* ending).

PRACTICE EXERCISE

Give the chemical formulas for **(a)** hydrobromic acid, **(b)** carbonic acid.

Answers: **(a)** HBr, **(b)** H_2CO_3

Names and Formulas of Binary Molecular Compounds

The procedures used for naming *binary* (two-element) molecular compounds are similar to those used for naming ionic compounds:

1. *The name of the element farther to the left in the periodic table (closest to the metals) is usually written first.* An exception occurs when the compound contains oxygen and chlorine, bromine, or iodine (any halogen except fluorine), in which case oxygen is written last.

2. *If both elements are in the same group, the lower one is named first.*

3. *The name of the second element is given an -ide ending.*

4. *Greek prefixes* (▶ **TABLE 2.6**) are used to indicate the number of atoms of each element. The prefix *mono-* is never used with the first element. When the prefix ends in *a* or *o* and the name of the second element begins with a vowel, the *a* or *o* of the prefix is often dropped.

The following examples illustrate these rules:

Cl_2O	dichlorine monoxide	NF_3	nitrogen trifluoride
N_2O_4	dinitrogen tetroxide	P_4S_{10}	tetraphosphorus decasulfide

Rule 4 is necessary because we cannot predict formulas for most molecular substances the way we can for ionic compounds. Molecular compounds that contain hydrogen and one other element are an important exception, however. These compounds can be treated as if they were neutral substances containing H^+ ions and anions. Thus, you can predict that the substance named hydrogen chloride has the formula HCl, containing one H^+ to balance the charge of one Cl^-. (The name hydrogen chloride is used only for the pure compound; water solutions of HCl are called hydrochloric acid.) Similarly, the formula for hydrogen sulfide is H_2S because two H^+ are needed to balance the charge on S^{2-}.

TABLE 2.6 • Prefixes Used in Naming Binary Compounds Formed between Nonmetals

Prefix	Meaning
Mono-	*1*
Di-	*2*
Tri-	*3*
Tetra-	*4*
Penta-	*5*
Hexa-	*6*
Hepta-	*7*
Octa-	*8*
Nona-	*9*
Deca-	*10*

SAMPLE EXERCISE 2.15 | Relating the Names and Formulas of Binary Molecular Compounds

Name the compounds (a) SO_2, (b) PCl_5, (c) Cl_2O_3.

SOLUTION

The compounds consist entirely of nonmetals, so they are molecular rather than ionic. Using the prefixes in Table 2.6, we have (a) sulfur dioxide, (b) phosphorus pentachloride, and (c) dichlorine trioxide.

PRACTICE EXERCISE

Give the chemical formulas for (a) silicon tetrabromide, (b) disulfur dichloride.

Answers: (a) $SiBr_4$, (b) S_2Cl_2

2.9 | SOME SIMPLE ORGANIC COMPOUNDS

The study of compounds of carbon is called **organic chemistry**, and as noted earlier, compounds that contain carbon and hydrogen, often in combination with oxygen, nitrogen, or other elements, are called *organic compounds*. We will examine organic compounds in Chapter 24, but here we present a brief introduction to some of the simplest organic compounds.

Alkanes

Compounds that contain only carbon and hydrogen are called **hydrocarbons**. In the simplest class of hydrocarbons, **alkanes**, each carbon is bonded to four other atoms. The three smallest alkanes are methane (CH_4), ethane (C_2H_6), and propane (C_3H_8). The structural formulas of these three alkanes are as follows:

Although hydrocarbons are binary molecular compounds, they are not named like the binary inorganic compounds discussed in Section 2.8. Instead, each alkane has a name that ends in *-ane*. The alkane with four carbons is called *butane*. For alkanes with five or more carbons, the names are derived from prefixes like those in Table 2.6. An alkane with eight carbon atoms, for example, is *octane* (C_8H_{18}), where the *octa-* prefix for eight is combined with the *-ane* ending for an alkane.

Some Derivatives of Alkanes

Other classes of organic compounds are obtained when one or more hydrogen atoms in an alkane are replaced with *functional groups*, which are specific groups of atoms. An **alcohol**, for example, is obtained by replacing an H atom of an alkane with an —OH group. The name of the alcohol is derived from that of the alkane by adding an *-ol* ending:

Alcohols have properties that are very different from the properties of the alkanes from which the alcohols are obtained. For example, methane, ethane, and propane are all colorless gases under normal conditions, whereas methanol, ethanol, and propanol are colorless liquids. We will discuss the reasons for these differences in Chapter 11.

The prefix "1" in the name 1-propanol indicates that the replacement of H with OH has occurred at one of the "outer" carbon atoms rather than the "middle" carbon atom. A different compound, called either 2-propanol or isopropyl alcohol, is obtained when the OH functional group is attached to the middle carbon atom (▶ FIGURE 2.27).

Compounds with the same molecular formula but different arrangements of atoms are called **isomers**. There are many different kinds of isomers, as we will discover later in this book. What we have here with 1-propanol and 2-propanol are *structural isomers,* compounds having the same molecular formula but different structural formulas.

 GIVE IT SOME THOUGHT

Draw the structural formulas of the two isomers of butane, C_4H_{10}.

Much of the richness of organic chemistry is possible because organic compounds can form long chains of carbon–carbon bonds. The series of alkanes that begins with methane, ethane, and propane and the series of alcohols that begins with methanol, ethanol, and propanol can both be extended for as long as we desire, in principle. The properties of alkanes and alcohols change as the chains get longer. Octanes, which are alkanes with eight carbon atoms, are liquids under normal conditions. If the alkane series is extended to tens of thousands of carbon atoms, we obtain *polyethylene,* a solid substance that is used to make thousands of plastic products, such as plastic bags, food containers, and laboratory equipment.

OH group on end carbon

1-Propanol

OH group on middle carbon

2-Propanol

▲ FIGURE 2.27 **The two forms (isomers) of propanol.**

SAMPLE EXERCISE 2.16 **Writing Structural and Molecular Formulas for Hydrocarbons**

Assuming the carbon atoms in *pentane* are in a linear chain, write **(a)** the structural formula and **(b)** the molecular formula for this alkane.

SOLUTION

(a) Alkanes contain only carbon and hydrogen, and each carbon is attached to four other atoms. The name pentane contains the prefix *penta-* for five (Table 2.6), and we are told that the carbons are in a linear chain. If we then add enough hydrogen atoms to make four bonds to each carbon, we obtain the structural formula

This form of pentane is often called *n-*pentane, where the *n-* stands for "normal" because all five carbon atoms are in one line in the structural formula.

(b) Once the structural formula is written, we determine the molecular formula by counting the atoms present. Thus, *n-*pentane has the molecular formula C_5H_{12}.

PRACTICE EXERCISE

(a) What is the molecular formula of butane, the alkane with four carbons? **(b)** What are the name and molecular formula of an alcohol derived from butane?

Answers: **(a)** C_4H_{10}, **(b)** butanol, $C_4H_{10}O$ or C_4H_9OH

CHAPTER SUMMARY AND KEY TERMS

SECTIONS 2.1 AND 2.2 **Atoms** are the basic building blocks of matter. They are the smallest units of an element that can combine with other elements. Atoms are composed of even smaller particles, called **subatomic particles.** Some of these subatomic particles are charged and follow the usual behavior of charged particles: Particles with the same charge repel one another, whereas particles with unlike charges are attracted to one another. We considered some of the important experiments that led to the discovery and characterization of subatomic particles. Thomson's experiments on the behavior of

cathode rays in magnetic and electric fields led to the discovery of the electron and allowed its charge-to-mass ratio to be measured. Millikan's oil-drop experiment determined the charge of the electron. Becquerel's discovery of **radioactivity**, the spontaneous emission of radiation by atoms, gave further evidence that the atom has a substructure. Rutherford's studies of how thin metal foils scatter α particles led to the **nuclear model** of the atom, showing that the atom has a dense, positively charged **nucleus.**

SECTION 2.3 Atoms have a nucleus that contains **protons** and **neutrons; electrons** move in the space around the nucleus. The magnitude of the charge of the electron, 1.602×10^{-19} C, is called the **electronic charge**. The charges of particles are usually represented as multiples of this charge—an electron has a $1-$ charge, and a proton has a $1+$ charge. The masses of atoms are usually expressed in terms of **atomic mass units** (1 amu $= 1.66054 \times 10^{-24}$ g). The dimensions of atoms are often expressed in units of **angstroms** (1 Å $= 10^{-10}$ m).

Elements can be classified by **atomic number**, the number of protons in the nucleus of an atom. All atoms of a given element have the same atomic number. The **mass number** of an atom is the sum of the numbers of protons and neutrons. Atoms of the same element that differ in mass number are known as **isotopes**.

SECTION 2.4 The atomic mass scale is defined by assigning a mass of exactly 12 amu to a ^{12}C atom. The **atomic weight** (average atomic mass) of an element can be calculated from the relative abundances and masses of that element's isotopes. The **mass spectrometer** provides the most direct and accurate means of experimentally measuring atomic (and molecular) weights.

SECTION 2.5 The **periodic table** is an arrangement of the elements in order of increasing atomic number. Elements with similar properties are placed in vertical columns. The elements in a column are known as a **group**. The elements in a horizontal row are known as a **period**. The **metallic elements** (**metals**), which comprise the majority of the elements, dominate the left side and the middle of the table; the **nonmetallic elements** (**nonmetals**) are located on the upper right side. Many of the elements that lie along the line that separates metals from nonmetals are **metalloids**.

SECTION 2.6 Atoms can combine to form **molecules**. Compounds composed of molecules (**molecular compounds**) usually contain only nonmetallic elements. A molecule that contains two atoms is called a **diatomic molecule**. The composition of a substance is given by its **chemical formula**. A molecular substance can be represented by its **empirical formula**, which gives the relative numbers of atoms of each kind. It is usually represented by its **molecular formula**, however, which gives the actual numbers of each type of atom in a molecule.

Structural formulas show the order in which the atoms in a molecule are connected. Ball-and-stick models and space-filling models are often used to represent molecules.

SECTION 2.7 Atoms can either gain or lose electrons, forming charged particles called **ions**. Metals tend to lose electrons, becoming positively charged ions (**cations**). Nonmetals tend to gain electrons, forming negatively charged ions (**anions**). Because **ionic compounds** are electrically neutral, containing both cations and anions, they usually contain both metallic and nonmetallic elements. Atoms that are joined together, as in a molecule, but carry a net charge are called **polyatomic ions**. The chemical formulas used for ionic compounds are empirical formulas, which can be written readily if the charges of the ions are known. The total positive charge of the cations in an ionic compound equals the total negative charge of the anions.

SECTION 2.8 The set of rules for naming chemical compounds is called **chemical nomenclature**. We studied the systematic rules used for naming three classes of inorganic substances: ionic compounds, acids, and binary molecular compounds. In naming an ionic compound, the cation is named first and then the anion. Cations formed from metal atoms have the same name as the metal. If the metal can form cations of differing charges, the charge is given using Roman numerals. Monatomic anions have names ending in *-ide*. Polyatomic anions containing oxygen and another element (**oxyanions**) have names ending in *-ate* or *-ite*.

SECTION 2.9 **Organic chemistry** is the study of compounds that contain carbon. The simplest class of organic molecules is the **hydrocarbons**, which contain only carbon and hydrogen. Hydrocarbons in which each carbon atom is attached to four other atoms are called **alkanes**. Alkanes have names that end in *-ane,* such as methane and ethane. Other organic compounds are formed when an H atom of a hydrocarbon is replaced with a functional group. An **alcohol**, for example, is a compound in which an H atom of a hydrocarbon is replaced by an OH functional group. Alcohols have names that end in *-ol,* such as methanol and ethanol. Compounds with the same molecular formula but a different bonding arrangement of their constituent atoms are called **isomers**.

KEY SKILLS

- Describe the basic postulates of Dalton's atomic theory. (Section 2.1)
- Describe the key experiments that led to the discovery of electrons and to the nuclear model of the atom. (Section 2.2)
- Describe the structure of the atom in terms of protons, neutrons, and electrons. (Section 2.3)
- Describe the electrical charge and relative masses of protons, neutrons, and electrons. (Section 2.3)
- Use chemical symbols together with atomic number and mass number to express the subatomic composition of isotopes. (Section 2.3)
- Understand how atomic weights relate to the masses of individual atoms and to their natural abundances. (Section 2.4)
- Describe how elements are organized in the periodic table by atomic number and by similarities in chemical behavior, giving rise to periods and groups. (Section 2.5)
- Describe the locations of metals and nonmetals in the periodic table. (Section 2.5)
- Distinguish between molecular substances and ionic substances in terms of their composition. (Sections 2.6 and 2.7)
- Distinguish between empirical formulas and molecular formulas. (Section 2.6)
- Describe how molecular formulas and structural formulas are used to represent the compositions of molecules. (Section 2.6)
- Explain how ions are formed by the gain or loss of electrons and be able to use the periodic table to predict the charges of common ions. (Section 2.7)
- Write the empirical formulas of ionic compounds, given the charges of their component ions. (Section 2.7)
- Write the name of an ionic compound given its chemical formula, or write the chemical formula given its name. (Section 2.8)
- Name or write chemical formulas for binary inorganic compounds and for acids. (Section 2.8)
- Identify organic compounds and name simple alkanes and alcohols. (Section 2.9)

EXERCISES

VISUALIZING CONCEPTS

These exercises are intended to probe your understanding of key concepts rather than your ability to utilize formulas and perform calculations. Exercises with red exercise numbers have answers in the back of the book.

2.1 A charged particle is caused to move between two electrically charged plates, as shown here.

(a) Why does the path of the charged particle bend? (b) What is the sign of the electrical charge on the particle? (c) As the charge on the plates is increased, would you expect the bending to increase, decrease, or stay the same? (d) As the mass of the particle is increased while the speed of the particles remains the same, would you expect the bending to increase, decrease, or stay the same? [Section 2.2]

2.2 The following diagram is a representation of 20 atoms of a fictitious element, which we will call nevadium (Nv). The red spheres are ^{293}Nv, and the blue spheres are ^{295}Nv. (a) Assuming that this sample is a statistically representative sample of the element, calculate the percent abundance of each element. (b) If the mass of ^{293}Nv is 293.15 amu and that of ^{295}Nv is 295.15 amu, what is the atomic weight of Nv? [Section 2.4]

2.3 Four of the boxes in the following periodic table are colored. Which of these are metals and which are nonmetals? Which one is an alkaline earth metal? Which one is a noble gas? [Section 2.5]

2.4 Does the following drawing represent a neutral atom or an ion? Write its complete chemical symbol including mass number, atomic number, and net charge (if any). [Sections 2.3 and 2.7]

16 protons + 16 neutrons

18 electrons

2.5 Which of the following diagrams most likely represents an ionic compound, and which represents a molecular one? Explain your choice. [Sections 2.6 and 2.7]

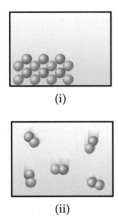

(i)

(ii)

2.6 Write the chemical formula for the following compound. Is the compound ionic or molecular? Name the compound. [Sections 2.6 and 2.8]

2.7 Five of the boxes in the following periodic table are colored. Predict the charge on the ion associated with each of these elements. [Section 2.7]

2.8 The following diagram represents an ionic compound in which the red spheres represent cations and blue spheres represent anions. Which of the following formulas is consistent with the drawing: KBr, K_2SO_4, $Ca(NO_3)_2$, $Fe_2(SO_4)_3$? Name the compound. [Sections 2.7 and 2.8]

These exercises are divided into sections that deal with specific topics in the chapter. The exercises are grouped in pairs, with the answers given in the back of the book to the odd-numbered exercises, as indicated by the red exercise numbers. Those exercises whose numbers appear in brackets are more challenging than the nonbracketed exercises.

ATOMIC THEORY AND THE DISCOVERY OF ATOMIC STRUCTURE (sections 2.1–2.2)

2.9 How does Dalton's atomic theory account for the fact that when 1.000 g of water is decomposed into its elements, 0.111 g of hydrogen and 0.889 g of oxygen are obtained regardless of the source of the water?

2.10 Hydrogen sulfide is composed of two elements: hydrogen and sulfur. In an experiment, 6.500 g of hydrogen sulfide is fully decomposed into its elements. **(a)** If 0.384 g of hydrogen is obtained in this experiment, how many grams of sulfur must be obtained? **(b)** What fundamental law does this experiment demonstrate? **(c)** How is this law explained by Dalton's atomic theory?

2.11 A chemist finds that 30.82 g of nitrogen will react with 17.60 g, 35.20 g, 70.40 g, or 88.00 g of oxygen to form four different compounds. **(a)** Calculate the mass of oxygen per gram of nitrogen in each compound. **(b)** How do the numbers in part (a) support Dalton's atomic theory?

2.12 In a series of experiments, a chemist prepared three different compounds that contain only iodine and fluorine and determined the mass of each element in each compound:

Compound	Mass of Iodine (g)	Mass of Fluorine (g)
1	4.75	3.56
2	7.64	3.43
3	9.41	9.86

(a) Calculate the mass of fluorine per gram of iodine in each compound. **(b)** How do the numbers in part (a) support the atomic theory?

2.13 Summarize the evidence used by J. J. Thomson to argue that cathode rays consist of negatively charged particles.

2.14 An unknown particle is caused to move between two electrically charged plates, as illustrated in Figure 2.8. Its path is deflected by a smaller magnitude in the opposite direction from that of a beta particle. What can you conclude about the charge and mass of this unknown particle?

2.15 How did Rutherford interpret the following observations made during his α-particle scattering experiments? **(a)** Most α particles were not appreciably deflected as they passed through the gold foil. **(b)** A few α particles were deflected at very large angles. **(c)** What differences would you expect if beryllium foil were used instead of gold foil in the α-particle scattering experiment?

2.16 Millikan determined the charge on the electron by studying the static charges on oil drops falling in an electric field (Figure 2.5). A student carried out this experiment using several oil drops for her measurements and calculated the charges on the drops. She obtained the following data:

Droplet	Calculated Charge (C)
A	1.60×10^{-19}
B	3.15×10^{-19}
C	4.81×10^{-19}
D	6.31×10^{-19}

(a) What is the significance of the fact that the droplets carried different charges? **(b)** What conclusion can the student draw from these data regarding the charge of the electron? **(c)** What value (and to how many significant figures) should she report for the electronic charge?

MODERN VIEW OF ATOMIC STRUCTURE; ATOMIC WEIGHTS (sections 2.3–2.4)

2.17 The radius of an atom of gold (Au) is about 1.35 Å. **(a)** Express this distance in nanometers (nm) and in picometers (pm). **(b)** How many gold atoms would have to be lined up to span 1.0 mm? **(c)** If the atom is assumed to be a sphere, what is the volume in cm^3 of a single Au atom?

2.18 An atom of rhodium (Rh) has a diameter of about 2.7×10^{-8} cm. **(a)** What is the radius of a rhodium atom in angstroms (Å) and in meters (m)? **(b)** How many Rh atoms would have to be placed side by side to span a distance of $6.0 \ \mu m$? **(c)** If you assume that the Rh atom is a sphere, what is the volume in m^3 of a single atom?

2.19 Answer the following questions without referring to Table 2.1: **(a)** What are the main subatomic particles that make up the atom? **(b)** What is the relative charge (in multiples of the electronic charge) of each of the particles? **(c)** Which of the particles is the most massive? **(d)** Which is the least massive?

2.20 Determine whether each of the following statements is true or false. If false, correct the statement to make it true: **(a)** The nucleus has most of the mass and comprises most of the volume of an atom. **(b)** Every atom of a given element has the same number of protons. **(c)** The number of electrons in an atom equals the number of neutrons in the atom. **(d)** The protons in the nucleus of the helium atom are held together by a force called the strong nuclear force.

2.21 **(a)** Define atomic number and mass number. **(b)** Which of these can vary without changing the identity of the element?

2.22 **(a)** Which two of the following are isotopes of the same element: $^{31}_{16}X$, $^{31}_{15}X$, $^{32}_{16}X$? **(b)** What is the identity of the element whose isotopes you have selected?

2.23 How many protons, neutrons, and electrons are in the following atoms: **(a)** ^{40}Ar, **(b)** ^{65}Zn, **(c)** ^{70}Ga, **(d)** ^{80}Br, **(e)** ^{184}W, **(f)** ^{243}Am?

2.24 Each of the following isotopes is used in medicine. Indicate the number of protons and neutrons in each isotope: (a) phosphorus-32, (b) chromium-51, (c) cobalt-60, (d) technetium-99, (e) iodine-131, (f) thallium-201.

2.25 Fill in the gaps in the following table, assuming each column represents a neutral atom.

Symbol	^{52}Cr				
Protons		25			82
Neutrons		30	64		
Electrons			48	86	
Mass no.				222	207

2.26 Fill in the gaps in the following table, assuming each column represents a neutral atom.

Symbol	^{65}Zn				
Protons		38			92
Neutrons		58	49		
Electrons			38	36	
Mass no.				81	235

2.27 Write the correct symbol, with both superscript and subscript, for each of the following. Use the list of elements inside the front cover as needed: (a) the isotope of platinum that contains 118 neutrons, (b) the isotope of krypton with mass number 84, (c) the isotope of arsenic with mass number 75, (d) the isotope of magnesium that has an equal number of protons and neutrons.

2.28 One way in which Earth's evolution as a planet can be understood is by measuring the amounts of certain isotopes in rocks. One quantity recently measured is the ratio of ^{129}Xe to ^{130}Xe in some minerals. In what way do these two isotopes differ from one another? In what respects are they the same?

2.29 (a) What isotope is used as the standard in establishing the atomic mass scale? (b) The atomic weight of boron is reported as 10.81, yet no atom of boron has the mass of 10.81 amu. Explain.

2.30 (a) What is the mass in amu of a carbon-12 atom? (b) Why is the atomic weight of carbon reported as 12.011 in the table of elements and the periodic table in the front inside cover of this text?

2.31 Only two isotopes of copper occur naturally, ^{63}Cu (atomic mass = 62.9296 amu; abundance 69.17%) and ^{65}Cu (atomic mass = 64.9278 amu; abundance 30.83%). Calculate the atomic weight (average atomic mass) of copper.

2.32 Rubidium has two naturally occurring isotopes, rubidium-85 (atomic mass = 84.9118 amu; abundance = 72.15%) and rubidium-87 (atomic mass = 86.9092 amu; abundance = 27.85%). Calculate the atomic weight of rubidium.

2.33 (a) In what fundamental way is mass spectrometry related to Thomson's cathode-ray experiments (Figure 2.4)? (b) What are the labels on the axes of a mass spectrum? (c) To measure the mass spectrum of an atom, the atom must first lose one or more electrons. Why is this so?

2.34 (a) The mass spectrometer in Figure 2.12 has a magnet as one of its components. What is the purpose of the magnet? (b) The atomic weight of Cl is 35.5 amu. However, the mass spectrum of Cl (Figure 2.13) does not show a peak at this mass. Explain. (c) A mass spectrum of phosphorus (P) atoms shows only a single peak at a mass of 31. What can you conclude from this observation?

2.35 Naturally occurring magnesium has the following isotopic abundances:

Isotope	Abundance	Atomic mass (amu)
^{24}Mg	78.99 %	23.98504
^{25}Mg	10.00 %	24.98584
^{26}Mg	11.01 %	25.98259

(a) What is the average atomic mass of Mg? (b) Sketch the mass spectrum of Mg.

2.36 Mass spectrometry is more often applied to molecules than to atoms. We will see in Chapter 3 that the *molecular weight* of a molecule is the sum of the atomic weights of the atoms in the molecule. The mass spectrum of H_2 is taken under conditions that prevent decomposition into H atoms. The two naturally occurring isotopes of hydrogen are ^{1}H (atomic mass = 1.00783 amu; abundance 99.9885%) and ^{2}H (atomic mass = 2.01410 amu; abundance 0.0115%). (a) How many peaks will the mass spectrum have? (b) Give the relative atomic masses of each of these peaks. (c) Which peak will be the largest and which the smallest?

THE PERIODIC TABLE; MOLECULES AND IONS (sections 2.5–2.7)

2.37 For each of the following elements, write its chemical symbol, locate it in the periodic table, give its atomic number, and indicate whether it is a metal, metalloid, or nonmetal: (a) chromium, (b) helium, (c) phosphorus, (d) zinc, (e) magnesium, (f) bromine, (g) arsenic.

2.38 Locate each of the following elements in the periodic table; give its name and atomic number, and indicate whether it is a metal, metalloid, or nonmetal: (a) Li, (b) Sc, (c) Ge, (d) Yb, (e) Mn, (f) Sb, (g) Xe.

2.39 For each of the following elements, write its chemical symbol, determine the name of the group to which it belongs (Table 2.3), and indicate whether it is a metal, metalloid, or nonmetal: (a) potassium, (b) iodine, (c) magnesium, (d) argon, (e) sulfur.

2.40 The elements of group 4A show an interesting change in properties moving down the group. Give the name and chemical symbol of each element in the group and label it as a nonmetal, metalloid, or metal.

2.41 What can we tell about a compound when we know the empirical formula? What additional information is conveyed by the molecular formula? By the structural formula? Explain in each case.

2.42 Two compounds have the same empirical formula. One substance is a gas, whereas the other is a viscous liquid. How is it possible for two substances with the same empirical formula to have markedly different properties?

2.43 Write the empirical formula corresponding to each of the following molecular formulas: (a) Al_2Br_6, (b) C_8H_{10}, (c) $C_4H_8O_2$, (d) P_4O_{10}, (e) $C_6H_4Cl_2$, (f) $B_3N_3H_6$.

2.44 Determine the molecular and empirical formulas of the following: **(a)** the organic solvent *benzene,* which has six carbon atoms and six hydrogen atoms; **(b)** the compound *silicon tetrachloride,* which has a silicon atom and four chlorine atoms and is used in the manufacture of computer chips; **(c)** the reactive substance *diborane,* which has two boron atoms and six hydrogen atoms; **(d)** the sugar called *glucose,* which has six carbon atoms, twelve hydrogen atoms, and six oxygen atoms.

2.45 How many hydrogen atoms are in each of the following: **(a)** C_2H_5OH, **(b)** $Ca(CH_3COO)_2$, **(c)** $(NH_4)_3PO_4$?

2.46 How many of the indicated atoms are represented by each chemical formula: **(a)** carbon atoms in $C_2H_5COOCH_3$, **(b)** oxygen atoms in $Ca(ClO_4)_2$, **(c)** hydrogen atoms in $(NH_4)_2HPO_4$?

2.47 Write the molecular and structural formulas for the compounds represented by the following molecular models:

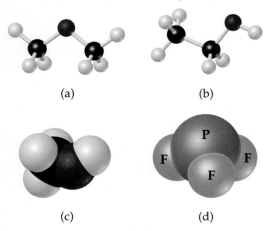

(a)   (b)

(c)   (d)

2.48 Write the molecular and structural formulas for the compounds represented by the following models:

(a)   (b)

(c)   (d)

2.49 Fill in the gaps in the following table:

Symbol	$^{59}Co^{3+}$			
Protons		34	76	80
Neutrons		46	116	120
Electrons		36		78
Net charge			2+	

2.50 Fill in the gaps in the following table:

Symbol	$^{31}P^{3-}$			
Protons		34	50	
Neutrons		45	69	118
Electrons			46	76
Net charge		2-		3+

2.51 Each of the following elements is capable of forming an ion in chemical reactions. By referring to the periodic table, predict the charge of the most stable ion of each: **(a)** Mg, **(b)** Al, **(c)** K, **(d)** S, **(e)** F.

2.52 Using the periodic table, predict the charges of the ions of the following elements: **(a)** Ga, **(b)** Sr, **(c)** As, **(d)** Br, **(e)** Se.

2.53 Using the periodic table to guide you, predict the chemical formula and name of the compound formed by the following elements: **(a)** Ga and F, **(b)** Li and H, **(c)** Al and I, **(d)** K and S.

2.54 The most common charge associated with scandium in its compounds is 3+. Indicate the chemical formulas you would expect for compounds formed between scandium and **(a)** iodine, **(b)** sulfur, **(c)** nitrogen.

2.55 Predict the chemical formula for the ionic compound formed by **(a)** Ca^{2+} and Br^-, **(b)** K^+ and CO_3^{2-}, **(c)** Al^{3+} and CH_3COO^-, **(d)** NH_4^+ and SO_4^{2-}, **(e)** Mg^{2+} and PO_4^{3-}.

2.56 Predict the chemical formulas of the compounds formed by the following pairs of ions: **(a)** Cr^{3+} and Br^-, **(b)** Fe^{3+} and O^{2-}, **(c)** Hg_2^{2+} and CO_3^{2-}, **(d)** Ca^{2+} and ClO_3^-, **(e)** NH_4^+ and PO_4^{3-}.

2.57 Complete the table by filling in the formula for the ionic compound formed by each pair of cations and anions, as shown for the first pair.

Ion	K^+	NH_4^+	Mg^{2+}	Fe^{3+}
Cl^-	KCl			
OH^-				
CO_3^{2-}				
PO_4^{3-}				

2.58 Complete the table by filling in the formula for the ionic compound formed by each pair of cations and anions, as shown for the first pair.

Ion	Na^+	Ca^{2+}	Fe^{2+}	Al^{3+}
O^{2-}	Na_2O			
NO_3^-				
SO_4^{2-}				
AsO_4^{3-}				

2.59 Predict whether each of the following compounds is molecular or ionic: **(a)** B_2H_6, **(b)** CH_3OH, **(c)** $LiNO_3$, **(d)** Sc_2O_3, **(e)** CsBr, **(f)** NOCl, **(g)** NF_3, **(h)** Ag_2SO_4.

2.60 Which of the following are ionic, and which are molecular? **(a)** PF_5, **(b)** NaI, **(c)** SCl_2, **(d)** $Ca(NO_3)_2$, **(e)** $FeCl_3$, **(f)** LaP, **(g)** $CoCO_3$, **(h)** N_2O_4.

NAMING INORGANIC COMPOUNDS; ORGANIC MOLECULES (sections 2.8–2.9)

2.61 Give the chemical formula for (a) chlorite ion, (b) chloride ion, (c) chlorate ion, (d) perchlorate ion, (e) hypochlorite ion.

2.62 Selenium, an element required nutritionally in trace quantities, forms compounds analogous to sulfur. Name the following ions: (a) SeO_4^{2-}, (b) Se^{2-}, (c) HSe^-, (d) $HSeO_3^-$.

2.63 Give the names and charges of the cation and anion in each of the following compounds: (a) CaO, (b) Na_2SO_4, (c) $KClO_4$, (d) $Fe(NO_3)_2$, (e) $Cr(OH)_3$.

2.64 Give the names and charges of the cation and anion in each of the following compounds: (a) CuS, (b) Ag_2SO_4, (c) $Al(ClO_3)_3$, (d) $Co(OH)_2$, (e) $PbCO_3$.

2.65 Name the following ionic compounds: (a) Li_2O, (b) $FeCl_3$, (c) $NaClO$, (d) $CaSO_3$, (e) $Cu(OH)_2$, (f) $Fe(NO_3)_2$, (g) $Ca(CH_3COO)_2$, (h) $Cr_2(CO_3)_3$, (i) K_2CrO_4, (j) $(NH_4)_2SO_4$.

2.66 Name the following ionic compounds: (a) KCN, (b) $NaBrO_2$, (c) $Sr(OH)_2$, (d) CoS, (e) $Fe_2(CO_3)_3$, (f) $Cr(NO_3)_3$, (g) $(NH_4)_2SO_3$, (h) NaH_2PO_4, (i) $KMnO_4$, (j) $Ag_2Cr_2O_7$.

2.67 Write the chemical formulas for the following compounds: (a) aluminum hydroxide, (b) potassium sulfate, (c) copper(I) oxide, (d) zinc nitrate, (e) mercury(II) bromide, (f) iron(III) carbonate, (g) sodium hypobromite.

2.68 Give the chemical formula for each of the following ionic compounds: (a) sodium phosphate, (b) zinc nitrate, (c) barium bromate, (d) iron(II) perchlorate, (e) cobalt(II) hydrogen carbonate, (f) chromium(III) acetate, (g) potassium dichromate.

2.69 Give the name or chemical formula, as appropriate, for each of the following acids: (a) $HBrO_3$, (b) HBr, (c) H_3PO_4, (d) hypochlorous acid, (e) iodic acid, (f) sulfurous acid.

2.70 Provide the name or chemical formula, as appropriate, for each of the following acids: (a) hydroiodic acid, (b) chloric acid, (c) nitrous acid, (d) H_2CO_3, (e) $HClO_4$, (f) CH_3COOH

2.71 Give the name or chemical formula, as appropriate, for each of the following binary molecular substances: (a) SF_6, (b) IF_5, (c) XeO_3, (d) dinitrogen tetroxide, (e) hydrogen cyanide, (f) tetraphosphorus hexasulfide.

2.72 The oxides of nitrogen are very important components in urban air pollution. Name each of the following compounds: (a) N_2O, (b) NO, (c) NO_2, (d) N_2O_5, (e) N_2O_4.

2.73 Write the chemical formula for each substance mentioned in the following word descriptions (use the front inside cover to find the symbols for the elements you don't know). (a) Zinc carbonate can be heated to form zinc oxide and carbon dioxide. (b) On treatment with hydrofluoric acid, silicon dioxide forms silicon tetrafluoride and water. (c) Sulfur dioxide reacts with water to form sulfurous acid. (d) The substance phosphorus trihydride, commonly called phosphine, is a toxic gas. (e) Perchloric acid reacts with cadmium to form cadmium(II) perchlorate. (f) Vanadium(III) bromide is a colored solid.

2.74 Assume that you encounter the following sentences in your reading. What is the chemical formula for each substance mentioned? (a) Sodium hydrogen carbonate is used as a deodorant. (b) Calcium hypochlorite is used in some bleaching solutions. (c) Hydrogen cyanide is a very poisonous gas. (d) Magnesium hydroxide is used as a cathartic. (e) Tin(II) fluoride has been used as a fluoride additive in toothpastes. (f) When cadmium sulfide is treated with sulfuric acid, fumes of hydrogen sulfide are given off.

2.75 (a) What is a hydrocarbon? (b) Butane is the alkane with a chain of four carbon atoms. Write a structural formula for this compound and determine its molecular and empirical formulas.

2.76 (a) What ending is used for the names of alkanes? (b) Hexane is an alkane whose structural formula has all its carbon atoms in a straight chain. Draw the structural formula for this compound and determine its molecular and empirical formulas. (*Hint:* You might need to refer to Table 2.6.)

2.77 (a) What is a functional group? (b) What functional group characterizes an alcohol? (c) With reference to Exercise 2.75, write a structural formula for 1-butanol, the alcohol derived from butane, by making a substitution on one of the carbon atoms.

2.78 (a) What do ethane and ethanol have in common? (b) How does 1-propanol differ from propane?

2.79 Chloropropane is a compound derived from propane by substituting Cl for H on one of the carbon atoms. (a) Draw the structural formulas for the two isomers of chloropropane. (b) Suggest names for these two compounds.

2.80 Draw the structural formulas for three isomers of pentane, C_5H_{12}.

ADDITIONAL EXERCISES

These exercises are not divided by category, although they are roughly in the order of the topics in the chapter. They are not paired.

2.81 Suppose a scientist repeats the Millikan oil-drop experiment but reports the charges on the drops using an unusual (and imaginary) unit called the *warmomb* (wa). The scientist obtains the following data for four of the drops:

(a) If all the droplets were the same size, which would fall most slowly through the apparatus? (b) From these data, what is the best choice for the charge of the electron in warmombs?

Droplet	Calculated Charge (wa)
A	3.84×10^{-8}
B	4.80×10^{-8}
C	2.88×10^{-8}
D	8.64×10^{-8}

(c) Based on your answer to part (b), how many electrons are there on each of the droplets? (d) What is the conversion factor between warmombs and coulombs?

2.82 The natural abundance of ^{3}He is 0.000137%. **(a)** How many protons, neutrons, and electrons are in an atom of ^{3}He? **(b)** Based on the sum of the masses of their subatomic particles, which is expected to be more massive, an atom of ^{3}He or an atom of ^{3}H (which is also called *tritium*)? **(c)** Based on your answer to part (b), what would need to be the precision of a mass spectrometer that is able to differentiate between peaks that are due to ^{3}He$^+$ and ^{3}H$^+$?

2.83 A cube of gold that is 1.00 cm on a side has a mass of 19.3 g. A single gold atom has a mass of 197.0 amu. **(a)** How many gold atoms are in the cube? **(b)** From the information given, estimate the diameter in Å of a single gold atom. **(c)** What assumptions did you make in arriving at your answer for part (b)?

2.84 The diameter of a rubidium atom is 4.95 Å. We will consider two different ways of placing the atoms on a surface. In arrangement A, all the atoms are lined up with one another to form a square grid. Arrangement B is called a *close-packed* arrangement because the atoms sit in the "depressions" formed by the previous row of atoms:

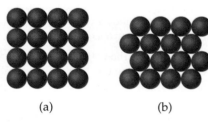

(a)   (b)

(a) Using arrangement A, how many Rb atoms could be placed on a square surface that is 1.0 cm on a side? **(b)** How many Rb atoms could be placed on a square surface that is 1.0 cm on a side, using arrangement B? **(c)** By what factor has the number of atoms on the surface increased in going to arrangement B from arrangement A? If extended to three dimensions, which arrangement would lead to a greater density for Rb metal?

2.85 **(a)** Assuming the dimensions of the nucleus and atom shown in Figure 2.11, what fraction of the *volume* of the atom is taken up by the nucleus? **(b)** Using the mass of the proton from Table 2.1 and assuming its diameter is 1.0×10^{-15} m , calculate the density of a proton in g/cm^3.

2.86 Identify the element represented by each of the following symbols and give the number of protons and neutrons in each: **(a)** $^{74}_{33}$X, **(b)** $^{127}_{53}$X, **(c)** $^{152}_{63}$X, **(d)** $^{209}_{83}$X.

2.87 The element oxygen has three naturally occurring isotopes, with 8, 9, and 10 neutrons in the nucleus, respectively. **(a)** Write the full chemical symbols for these three isotopes. **(b)** Describe the similarities and differences between the three kinds of atoms of oxygen.

2.88 Use Coulomb's law, $F = kQ_1Q_2/d^2$, to calculate the electric force on an electron ($Q = -1.6 \times 10^{-19}$ C) exerted by a single proton if the particles are 0.53×10^{-10} m apart. The constant k in Coulomb's law is 9.0×10^9 N$\cdot$m^2/C^2. (The unit abbreviated N is the newton, the SI unit of force.)

2.89 The element lead (Pb) consists of four naturally occurring isotopes with atomic masses 203.97302, 205.97444, 206.97587, and 207.97663 amu. The relative abundances of these four isotopes are 1.4, 24.1, 22.1, and 52.4%, respectively. From these data, calculate the atomic weight of lead.

2.90 Gallium (Ga) consists of two naturally occurring isotopes with masses of 68.926 and 70.925 amu. **(a)** How many protons and neutrons are in the nucleus of each isotope? Write the complete atomic symbol for each, showing the atomic number and mass number. **(b)** The average atomic mass of Ga is 69.72 amu. Calculate the abundance of each isotope.

2.91 Using a suitable reference such as the *CRC Handbook of Chemistry and Physics* or http://www.webelements.com, look up the following information for nickel: **(a)** the number of known isotopes, **(b)** the atomic masses (in amu) and **(c)** the natural abundances of the five most abundant isotopes.

2.92 There are two different isotopes of bromine atoms. Under normal conditions, elemental bromine consists of Br$_2$ molecules, and the mass of a Br$_2$ molecule is the sum of the masses of the two atoms in the molecule. The mass spectrum of Br$_2$ consists of three peaks:

Mass (amu)	Relative Size
157.836	0.2569
159.834	0.4999
161.832	0.2431

(a) What is the origin of each peak (of what isotopes does each consist)? **(b)** What is the mass of each isotope? **(c)** Determine the average molecular mass of a Br$_2$ molecule. **(d)** Determine the average atomic mass of a bromine atom. **(e)** Calculate the abundances of the two isotopes.

2.93 It is common in mass spectrometry to assume that the mass of a cation is the same as that of its parent atom. **(a)** Using data in Table 2.1, determine the number of significant figures that must be reported before the difference in mass of ^{1}H and ^{1}H$^+$ is significant. **(b)** What percentage of the mass of an ^{1}H atom does the electron represent?

2.94 From the following list of elements—Ar, H, Ga, Al, Ca, Br, Ge, K, O—pick the one that best fits each description. Use each element only once: **(a)** an alkali metal, **(b)** an alkaline earth metal, **(c)** a noble gas, **(d)** a halogen, **(e)** a metalloid, **(f)** a nonmetal listed in group 1A, **(g)** a metal that forms a 3+ ion, **(h)** a nonmetal that forms a 2− ion, **(i)** an element that resembles aluminum.

2.95 The first atoms of seaborgium (Sg) were identified in 1974. The longest-lived isotope of Sg has a mass number of 266. **(a)** How many protons, electrons, and neutrons are in an ^{266}Sg atom? **(b)** Atoms of Sg are very unstable, and it is therefore difficult to study this element's properties. Based on the position of Sg in the periodic table, what element should it most closely resemble in its chemical properties?

2.96 The explosion of an atomic bomb releases many radioactive isotopes, including strontium-90. Considering the location of strontium in the periodic table, suggest a reason for the fact that this isotope is particularly harmful to humans.

2.97 From the molecular structures shown here, identify the one that corresponds to each of the following species: **(a)** chlorine gas, **(b)** propane, **(c)** nitrate ion, **(d)** sulfur trioxide, **(e)** methyl chloride, CH_3Cl.

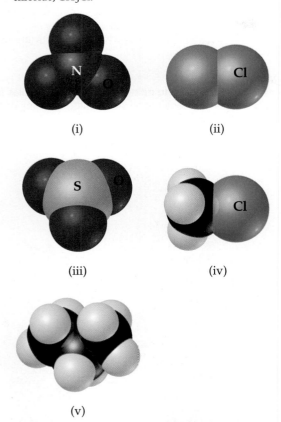

(i)   (ii)

(iii)   (iv)

(v)

2.98 Name each of the following oxides. Assuming that the compounds are ionic, what charge is associated with the metallic element in each case? **(a)** NiO, **(b)** MnO_2, **(c)** Cr_2O_3, **(d)** MoO_3.

2.99 Fill in the blanks in the following table:

Cation	Anion	Formula	Name
			Lithium oxide
Fe^{2+}	PO_4^{3-}		
		$Al_2(SO_4)_3$	
			Copper(II) nitrate
Cr^{3+}	I^-		
		$MnClO_2$	
			Ammonium carbonate
			Zinc perchlorate

2.100 Iodic acid has the molecular formula HIO_3. Write the formulas for the following: **(a)** the iodate anion, **(b)** the periodate anion, **(c)** the hypoiodite anion, **(d)** hypoiodous acid, **(e)** periodic acid.

2.101 Elements in the same group of the periodic table often form oxyanions with the same general formula. The anions are also named in a similar fashion. Based on these observations, suggest a chemical formula or name, as appropriate, for each of the following ions: **(a)** BrO_4^-, **(b)** SeO_3^{2-}, **(c)** arsenate ion, **(d)** hydrogen tellurate ion.

2.102 Carbonic acid occurs in carbonated beverages. When allowed to react with lithium hydroxide it produces lithium carbonate. Lithium carbonate is used to treat depression and bipolar disorder. Write chemical formulas for carbonic acid, lithium hydroxide, and lithium carbonate.

2.103 Give the chemical names of each of the following familiar compounds: **(a)** NaCl (table salt), **(b)** $NaHCO_3$ (baking soda), **(c)** NaOCl (in many bleaches), **(d)** NaOH (caustic soda), **(e)** $(NH_4)_2CO_3$ (smelling salts), **(f)** $CaSO_4$ (plaster of Paris).

2.104 Many familiar substances have common, unsystematic names. For each of the following, give the correct systematic name: **(a)** saltpeter, KNO_3; **(b)** soda ash, Na_2CO_3; **(c)** lime, CaO; **(d)** muriatic acid, HCl; **(e)** Epsom salts, $MgSO_4$; **(f)** milk of magnesia, $Mg(OH)_2$.

2.105 Because many ions and compounds have very similar names, there is great potential for confusing them. Write the correct chemical formulas to distinguish between **(a)** calcium sulfide and calcium hydrogen sulfide, **(b)** hydrobromic acid and bromic acid, **(c)** aluminum nitride and aluminum nitrite, **(d)** iron(II) oxide and iron(III) oxide, **(e)** ammonia and ammonium ion, **(f)** potassium sulfite and potassium bisulfite, **(g)** mercurous chloride and mercuric chloride, **(h)** chloric acid and perchloric acid.

2.106 The compound *cyclohexane* is an alkane in which six carbon atoms form a ring. The partial structural formula of the compound is as follows:

(a) Complete the structural formula for cyclohexane. **(b)** Is the molecular formula for cyclohexane the same as that for *n*-hexane, in which the carbon atoms are in a straight line? If possible, comment on the source of any differences. **(c)** Propose a structural formula for *cyclohexanol*, the alcohol derived from cyclohexane.

WHAT'S AHEAD

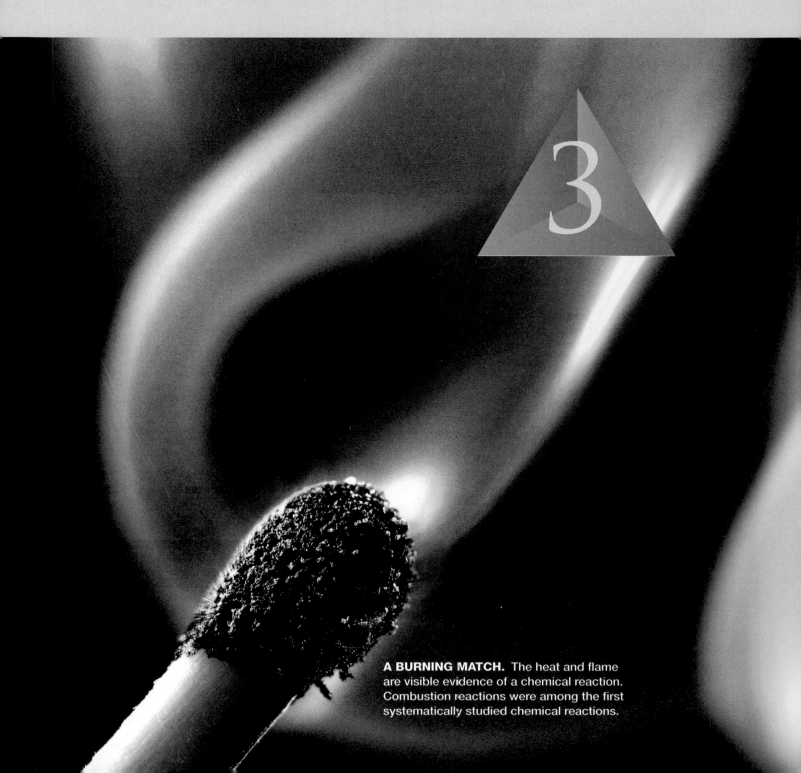

A BURNING MATCH. The heat and flame are visible evidence of a chemical reaction. Combustion reactions were among the first systematically studied chemical reactions.

3.6 QUANTITATIVE INFORMATION FROM BALANCED EQUATIONS
We use the quantitative information inherent in chemical formulas and equations together with the mole concept to predict the amounts of substances consumed or produced in chemical reactions.

3.7 LIMITING REACTANTS
We recognize that one reactant may be used up before others in a chemical reaction. This is the *limiting reactant*. The reaction stops, leaving some excess starting material.

STOICHIOMETRY: CALCULATIONS WITH CHEMICAL FORMULAS AND EQUATIONS

YOU POUR VINEGAR INTO a glass of water containing baking soda and bubbles form. You strike a match and use the flame to light a candle. You heat sugar in a pan and it turns brown. The bubbles, flame, and color change are visual evidence that something is happening.

To an experienced eye, these visual changes indicate a chemical change, or chemical reaction. Some chemical changes are simple; others are complex. Some are dramatic; some are very subtle. Even as you sit reading this chapter, chemical changes are occurring in your body. Those occurring in your eyes and brain, for example, allow you to see these words and think about them. Although not as obvious as those we see

▲ **FIGURE 3.1 Antoine Lavoisier (1734–1794).** The science career of Lavoisier, who conducted many important studies on combustion reactions, was cut short by the French Revolution. Guillotined in 1794 during the Reign of Terror, he is generally considered the father of modern chemistry because he conducted carefully controlled experiments and used quantitative measurements.

in the laboratory, the chemical changes taking place in our bodies are nevertheless remarkable for how they allow us to function.

In this chapter we explore some important aspects of chemical change. Our focus will be both on the use of chemical formulas to represent reactions and on the quantitative information we can obtain about the amounts of substances involved in reactions. **Stoichiometry** (pronounced stoy-key-OM-uh-tree) is the area of study that examines the quantities of substances consumed and produced in chemical reactions. Stoichiometry (Greek *stoicheion,* "element," and *metron,* "measure") provides an essential set of tools widely used in chemistry, including such diverse applications as measuring ozone concentrations in the atmosphere and assessing different processes for converting coal into gaseous fuels.

Stoichiometry is built on an understanding of atomic masses ∞∞ (Section 2.4), chemical formulas, and the law of conservation of mass. ∞∞ (Section 2.1) The French nobleman and scientist Antoine Lavoisier (◀ **FIGURE 3.1**) discovered this important chemical law during the late 1700s. Lavoisier stated the law in this eloquent way: "We may lay it down as an incontestable axiom that, in all the operations of art and nature, nothing is created; an equal quantity of matter exists both before and after the experiment. Upon this principle, the whole art of performing chemical experiments depends." With the advent of Dalton's atomic theory, chemists came to understand the basis for this law: *Atoms are neither created nor destroyed during a chemical reaction.* The changes that occur during any reaction merely rearrange the atoms. The same collection of atoms is present both before and after the reaction.

3.1 | CHEMICAL EQUATIONS

We represent chemical reactions by **chemical equations**. When the gas hydrogen (H_2) burns, for example, it reacts with oxygen (O_2) in the air to form water (H_2O). We write the chemical equation for this reaction as

$$2 H_2 + O_2 \longrightarrow 2 H_2O \qquad [3.1]$$

We read the $+$ sign as "reacts with" and the arrow as "produces." The chemical formulas to the left of the arrow represent the starting substances, called **reactants**. The chemical formulas to the right of the arrow represent substances produced in the reaction, called **products**. The numbers in front of the formulas, called *coefficients,* indicate the relative numbers of molecules of each kind involved in the reaction. (As in algebraic equations, *the coefficient 1 is usually not written.*)

Because atoms are neither created nor destroyed in any reaction, a chemical equation must have an equal number of atoms of each element on each side of the arrow. When this condition is met, the equation is *balanced.* On the right side of Equation 3.1, for example, there are two molecules of H_2O, each composed of two atoms of hydrogen and one atom of oxygen (◀ **FIGURE 3.2**). Thus, $2 H_2O$ (read "two molecules of water") contains $2 \times 2 = 4$ H atoms and $2 \times 1 = 2$ O atoms. Notice that *the number of atoms is obtained by multiplying each subscript in a chemical formula by the coefficient for the formula.* Because there are four H atoms and two O atoms on each side of the equation, the equation is balanced.

▲ GIVE IT SOME THOUGHT

How many atoms of Mg, O, and H are represented by the notation 3 $Mg(OH)_2$?

Balancing Equations

Once we know the formulas of the reactants and products in a reaction, we can write an unbalanced equation. We then balance the equation by determining the coefficients that provide equal numbers of each type of atom on the two sides of the equation. For most purposes, a balanced equation should contain the smallest possible whole-number coefficients.

Reactants   Products

$2 H_2 + O_2 \longrightarrow 2 H_2O$

▲ **FIGURE 3.2 A balanced chemical equation.**

⚠️ **GO FIGURE**

What is the difference in atom count between the notation CO_2 and the notation 2 CO?

Changing coefficient changes amount → 2 H_2O 2 molecules water (contain 4 H atoms and 2 O atoms)

H_2O

Changing subscript changes composition and identity → H_2O_2 1 molecule hydrogen peroxide (contains 2 H atoms and 2 O atoms)

▲ **FIGURE 3.3** **The difference between changing subscripts and changing coefficients in chemical equations.**

In balancing an equation, you need to understand the difference between coefficients and subscripts. As ▲ **FIGURE 3.3** illustrates, changing a subscript in a formula—from H_2O to H_2O_2, for example—changes the identity of the substance. The substance H_2O_2, hydrogen peroxide, is quite different from the substance H_2O, water. *Never change subscripts when balancing an equation.* In contrast, placing a coefficient in front of a formula changes only the *amount* of the substance and not its *identity*. Thus, 2 H_2O means two molecules of water, 3 H_2O means three molecules of water, and so forth.

To illustrate the process of balancing an equation, consider the reaction that occurs when methane (CH_4), the principal component of natural gas, burns in air to produce carbon dioxide gas (CO_2) and water vapor (H_2O) (▼ **FIGURE 3.4**). Both products contain oxygen atoms that come from O_2 in the air. Thus, O_2 is a reactant, and the unbalanced equation is

$$CH_4 + O_2 \longrightarrow CO_2 + H_2O \quad \text{(unbalanced)} \qquad [3.2]$$

It is usually best to balance first those elements that occur in the fewest chemical formulas in the equation. In our example, C appears in only one reactant (CH_4) and one product (CO_2). The same is true for H (CH_4 and H_2O). Notice, however, that O appears in one reactant (O_2) and two products (CO_2 and H_2O). So, let's begin with C. Because one molecule of CH_4 contains the same number of C atoms (one) as one molecule of CO_2 the coefficients for these substances *must* be the same in the balanced equation. Therefore, we start by choosing the coefficient 1 (unwritten) for both CH_4 and CO_2.

Reactants

CH_4 + O_2

Products

CO_2 and H_2O

▲ **FIGURE 3.4**   **Methane reacts with oxygen in a Bunsen burner.**

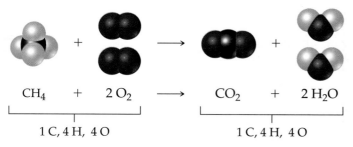

$$CH_4 \quad + \quad 2\,O_2 \quad \longrightarrow \quad CO_2 \quad + \quad 2\,H_2O$$

1 C, 4 H, 4 O   1 C, 4 H, 4 O

▲ **FIGURE 3.5** **Balanced chemical equation for the combustion of CH$_4$.**

Next we focus on H. Because CH$_4$ contains four H atoms and H$_2$O contains two H atoms, we balance the H atoms by placing the coefficient 2 in front of H$_2$O. There are then four H atoms on each side of the equation:

$$CH_4 + O_2 \longrightarrow CO_2 + 2\,H_2O \quad \text{(unbalanced)} \qquad [3.3]$$

Finally, a coefficient 2 in front of O$_2$ balances the equation by giving four C atoms on each side (2 × 2 left, 2 + 2 × 1 right):

$$CH_4 + 2\,O_2 \longrightarrow CO_2 + 2\,H_2O \quad \text{(balanced)} \qquad [3.4]$$

The molecular view of the balanced equation is shown in ◀ **FIGURE 3.5.**

SAMPLE EXERCISE 3.1 **Interpreting and Balancing Chemical Equations**

The following diagram represents a chemical reaction in which the red spheres are oxygen atoms and the blue spheres are nitrogen atoms. **(a)** Write the chemical formulas for the reactants and products. **(b)** Write a balanced equation for the reaction. **(c)** Is the diagram consistent with the law of conservation of mass?

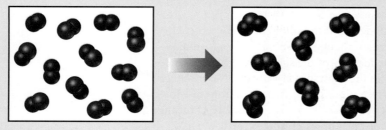

SOLUTION

(a) The left box, which represents reactants, contains two kinds of molecules, those composed of two oxygen atoms (O$_2$) and those composed of one nitrogen atom and one oxygen atom (NO). The right box, which represents products, contains only molecules composed of one nitrogen atom and two oxygen atoms (NO$_2$).

(b) The unbalanced chemical equation is

$$O_2 + NO \longrightarrow NO_2 \quad \text{(unbalanced)}$$

An inventory of atoms on each side of the equation shows that there are one N and three O on the left side of the arrow and one N and two O on the right. To balance O we must increase the number of O atoms on the right while keeping the coefficients for NO and NO$_2$ equal. Sometimes we need to go back and forth several times from one side of an equation to the other, changing coefficients first on one side of the equation and then the other until it is balanced. In our present case, we can increase the number of O atoms by placing the coefficient 2 in front of NO$_2$:

$$O_2 + NO \longrightarrow 2\,NO_2 \quad \text{(unbalanced)}$$

That gives two N atoms and four O atoms on the right, so we go back to the left side. Placing the coefficient 2 in front of NO balances both N and O:

$$O_2 + 2\,NO \longrightarrow 2\,NO_2 \quad \text{(balanced)}$$

2 N, 4 O   2 N, 4 O

(c) The reactants box contains four O$_2$ and eight NO. Thus, the molecular ratio is one O$_2$ for each two NO, as required by the balanced equation. The products box contains eight NO$_2$, which means the number of NO$_2$ product molecules equals the number of NO reactant molecules, as the balanced equation requires.

There are eight N atoms in the eight NO molecules in the reactants box. There are also 4 × 2 = 8 O atoms in the O$_2$ molecules and eight O atoms in the NO molecules, giving a total of 16 O atoms. In the products box, we find eight N atoms and 8 × 2 = 16 O atoms in the eight NO$_2$ molecules. Because there are equal numbers of N and O atoms in the two boxes, the drawing is consistent with the law of conservation of mass.

PRACTICE EXERCISE

In the following diagram, the white spheres represent hydrogen atoms and the blue spheres represent nitrogen atoms.

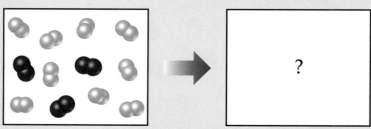

To be consistent with the law of conservation of mass, how many NH$_3$ molecules should be shown in the right (products) box?

Answer: Six NH$_3$ molecules

Indicating the States of Reactants and Products

Symbols indicating the physical state of each reactant and product are often shown in chemical equations. We use the symbols (g), (l), (s), and (aq) for gas, liquid, solid, and aqueous (water) solution, respectively. Thus, Equation 3.4 can be written

$$CH_4(g) + 2\,O_2(g) \longrightarrow CO_2(g) + 2\,H_2O(g) \qquad [3.5]$$

Sometimes the conditions under which the reaction proceeds appear above or below the reaction arrow. The symbol Δ (Greek uppercase delta) above the arrow indicates addition of heat.

SAMPLE EXERCISE 3.2   **Balancing Chemical Equations**

Balance the equation

$$Na(s) + H_2O(l) \longrightarrow NaOH(aq) + H_2(g)$$

SOLUTION

Begin by counting each kind of atom on the two sides of the arrow. There are one Na, one O, and two H on the left side, and one Na, one O, and three H on the right. To increase the number of H atoms on the left, let's try placing the coefficient 2 in front of H_2O:

$$Na(s) + 2\,H_2O(l) \longrightarrow NaOH(aq) + H_2(g)$$

Although beginning this way does not balance H, it does increase the number of reactant H atoms, which we need to do. (Also, adding the coefficient 2 on H_2O unbalances O, but we will take care of that after we balance H.) Now that we have 2 H_2O on the left, we balance H by putting the coefficient 2 in front of NaOH:

$$Na(s) + 2\,H_2O(l) \longrightarrow 2\,NaOH(aq) + H_2(g)$$

Balancing H in this way brings O into balance, but now Na is unbalanced, with one Na on the left and two on the right. To rebalance Na, we put the coefficient 2 in front of the reactant:

$$2\,Na(s) + 2\,H_2O(l) \longrightarrow 2\,NaOH(aq) + H_2(g)$$

We now have two Na atoms, four H atoms, and two O atoms on each side. The equation is balanced.

Comment Notice that we moved back and forth, placing a coefficient in front of H_2O, then NaOH, and finally Na. In balancing equations, we often find ourselves following this pattern of moving back and forth from one side of the arrow to the other, placing coefficients first in front of a formula on one side and then in front of a formula on the other side until the equation is balanced. You can always tell if you have balanced your equation correctly by checking that the number of atoms of each element is the same on the two sides of the arrow.

PRACTICE EXERCISE

Balance these equations by providing the missing coefficients:

(a) __ Fe(s) + __ $O_2(g)$ $\longrightarrow$ __ $Fe_2O_3(s)$

(b) __ $C_2H_4(g)$ + __ $O_2(g)$ $\longrightarrow$ __ $CO_2(g)$ + __ $H_2O(g)$

(c) __ Al(s) + __ HCl(aq) $\longrightarrow$ __ $AlCl_3(aq)$ + __ $H_2(g)$

Answers: (a) 4, 3, 2; (b) 1, 3, 2, 2; (c) 2, 6, 2, 3

3.2 | SOME SIMPLE PATTERNS OF CHEMICAL REACTIVITY

In this section we examine three types of reactions that we see frequently throughout this chapter: combination reactions, decomposition reactions, and combustion reactions. Our first reason for examining these reactions is to become better acquainted with chemical reactions and their balanced equations. Our second reason is to consider how we might predict the products of some of these reactions knowing only their reactants. The key to predicting the products formed by a given combination of reactants is recognizing general patterns of chemical reactivity. Recognizing a pattern of reactivity for a class of substances gives you a broader understanding than merely memorizing a large number of unrelated reactions.

Combination and Decomposition Reactions

In **combination reactions** two or more substances react to form one product (▼ TABLE 3.1). For example, magnesium metal burns brilliantly in air to produce magnesium oxide (▼ FIGURE 3.6):

$$2\,Mg(s) + O_2(g) \longrightarrow 2\,MgO(s) \qquad [3.6]$$

This reaction is used to produce the bright flame generated by flares and some fireworks.

A combination reaction between a metal and a nonmetal, as in Equation 3.6, produces an ionic solid. Recall that the formula of an ionic compound can be determined from the charges of its ions. ∞ (Section 2.7) When magnesium reacts with oxygen, the magnesium loses electrons and forms the magnesium ion, Mg^{2+}. The oxygen gains electrons and forms the oxide ion, O^{2-}. Thus, the reaction product is MgO.

You should be able to recognize when a reaction is a combination reaction and to predict the products when the reactants are a metal and a nonmetal.

TABLE 3.1 • Combination and Decomposition Reactions

Combination Reactions

$A + B \longrightarrow C$	Two or more reactants combine to form a
$C(s) + O_2(g) \longrightarrow CO_2(g)$	single product. Many elements react with one
$N_2(g) + 3\,H_2(g) \longrightarrow 2\,NH_3(g)$	another in this fashion to form compounds.
$CaO(s) + H_2O(l) \longrightarrow Ca(OH)_2(s)$	

Decomposition Reactions

$C \longrightarrow A + B$	A single reactant breaks apart to form two or
$2\,KClO_3(s) \longrightarrow 2\,KCl(s) + 3\,O_2(g)$	more substances. Many compounds react this
$PbCO_3(s) \longrightarrow PbO(s) + CO_2(g)$	way when heated.
$Cu(OH)_2(s) \longrightarrow CuO(s) + H_2O(l)$	

▼ FIGURE 3.6 **Combustion of magnesium metal in air, a combination reaction.**

The ribbon of magnesium metal is surrounded by oxygen gas in the air.

An intense flame is produced as the Mg atoms react with O_2.

The reaction forms MgO, a white, ionic solid.

Reactants   *Products*

$2\,Mg(s) + O_2(g) \longrightarrow 2\,MgO(s)$

⚠️ **GIVE IT SOME THOUGHT**

When Na and S undergo a combination reaction, what is the chemical formula of the product?

In a **decomposition reaction** one substance undergoes a reaction to produce two or more other substances (Table 3.1). For example, many metal carbonates decompose to form metal oxides and carbon dioxide when heated:

$$CaCO_3(s) \xrightarrow{\Delta} CaO(s) + CO_2(g) \qquad [3.7]$$

Decomposition of $CaCO_3$ is an important commercial process. Limestone or seashells, which are both primarily $CaCO_3$, are heated to prepare CaO, known as lime or quicklime. About 2×10^{10} kg (20 million tons) of CaO is used in the United States each year, principally in making glass, in obtaining iron from its ores, and in making mortar to bind bricks.

The decomposition of sodium azide (NaN_3) rapidly releases $N_2(g)$, so this reaction is used to inflate safety air bags in automobiles (▶ **FIGURE 3.7**):

$$2\,NaN_3(s) \longrightarrow 2\,Na(s) + 3\,N_2(g) \qquad [3.8]$$

The system is designed so that an impact ignites a detonator cap, which in turn causes NaN_3 to decompose explosively. A small quantity of NaN_3 (about 100 g) forms a large quantity of gas (about 50 L).

▲ **FIGURE 3.7** Decomposition of sodium azide, NaN₃(s), is used to inflate automobile air bags.

SAMPLE EXERCISE 3.3 | **Writing Balanced Equations for Combination and Decomposition Reactions**

Write a balanced equation for **(a)** the combination reaction between lithium metal and fluorine gas and **(b)** the decomposition reaction that occurs when solid barium carbonate is heated (two products form, a solid and a gas).

SOLUTION

(a) With the exception of mercury, all metals are solids at room temperature. Fluorine occurs as a diatomic molecule. Thus, the reactants are Li(s) and $F_2(g)$. The product will be composed of a metal and a nonmetal, so we expect it to be an ionic solid. Lithium ions have a 1+ charge, Li^+, whereas fluoride ions have a 1− charge, F^-. Thus, the chemical formula for the product is LiF. The balanced chemical equation is

$$2\,Li(s) + F_2(g) \longrightarrow 2\,LiF(s)$$

(b) The chemical formula for barium carbonate is $BaCO_3$. As noted in the text, many metal carbonates decompose to metal oxides and carbon dioxide when heated. In Equation 3.7, for example, $CaCO_3$ decomposes to form CaO and CO_2. Thus, we expect $BaCO_3$ to decompose to BaO and CO_2. Barium and calcium are both in group 2A in the periodic table, which further suggests they react in the same way:

$$BaCO_3(s) \longrightarrow BaO(s) + CO_2(g)$$

PRACTICE EXERCISE

Write a balanced equation for **(a)** solid mercury(II) sulfide decomposing into its component elements when heated and **(b)** aluminum metal combining with oxygen in the air.

Answers: **(a)** $HgS(s) \longrightarrow Hg(l) + S(s)$, **(b)** $4\,Al(s) + 3\,O_2(g) \longrightarrow 2\,Al_2O_3(s)$

Combustion Reactions

Combustion reactions are rapid reactions that produce a flame. Most combustion reactions we observe involve O_2 from air as a reactant. Equation 3.5 illustrates a general class of reactions involving the burning, or combustion, of hydrocarbons (compounds that contain only carbon and hydrogen, such as CH_4 and C_2H_4). ⚬⚬ (Section 2.9)

Hydrocarbons combusted in air react with O_2 to form CO_2 and H_2O.* The number of molecules of O_2 required and the number of molecules of CO_2 and H_2O formed

---

*When there is an insufficient quantity of O_2 present, carbon monoxide (CO) is produced along with CO_2; this is called incomplete combustion. If the O_2 quantity is severely restricted, the fine particles of carbon we call soot are produced. Complete combustion produces only CO_2 and H_2O. Unless stated to the contrary, we will always take combustion to mean complete combustion.

▲ GO FIGURE

In what ways are the reactions depicted in Figures 3.4 and 3.8 alike?

▲ **FIGURE 3.8** **Propane burning in air.** Liquid propane in the tank, C_3H_8, vaporizes and mixes with air as it escapes through the nozzle. The combustion reaction of C_3H_8 and O_2 produces a blue flame.

depend on the composition of the hydrocarbon, which acts as the fuel in the reaction. For example, the combustion of propane (C_3H_8, ◄ **FIGURE 3.8**), a gas used for cooking and home heating, is described by the equation

$$C_3H_8(g) + 5\,O_2(g) \longrightarrow 3\,CO_2(g) + 4\,H_2O(g) \qquad [3.9]$$

The state of the water in this reaction, $H_2O(g)$ or $H_2O(l)$, depends on the reaction conditions. Water vapor, $H_2O(g)$, is formed at high temperature in an open container.

Combustion of oxygen-containing derivatives of hydrocarbons, such as CH_3OH, also produces CO_2 and H_2O. The rule that hydrocarbons and their oxygen-containing derivatives form CO_2 and H_2O when they burn in air summarizes the behavior of about 3 million compounds. Many substances that our bodies use as energy sources, such as the sugar glucose ($C_6H_{12}O_6$), react with O_2 to form CO_2 and H_2O. In our bodies, however, the reactions take place in a series of intermediate steps that occur at body temperature. These reactions that involve intermediate steps are described as *oxidation reactions* instead of combustion reactions.

SAMPLE EXERCISE 3.4 | **Writing Balanced Equations for Combustion Reactions**

Write the balanced equation for the reaction that occurs when methanol, $CH_3OH(l)$, is burned in air.

SOLUTION

When any compound containing C, H, and O is combusted, it reacts with the $O_2(g)$ in air to produce $CO_2(g)$ and $H_2O(g)$. Thus the unbalanced equation is

$$CH_3OH(l) + O_2(g) \longrightarrow CO_2(g) + H_2O(g)$$

The C atoms are balanced, one on each side of the arrow. Because CH_3OH has four H atoms, we place the coefficient 2 in front of H_2O to balance the H atoms:

$$CH_3OH(l) + O_2(g) \longrightarrow CO_2(g) + 2\,H_2O(g)$$

Adding this coefficient balances H but gives four O atoms in the products. Because there are only three O atoms in the reactants, we are not finished. We can place the coefficient $\frac{3}{2}$ in front of O_2 to give four O atoms in the reactants ($\frac{3}{2} \times 2 = 3$ O atoms in $\frac{3}{2}\,O_2$):

$$CH_3OH(l) + \tfrac{3}{2}\,O_2(g) \longrightarrow CO_2(g) + 2\,H_2O(g)$$

Although this equation is balanced, it is not in its most conventional form because it contains a fractional coefficient. However, multiplying through by 2 removes the fraction and keeps the equation balanced:

$$2\,CH_3OH(l) + 3\,O_2(g) \longrightarrow 2\,CO_2(g) + 4\,H_2O(g)$$

PRACTICE EXERCISE

Write the balanced equation for the reaction that occurs when ethanol, $C_2H_5OH(l)$, burns in air.

Answer: $C_2H_5OH(l) + 3\,O_2(g) \longrightarrow 2\,CO_2(g) + 3\,H_2O(g)$

3.3 | FORMULA WEIGHTS

Chemical formulas and chemical equations both have a *quantitative* significance in that the subscripts in formulas and the coefficients in equations represent precise quantities. The formula H_2O indicates that a molecule of this substance (water) contains exactly two atoms of hydrogen and one atom of oxygen. Similarly, the coefficients in a balanced chemical equation indicate the relative quantities of reactants and products. But how do we relate the numbers of atoms or molecules to the amounts we measure in the laboratory? Although we cannot directly count atoms or molecules, we can indirectly determine their numbers if we know their masses. Therefore, before we can pursue the quantitative aspects of chemical formulas and equations, we must examine the masses of atoms and molecules.

Formula and Molecular Weights

The **formula weight** of a substance is the sum of the atomic weights of the atoms in the chemical formula of the substance. Using atomic weights, we find, for example, that the formula weight of sulfuric acid (H_2SO_4) is 98.1 amu:*

$$FW \text{ of } H_2SO_4 = 2(AW \text{ of } H) + (AW \text{ of } S) + 4(AW \text{ of } O)$$
$$= 2(1.0 \text{ amu}) + 32.1 \text{ amu} + 4(16.0 \text{ amu})$$
$$= 98.1 \text{ amu}$$

For convenience, we have rounded off the atomic weights to one decimal place, a practice we will follow in most calculations in this book.

If the chemical formula is the chemical symbol of an element, such as Na, the formula weight equals the atomic weight of the element, in this case 23.0 amu. If the chemical formula is that of a molecule, the formula weight is also called the **molecular weight**. The molecular weight of glucose ($C_6H_{12}O_6$), for example, is

$$MW \text{ of } C_6H_{12}O_6 = 6(12.0 \text{ amu}) + 12(1.0 \text{ amu}) + 6(16.0 \text{ amu}) = 180.0 \text{ amu}$$

Because ionic substances exist as three-dimensional arrays of ions (see Figure 2.21), it is inappropriate to speak of molecules of these substances. Instead, we speak of *formula units*. The formula unit of NaCl, for instance, consists of one Na^+ ion and one Cl^- ion. Thus, the formula weight of NaCl is defined as the mass of one formula unit:

$$FW \text{ of } NaCl = 23.0 \text{ amu} + 35.5 \text{ amu} = 58.5 \text{ amu}$$

SAMPLE EXERCISE 3.5 **Calculating Formula Weights**

Calculate the formula weight of (a) sucrose, $C_{12}H_{22}O_{11}$ (table sugar), and (b) calcium nitrate, $Ca(NO_3)_2$.

SOLUTION

(a) By adding the atomic weights of the atoms in sucrose, we find the formula weight to be 342.0 amu:

12 C atoms = 12(12.0 amu) = 144.0 amu
22 H atoms = 22(1.0 amu) = 22.0 amu
11 O atoms = 11(16.0 amu) = 176.0 amu
                             342.0 amu

(b) If a chemical formula has parentheses, the subscript outside the parentheses is a multiplier for all atoms inside. Thus, for $Ca(NO_3)_2$ we have

1 Ca atom = 1(40.1 amu) = 40.1 amu
2 N atoms = 2(14.0 amu) = 28.0 amu
6 O atoms = 6(16.0 amu) = 96.0 amu
                          164.1 amu

PRACTICE EXERCISE

Calculate the formula weight of (a) $Al(OH)_3$ and (b) CH_3OH.
Answers: (a) 78.0 amu, (b) 32.0 amu

Percentage Composition from Chemical Formulas

Chemists must sometimes calculate the *percentage composition* of a compound—that is, the percentage by mass contributed by each element in the substance. Forensic chemists, for example, will measure the percentage composition of an unknown powder and compare it with the percentage compositions for sugar, salt, or cocaine to identify the powder.

Calculating the percentage composition of any element in a substance is straightforward if the chemical formula is known. The calculation depends on the formula weight of the substance, the atomic weight of the element of interest, and the number of atoms of that element in the chemical formula:

$$\% \text{ composition of element} = \frac{\left(\begin{array}{c}\text{number of atoms}\\\text{of element}\end{array}\right)\left(\begin{array}{c}\text{atomic weight}\\\text{of element}\end{array}\right)}{\text{formula weight of substance}} \times 100\% \quad [3.10]$$

*The abbreviation AW is used for atomic weight, FW for formula weight, and MW for molecular weight.

SAMPLE EXERCISE 3.6 **Calculating Percentage Composition**

Calculate the percentage of carbon, hydrogen, and oxygen (by mass) in $C_{12}H_{22}O_{11}$.

SOLUTION

Let's examine this question using the problem-solving steps in the accompanying "Strategies in Chemistry: Problem Solving" essay.

Analyze We are given a chemical formula and asked to calculate the percentage by mass of each element.

Plan We use Equation 3.10, obtaining our atomic weights from a periodic table. We know the denominator in Equation 3.10, the formula weight of $C_{12}H_{22}O_{11}$, from Sample Exercise 3.5. We must use that value in three calculations, one for each element.

Solve

$$\%C = \frac{(12)(12.0\ \text{amu})}{342.0\ \text{amu}} \times 100\% = 42.1\%$$

$$\%H = \frac{(22)(1.0\ \text{amu})}{342.0\ \text{amu}} \times 100\% = 6.4\%$$

$$\%O = \frac{(11)(16.0\ \text{amu})}{342.0\ \text{amu}} \times 100\% = 51.5\%$$

Check Our calculated percentages must add up to 100%, which they do. We could have used more significant figures for our atomic weights, giving more significant figures for our percentage composition, but we have adhered to our suggested guideline of rounding atomic weights to one digit beyond the decimal point.

PRACTICE EXERCISE

Calculate the percentage of nitrogen, by mass, in $Ca(NO_3)_2$.

Answer: 17.1%

3.4 | AVOGADRO'S NUMBER AND THE MOLE

Even the smallest samples we deal with in the laboratory contain enormous numbers of atoms, ions, or molecules. For example, a teaspoon of water (about 5 mL) contains 2×10^{23} water molecules, a number so large it almost defies comprehension. Chemists therefore have devised a counting unit for describing such large numbers of atoms or molecules.

In everyday life we use such familiar counting units as dozen (12 objects) and gross (144 objects). In chemistry the counting unit for numbers of atoms, ions, or molecules in a laboratory-size sample is the **mole**, abbreviated mol.* One mole is the amount of matter that contains as many objects (atoms, molecules, or whatever other objects we are considering) as the number of atoms in exactly 12 g of isotopically pure ^{12}C. From experiments, scientists have determined this number to be 6.0221421×10^{23}, which we will usually round to 6.02×10^{23}. Scientists call this value **Avogadro's number**, N_A, in honor

STRATEGIES IN CHEMISTRY

PROBLEM SOLVING

Practice is the key to success in solving problems. As you practice, you can improve your skills by following these steps:

Step 1: Analyze the problem. Read the problem carefully. What does it say? Draw a picture or diagram that will help you to visualize the problem. Write down both the data you are given and the quantity you need to obtain (the unknown).

Step 2: Develop a plan for solving the problem. Consider a possible path between the given information and the unknown. What principles or equations relate the known data to the unknown?

Recognize that some data may not be given explicitly in the problem; you may be expected to know certain quantities (such as Avogadro's number) or look them up in tables (such as atomic weights). Recognize also that your plan may involve either a single step or a series of steps with intermediate answers.

Step 3: Solve the problem. Use the known information and suitable equations or relationships to solve for the unknown. Dimensional analysis ⬭ (Section 1.6) is a useful tool for solving a great number of problems. Be careful with significant figures, signs, and units.

Step 4: Check the solution. Read the problem again to make sure you have found all the solutions asked for in the problem. Does your answer make sense? That is, is the answer outrageously large or small or is it in the ballpark? Finally, are the units and significant figures correct?

*The term *mole* comes from the Latin word *moles,* meaning "a mass." The term *molecule* is the diminutive of this word and means "a small mass."

of the Italian scientist Amedeo Avogadro (1776–1856), and it is often cited with units of reciprocal moles, $6.02 \times 10^{23} \, mol^{-1}$. The unit (read as either "inverse mole" or "per mole") reminds us that there are 6.02×10^{23} objects per one mole. A mole of atoms, a mole of molecules, or a mole of anything else all contain Avogadro's number of objects:

$$1 \text{ mol } {}^{12}\text{C atoms} = 6.02 \times 10^{23} \text{ } {}^{12}\text{C atoms}$$

$$1 \text{ mol } H_2O \text{ molecules} = 6.02 \times 10^{23} \text{ } H_2O \text{ molecules}$$

$$1 \text{ mol } NO_3^- \text{ ions} = 6.02 \times 10^{23} \text{ } NO_3^- \text{ ions}$$

Avogadro's number is so large that it is difficult to imagine. Spreading 6.02×10^{23} marbles over Earth's surface would produce a layer about 3 miles thick. Avogadro's number of pennies placed side by side in a straight line would encircle Earth 300 trillion (3×10^{14}) times.

SAMPLE EXERCISE 3.7   **Estimating Numbers of Atoms**

Without using a calculator, arrange these samples in order of increasing numbers of carbon atoms: 12 g ^{12}C, 1 mol C_2H_2, 9×10^{23} molecules of CO_2.

SOLUTION

Analyze We are given amounts of three substances expressed in grams, moles, and number of molecules and asked to arrange the samples in order of increasing numbers of C atoms.

Plan To determine the number of C atoms in each sample, we must convert 12 g ^{12}C, 1 mol C_2H_2, and 9×10^{23} molecules CO_2 to numbers of C atoms. To make these conversions, we use the definition of mole and Avogadro's number.

Solve One mole is defined as the amount of matter that contains as many units of the matter as there are C atoms in exactly 12 g of ^{12}C. Thus, 12 g of ^{12}C contains 1 mol of C atoms = 6.02×10^{23} C atoms. One mol of C_2H_2 contains 6×10^{23} C_2H_2 molecules. Because

there are two C atoms in each molecule, this sample contains 12×10^{23} C atoms. Because each CO_2 molecule contains one C atom, the CO_2 sample contains 9×10^{23} C atoms. Hence, the order is 12 g ^{12}C (6×10^{23} C atoms) $< 9 \times 10^{23}$ CO_2 molecules (9×10^{23} C atoms) < 1 mol C_2H_2 (12×10^{23} C atoms).

Check We can check our results by comparing numbers of moles of C atoms in the samples because the number of moles is proportional to the number of atoms. Thus, 12 g of ^{12}C is 1 mol C; 1 mol of C_2H_2 contains 2 mol C, and 9×10^{23} molecules of CO_2 contain 1.5 mol C, giving the same order as stated previously.

PRACTICE EXERCISE

Without using a calculator, arrange these samples in order of increasing number of O atoms: 1 mol H_2O, 1 mol CO_2, 3×10^{23} molecules O_3.

Answer: 1 mol H_2O (6×10^{23} O atoms) $< 3 \times 10^{23}$ molecules O_3 (9×10^{23} O atoms) < 1 mol CO_2 (12×10^{23} O atoms)

SAMPLE EXERCISE 3.8   **Converting Moles to Number of Atoms**

Calculate the number of H atoms in 0.350 mol of $C_6H_{12}O_6$.

SOLUTION

Analyze We are given the amount of a substance (0.350 mol) and its chemical formula $C_6H_{12}O_6$. The unknown is the number of H atoms in the sample.

Plan Avogadro's number provides the conversion factor between number of moles of $C_6H_{12}O_6$ and number of molecules of $C_6H_{12}O_6$: 1 mol $C_6H_{12}O_6$ = 6.02×10^{23} molecules $C_6H_{12}O_6$. Once we know the number of molecules of $C_6H_{12}O_6$, we can use the chemical formula, which tells us that each molecule of $C_6H_{12}O_6$ contains 12 H atoms. Thus, we convert moles of $C_6H_{12}O_6$ to molecules of $C_6H_{12}O_6$ and then determine the number of atoms of H from the number of molecules of $C_6H_{12}O_6$:

$$\text{Moles } C_6H_{12}O_6 \longrightarrow \text{ molecules } C_6H_{12}O_6 \longrightarrow \text{ atoms H}$$

Solve

$$H \text{ atoms} = (0.350 \text{ mol } C_6H_{12}O_6)\left(\frac{6.02 \times 10^{23} \text{ molecules } C_6H_{12}O_6}{1 \text{ mol } C_6H_{12}O_6}\right)$$

$$\times \left(\frac{12 \text{ H atoms}}{1 \text{ molecule } C_6H_{12}O_6}\right) = 2.53 \times 10^{24} \text{ H atoms}$$

Check We can do a ballpark calculation: First, $0.35(6 \times 10^{23})$ is about 2×10^{23} molecules of $C_6H_{12}O_6$, and each one of these molecules contains 12 H atoms. So $12(2 \times 10^{23})$ gives $24 \times 10^{23} = 2.4 \times 10^{24}$ H atoms, which agrees with our result. Because we were asked for the number of H atoms, the units of our answer are correct. The given data had three significant figures, so our answer has three significant figures.

PRACTICE EXERCISE

How many oxygen atoms are in **(a)** 0.25 mol $Ca(NO_3)_2$ and **(b)** 1.50 mol of sodium carbonate?

Answers: **(a)** 9.0×10^{23}, **(b)** 2.71×10^{24}

GO FIGURE

How many H_2O molecules are in a 9.00-g sample of water?

Single molecule

1 molecule H_2O
(18.0 amu)

Laboratory-size sample

Avogadro's number of molecules
(6.02×10^{23})

1 mol H_2O
(18.0 g)

▲ **FIGURE 3.9** **Comparing the mass of 1 molecule and 1 mol of H_2O.** Both masses have the same number but different units (atomic mass units and grams). Expressing both masses in grams indicates their huge difference: 1 molecule H_2O has a mass of 2.99×10^{-23} g whereas 1 mol H_2O has a mass of 18.0 g.

Molar Mass

A dozen is the same number, 12, whether we have a dozen eggs or a dozen elephants. Clearly, however, a dozen eggs does not have the same mass as a dozen elephants. Similarly, a mole is always the *same number* (6.02×10^{23}), but 1-mol samples of different substances have *different masses*. Compare, for example, 1 mol of ^{12}C and 1 mol of ^{24}Mg. A single ^{12}C atom has a mass of 12 amu, whereas a single ^{24}Mg atom is twice as massive, 24 amu (to two significant figures). Because a mole of anything always contains the same number of particles, a mole of ^{24}Mg must be twice as massive as a mole of ^{12}C. Because a mole of ^{12}C has a mass of 12 g (by definition), a mole of ^{24}Mg must have a mass of 24 g. This example illustrates a general rule relating the mass of an atom to the mass of Avogadro's number (1 mol) of these atoms: *The atomic weight of an element in atomic mass units is numerically equal to the mass in grams of 1 mol of that element.* For example,

Cl has an atomic weight of 35.5 amu $\Rightarrow$ 1 mol Cl has a mass of 35.5 g

Au has an atomic weight of 197 amu $\Rightarrow$ 1 mol Au has a mass of 197 g

For other kinds of substances, the same numerical relationship exists between formula weight and mass of one mole of a substance:

H_2O has a formula weight of 18.0 amu $\Rightarrow$ 1 mol H_2O has a mass of 18.0 g

(◀ **FIGURE 3.9**)

NO_3^- has a formula weight of 62.0 amu $\Rightarrow$ 1 mol NO_3^- has a mass of 62.0 g

$NaCl$ has a formula weight of 58.5 amu $\Rightarrow$ 1 mol $NaCl$ has a mass of 58.5 g

GIVE IT SOME THOUGHT

a. Which has more mass, a mole of water (H_2O) or a mole of glucose ($C_6H_{12}O_6$)?
b. Which contains more molecules, a mole of water or a mole of glucose?

The mass in grams of one mole of a substance (that is, the mass in grams per mole) is called the **molar mass** of the substance. *The molar mass in grams per mole of any substance is numerically equal to its formula weight in atomic mass units.* For NaCl, for example, the formula weight is 58.5 amu and the molar mass is 58.5 g/mol. Mole relationships for several other substances are shown in ▼ **TABLE 3.2**, and ▶ **FIGURE 3.10** shows 1-mol quantities of three common substances.

The entries in Table 3.2 for N and N_2 point out the importance of stating the chemical form of a substance when using the mole concept. Suppose you read that 1 mol of nitrogen is produced in a particular reaction. You might interpret this statement to mean 1 mol of nitrogen atoms (14.0 g). Unless otherwise stated, however, what is

TABLE 3.2 • Mole Relationships				
Name of Substance	**Formula**	**Formula Weight (amu)**	**Molar Mass (g/mol)**	**Number and Kind of Particles in One Mole**
Atomic nitrogen	N	14.0	14.0	6.02×10^{23} N atoms
Molecular nitrogen	N_2	28.0	28.0	$\begin{cases} 6.02 \times 10^{23} \text{ } N_2 \text{ molecules} \\ 2(6.02 \times 10^{23}) \text{ N atoms} \end{cases}$
Silver	Ag	107.9	107.9	6.02×10^{23} Ag atoms
Silver ions	Ag^+	107.9*	107.9	6.02×10^{23} Ag^+ ions
Barium chloride	$BaCl_2$	208.2	208.2	$\begin{cases} 6.02 \times 10^{23} \text{ } BaCl_2 \text{ formula units} \\ 6.02 \times 10^{23} \text{ } Ba^{2+} \text{ ions} \\ 2(6.02 \times 10^{23}) \text{ } Cl^- \text{ ions} \end{cases}$

*Recall that the electron has negligible mass; thus, ions and atoms have essentially the same mass.

1 mol $O_2(g)$ has a mass of 32.0 g

1 mol $H_2O(l)$ has a mass of 18.0 g

1 mol $NaCl(s)$ has a mass of 58.45 g

▲ **FIGURE 3.10   One mole each of a solid (NaCl), a liquid (H_2O), and a gas (O_2).** In each case, the mass in grams of 1 mol—that is, the molar mass—is numerically equal to the formula weight in atomic mass units. Each of these samples contains 6.02×10^{23} formula units.

probably meant is 1 mol of nitrogen molecules, N_2 (28.0 g), because N_2 is the most common chemical form of the element. To avoid ambiguity, it is important to state explicitly the chemical form being discussed. Using the chemical formula—N or N_2, for instance—avoids ambiguity.

SAMPLE EXERCISE 3.9 | Calculating Molar Mass

What is the molar mass of glucose, $C_6H_{12}O_6$?

SOLUTION

Analyze We are given a chemical formula and asked to determine its molar mass.

Plan Because the molar mass of any substance is numerically equal to its formula weight, we first determine the formula weight of glucose by adding the atomic weights of its component atoms. The formula weight will have units of amu, whereas the molar mass has units of g/mol.

Solve Our first step is to determine the formula weight of glucose:

$$6 \text{ C atoms} = 6(12.0 \text{ amu}) = 72.0 \text{ amu}$$
$$12 \text{ H atoms} = 12(1.0 \text{ amu}) = 12.0 \text{ amu}$$
$$6 \text{ O atoms} = 6(16.0 \text{ amu}) = 96.0 \text{ amu}$$
$$\overline{\phantom{6 \text{ O atoms} = 6(16.0 \text{ amu}) = }180.0 \text{ amu}}$$

Because glucose has a formula weight of 180.0 amu, 1 mol of this substance (6.02×10^{23} molecules) has a mass of 180.0 g. In other words, $C_6H_{12}O_6$ has a molar mass of 180.0 g/mol.

Check A magnitude below 250 seems reasonable based on the earlier examples we have encountered, and grams per mole is the appropriate unit for the molar mass.

Comment Glucose, also known as blood sugar, is found in nature in honey and fruits. Other sugars used as food are converted into glucose in the stomach or liver before the body uses them as energy sources. Because glucose requires no conversion, it is often given intravenously to patients who need immediate nourishment.

PRACTICE EXERCISE

Calculate the molar mass of $Ca(NO_3)_2$.

Answer: 164.1 g/mol

CHEMISTRY AND LIFE

GLUCOSE MONITORING

Over 20 million Americans have diabetes, and globally the number approaches 172 million. Diabetes is a metabolic disorder in which the body either cannot produce or cannot properly use the hormone insulin. One signal that a person is diabetic is that the concentration of glucose in the blood is higher than normal. Therefore, people who are diabetic need to measure their blood glucose concentrations regularly. Untreated diabetes can cause severe complications such as blindness and loss of limbs.

The body converts most of the food we eat into glucose. After digestion, glucose is delivered to cells via the blood. Cells need glucose to live, and insulin must be present in order for glucose to enter the cells. Normally, the body adjusts the concentration of insulin automatically, in concert with the glucose concentration after eating. However, in a diabetic person, either little or no insulin is produced (Type 1 diabetes) or insulin is produced but the cells cannot take it up properly (Type 2 diabetes). The result is that the blood glucose concentration is too high. People normally have a range of 70–120 mg glucose per deciliter of blood. A person who has not eaten for 8 hours or more is diagnosed as diabetic if his or her glucose level is 126 mg/dL or higher.

Glucose meters work by the introduction of blood from a person, usually by a prick of the finger, onto a small strip of paper that contains chemicals that react with glucose. Insertion of the strip into a small battery-operated reader gives the glucose concentration (▼ FIGURE 3.11). The mechanism of the readout varies from one monitor to another—it may be a measurement of a small electrical current or measurement of light produced in a chemical reaction. Depending on the reading on any given day, a diabetic person may need to receive an injection of insulin or simply stop eating sweets for a while.

▲ FIGURE 3.11   **Glucose meter.**

Interconverting Masses and Moles

Conversions of mass to moles and of moles to mass are frequently encountered in calculations using the mole concept. These calculations are simplified using dimensional analysis, as shown in Sample Exercises 3.10 and 3.11.

SAMPLE EXERCISE 3.10   **Converting Grams to Moles**

Calculate the number of moles of glucose ($C_6H_{12}O_6$) in 5.380 g of $C_6H_{12}O_6$.

SOLUTION

Analyze We are given the number of grams of a substance and its chemical formula and asked to calculate the number of moles.

Plan The molar mass of a substance provides the factor for converting grams to moles. The molar mass of $C_6H_{12}O_6$ is 180.0 g/mol (Sample Exercise 3.9).

Solve Using 1 mol $C_6H_{12}O_6$ = 180.0 g $C_6H_{12}O_6$ to write the appropriate conversion factor, we have

$$\text{Moles } C_6H_{12}O_6 = (5.380 \text{ g } C_6H_{12}O_6)\left(\frac{1 \text{ mol } C_6H_{12}O_6}{180.0 \text{ g } C_6H_{12}O_6}\right) = 0.02989 \text{ mol } C_6H_{12}O_6$$

Check Because 5.380 g is less than the molar mass, an answer less than one mole is reasonable. The unit mol is appropriate. The original data had four significant figures, so our answer has four significant figures.

PRACTICE EXERCISE

How many moles of sodium bicarbonate ($NaHCO_3$) are in 508 g of $NaHCO_3$?

Answer: 6.05 mol $NaHCO_3$

SAMPLE EXERCISE 3.11   **Converting Moles to Grams**

Calculate the mass, in grams, of 0.433 mol of calcium nitrate.

SOLUTION

Analyze We are given the number of moles and the name of a substance and asked to calculate the number of grams in the sample.

Plan To convert moles to grams, we need the molar mass, which we can calculate using the chemical formula and atomic weights.

Solve Because the calcium ion is Ca^{2+} and the nitrate ion is NO_3^-, calcium nitrate is $Ca(NO_3)_2$. Adding the atomic weights of the elements in the compound gives a formula weight of 164.1 amu. Using 1 mol $Ca(NO_3)_2$ = 164.1 g $Ca(NO_3)_2$ to write the appropriate conversion factor, we have

$$\text{Grams } Ca(NO_3)_2 = (0.433 \text{ mol } Ca(NO_3)_2)\left(\frac{164.1 \text{ g } Ca(NO_3)_2}{1 \text{ mol } Ca(NO_3)_2}\right) = 71.1 \text{ g } Ca(NO_3)_2$$

Check The number of moles is less than 1, so the number of grams must be less than the molar mass, 164.1 g. Using rounded numbers to estimate, we have $0.5 \times 150 = 75$ g, which means the magnitude of our answer is reasonable. Both the units (g) and the number of significant figures (3) are correct.

PRACTICE EXERCISE

What is the mass, in grams, of **(a)** 6.33 mol of $NaHCO_3$ and **(b)** 3.0×10^{-5} mol of sulfuric acid?

Answers: **(a)** 532 g, **(b)** 2.9×10^{-3} g

Interconverting Masses and Numbers of Particles

The mole concept provides the bridge between mass and number of particles. To illustrate how this bridge works, let's calculate the number of copper atoms in an old copper penny. Such a penny has a mass of about 3 g, and we assume it is 100% copper:

$$\text{Cu atoms} = (3 \text{ g Cu})\left(\frac{1 \text{ mol Cu}}{63.5 \text{ g Cu}}\right)\left(\frac{6.02 \times 10^{23} \text{ Cu atoms}}{1 \text{ mol Cu}}\right)$$

$$= 3 \times 10^{22} \text{ Cu atoms}$$

We have rounded our answer to one significant figure because we used only one significant figure for the mass of the penny. Notice how dimensional analysis ∞ (Section 1.6) provides a straightforward route from grams to numbers of atoms. The molar mass and Avogadro's number are used as conversion factors to convert grams to moles and then moles to atoms. Notice also that our answer is a very large number. Any time you calculate the number of atoms, molecules, or ions in an ordinary sample of matter, you can expect the answer to be very large. In contrast, the number of moles in a sample will usually be small, often less than 1.

The general procedure for interconverting mass and number of formula units (atoms, molecules, ions, or whatever else is represented by the chemical formula) is summarized in ▼ **FIGURE 3.12**.

⚠ **GO FIGURE**

What number would you use to convert **(a)** moles of CH_4 to grams of CH_4 and **(b)** number of molecules of CH_4 to moles of CH_4?

▲ **FIGURE 3.12 Procedure for interconverting mass and number of formula units.** The number of moles of the substance is central to the calculation. Thus, the mole concept can be thought of as the bridge between the mass of a sample in grams and the number of formula units contained in the sample.

| **SAMPLE EXERCISE 3.12** | **Calculating Numbers of Molecules and Atoms from Mass** |

(a) How many glucose molecules are in 5.23 g of $C_6H_{12}O_6$? **(b)** How many oxygen atoms are in this sample?

SOLUTION

Analyze We are given the number of grams and the chemical formula and asked to calculate **(a)** the number of molecules and **(b)** the number of O atoms in the sample.

(a) Plan The strategy for determining the number of molecules in a given quantity of a substance is summarized in Figure 3.12. We must convert 5.23 g to moles of $C_6H_{12}O_6$ and then convert moles to molecules of $C_6H_{12}O_6$. The first conversion uses the molar mass of $C_6H_{12}O_6$, 180.0 g, and the second conversion uses Avogadro's number.

Solve Molecules $C_6H_{12}O_6$

$$= (5.23 \text{ g } C_6H_{12}O_6)\left(\frac{1 \text{ mol } C_6H_{12}O_6}{180.0 \text{ g } C_6H_{12}O_6}\right)\left(\frac{6.02 \times 10^{23} \text{ molecules } C_6H_{12}O_6}{1 \text{ mol } C_6H_{12}O_6}\right)$$

$$= 1.75 \times 10^{22} \text{ molecules } C_6H_{12}O_6$$

Check Because the mass we began with is less than a mole, there should be fewer than 6.02×10^{23} molecules in the sample, which means the magnitude of our answer is reasonable. We can make a ballpark estimate of the answer: $5/200 = 2.5 \times 10^{-2}$ mol; $2.5 \times 10^{-2} \times 6 \times 10^{23} = 15 \times 10^{21} = 1.5 \times 10^{22}$ molecules. The units (molecules) and significant figures (three) are appropriate.

(b) Plan To determine the number of O atoms, we use the fact that there are six O atoms in each $C_6H_{12}O_6$ molecule. Thus, multiplying the number of molecules we calculated in (a) by the factor (6 atoms O/1 molecule $C_6H_{12}O_6$) gives the number of O atoms.

Solve

$$\text{Atoms O} = (1.75 \times 10^{22} \text{ molecules } C_6H_{12}O_6)\left(\frac{6 \text{ atoms O}}{1 \text{ molecule } C_6H_{12}O_6}\right)$$

$$= 1.05 \times 10^{23} \text{ atoms O}$$

Check The answer is 6 times as large as the answer to part (a), exactly what it should be. The number of significant figures (three) and the units (atoms O) are correct.

PRACTICE EXERCISE

(a) How many nitric acid molecules are in 4.20 g of HNO_3? **(b)** How many O atoms are in this sample?

Answers: **(a)** 4.01×10^{22} molecules HNO_3, **(b)** 1.20×10^{23} atoms O

3.5 | EMPIRICAL FORMULAS FROM ANALYSES

As we learned in Section 2.6, the empirical formula for a substance tells us the relative number of atoms of each element in the substance. The empirical formula H_2O shows that water contains two H atoms for each O atom. This ratio also applies on the molar level: 1 mol of H_2O contains 2 mol of H atoms and 1 mol of O atoms. Conversely, *the ratio of the numbers of moles of all elements in a compound gives the subscripts in the compound's empirical formula.* Thus, the mole concept provides a way of calculating empirical formulas.

Mercury and chlorine, for example, combine to form a compound that is 73.9% mercury and 26.1% chlorine by mass. Thus, if we had a 100.0-g sample of the compound, it would contain 73.9 g of mercury and 26.1 g of chlorine. (Samples of any size can be used in problems of this type, but we will generally use 100.0 g to simplify the calculation of mass from percentage.) Using atomic weights to get molar masses, we can calculate the number of moles of each element in the sample:

$$(73.9 \text{ g Hg})\left(\frac{1 \text{ mol Hg}}{200.6 \text{ g Hg}}\right) = 0.368 \text{ mol Hg}$$

$$(26.1 \text{ g Cl})\left(\frac{1 \text{ mol Cl}}{35.5 \text{ g Cl}}\right) = 0.735 \text{ mol Cl}$$

GO FIGURE

How do you calculate the mole ratio of each element in any compound?

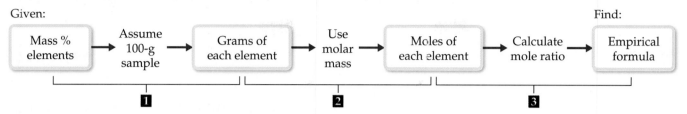

▲ FIGURE 3.13   Procedure for calculating an empirical formula from percentage composition. The key step in the calculation is step 2, determining the number of moles of each element in the compound.

We then divide the larger number of moles by the smaller number to obtain the Cl:Hg mole ratio:

$$\frac{\text{moles of Cl}}{\text{moles of Hg}} = \frac{0.735 \text{ mol Cl}}{0.368 \text{ mol Hg}} = \frac{1.99 \text{ mol Cl}}{1 \text{ mol Hg}}$$

Because of experimental errors, calculated values for a mole ratio may not be whole numbers, as in the calculation here. The number 1.99 is very close to 2, however, and so we can confidently conclude that the empirical formula for the compound is $HgCl_2$. The empirical formula is correct because its subscripts are the smallest integers that express the *ratio* of atoms present in the compound. ∞ (Section 2.6).

The general procedure for determining empirical formulas is outlined in ▲ FIGURE 3.13.

GIVE IT SOME THOUGHT

What is the mole ratio of nitrogen to hydrogen in N_2H_4?

SAMPLE EXERCISE 3.13   **Calculating an Empirical Formula**

Ascorbic acid (vitamin C) contains 40.92% C, 4.58% H, and 54.50% O by mass. What is the empirical formula of ascorbic acid?

SOLUTION

Analyze We are to determine the empirical formula of a compound from the mass percentages of its elements.

Plan The strategy for determining the empirical formula involves the three steps given in Figure 3.13.

Solve

1. For simplicity, we assume we have exactly 100 g of material (although any other mass could also be used). In 100 g of ascorbic acid, we have

   40.92 g C, 4.58 g H, and 54.50 g O.

2. We calculate the number of moles of each element:

   $$\text{Moles C} = (40.92 \text{ g C})\left(\frac{1 \text{ mol C}}{12.01 \text{ g C}}\right) = 3.407 \text{ mol C}$$

   $$\text{Moles H} = (4.58 \text{ g H})\left(\frac{1 \text{ mol H}}{1.008 \text{ g H}}\right) = 4.54 \text{ mol H}$$

   $$\text{Moles O} = (54.50 \text{ g O})\left(\frac{1 \text{ mol O}}{16.00 \text{ g O}}\right) = 3.406 \text{ mol O}$$

3. We determine the simplest whole-number ratio of moles by dividing each number of moles by the smallest number of moles:

   $$\text{C:}\ \frac{3.407}{3.406} = 1.000 \quad \text{H:}\ \frac{4.54}{3.406} = 1.33 \quad \text{O:}\ \frac{3.406}{3.406} = 1.000$$

   The ratio for H is too far from 1 to attribute the difference to experimental error; in fact, it is quite close to $1\frac{1}{3}$. This suggests we should multiply the ratios by 3 to obtain whole numbers:

   $$\text{C:H:O} = 3(1:1.33:1) = 3:4:3$$

   Thus, the empirical formula is

   $$C_3H_4O_3$$

Check It is reassuring that the subscripts are moderate-size whole numbers. Also, calculating the percentage composition of C_3H_8O gives values very close to the original percentages.

PRACTICE EXERCISE

A 5.325-g sample of methyl benzoate, a compound used in the manufacture of perfumes, contains 3.758 g of carbon, 0.316 g of hydrogen, and 1.251 g of oxygen. What is the empirical formula of this substance?

Answer: C_4H_4O

Molecular Formulas from Empirical Formulas

We can obtain a molecular formula for any compound from its empirical formula if we know either the molecular weight or the molar mass of the compound. *The subscripts in the molecular formula of a substance are always whole-number multiples of the subscripts in its empirical formula.* ∞ (Section 2.6) This multiple can be found by dividing the molecular weight by the empirical formula weight:

$$\text{Whole-number multiple} = \frac{\text{molecular weight}}{\text{empirical formula weight}} \qquad [3.11]$$

In Sample Exercise 3.13, for example, the empirical formula of ascorbic acid was determined to be $C_3H_4O_3$. This means the empirical formula weight is $3(12.0 \text{ amu}) + 4(1.0 \text{ amu}) + 3(16.0 \text{ amu}) = 88.0$ amu. The experimentally determined molecular weight is 176 amu. Thus, we find the whole-number multiple that converts the empirical formula to the molecular formula by dividing:

$$\text{Whole-number multiple} = \frac{\text{molecular weight}}{\text{empirical formula weight}} = \frac{176 \text{ amu}}{88.0 \text{ amu}} = 2$$

Consequently, we multiply the subscripts in the empirical formula by this multiple, giving the molecular formula: $C_6H_8O_6$.

SAMPLE EXERCISE 3.14   **Determining a Molecular Formula**

Mesitylene, a hydrocarbon found in crude oil, has an empirical formula of C_3H_4 and an experimentally determined molecular weight of 121 amu. What is its molecular formula?

SOLUTION

Analyze We are given an empirical formula and a molecular weight and asked to determine a molecular formula.

Plan The subscripts in a compound's molecular formula are whole-number multiples of the subscripts in its empirical formula. We find the appropriate multiple by using Equation 3.11.

Solve The formula weight of the empirical formula C_3H_4 is

$$3(12.0 \text{ amu}) + 4(1.0 \text{ amu}) = 40.0 \text{ amu}$$

Next, we use this value in Equation 3.11:

$$\text{Whole-number multiple} = \frac{\text{molecular weight}}{\text{empirical formula weight}} = \frac{121}{40.0} = 3.02$$

Only whole-number ratios make physical sense because molecules contain whole atoms. The 3.02 in this case could result from a small experimental error in the molecular weight. We therefore multiply each subscript in the empirical formula by 3 to give the molecular formula: C_9H_{12}.

Check We can have confidence in the result because dividing molecular weight by empirical formula weight yields nearly a whole number.

PRACTICE EXERCISE

Ethylene glycol, used in automobile antifreeze, is 38.7% C, 9.7% H, and 51.6% O by mass. Its molar mass is 62.1 g/mol. **(a)** What is the empirical formula of ethylene glycol? **(b)** What is its molecular formula?

Answers: **(a)** CH_3O, **(b)** $C_2H_6O_2$

Combustion Analysis

One technique for determining empirical formulas in the laboratory is *combustion analysis*, commonly used for compounds containing principally carbon and hydrogen.

When a compound containing carbon and hydrogen is completely combusted in an apparatus such as that shown in ▶ **FIGURE 3.14**, the carbon is converted to CO_2 and the hydrogen is converted to H_2O. ∞ (Section 3.2) The amounts of CO_2 and H_2O produced are determined by measuring the mass increase in the CO_2 and H_2O absorbers. From the masses of CO_2 and H_2O we can calculate the number of moles of C and H in the original sample and thereby the empirical formula. If a third element is present in the compound, its mass can be determined by subtracting the measured masses of C and H from the original sample mass.

Sample combusted, producing CO_2 and H_2O

H_2O and CO_2 are trapped in separate absorbers

$O_2 \rightarrow$ Sample

Furnace H_2O absorber CO_2 absorber

Mass gained by each absorber corresponds to mass of CO_2 or H_2O produced

▲ **FIGURE 3.14 Apparatus for combustion analysis.**

SAMPLE EXERCISE 3.15   Determining an Empirical Formula by Combustion Analysis

Isopropyl alcohol, sold as rubbing alcohol, is composed of C, H, and O. Combustion of 0.255 g of isopropyl alcohol produces 0.561 g of CO_2 and 0.306 g of H_2O. Determine the empirical formula of isopropyl alcohol.

SOLUTION

Analyze We are told that isopropyl alcohol contains C, H, and O atoms and given the quantities of CO_2 and H_2O produced when a given quantity of the alcohol is combusted. We must determine the empirical formula for isopropyl alcohol, a task that requires us to calculate the number of moles of C, H, and O in the sample.

Plan We can use the mole concept to calculate grams of C in the CO_2 and grams of H in the H_2O. These masses are the masses of C and H in the alcohol before combustion. The mass of O in the compound equals the mass of the original sample minus the sum of the C and H masses. Once we have the C, H, and O masses, we can proceed as in Sample Exercise 3.13.

Solve

To calculate the mass of C from the measured mass of CO_2, we first use the molar mass of CO_2, 44.0 g/mol, to convert grams of CO_2 to moles of CO_2. Because each CO_2 molecule has only one C atom, there is 1 mol of C atoms per mole of CO_2 molecules. This fact allows us to convert moles of CO_2 to moles of C. Finally, we use the molar mass of C, 12.0 g, to convert moles of C to grams of C:

$$\text{Grams C} = (0.561 \text{ g CO}_2)\left(\frac{1 \text{ mol CO}_2}{44.0 \text{ g CO}_2}\right)\left(\frac{1 \text{ mol C}}{1 \text{ mol CO}_2}\right)\left(\frac{12.0 \text{ g C}}{1 \text{ mol C}}\right) = 0.153 \text{ g C}$$

The calculation for determining H mass from H_2O mass is similar, although we must remember that there are 2 mol of H atoms per 1 mol of H_2O molecules:

$$\text{Grams H} = (0.306 \text{ g H}_2\text{O})\left(\frac{1 \text{ mol H}_2\text{O}}{18.0 \text{ g H}_2\text{O}}\right)\left(\frac{2 \text{ mol H}}{1 \text{ mol H}_2\text{O}}\right)\left(\frac{1.01 \text{ g H}}{1 \text{ mol H}}\right) = 0.0343 \text{ g H}$$

The mass of the sample, 0.255 g, is the sum of the masses of C, H, and O. Thus, the O mass is

$$\text{Mass of O} = \text{mass of sample} - (\text{mass of C} + \text{mass of H})$$
$$= 0.255 \text{ g} - (0.153 \text{ g} + 0.0343 \text{ g}) = 0.068 \text{ g O}$$

The number of moles of C, H, and O in the sample is therefore

$$\text{Moles C} = (0.153 \text{ g C})\left(\frac{1 \text{ mol C}}{12.0 \text{ g C}}\right) = 0.0128 \text{ mol C}$$

$$\text{Moles H} = (0.0343 \text{ g H})\left(\frac{1 \text{ mol H}}{1.01 \text{ g H}}\right) = 0.0340 \text{ mol H}$$

$$\text{Moles O} = (0.068 \text{ g O})\left(\frac{1 \text{ mol O}}{16.0 \text{ g O}}\right) = 0.0043 \text{ mol O}$$

To find the empirical formula, we must compare the relative number of moles of each element in the sample. We determine relative number of moles by dividing each of our calculated number of moles by the smallest number:

$$\text{C:} \frac{0.0128}{0.0043} = 3.0 \quad \text{H:} \frac{0.0340}{0.0043} = 7.9 \quad \text{O:} \frac{0.0043}{0.0043} = 1.0$$

The first two numbers are very close to the whole numbers 3 and 8, giving the empirical formula

$$C_3H_8O.$$

Check The subscripts work out to be moderate-size whole numbers, as expected.

PRACTICE EXERCISE

(a) Caproic acid, responsible for the odor of dirty socks, is composed of C, H, and O atoms. Combustion of a 0.225-g sample of this compound produces 0.512 g CO_2 and 0.209 g H_2O. What is the empirical formula of caproic acid? **(b)** Caproic acid has a molar mass of 116 g/mol. What is its molecular formula?

Answers: **(a)** C_3H_6O, **(b)** $C_6H_{12}O_2$

 GIVE IT SOME THOUGHT

In Sample Exercise 3.15, how do you explain the fact that the values in our calculated C:H:O ratio are 3.0:7.9:1.0 rather than exact integers 3:8:1?

3.6 | QUANTITATIVE INFORMATION FROM BALANCED EQUATIONS

The coefficients in a chemical equation represent the relative numbers of molecules in a reaction. The mole concept allows us to convert this information to the masses of the substances in the reaction. For instance, the coefficients in the balanced equation

$$2\ H_2(g) + O_2(g) \longrightarrow 2\ H_2O(l) \qquad [3.12]$$

indicate that two molecules of H_2 react with one molecule of O_2 to form two molecules of H_2O. It follows that the relative numbers of moles are identical to the relative numbers of molecules:

$2\ H_2(g)$	$+$	$O_2(g)$	$\longrightarrow$	$2\ H_2O(l)$
2 molecules		1 molecule		2 molecules
$2(6.02 \times 10^{23}$ molecules)		$1(6.02 \times 10^{23}$ molecules)		$2(6.02 \times 10^{23}$ molecules)
2 mol		1 mol		2 mol

We can generalize this observation to all balanced chemical equations: *The coefficients in a balanced chemical equation indicate both the relative numbers of molecules (or formula units) in the reaction and the relative numbers of moles.* ▼ **FIGURE 3.15** shows how this result corresponds to the law of conservation of mass.

The quantities 2 mol H_2, 1 mol O_2, and 2 mol H_2O given by the coefficients in Equation 3.12 are called *stoichiometrically equivalent quantities*. The relationship between these quantities can be represented as

$$2\ \text{mol}\ H_2 \approx 1\ \text{mol}\ O_2 \approx 2\ \text{mol}\ H_2O$$

where the $\approx$ symbol means "is stoichiometrically equivalent to." Stoichiometric relations such as these can be used to convert between quantities of reactants and products

▶ **FIGURE 3.15 Interpreting a balanced chemical equation quantitatively.**

in a chemical reaction. For example, the number of moles of H_2O produced from 1.57 mol of O_2 is

$$\text{Moles } H_2O = (1.57 \text{ mol } O_2)\left(\frac{2 \text{ mol } H_2O}{1 \text{ mol } O_2}\right) = 3.14 \text{ mol } H_2O$$

 GIVE IT SOME THOUGHT

When 1.57 mol O_2 reacts with H_2 to form H_2O, how many moles of H_2 are consumed in the process?

As an additional example, consider the combustion of butane (C_4H_{10}), the fuel in disposable general-purpose lighters:

$$2\,C_4H_{10}(l) + 13\,O_2(g) \longrightarrow 8\,CO_2(g) + 10\,H_2O(g) \qquad [3.13]$$

Let's calculate the mass of CO_2 produced when 1.00 g of C_4H_{10} is burned. The coefficients in Equation 3.13 tell us how the amount of C_4H_{10} consumed is related to the amount of CO_2 produced: 2 mol C_4H_{10} ≏ 8 mol CO_2. To use this stoichiometric relationship, we must convert grams of C_4H_{10} to moles using the molar mass of C_4H_{10}, 58.0 g/mol:

$$\text{Moles } C_4H_{10} = (1.00 \text{ g } C_4H_{10})\left(\frac{1 \text{ mol } C_4H_{10}}{58.0 \text{ g } C_4H_{10}}\right)$$

$$= 1.72 \times 10^{-2} \text{ mol } C_4H_{10}$$

We then use the stoichiometric factor from the balanced equation to calculate moles of CO_2:

$$\text{Moles } CO_2 = (1.72 \times 10^{-2} \text{ mol } C_4H_{10})\left(\frac{8 \text{ mol } CO_2}{2 \text{ mol } C_4H_{10}}\right)$$

$$= 6.88 \times 10^{-2} \text{ mol } CO_2$$

Finally, we use the molar mass of CO_2, 44.0 g/mol, to calculate the CO_2 mass in grams:

$$\text{Grams } CO_2 = (6.88 \times 10^{-2} \text{ mol } CO_2)\left(\frac{44.0 \text{ g } CO_2}{1 \text{ mol } CO_2}\right)$$

$$= 3.03 \text{ g } CO_2$$

This conversion sequence involves three steps, as illustrated in ▼ **FIGURE 3.16**. These three conversions can be combined in a single equation:

$$\text{Grams } CO_2 = (1.00 \text{ g } C_4H_{10})\left(\frac{1 \text{ mol } C_4H_{10}}{58.0 \text{ g } C_4H_{10}}\right)\left(\frac{8 \text{ mol } CO_2}{2 \text{ mol } C_4H_{10}}\right)\left(\frac{44.0 \text{ g } CO_2}{1 \text{ mol } CO_2}\right)$$

$$= 3.03 \text{ g } CO_2$$

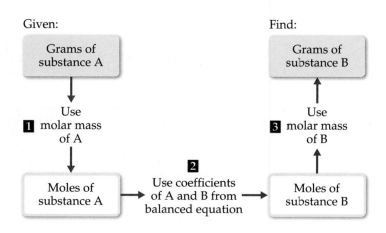

◀ **FIGURE 3.16   Procedure for calculating amounts of reactants consumed or products formed in a reaction.** The number of grams of a reactant consumed or product formed can be calculated in three steps, starting with the number of grams of any reactant or product. Notice how molar masses and the coefficients in the balanced equation are used.

To calculate the amount of O_2 consumed in the reaction of Equation 3.13, we again rely on the coefficients in the balanced equation for our stoichiometric factor: 2 mol C_4H_{10} ≏ 13 mol O_2:

$$\text{Grams } O_2 = (1.00 \text{ g } C_4H_{10})\left(\frac{1 \text{ mol } C_4H_{10}}{58.0 \text{ g } C_4H_{10}}\right)\left(\frac{13 \text{ mol } O_2}{2 \text{ mol } C_4H_{10}}\right)\left(\frac{32.0 \text{ g } O_2}{1 \text{ mol } O_2}\right)$$

$$= 3.59 \text{ g } O_2$$

▲ GIVE IT SOME THOUGHT

If 20.00 g of a compound reacts completely with 30.00 g of another compound in a combination reaction, how many grams of product are formed?

SAMPLE EXERCISE 3.16	Calculating Amounts of Reactants and Products

Determine how many grams of water are produced in the oxidation of 1.00 g of glucose, $C_6H_{12}O_6$:

$$C_6H_{12}O_6(s) + 6 O_2(g) \longrightarrow 6 CO_2(g) + 6 H_2O(l)$$

SOLUTION

Analyze We are given the mass of a reactant and must determine the mass of a product in the given reaction.

Plan The general strategy, as outlined in Figure 3.16, requires three steps:
1. Convert grams of $C_6H_{12}O_6$ to moles using the molar mass of $C_6H_{12}O_6$.
2. Convert moles of $C_6H_{12}O_6$ to moles of H_2O using the stoichiometric relationship 1 mol $C_6H_{12}O_6$ ≏ 6 mol H_2O.
3. Convert moles of H_2O to grams using the molar mass of H_2O.

Solve

1. $\text{Moles } C_6H_{12}O_6 = (1.00 \text{ g } C_6H_{12}O_6)\left(\frac{1 \text{ mol } C_6H_{12}O_6}{180.0 \text{ g } C_6H_{12}O_6}\right)$

2. $\text{Moles } H_2O = (1.00 \text{ g } C_6H_{12}O_6)\left(\frac{1 \text{ mol } C_6H_{12}O_6}{180.0 \text{ g } C_6H_{12}O_6}\right)\left(\frac{6 \text{ mol } H_2O}{1 \text{ mol } C_6H_{12}O_6}\right)$

3. $\text{Grams } H_2O = (1.00 \text{ g } C_6H_{12}O_6)\left(\frac{1 \text{ mol } C_6H_{12}O_6}{180.0 \text{ g } C_6H_{12}O_6}\right)\left(\frac{6 \text{ mol } H_2O}{1 \text{ mol } C_6H_{12}O_6}\right)\left(\frac{18.0 \text{ g } H_2O}{1 \text{ mol } H_2O}\right)$

    $= 0.600 \text{ g } H_2O$

The steps can be summarized in a diagram like that in Figure 3.16:

Check We can check how reasonable our result is by doing a ballpark estimate of the mass of H_2O. Because the molar mass of glucose is 180 g/mol, 1 gram of glucose equals 1/180 mol. Because one mole of glucose yields 6 mol H_2O, we would have 6/180 = 1/30 mol H_2O. The molar mass of water is 18 g/mol, so we have 1/30 × 18 = 6/10 = 0.6 g of H_2O, which agrees with the full calculation. The units, grams H_2O, are correct. The initial data had three significant figures, so three significant figures for the answer is correct.

Comment An average adult ingests 2 L of water daily and eliminates 2.4 L. The "extra" 0.4 L is produced in the metabolism of foodstuffs, such as oxidation of glucose. The desert rat (kangaroo rat), on the other hand, apparently never drinks water. It survives on its metabolic water.

PRACTICE EXERCISE

Decomposition of $KClO_3$ is sometimes used to prepare small amounts of O_2 in the laboratory: $2 KClO_3(s) \longrightarrow 2 KCl(s) + 3 O_2(g)$. How many grams of O_2 can be prepared from 4.50 g of $KClO_3$?

Answer: 1.77 g

SAMPLE EXERCISE 3.17	Calculating Amounts of Reactants and Products

Solid lithium hydroxide is used in space vehicles to remove the carbon dioxide gas exhaled by astronauts. The hydroxide reacts with the carbon dioxide to form solid lithium carbonate and liquid water. How many grams of carbon dioxide can be absorbed by 1.00 g of lithium hydroxide?

SOLUTION

Analyze We are given a verbal description of a reaction and asked to calculate the number of grams of one reactant that reacts with 1.00 g of another.

Plan The verbal description of the reaction can be used to write a balanced equation:

$$2 LiOH(s) + CO_2(g) \longrightarrow Li_2CO_3(s) + H_2O(l)$$

We are given the mass in grams of LiOH and asked to calculate the mass in grams of CO_2. We can accomplish this task by using the three conversion steps in Figure 3.16. The conversion of step 1 requires the molar mass of LiOH ($6.94 + 16.00 + 1.01 = 23.95$ g/mol). The conversion of step 2 is based on a stoichiometric relationship from the balanced chemical equation: $2 \text{ mol LiOH} \cong 1 \text{ mol } CO_2$. For the step 3 conversion, we use the molar mass of CO_2: $12.01 + 2(16.00) = 44.01$ g/mol.

Solve

$$(1.00 \text{ g LiOH})\left(\frac{1 \text{ mol LiOH}}{23.95 \text{ g LiOH}}\right)\left(\frac{1 \text{ mol } CO_2}{2 \text{ mol LiOH}}\right)\left(\frac{44.01 \text{ g } CO_2}{1 \text{ mol } CO_2}\right) = 0.919 \text{ g } CO_2$$

Check Notice that 23.95 g LiOH/mol $\approx$ 24 g LiOH/mol, that 24 g LiOH/mol $\times$ 2 mol LiOH = 48 g LiOH, and (44 g CO_2/mol)/(48 g LiOH) is slightly less than 1. Thus, the magnitude of our answer, 0.919 g CO_2, is reasonable based on the amount of starting LiOH. The significant figures and units are also appropriate.

PRACTICE EXERCISE

Propane, C_3H_8 (Figure 3.8), is a common fuel used for cooking and home heating. What mass of O_2 is consumed in the combustion of 1.00 g of propane?

Answer: 3.64 g

3.7 | LIMITING REACTANTS

Suppose you wish to make several sandwiches using one slice of cheese and two slices of bread for each. Using Bd = bread, Ch = cheese, and Bd_2Ch = sandwich, the recipe for making a sandwich can be represented like a chemical equation:

$$2 Bd + Ch \longrightarrow Bd_2Ch$$

If you have 10 slices of bread and 7 slices of cheese, you can make only 5 sandwiches and will have 2 slices of cheese left over. The amount of bread available limits the number of sandwiches.

An analogous situation occurs in chemical reactions when one reactant is used up before the others. The reaction stops as soon as any reactant is totally consumed, leaving the excess reactants as leftovers. Suppose, for example, we have a mixture of 10 mol H_2 and 7 mol O_2, which react to form water:

$$2 H_2(g) + O_2(g) \longrightarrow 2 H_2O(g)$$

Because 2 mol $H_2 \cong 1$ mol O_2, the number of moles of O_2 needed to react with all the H_2 is

$$\text{Moles } O_2 = (10 \text{ mol } H_2)\left(\frac{1 \text{ mol } O_2}{2 \text{ mol } H_2}\right) = 5 \text{ mol } O_2$$

GO FIGURE

If O_2 had been the limiting reactant, how many moles of H_2O would have formed?

Before reaction

After reaction

10 H_2 and 7 O_2

10 H_2O and 2 O_2 (no H_2 molecules)

▲ FIGURE 3.17 **Limiting reactant.** Because H_2 is completely consumed, it is the limiting reactant. Because some O_2 is left over after the reaction is complete, O_2 is the excess reactant. The amount of H_2O formed depends on the amount of limiting reactant, H_2.

Because 7 mol O_2 is available at the start of the reaction, 7 mol O_2 − 5 mol O_2 = 2 mol O_2 is present when all the H_2 is consumed.

The reactant that is completely consumed in a reaction is called the **limiting reactant** because it determines, or limits, the amount of product formed. The other reactants are sometimes called *excess reactants*. In our example, shown in ◄ FIGURE 3.17, H_2 is the limiting reactant, which means that once all the H_2 has been consumed, the reaction stops. The excess reactant is O_2; some is left over when the reaction stops.

There are no restrictions on the starting amounts of reactants in any reaction. Indeed, many reactions are carried out using an excess of one reactant. The quantities of reactants consumed and products formed, however, are restricted by the quantity of the limiting reactant. For example, when a combustion reaction takes place in the open air, oxygen is plentiful and is therefore the excess reactant. If you run out of gasoline while driving, the car stops because the gasoline is the limiting reactant in the combustion reaction that moves the car.

Before we leave the example illustrated in Figure 3.17, let's summarize the data:

	2 $H_2(g)$	+	$O_2(g)$	⟶	2 $H_2O(g)$
Initial quantities:	10 mol		7 mol		0 mol
Change (reaction):	−10 mol		−5 mol		+10 mol
Final quantities:	0 mol		2 mol		10 mol

The second line in the table (Change) summarizes the amounts of reactants consumed (where this consumption is indicated by the minus signs) and the amount of the product formed (indicated by the plus sign). These quantities are restricted by the quantity of the limiting reactant and depend on the coefficients in the balanced equation. The mole ratio H_2:O_2:H_2O = 10:5:10 conforms to the ratio of the coefficients in the balanced equation, 2:1:2. The final quantities, which depend on the initial quantities and their changes, are found by adding the initial quantity and change quantity for each column. None of the limiting reactant (H_2) remains at the end of the reaction. What remains is 2 mol O_2 (excess reactant) and 10 mol H_2O (product).

SAMPLE EXERCISE 3.18 | **Calculating the Amount of Product Formed from a Limiting Reactant**

The most important commercial process for converting N_2 from the air into nitrogen-containing compounds is based on the reaction of N_2 and H_2 to form ammonia (NH_3):

$$N_2(g) + 3 H_2(g) \longrightarrow 2 NH_3(g)$$

How many moles of NH_3 can be formed from 3.0 mol of N_2 and 6.0 mol of H_2?

SOLUTION

Analyze We are asked to calculate the number of moles of product, NH_3, given the quantities of each reactant, N_2 and H_2, available in a reaction. This is a limiting reactant problem.

Plan If we assume one reactant is completely consumed, we can calculate how much of the second reactant is needed. By comparing the calculated quantity of the second reactant with the amount available, we can determine which reactant is limiting. We then proceed with the calculation, using the quantity of the limiting reactant.

Solve

The number of moles of H_2 needed for complete consumption of 3.0 mol of N_2 is:

$$\text{Moles } H_2 = (3.0 \text{ mol } N_2)\left(\frac{3 \text{ mol } H_2}{1 \text{ mol } N_2}\right) = 9.0 \text{ mol } H_2$$

Because only 6.0 mol H_2 is available, we will run out of H_2 before the N_2 is gone, which tells us that H_2 is the limiting reactant. Therefore, we use the quantity of H_2 to calculate the quantity of NH_3 produced:

$$\text{Moles } NH_3 = (6.0 \text{ mol } H_2)\left(\frac{2 \text{ mol } NH_3}{3 \text{ mol } H_2}\right) = 4.0 \text{ mol } NH_3$$

Comment The table on the right summarizes this example:

	N₂(g)	+	3 H₂(g)	⟶	2 NH₃(g)
Initial quantities:	3.0 mol		6.0 mol		0 mol
Change (reaction):	−2.0 mol		−6.0 mol		+4.0 mol
Final quantities:	1.0 mol		0 mol		4.0 mol

Notice that we can calculate not only the number of moles of NH_3 formed but also the number of moles of each reactant remaining after the reaction. Notice also that although the initial number of moles of H_2 is greater than the final number of moles of N_2, the H_2 is nevertheless the limiting reactant because of its larger coefficient in the balanced equation.

Check The Change row of the summary table shows that the mole ratio of reactants consumed and product formed, 2:6:4, conforms to the coefficients in the balanced equation, 1:3:2. Because H_2 is the limiting reactant, it is completely consumed in the reaction, leaving 0 mol at the end. Because 6.0 mol H_2 has two significant figures, our answer has two significant figures.

PRACTICE EXERCISE

(a) When 1.50 mol of Al and 3.00 mol of Cl_2 combine in the reaction $2\,Al(s) + 3\,Cl_2(g) \longrightarrow 2\,AlCl_3(s)$, which is the limiting reactant? **(b)** How many moles of $AlCl_3$ are formed? **(c)** How many moles of the excess reactant remain at the end of the reaction?

Answers: **(a)** Al, **(b)** 1.50 mol, **(c)** 0.75 mol Cl_2

SAMPLE EXERCISE 3.19 **Calculating the Amount of Product Formed from a Limiting Reactant**

The reaction

$$2\,H_2(g) + O_2(g) \longrightarrow 2\,H_2O(g)$$

is used to produce electricity in a hydrogen fuel cell. Suppose a fuel cell contains 150 g of $H_2(g)$ and 1500 g of $O_2(g)$ (each measured to two significant figures). How many grams of water can form?

SOLUTION

Analyze We are asked to calculate the amount of a product, given the amounts of two reactants, so this is a limiting reactant problem.

Plan To identify the limiting reactant, we can calculate the number of moles of each reactant and compare their ratio with the ratio of coefficients in the balanced equation. We then use the quantity of the limiting reactant to calculate the mass of water that forms.

Solve From the balanced equation, we have the stoichiometric relations

$$2\text{ mol }H_2 \backsimeq 1\text{ mol }O_2 \backsimeq 2\text{ mol }H_2O$$

Using the molar mass of each substance, we calculate the number of moles of each reactant:

$$\text{Moles }H_2 = (150\text{ g }H_2)\left(\frac{1\text{ mol }H_2}{2.00\text{ g }H_2}\right) = 75\text{ mol }H_2$$

$$\text{Moles }O_2 = (1500\text{ g }O_2)\left(\frac{1\text{ mol }O_2}{32.0\text{ g }O_2}\right) = 47\text{ mol }O_2$$

The coefficients in the balanced equation indicate that the reaction requires 2 mol of H_2 for every 1 mol of O_2. Therefore, for all the O_2 to completely react, we would need $2 \times 47 = 94$ mol of H_2. Since there are only 75 mol of H_2, all of the O_2 cannot react, so it is the excess reactant, and H_2 must be the limiting reactant. (Notice that the limiting reactant is not merely the one present in the lowest amount.)

We use the given quantity of H_2 (the limiting reactant) to calculate the quantity of water formed. We could begin this calculation with the given H_2 mass, 150 g, but we can save a step by starting with the moles of H_2, 75 mol, we just calculated:

$$\text{Grams }H_2O = (75\text{ mol }H_2)\left(\frac{2\text{ mol }H_2O}{2\text{ mol }H_2}\right)\left(\frac{18.0\text{ g }H_2O}{1\text{ mol }H_2O}\right)$$

$$= 1400\text{ g }H_2O = 1.4 \times 10^2\text{ g }H_2O \text{ (two significant figures)}$$

Check The magnitude of the answer seems reasonable based on the amounts of the reactants. The units are correct, and the number of significant figures (two) corresponds to those in the values given in the problem statement.

Comment The quantity of the limiting reactant, H_2, can also be used to determine the quantity of O_2 used:

$$\text{Grams } O_2 = (75 \text{ mol } H_2)\left(\frac{1 \text{ mol } O_2}{2 \text{ mol } H_2}\right)\left(\frac{32.0 \text{ g } O_2}{1 \text{ mol } O_2}\right)$$

$$= 1.2 \times 10^3 \text{ g } H_2O$$

The mass of O_2 remaining at the end of the reaction equals the starting amount minus the amount consumed:

$$1500 \text{ g} - 1200 \text{ g} = 300 \text{ g.}$$

PRACTICE EXERCISE

When a 2.00-g strip of zinc metal is placed in an aqueous solution containing 2.50 g of silver nitrate, the reaction is

$$Zn(s) + 2\,AgNO_3(aq) \longrightarrow 2\,Ag(s) + Zn(NO_3)_2(aq)$$

(a) Which reactant is limiting? **(b)** How many grams of Ag form? **(c)** How many grams of $Zn(NO_3)_2$ form? **(d)** How many grams of the excess reactant are left at the end of the reaction?
Answers: **(a)** $AgNO_3$, **(b)** 1.59 g, **(c)** 1.39 g, **(d)** 1.52 g Zn

Theoretical Yields

The quantity of product calculated to form when all of a limiting reactant is consumed is called the **theoretical yield**. The amount of product actually obtained, called the *actual yield,* is almost always less than (and can never be greater than) the theoretical yield. There are many reasons for this difference. Part of the reactants may not react, for example, or they may react in a way different from that desired (side reactions). In addition, it is not always possible to recover all of the product from the reaction mixture. The **percent yield** of a reaction relates actual and theoretical yields:

$$\text{Percent yield} = \frac{\text{actual yield}}{\text{theoretical yield}} \times 100\% \qquad [3.14]$$

SAMPLE EXERCISE 3.20 | **Calculating Theoretical Yield and Percent Yield**

Adipic acid, $H_2C_6H_8O_4$, used to produce nylon, is made commercially by a reaction between cyclohexane (C_6H_{12}) and O_2:

$$2\,C_6H_{12}(l) + 5\,O_2(g) \longrightarrow 2\,H_2C_6H_8O_4(l) + 2\,H_2O(g)$$

(a) Assume that you carry out this reaction with 25.0 g of cyclohexane and that cyclohexane is the limiting reactant. What is the theoretical yield of adipic acid? **(b)** If you obtain 33.5 g of adipic acid, what is the percent yield for the reaction?

SOLUTION

Analyze We are given a chemical equation and the quantity of the limiting reactant (25.0 g of C_6H_{12}). We are asked to calculate the theoretical yield of a product $H_2C_6H_8O_4$ and the percent yield if only 33.5 g of product is obtained.

Plan

(a) The theoretical yield, which is the calculated quantity of adipic acid formed, can be calculated using the sequence of conversions shown in Figure 3.16.

(b) The percent yield is calculated by using Equation 3.14 to compare the given actual yield (33.5 g) with the theoretical yield.

Solve

(a) The theoretical yield is

$$\text{Grams } H_2C_6H_8O_4 = (25.0 \text{ g } C_6H_{12})\left(\frac{1 \text{ mol } C_6H_{12}}{84.0 \text{ g } C_6H_{12}}\right)\left(\frac{2 \text{ mol } H_2C_6H_8O_4}{2 \text{ mol } C_6H_{12}}\right)\left(\frac{146.0 \text{ g } H_2C_6H_8O_4}{1 \text{ mol } H_2C_6H_8O_4}\right)$$

$$= 43.5 \text{ g } H_2C_6H_8O_4$$

(b) Percent yield $= \dfrac{\text{actual yield}}{\text{theoretical yield}} \times 100\% = \dfrac{33.5\text{ g}}{43.5\text{ g}} \times 100\% = 77.0\%$

Check We can check our answer in (a) by doing a ballpark calculation. From the balanced equation we know that each mole of cyclohexane gives 1 mol adipic acid. We have $25/84 \approx 25/75 = 0.3$ mol hexane, so we expect 0.3 mol adipic acid, which equals about $0.3 \times 150 = 45$ g, about the same magnitude as the 43.5 g obtained in the more detailed calculation given previously. In addition, our answer has the appropriate units and significant figures. In (b) the answer is less than 100%, as it must be from the definition of percent yield.

PRACTICE EXERCISE

Imagine you are working on ways to improve the process by which iron ore containing Fe_2O_3 is converted into iron:

$$Fe_2O_3(s) + 3\,CO(g) \longrightarrow 2\,Fe(s) + 3\,CO_2(g)$$

(a) If you start with 150 g of Fe_2O_3 as the limiting reactant, what is the theoretical yield of Fe?
(b) If your actual yield is 87.9 g, what is the percent yield?
Answers: **(a)** 105 g Fe, **(b)** 83.7%

STRATEGIES IN CHEMISTRY

HOW TO TAKE A TEST

At about this time in your study of chemistry, you are likely to face your first hour-long examination. The best way to prepare is to study, do homework diligently, and get help from the instructor on any material that is unclear or confusing. (See the advice for learning and studying chemistry presented in the preface of the book.) We present here some general guidelines for taking tests.

Depending on the nature of your course, the exam could consist of a variety of different types of questions.

1. **Multiple-choice questions** In large-enrollment courses, the most common kind of test question is the multiple-choice question. You are given the problem and presented with four or five answers from which you must select the correct one. The first thing to realize is that the instructor has written the question so that at first glance all the answers appear to be correct. (There would be little point in offering choices you could tell were wrong even without knowing much about the concept being tested.) Thus, you should not jump to the conclusion that because one of the choices looks correct, it must be correct.

If a multiple-choice question involves a calculation, do the calculation, check your work, and *only then* compare your answer with the choices. If you find a match, you have probably found the correct answer. Keep in mind, though, that your instructor has anticipated the most common errors you might make in solving a given problem and has probably listed the incorrect answers resulting from those errors. Always double-check your reasoning and use dimensional analysis to arrive at the correct numeric answer and the correct units.

In multiple-choice questions that do not involve calculations, if you are not sure of the correct choice, eliminate all the choices you know for sure to be incorrect. The reasoning you use in eliminating incorrect choices will help you in reasoning about which of the remaining choices is correct.

2. **Calculations in which you must show your work** In questions of this kind, you may receive partial credit even if you do not arrive at the correct answer, depending on whether the instructor can follow your line of reasoning. It is important, therefore, to be neat and organized in your calculations. Pay particular attention to what information is given and to what your unknown is. Think about how you can get from the given information to your unknown.

You may want to write a few words or a diagram on the test paper to indicate your approach. Then write out your calculations as neatly as you can. Show the units for every number you write down, and use dimensional analysis as much as you can, showing how units cancel.

3. **Questions requiring drawings** Questions of this kind will come later in the course, but it is useful to talk about them here. (You should review this box before each exam to remind yourself of good exam-taking practices.) Be sure to label your drawing as completely as possible.

4. **Other types of questions** Other exam questions you might encounter include true-false questions and ones in which you are given a list and asked to indicate which members of the list match some criterion given in the question. Often students answer such questions incorrectly because, in their haste, they misunderstand the nature of the question. Whatever the form of the question, ask yourself this: What is the instructor testing here? What material am I supposed to know that this question covers?

Finally, if you find that you simply do not understand how to arrive at a reasoned response to a question, do not linger over the question. Put a check next to it and go on to the next one. If time permits, you can come back to the unanswered questions, but lingering over a question when nothing is coming to mind is wasting time you may need to finish the exam.

CHAPTER SUMMARY AND KEY TERMS

INTRODUCTION AND SECTION 3.1 The study of the quantitative relationships between chemical formulas and chemical equations is known as **stoichiometry**. One of the important concepts of stoichiometry is the law of conservation of mass, which states that the total mass of the products of a chemical reaction is the same as the total mass of the reactants. The same numbers of atoms of each type are present before and after a chemical reaction. A balanced **chemical equation** shows equal numbers of atoms of each element on each side of the equation. Equations are balanced by placing coefficients in front of the chemical formulas for the **reactants** and **products** of a reaction, *not* by changing the subscripts in chemical formulas.

SECTION 3.2 Among the reaction types described in this chapter are (1) **combination reactions**, in which two reactants combine to form one product; (2) **decomposition reactions**, in which a single reactant forms two or more products; and (3) **combustion reactions** in oxygen, in which a hydrocarbon or related compound reacts with O_2 to form CO_2 and H_2O.

SECTION 3.3 Much quantitative information can be determined from chemical formulas and balanced chemical equations by using atomic weights. The **formula weight** of a compound equals the sum of the atomic weights of the atoms in its formula. If the formula is a molecular formula, the formula weight is also called the **molecular weight**. Atomic weights and formula weights can be used to determine the elemental composition of a compound.

SECTION 3.4 A mole of any substance is **Avogadro's number** (6.02×10^{23}) of formula units of that substance. The mass of a **mole** of atoms, molecules, or ions (the **molar mass**) equals the formula weight of that material expressed in grams. The mass of one molecule of H_2O, for example, is 18 amu, so the mass of 1 mol of H_2O is 18 g. That is, the molar mass of H_2O is 18 g/mol.

SECTION 3.5 The empirical formula of any substance can be determined from its percent composition by calculating the relative number of moles of each atom in 100 g of the substance. If the substance is molecular in nature, its molecular formula can be determined from the empirical formula if the molecular weight is also known.

SECTIONS 3.6 AND 3.7 The mole concept can be used to calculate the relative quantities of reactants and products in chemical reactions. The coefficients in a balanced equation give the relative numbers of moles of the reactants and products. To calculate the number of grams of a product from the number of grams of a reactant, first convert grams of reactant to moles of reactant. Then use the coefficients in the balanced equation to convert the number of moles of reactant to moles of product. Finally, convert moles of product to grams of product.

A **limiting reactant** is completely consumed in a reaction. When it is used up, the reaction stops, thus limiting the quantities of products formed. The **theoretical yield** of a reaction is the quantity of product calculated to form when all of the limiting reactant reacts. The actual yield of a reaction is always less than the theoretical yield. The **percent yield** compares the actual and theoretical yields.

KEY SKILLS

- Balance chemical equations. (Section 3.1)
- Predict the products of simple combination, decomposition, and combustion reactions. (Section 3.2)
- Calculate formula weights. (Section 3.3)
- Convert grams to moles and moles to grams using molar masses. (Section 3.4)
- Convert number of molecules to moles and moles to number of molecules using Avogadro's number. (Section 3.4)
- Calculate the empirical and molecular formulas of a compound from percentage composition and molecular weight. (Section 3.5)
- Calculate amounts, in grams or moles, of reactants and products for a reaction. (Section 3.6)
- Calculate the percent yield of a reaction. (Section 3.7)

KEY EQUATIONS

- $$\% \text{ element} = \frac{\left(\begin{array}{c}\text{number of atoms}\\\text{of that element}\end{array}\right)\left(\begin{array}{c}\text{atomic weight}\\\text{of element}\end{array}\right)}{(\text{formula weight of compound})} \times 100\% \qquad [3.10]$$

  This is the formula to calculate the mass percentage of each element in a compound. The sum of all the percentages of all the elements in a compound should add up to 100%.

- $$\% \text{ yield} = \frac{(\text{actual yield})}{(\text{theoretical yield})} \times 100\% \qquad [3.14]$$

  This is the formula to calculate the percent yield of a reaction. The percent yield can never be more than 100%.

EXERCISES

VISUALIZING CONCEPTS

3.1 The reaction between reactant A (blue spheres) and reactant B (red spheres) is shown in the following diagram:

Based on this diagram, which equation best describes the reaction? [Section 3.1]

(a) $A_2 + B \longrightarrow A_2B$

(b) $A_2 + 4B \longrightarrow 2AB_2$

(c) $2A + B_4 \longrightarrow 2AB_2$

(d) $A + B_2 \longrightarrow AB_2$

3.2 Under appropriate experimental conditions, H_2 and CO undergo a combination reaction to form CH_3OH. The following drawing represents a sample of H_2. Make a corresponding drawing of the CO needed to react completely with the H_2. How did you arrive at the number of CO molecules in your drawing? [Section 3.2]

3.3 The following diagram represents the collection of elements formed by a decomposition reaction. (a) If the blue spheres represent N atoms and the red ones represent O atoms, what was the empirical formula of the original compound? (b) Could you draw a diagram representing the molecules of the compound that had been decomposed? Why or why not? [Section 3.2]

3.4 The following diagram represents the collection of CO_2 and H_2O molecules formed by complete combustion of a hydrocarbon. What is the empirical formula of the hydrocarbon? [Section 3.2]

3.5 Glycine, an amino acid used by organisms to make proteins, is represented by the following molecular model.

(a) Write its molecular formula.

(b) Determine its molar mass.

(c) Calculate the mass of 3 moles of glycine.

(d) Calculate the percent nitrogen by mass in glycine. [Sections 3.3 and 3.5]

3.6 The following diagram represents a high-temperature reaction between CH_4 and H_2O. Based on this reaction, how many moles of each product can be obtained starting with 4.0 mol CH_4? [Section 3.6]

3.7 Nitrogen (N_2) and hydrogen (H_2) react to form ammonia (NH_3). Consider the mixture of N_2 and H_2 shown in the accompanying diagram. The blue spheres represent N, and the white ones represent H. Draw a representation of the product mixture, assuming that the reaction goes to completion. How did you arrive at your representation? What is the limiting reactant in this case? [Section 3.7]

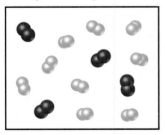

3.8 Nitrogen monoxide and oxygen react to form nitrogen dioxide. Consider the mixture of NO and O_2 shown in the accompanying diagram. The blue spheres represent N, and the red ones represent O. (a) Draw a representation of the product mixture, assuming that the reaction goes to completion. What is the limiting reactant in this case? (b) How many NO_2 molecules would you draw as products if the reaction had a percent yield of 75%? [Section 3.7]

BALANCING CHEMICAL EQUATIONS (section 3.1)

3.9 **(a)** What scientific principle or law is used in the process of balancing chemical equations? **(b)** In balancing equations, why should you not change subscripts in chemical formulas? **(c)** How would you write out liquid water, water vapor, aqueous sodium chloride, and solid sodium chloride in chemical equations?

3.10 **(a)** What is the difference between adding a subscript 2 to the end of the formula for CO to give CO_2 and adding a coefficient in front of the formula to give 2 CO? **(b)** Is the following chemical equation, as written, consistent with the law of conservation of mass?

$$3\ Mg(OH)_2(s) + 2\ H_3PO_4(aq) \longrightarrow$$
$$Mg_3(PO_4)_2(s) + 6\ H_2O(l)$$

Why or why not?

3.11 Balance the following equations:
(a) $CO(g) + O_2(g) \longrightarrow CO_2(g)$
(b) $N_2O_5(g) + H_2O(l) \longrightarrow HNO_3(aq)$
(c) $CH_4(g) + Cl_2(g) \longrightarrow CCl_4(l) + HCl(g)$
(d) $Al_4C_3(s) + H_2O(l) \longrightarrow Al(OH)_3(s) + CH_4(g)$
(e) $C_5H_{10}O_2(l) + O_2(g) \longrightarrow CO_2(g) + H_2O(g)$
(f) $Fe(OH)_3(s) + H_2SO_4(aq) \longrightarrow$
$$Fe_2(SO_4)_3(aq) + H_2O(l)$$
(g) $Mg_3N_2(s) + H_2SO_4(aq) \longrightarrow$
$$MgSO_4(aq) + (NH_4)_2SO_4(aq)$$

3.12 Balance the following equations:
(a) $Li(s) + N_2(g) \longrightarrow Li_3N(s)$
(b) $TiCl_4(l) + H_2O(l) \longrightarrow TiO_2(s) + HCl(aq)$
(c) $NH_4NO_3(s) \longrightarrow N_2(g) + O_2(g) + H_2O(g)$

(d) $Ca_3P_2(s) + H_2O(l) \longrightarrow Ca(OH)_2(aq) + PH_3(g)$
(e) $Al(OH)_3(s) + H_2SO_4(aq) \longrightarrow Al_2(SO_4)_3(aq) + H_2O(l)$
(f) $AgNO_3(aq) + Na_2CO_3(aq) \longrightarrow$
$$Ag_2NO_3(s) + Na_2CO_3(aq)$$
(g) $C_2H_5NH_2(g) + O_2(g) \longrightarrow$
$$CO_2(g) + H_2O(g) + N_2(g)$$

3.13 Write balanced chemical equations to correspond to each of the following descriptions: **(a)** Solid calcium carbide, CaC_2, reacts with water to form an aqueous solution of calcium hydroxide and acetylene gas, C_2H_2. **(b)** When solid potassium chlorate is heated, it decomposes to form solid potassium chloride and oxygen gas. **(c)** Solid zinc metal reacts with sulfuric acid to form hydrogen gas and an aqueous solution of zinc sulfate. **(d)** When liquid phosphorus trichloride is added to water, it reacts to form aqueous phosphorous acid, $H_3PO_3(aq)$, and aqueous hydrochloric acid. **(e)** When hydrogen sulfide gas is passed over solid hot iron(III) hydroxide, the resultant reaction produces solid iron(III) sulfide and gaseous water.

3.14 Write balanced chemical equations to correspond to each of the following descriptions: **(a)** When sulfur trioxide gas reacts with water, a solution of sulfuric acid forms. **(b)** Boron sulfide, $B_2S_3(s)$, reacts violently with water to form dissolved boric acid, H_3BO_3, and hydrogen sulfide gas. **(c)** Phosphine, $PH_3(g)$, combusts in oxygen gas to form water vapor and solid tetraphosphorus decaoxide. **(d)** When solid mercury(II) nitrate is heated, it decomposes to form solid mercury(II) oxide, gaseous nitrogen dioxide, and oxygen. **(e)** Copper metal reacts with hot concentrated sulfuric acid solution to form aqueous copper(II) sulfate, sulfur dioxide gas, and water.

PATTERNS OF CHEMICAL REACTIVITY (section 3.2)

3.15 **(a)** When the metallic element sodium combines with the nonmetallic element bromine, $Br_2(l)$, how can you determine the chemical formula of the product? How do you know whether the product is a solid, liquid, or gas at room temperature? Write the balanced chemical equation for the reaction. **(b)** When a hydrocarbon burns in air, what reactant besides the hydrocarbon is involved in the reaction? What products are formed? Write a balanced chemical equation for the combustion of benzene, $C_6H_6(l)$, in air.

3.16 **(a)** Determine the chemical formula of the product formed when the metallic element aluminum combines with the nonmetallic element bromine, Br_2. Write the balanced chemical equation for the reaction. **(b)** What products form when a compound containing C, H, and O is completely combusted in air? Write a balanced chemical equation for the combustion of acetone, $C_3H_6O(l)$, in air.

3.17 Write a balanced chemical equation for the reaction that occurs when **(a)** $Mg(s)$ reacts with $Cl_2(g)$; **(b)** barium carbonate decomposes into barium oxide and carbon dioxide gas when heated; **(c)** the hydrocarbon styrene, $C_8H_8(l)$, is combusted in air; **(d)** dimethylether, $CH_3OCH_3(g)$, is combusted in air.

3.18 Write a balanced chemical equation for the reaction that occurs when **(a)** calcium metal undergoes a combination reaction with $O_2(g)$; **(b)** copper(II) hydroxide decomposes into copper(II) oxide and water when heated; **(c)** heptane, $C_7H_{16}(l)$, burns in air; **(d)** methyl tert-butyl ether, $C_5H_{12}O(l)$, burns in air.

3.19 Balance the following equations and indicate whether they are combination, decomposition, or combustion reactions:
(a) $C_3H_6(g) + O_2(g) \longrightarrow CO_2(g) + H_2O(g)$
(b) $NH_4NO_3(s) \longrightarrow N_2O(g) + H_2O(g)$
(c) $C_5H_6O(l) + O_2(g) \longrightarrow CO_2(g) + H_2O(g)$
(d) $N_2(g) + H_2(g) \longrightarrow NH_3(g)$
(e) $K_2O(s) + H_2O(l) \longrightarrow KOH(aq)$

3.20 Balance the following equations and indicate whether they are combination, decomposition, or combustion reactions:
(a) $PbCO_3(s) \longrightarrow PbO(s) + CO_2(g)$
(b) $C_2H_4(g) + O_2(g) \longrightarrow CO_2(g) + H_2O(g)$
(c) $Mg(s) + N_2(g) \longrightarrow Mg_3N_2(s)$
(d) $C_7H_8O_2(l) + O_2(g) \longrightarrow CO_2(g) + H_2O(g)$
(e) $Al(s) + Cl_2(g) \longrightarrow AlCl_3(s)$

FORMULA WEIGHTS (section 3.3)

3.21 Determine the formula weights of each of the following compounds: **(a)** nitric acid, HNO_3; **(b)** $KMnO_4$; **(c)** $Ca_3(PO_4)_2$; **(d)** quartz, SiO_2; **(e)** gallium sulfide, **(f)** chromium(III) sulfate, **(g)** phosphorus trichloride.

3.22 Determine the formula weights of each of the following compounds: **(a)** nitrous oxide, N_2O, known as laughing gas and used as an anesthetic in dentistry; **(b)** benzoic acid, $HC_7H_5O_2$, a substance used as a food preservative; **(c)** $Mg(OH)_2$, the active ingredient in milk of magnesia; **(d)** urea, $(NH_2)_2CO$, a compound used as a nitrogen fertilizer; **(e)** isopentyl acetate, $CH_3CO_2C_5H_{11}$, responsible for the odor of bananas.

3.23 Calculate the percentage by mass of oxygen in the following compounds: **(a)** morphine, $C_{17}H_{19}NO_3$; **(b)** codeine, $C_{18}H_{21}NO_3$ **(c)** cocaine, $C_{17}H_{21}NO_4$; **(d)** tetracycline, $C_{22}H_{24}N_2O_8$; **(e)** digitoxin, $C_{41}H_{64}O_{13}$; **(f)** vancomycin, $C_{66}H_{75}Cl_2N_9O_{24}$.

3.24 Calculate the percentage by mass of the indicated element in the following compounds: **(a)** carbon in acetylene, C_2H_2, a gas used in welding; **(b)** hydrogen in ascorbic acid, $HC_6H_7O_6$, also known as vitamin C; **(c)** hydrogen in ammonium sulfate, $(NH_4)_2SO_4$, a substance used as a nitrogen fertilizer; **(d)** platinum in $PtCl_2(NH_3)_2$, a chemotherapy agent called cisplatin; **(e)** oxygen in the female sex hormone estradiol, $C_{18}H_{24}O_2$; **(f)** carbon in capsaicin, $C_{18}H_{27}NO_3$, the compound that gives the hot taste to chili peppers.

3.25 Based on the following structural formulas, calculate the percentage of carbon by mass present in each compound:

(a) Benzaldehyde (almond fragrance)

(b) Vanillin (vanilla flavor)

(c) Isopentyl acetate (banana flavor)

3.26 Calculate the percentage of carbon by mass in each of the compounds represented by the following models:

(a) **(b)**

(c) **(d)**

AVOGADRO'S NUMBER AND THE MOLE (section 3.4)

3.27 **(a)** What is Avogadro's number, and how is it related to the mole? **(b)** What is the relationship between the formula weight of a substance and its molar mass?

3.28 **(a)** What is the mass, in grams, of a mole of ^{12}C? **(b)** How many carbon atoms are present in a mole of ^{12}C?

3.29 Without doing any detailed calculations (but using a periodic table to give atomic weights), rank the following samples in order of increasing number of atoms: 0.50 mol H_2O, 23 g Na, 6.0×10^{23} N_2 molecules.

3.30 Without doing any detailed calculations (but using a periodic table to give atomic weights), rank the following samples in order of increasing number of atoms: 9.0×10^{23} molecules of H_2O_2, 2.0 mol CH_4, 16 g O_2.

3.31 What is the mass, in kilograms, of an Avogadro's number of people, if the average mass of a person is 160 lb? How does this compare with the mass of Earth, 5.98×10^{24} kg?

3.32 If Avogadro's number of pennies is divided equally among the 300 million men, women, and children in the United States, how many dollars would each receive? How does this compare with the gross domestic product (GDP) of the United States, which was $14.4 trillion in 2008? (The GDP is the total market value of the nation's goods and services.)

3.33 Calculate the following quantities:
(a) mass, in grams, of 0.105 mole of sucrose ($C_{12}H_{22}O_{11}$)
(b) moles of $Zn(NO_3)_2$ in 143.50 g of this substance
(c) number of molecules in 1.0×10^{-6} mol CH_3CH_2OH
(d) number of N atoms in 0.410 mol NH_3

3.34 Calculate the following quantities:
(a) mass, in grams, of 1.50×10^{-2} mol of CdS
(b) number of moles of NH_4Cl in 86.6 g of this substance
(c) number of molecules in 8.447×10^{-2} mol C_6H_6
(d) number of O atoms in 6.25×10^{-3} mol $Al(NO_3)_3$

3.35 **(a)** What is the mass, in grams, of 2.50×10^{-3} mol of ammonium phosphate?
(b) How many moles of chloride ions are in 0.2550 g of aluminum chloride?

(c) What is the mass, in grams, of 7.70×10^{20} molecules of caffeine, $C_8H_{10}N_4O_2$?

(d) What is the molar mass of cholesterol if 0.00105 mol has a mass of 0.406 g?

3.36 (a) What is the mass, in grams, of 1.223 mol of iron(III) sulfate?

(b) How many moles of ammonium ions are in 6.955 g of ammonium carbonate?

(c) What is the mass, in grams, of 1.50×10^{21} molecules of aspirin, $C_9H_8O_4$?

(d) What is the molar mass of diazepam (Valium®) if 0.05570 mol has a mass of 15.86 g?

3.37 The molecular formula of allicin, the compound responsible for the characteristic smell of garlic, is $C_6H_{10}OS_2$. (a) What is the molar mass of allicin? (b) How many moles of allicin are present in 5.00 mg of this substance? (c) How many molecules of allicin are in 5.00 mg of this substance? (d) How many S atoms are present in 5.00 mg of allicin?

3.38 The molecular formula of aspartame, the artificial sweetener marketed as NutraSweet®, is $C_{14}H_{18}N_2O_5$. (a) What is the molar mass of aspartame? (b) How many moles of aspartame are present in 1.00 mg of aspartame? (c) How many molecules

of aspartame are present in 1.00 mg of aspartame? (d) How many hydrogen atoms are present in 1.00 mg of aspartame?

3.39 A sample of glucose, $C_6H_{12}O_6$, contains 1.250×10^{21} carbon atoms. (a) How many atoms of hydrogen does it contain? (b) How many molecules of glucose does it contain? (c) How many moles of glucose does it contain? (d) What is the mass of this sample in grams?

3.40 A sample of the male sex hormone testosterone, $C_{19}H_{28}O_2$, contains 3.88×10^{21} hydrogen atoms. (a) How many atoms of carbon does it contain? (b) How many molecules of testosterone does it contain? (c) How many moles of testosterone does it contain? (d) What is the mass of this sample in grams?

3.41 The allowable concentration level of vinyl chloride, C_2H_3Cl, in the atmosphere in a chemical plant is 2.0×10^{-6} g/L. How many moles of vinyl chloride in each liter does this represent? How many molecules per liter?

3.42 At least 25 μg of tetrahydrocannabinol (THC), the active ingredient in marijuana, is required to produce intoxication. The molecular formula of THC is $C_{21}H_{30}O_2$. How many moles of THC does this 25 μg represent? How many molecules?

EMPIRICAL FORMULAS (section 3.5)

3.43 Give the empirical formula of each of the following compounds if a sample contains (a) 0.0130 mol C, 0.0390 mol H, and 0.0065 mol O; (b) 11.66 g iron and 5.01 g oxygen; (c) 40.0% C, 6.7% H, and 53.3% O by mass.

3.44 Determine the empirical formula of each of the following compounds if a sample contains (a) 0.104 mol K, 0.052 mol C, and 0.156 mol O; (b) 5.28 g Sn and 3.37 g F; (c) 87.5% N and 12.5% H by mass.

3.45 Determine the empirical formulas of the compounds with the following compositions by mass:

(a) 10.4% C, 27.8% S, and 61.7% Cl

(b) 21.7% C, 9.6% O, and 68.7% F

(c) 32.79% Na, 13.02% Al, and the remainder F

3.46 Determine the empirical formulas of the compounds with the following compositions by mass:

(a) 55.3% K, 14.6% P, and 30.1% O

(b) 24.5% Na, 14.9% Si, and 60.6% F

(c) 62.1% C, 5.21% H, 12.1% N, and the remainder O

3.47 A compound whose empirical formula is XF_3 consists of 65% F by mass. What is the atomic mass of X?

3.48 The compound XCl_4 contains 75.0% Cl by mass. What is the element X?

3.49 What is the molecular formula of each of the following compounds?

(a) empirical formula CH_2, molar mass = 84 g/mol

(b) empirical formula NH_2Cl, molar mass = 51.5 g/mol

3.50 What is the molecular formula of each of the following compounds?

(a) empirical formula HCO_2, molar mass = 90.0 g/mol

(b) empirical formula C_2H_4O, molar mass = 88 g/mol

3.51 Determine the empirical and molecular formulas of each of the following substances:

(a) Styrene, a compound substance used to make Styrofoam® cups and insulation, contains 92.3% C and 7.7% H by mass and has a molar mass of 104 g/mol.

(b) Caffeine, a stimulant found in coffee, contains 49.5% C, 5.15% H, 28.9% N, and 16.5% O by mass and has a molar mass of 195 g/mol.

(c) Monosodium glutamate (MSG), a flavor enhancer in certain foods, contains 35.51% C, 4.77% H, 37.85% O, 8.29% N, and 13.60% Na, and has a molar mass of 169 g/mol.

3.52 Determine the empirical and molecular formulas of each of the following substances:

(a) Ibuprofen, a headache remedy, contains 75.69% C, 8.80% H, and 15.51% O by mass, and has a molar mass of 206 g/mol.

(b) Cadaverine, a foul-smelling substance produced by the action of bacteria on meat, contains 58.55% C, 13.81% H, and 27.40% N by mass; its molar mass is 102.2 g/mol.

(c) Epinephrine (adrenaline), a hormone secreted into the bloodstream in times of danger or stress, contains 59.0% C, 7.1% H, 26.2% O, and 7.7% N by mass; its MW is about 180 amu.

3.53 (a) Combustion analysis of toluene, a common organic solvent, gives 5.86 mg of CO_2 and 1.37 mg of H_2O. If the compound contains only carbon and hydrogen, what is its empirical formula? (b) Menthol, the substance we can smell in mentholated cough drops, is composed of C, H, and O. A 0.1005-g sample of menthol is combusted, producing 0.2829 g of CO_2 and 0.1159 g of H_2O. What is the empirical formula for menthol? If menthol has a molar mass of 156 g/mol, what is its molecular formula?

3.54 (a) The characteristic odor of pineapple is due to ethyl butyrate, a compound containing carbon, hydrogen, and oxygen. Combustion of 2.78 mg of ethyl butyrate produces 6.32 mg of CO_2 and 2.58 mg of H_2O. What is the empirical formula of the compound? (b) Nicotine, a component of tobacco, is composed of C, H, and N. A 5.250-mg sample of nicotine was combusted, producing 14.242 mg of CO_2 and 4.083 mg of

H_2O. What is the empirical formula for nicotine? If nicotine has a molar mass of 160 ± 5 g/mol, what is its molecular formula?

3.55 Valproic acid, used to treat seizures and bipolar disorder, is composed of C, H, and O. A 0.165-g sample is combusted in an apparatus such as that shown in Figure 3.14. The gain in mass of the H_2O absorber is 0.166 g, whereas that of the CO_2 absorber is 0.403 g. What empirical formula for valproic acid do these results indicate? Is this empirical formula consistent with the molecular model shown here?

3.56 Propenoic acid, as shown here,

is a reactive organic liquid used in the manufacture of plastics, coatings, and adhesives. An unlabeled container is thought to contain this acid. A 0.2033-g sample is combusted in an apparatus such as that shown in Figure 3.14. The gain in mass of the H_2O absorber is 0.102 g, whereas that of the CO_2 absorber is 0.374 g. Is this analysis consistent with the contents of the container being propenoic acid?

3.57 Washing soda, a compound used to prepare hard water for washing laundry, is a hydrate, which means that a certain number of water molecules are included in the solid structure. Its formula can be written as $Na_2CO_3 \cdot xH_2O$, where x is the number of moles of H_2O per mole of Na_2CO_3. When a 2.558-g sample of washing soda is heated at 25 °C, all the water of hydration is lost, leaving 0.948 g of Na_2CO_3. What is the value of x?

3.58 Epsom salts, a strong laxative used in veterinary medicine, is a hydrate, which means that a certain number of water molecules are included in the solid structure. The formula for Epsom salts can be written as $MgSO_4 \cdot xH_2O$, where x indicates the number of moles of H_2O per mole of $MgSO_4$. When 5.061 g of this hydrate is heated to 250 °C, all the water of hydration is lost, leaving 2.472 g of $MgSO_4$. What is the value of x?

CALCULATIONS BASED ON CHEMICAL EQUATIONS (section 3.6)

3.59 Why is it essential to use balanced chemical equations when determining the quantity of a product formed from a given quantity of a reactant?

3.60 What parts of balanced chemical equations give information about the relative numbers of moles of reactants and products involved in a reaction?

3.61 Hydrofluoric acid, HF(aq), cannot be stored in glass bottles because compounds called silicates in the glass are attacked by the HF(aq). Sodium silicate (Na_2SiO_3), for example, reacts as follows:

$$Na_2SiO_3(s) + 8\,HF(aq) \longrightarrow$$
$$H_2SiF_6(aq) + 2\,NaF(aq) + 3\,H_2O(l)$$

(a) How many moles of HF are needed to react with 0.300 mol of Na_2SiO_3?

(b) How many grams of NaF form when 0.500 mol of HF reacts with excess Na_2SiO_3?

(c) How many grams of Na_2SiO_3 can react with 0.800 g of HF?

3.62 The reaction between potassium superoxide, KO_2, and CO_2,

$$4\,KO_2 + 2\,CO_2 \longrightarrow 2\,K_2CO_3 + 3\,O_2$$

is used as a source of O_2 and absorber of CO_2 in self-contained breathing equipment used by rescue workers.

(a) How many moles of O_2 are produced when 0.400 mol of KO_2 reacts in this fashion?

(b) How many grams of KO_2 are needed to form 7.50 g of O_2?

(c) How many grams of CO_2 are used when 7.50 g of O_2 are produced?

3.63 Several brands of antacids use $Al(OH)_3$ to react with stomach acid, which contains primarily HCl:

$$Al(OH)_3(s) + HCl(aq) \longrightarrow AlCl_3(aq) + H_2O(l)$$

(a) Balance this equation.

(b) Calculate the number of grams of HCl that can react with 0.500 g of $Al(OH)_3$.

(c) Calculate the number of grams of $AlCl_3$ and the number of grams of H_2O formed when 0.500 g of $Al(OH)_3$ reacts.

(d) Show that your calculations in parts (b) and (c) are consistent with the law of conservation of mass.

3.64 An iron ore sample contains Fe_2O_3 together with other substances. Reaction of the ore with CO produces iron metal:

$$Fe_2O_3(s) + CO(g) \longrightarrow Fe(s) + CO_2(g)$$

(a) Balance this equation.

(b) Calculate the number of grams of CO that can react with 0.350 kg of Fe_2O_3.

(c) Calculate the number of grams of Fe and the number of grams of CO_2 formed when 0.350 kg of Fe_2O_3 reacts.

(d) Show that your calculations in parts (b) and (c) are consistent with the law of conservation of mass.

3.65 Aluminum sulfide reacts with water to form aluminum hydroxide and hydrogen sulfide. (a) Write the balanced chemical equation for this reaction. (b) How many grams of aluminum hydroxide are obtained from 14.2 g of aluminum sulfide?

3.66 Calcium hydride reacts with water to form calcium hydroxide and hydrogen gas. (a) Write a balanced chemical equation for the reaction. (b) How many grams of calcium hydride are needed to form 4.500 g of hydrogen?

3.67 Automotive air bags inflate when sodium azide, NaN_3, rapidly decomposes to its component elements:

$$2\,NaN_3(s) \longrightarrow 2\,Na(s) + 3\,N_2(g)$$

(a) How many moles of N_2 are produced by the decomposition of 1.50 mol of NaN_3?

(b) How many grams of NaN_3 are required to form 10.0 g of nitrogen gas?

(c) How many grams of NaN_3 are required to produce 10.0 ft^3 of nitrogen gas, about the size of an automotive air bag, if the gas has a density of 1.25 g/L?

3.68 The complete combustion of octane, C_8H_{18}, the main component of gasoline, proceeds as follows:

$$2\,C_8H_{18}(l) + 25\,O_2(g) \longrightarrow 16\,CO_2(g) + 18\,H_2O(g)$$

(a) How many moles of O_2 are needed to burn 1.50 mol of C_8H_{18}?

(b) How many grams of O_2 are needed to burn 10.0 g of C_8H_{18}?

(c) Octane has a density of 0.692 g/mL at 20 °C. How many grams of O_2 are required to burn 15.0 gal of C_8H_{18} (the capacity of an average fuel tank)?

(d) How many grams of CO_2 are produced when 15.0 gal of C_8H_{18} are combusted?

3.69 A piece of aluminum foil 1.00 cm square and 0.550 mm thick is allowed to react with bromine to form aluminum bromide.

(a) How many moles of aluminum were used? (The density of aluminum is 2.699 g/cm^3.) (b) How many grams of aluminum bromide form, assuming the aluminum reacts completely?

3.70 Detonation of nitroglycerin proceeds as follows:

$$4\,C_3H_5N_3O_9(l) \longrightarrow$$
$$12\,CO_2(g) + 6\,N_2(g) + O_2(g) + 10\,H_2O(g)$$

(a) If a sample containing 2.00 mL of nitroglycerin (density = 1.592 g/mL) is detonated, how many total moles of gas are produced? (b) If each mole of gas occupies 55 L under the conditions of the explosion, how many liters of gas are produced? (c) How many grams of N_2 are produced in the detonation?

LIMITING REACTANTS (section 3.7)

3.71 (a) Define the terms *limiting reactant* and *excess reactant*. (b) Why are the amounts of products formed in a reaction determined only by the amount of the limiting reactant? (c) Why should you base your choice of which compound is the limiting reactant on its number of initial moles, not on its initial mass in grams?

3.72 (a) Define the terms *theoretical yield, actual yield,* and *percent yield.* (b) Why is the actual yield in a reaction almost always less than the theoretical yield? (c) Can a reaction ever have 110% actual yield?

3.73 A manufacturer of bicycles has 4815 wheels, 2305 frames, and 2255 handlebars. (a) How many bicycles can be manufactured using these parts? (b) How many parts of each kind are left over? (c) Which part limits the production of bicycles?

3.74 A bottling plant has 126,515 bottles with a capacity of 355 mL, 108,500 caps, and 48,775 L of beverage. (a) How many bottles can be filled and capped? (b) How much of each item is left over? (c) Which component limits the production?

3.75 Sodium hydroxide reacts with carbon dioxide as follows:

$$2\,NaOH(s) + CO_2(g) \longrightarrow Na_2CO_3(s) + H_2O(l)$$

Which is the limiting reactant when 1.85 mol NaOH and 1.00 mol CO_2 are allowed to react? How many moles of Na_2CO_3 can be produced? How many moles of the excess reactant remain after the completion of the reaction?

3.76 Aluminum hydroxide reacts with sulfuric acid as follows:

$$2\,Al(OH)_3(s) + 3\,H_2SO_4(aq) \longrightarrow$$
$$Al_2(SO_4)_3(aq) + 6\,H_2O(l)$$

Which is the limiting reactant when 0.500 mol $Al(OH)_3$ and 0.500 mol H_2SO_4 are allowed to react? How many moles of $Al_2(SO_4)_3$ can form under these conditions? How many moles of the excess reactant remain after the completion of the reaction?

3.77 The fizz produced when an Alka-Seltzer® tablet is dissolved in water is due to the reaction between sodium bicarbonate ($NaHCO_3$) and citric acid ($H_3C_6H_5O_7$):

$$3\ NaHCO_3(aq) + H_3C_6H_5O_7(aq) \longrightarrow$$
$$3\ CO_2(g) + 3\ H_2O(l) + Na_3C_6H_5O_7(aq)$$

In a certain experiment 1.00 g of sodium bicarbonate and 1.00 g of citric acid are allowed to react. **(a)** Which is the limiting reactant? **(b)** How many grams of carbon dioxide form? **(c)** How many grams of the excess reactant remain after the limiting reactant is completely consumed?

3.78 One of the steps in the commercial process for converting ammonia to nitric acid is the conversion of NH_3 to NO:

$$4\ NH_3(g) + 5\ O_2(g) \longrightarrow 4\ NO(g) + 6\ H_2O(g)$$

In a certain experiment, 2.00 g of NH_3 reacts with 2.50 g of O_2 **(a)** Which is the limiting reactant? **(b)** How many grams of NO and of H_2O form? **(c)** How many grams of the excess reactant remain after the limiting reactant is completely consumed? **(d)** Show that your calculations in parts (b) and (c) are consistent with the law of conservation of mass.

3.79 Solutions of sodium carbonate and silver nitrate react to form solid silver carbonate and a solution of sodium nitrate. A solution containing 3.50 g of sodium carbonate is mixed with one containing 5.00 g of silver nitrate. How many grams of sodium carbonate, silver nitrate, silver carbonate, and sodium nitrate are present after the reaction is complete?

3.80 Solutions of sulfuric acid and lead(II) acetate react to form solid lead(II) sulfate and a solution of acetic acid. If 5.00 g of sulfuric acid and 5.00 g of lead(II) acetate are mixed, calculate the number of grams of sulfuric acid, lead(II) acetate, lead(II) sulfate, and acetic acid present in the mixture after the reaction is complete.

3.81 When benzene (C_6H_6) reacts with bromine (Br_2), bromobenzene (C_6H_5Br) is obtained:

$$C_6H_6 + Br_2 \longrightarrow C_6H_5Br + HBr$$

(a) When 30.0 g of benzene reacts with 65.0 g of bromine, what is the theoretical yield of bromobenzene? **(b)** If the actual yield of bromobenzene is 42.3 g, what is the percentage yield?

3.82 When ethane (C_2H_6) reacts with chlorine (Cl_2), the main product is C_2H_5Cl, but other products containing Cl, such as $C_2H_4Cl_2$, are also obtained in small quantities. The formation of these other products reduces the yield of C_2H_5Cl. **(a)** Calculate the theoretical yield of C_2H_5Cl when 125 g of C_2H_6 reacts with 255 g of Cl_2, assuming that C_2H_6 and Cl_2 react only to form C_2H_2Cl and HCl. **(b)** Calculate the percent yield of C_2H_5Cl if the reaction produces 206 g of C_2H_5Cl.

3.83 Hydrogen sulfide is an impurity in natural gas that must be removed. One common removal method is called the Claus process, which relies on the reaction:

$$8\ H_2S(g) + 4\ O_2(g) \longrightarrow S_8(l) + 8\ H_2O(g)$$

Under optimal conditions the Claus process gives 98% yield of S_8 from H_2S. If you started with 30.0 grams of H_2S and 50.0 grams of O_2, how many grams of S_8 would be produced, assuming 98% yield?

3.84 When hydrogen sulfide gas is bubbled into a solution of sodium hydroxide, the reaction forms sodium sulfide and water. How many grams of sodium sulfide are formed if 1.25 g of hydrogen sulfide is bubbled into a solution containing 2.00 g of sodium hydroxide, assuming that the sodium sulfide is made in 92.0% yield?

ADDITIONAL EXERCISES

3.85 Write the balanced chemical equations for **(a)** the complete combustion of acetic acid (CH_3COOH), the main active ingredient in vinegar; **(b)** the decomposition of solid calcium hydroxide into solid calcium(II) oxide (lime) and water vapor; **(c)** the combination reaction between nickel metal and chlorine gas.

3.86 If 1.5 mol C_2H_5OH, 1.5 mol C_3H_8, and 1.5 mol $CH_3CH_2COCH_3$ are completely combusted in oxygen, which produces the largest number of moles of H_2O? Which produces the least? Explain.

3.87 The effectiveness of nitrogen fertilizers depends on both their ability to deliver nitrogen to plants and the amount of nitrogen they can deliver. Four common nitrogen-containing fertilizers are ammonia, ammonium nitrate, ammonium sulfate, and urea [$(NH_2)_2CO$]. Rank these fertilizers in terms of the mass percentage nitrogen they contain.

3.88 **(a)** The molecular formula of acetylsalicylic acid (aspirin), one of the most common pain relievers, is $C_9H_8O_4$. How many moles of $C_9H_8O_4$ are in a 0.500-g tablet of aspirin? **(b)** How many molecules of $C_9H_8O_4$ are in this tablet? **(c)** How many carbon atoms are in the tablet?

3.89 Very small crystals composed of 1000 to 100,000 atoms, called quantum dots, are being investigated for use in electronic devices.
(a) A quantum dot was made of solid silicon in the shape of a sphere, with a diameter of 4 nm. Calculate the mass of the quantum dot, using the density of silicon ($2.3\ g/cm^3$).
(b) How many silicon atoms are in the quantum dot?
(c) The density of germanium is $5.325\ g/cm^3$. If you made a 4-nm quantum dot of germanium, how many Ge atoms would it contain? Assume the dot is spherical.

3.90 **(a)** One molecule of the antibiotic penicillin G has a mass of 5.342×10^{-21} g. What is the molar mass of penicillin G? **(b)** Hemoglobin, the oxygen-carrying protein in red blood cells, has four iron atoms per molecule and contains 0.340% iron by mass. Calculate the molar mass of hemoglobin.

3.91 Serotonin is a compound that conducts nerve impulses in the brain. It contains 68.2 mass percent C, 6.86 mass percent H, 15.9 mass percent N, and 9.08 mass percent O. Its molar mass is 176 g/mol. Determine its molecular formula.

3.92 The koala dines exclusively on eucalyptus leaves. Its digestive system detoxifies the eucalyptus oil, a poison to other animals. The chief constituent in eucalyptus oil is a substance called eucalyptol, which contains 77.87% C, 11.76% H, and the remainder O. **(a)** What is the empirical formula for this substance? **(b)** A mass spectrum of eucalyptol shows a peak at about 154 amu. What is the molecular formula of the substance?

3.93 Vanillin, the dominant flavoring in vanilla, contains C, H, and O. When 1.05 g of this substance is completely combusted, 2.43 g of CO_2 and 0.50 g of H_2O are produced. What is the empirical formula of vanillin?

[3.94] An organic compound was found to contain only C, H, and Cl. When a 1.50-g sample of the compound was completely combusted in air, 3.52 g of CO_2 was formed. In a separate experiment the chlorine in a 1.00-g sample of the compound was converted to 1.27 g of AgCl. Determine the empirical formula of the compound.

[3.95] A compound, $KBrO_x$, where x is unknown, is analyzed and found to contain 52.92% Br. What is the value of x?

[3.96] An element X forms an iodide (XI_3) and a chloride (XCl_3). The iodide is quantitatively converted to the chloride when it is heated in a stream of chlorine:

$$2 XI_3 + 3 Cl_2 \longrightarrow 2 XCl_3 + 3 I_2$$

If 0.5000 g of XI_3 is treated, 0.2360 g of XCl_3 is obtained. **(a)** Calculate the atomic weight of the element X. **(b)** Identify the element X.

3.97 A method used by the U.S. Environmental Protection Agency (EPA) for determining the concentration of ozone in air is to pass the air sample through a "bubbler" containing sodium iodide, which removes the ozone according to the following equation:

$$O_3(g) + 2 NaI(aq) + H_2O(l) \longrightarrow$$
$$O_2(g) + I_2(s) + 2 NaOH(aq)$$

(a) How many moles of sodium iodide are needed to remove 5.95×10^{-6} mol of O_3? **(b)** How many grams of sodium iodide are needed to remove 1.3 mg of O_3?

3.98 A chemical plant uses electrical energy to decompose aqueous solutions of NaCl to give Cl_2, H_2, and NaOH:

$$2 NaCl(aq) + 2 H_2O(l) \longrightarrow$$
$$2 NaOH(aq) + H_2(g) + Cl_2(g)$$

If the plant produces 1.5×10^6 kg (1500 metric tons) of Cl_2 daily, estimate the quantities of H_2 and NaOH produced.

3.99 The fat stored in a camel's hump is a source of both energy and water. Calculate the mass of H_2O produced by metabolism of 1.0 kg of fat, assuming the fat consists entirely of tristearin ($C_{57}H_{110}O_6$), a typical animal fat, and assuming that during metabolism, tristearin reacts with O_2 to form only CO_2 and H_2O.

[3.100] When hydrocarbons are burned in a limited amount of air, both CO and CO_2 form. When 0.450 g of a particular hydrocarbon was burned in air, 0.467 g of CO, 0.733 g of CO_2, and 0.450 g of H_2O were formed. **(a)** What is the empirical formula of the compound? **(b)** How many grams of O_2 were used in the reaction? **(c)** How many grams would have been required for complete combustion?

3.101 A mixture of $N_2(g)$ and $H_2(g)$ reacts in a closed container to form ammonia, $NH_3(g)$. The reaction ceases before either reactant has been totally consumed. At this stage 3.0 mol N_2, 3.0 mol H_2, and 3.0 mol NH_3 are present. How many moles of N_2 and H_2 were present originally?

[3.102] A mixture containing $KClO_3$, K_2CO_3, $KHCO_3$, and KCl was heated, producing CO_2, O_2, and H_2O gases according to the following equations:

$$2 KClO_3(s) \longrightarrow 2 KCl(s) + 3 O_2(g)$$
$$2 KHCO_3(s) \longrightarrow K_2O(s) + H_2O(g) + 2 CO_2(g)$$
$$K_2CO_3(s) \longrightarrow K_2O(s) + CO_2(g)$$

The KCl does not react under the conditions of the reaction. If 100.0 g of the mixture produces 1.80 g of H_2O, 13.20 g of CO_2, and 4.00 g of O_2, what was the composition of the original mixture? (Assume complete decomposition of the mixture.)

3.103 When a mixture of 10.0 g of acetylene (C_2H_2); and 10.0 g of oxygen (O_2) is ignited, the resultant combustion reaction produces CO_2 and H_2O. **(a)** Write the balanced chemical equation for this reaction. **(b)** Which is the limiting reactant? **(c)** How many grams of C_2H_2, O_2, CO_2, and H_2O are present after the reaction is complete?

3.104 Aspirin ($C_9H_8O_4$) is produced from salicylic acid ($C_7H_6O_3$) and acetic anhydride ($C_4H_6O_3$):

$$C_7H_6O_3 + C_4H_6O_3 \longrightarrow C_9H_8O_4 + HC_2H_3O_2$$

(a) How much salicylic acid is required to produce 1.5×10^2 kg of aspirin, assuming that all of the salicylic acid is converted to aspirin? **(b)** How much salicylic acid would be required if only 80% of the salicylic acid is converted to aspirin? **(c)** What is the theoretical yield of aspirin if 185 kg of salicylic acid is allowed to react with 125 kg of acetic anhydride? **(d)** If the situation described in part **(c)** produces 182 kg of aspirin, what is the percentage yield?

INTEGRATIVE EXERCISES

These exercises require skills from earlier chapters as well as skills from the present chapter.

3.105 Consider a sample of calcium carbonate in the form of a cube measuring 2.005 in. on each edge. If the sample has a density of 2.71 g/cm^3, how many oxygen atoms does it contain?

3.106 **(a)** You are given a cube of silver metal that measures 1.000 cm on each edge. The density of silver is 10.5 g/cm^3. How many atoms are in this cube? **(b)** Because atoms are spherical, they cannot occupy all of the space of the cube. The silver atoms pack in the solid in such a way that 74% of the volume of the solid is actually filled with the silver atoms. Calculate the volume of a single silver atom. **(c)** Using the volume of a silver atom and the formula for the volume of a sphere, calculate the radius in angstroms of a silver atom.

3.107 **(a)** If an automobile travels 225 mi with a gas mileage of 20.5 mi/gal, how many kilograms of CO_2 are produced? Assume that the gasoline is composed of octane, $C_8H_{18}(l)$, whose density is 0.69 g/mL. **(b)** Repeat the calculation for a truck that has a gas mileage of 5 mi/gal.

3.108 ∞ Section 2.9 introduced the idea of structural isomerism, with 1-propanol and 2-propanol as examples. Determine which of these properties would distinguish these two substances: **(a)** boiling point; **(b)** combustion analysis results; **(c)** molecular weight; **(d)** density at a given temperature and pressure. You can check on the properties of these two compounds in *Wolfram Alpha* (*http://www.wolframalpha.com/*) or the *CRC Handbook of Chemistry and Physics*.

3.109 A particular coal contains 2.5% sulfur by mass. When this coal is burned at a power plant, the sulfur is converted into sulfur dioxide gas, which is a pollutant. To reduce sulfur dioxide emissions, calcium oxide (lime) is used. The sulfur dioxide reacts with calcium oxide to form solid calcium sulfite. **(a)** Write the balanced chemical equation for the reaction. **(b)** If the coal is burned in a power plant that uses 2000 tons of coal per day, what mass of calcium oxide is required daily to eliminate the sulfur dioxide? **(c)** How many grams of calcium sulfite are produced daily by this power plant?

3.110 Copper is an excellent electrical conductor widely used in making electric circuits. In producing a printed circuit board for the electronics industry, a layer of copper is laminated on a plastic board. A circuit pattern is then printed on the board using a chemically resistant polymer. The board is then exposed to a chemical bath that reacts with the exposed copper, leaving the desired copper circuit, which has been protected by the overlaying polymer. Finally, a solvent removes the polymer. One reaction used to remove the exposed copper from the circuit board is

$$Cu(s) + Cu(NH_3)_4Cl_2(aq) + 4 NH_3(aq) \longrightarrow$$
$$2 Cu(NH_3)_4Cl(aq)$$

A plant needs to produce 5000 circuit boards, each with a surface area measuring 2.0 in. $\times$ 3.0 in. The boards are covered with a 0.65-mm layer of copper. In subsequent processing, 85% of the copper is removed. Copper has a density of 8.96 g/cm^3. Calculate the masses of $Cu(NH_3)_4Cl_2$ and NH_3 needed to produce the circuit boards, assuming that the reaction used gives a 97% yield.

3.111 Hydrogen cyanide, HCN, is a poisonous gas. The lethal dose is approximately 300 mg HCN per kilogram of air when inhaled. **(a)** Calculate the amount of HCN that gives the lethal dose in a small laboratory room measuring 12 $\times$ 15 $\times$ 8.0 ft. The density of air at 26 °C is 0.00118 g/cm^3. **(b)** If the HCN is formed by reaction of NaCN with an acid such as H_2SO_4, what mass of NaCN gives the lethal dose in the room?

$$2 NaCN(s) + H_2SO_4(aq) \longrightarrow Na_2SO_4(aq) + 2 HCN(g)$$

(c) HCN forms when synthetic fibers containing Orlon® or Acrilan® burn. Acrilan® has an empirical formula of CH_2CHCN, so HCN is 50.9% of the formula by mass. A rug measures 12 $\times$ 15 ft and contains 30 oz of Acrilan® fibers per square yard of carpet. If the rug burns, will a lethal dose of HCN be generated in the room? Assume that the yield of HCN from the fibers is 20% and that the carpet is 50% consumed.

3.112 The source of oxygen that drives the internal combustion engine in an automobile is air. Air is a mixture of gases, principally N_2 (~79%) and O_2 (~20%). In the cylinder of an automobile engine, nitrogen can react with oxygen to produce nitric oxide gas, NO. As NO is emitted from the tailpipe of the car, it can react with more oxygen to produce nitrogen dioxide gas. **(a)** Write balanced chemical equations for both reactions. **(b)** Both nitric oxide and nitrogen dioxide are pollutants that can lead to acid rain and global warming; collectively, they are called "NO_x" gases. In 2007, the United States emitted an estimated 22 million tons of nitrogen dioxide into the atmosphere. How many grams of nitrogen dioxide is this? **(c)** The production of NO_x gases is an unwanted side reaction of the main engine combustion process that turns octane, C_8H_{18}, into CO_2 and water. If 85% of the oxygen in an engine is used to combust octane and the remainder used to produce nitrogen dioxide, calculate how many grams of nitrogen dioxide would be produced during the combustion of 500 grams of octane.

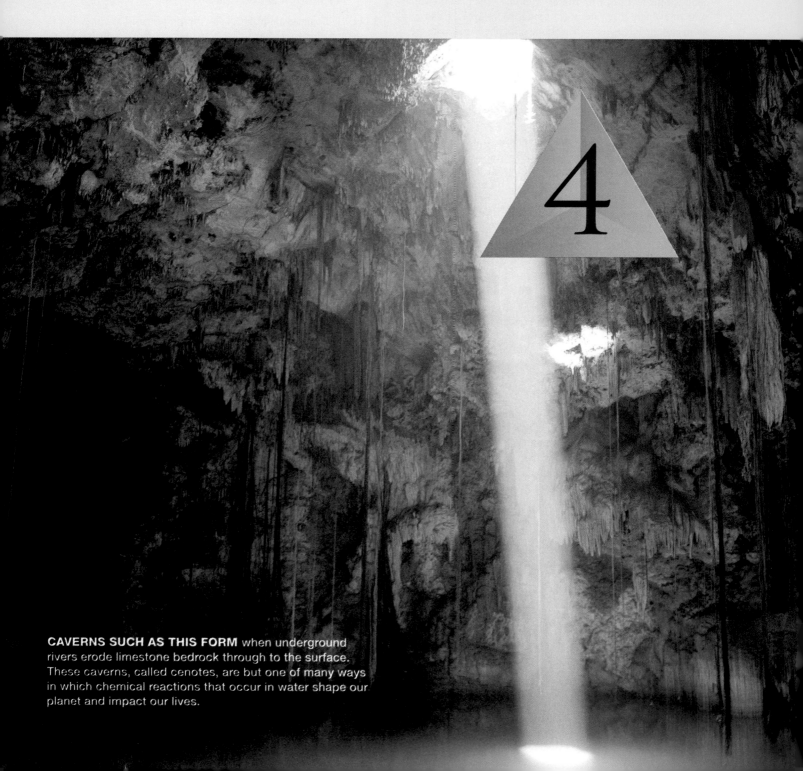

CAVERNS SUCH AS THIS FORM when underground rivers erode limestone bedrock through to the surface. These caverns, called cenotes, are but one of many ways in which chemical reactions that occur in water shape our planet and impact our lives.

REACTIONS IN AQUEOUS SOLUTION

WATER COVERS NEARLY TWO-THIRDS of our planet, and this simple substance has been the key to much of Earth's evolutionary history. Life almost certainly originated in water, and the need for water by all forms of life has helped determine diverse biological structures.

Given the importance of water for life, it should come as no surprise that development of civilizations has been closely tied to reliable sources of fresh water. During the first millennium, Mayan civilization was one of the most advanced on Earth. Mayan city-states covered much of the Yucatan peninsula in what is now easternmost Mexico. The northern half of the peninsula is a flat shelf of land composed largely of carbonate rocks, such as limestone. Because there are no rivers and very few lakes, the Mayans depended on sinkholes called *cenotes*, for their fresh water (▶ **FIGURE 4.1**).

Chemical reactions that occur in water are responsible for creation of cenotes. When carbon dioxide, CO_2, dissolves in water, the resulting solution is slightly acidic and reacts with $CaCO_3$ in the limestone:

$$CaCO_3(s) + H_2O(l) + CO_2(aq) \longrightarrow Ca(HCO_3)_2(aq) \qquad [4.1]$$

A solution in which water is the dissolving medium is called an **aqueous solution**. In this chapter we examine chemical reactions that take place in aqueous solutions. In addition, we extend the concepts of stoichiometry learned in Chapter 3 by considering how solution concentrations are expressed and used.

115

▲ FIGURE 4.1 **Cenote formation.**

4.1 | GENERAL PROPERTIES OF AQUEOUS SOLUTIONS

A *solution* is a homogeneous mixture of two or more substances. ∞ (Section 1.2) The substance present in the greatest quantity is usually called the **solvent**, and the other substances are called **solutes**; they are said to be *dissolved in* the solvent. When a small amount of sodium chloride (NaCl) is dissolved in a large quantity of water, for example, water is the solvent and sodium chloride is the solute.

Electrolytic Properties

At a young age we learn not to bring electrical devices into the bathtub so as not to electrocute ourselves. That's a useful lesson because most of the water you encounter in daily life is electrically conducting. Pure water, however, is a very poor conductor of electricity. The conductivity of bathwater originates from the substances dissolved in the water, not from the water itself.

Not all substances that dissolve in water make the resulting solution conducting. Imagine preparing two aqueous solutions—one by dissolving a teaspoon of table salt (sodium chloride) in a cup of water and the other by dissolving a teaspoon of table sugar (sucrose) in a cup of water (▶ FIGURE 4.2). Both solutions are clear and colorless, but they possess very different electrical conductivities: the salt solution is a good conductor of electricity, whereas the sugar solution is not.

In order for the bulb in the device of Figure 4.2 to light up, there must be a current (that is, a *flow* of electrically charged particles) between two electrodes immersed in the solution. The conductivity of pure water is not sufficient to complete the electrical circuit and light the bulb. The situation changes when ions are present in solution because the ions carry electrical charge from one electrode to the other, completing the circuit. Thus, the conductivity of NaCl solutions indicates the presence of ions. The lack of conductivity of sucrose solutions indicates the absence of ions. When NaCl dissolves in water, the solution contains Na^+ and Cl^- ions, each surrounded by water molecules. When sucrose ($C_{12}H_{22}O_{11}$) dissolves in water, the solution contains only neutral sucrose molecules surrounded by water molecules.

Not lit

Pure water,
H₂O(*l*)
does not conduct electricity

Not lit

Sucrose solution,
C₁₂H₂₂O₁₁(*aq*)
Nonelectrolyte
does not conduct electricity

Lit

Sodium chloride solution,
NaCl(*aq*)
Electrolyte
conducts electricity

◀ **FIGURE 4.2**
Electrical
conductivities of
water and two
aqueous solutions.

A substance (such as NaCl) whose aqueous solutions contain ions is called an **electrolyte**. A substance (such as C₁₂H₂₂O₁₁) that does not form ions in solution is called a **nonelectrolyte**. The different classifications of NaCl and C₁₂H₂₂O₁₁ arise largely because NaCl is ionic, whereas C₁₂H₂₂O₁₁ is molecular.

Ionic Compounds in Water

Recall from Figure 2.21 that solid NaCl consists of an orderly arrangement of Na⁺ and Cl⁻ ions. When NaCl dissolves in water, each ion separates from the solid structure and disperses throughout the solution [▼ **FIGURE 4.3**(a)]. The ionic solid *dissociates* into its component ions as it dissolves.

GO FIGURE

Which solution, NaCl(*aq*) or CH₃OH(*aq*), conducts electricity?

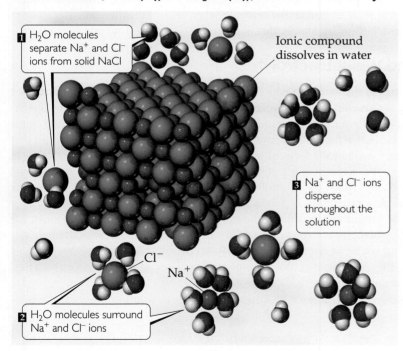

1 H₂O molecules separate Na⁺ and Cl⁻ ions from solid NaCl

Ionic compound dissolves in water

3 Na⁺ and Cl⁻ ions disperse throughout the solution

Cl⁻

Na⁺

2 H₂O molecules surround Na⁺ and Cl⁻ ions

(a) Ionic compounds like sodium chloride, NaCl, form ions when they dissolve

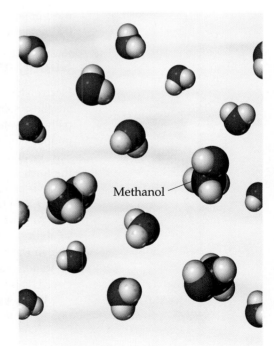

Methanol

(b) Molecular substances like methanol, CH₃OH, dissolve without forming ions

▲ **FIGURE 4.3   Dissolution in water.** (a) When an ionic compound, such as sodium chloride, NaCl, dissolves in water, H₂O molecules separate, surround, and uniformly disperse the ions into the liquid. (b) Molecular substances that dissolve in water, such as methanol, CH₃OH, usually do so without forming ions. We can think of this as a simple mixing of two molecular species. In both (a) and (b) the water molecules have been moved apart so that the solute particles can be seen clearly.

Water is a very effective solvent for ionic compounds. Although H_2O is an electrically neutral molecule, the O atom is rich in electrons and has a partial negative charge, denoted by δ^-. Each H atom has a partial positive charge, denoted by δ^+. Cations are attracted by the negative end of H_2O, and anions are attracted by the positive end.

As an ionic compound dissolves, the ions become surrounded by H_2O molecules, as shown in Figure 4.3(a). The ions are said to be *solvated*. In chemical equations, we denote solvated ions by writing them as $Na^+(aq)$ and $Cl^-(aq)$, where *aq* is an abbreviation for "aqueous." ∞∞ (Section 3.1) **Solvation** helps stabilize the ions in solution and prevents cations and anions from recombining. Furthermore, because the ions and their shells of surrounding water molecules are free to move about, the ions become dispersed uniformly throughout the solution.

We can usually predict the nature of the ions in a solution of an ionic compound from the chemical name of the substance. Sodium sulfate (Na_2SO_4), for example, dissociates into sodium ions (Na^+) and sulfate ions (SO_4^{2-}). You must remember the formulas and charges of common ions (Tables 2.4 and 2.5) to understand the forms in which ionic compounds exist in aqueous solution.

 GIVE IT SOME THOUGHT

What dissolved species are present in a solution of
a. KCN,
b. $NaClO_4$?

Molecular Compounds in Water

When a molecular compound dissolves in water, the solution usually consists of intact molecules dispersed throughout the solution. Consequently, most molecular compounds are nonelectrolytes. As we have seen, table sugar (sucrose) is a nonelectrolyte. As another example, a solution of methanol (CH_3OH) in water consists entirely of CH_3OH molecules dispersed in the water [Figure 4.3(b)].

A few molecular substances have aqueous solutions that contain ions. Acids are the most important of these solutions. For example, when $HCl(g)$ dissolves in water to form hydrochloric acid, $HCl(aq)$, it *ionizes*; that is, it dissociates into $H^+(aq)$ and $Cl^-(aq)$ ions.

Strong and Weak Electrolytes

Electrolytes differ in the extent to which they conduct electricity. **Strong electrolytes** are those solutes that exist in solution completely or nearly completely as ions. Essentially all water-soluble ionic compounds (such as NaCl) and a few molecular compounds (such as HCl) are strong electrolytes. **Weak electrolytes** are those solutes that exist in solution mostly in the form of neutral molecules with only a small fraction in the form of ions. For example, in a solution of acetic acid (CH_3COOH) most of the solute is present as $CH_3COOH(aq)$ molecules. Only a small fraction (about 1%) of the CH_3COOH has dissociated into $H^+(aq)$ and $CH_3COO^-(aq)$ ions.*

We must be careful not to confuse the extent to which an electrolyte dissolves (its solubility) with whether it is strong or weak. For example, CH_3COOH is extremely soluble in water but is a weak electrolyte. $Ca(OH)_2$, on the other hand, is not very soluble in water, but the amount that does dissolve dissociates almost completely. Thus, $Ca(OH)_2$ is a strong electrolyte.

When a weak electrolyte, such as acetic acid, ionizes in solution, we write the reaction in the form

$$CH_3COOH(aq) \rightleftharpoons CH_3COO^-(aq) + H^+(aq) \qquad [4.2]$$

The half-arrows pointing in opposite directions mean that the reaction is significant in both directions. At any given moment some CH_3COOH molecules are ionizing to

*The chemical formula of acetic acid is sometimes written $HC_2H_3O_2$ so that the formula looks like that of other common acids such as HCl. The formula CH_3COOH conforms to the molecular structure of acetic acid, with the acidic H on the O atom at the end of the formula.

form H^+ and CH_3COO^- ions but H^+ and CH_3COO^- ions are recombining to form CH_3COOH. The balance between these opposing processes determines the relative numbers of ions and neutral molecules. This balance produces a state of **chemical equilibrium** in which the relative numbers of each type of ion or molecule in the reaction are constant over time. Chemists use half-arrows pointing in opposite directions to represent the ionization of weak electrolytes and a single arrow to represent the ionization of strong electrolytes. Because HCl is a strong electrolyte, we write the equation for the ionization of HCl as

$$HCl(aq) \longrightarrow H^+(aq) + Cl^-(aq) \qquad [4.3]$$

The absence of a left-pointing arrow indicates that the H^+ and Cl^- ions have no tendency to recombine to form HCl molecules.

In the following sections we will look at how a compound's composition lets us predict whether it is a strong electrolyte, weak electrolyte, or nonelectrolyte. For the moment, you need only to remember that *water-soluble ionic compounds are strong electrolytes*. Ionic compounds can usually be identified by the presence of both metals and nonmetals [for example, NaCl, $FeSO_4$, and $Al(NO_3)_3$]. Ionic compounds containing the ammonium ion, NH_4^+ [for example, NH_4Br and $(NH_4)_2CO_3$], are exceptions to this rule of thumb.

 GIVE IT SOME THOUGHT

Which solute will cause the lightbulb in Figure 4.2 to glow most brightly, CH_3OH, NaOH, or CH_3COOH?

| **SAMPLE EXERCISE 4.1** | **Relating Relative Numbers of Anions and Cations to Chemical Formulas** |

The accompanying diagram represents an aqueous solution of either $MgCl_2$, KCl, or K_2SO_4. Which solution does the drawing best represent?

SOLUTION

Analyze We are asked to associate the charged spheres in the diagram with ions present in a solution of an ionic substance.

Plan We examine each ionic substance given to determine the relative numbers and charges of its ions. We then correlate these ionic species with the ones shown in the diagram.

Solve The diagram shows twice as many cations as anions, consistent with the formulation K_2SO_4.

Check Notice that the net charge in the diagram is zero, as it must be if it is to represent an ionic substance.

PRACTICE EXERCISE

If you were to draw diagrams representing aqueous solutions of (a) $NiSO_4$, (b) $Ca(NO_3)_2$, (c) Na_3PO_4, (d) $Al_2(SO_4)_3$, how many anions would you show if each diagram contained six cations?

Answers: (a) 6, (b) 12, (c) 2, (d) 9

4.2 | PRECIPITATION REACTIONS

▶ **FIGURE 4.4** shows two clear solutions being mixed. One solution contains potassium iodide, KI, dissolved in water and the other contains lead nitrate, $Pb(NO_3)_2$, dissolved in water. The reaction between these two solutes produces a water-insoluble yellow solid. Reactions that result in the formation of an insoluble product are called **precipitation reactions**. A **precipitate** is an insoluble solid formed by a reaction in solution. In Figure 4.4 the precipitate is lead iodide (PbI_2), a compound that has a very low solubility in water:

$$Pb(NO_3)_2(aq) + 2\,KI(aq) \longrightarrow PbI_2(s) + 2\,KNO_3(aq) \qquad [4.4]$$

The other product of this reaction, potassium nitrate (KNO_3), remains in solution.

▲ GO FIGURE

Which ions remain in solution after PbI₂ precipitation is complete?

Reactants	Pb²⁺(aq) and I⁻(aq) combine	Products
2 KI(aq) + Pb(NO₃)₂(aq)	to form precipitate	PbI₂(s) + 2 KI(aq)

I⁻
K⁺
Pb²⁺
NO₃⁻

▲ FIGURE 4.4 **A precipitation reaction.**

Precipitation reactions occur when pairs of oppositely charged ions attract each other so strongly that they form an insoluble ionic solid. To predict whether certain combinations of ions form insoluble compounds, we must consider some guidelines concerning the solubilities of common ionic compounds.

Solubility Guidelines for Ionic Compounds

The **solubility** of a substance at a given temperature is the amount of the substance that can be dissolved in a given quantity of solvent at the given temperature. In our discussions, any substance with a solubility less than 0.01 mol/L will be referred to as *insoluble*. In those cases the attraction between the oppositely charged ions in the solid is too great for the water molecules to separate the ions to any significant extent; the substance remains largely undissolved.

Unfortunately, there are no rules based on simple physical properties such as ionic charge to guide us in predicting whether a particular ionic compound will be soluble. Experimental observations, however, have led to guidelines for predicting solubility for ionic compounds. For example, experiments show that all common ionic compounds that contain the nitrate anion, NO_3^-, are soluble in water. ▶ TABLE 4.1 summarizes the solubility guidelines for common ionic compounds. The table is organized according to the anion in the compound, but it also reveals many important facts about cations. Note that *all common ionic compounds of the alkali metal ions (group 1A of the periodic table) and of the ammonium ion* (NH_4^+) *are soluble in water.*

TABLE 4.1 • Solubility Guidelines for Common Ionic Compounds in Water		
Soluble Ionic Compounds		**Important Exceptions**
Compounds containing	NO_3^-	None
	CH_3COO^-	None
	Cl^-	Compounds of Ag^+, Hg_2^{2+}, and Pb^{2+}
	Br^-	Compounds of Ag^+, Hg_2^{2+}, and Pb^{2+}
	I^-	Compounds of Ag^+, Hg_2^{2+}, and Pb^{2+}
	SO_4^{2-}	Compounds of Sr^{2+}, Ba^{2+}, Hg_2^{2+}, and Pb^{2+}
Insoluble Ionic Compounds		**Important Exceptions**
Compounds containing	S^{2-}	Compounds of NH_4^+, the alkali metal cations, Ca^{2+}, Sr^{2+}, and Ba^{2+}
	CO_3^{2-}	Compounds of NH_4^+ and the alkali metal cations
	PO_4^{3-}	Compounds of NH_4^+ and the alkali metal cations
	OH^-	Compounds of NH_4^+, the alkali metal cations, Ca^{2+}, Sr^{2+}, and Ba^{2+}

SAMPLE EXERCISE 4.2 **Using Solubility Rules**

Classify these ionic compounds as soluble or insoluble in water: **(a)** sodium carbonate, Na_2CO_3, **(b)** lead sulfate, $PbSO_4$.

SOLUTION

Analyze We are given the names and formulas of two ionic compounds and asked to predict whether they are soluble or insoluble in water.

Plan We can use Table 4.1 to answer the question. Thus, we need to focus on the anion in each compound because the table is organized by anions.

Solve

(a) According to Table 4.1, most carbonates are insoluble. But carbonates of the alkali metal cations (such as sodium ion) are an exception to this rule and are soluble. Thus, Na_2CO_3 is soluble in water.

(b) Table 4.1 indicates that although most sulfates are water soluble, the sulfate of Pb^{2+} is an exception. Thus, $PbSO_4$ is insoluble in water.

PRACTICE EXERCISE

Classify the following compounds as soluble or insoluble in water: **(a)** cobalt(II) hydroxide, **(b)** barium nitrate, **(c)** ammonium phosphate.

Answers: **(a)** insoluble, **(b)** soluble, **(c)** soluble

To predict whether a precipitate forms when we mix aqueous solutions of two strong electrolytes, we must (1) note the ions present in the reactants, (2) consider the possible cation-anion combinations, and (3) use Table 4.1 to determine if any of these combinations is insoluble. For example, will a precipitate form when solutions of $Mg(NO_3)_2$ and NaOH are mixed? Both substances are soluble ionic compounds and strong electrolytes. Mixing the solutions first produces a solution containing Mg^{2+}, NO_3^-, Na^+, and OH^- ions. Will either cation interact with either anion to form an insoluble compound? Knowing from Table 4.1 that $Mg(NO_3)_2$ and NaOH are both soluble in water, our only possibilities are Mg^{2+} with OH^- and Na^+ with NO_3^-. From Table 4.1 we see that hydroxides are generally insoluble. Because Mg^{2+} is not an exception, $Mg(OH)_2$ is insoluble and thus forms a precipitate. $NaNO_3$, however, is soluble, so Na^+ and NO_3^- remain in solution. The balanced equation for the precipitation reaction is

$$Mg(NO_3)_2(aq) + 2\,NaOH(aq) \longrightarrow Mg(OH)_2(s) + 2\,NaNO_3(aq) \quad [4.5]$$

Exchange (Metathesis) Reactions

Notice in Equation 4.5 that the reactant cations exchange anions—Mg^{2+} ends up with OH^-, and Na^+ ends up with NO_3^-. The chemical formulas of the products are based on the charges of the ions—two OH^- ions are needed to give a neutral compound with Mg^{2+}, and one NO_3^- ion is needed to give a neutral compound with Na^+. ∞ (Section 2.7) *The equation can be balanced only after the chemical formulas of the products have been determined.*

Reactions in which cations and anions appear to exchange partners conform to the general equation

$$AX + BY \longrightarrow AY + BX \qquad [4.6]$$

Example: $\qquad AgNO_3(aq) + KCl(aq) \longrightarrow AgCl(s) + KNO_3(aq)$

Such reactions are called either **exchange reactions** or **metathesis reactions** (meh-TATH-eh-sis, Greek for "to transpose"). Precipitation reactions conform to this pattern, as do many neutralization reactions between acids and bases, as we will see in Section 4.3.

To complete and balance the equation for a metathesis reaction, we follow these steps:

1. Use the chemical formulas of the reactants to determine which ions are present.
2. Write the chemical formulas of the products by combining the cation from one reactant with the anion of the other, using the ionic charges to determine the subscripts in the chemical formulas.
3. Check the water solubilities of the products. For a precipitation reaction to occur, at least one product must be insoluble in water.
4. Balance the equation.

SAMPLE EXERCISE 4.3 | **Predicting a Metathesis Reaction**

(a) Predict the identity of the precipitate that forms when aqueous solutions of $BaCl_2$ and K_2SO_4 are mixed. (b) Write the balanced chemical equation for the reaction.

SOLUTION

Analyze We are given two ionic reactants and asked to predict the insoluble product that they form.

Plan We need to write the ions present in the reactants and exchange the anions between the two cations. Once we have written the chemical formulas for these products, we can use Table 4.1 to determine which is insoluble in water. Knowing the products also allows us to write the equation for the reaction.

Solve

(a) The reactants contain Ba^{2+}, Cl^-, K^+, and SO_4^{2-} ions. Exchanging the anions gives us $BaSO_4$ and KCl. According to Table 4.1, most compounds of SO_4^{2-} are soluble but those of Ba^{2+} are not. Thus, $BaSO_4$ is insoluble and will precipitate from solution. KCl is soluble.

(b) From part (a) we know the chemical formulas of the products, $BaSO_4$ and KCl. The balanced equation is

$$BaCl_2(aq) + K_2SO_4(aq) \longrightarrow BaSO_4(s) + 2\ KCl(aq)$$

PRACTICE EXERCISE

(a) What compound precipitates when aqueous solutions of $Fe_2(SO_4)_3$ and $LiOH$ are mixed? (b) Write a balanced equation for the reaction. (c) Will a precipitate form when solutions of $Ba(NO_3)_2$ and KOH are mixed?

Answers: (a) $Fe(OH)_3$, (b) $Fe_2(SO_4)_3(aq) + 6\ LiOH(aq) \longrightarrow 2\ Fe(OH)_3(s) + 3\ Li_2SO_4(aq)$, (c) no (both possible products, $Ba(OH)_2$ and KNO_3, are water soluble)

Ionic Equations

In writing equations for reactions in aqueous solution, it is often useful to indicate whether the dissolved substances are present predominantly as ions or as molecules. Let's reconsider the precipitation reaction between $Pb(NO_3)_2$ and 2 KI:

$$Pb(NO_3)_2(aq) + 2\ KI(aq) \longrightarrow PbI_2(s) + 2\ KNO_3(aq)$$

An equation written in this fashion, showing the complete chemical formulas of reactants and products, is called a **molecular equation** because it shows chemical formulas without indicating ionic character. Because $Pb(NO_3)_2$, KI, and KNO_3 are all water-soluble ionic compounds and therefore strong electrolytes, we can write the equation in a form that indicates which species exist as ions in the solution:

$$Pb^{2+}(aq) + 2\,NO_3^-(aq) + 2\,K^+(aq) + 2\,I^-(aq) \longrightarrow$$
$$PbI_2(s) + 2\,K^+(aq) + 2\,NO_3^-(aq) \quad [4.7]$$

An equation written in this form, with all soluble strong electrolytes shown as ions, is called a **complete ionic equation**.

Notice that $K^+(aq)$ and $NO_3^-(aq)$ appear on both sides of Equation 4.7. Ions that appear in identical forms on both sides of a complete ionic equation, called **spectator ions**, play no direct role in the reaction. When spectator ions are omitted from the equation (they cancel out like algebraic quantities), we are left with the **net ionic equation**, which is one that includes only the ions and molecules directly involved in the reaction:

$$Pb^{2+}(aq) + 2\,I^-(aq) \longrightarrow PbI_2(s) \quad [4.8]$$

Because charge is conserved in reactions, the sum of the ionic charges must be the same on both sides of a balanced net ionic equation. In this case the 2+ charge of the cation and the two 1− charges of the anions add to zero, the charge of the electrically neutral product. *If every ion in a complete ionic equation is a spectator, no reaction occurs.*

 GIVE IT SOME THOUGHT

Which ions, if any, are spectator ions in the reaction $AgNO_3(aq) + NaCl(aq) \longrightarrow$ $AgCl(s) + NaNO_3(aq)$?

Net ionic equations illustrate the similarities between various reactions involving electrolytes. For example, Equation 4.8 expresses the essential feature of the precipitation reaction between any strong electrolyte containing $Pb^{2+}(aq)$ and any strong electrolyte containing $I^-(aq)$: The ions combine to form a precipitate of PbI_2. Thus, a net ionic equation demonstrates that more than one set of reactants can lead to the same net reaction. For example, aqueous solutions of KI and MgI_2 share many chemical similarities because both contain I^- ions. Either solution when mixed with a $Pb(NO_3)_2$ solution produces $PbI_2(s)$. The complete ionic equation, on the other hand, identifies the actual reactants that participate in a reaction.

The following steps summarize the procedure for writing net ionic equations:

1. Write a balanced molecular equation for the reaction.
2. Rewrite the equation to show the ions that form in solution when each soluble strong electrolyte dissociates into its ions. *Only strong electrolytes dissolved in aqueous solution are written in ionic form.*
3. Identify and cancel spectator ions.

SAMPLE EXERCISE 4.4   **Writing a Net Ionic Equation**

Write the net ionic equation for the precipitation reaction that occurs when aqueous solutions of calcium chloride and sodium carbonate are mixed.

SOLUTION

Analyze Our task is to write a net ionic equation for a precipitation reaction, given the names of the reactants present in solution.

Plan We write the chemical formulas of the reactants and products and then determine which product is insoluble. We then write and balance the molecular equation. Next, we write each soluble strong electrolyte as separated ions to obtain the complete ionic equation. Finally, we eliminate the spectator ions to obtain the net ionic equation.

Solve Calcium chloride is composed of calcium ions, Ca^{2+}, and chloride ions, Cl^-; hence, an aqueous solution of the substance is $CaCl_2(aq)$. Sodium carbonate is composed of Na^+ ions and CO_3^{2-} ions; hence, an aqueous solution of the compound is $Na_2CO_3(aq)$. In the molecular

▲ **FIGURE 4.5** Vinegar and lemon juice are common household acids. Ammonia and baking soda (sodium bicarbonate) are common household bases.

equations for precipitation reactions, the anions and cations appear to exchange partners. Thus, we put Ca^{2+} and CO_3^{2-} together to give $CaCO_3$ and Na^+ and Cl^- together to give $NaCl$. According to the solubility guidelines in Table 4.1, $CaCO_3$ is insoluble and $NaCl$ is soluble. The balanced molecular equation is

$$CaCl_2(aq) + Na_2CO_3(aq) \longrightarrow CaCO_3(s) + 2\,NaCl(aq)$$

In a complete ionic equation, *only* dissolved strong electrolytes (such as soluble ionic compounds) are written as separate ions. As the (aq) designations remind us, $CaCl_2$, Na_2CO_3, and $NaCl$ are all dissolved in the solution. Furthermore, they are all strong electrolytes. $CaCO_3$ is an ionic compound, but it is not soluble. We do not write the formula of any insoluble compound as its component ions. Thus, the complete ionic equation is

$$Ca^{2+}(aq) + 2\,Cl^-(aq) + 2\,Na^+(aq) + CO_3^{2-}(aq) \longrightarrow$$
$$CaCO_3(s) + 2\,Na^+(aq) + 2\,Cl^-(aq)$$

Cl^- and Na^+ are spectator ions. Canceling them gives the following net ionic equation:

$$Ca^{2+}(aq) + CO_3^{2-}(aq) \longrightarrow CaCO_3(s)$$

Check We can check our result by confirming that both the elements and the electric charge are balanced. Each side has one Ca, one C, and three O, and the net charge on each side equals 0.

Comment If none of the ions in an ionic equation is removed from solution or changed in some way, all ions are spectator ions and a reaction does not occur.

PRACTICE EXERCISE

Write the net ionic equation for the precipitation reaction that occurs when aqueous solutions of silver nitrate and potassium phosphate are mixed.

Answer: $3\,Ag^+(aq) + PO_4^{3-}(aq) \longrightarrow Ag_3PO_4(s)$

4.3 | ACIDS, BASES, AND NEUTRALIZATION REACTIONS

Many acids and bases are industrial and household substances (◀ **FIGURE 4.5**), and some are important components of biological fluids. Hydrochloric acid, for example, is an important industrial chemical and the main constituent of gastric juice in your stomach. Acids and bases are also common electrolytes.

Acids

As noted in Section 2.8, **acids** are substances that ionize in aqueous solution to form hydrogen ions $H^+(aq)$. Because a hydrogen atom consists of a proton and an electron, H^+ is simply a proton. Thus, acids are often called *proton donors*. Molecular models of three common acids are shown in ◀ **FIGURE 4.6**.

Protons in aqueous solution are solvated by water molecules, just as other cations are [Figure 4.3(a)]. In writing chemical equations involving protons in water, therefore, we write $H^+(aq)$.

Molecules of different acids ionize to form different numbers of H^+ ions. Both HCl and HNO_3 are *monoprotic* acids, yielding one H^+ per molecule of acid. Sulfuric acid, H_2SO_4, is a *diprotic* acid, one that yields two H^+ per molecule of acid. The ionization of H_2SO_4 and other diprotic acids occurs in two steps:

$$H_2SO_4(aq) \longrightarrow H^+(aq) + HSO_4^-(aq) \qquad [4.9]$$
$$HSO_4^-(aq) \rightleftharpoons H^+(aq) + SO_4^{2-}(aq) \qquad [4.10]$$

Although H_2SO_4 is a strong electrolyte, only the first ionization (Equation 4.9) is complete. Thus, aqueous solutions of sulfuric acid contain a mixture of $H^+(aq)$, $HSO_4^-(aq)$, and $SO_4^{2-}(aq)$.

The molecule CH_3COOH (acetic acid) that we have mentioned frequently is the primary component in vinegar. Acetic acid has four hydrogens, as Figure 4.6 shows, but only one of them, the H in the COOH group, is ionized in water. The three other hydrogens are bound to carbon and do not break their C—H bonds in water.

Hydrochloric acid, HCl

Nitric acid, HNO_3

| H |
| Cl |
| N |
| O |
| C |

Acetic acid, CH_3COOH

▲ **FIGURE 4.6** Molecular models of three common acids.

GIVE IT SOME THOUGHT

The structural formula of citric acid, a main component of citrus fruits, is

▲ **FIGURE 4.7   Hydrogen ion transfer.** An H_2O molecule acts as a proton donor (acid), and NH_3 acts as a proton acceptor (base). Only a fraction of the NH_3 molecules react with H_2O. Consequently, NH_3 is a weak electrolyte.

$$
\begin{array}{c}
\text{H} \\
| \\
\text{H}-\text{C}-\text{COOH} \\
| \\
\text{HO}-\text{C}-\text{COOH} \\
| \\
\text{H}-\text{C}-\text{COOH} \\
| \\
\text{H}
\end{array}
$$

How many $H^+(aq)$ can be generated by each citric acid molecule dissolved in water?

Bases

Bases are substances that accept (react with) H^+ ions. Bases produce hydroxide ions (OH^-) when they dissolve in water. Ionic hydroxide compounds, such as NaOH, KOH, and $Ca(OH)_2$, are among the most common bases. When dissolved in water, they dissociate into ions, introducing OH^- ions into the solution.

Compounds that do not contain OH^- ions can also be bases. For example, ammonia (NH_3) is a common base. When added to water, it accepts an H^+ ion from a water molecule and thereby produces an OH^- ion (▶ **FIGURE 4.7**):

$$NH_3(aq) + H_2O(l) \rightleftharpoons NH_4^+(aq) + OH^-(aq) \qquad [4.11]$$

Ammonia is a weak electrolyte because only about 1% of the NH_3 forms NH_4^+ and OH^- ions.

Strong and Weak Acids and Bases

Acids and bases that are strong electrolytes (completely ionized in solution) are **strong acids** and **strong bases**. Those that are weak electrolytes (partly ionized) are **weak acids** and **weak bases**. When reactivity depends only on $H^+(aq)$ concentration, strong acids are more reactive than weak acids. The reactivity of an acid, however, can depend on the anion as well as on $H^+(aq)$ concentration. For example, hydrofluoric acid (HF) is a weak acid (only partly ionized in aqueous solution), but it is very reactive and vigorously attacks many substances, including glass. This reactivity is due to the combined action of $H^+(aq)$ and $F^-(aq)$.

▼ **TABLE 4.2** lists the strong acids and bases we are most likely to encounter. You need to commit this information to memory in order to correctly identify strong electrolytes and write net ionic equations. The brevity of this list tells us that most acids are weak. (For H_2SO_4, as we noted earlier, only the first proton completely ionizes.) The only common strong bases are the common soluble metal hydroxides. Most other metal hydroxides are insoluble in water. The most common weak base is NH_3, which reacts with water to form OH^- ions (Equation 4.11).

TABLE 4.2 • Common Strong Acids and Bases	
Strong Acids	**Strong Bases**
Hydrochloric, HCl	Group 1A metal hydroxides [LiOH, NaOH, KOH, RbOH, CsOH]
Hydrobromic, HBr	Heavy group 2A metal hydroxides [$Ca(OH)_2$, $Sr(OH)_2$, $Ba(OH)_2$]
Hydroiodic, HI	
Chloric, $HClO_3$	
Perchloric, $HClO_4$	
Nitric, HNO_3	
Sulfuric, H_2SO_4	

▲ **GIVE IT SOME THOUGHT**

Why isn't $Al(OH)_3$ classified as a strong base?

SAMPLE EXERCISE 4.5 | **Comparing Acid Strengths**

The following diagrams represent aqueous solutions of acids HX, HY, and HZ, with water molecules omitted for clarity. Rank the acids from strongest to weakest.

HX	HY	HZ

SOLUTION

Analyze We are asked to rank three acids from strongest to weakest, based on schematic drawings of their solutions.

Plan We can determine the relative numbers of uncharged molecular species in the diagrams. The strongest acid is the one with the most H^+ ions and fewest undissociated molecules in solution. The weakest acid is the one with the largest number of undissociated molecules.

Solve The order is HY > HZ > HX. HY is a strong acid because it is totally ionized (no HY molecules in solution), whereas both HX and HZ are weak acids, whose solutions consist of a mixture of molecules and ions. Because HZ contains more H^+ ions and fewer molecules than HX, it is a stronger acid.

PRACTICE EXERCISE

Imagine a diagram showing 10 Na^+ ions and 10 OH^- ions. If this solution were mixed with the one pictured above for HY, what species would be present in a diagram that represents the combined solutions after any possible reaction?

Answer: The diagram would show 10 Na^+ ions, 2 OH^- ions, 8 Y^- ions, and 8 H_2O molecules.

Identifying Strong and Weak Electrolytes

If we remember the common strong acids and bases (Table 4.2) and also remember that NH_3 is a weak base, we can make reasonable predictions about the electrolytic strength of a great number of *water-soluble* substances. ▼ TABLE 4.3 summarizes our observations about electrolytes. To classify a soluble substance as strong electrolyte, weak electrolyte, or nonelectrolyte, we work our way down and across this table. We first ask whether the substance is ionic or molecular. If it is ionic, it is a strong electrolyte. The second column of Table 4.3 tells us that all ionic compounds are strong electrolytes. If the substance is molecular, we ask whether it is an acid or a base. (It is an acid if it either has H first in the chemical formula or contains a COOH group.) If it is an acid, we use Table 4.2 to determine whether it is a strong or weak electrolyte: All strong acids are strong electrolytes, and all weak acids are weak electrolytes. If an acid is not listed in Table 4.2, it is probably a weak acid and therefore a weak electrolyte.

TABLE 4.3 • **Summary of the Electrolytic Behavior of Common Soluble Ionic and Molecular Compounds**

	Strong Electrolyte	Weak Electrolyte	Nonelectrolyte
Ionic	All	None	None
Molecular	Strong acids (see Table 4.2)	Weak acids, weak bases	All other compounds

If our substance is a base, we use Table 4.2 to determine whether it is a strong base. NH_3 is the only molecular base that we consider in this chapter, and Table 4.3 tells us it is a weak electrolyte. Finally, any molecular substance that we encounter in this chapter that is not an acid or NH_3 is probably a nonelectrolyte.

SAMPLE EXERCISE 4.6   Identifying Strong, Weak, and Nonelectrolytes

Classify these dissolved substances as strong, weak, or nonelectrolyte: $CaCl_2$, HNO_3, C_2H_5OH (ethanol), $HCOOH$ (formic acid), KOH.

SOLUTION

Analyze We are given several chemical formulas and asked to classify each substance as a strong electrolyte, weak electrolyte, or nonelectrolyte.

Plan The approach we take is outlined in Table 4.3. We can predict whether a substance is ionic or molecular based on its composition. As we saw in Section 2.7, most ionic compounds we encounter in this text are composed of a metal and a nonmetal, whereas most molecular compounds are composed only of nonmetals.

Solve Two compounds fit the criteria for ionic compounds: $CaCl_2$ and KOH. Because Table 4.3 tells us that all ionic compounds are strong electrolytes, that is how we classify these two substances. The three remaining compounds are molecular. Two, HNO_3 and $HCOOH$, are acids. Nitric acid, HNO_3, is a common strong acid, as shown in Table 4.2, and therefore is a strong electrolyte. Because most acids are weak acids, our best guess would be that $HCOOH$ is a weak acid (weak electrolyte). This is correct. The remaining molecular compound, C_2H_5OH, is neither an acid nor a base, so it is a nonelectrolyte.

Comment Although C_2H_5OH has an OH group, it is not a metal hydroxide and so not a base. Rather, it is a member of a class of organic compounds that have C—OH bonds, which are known as alcohols. ∞ (Section 2.9) Organic compounds containing the COOH group are called carboxylic acids (Chapter 16). Molecules that have this group are weak acids.

PRACTICE EXERCISE

Consider solutions in which 0.1 mol of each of the following compounds is dissolved in 1 L of water: $Ca(NO_3)_2$ (calcium nitrate), $C_6H_{12}O_6$ (glucose), $NaCH_3COO$ (sodium acetate), and CH_3COOH (acetic acid). Rank the solutions in order of increasing electrical conductivity, based on the fact that the greater the number of ions in solution, the greater the conductivity.

Answers: $C_6H_{12}O_6$ (nonelectrolyte) $<$ CH_3COOH (weak electrolyte, existing mainly in the form of molecules with few ions) $<$ $NaCH_3COO$ (strong electrolyte that provides two ions, Na^+ and CH_3COO^-) $<$ $Ca(NO_3)_2$ (strong electrolyte that provides three ions, Ca^{2+} and $2 NO_3^-$)

Neutralization Reactions and Salts

The properties of acidic solutions are quite different from those of basic solutions. Acids have a sour taste, whereas bases have a bitter taste.* Acids change the colors of certain dyes in a way that differs from the way bases affect the same dyes. This is the principle behind the indicator known as litmus paper (▶ FIGURE 4.8). In addition, acidic and basic solutions differ in chemical properties in several other important ways that we explore in this chapter and in later chapters.

When a solution of an acid and a solution of a base are mixed, a **neutralization reaction** occurs. The products of the reaction have none of the characteristic properties of either the acidic solution or the basic solution. For example, when hydrochloric acid is mixed with a solution of sodium hydroxide, the reaction is

Base turns litmus paper blue

Acid turns litmus paper red

$$\underset{\text{(acid)}}{HCl(aq)} + \underset{\text{(base)}}{NaOH(aq)} \longrightarrow \underset{\text{(water)}}{H_2O(l)} + \underset{\text{(salt)}}{NaCl(aq)} \qquad [4.12]$$

▲ **FIGURE 4.8 Litmus paper.** Litmus paper is coated with dyes that change color in response to exposure to either acids or bases.

---

*Tasting chemical solutions is not a good practice. However, we have all had acids such as ascorbic acid (vitamin C), acetylsalicylic acid (aspirin), and citric acid (in citrus fruits) in our mouths, and we are familiar with their characteristic sour taste. Soaps, which are basic, have the characteristic bitter taste of bases.

Water and table salt, NaCl, are the products of the reaction. By analogy to this reaction, the term **salt** has come to mean any ionic compound whose cation comes from a base (for example, Na^+ from NaOH) and whose anion comes from an acid (for example, Cl^- from HCl). In general, *a neutralization reaction between an acid and a metal hydroxide produces water and a salt.*

Because HCl, NaOH, and NaCl are all water-soluble strong electrolytes, the complete ionic equation associated with Equation 4.12 is

$$H^+(aq) + Cl^-(aq) + Na^+(aq) + OH^-(aq) \longrightarrow$$
$$H_2O(l) + Na^+(aq) + Cl^-(aq) \qquad [4.13]$$

Therefore, the net ionic equation is

$$H^+(aq) + OH^-(aq) \longrightarrow H_2O(l) \qquad [4.14]$$

Equation 4.14 summarizes the main feature of the neutralization reaction between any strong acid and any strong base: $H^+(aq)$ and $OH^-(aq)$ ions combine to form H_2O.

▼ FIGURE 4.9 shows the neutralization reaction between hydrochloric acid and the water-insoluble base $Mg(OH)_2$:

Molecular equation:

$$Mg(OH)_2(s) + 2\,HCl(aq) \longrightarrow MgCl_2(aq) + 2\,H_2O(l) \qquad [4.15]$$

Net ionic equation:

$$Mg(OH)_2(s) + 2\,H^+(aq) \longrightarrow Mg^{2+}(aq) + 2\,H_2O(l) \qquad [4.16]$$

Notice that the OH^- ions (this time in a solid reactant) and H^+ ions combine to form H_2O. Because the ions exchange partners, neutralization reactions between acids and metal hydroxides are metathesis reactions.

◢ GO FIGURE

Adding just a few drops of hydrochloric acid would not be sufficient to dissolve all the $Mg(OH)_2(s)$. Why not?

Reactants
$Mg(OH)_2(s) + 2\,HCl(aq)$

$H^+(aq)$ combines with hydroxide ions in $Mg(OH)_2(s)$, forming $H_2O(l)$

Products
$MgCl_2(aq) + 2\,H_2O(l)$

▲ FIGURE 4.9 **Neutralization reaction between $Mg(OH)_2(s)$ and hydrochloric acid.** Milk of magnesia is a suspension of water-insoluble magnesium hydroxide, $Mg(OH)_2(s)$, in water. When sufficient hydrochloric acid, HCl(*aq*), is added a reaction ensues that leads to an aqueous solution containing $Mg^{2+}(aq)$ and $Cl^-(aq)$ ions.

SAMPLE EXERCISE 4.7   **Writing Chemical Equations for a Neutralization Reaction**

For the reaction between aqueous solutions of acetic acid (CH_3COOH) and barium hydroxide, $Ba(OH)_2$, write **(a)** the balanced molecular equation, **(b)** the complete ionic equation, **(c)** the net ionic equation.

SOLUTION

Analyze We are given the chemical formulas for an acid and a base and asked to write a balanced molecular equation, a complete ionic equation, and a net ionic equation for their neutralization reaction.

Plan As Equation 4.12 and the italicized statement that follows it indicate, neutralization reactions form two products, H_2O and a salt. We examine the cation of the base and the anion of the acid to determine the composition of the salt.

Solve

(a) The salt contains the cation of the base (Ba^{2+}) and the anion of the acid (CH_3COO^-). Thus, the salt formula is $Ba(CH_3COO)_2$. According to Table 4.1, this compound is soluble in water. The unbalanced molecular equation for the neutralization reaction is

$$CH_3COOH(aq) + Ba(OH)_2(aq) \longrightarrow H_2O(l) + Ba(CH_3COO)_2(aq)$$

To balance this equation, we must provide two molecules of CH_3COOH to furnish the two CH_3COO^- ions and to supply the two H^+ ions needed to combine with the two OH^- ions of the base. The balanced molecular equation is

$$2\,CH_3COOH(aq) + Ba(OH)_2(aq) \longrightarrow$$
$$2\,H_2O(l) + Ba(CH_3COO)_2(aq)$$

(b) To write the complete ionic equation, we identify the strong electrolytes and break them into ions. In this case $Ba(OH)_2$ and $Ba(CH_3COO)_2$ are both water-soluble ionic compounds and hence strong electrolytes. Thus, the complete ionic equation is

$$2\,CH_3COOH(aq) + Ba^{2+}(aq) + 2\,OH^-(aq) \longrightarrow$$
$$2\,H_2O(l) + Ba^{2+}(aq) + 2\,CH_3COO^-(aq)$$

(c) Eliminating the spectator ion, Ba^{2+}, and simplifying coefficients gives the net ionic equation:

$$2\,CH_3COOH(aq) + 2\,OH^-(aq) \longrightarrow 2\,H_2O(l) + 2\,CH_3COO^-(aq)$$
$$CH_3COOH(aq) + OH^-(aq) \longrightarrow H_2O(l) + CH_3COO^-(aq)$$

Check We can determine whether the molecular equation is balanced by counting the number of atoms of each kind on both sides of the arrow (10 H, 6 O, 4 C, and 1 Ba on each side). However, it is often easier to check equations by counting groups: There are

2 CH_3COO groups, as well as 1 Ba, and 4 additional H atoms and 2 additional O atoms on each side of the equation. The net ionic equation checks out because the numbers of each kind of element and the net charge are the same on both sides of the equation.

PRACTICE EXERCISE

For the reaction of phosphorous acid (H_3PO_3) and potassium hydroxide (KOH), write **(a)** the balanced molecular equation and **(b)** the net ionic equation.

Answers: (a) $H_3PO_3(aq) + 3\,KOH(aq) \longrightarrow 3\,H_2O(l) + K_3PO_3(aq)$,
(b) $H_3PO_3(aq) + 3\,OH^-(aq) \longrightarrow 3\,H_2O(l) + PO_3^{3-}(aq)$. ($H_3PO_3$ is a weak acid and therefore a weak electrolyte, whereas KOH, a strong base, and K_3PO_3, an ionic compound, are strong electrolytes.)

Neutralization Reactions with Gas Formation

Many bases besides OH^- react with H^+ to form molecular compounds. Two of these that you might encounter in the laboratory are the sulfide ion and the carbonate ion. Both of these anions react with acids to form gases that have low solubilities in water. Hydrogen sulfide (H_2S), the substance that gives rotten eggs their foul odor, forms when an acid such as HCl(aq) reacts with a metal sulfide such as Na_2S:

Molecular equation:

$$2\,HCl(aq) + Na_2S(aq) \longrightarrow H_2S(g) + 2\,NaCl(aq) \qquad [4.17]$$

Net ionic equation:

$$2\,H^+(aq) + S^{2-}(aq) \longrightarrow H_2S(g) \qquad [4.18]$$

Carbonates and bicarbonates react with acids to form $CO_2(g)$. Reaction of CO_3^{2-} or HCO_3^- with an acid first gives carbonic acid (H_2CO_3). For example, when hydrochloric acid is added to sodium bicarbonate, the reaction is

$$HCl(aq) + NaHCO_3(aq) \longrightarrow NaCl(aq) + H_2CO_3(aq) \qquad [4.19]$$

Carbonic acid is unstable. If present in solution in sufficient concentrations, it decomposes to H_2O and CO_2, which escapes from the solution as a gas:

$$H_2CO_3(aq) \longrightarrow H_2O(l) + CO_2(g) \qquad [4.20]$$

The overall reaction is summarized by the equations

Molecular equation:

$$HCl(aq) + NaHCO_3(aq) \longrightarrow NaCl(aq) + H_2O(l) + CO_2(g) \qquad [4.21]$$

Net ionic equation:

$$H^+(aq) + HCO_3^-(aq) \longrightarrow H_2O(l) + CO_2(g) \qquad [4.22]$$

Both $NaHCO_3(s)$ and $Na_2CO_3(s)$ are used as neutralizers in acid spills, either salt is added until the fizzing caused by $CO_2(g)$ formation stops. Sometimes sodium bicarbonate is used as an antacid to soothe an upset stomach. In that case the HCO_3^- reacts with stomach acid to form $CO_2(g)$.

 GIVE IT SOME THOUGHT

By analogy to examples given in the text, predict what gas forms when $Na_2SO_3(s)$ reacts with $HCl(aq)$.

CHEMISTRY PUT TO WORK

Antacids

Your stomach secretes acids to help digest foods. These acids, which include hydrochloric acid, contain about 0.1 mol of H^+ per liter of solution. The stomach and digestive tract are normally protected from the corrosive effects of stomach acid by a mucosal lining. Holes can develop in this lining, however, allowing the acid to attack the underlying tissue, causing painful damage. These holes, known as ulcers, can be caused by the secretion of excess acids or by a weakness in the digestive lining. Studies indicate, however, that many ulcers are caused by bacterial infection. Between 10 and 20% of Americans suffer from ulcers at some point in their lives. Many others experience occasional indigestion or heartburn due to digestive acids entering the esophagus.

We can address the problem of excess stomach acid in two ways: (1) removing the excess acid or (2) decreasing the production of acid. Substances that remove excess acid are called *antacids*, whereas those that decrease acid production are called *acid inhibitors*. ◄ FIGURE 4.10 shows several common over-the-counter antacids, which usually contain hydroxide, carbonate, or bicarbonate ions (▼ TABLE 4.4). Antiulcer drugs, such as Tagamet® and Zantac®, are acid inhibitors. They act on acid-producing cells in the lining of the stomach. Formulations that control acid in this way are now available as over-the-counter drugs.

RELATED EXERCISE: 4.95

▲ FIGURE 4.10 **Antacids.** These products all serve as acid-neutralizing agents in the stomach.

TABLE 4.4 • Some Common Antacids	
Commercial Name	**Acid-Neutralizing Agents**
Alka-Seltzer®	$NaHCO_3$
Amphojel®	$Al(OH)_3$
Di-Gel®	$Mg(OH)_2$ and $CaCO_3$
Milk of Magnesia	$Mg(OH)_2$
Maalox®	$Mg(OH)_2$ and $Al(OH)_3$
Mylanta®	$Mg(OH)_2$ and $Al(OH)_3$
Rolaids®	$NaAl(OH)_2CO_3$
Tums®	$CaCO_3$

4.4 | OXIDATION-REDUCTION REACTIONS

In precipitation reactions, cations and anions come together to form an insoluble ionic compound. In neutralization reactions, H^+ ions and OH^- ions come together to form H_2O molecules. Now let's consider a third kind of reaction, one in which electrons are transferred from one reactant to another. Such reactions are called either **oxidation-reduction reactions** or **redox reactions**. In this chapter we concentrate on redox reactions where one of the reactants is a metal in its elemental form.

Oxidation and Reduction

One of the most familiar redox reactions is *corrosion* of a metal (▼ FIGURE 4.11). In some instances corrosion is limited to the surface of the metal, with the green coating that forms on copper roofs and statues being one such case. In other instances the corrosion goes deeper, eventually compromising the structural integrity of the metal. Iron rusting is an important example.

Corrosion is the conversion of a metal into a metal compound by a reaction between the metal and some substance in its environment. When a metal corrodes, each metal atom loses electrons and so forms a cation, which can combine with an anion to form an ionic compound. The green coating on the Statue of Liberty contains Cu^{2+} combined with carbonate and hydroxide anions, rust contains Fe^{3+} combined with oxide and hydroxide anions, and silver tarnish contains Ag^+ combined with sulfide anions.

When an atom, ion, or molecule becomes more positively charged (that is, when it loses electrons), we say that it has been oxidized. *Loss of electrons by a substance is called* **oxidation**. The term *oxidation* is used because the first reactions of this sort to be studied were reactions with oxygen. Many metals react directly with O_2 in air to form metal oxides. In these reactions the metal loses electrons to oxygen, forming an ionic compound of the metal ion and oxide ion. The familiar example of rusting involves the reaction between iron metal and oxygen in the presence of water. In this process Fe is *oxidized* (loses electrons) to form Fe^{3+}.

The reaction between iron and oxygen tends to be relatively slow, but other metals, such as the alkali and alkaline earth metals, react quickly upon exposure to air. ▶ FIGURE 4.12 shows how the bright metallic surface of calcium tarnishes as CaO forms in the reaction

$$2\,Ca(s) + O_2(g) \longrightarrow 2\,CaO(s) \qquad [4.23]$$

In this reaction Ca is oxidized to Ca^{2+} and neutral O_2 is transformed to O^{2-} ions. When an atom, ion, or molecule becomes more negatively charged (gains electrons), we say that it is *reduced. The gain of electrons by a substance is called* **reduction**. When one reactant loses electrons (that is, when it is *oxidized*), another reactant must gain them. In other words, oxidation of one substance must be accompanied by reduction of some other substance.

(a)　　　　　　　　　　　(b)　　　　　　　　　　　(c)

▲ **FIGURE 4.11 Familiar corrosion products.** (a) A green coating forms when copper is oxidized. (b) Rust forms when iron corrodes. (c) A black tarnish forms as silver corrodes.

Ca(*s*) is oxidized (loses electrons)   O$_2$(*g*) is reduced (gains electrons)   Ca^{2+} and O^{2-} ions combine to form CaO(*s*)

Reactants
2 Ca(*s*) + O$_2$(*g*)

Products
2 CaO(*s*)

▲ **FIGURE 4.12 Oxidation of calcium metal by molecular oxygen.** The oxidation involves transfer of electrons from the calcium metal to the O$_2$, leading to formation of CaO.

Oxidation Numbers

Before we can identify an oxidation-reduction reaction, we must have a bookkeeping system—a way of keeping track of electrons gained by the substance being reduced and electrons lost by the substance being oxidized. The concept of oxidation numbers (also called *oxidation states*) was devised as a way of doing this. Each atom in a neutral substance or ion is assigned an **oxidation number**. For monatomic ions the oxidation number is the same as the charge. For neutral molecules and polyatomic ions, the oxidation number of a given atom is a hypothetical charge. This charge is assigned by artificially dividing up the electrons among the atoms in the molecule or ion. We use the following rules for assigning oxidation numbers:

1. *For an atom in its **elemental form**, the oxidation number is always zero.* Thus, each H atom in the H$_2$ molecule has an oxidation number of 0 and each P atom in the P$_4$ molecule has an oxidation number of 0.

2. *For any **monatomic ion** the oxidation number equals the ionic charge.* Thus, K$^+$ has an oxidation number of +1, S^{2-} has an oxidation number of −2, and so forth. In ionic compounds the alkali metal ions (group 1A) always have a 1+ charge and therefore an oxidation number of +1. The alkaline earth metals (group 2A) are always +2, and aluminum (group 3A) is always +3 in ionic compounds. (In writing oxidation numbers we will write the sign before the number to distinguish them from the actual electronic charges, which we write with the number first.)

3. **Nonmetals** usually have negative oxidation numbers, although they can sometimes be positive:

   (a) *The oxidation number of **oxygen** is usually −2 in both ionic and molecular compounds.* The major exception is in compounds called peroxides, which contain the O$_2{}^{2-}$ ion, giving each oxygen an oxidation number of −1.

   (b) *The oxidation number of **hydrogen** is usually +1 when bonded to nonmetals and −1 when bonded to metals.*

   (c) *The oxidation number of **fluorine** is −1 in all compounds.* The other **halogens** have an oxidation number of −1 in most binary compounds. When combined with oxygen, as in oxyanions, however, they have positive oxidation states.

4. ***The sum of the oxidation numbers** of all atoms in a neutral compound is zero. The sum of the oxidation numbers in a polyatomic ion equals the charge of the ion.* For example, in the hydronium ion H$_3$O$^+$ the oxidation number of each hydrogen is +1 and that of oxygen is −2. Thus, the sum of the oxidation numbers is $3(+1) + (-2) = +1$, which equals the net charge of the ion. This rule is useful in obtaining the oxidation number of one atom in a compound or ion if you know the oxidation numbers of the other atoms, as illustrated in Sample Exercise 4.8.

It's important to remember that in every oxidation-reduction reaction, the oxidation numbers of at least two atoms must change. The oxidation number increases for any atom that is oxidized and decreases for any atom that is reduced.

GIVE IT SOME THOUGHT

What is the oxidation number of nitrogen (a) in aluminum nitride, AlN, and (b) in nitric acid, HNO_3?

SAMPLE EXERCISE 4.8   **Determining Oxidation Numbers**

Determine the oxidation number of sulfur in **(a)** H_2S, **(b)** S_8, **(c)** SCl_2, **(d)** Na_2SO_3, **(e)** SO_4^{2-}.

SOLUTION

Analyze We are asked to determine the oxidation number of sulfur in two molecular species, in the elemental form, and in two substances containing ions.

Plan In each species the sum of oxidation numbers of all the atoms must equal the charge on the species. We will use the rules outlined previously to assign oxidation numbers.

Solve

(a) When bonded to a nonmetal, hydrogen has an oxidation number of $+1$ (rule 3b). Because the H_2S molecule is neutral, the sum of the oxidation numbers must equal zero (rule 4). Letting x equal the oxidation number of S, we have $2(+1) + x = 0$. Thus, S has an oxidation number of -2.

(b) Because this is an elemental form of sulfur, the oxidation number of S is 0 (rule 1).

(c) Because this is a binary compound, we expect chlorine to have an oxidation number of -1 (rule 3c). The sum of the oxidation numbers must equal zero (rule 4). Letting x equal the oxidation number of S, we have $x + 2(-1) = 0$. Consequently, the oxidation number of S must be $+2$.

(d) Sodium, an alkali metal, always has an oxidation number of $+1$ in its compounds (rule 2). Oxygen has a common oxidation state of -2 (rule 3a). Letting x equal the oxidation number of S, we have $2(+1) + x + 3(-2) = 0$. Therefore, the oxidation number of S in this compound is $+4$.

(e) The oxidation state of O is -2 (rule 3a). The sum of the oxidation numbers equals -2, the net charge of the SO_4^{2-} ion (rule 4). Thus, we have $x + 4(-2) = -2$. From this relation we conclude that the oxidation number of S in this ion is $+6$.

Comment These examples illustrate that the oxidation number of a given element depends on the compound in which it occurs. The oxidation numbers of sulfur, as seen in these examples, range from -2 to $+6$.

PRACTICE EXERCISE

What is the oxidation state of the boldfaced element in **(a)** $\mathbf{P}_2O_5$, **(b)** $Na\mathbf{H}$, **(c)** $\mathbf{Cr}_2O_7^{2-}$, **(d)** $\mathbf{Sn}Br_4$, **(e)** $Ba\mathbf{O}_2$?
Answers: **(a)** $+5$, **(b)** -1, **(c)** $+6$, **(d)** $+4$, **(e)** -1

Oxidation of Metals by Acids and Salts

The reaction between a metal and either an acid or a metal salt conforms to the general pattern

$$A + BX \longrightarrow AX + B \qquad [4.24]$$

Examples:
$$Zn(s) + 2\,HBr(aq) \longrightarrow ZnBr_2(aq) + H_2(g)$$

$$Mn(s) + Pb(NO_3)_2(aq) \longrightarrow Mn(NO_3)_2(aq) + Pb(s)$$

These reactions are called **displacement reactions** because the ion in solution is *displaced* (replaced) through oxidation of an element.

▲ **FIGURE 4.13** **Reaction of magnesium metal with hydrochloric acid.** The metal is readily oxidized by the acid, producing hydrogen gas, $H_2(g)$, and $MgCl_2(aq)$.

Many metals undergo displacement reactions with acids, producing salts and hydrogen gas. For example, magnesium metal reacts with hydrochloric acid to form magnesium chloride and hydrogen gas (▲ **FIGURE 4.13**):

$$Mg(s) + 2\,HCl(aq) \longrightarrow MgCl_2(aq) + H_2(g) \qquad [4.25]$$

Oxidation number $\quad 0 \qquad +1\ -1 \qquad +2\ -1 \qquad 0$

The oxidation number of Mg changes from 0 to $+2$, an increase that indicates the atom has lost electrons and has therefore been oxidized. The oxidation number of H^+ in the acid decreases from $+1$ to 0, indicating that this ion has gained electrons and has therefore been reduced. Chlorine has an oxidation number of -1 both before and after the reaction, indicating that it is neither oxidized nor reduced. In fact the Cl^- ions are spectator ions, dropping out of the net ionic equation:

$$Mg(s) + 2\,H^+(aq) \longrightarrow Mg^{2+}(aq) + H_2(g) \qquad [4.26]$$

Metals can also be oxidized by aqueous solutions of various salts. Iron metal, for example, is oxidized to Fe^{2+} by aqueous solutions of Ni^{2+} such as $Ni(NO_3)_2(aq)$:

Molecular equation: $\quad Fe(s) + Ni(NO_3)_2(aq) \longrightarrow Fe(NO_3)_2(aq) + Ni(s) \quad [4.27]$

Net ionic equation: $\quad\quad Fe(s) + Ni^{2+}(aq) \longrightarrow Fe^{2+}(aq) + Ni(s) \quad [4.28]$

The oxidation of Fe to Fe^{2+} in this reaction is accompanied by the reduction of Ni^{2+} to Ni. Remember: *Whenever one substance is oxidized, another substance must be reduced.*

SAMPLE EXERCISE 4.9   **Writing Equations for Oxidation-Reduction Reactions**

Write the balanced molecular and net ionic equations for the reaction of aluminum with hydrobromic acid.

SOLUTION

Analyze We must write two equations—molecular and net ionic—for the redox reaction between a metal and an acid.

Plan Metals react with acids to form salts and H_2 gas. To write the balanced equations, we must write the chemical formulas for the two reactants and then determine the formula of the salt, which is composed of the cation formed by the metal and the anion of the acid.

Solve The reactants are Al and HBr. The cation formed by Al is Al^{3+}, and the anion from hydrobromic acid is Br^-. Thus, the salt formed in the reaction is $AlBr_3$. Writing the reactants and products and then balancing the equation gives the molecular equation:

$$2\,Al(s) + 6\,HBr(aq) \longrightarrow 2\,AlBr_3(aq) + 3\,H_2(g)$$

Both HBr and $AlBr_3$ are soluble strong electrolytes. Thus, the complete ionic equation is

$$2\,Al(s) + 6\,H^+(aq) + 6\,Br^-(aq) \longrightarrow 2\,Al^{3+}(aq) + 6\,Br^-(aq) + 3\,H_2(g)$$

Because Br^- is a spectator ion, the net ionic equation is

$$2\,Al(s) + 6\,H^+(aq) \longrightarrow 2\,Al^{3+}(aq) + 3\,H_2(g)$$

Comment The substance oxidized is the aluminum metal because its oxidation state changes from 0 in the metal to +3 in the cation, thereby increasing in oxidation number. The H^+ is reduced because its oxidation state changes from +1 in the acid to 0 in H_2.

PRACTICE EXERCISE

(a) Write the balanced molecular and net ionic equations for the reaction between magnesium and cobalt(II) sulfate. (b) What is oxidized and what is reduced in the reaction?

Answers: (a) $Mg(s) + CoSO_4(aq) \longrightarrow MgSO_4(aq) + Co(s)$;
$Mg(s) + Co^{2+}(aq) \longrightarrow Mg^{2+}(aq) + Co(s)$, (b) Mg is oxidized and Co^{2+} is reduced.

The Activity Series

Can we predict whether a certain metal will be oxidized either by an acid or by a particular salt? This question is of practical importance as well as chemical interest. According to Equation 4.27, for example, it would be unwise to store a solution of nickel nitrate in an iron container because the solution would dissolve the container. When a metal is oxidized, it forms various compounds. Extensive oxidation can lead to the failure of metal machinery parts or the deterioration of metal structures.

Different metals vary in the ease with which they are oxidized. Zn is oxidized by aqueous solutions of Cu^{2+}, for example, but Ag is not. Zn, therefore, loses electrons more readily than Ag; that is, Zn is easier to oxidize than Ag.

A list of metals arranged in order of decreasing ease of oxidation, such as ▶ TABLE 4.5, is called an **activity series**. The metals at the top of the table, such as the alkali metals and the alkaline earth metals, are most easily oxidized; that is, they react most readily to form compounds. They are called the *active metals*. The metals at the bottom of the activity series, such as the transition elements from groups 8B and 1B, are very stable and form compounds less readily. These metals, which are used to make coins and jewelry, are called *noble metals* because of their low reactivity.

The activity series can be used to predict the outcome of reactions between metals and either metal salts or acids. *Any metal on the list can be oxidized by the ions of elements below it.* For example, copper is above silver in the series. Thus, copper metal is oxidized by silver ions:

$$Cu(s) + 2\,Ag^+(aq) \longrightarrow Cu^{2+}(aq) + 2\,Ag(s) \qquad [4.29]$$

Metal	Oxidation Reaction
Lithium	$Li(s) \longrightarrow Li^+(aq) + e^-$
Potassium	$K(s) \longrightarrow K^+(aq) + e^-$
Barium	$Ba(s) \longrightarrow Ba^{2+}(aq) + 2e^-$
Calcium	$Ca(s) \longrightarrow Ca^{2+}(aq) + 2e^-$
Sodium	$Na(s) \longrightarrow Na^+(aq) + e^-$
Magnesium	$Mg(s) \longrightarrow Mg^{2+}(aq) + 2e^-$
Aluminum	$Al(s) \longrightarrow Al^{3+}(aq) + 3e^-$
Manganese	$Mn(s) \longrightarrow Mn^{2+}(aq) + 2e^-$
Zinc	$Zn(s) \longrightarrow Zn^{2+}(aq) + 2e^-$
Chromium	$Cr(s) \longrightarrow Cr^{3+}(aq) + 3e^-$
Iron	$Fe(s) \longrightarrow Fe^{2+}(aq) + 2e^-$
Cobalt	$Co(s) \longrightarrow Co^{2+}(aq) + 2e^-$
Nickel	$Ni(s) \longrightarrow Ni^{2+}(aq) + 2e^-$
Tin	$Sn(s) \longrightarrow Sn^{2+}(aq) + 2e^-$
Lead	$Pb(s) \longrightarrow Pb^{2+}(aq) + 2e^-$
Hydrogen	$H_2(g) \longrightarrow 2\,H^+(aq) + 2e^-$
Copper	$Cu(s) \longrightarrow Cu^{2+}(aq) + 2e^-$
Silver	$Ag(s) \longrightarrow Ag^+(aq) + e^-$
Mercury	$Hg(l) \longrightarrow Hg^{2+}(aq) + 2e^-$
Platinum	$Pt(s) \longrightarrow Pt^{2+}(aq) + 2e^-$
Gold	$Au(s) \longrightarrow Au^{3+}(aq) + 3e^-$

TABLE 4.5 • Activity Series of Metals in Aqueous Solution

Ease of oxidation increases

The oxidation of copper to copper ions is accompanied by the reduction of silver ions to silver metal. The silver metal is evident on the surface of the copper wire in ▶ **FIGURE 4.14**. The copper(II) nitrate produces a blue color in the solution, as can be seen most clearly in the photograph on the right of Figure 4.14.

GIVE IT SOME THOUGHT

Does a reaction occur (a) when an aqueous solution of $NiCl_2(aq)$ is added to a test tube containing strips of metallic zinc, and (b) when $NiCl_2(aq)$ is added to a test tube containing $Zn(NO_3)_2(aq)$?

Only metals above hydrogen in the activity series are able to react with acids to form H_2. For example, Ni reacts with $HCl(aq)$ to form H_2:

$$Ni(s) + 2\,HCl(aq) \longrightarrow NiCl_2(aq) + H_2(g) \qquad [4.30]$$

Because elements below hydrogen in the activity series are not oxidized by H^+, Cu does not react with $HCl(aq)$. Interestingly, copper does react with nitric acid, as shown in Figure 1.11, but the reaction is not oxidation of Cu by H^+ ions. Instead, the metal is oxidized to Cu^{2+} by the nitrate ion, accompanied by the formation of brown nitrogen dioxide, $NO_2(g)$:

$$Cu(s) + 4\,HNO_3(aq) \longrightarrow Cu(NO_3)_2(aq) + 2\,H_2O(l) + 2\,NO_2(g) \quad [4.31]$$

As the copper is oxidized in this reaction, NO_3^-, where the oxidation number of nitrogen is +5, is reduced to NO_2, where the oxidation number of nitrogen is +4. We will examine reactions of this type in Chapter 20.

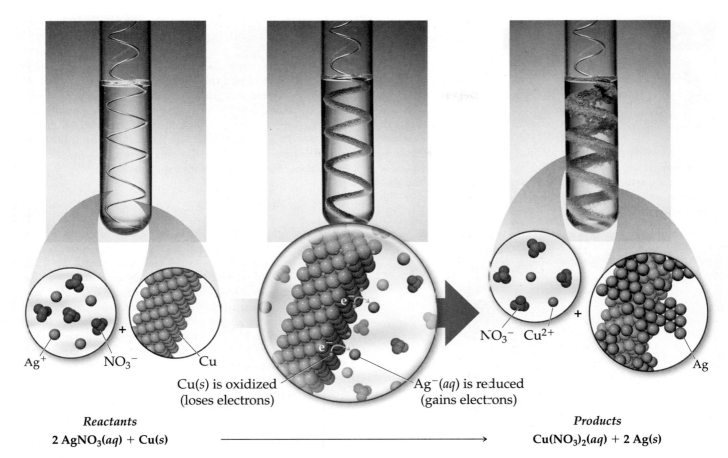

Cu(s) is oxidized
(loses electrons)

Ag⁻(aq) is reduced
(gains electrons)

Reactants

2 AgNO₃(aq) + Cu(s)

Products

Cu(NO₃)₂(aq) + 2 Ag(s)

▲ **FIGURE 4.14 Reaction of copper metal with silver ion.** When copper metal is placed in a solution of silver nitrate, a redox reaction forms silver metal and a blue solution of copper(II) nitrate.

SAMPLE EXERCISE 4.10 | **Determining When an Oxidation-Reduction Reaction Can Occur**

Will an aqueous solution of iron(II) chloride oxidize magnesium metal? If so, write the balanced molecular and net ionic equations for the reaction.

SOLUTION

Analyze We are given two substances—an aqueous salt, $FeCl_2$, and a metal, Mg—and asked if they react with each other.

Plan A reaction occurs if the reactant that is a metal in its elemental form (Mg) is located above the reactant that is a metal in its oxidized form (Fe^{2+}) in Table 4.5. If the reaction occurs, the Fe^{2+} ion in $FeCl_2$ is reduced to Fe, and the Mg is oxidized to Mg^{2+}.

Solve Because Mg is above Fe in the table, the reaction occurs. To write the formula for the salt produced in the reaction, we must remember the charges on common ions. Magnesium is always present in compounds as Mg^{2+}; the chloride ion is Cl^-. The magnesium salt formed in the reaction is $MgCl_2$, meaning the balanced molecular equation is

$$Mg(s) + FeCl_2(aq) \longrightarrow MgCl_2(aq) + Fe(s)$$

Both $FeCl_2$ and $MgCl_2$ are soluble strong electrolytes and can be written in ionic form, which shows us that Cl^- is a spectator ion in the reaction. The net ionic equation is

$$Mg(s) + Fe^{2+}(aq) \longrightarrow Mg^{2+}(aq) + Fe(s)$$

The net ionic equation shows that Mg is oxidized and Fe^{2+} is reduced in this reaction.

Check Note that the net ionic equation is balanced with respect to both charge and mass.

PRACTICE EXERCISE

Which of the following metals will be oxidized by $Pb(NO_3)_2$: Zn, Cu, Fe?

Answer: Zn and Fe

A CLOSER LOOK

THE AURA OF GOLD

Throughout history, people have cherished gold, fought for it, and even died for it.

The physical and chemical properties of gold make it special. First, its intrinsic beauty and rarity make it precious. Second, it is soft and can be easily formed into jewelry, coins, and other objects. Third, it is one of the least active metals (Table 4.5). It is not oxidized in air and does not react with water (▼ FIGURE 4.15), with basic solutions, or with most acidic solutions.

▲ FIGURE 4.15 **The chemical inertness of gold.** Two, stamped, weighed, and priced (in the 1800's) gold bars recently recovered from a steamship that sank off the coast of Central America in 1857.

Many of the early studies on gold arose from *alchemy*, in which people attempted to turn cheap metals, such as lead, into gold. Alchemists discovered that gold can be dissolved in a 3:1 mixture of concentrated hydrochloric and nitric acids, known as aqua regia ("royal water"). The action of the nitric acid on gold is similar to that on copper (Equation 4.31) in that the nitrate ion, rather than H^+, oxidizes the metal to Au^{3+}. The Cl^- ions interact with Au^{3+} to form highly stable $AuCl_4^-$ ions. The net ionic equation is

$$Au(s) - NO_3^-(aq) + 4\,H^+(aq) + 4\,Cl^-(aq) \longrightarrow$$
$$AuCl_4^-(aq) + 2\,H_2O(l) + NO(g)$$

All the gold ever mined would fit in a cube 21 m on a side and weighing about 1.6×10^8 kg. More than 90% of this amount has been produced since the 1848 California gold rush. Annual worldwide production of gold is about 2.4×10^6 kg. By contrast 16,000 times more aluminum, over 3.97×10^{10} kg, are produced annually.

Roughly three-quarters of gold production goes to make jewelry, where it is often alloyed with other metals. Approximately 12% of gold production is used to meet a variety of industrial applications, most notably in electronic devices where its excellent conductivity and corrosion resistance make it a valuable component. A typical touch-tone telephone contains 33 gold-plated contacts. Gold is also used in computers and other microelectronic devices where fine gold wire is used to link components.

Because of its resistance to corrosion, gold is an ideal metal for dental crowns and caps, which accounts for about 3% of the annual use of the element. The pure metal is too soft to use in dentistry, so it is combined with other metals to form alloys.

RELATED EXERCISE: 4.91

STRATEGIES IN CHEMISTRY

ANALYZING CHEMICAL REACTIONS

In this chapter you have been introduced to a great number of chemical reactions. A major difficulty students face in trying to master material of this sort is gaining a "feel" for what happens when chemicals react. In fact, you might marvel at the ease with which your professor or teaching assistant can figure out the results of a chemical reaction. One of our goals in this textbook is to help you become more adept at predicting the outcomes of reactions. The key to gaining this "chemical intuition" is understanding how to categorize reactions.

Attempting to memorize individual reactions would be a futile task. It is far more fruitful to recognize patterns to determine the general category of a reaction, such as metathesis or oxidation-reduction. Thus, when you are faced with the challenge of predicting the outcome of a chemical reaction, ask yourself the following questions:

- What are the reactants?
- Are they electrolytes or nonelectrolytes?

- Are they acids and bases?
- If the reactants are electrolytes, will metathesis produce a precipitate? Water? A gas?
- If metathesis cannot occur, can the reactants engage in an oxidation-reduction reaction? This requires that there be both a reactant that can be oxidized and a reactant that can be reduced.

By asking questions such as these, you should be able to predict what happens during the reaction. You might not always be entirely correct, but if you keep your wits about you, you will not be far off. As you gain experience, you will begin to look for reactants that might not be immediately obvious, such as water from the solution or oxygen from the atmosphere.

One of the greatest tools available to chemists is experimentation. If you perform an experiment in which two solutions are mixed, you can make observations that help you understand what is happening. For example, using Table 4.1 to predict whether a precipitate will form is not nearly as exciting as seeing the precipitate form, as in Figure 4.4. Careful observations in the laboratory portion of the course will make your lecture material easier to master.

4.5 | CONCENTRATIONS OF SOLUTIONS

Scientists use the term **concentration** to designate the amount of solute dissolved in a given quantity of solvent or quantity of solution. The greater the amount of solute dissolved in a certain amount of solvent, the more concentrated the resulting solution. In chemistry we often need to express the concentrations of solutions quantitatively.

Molarity

Molarity (symbol M) expresses the concentration of a solution as the number of moles of solute in a liter of solution (soln):

$$\text{Molarity} = \frac{\text{moles solute}}{\text{volume of solution in liters}} \qquad [4.32]$$

A 1.00 molar solution (written 1.00 M) contains 1.00 mol of solute in every liter of solution. ▼ FIGURE 4.16 shows the preparation of 250.0 mL of a 1.00 M solution of $CuSO_4$. The molarity of the solution is $(0.250 \text{ mol } CuSO_4)/(0.250 \text{ L soln}) = 1.00\ M$.

 GIVE IT SOME THOUGHT

> Which is more concentrated, a solution prepared by dissolving 21.0 g of NaF (0.500 mol) in enough water to make 500 mL of solution or a solution prepared by dissolving 10.5 g (0.250 mol) of NaF in enough water to make 100 mL of solution?

1 Weigh out 39.9 g (0.250 mol) $CuSO_4$

2 Put $CuSO_4$ (solute) into 250-mL volumetric flask; add water and swirl to dissolve solute

3 Add water until solution just reaches calibration mark on neck of flask

◄ FIGURE 4.16   **Preparing 0.250 L of a 1.00 *M* solution of $CuSO_4$.**

SAMPLE EXERCISE 4.11   **Calculating Molarity**

Calculate the molarity of a solution made by dissolving 23.4 g of sodium sulfate (Na_2SO_4) in enough water to form 125 mL of solution.

SOLUTION

Analyze We are given the number of grams of solute (23.4 g), its chemical formula (Na_2SO_4), and the volume of the solution (125 mL) and asked to calculate the molarity of the solution.

Plan We can calculate molarity using Equation 4.32. To do so, we must convert the number of grams of solute to moles and the volume of the solution from milliliters to liters.

Solve The number of moles of Na_2SO_4 is obtained by using its molar mass:

$$\text{Moles } Na_2SO_4 = (23.4 \text{ g } Na_2SO_4)\left(\frac{1 \text{ mol } Na_2SO_4}{142 \text{ g } Na_2SO_4}\right) = 0.165 \text{ mol } Na_2SO_4$$

Converting the volume of the solution to liters:

$$\text{Liters soln} = (125 \text{ mL})\left(\frac{1 \text{ L}}{1000 \text{ mL}}\right) = 0.125 \text{ L}$$

Thus, the molarity is

$$\text{Molarity} = \frac{0.165 \text{ mol } Na_2SO_4}{0.125 \text{ L soln}} = 1.32 \frac{\text{mol } Na_2SO_4}{\text{L soln}} = 1.32 \text{ } M$$

Check Because the numerator is only slightly larger than the denominator, it is reasonable for the answer to be a little over 1 M. The units (mol/L) are appropriate for molarity, and three signifi- cant figures are appropriate for the answer because each of the initial pieces of data had three significant figures.

PRACTICE EXERCISE

Calculate the molarity of a solution made by dissolving 5.00 g of glucose ($C_6H_{12}O_6$) in sufficient water to form exactly 100 mL of solution.

Answer: 0.278 M

Expressing the Concentration of an Electrolyte

When an ionic compound dissolves, the relative concentrations of the ions in the solution depend on the chemical formula of the compound. For example, a 1.0 M solution of NaCl is 1.0 M in Na^+ ions and 1.0 M in Cl^- ions, and a 1.0 M solution of Na_2SO_4 is 2.0 M in Na^+ ions and 1.0 M in SO_4^{2-} ions. Thus, the concentration of an electrolyte solution can be specified either in terms of the compound used to make the solution (1.0 M Na_2SO_4) or in terms of the ions in the solution (2.0 M Na^+ and 1.0 M SO_4^{2-}).

SAMPLE EXERCISE 4.12 | **Calculating Molar Concentrations of Ions**

What is the molar concentration of each ion present in a 0.025 M aqueous solution of calcium nitrate?

SOLUTION:

Analyze We are given the concentration of the ionic compound used to make the solution and asked to determine the concentrations of the ions in the solution.

Plan We can use the subscripts in the chemical formula of the compound to determine the relative ion concentrations.

Solve Calcium nitrate is composed of calcium ions (Ca^{2+}) and nitrate ions (NO_3^-), so its chemical formula is $Ca(NO_3)_2$. Because there are two NO_3^- ions for each Ca^{2+} ion, each mole of $Ca(NO_3)_2$ that dissolves dissociates into 1 mol of Ca^{2+} and 2 mol of NO_3^-. Thus, a solution that is 0.025 M in $Ca(NO_3)_2$ is 0.025 M in Ca^{2+} and 2 × 0.025 M = 0.050 M in NO_3^-:

$$\frac{\text{mol } NO_3^-}{L} = \left(\frac{0.025 \text{ mol } Ca(NO_3)_2}{L}\right)\left(\frac{2 \text{ mol } NO_3^-}{1 \text{ mol } Ca(NO_3)_2}\right) = 0.050 \text{ } M$$

Check The concentration of NO_3^- ions is twice that of Ca^{2+} ions, as the subscript 2 after the NO_3^- in the chemical formula $Ca(NO_3)_2$ suggests it should be.

PRACTICE EXERCISE

What is the molar concentration of K^+ ions in a 0.015 M solution of potassium carbonate?

Answer: 0.030 M

Interconverting Molarity, Moles, and Volume

If we know any two of the three quantities in Equation 4.32, we can calculate the third. For example, if we know the molarity of an HNO_3 solution to be 0.200 M, which means 0.200 mol of HNO_3 per liter of solution, we can calculate the number of moles of solute in a given volume, say 2.0 L. Molarity therefore is a conversion factor between volume of solution and moles of solute:

$$\text{Moles } HNO_3 = (2.0 \text{ L soln})\left(\frac{0.200 \text{ mol } HNO_3}{1 \text{ L soln}}\right) = 0.40 \text{ mol } HNO_3$$

To illustrate the conversion of moles to volume, let's calculate the volume of 0.30 M HNO_3 solution required to supply 2.0 mol of HNO_3:

$$\text{Liters soln} = (2.0 \text{ mol HNO}_3)\left(\frac{1 \text{ L soln}}{0.30 \text{ mol HNO}_3}\right) = 6.7 \text{ L soln}$$

In this case we must use the reciprocal of molarity in the conversion: Liters = moles $\times$ $1/M$ = moles $\times$ liters/mole.

SAMPLE EXERCISE 4.13   **Using Molarity to Calculate Grams of Solute**

How many grams of Na_2SO_4 are required to make 0.350 L of 0.500 M Na_2SO_4?

SOLUTION

Analyze We are given the volume of the solution (0.350 L), its concentration (0.500 M), and the identity of the solute Na_2SO_4 and asked to calculate the number of grams of the solute in the solution.

Plan We can use the definition of molarity (Equation 4.32) to determine the number of moles of solute, and then convert moles to grams using the molar mass of the solute.

$$M_{Na_2SO_4} = \frac{\text{moles Na}_2SO_4}{\text{liters soln}}$$

Solve Calculating the moles of Na_2SO_4 using the molarity and volume of solution gives

$$M_{Na_2SO_4} = \frac{\text{moles Na}_2SO_4}{\text{liters soln}}$$

$$\text{Moles Na}_2SO_4 = \text{liters soln} \times M_{Na_2SO_4}$$

$$= (0.350 \text{ L soln})\left(\frac{0.500 \text{ mol Na}_2SO_4}{1 \text{ L soln}}\right)$$

$$= 0.175 \text{ mol Na}_2SO_4$$

Because each mole of Na_2SO_4 has a mass of 142 g, the required number of grams of Na_2SO_4 is

$$\text{Grams Na}_2SO_4 = (0.175 \text{ mol Na}_2SO_4)\left(\frac{142 \text{ g Na}_2SO_4}{1 \text{ mol Na}_2SO_4}\right) = 24.9 \text{ g Na}_2SO_4$$

Check The magnitude of the answer, the units, and the number of significant figures are all appropriate.

PRACTICE EXERCISE

(a) How many grams of Na_2SO_4 are there in 15 mL of 0.50 M Na_2SO_4? **(b)** How many milliliters of 0.50 M Na_2SO_4 solution are needed to provide 0.038 mol of this salt?

Answers: **(a)** 1.1 g, **(b)** 76 mL

Dilution

Solutions used routinely in the laboratory are often purchased or prepared in concentrated form (called *stock solutions*). Solutions of lower concentrations can then be obtained by adding water, a process called **dilution**.*

Let's see how we can prepare a dilute solution from a concentrated one. Suppose we want to prepare 250.0 mL (that is, 0.2500 L) of 0.100 M $CuSO_4$ solution by diluting a 1.00 M $CuSO_4$ stock solution. The main point to remember is that when solvent is added to a solution, the number of moles of solute remains unchanged:

$$\text{Moles solute before dilution} = \text{moles solute after dilution} \qquad [4.33]$$

---

*In diluting a concentrated acid or base, the acid or base should be added to water and then further diluted by adding more water. Adding water directly to concentrated acid or base can cause spattering because of the intense heat generated.

Because we know both the volume (250 mL) and the concentration (0.100 mol/L) of the dilute solution, we can calculate the number of moles of CuSO$_4$ it contains:

$$\text{Moles CuSO}_4 \text{ in dilute soln} = (0.2500 \text{ L soln})\left(\frac{0.100 \text{ mol CuSO}_4}{\text{L soln}}\right)$$

$$= 0.0250 \text{ mol CuSO}_4$$

The volume of stock solution needed to provide 0.0250 mol CuSO$_4$ is therefore:

$$\text{Liters of conc soln} = (0.0250 \text{ mol CuSO}_4)\left(\frac{1 \text{ L soln}}{1.00 \text{ mol CuSO}_4}\right) = 0.0250 \text{ L}$$

▼ **FIGURE 4.17** shows the dilution carried out in the laboratory. Notice that the diluted solution is less intensely colored than the concentrated one.

△ GIVE IT SOME THOUGHT

How is the molarity of a 0.50 *M* KBr solution changed when water is added to double its volume?

In laboratory situations, calculations of this sort are often made with an equation derived by remembering that the number of moles of solute is the same in both the concentrated and dilute solutions and that moles = molarity × liters:

$$\text{Moles solute in conc soln} = \text{moles solute in dilute soln}$$

$$M_{\text{conc}} \times V_{\text{conc}} = M_{\text{dil}} \times V_{\text{dil}} \qquad [4.34]$$

Although we derived Equation 4.34 in terms of liters, any volume unit can be used as long as it is used on both sides of the equation. For example, in the calculation we did for the CuSO$_4$ solution, we have

$$(1.00 \, M)(V_{\text{conc}}) = (0.100 \, M)(250. \text{ mL})$$

Solving for V_{conc} gives $V_{\text{conc}} = 25.0$ mL as before.

 1 Draw 25.0 mL of 1.00 *M* stock solution into pipet

 2 Add concentrated solution in pipet to 250–mL volumetric flask

 3 Dilute with water until solution reaches calibration mark on neck of flask and mix to create 0.100 *M* solution

▲ **FIGURE 4.17** Preparing 250 mL of 0.100 *M* CuSO$_4$ by dilution of 1.00 *M* CuSO$_4$.

CHEMISTRY AND LIFE

DRINKING TOO MUCH WATER CAN KILL YOU

For a long time dehydration was considered a potential danger for people engaged in extended vigorous activity. Thus, athletes were encouraged to drink lots of water while engaged in active sport. The trend toward extensive hydration has spread throughout society, so that today many people carry water bottles everywhere and dutifully keep well hydrated.

In some circumstances, however, drinking too much water is a greater danger than not drinking enough. Excess water consumption can lead to *hyponatremia*, a condition in which the concentration of sodium ion in the blood is too low. In the past decade at least four marathon runners have died from hyponatremia-related trauma, and dozens more have become seriously ill. For example, a first-time marathoner named Hillary Bellamy, running in the Marine Corps marathon in 2003, collapsed near mile 22 and died the next day. One physician who treated her said that she died from hyponatremia-induced brain swelling, the result of drinking too much water before and during the race.

The normal blood sodium level is 135 to 145 m*M* (*millimolar*). When that level drops to 125 m*M*, dizziness and confusion set in. A concentration below 120 m*M* can be critical. Dangerously low levels can occur in any active athlete who is sweating out salt (NaCl) at the same time that excessive amounts of NaCl-free water are being drunk to compensate for water loss. The condition affects women more than men because of differences in body composition and patterns of metabolism. Drinking a sport drink that contains some electrolytes helps to prevent hyponatremia.

RELATED EXERCISES: 4.63, 4.64

SAMPLE EXERCISE 4.14   Preparing a Solution by Dilution

How many milliliters of 3.0 *M* H_2SO_4 are needed to make 450 mL of 0.10 *M* H_2SO_4?

SOLUTION

Analyze We need to dilute a concentrated solution. We are given the molarity of a more concentrated solution (3.0 *M*) and the volume and molarity of a more dilute one containing the same solute (450 mL of 0.10 *M* solution). We must calculate the volume of the concentrated solution needed to prepare the dilute solution.

Plan We can calculate the number of moles of solute, H_2SO_4, in the dilute solution and then calculate the volume of the concentrated solution needed to supply this amount of solute. Alternatively, we can directly apply Equation 4.34. Let's compare the two methods.

Solve Calculating the moles of H_2SO_4 in the dilute solution:

$$\text{Moles } H_2SO_4 \text{ in dilute solution} = (0.450 \text{ L soln})\left(\frac{0.10 \text{ mol } H_2SO_4}{1 \text{ L soln}}\right)$$

$$= 0.045 \text{ mol } H_2SO_4$$

Calculating the volume of the concentrated solution that contains 0.045 mol H_2SO_4:

$$\text{L conc soln} = (0.045 \text{ mol } H_2SO_4)\left(\frac{1 \text{ L soln}}{3.0 \text{ mol } H_2SO_4}\right) = 0.015 \text{ L soln}$$

Converting liters to milliliters gives 15 mL.
If we apply Equation 4.34, we get the same result:

$$(3.0 \, M)(V_{\text{conc}}) = (0.10 \, M)(450 \text{ mL})$$

$$(V_{\text{conc}}) = \frac{(0.10 \, M)(450 \text{ mL})}{3.0 \, M} = 15 \text{ mL}$$

Either way, we see that if we start with 15 mL of 3.0 *M* H_2SO_4 and dilute it to a total volume of 450 mL, the desired 0.10 *M* solution will be obtained.

Check The calculated volume seems reasonable because a small volume of concentrated solution is used to prepare a large volume of dilute solution.

Comment The first approach can also be used to find the final concentration when two solutions of different concentrations are mixed, whereas the second approach, using Equation 4.34, can be used only for diluting a concentrated solution with pure solvent.

PRACTICE EXERCISE

(a) What volume of 2.50 *M* lead(II) nitrate solution contains 0.0500 mol of Pb^{2+}? **(b)** How many milliliters of 5.0 *M* $K_2Cr_2O_7$ solution must be diluted to prepare 250 mL of 0.10 *M* solution? **(c)** If 10.0 mL of a 10.0 *M* stock solution of NaOH is diluted to 250 mL, what is the concentration of the resulting stock solution?

Answers: **(a)** 0.0200 L = 20.0 mL, **(b)** 5.0 mL, **(c)** 0.40 *M*

4.6 | SOLUTION STOICHIOMETRY AND CHEMICAL ANALYSIS

In Chapter 3 we learned that given the chemical equation for a reaction and the amount of one reactant consumed in the reaction, you can calculate the quantities of other reactants and products. In this section we extend this concept to reactions involving solutions.

Recall that the coefficients in a balanced equation give the relative number of moles of reactants and products. ∞ (Section 3.6) To use this information, we must convert the masses of substances involved in a reaction into moles. When dealing with pure substances, as we were in Chapter 3, we use molar mass to convert between grams and moles of the substances. This conversion is not valid when working with a solution because both solute and solvent contribute to its mass. However, if we know the solute concentration, we can use molarity and volume to determine the number of moles (moles solute $= M \times V$). ▼ FIGURE 4.18 summarizes this approach to using stoichiometry for the reaction between a pure substance and a solution.

SAMPLE EXERCISE 4.15 | Using Mass Relations in a Neutralization Reaction

How many grams of $Ca(OH)_2$ are needed to neutralize 25.0 mL of 0.100 M HNO_3?

SOLUTION

Analyze The reactants are an acid, HNO_3, and a base, $Ca(OH)_2$. The volume and molarity of HNO_3 are given, and we are asked how many grams of $Ca(OH)_2$ are needed to neutralize this quantity of HNO_3.

Plan Following the steps outlined by the green arrows in Figure 4.18, we use the molarity and volume of the HNO_3 solution (substance B in Figure 4.18) to calculate the number of moles of HNO_3. We then use the balanced equation to relate moles of HNO_3 to moles of $Ca(OH)_2$ (substance A). Finally, we use the molar mass to convert moles to grams of $Ca(OH)_2$:

$$V_{HNO_3} \times M_{HNO_3} \Rightarrow \text{mol } HNO_3 \Rightarrow \text{mol } Ca(OH)_2 \Rightarrow \text{g } Ca(OH)_2$$

Solve The product of the molar concentration of a solution and its volume in liters gives the number of moles of solute:

$$\text{Moles } HNO_3 = V_{HNO_3} \times M_{HNO_3} = (0.0250 \, \cancel{L})\left(\frac{0.100 \, \text{mol } HNO_3}{\cancel{L}}\right)$$

$$= 2.50 \times 10^{-3} \, \text{mol } HNO_3$$

▶ FIGURE 4.18 **Procedure for solving stoichiometry problems involving reactions between a pure substance A and a solution containing a known concentration of substance B.** Starting from a known mass of substance A, we follow the red arrows to determine either the volume of the solution containing B (if the molarity of B is known) or the molarity of the solution containing B (if the volume of B is known). Starting from either a known volume or known molarity of the solution containing B, we follow the green arrows to determine the mass of substance A.

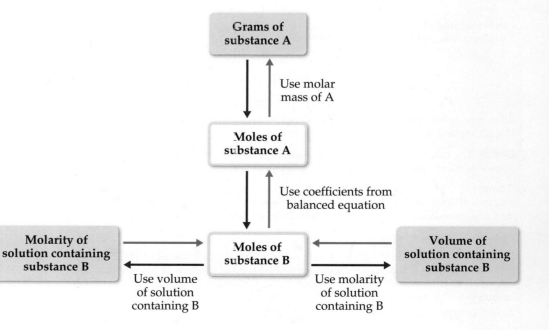

Because this is a neutralization reaction, HNO_3 and $Ca(OH)_2$ react to form H_2O and the salt containing Ca^{2+} and NO_3^-:

$$2\ HNO_3(aq) + Ca(OH)_2(s) \longrightarrow 2\ H_2O(l) + Ca(NO_3)_2(aq)$$

Thus, 2 mol $HNO_3 \simeq$ mol $Ca(OH)_2$. Therefore,

$$\text{Grams } Ca(OH)_2 = (2.50 \times 10^{-3}\ \text{mol } HNO_3)\left(\frac{1\ \text{mol } Ca(OH)_2}{2\ \text{mol } HNO_3}\right)\left(\frac{74.1\ \text{g } Ca(OH)_2}{1\ \text{mol } Ca(OH)_2}\right)$$

$$= 0.0926\ \text{g } Ca(OH)_2$$

Check The answer is reasonable because a small volume of dilute acid requires only a small amount of base to neutralize it.

PRACTICE EXERCISE

(a) How many grams of NaOH are needed to neutralize 20.0 mL of 0.150 M H_2SO_4 solution?
(b) How many liters of 0.500 M HCl(aq) are needed to react completely with 0.100 mol of $Pb(NO_3)_2(aq)$, forming a precipitate of $PbCl_2(s)$?

Answers: (a) 0.240 g, (b) 0.400 L

Titrations

To determine the concentration of a particular solute in a solution, chemists often carry out a **titration**, which involves combining a solution where the solute concentration is not known with a reagent solution of known concentration, called a **standard solution**. Just enough standard solution is added to completely react with the solute in the solution of unknown concentration. The point at which stoichiometrically equivalent quantities are brought together is known as the **equivalence point**.

Titrations can be conducted using neutralization, precipitation, or oxidation-reduction reactions. ▼ FIGURE 4.19 illustrates a typical neutralization titration, one between a HCl solution of unknown concentration and a NaOH solution we know to have a concentration of 0.100 M (our standard solution). To determine the HCl concentration, we first add a specific volume of the HCl solution, 20.0 mL in this example, to a flask. Next

GO FIGURE

How would the volume of standard solution added change if that solution were Ba(OH)$_2$(aq) instead of NaOH(aq)?

1 20.0 mL of acid solution added to flask

2 A few drops of acid–base indicator added

3 Standard NaOH solution added from buret

Initial volume reading

Buret

4 Solution becomes basic on passing equivalence point, triggering indicator color change

Final volume reading

▲ FIGURE 4.19 **Procedure for titrating an acid against a standard solution of NaOH.**
The acid–base indicator, phenolphthalein, is colorless in acidic solution but takes on a pink color in basic solution.

▶ **FIGURE 4.20 Procedure for determining the concentration of a solution from titration with a standard solution.**

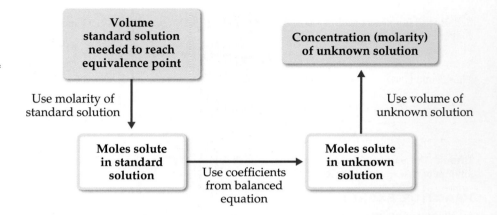

a few drops of an acid–base indicator are added. The acid–base indicator is a dye that changes color on passing the equivalence point.* For example, the dye phenolphthalein is colorless in acidic solution but pink in basic solution. The standard solution is then slowly added until the solution turns pink, telling us that the neutralization reaction between HCl and NaOH is complete. The standard solution is added from a *buret* so that we can accurately determine the added volume of NaOH solution. Knowing the volumes of both solutions and the concentration of the standard solution we can calculate the concentration of the unknown solution as diagrammed in ▲ **FIGURE 4.20**.

SAMPLE EXERCISE 4.16 | **Determining Solution Concentration by an Acid–Base Titration**

One commercial method used to peel potatoes is to soak them in a NaOH solution for a short time, then remove them and spray off the peel. The NaOH concentration is normally 3 to 6 M, and the solution must be analyzed periodically. In one such analysis, 45.7 mL of 0.500 M H_2SO_4 is required to neutralize 20.0 mL of NaOH solution. What is the concentration of the NaOH solution?

SOLUTION

Analyze We are given the volume (45.7 mL) and molarity (0.500 M) of an H_2SO_4 solution (the standard solution) that reacts completely with 20.0 mL of NaOH solution. We are asked to calculate the molarity of the NaOH solution.

Plan Following the steps of Figure 4.20, we use the H_2SO_4 volume and molarity to calculate the number of moles of H_2SO_4. Then we can use this quantity and the balanced equation for the reaction to calculate moles of NaOH. Finally, we can use moles of NaOH and the NaOH volume to calculate NaOH molarity.

Solve The number of moles of H_2SO_4 is the product of the volume and molarity of this solution:

$$\text{Moles } H_2SO_4 = (45.7 \text{ mL soln})\left(\frac{1 \text{ L soln}}{1000 \text{ mL soln}}\right)\left(\frac{0.500 \text{ mol } H_2SO_4}{\text{L soln}}\right)$$

$$= 2.28 \times 10^{-2} \text{ mol } H_2SO_4$$

Acids react with metal hydroxides to form water and a salt. Thus, the balanced equation for the neutralization reaction is

$$H_2SO_4(aq) + 2\,NaOH(aq) \longrightarrow 2\,H_2O(l) + Na_2SO_4(aq)$$

According to the balanced equation, 1 mol $H_2SO_4 \simeq 2$ mol NaOH. Therefore,

$$\text{Moles NaOH} = (2.28 \times 10^{-2} \text{ mol } H_2SO_4)\left(\frac{2 \text{ mol NaOH}}{1 \text{ mol } H_2SO_4}\right)$$

$$= 4.56 \times 10^{-2} \text{ mol NaOH}$$

---

*More precisely, the color change of an indicator signals the end point of the titration, which if the proper indicator is chosen lies very near the equivalence point. Acid–base titrations are discussed in more detail in Section 17.3.

Knowing the number of moles of NaOH in 20.0 mL of solution allows us to calculate the molarity of this solution:

$$\text{Molarity NaOH} = \frac{\text{mol NaOH}}{\text{L soln}} = \left(\frac{4.56 \times 10^{-2} \text{ mol NaOH}}{20.0 \text{ mL soln}}\right)\left(\frac{1000 \text{ mL soln}}{1 \text{ L soln}}\right)$$

$$= 2.28 \frac{\text{mol NaOH}}{\text{L soln}} = 2.28 \ M$$

PRACTICE EXERCISE

What is the molarity of an NaOH solution if 48.0 mL neutralizes 35.0 mL of 0.144 M H$_2$SO$_4$?

Answer: 0.210 M

SAMPLE EXERCISE 4.17 | **Determining the Quantity of Solute by Titration**

The quantity of Cl$^-$ in a municipal water supply is determined by titrating the sample with Ag$^+$. The precipitation reaction taking place during the titration is

$$\text{Ag}^+(aq) + \text{Cl}^-(aq) \longrightarrow \text{AgCl}(s)$$

The end point in this type of titration is marked by a change in color of a special type of indicator. **(a)** How many grams of chloride ion are in a sample of the water if 20.2 mL of 0.100 M Ag$^+$ is needed to react with all the chloride in the sample? **(b)** If the sample has a mass of 10.0 g, what percent Cl$^-$ does it contain?

SOLUTION

Analyze We are given the volume (20.2 mL) and molarity (0.100 M) of a solution of Ag$^+$ and the chemical equation for reaction of this ion with Cl$^-$. We are asked to calculate the number of grams of Cl$^-$ in the sample and the mass percent of Cl$^-$ in the sample.

(a) Plan We can use the procedure outlined by the green arrows in Figure 4.18. We begin by using the volume and molarity of Ag$^+$ to calculate the number of moles of Ag$^+$ used in the titration. We then use the balanced equation to determine the moles of Cl$^-$ in the sample and from that the grams of Cl$^-$.

Solve

$$\text{Moles Ag}^+ = (20.2 \text{ mL soln})\left(\frac{1 \text{ L soln}}{1000 \text{ mL soln}}\right)\left(\frac{0.100 \text{ mol Ag}^+}{\text{L soln}}\right)$$

$$= 2.02 \times 10^{-3} \text{ mol Ag}^+$$

From the balanced equation we see that 1 mol Ag$^+ \simeq$ 1 mol Cl$^-$. Using this information and the molar mass of Cl, we have

$$\text{Grams Cl}^- = (2.02 \times 10^{-3} \text{ mol Ag}^+)\left(\frac{1 \text{ mol Cl}^-}{1 \text{ mol Ag}^+}\right)\left(\frac{35.5 \text{ g Cl}^-}{\text{mol Cl}^-}\right)$$

$$= 7.17 \times 10^{-2} \text{ g Cl}^-$$

(b) Plan To calculate the percentage of Cl$^-$ in the sample, we compare the number of grams of Cl$^-$ in the sample, 7.17×10^{-2} g, with the original mass of the sample, 10.0 g.

Solve

$$\text{Percent Cl}^- = \frac{7.17 \times 10^{-2} \text{ g}}{10.0 \text{ g}} \times 100\% = 0.717\% \text{ Cl}^-$$

Comment Chloride ion is one of the most common ions in water and sewage. Ocean water contains 1.92% Cl$^-$. Whether water containing Cl$^-$ tastes salty depends on the other ions present. If the only accompanying ions are Na$^+$, a salty taste may be detected with as little as 0.03% Cl$^-$.

PRACTICE EXERCISE

A sample of an iron ore is dissolved in acid, and the iron is converted to Fe^{2+}. The sample is then titrated with 47.20 mL of 0.02240 M MnO_4^- solution. The oxidation-reduction reaction that occurs during titration is

$$MnO_4^-(aq) + 5\,Fe^{2+}(aq) + 8\,H^+(aq) \longrightarrow Mn^{2+}(aq) + 5\,Fe^{3+}(aq) + 4\,H_2O(l)$$

(a) How many moles of MnO_4^- were added to the solution? **(b)** How many moles of Fe^{2+} were in the sample? **(c)** How many grams of iron were in the sample? **(d)** If the sample had a mass of 0.8890 g, what is the percentage of iron in the sample?

Answers: **(a)** 1.057×10^{-3} mol MnO_4^-, **(b)** 5.286×10^{-3} mol Fe^{2+}, **(c)** 0.2952 g, **(d)** 33.21%

SAMPLE INTEGRATIVE EXERCISE | **Putting Concepts Together**

Note: Integrative exercises require skills from earlier chapters as well as ones from the present chapter.

A sample of 70.5 mg of potassium phosphate is added to 15.0 mL of 0.050 M silver nitrate, resulting in the formation of a precipitate. **(a)** Write the molecular equation for the reaction. **(b)** What is the limiting reactant in the reaction? **(c)** Calculate the theoretical yield, in grams, of the precipitate that forms.

SOLUTION

(a) Potassium phosphate and silver nitrate are both ionic compounds. Potassium phosphate contains K^+ and PO_4^{3-} ions, so its chemical formula is K_3PO_4. Silver nitrate contains Ag^+ and NO_3^- ions, so its chemical formula is $AgNO_3$. Because both reactants are strong electrolytes, the solution contains K^+, PO_4^{3-}, Ag^+, and NO_3^- ions before the reaction occurs. According to the solubility guidelines in Table 4.1, Ag^+ and PO_4^{3-} form an insoluble compound, so Ag_3PO_4 will precipitate from the solution. In contrast, K^+ and NO_3^- will remain in solution because KNO_3 is water soluble. Thus, the balanced molecular equation for the reaction is

$$K_3PO_4(aq) + 3\,AgNO_3(aq) \longrightarrow Ag_3PO_4(s) + 3\,KNO_3(aq)$$

(b) To determine the limiting reactant, we must examine the number of moles of each reactant. ∞ (Section 3.7) The number of moles of K_3PO_4 is calculated from the mass of the sample using the molar mass as a conversion factor. ∞ (Section 3.4) The molar mass of K_3PO_4 is $3(39.1) + 31.0 + 4(16.0) = 212.3$ g/mol. Converting milligrams to grams and then to moles, we have

$$(70.5 \text{ mg } K_3PO_4)\left(\frac{10^{-3}\text{ g } K_3PO_4}{1\text{ mg } K_3PO_4}\right)\left(\frac{1\text{ mol } K_3PO_4}{212.3\text{ g } K_3PO_4}\right) = 3.32 \times 10^{-4}\text{ mol } K_3PO_4$$

We determine the number of moles of $AgNO_3$ from the volume and molarity of the solution. (Section 4.5) Converting milliliters to liters and then to moles, we have

$$(15.0 \text{ mL})\left(\frac{10^{-3}\text{ L}}{1\text{ mL}}\right)\left(\frac{0.050\text{ mol } AgNO_3}{\text{L}}\right) = 7.5 \times 10^{-4}\text{ mol } AgNO_3$$

Comparing the amounts of the two reactants, we find that there are $(7.5 \times 10^{-4})/(3.32 \times 10^{-4}) = 2.3$ times as many moles of $AgNO_3$ as there are moles of K_3PO_4. According to the balanced equation, however, 1 mol K_3PO_4 requires 3 mol $AgNO_3$. Thus, there is insufficient $AgNO_3$ to consume the K_3PO_4, and $AgNO_3$ is the limiting reactant.

(c) The precipitate is Ag_3PO_4, whose molar mass is $3(107.9) + 31.0 + 4(16.0) = 418.7$ g/mol. To calculate the number of grams of Ag_3PO_4 that could be produced in this reaction (the theoretical yield), we use the number of moles of the limiting reactant, converting mol $AgNO_3 \Rightarrow$ mol $Ag_3PO_4 \Rightarrow$ g Ag_3PO_4. We use the coefficients in the balanced equation to convert moles of $AgNO_3$ to moles Ag_3PO_4, and we use the molar mass of Ag_3PO_4 to convert the number of moles of this substance to grams.

$$(7.5 \times 10^{-4}\text{ mol } AgNO_3)\left(\frac{1\text{ mol } Ag_3PO_4}{3\text{ mol } AgNO_3}\right)\left(\frac{418.7\text{ g } Ag_3PO_4}{1\text{ mol } Ag_3PO_4}\right) = 0.10\text{ g } Ag_3PO_4$$

The answer has only two significant figures because the quantity of $AgNO_3$ is given to only two significant figures.

CHAPTER SUMMARY AND KEY TERMS

INTRODUCTION AND SECTION 4.1 Solutions in which water is the dissolving medium are called **aqueous solutions**. The component of the solution that is present in the greatest quantity is the **solvent**. The other components are **solutes**.

Any substance whose aqueous solution contains ions is called an **electrolyte**. Any substance that forms a solution containing no ions is a **nonelectrolyte**. Electrolytes that are present in solution entirely as ions are **strong electrolytes**, whereas those that are present partly as ions and partly as molecules are **weak electrolytes**. Ionic compounds dissociate into ions when they dissolve, and they are strong electrolytes. The solubility of ionic substances is made possible by **solvation**, the interaction of ions with polar solvent molecules. Most molecular compounds are nonelectrolytes, although some are weak electrolytes, and a few are strong electrolytes. When representing the ionization of a weak electrolyte in solution, half-arrows in both directions are used, indicating that the forward and reverse reactions can achieve a chemical balance called a **chemical equilibrium**.

SECTION 4.2 **Precipitation reactions** are those in which an insoluble product, called a **precipitate**, forms. Solubility guidelines help determine whether or not an ionic compound will be soluble in water. (The **solubility** of a substance is the amount that dissolves in a given quantity of solvent.) Reactions such as precipitation reactions, in which cations and anions appear to exchange partners, are called **exchange reactions**, or **metathesis reactions**.

Chemical equations can be written to show whether dissolved substances are present in solution predominantly as ions or molecules. When the complete chemical formulas of all reactants and products are used, the equation is called a **molecular equation**. A **complete ionic equation** shows all dissolved strong electrolytes as their component ions. In a **net ionic equation**, those ions that go through the reaction unchanged (**spectator ions**) are omitted.

SECTION 4.3 Acids and bases are important electrolytes. **Acids** are proton donors; they increase the concentration of $H^+(aq)$ in aqueous solutions to which they are added. **Bases** are proton acceptors; they increase the concentration of $OH^-(aq)$ in aqueous solutions. Those acids and bases that are strong electrolytes are called **strong acids** and **strong bases**, respectively. Those that are weak electrolytes are **weak acids** and **weak bases**. When solutions of acids and bases are mixed, a neutralization reaction occurs. The **neutralization reaction** between an acid and a metal hydroxide produces water and a **salt**. Gases can also be formed as a result of neutralization reactions. The reaction of a sulfide with an acid forms $H_2S(g)$; the reaction between a carbonate and an acid forms $CO_2(g)$.

SECTION 4.4 **Oxidation** is the loss of electrons by a substance, whereas **reduction** is the gain of electrons by a substance. **Oxidation numbers** keep track of electrons during chemical reactions and are assigned to atoms using specific rules. The oxidation of an element results in an increase in its oxidation number, whereas reduction is accompanied by a decrease in oxidation number. Oxidation is always accompanied by reduction, giving **oxidation-reduction**, or **redox**, **reactions**.

Many metals are oxidized by O_2, acids, and salts. The redox reactions between metals and acids as well as those between metals and salts are called **displacement reactions**. The products of these displacement reactions are always an element (H_2 or a metal) and a salt. Comparing such reactions allows us to rank metals according to their ease of oxidation. A list of metals arranged in order of decreasing ease of oxidation is called an **activity series**. Any metal on the list can be oxidized by ions of metals (or H^+) below it in the series.

SECTION 4.5 The **concentration** of a solution expresses the amount of a solute dissolved in the solution. One of the common ways to express the concentration of a solute is in terms of molarity. The **molarity** of a solution is the number of moles of solute per liter of solution. Molarity makes it possible to interconvert solution volume and number of moles of solute. Solutions of known molarity can be formed either by weighing out the solute and diluting it to a known volume or by the **dilution** of a more concentrated solution of known concentration (a stock solution). Adding solvent to the solution (the process of dilution) decreases the concentration of the solute without changing the number of moles of solute in the solution ($M_{conc} \times V_{conc} = M_{dil} \times V_{dil}$).

SECTION 4.6 In the process called **titration**, we combine a solution of known concentration (a **standard solution**) with a solution of unknown concentration to determine the unknown concentration or the quantity of solute in the unknown. The point in the titration at which stoichiometrically equivalent quantities of reactants are brought together is called the **equivalence point**. An indicator can be used to show the **end point** of the titration, which coincides closely with the equivalence point.

KEY SKILLS

- Recognize compounds as acids or bases, and as strong, weak, or nonelectrolytes. (Sections 4.1 and 4.3)
- Recognize reactions by type and be able to predict the products of simple acid–base, precipitation, and redox reactions. (Sections 4.2–4.4)
- Be able to calculate molarity and use it to convert between moles of a substance in solution and volume of the solution. (Section 4.5)
- Understand how to carry out a dilution to achieve a desired solution concentration. (Section 4.5)
- Understand how to perform and interpret the results of a titration. (Section 4.6)

KEY EQUATIONS

- $\text{Molarity} = \dfrac{\text{moles solute}}{\text{volume of solution in liters}}$ [4.32]   Molarity is the most commonly used unit of concentration in chemistry.

- $M_{conc} \times V_{conc} = M_{dil} \times V_{dil}$ [4.34]   When adding solvent to a concentrated solution to make a dilute solution, molarities and volumes of both concentrated and dilute solutions can be calculated if three of the quantities are known.

EXERCISES

VISUALIZING CONCEPTS

4.1 Which of the following schematic drawings best describes a solution of Li_2SO_4 in water (water molecules not shown for simplicity)? [Section 4.1]

    (a)   (b)   (c)

4.2 Aqueous solutions of three different substances, AX, AY, and AZ, are represented by the three accompanying diagrams. Identify each substance as a strong electrolyte, weak electrolyte, or non-electrolyte. [Section 4.1]

    AX   AY   AZ

    (a)   (b)   (c)

4.3 Use the molecular representations shown here to classify each compound as either a nonelectrolyte, a weak electrolyte, or a strong electrolyte (see inside back cover for element color scheme). [Sections 4.1 and 4.3]

    (a)   (b)   (c)

4.4 A 0.1 M solution of acetic acid, CH_3COOH, causes the light-bulb in the apparatus of Figure 4.2 to glow about as brightly as a 0.001 M solution of HBr. How do you account for this fact? [Section 4.1]

4.5 You are presented with a white solid and told that due to careless labeling it is not clear if the substance is barium chloride, lead chloride, or zinc chloride. When you transfer the solid to a beaker and add water, the solid dissolves to give a clear solution. Next a $Na_2SO_4(aq)$ solution is added and a white precipitate forms. What is the identity of the unknown white solid? [Section 4.2]

4.6 We have seen that ions in aqueous solution are stabilized by the attractions between the ions and the water molecules. Why then do some pairs of ions in solution form precipitates? [Section 4.2]

4.7 Which of the following ions will *always* be a spectator ion in a precipitation reaction? (a) Cl^-, (b) NO_3^-, (c) NH_4^+, (d) S^{2-}, (e) SO_4^{2-}. Explain briefly. [Section 4.2]

4.8 The labels have fallen off three bottles containing powdered samples of metals; one contains zinc, one lead, and the other platinum. You have three solutions at your disposal: 1 M sodium nitrate, 1 M nitric acid, and 1 M nickel nitrate. How could you use these solutions to determine the identities of each metal powder? [Section 4.4]

4.9 Explain how a redox reaction involves electrons in the same way that a neutralization reaction involves protons. [Sections 4.3 and 4.4]

4.10 If you want to double the concentration of a solution, how could you do it? [Section 4.5]

GENERAL PROPERTIES OF AQUEOUS SOLUTIONS (section 4.1)

4.11 When asked what causes electrolyte solutions to conduct electricity, a student responds that it is due to the movement of electrons through the solution. Is the student correct? If not, what is the correct response?

4.12 When methanol, CH_3OH, is dissolved in water, a nonconducting solution results. When acetic acid, CH_3COOH, dissolves in water, the solution is weakly conducting and acidic in nature. Describe what happens upon dissolution in the two cases, and account for the different results.

4.13 We have learned in this chapter that many ionic solids dissolve in water as strong electrolytes, that is, as separated ions in solution. What properties of water facilitate this process? Would you expect ionic compounds to be soluble in elemental liquids like bromine or mercury, just as they are in water? Explain.

4.14 What does it mean to say that ions are solvated when an ionic substance dissolves in water?

4.15 Specify what ions are present in solution upon dissolving each of the following substances in water: (a) $ZnCl_2$, (b) HNO_3, (c) $(NH_4)_2SO_4$, (d) $Ca(OH)_2$.

4.16 Specify what ions are present upon dissolving each of the following substances in water: (a) MgI_2, (b) $Al(NO_3)_3$, (c) $HClO_4$, (d) $NaCH_3COO$.

4.17 Formic acid, HCOOH, is a weak electrolyte. What solute particles are present in an aqueous solution of this compound? Write the chemical equation for the ionization of HCOOH.

4.18 Acetone, CH_3COCH_3, is a nonelectrolyte; hypochlorous acid, HClO, is a weak electrolyte; and ammonium chloride, NH_4Cl, is a strong electrolyte. (a) What are the solute particles present in aqueous solutions of each compound? (b) If 0.1 mol of each compound is dissolved in solution, which one contains 0.2 mol of solute particles, which contains 0.1 mol of solute particles, and which contains somewhere between 0.1 and 0.2 mol of solute particles?

PRECIPITATION REACTIONS (section 4.2)

4.19 Using solubility guidelines, predict whether each of the following compounds is soluble or insoluble in water: (a) $MgBr_2$, (b) PbI_2, (c) $(NH_4)_2CO_3$, (d) $Sr(OH)_2$, (e) $ZnSO_4$.

4.20 Predict whether each of the following compounds is soluble in water: (a) AgI, (b) Na_2CO_3, (c) $BaCl_2$, (d) $Al(OH)_3$, (e) $Zn(CH_3COO)_2$.

4.21 Will precipitation occur when the following solutions are mixed? If so, write a balanced chemical equation for the reaction. (a) Na_2CO_3 and $AgNO_3$, (b) $NaNO_3$ and $NiSO_4$, (c) $FeSO_4$ and $Pb(NO_3)_2$.

4.22 Identify the precipitate (if any) that forms when the following solutions are mixed, and write a balanced equation for each reaction. (a) $NaCH_3COO$ and HCl, (b) KOH and $Cu(NO_3)_2$, (c) Na_2S and $CdSO_4$.

4.23 Name the spectator ions in any reactions that may be involved when each of the following pairs of solutions are mixed.
(a) $Na_2CO_3(aq)$ and $MgSO_4(aq)$
(b) $Pb(NO_3)_2(aq)$ and $Na_2S(aq)$
(c) $(NH_4)_3PO_4(aq)$ and $CaCl_2(aq)$

4.24 Write balanced net ionic equations for the reactions that occur in each of the following cases. Identify the spectator ion or ions in each reaction.
(a) $Cr_2(SO_4)_3(aq) + (NH_4)_2CO_3(aq) \longrightarrow$
(b) $Ba(NO_3)_2(aq) + K_2SO_4(aq) \longrightarrow$
(c) $Fe(NO_3)_2(aq) + KOH(aq) \longrightarrow$

4.25 Separate samples of a solution of an unknown salt are treated with dilute solutions of HBr, H_2SO_4, and $NaOH$. A precipitate forms in all three cases. Which of the following cations could the solution contain: K^+, Pb^{2+}, Ba^{2+}?

4.26 Separate samples of a solution of an unknown ionic compound are treated with dilute $AgNO_3$, $Pb(NO_3)_2$, and $BaCl_2$. Precipitates form in all three cases. Which of the following could be the anion of the unknown salt: Br^-, CO_3^{2-}, NO_3^-?

4.27 You know that an unlabeled bottle contains a solution of one of the following: $AgNO_3$, $CaCl_2$, or $Al_2(SO_4)_3$. A friend suggests that you test a portion of the solution with $Ba(NO_3)_2$ and then with $NaCl$ solutions. Explain how these two tests together would be sufficient to determine which salt is present in the solution.

4.28 Three solutions are mixed together to form a single solution. One contains 0.2 mol $Pb(CH_3COO)_2$, the second contains 0.1 mol Na_2S, and the third contains 0.1 mol $CaCl_2$. (a) Write the net ionic equations for the precipitation reaction or reactions that occur. (b) What are the spectator ions in the solution?

ACIDS, BASES, AND NEUTRALIZATION REACTIONS (section 4.3)

4.29 Which of the following solutions has the largest concentration of solvated protons: (a) 0.2 M $LiOH$, (b) 0.2 M HI, (c) 1.0 M methyl alcohol (CH_3OH)? Explain

4.30 Which of the following solutions is the most basic? (a) 0.6 M NH_3, (b) 0.150 M KOH, (c) 0.100 M $Ba(OH)_2$. Explain.

4.31 What is the difference between (a) a monoprotic acid and a diprotic acid, (b) a weak acid and a strong acid, (c) an acid and a base?

4.32 Explain the following observations: (a) NH_3 contains no OH^- ions, and yet its aqueous solutions are basic; (b) HF is called a weak acid, and yet it is very reactive; (c) although sulfuric acid is a strong electrolyte, an aqueous solution of H_2SO_4 contains more HSO_4^- ions than SO_4^{2-} ions.

4.33 Is there any correlation between the anions that form when each of the strong acids in Table 4.2 dissociates and the anions that normally form soluble ionic compounds (Table 4.1)? Which anions if any are exceptions to the general trend?

4.34 What is the relationship between the solubility rules in Table 4.1 and the list of strong bases in Table 4.2? Another way of asking this question is, why is $Cd(OH)_2$, for example, not listed as a strong base in Table 4.2?

4.35 Label each of the following substances as an acid, base, salt, or none of the above. Indicate whether the substance exists in aqueous solution entirely in molecular form, entirely as ions, or as a mixture of molecules and ions. (a) HF, (b) acetonitrile, CH_3CN, (c) $NaClO_4$, (d) $Ba(OH)_2$.

4.36 An aqueous solution of an unknown solute is tested with litmus paper and found to be acidic. The solution is weakly conducting compared with a solution of $NaCl$ of the same concentration. Which of the following substances could the unknown be: KOH, NH_3, HNO_3, $KClO_2$, H_3PO_3, CH_3COCH_3 (acetone)?

4.37 Classify each of the following substances as a nonelectrolyte, weak electrolyte, or strong electrolyte in water: (a) H_2SO_3, (b) C_2H_5OH (ethanol), (c) NH_3, (d) $KClO_3$, (e) $Cu(NO_3)_2$.

4.38 Classify each of the following aqueous solutions as a nonelectrolyte, weak electrolyte, or strong electrolyte: (a) $LiClO_4$, (b) $HClO$, (c) $CH_3CH_2CH_2OH$ (propanol), (d) $HClO_3$, (e) $CuSO_4$, (f) $C_{12}H_{22}O_{11}$ (sucrose).

4.39 Complete and balance the following molecular equations, and then write the net ionic equation for each:
(a) $HBr(aq) + Ca(OH)_2(aq) \longrightarrow$
(b) $Cu(OH)_2(s) + HClO_4(aq) \longrightarrow$
(c) $Al(OH)_3(s) + HNO_3(aq) \longrightarrow$

4.40 Write the balanced molecular and net ionic equations for each of the following neutralization reactions:
(a) Aqueous acetic acid is neutralized by aqueous barium hydroxide.
(b) Solid chromium(III) hydroxide reacts with nitrous acid.
(c) Aqueous nitric acid and aqueous ammonia react.

4.41 Write balanced molecular and net ionic equations for the following reactions, and identify the gas formed in each: (a) solid cadmium sulfide reacts with an aqueous solution of sulfuric acid; (b) solid magnesium carbonate reacts with an aqueous solution of perchloric acid.

4.42 Because the oxide ion is basic, metal oxides react readily with acids. (a) Write the net ionic equation for the following reaction:

$FeO(s) + 2HClO_4(aq) \longrightarrow Fe(ClO_4)_2(aq) + H_2O(l)$

(b) Based on the equation in part (a), write the net ionic equation for the reaction that occurs between NiO(s) and an aqueous solution of nitric acid.

4.43 Magnesium carbonate, magnesium oxide, and magnesium hydroxide are all white solids that react with acidic solutions. **(a)** Write a balanced molecular equation and a net ionic equation for the reaction that occurs when each substance reacts with a hydrochloric acid solution. **(b)** By observing the reactions in part (a) could you distinguish any of the three magnesium substances from the other two? If so how? **(c)** If excess HCl(aq) is added, would the clear solutions left behind after the reaction is complete contain the same or different ions in each case?

4.44 As K_2O dissolves in water, the oxide ion reacts with water molecules to form hydroxide ions. Write the molecular and net ionic equations for this reaction. Based on the definitions of acid and base, what ion is the base in this reaction? What is the acid? What is the spectator ion in the reaction?

OXIDATION-REDUCTION REACTIONS (section 4.4)

4.45 Define oxidation and reduction in terms of **(a)** electron transfer and **(b)** oxidation numbers.

4.46 Can oxidation occur without oxygen? Can oxidation occur without reduction?

4.47 Which region of the periodic table shown here contains the most readily oxidized elements? Which region contains the least readily oxidized?

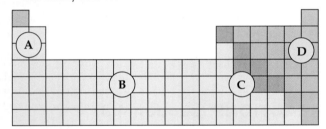

4.48 Determine the oxidation number of sulfur in each of the following substances: **(a)** barium sulfate, $BaSO_4$, **(b)** sulfurous acid, H_2SO_3, **(c)** strontium sulfide, SrS, **(d)** hydrogen sulfide, H_2S. **(e)** Based on these compounds what is the range of oxidation numbers seen for sulfur? Is there any relationship between the range of accessible oxidation states and sulfur's position on the periodic table?

4.49 Determine the oxidation number for the indicated element in each of the following substances: **(a)** S in SO_2, **(b)** C in $COCl_2$, **(c)** Mn in $KMnO_4$, **(d)** Br in HBrO, **(e)** As in As_4, **(f)** O in K_2O_2.

4.50 Determine the oxidation number for the indicated element in each of the following compounds: **(a)** Co in $LiCoO_2$, **(b)** Al in $NaAlH_4$, **(c)** C in CH_3OH (methanol), **(d)** N in GaN, **(e)** Cl in $HClO_2$, **(f)** Cr in $BaCrO_4$.

4.51 Which element is oxidized and which is reduced in the following reactions?
(a) $N_2(g) + 3 H_2(g) \longrightarrow 2 NH_3(g)$
(b) $3 Fe(NO_3)_2(aq) + 2 Al(s) \longrightarrow$
$$3 Fe(s) + 2 Al(NO_3)_3(aq)$$
(c) $Cl_2(aq) + 2 NaI(aq) \longrightarrow I_2(aq) + 2 NaCl(aq)$
(d) $PbS(s) + 4 H_2O_2(aq) \longrightarrow PbSO_4(s) + 4 H_2O(l)$

4.52 Which of the following are redox reactions? For those that are, indicate which element is oxidized and which is reduced. For those that are not, indicate whether they are precipitation or neutralization reactions.
(a) $P_4(s) + 10 HClO(aq) + 6 H_2O(l) \longrightarrow$
$$4 H_3PO_4(aq) + 10 HCl(aq)$$
(b) $Br_2(l) + 2 K(s) \longrightarrow 2 KBr(s)$

(c) $CH_3CH_2OH(l) + 3 O_2(g) \longrightarrow 3 H_2O(l) + 2 CO_2(g)$
(d) $ZnCl_2(aq) + 2 NaOH(aq) \longrightarrow Zn(OH)_2(s) + 2 NaCl(aq)$

4.53 Write balanced molecular and net ionic equations for the reactions of **(a)** manganese with dilute sulfuric acid, **(b)** chromium with hydrobromic acid, **(c)** tin with hydrochloric acid, **(d)** aluminum with formic acid, HCOOH.

4.54 Write balanced molecular and net ionic equations for the reactions of **(a)** hydrochloric acid with nickel, **(b)** dilute sulfuric acid with iron, **(c)** hydrobromic acid with magnesium, **(d)** acetic acid, CH_3COOH, with zinc.

4.55 Using the activity series (Table 4.5), write balanced chemical equations for the following reactions. If no reaction occurs, simply write NR. **(a)** Iron metal is added to a solution of copper(II) nitrate; **(b)** zinc metal is added to a solution of magnesium sulfate; **(c)** hydrobromic acid is added to tin metal; **(d)** hydrogen gas is bubbled through an aqueous solution of nickel(II) chloride; **(e)** aluminum metal is added to a solution of cobalt(II) sulfate.

4.56 Using the activity series (Table 4.5), write balanced chemical equations for the following reactions. If no reaction occurs, simply write NR. **(a)** Nickel metal is added to a solution of copper(II) nitrate; **(b)** a solution of zinc nitrate is added to a solution of magnesium sulfate; **(c)** hydrochloric acid is added to gold metal; **(d)** chromium metal is immersed in an aqueous solution of cobalt(II) chloride; **(e)** hydrogen gas is bubbled through a solution of silver nitrate.

4.57 The metal cadmium tends to form Cd^{2+} ions. The following observations are made: (i) When a strip of zinc metal is placed in $CdCl_2(aq)$, cadmium metal is deposited on the strip. (ii) When a strip of cadmium metal is placed in $Ni(NO_3)_2(aq)$, nickel metal is deposited on the strip. **(a)** Write net ionic equations to explain each of the preceding observations. **(b)** What can you conclude about the position of cadmium in the activity series? **(c)** What experiments would you need to perform to locate more precisely the position of cadmium in the activity series?

4.58 **(a)** Use the following reactions to prepare an activity series for the halogens:
$$Br_2(aq) + 2 NaI(aq) \longrightarrow 2 NaBr(aq) + I_2(aq)$$
$$Cl_2(aq) + 2 NaBr(aq) \longrightarrow 2 NaCl(aq) + Br_2(aq)$$
(b) Relate the positions of the halogens in the periodic table with their locations in this activity series. **(c)** Predict whether a reaction occurs when the following reagents are mixed: $Cl_2(aq)$ and KI(aq); $Br_2(aq)$ and LiCl(aq).

CONCENTRATIONS OF SOLUTIONS (section 4.5)

4.59 (a) Is the concentration of a solution an intensive or an extensive property? (b) What is the difference between 0.50 mol HCl and 0.50 M HCl?

4.60 (a) Suppose you prepare 500 mL of a 0.10 M solution of some salt and then spill some of it. What happens to the concentration of the solution left in the container? (b) Suppose you prepare 500 mL of a 0.10 M aqueous solution of some salt and let it sit out, uncovered, for a long time, and some water evaporates. What happens to the concentration of the solution left in the container? (c) A certain volume of a 0.50 M solution contains 4.5 g of a salt. What mass of the salt is present in the same volume of a 2.50 M solution?

4.61 (a) Calculate the molarity of a solution that contains 0.175 mol $ZnCl_2$ in exactly 150 mL of solution. (b) How many moles of HCl are present in 35.0 mL of a 4.50 M solution of nitric acid? (c) How many milliliters of 6.00 M NaOH solution are needed to provide 0.325 mol of NaOH?

4.62 (a) Calculate the molarity of a solution made by dissolving 12.5 grams of Na_2CrO_4 in enough water to form exactly 550 mL of solution. (b) How many moles of KBr are present in 150 mL of a 0.275 M solution? (c) How many milliliters of 6.1 M HCl solution are needed to obtain 0.100 mol of HCl?

4.63 The average adult human male has a total blood volume of 5.0 L. If the concentration of sodium ion in this average individual is 0.135 M, what is the mass of sodium ion circulating in the blood?

4.64 A person suffering from hyponatremia has a sodium ion concentration in the blood of 0.118 M and a total blood volume of 4.6 L. What mass of sodium chloride would need to be added to the blood to bring the sodium ion concentration up to 0.138 M, assuming no change in blood volume?

4.65 The concentration of alcohol (CH_3CH_2OH) in blood, called the "blood alcohol concentration" or BAC, is given in units of grams of alcohol per 100 mL of blood. The legal definition of intoxication, in many states of the United States, is that the BAC is 0.08 or higher. What is the concentration of alcohol, in terms of molarity, in blood if the BAC is 0.08?

4.66 The average adult male has a total blood volume of 5.0 L. After drinking a few beers, he has a BAC of 0.10 (see Exercise 4.65). What mass of alcohol is circulating in his blood?

4.67 Calculate (a) the number of grams of solute in 0.250 L of 0.175 M KBr, (b) the molar concentration of a solution containing 14.75 g of $Ca(NO_3)_2$ in 1.375 L, (c) the volume of 1.50 M Na_3PO_4 in milliliters that contains 2.50 g of solute.

4.68 (a) How many grams of solute are present in 15.0 mL of 0.736 M $K_2Cr_2O_7$? (b) If 14.00 g of $(NH_4)_2SO_4$ is dissolved in enough water to form 250 mL of solution, what is the molarity of the solution? (c) How many milliliters of 0.0455 M $CuSO_4$ contain 3.65 g of solute?

4.69 (a) Which will have the highest concentration of potassium ion: 0.20 M KCl, 0.15 M K_2CrO_4, or 0.080 M K_3PO_4? (b) Which will contain the greater number of moles of potassium ion: 30.0 mL of 0.15 M K_2CrO_4 or 25.0 mL of 0.080 M K_3PO_4?

4.70 In each of the following pairs, indicate which has the higher concentration of I^- ion: (a) 0.10 M BaI_2 or 0.25 M KI solution, (b) 100 mL of 0.10 M KI solution or 200 mL of 0.040 M ZnI_2 solution, (c) 3.2 M HI solution or a solution made by dissolving 145 g of NaI in water to make 150 mL of solution.

4.71 Indicate the concentration of each ion or molecule present in the following solutions: (a) 0.25 M $NaNO_3$, (b) 1.3×10^{-2} M $MgSO_4$, (c) 0.0150 M $C_6H_{12}O_6$, (d) a mixture of 45.0 mL of 0.272 M NaCl and 65.0 mL of 0.0247 M $(NH_4)_2CO_3$. Assume that the volumes are additive.

4.72 Indicate the concentration of each ion present in the solution formed by mixing (a) 42.0 mL of 0.170 M NaOH and 37.6 mL of 0.400 M NaOH, (b) 44.0 mL of 0.100 M and Na_2SO_4 and 25.0 mL of 0.150 M KCl, (c) 3.60 g KCl in 75.0 mL of 0.250 M $CaCl_2$ solution. Assume that the volumes are additive.

4.73 (a) You have a stock solution of 14.8 M NH_3. How many milliliters of this solution should you dilute to make 1000.0 mL of 0.250 M NH_3? (b) If you take a 10.0-mL portion of the stock solution and dilute it to a total volume of 0.500 L, what will be the concentration of the final solution?

4.74 (a) How many milliliters of a stock solution of 6.0 M HNO_3 would you have to use to prepare 110 mL of 0.500 M HNO_3? (b) If you dilute 10.0 mL of the stock solution to a final volume of 0.250 L, what will be the concentration of the diluted solution?

4.75 (a) Starting with solid sucrose, $C_{12}H_{22}O_{11}$, describe how you would prepare 250 mL of a 0.250 M sucrose solution. (b) Describe how you would prepare 350.0 mL of 0.100 M $C_{12}H_{22}O_{11}$ starting with 3.00 L of 1.50 M $C_{12}H_{22}O_{11}$.

4.76 (a) How would you prepare 175.0 mL of 0.150 M $AgNO_3$ solution starting with pure $AgNO_3$? (b) An experiment calls for you to use 100 mL of 0.50 M HNO_3 solution. All you have available is a bottle of 3.6 M HNO_3. How would you prepare the desired solution?

4.77 Pure acetic acid, known as glacial acetic acid, is a liquid with a density of 1.049 g/mL at 25 °C. Calculate the molarity of a solution of acetic acid made by dissolving 20.00 mL of glacial acetic acid at 25 °C in enough water to make 250.0 mL of solution.

4.78 Glycerol, $C_3H_8O_3$, is a substance used extensively in the manufacture of cosmetics, foodstuffs, antifreeze, and plastics. Glycerol is a water-soluble liquid with a density of 1.2656 g/mL at 15 °C. Calculate the molarity of a solution of glycerol made by dissolving 50.000 mL glycerol at 15 °C in enough water to make 250.00 mL of solution.

SOLUTION STOICHIOMETRY AND CHEMICAL ANALYSIS (section 4.6)

4.79 What mass of KCl is needed to precipitate the silver ions from 15.0 mL of 0.200 M $AgNO_3$ solution?

4.80 What mass of NaOH is needed to precipitate the Cd^{2+} ions from 35.0 mL of 0.500 M $Cd(NO_3)_2$ solution?

4.81 (a) What volume of 0.115 M $HClO_4$ solution is needed to neutralize 50.00 mL of 0.0875 M NaOH? (b) What volume of 0.128 M HCl is needed to neutralize 2.87 g of $Mg(OH)_2$? (c) If 25.8 mL of $AgNO_3$ is needed to precipitate all the Cl^- ions in a

785-mg sample of KCl (forming AgCl), what is the molarity of the $AgNO_3$ solution? (d) If 45.3 mL of 0.108 M HCl solution is needed to neutralize a solution of KOH, how many grams of KOH must be present in the solution?

4.82 (a) How many milliliters of 0.120 M HCl are needed to completely neutralize 50.0 mL of 0.101 M $Ba(OH)_2$ solution? (b) How many milliliters of 0.125 M H_2SO_4 are needed to neutralize 0.200 g of NaOH? (c) If 55.8 mL of $BaCl_2$ solution is needed to precipitate all the sulfate ion in a 752-mg sample of Na_2SO_4, what is the molarity of the solution? (d) If 42.7 mL of 0.208 M HCl solution is needed to neutralize a solution of $Ca(OH)_2$, how many grams of $Ca(OH)_2$ must be in the solution?

4.83 Some sulfuric acid is spilled on a lab bench. You can neutralize the acid by sprinkling sodium bicarbonate on it and then mopping up the resultant solution. The sodium bicarbonate reacts with sulfuric acid as follows:

$$2\ NaHCO_3(s) + H_2SO_4(aq) \longrightarrow$$
$$Na_2SO_4(aq) + 2\ H_2O(l) + 2\ CO_2(g)$$

Sodium bicarbonate is added until the fizzing due to the formation of $CO_2(g)$ stops. If 27 mL of 6.0 M H_2SO_4 was spilled, what is the minimum mass of $NaHCO_3$ that must be added to the spill to neutralize the acid?

4.84 The distinctive odor of vinegar is due to acetic acid, CH_3COOH, which reacts with sodium hydroxide in the following fashion:

$$CH_3COOH(aq) + NaOH(aq) \longrightarrow$$
$$H_2O(l) + NaC_2H_3O_2(aq)$$

If 3.45 mL of vinegar needs 42.5 mL of 0.115 M NaOH to reach the equivalence point in a titration, how many grams of acetic acid are in a 1.00-qt sample of this vinegar?

4.85 A 4.36-g sample of an unknown alkali metal hydroxide is dissolved in 100.0 mL of water. An acid–base indicator is added and the resulting solution is titrated with 2.50 M HCl(aq) solution. The indicator changes color signaling that the equivalence point has been reached after 17.0 mL of the hydrochloric acid solution has been added. (a) What is the molar mass of the metal hydroxide? (b) What is the identity of the alkali metal cation: Li^+, Na^+, K^+, Rb^+, or Cs^+?

4.86 An 8.65-g sample of an unknown group 2A metal hydroxide is dissolved in 85.0 mL of water. An acid–base indicator is added and the resulting solution is titrated with 2.50 M HCl(aq) solution. The indicator changes color signaling that the equivalence point has been reached after 56.9 mL of the hydrochloric acid solution has been added. (a) What is the molar mass of the metal hydroxide? (b) What is the identity of the metal cation: Ca^{2+}, Sr^{2+}, Ba^{2+}?

4.87 A solution of 100.0 mL of 0.200 M KOH is mixed with a solution of 200.0 mL of 0.150 M $NiSO_4$. (a) Write the balanced chemical equation for the reaction that occurs. (b) What precipitate forms? (c) What is the limiting reactant? (d) How many grams of this precipitate form? (e) What is the concentration of each ion that remains in solution?

4.88 A solution is made by mixing 15.0 g of $Sr(OH)_2$ and 55.0 mL of 0.200 M HNO_3. (a) Write a balanced equation for the reaction that occurs between the solutes. (b) Calculate the concentration of each ion remaining in solution. (c) Is the resultant solution acidic or basic?

4.89 A 0.5895-g sample of impure magnesium hydroxide is dissolved in 100.0 mL of 0.2050 M HCl solution. The excess acid then needs 19.85 mL of 0.1020 M NaOH for neutralization. Calculate the percent by mass of magnesium hydroxide in the sample, assuming that it is the only substance reacting with the HCl solution.

4.90 A 1.248-g sample of limestone rock is pulverized and then treated with 30.00 mL of 1.035 M HCl solution. The excess acid then requires 11.56 mL of 1.010 M NaOH for neutralization. Calculate the percent by mass of calcium carbonate in the rock, assuming that it is the only substance reacting with the HCl solution.

ADDITIONAL EXERCISES

4.91 Gold is one of the few metals that can be obtained by panning, where a simple pan is used to separate gold from other deposits found in or near a stream bed. What two properties of gold make it possible to find gold, but not metals like copper, silver, lead, and aluminum, by panning?

4.92 The accompanying photo shows the reaction between a solution of $Cd(NO_3)_2$ and one of Na_2S. What is the identity of the precipitate? What ions remain in solution? Write the net ionic equation for the reaction.

4.93 Suppose you have a solution that might contain any or all of the following cations: Ni^{2+}, Ag^+, Sr^{2+}, and Mn^{2+}. Addition of HCl solution causes a precipitate to form. After filtering off the precipitate, H_2SO_4 solution is added to the resulting solution and another precipitate forms. This is filtered off, and a solution of NaOH is added to the resulting solution. No precipitate is observed. Which ions are present in each of the precipitates? Which of the four ions listed above must be absent from the original solution?

4.94 You choose to investigate some of the solubility guidelines for two ions not listed in Table 4.1, the chromate ion (CrO_4^{2-}) and the oxalate ion ($C_2O_4^{2-}$). You are given 0.01 M solutions (A, B, C, D) of four water-soluble salts:

Solution	Solute	Color of Solution
A	Na_2CrO_4	Yellow
B	$(NH_4)_2C_2O_4$	Colorless
C	$AgNO_3$	Colorless
D	$CaCl_2$	Colorless

When these solutions are mixed, the following observations are made:

Expt Number	Solutions Mixed	Result
1	A + B	No precipitate, yellow solution
2	A + C	Red precipitate forms
3	A + D	Yellow precipitate forms
4	B + C	White precipitate forms
5	B + D	White precipitate forms
6	C + D	White precipitate forms

(a) Write a net ionic equation for the reaction that occurs in each of the experiments. **(b)** Identify the precipitate formed, if any, in each of the experiments.

4.95 Antacids are often used to relieve pain and promote healing in the treatment of mild ulcers. Write balanced net ionic equations for the reactions between the HCl(aq) in the stomach and each of the following substances used in various antacids: **(a)** $Al(OH)_3(s)$, **(b)** $Mg(OH)_2(s)$, **(c)** $MgCO_3(s)$, **(d)** $NaAl(CO_3)(OH)_2(s)$, **(e)** $CaCO_3(s)$.

[4.96] The commercial production of nitric acid involves the following chemical reactions:

$$4\,NH_3(g) + 5\,O_2(g) \longrightarrow 4\,NO(g) + 6\,H_2O(g)$$
$$2\,NO(g) + O_2(g) \longrightarrow 2\,NO_2(g)$$
$$3\,NO_2(g) + H_2O(l) \longrightarrow 2\,HNO_3(aq) + NO(g)$$

(a) Which of these reactions are redox reactions? **(b)** In each redox reaction identify the element undergoing oxidation and the element undergoing reduction.

4.97 Consider the following reagents: zinc, copper, mercury (density 13.6 g/mL), silver nitrate solution, nitric acid solution. **(a)** Given a 500-mL Erlenmeyer flask and a balloon can you combine two or more of the foregoing reagents to initiate a chemical reaction that will inflate the balloon? Write a balanced chemical equation to represent this process. What is the identity of the substance that inflates the balloon? **(b)** What is the theoretical yield of the substance that fills the balloon? **(c)** Can you combine two or more of the foregoing reagents to initiate a chemical reaction that will produce metallic silver? Write a balanced chemical equation to represent this process. What ions are left behind in solution? **(d)** What is the theoretical yield of silver?

35.0 g Zn   42.0 g Cu   6.55 mL Hg

150 mL of 0.750 M AgNO$_3$(aq)   150 mL of 3.00 M HNO$_3$(aq)

[4.98] Lanthanum metal forms cations with a charge of 3+. Consider the following observations about the chemistry of lanthanum: When lanthanum metal is exposed to air, a white solid (compound A) is formed that contains lanthanum and one other element. When lanthanum metal is added to water, gas bubbles are observed and a different white solid (compound B) is formed. Both A and B dissolve in hydrochloric acid to give a clear solution. When either of these solutions is evaporated, a soluble white solid (compound C) remains. If compound C is dissolved in water and sulfuric acid is added, a white precipitate (compound D) forms. **(a)** Propose identities for the substances A, B, C, and D. **(b)** Write net ionic equations for all the reactions described. **(c)** Based on the preceding observations, what can be said about the position of lanthanum in the activity series (Table 4.5)?

4.99 A 35.0-mL sample of 1.00 M KBr and a 60.0-mL sample of 0.600 M KBr are mixed. The solution is then heated to evaporate water until the total volume is 50.0 mL. What is the molarity of the KBr in the final solution?

4.100 Using modern analytical techniques, it is possible to detect sodium ions in concentrations as low as 50 pg/mL. What is this detection limit expressed in **(a)** molarity of Na^+, **(b)** Na^+ ions per cubic centimeter?

4.101 Hard water contains Ca^{2+}, Mg^{2+}, and Fe^{2+}, which interfere with the action of soap and leave an insoluble coating on the insides of containers and pipes when heated. Water softeners replace these ions with Na^+. **(a)** If 1500 L of hard water contains 0.020 M Ca^{2+} and 0.0040 M Mg^{2+}, how many moles of Na^+ are needed to replace these ions? **(b)** If the sodium is added to the water softener in the form of NaCl, how many grams of sodium chloride are needed?

4.102 Tartaric acid, $H_2C_4H_4O_6$, has two acidic hydrogens. The acid is often present in wines and precipitates from solution as the wine ages. A solution containing an unknown concentration of the acid is titrated with NaOH. It requires 24.65 mL of 0.2500 M NaOH solution to titrate both acidic protons in 50.00 mL of the tartaric acid solution. Write a balanced net ionic equation for the neutralization reaction, and calculate the molarity of the tartaric acid solution.

4.103 **(a)** A strontium hydroxide solution is prepared by dissolving 10.45 g of $Sr(OH)_2$ in water to make 50.00 mL of solution. What is the molarity of this solution? **(b)** Next the strontium hydroxide solution prepared in part (a) is used to titrate a nitric acid solution of unknown concentration. Write a balanced chemical equation to represent the reaction between strontium hydroxide and nitric acid solutions. **(c)** If 23.9 mL of the strontium hydroxide solution was needed to neutralize a 31.5 mL aliquot of the nitric acid solution, what is the concentration (molarity) of the acid?

[4.104] A solid sample of $Zn(OH)_2$ is added to 0.350 L of 0.500 M aqueous HBr. The solution that remains is still acidic. It is then titrated with 0.500 M NaOH solution, and it takes 88.5 mL of the NaOH solution to reach the equivalence point. What mass of $Zn(OH)_2$ was added to the HBr solution?

INTEGRATIVE EXERCISES

4.105 Suppose you have 5.00 g of powdered magnesium metal, 1.00 L of 2.00 M potassium nitrate solution, and 1.00 L of 2.00 M silver nitrate solution. **(a)** Which one of the solutions will react with the magnesium powder? **(b)** What is the net ionic equation that describes this reaction? **(c)** What volume of solution is needed to completely react with the magnesium? **(d)** What is the molarity of the Mg^{2+} ions in the resulting solution?

4.106 **(a)** By titration, 15.0 mL of 0.1008 M sodium hydroxide is needed to neutralize a 0.2053-g sample of an organic acid. What is the molar mass of the acid if it is monoprotic? **(b)** An elemental analysis of the acid indicates that it is composed of 5.89% H, 70.6% C, and 23.5% O by mass. What is its molecular formula?

4.107 A 3.455-g sample of a mixture was analyzed for barium ion by adding a small excess of sulfuric acid to an aqueous solution of the sample. The resultant reaction produced a precipitate of barium sulfate, which was collected by filtration, washed, dried, and weighed. If 0.2815 g of barium sulfate was obtained, what was the mass percentage of barium in the sample?

4.108 A tanker truck carrying 5.0×10^3 kg of concentrated sulfuric acid solution tips over and spills its load. If the sulfuric acid is 95.0% H_2SO_4 by mass and has a density of 1.84 g/mL, how many kilograms of sodium carbonate must be added to neutralize the acid?

4.109 A sample of 5.53 g of $Mg(OH)_2$ is added to 25.0 mL of 0.200 M HNO_3. **(a)** Write the chemical equation for the reaction that occurs. **(b)** Which is the limiting reactant in the reaction? **(c)** How many moles of $Mg(OH)_2$, HNO_3, and $Mg(NO_3)_2$ are present after the reaction is complete?

4.110 A sample of 1.50 g of lead(II) nitrate is mixed with 125 mL of 0.100 M sodium sulfate solution. **(a)** Write the chemical equation for the reaction that occurs. **(b)** Which is the limiting reactant in the reaction? **(c)** What are the concentrations of all ions that remain in solution after the reaction is complete?

[4.111] The average concentration of bromide ion in seawater is 65 mg of bromide ion per kg of seawater. What is the molarity of the bromide ion if the density of the seawater is 1.025 g/mL?

[4.112] The mass percentage of chloride ion in a 25.00-mL sample of seawater was determined by titrating the sample with silver nitrate, precipitating silver chloride. It took 42.58 mL of 0.2997 M silver nitrate solution to reach the equivalence point in the titration. What is the mass percentage of chloride ion in the seawater if its density is 1.025 g/mL?

4.113 The arsenic in a 1.22-g sample of a pesticide was converted to AsO_4^{3-} by suitable chemical treatment. It was then titrated using Ag^+ to form Ag_3AsO_4 as a precipitate. **(a)** What is the oxidation state of As in AsO_4^{3-}? **(b)** Name Ag_3AsO_4 by analogy to the corresponding compound containing phosphorus in place of arsenic. **(c)** If it took 25.0 mL of 0.102 M Ag^+ to reach the equivalence point in this titration, what is the mass percentage of arsenic in the pesticide?

[4.114] The newest US standard for arsenate in drinking water, mandated by the Safe Drinking Water Act, required that by January 2006, public water supplies must contain no greater than 10 parts per billion (ppb) arsenic. If this arsenic is present as arsenate, AsO_4^{3-}, what mass of sodium arsenate would be present in a 1.00-L sample of drinking water that just meets the standard? Parts per billion is defined on a mass basis as

$$ppb = \frac{g\ solute}{g\ solution} \times 10^9.$$

[**4.115**] Federal regulations set an upper limit of 50 parts per million (ppm) of NH_3 in the air in a work environment [that is, 50 molecules of $NH_3(g)$ for every million molecules in the air]. Air from a manufacturing operation was drawn through a solution containing 1.00×10^2 mL of 0.0105 M HCl. The NH_3 reacts with HCl as follows:

$$NH_3(aq) + HCl(aq) \longrightarrow NH_4Cl(aq)$$

After drawing air through the acid solution for 10.0 min at a rate of 10.0 L/min, the acid was titrated. The remaining acid needed 13.1 mL of 0.0588 M NaOH to reach the equivalence point. **(a)** How many grams of NH_3 were drawn into the acid solution? **(b)** How many ppm of NH_3 were in the air? (Air has a density of 1.20 g/L and an average molar mass of 29.0 g/mol under the conditions of the experiment.) **(c)** Is this manufacturer in compliance with regulations?

▲ **FIGURE 16.1 Oxalic acid, $H_2C_2O_4$.**

pollutants washed out of the air by rain, and even the rates of reactions that maintain our lives all critically depend on the acidity or basicity of solutions.

We have encountered acids and bases many times in earlier discussions. For example, a portion of Chapter 4 focused on their reactions. In this chapter we reexamine acids and bases, taking a closer look at how they are identified and characterized. In doing so, we consider their behavior both in terms of their structure and bonding and in terms of the chemical equilibria in which they participate.

16.1 | ACIDS AND BASES: A BRIEF REVIEW

From the earliest days of experimental chemistry, scientists have recognized acids and bases by their characteristic properties. Acids have a sour taste and cause certain dyes to change color, whereas bases have a bitter taste and feel slippery (soap is a good example). Use of the term *base* comes from the old English meaning of the word, "to bring low." (We still use the word *debase* in this sense, meaning to lower the value of something.) When a base is added to an acid, the base "lowers" the amount of acid. Indeed, when acids and bases are mixed in certain proportions, their characteristic properties disappear altogether. ∞ (Section 4.3)

By 1830 it was evident that all acids contain hydrogen but not all hydrogen-containing substances are acids. During the 1880s, the Swedish chemist Svante Arrhenius (1859–1927) defined acids as substances that produce H^+ ions in water and bases as substances that produce OH^- ions in water. Over time the Arrhenius concept of acids and bases came to be stated in the following way:

- An *acid* is a substance that, when dissolved in water, increases the concentration of H^+ ions.

- A *base* is a substance that, when dissolved in water, increases the concentration of OH^- ions.

Hydrogen chloride is an Arrhenius acid. Hydrogen chloride gas is highly soluble in water because of its chemical reaction with water, which produces hydrated H^+ and Cl^- ions:

$$HCl(g) \xrightarrow{H_2O} H^+(aq) + Cl^-(aq) \qquad [16.1]$$

The aqueous solution of HCl is known as hydrochloric acid. Concentrated hydrochloric acid is about 37% HCl by mass and is 12 M in HCl.

Sodium hydroxide is an Arrhenius base. Because NaOH is an ionic compound, it dissociates into Na^+ and OH^- ions when it dissolves in water, thereby releasing OH^- ions into the solution.

GIVE IT SOME THOUGHT

What two ions are central to the Arrhenius definitions of acids and bases?

16.2 | BRØNSTED–LOWRY ACIDS AND BASES

The Arrhenius concept of acids and bases, while useful, has limitations. For one thing, it is restricted to aqueous solutions. In 1923 the Danish chemist Johannes Brønsted (1879–1947) and the English chemist Thomas Lowry (1874–1936) independently proposed a more general definition of acids and bases. Their concept is based on the fact that *acid–base reactions involve the transfer of H^+ ions from one substance to another.*

The H^+ Ion in Water

We might at first imagine that ionization of HCl in water produces just H^+ and Cl^-. A hydrogen ion is no more than a bare proton, however, and would interact strongly with any source of electron density, such as the nonbonding electron pairs on the oxygen atoms of water molecules. For example, the interaction of a proton with water forms the **hydronium ion**, $H_3O^+(aq)$:

$$H^+ \ + \ :\overset{\displaystyle .}{\underset{\displaystyle \underset{H}{|}}{O}}\!-\!H \ \longrightarrow \ \left[H\!-\!\overset{\displaystyle .}{\underset{\displaystyle \underset{H}{|}}{O}}\!-\!H \right]^- \qquad [16.2]$$

The behavior of H^+ ions in liquid water is complex because hydronium ions are not the only polyatomic ions that form when H^+ interacts with water molecules. The H_3O^+ ion can form hydrogen bonds to additional H_2O molecules to generate such ions as $H_5O_2^+$ and $H_9O_4^+$ (▶ **FIGURE 16.2**).

Chemists use the notations $H^+(aq)$ and $H_3O^+(aq)$ interchangeably to represent the hydrated proton responsible for the characteristic properties of aqueous solutions of acids. We often use the notation $H^+(aq)$ for simplicity and convenience, as we did in Chapter 4 and Equation 16.1. The notation $H_3O^+(aq)$, however, more closely represents reality.

Proton-Transfer Reactions

In the reaction that occurs when HCl dissolves in water, the HCl molecule transfers an H^+ ion (a proton) to a water molecule. Thus, we can represent the reaction as occurring between an HCl molecule and a water molecule to form hydronium and chloride ions:

$$HCl(g) \ + \ H_2O(l) \ \longrightarrow \ Cl^-(aq) \ + \ H_3O^+(aq)$$

$$:\!\overset{\displaystyle .}{\underset{\displaystyle .}{Cl}}\!-\!H \ + \ :\overset{\displaystyle .}{\underset{\displaystyle \underset{H}{|}}{O}}\!-\!H \ \longrightarrow \ :\!\overset{\displaystyle .}{\underset{\displaystyle .}{Cl}}\!:\!\!{}^- \ + \ \left[H\!-\!\overset{\displaystyle .}{\underset{\displaystyle \underset{H}{|}}{O}}\!-\!H \right]^+ \qquad [16.3]$$

Acid   Base

The polar H_2O molecule promotes the ionization of acids in water solution by accepting a proton to form H_3O^+.

Brønsted and Lowry proposed definitions of acids and bases in terms of their ability to transfer protons:

- An *acid* is a substance (molecule or ion) that donates a proton to another substance.

- A *base* is a substance that accepts a proton.

Thus, when HCl dissolves in water (Equation 16.3), HCl acts as a **Brønsted–Lowry acid** (it donates a proton to H_2O), and H_2O acts as a **Brønsted–Lowry base** (it accepts a proton from HCl).

Because the emphasis in the Brønsted–Lowry concept is on proton transfer, the concept also applies to reactions that do not occur in aqueous solution. In the reaction

▲ **GO FIGURE**

Which type of intermolecular force do the dotted lines in this figure represent?

$$\left[H\!-\!\overset{\displaystyle .}{\underset{\displaystyle \underset{H}{|}}{O}}\!:\cdots H\!-\!\overset{\displaystyle .}{\underset{\displaystyle \underset{H}{|}}{O}}\!-\!H \right]^+$$

$$H_5O_2^+$$

$$H_9O_4^+$$

▲ **FIGURE 16.2   Ball-and-stick models and Lewis structures for two hydrated hydronium ions.**

between gas phase HCl and NH_3, for example, a proton is transferred from the acid HCl to the base NH_3:

$$:\overset{..}{\underset{..}{Cl}}-H \;+\; :\overset{\displaystyle H}{\underset{\displaystyle H}{N}}-H \;\longrightarrow\; :\overset{..}{\underset{..}{Cl}}:^- \;+\; \left[\overset{\displaystyle H}{\underset{\displaystyle H}{H-N-H}}\right]^+ \qquad [16.4]$$

Acid   Base

The hazy film that forms on the windows of general chemistry laboratories and on glassware in the laboratory is largely solid NH_4Cl formed by the gas-phase reaction between HCl and NH_3.

Let's consider another example that compares the relationship between the Arrhenius and Brønsted–Lowry definitions of acids and bases—an aqueous solution of ammonia, in which we have the equilibrium:

$$\underset{\text{Base}}{NH_3(aq)} \;+\; \underset{\text{Acid}}{H_2O(l)} \;\rightleftharpoons\; NH_4^+(aq) \;+\; OH^-(aq) \qquad [16.5]$$

Ammonia is a Brønsted–Lowry base because it accepts a proton from H_2O. Ammonia is also an Arrhenius base because adding it to water leads to an increase in the concentration of $OH^-(aq)$.

An acid and a base always work together to transfer a proton. In other words, a substance can function as an acid only if another substance simultaneously behaves as a base. To be a Brønsted–Lowry acid, a molecule or ion must have a hydrogen atom it can lose as an H^+ ion. To be a Brønsted–Lowry base, a molecule or ion must have a nonbonding pair of electrons it can use to bind the H^+ ion.

Some substances can act as an acid in one reaction and as a base in another. For example, H_2O is a Brønsted–Lowry base in Equation 16.3 and a Brønsted–Lowry acid in Equation 16.5. A substance capable of acting as either an acid or a base is called **amphiprotic**. An amphiprotic substance acts as a base when combined with something more strongly acidic than itself and as an acid when combined with something more strongly basic than itself.

> ▲ **GIVE IT SOME THOUGHT**
>
> In the forward reaction of this equilibrium, which substance acts as the Brønsted–Lowry base?
>
> $$H_2S(aq) + CH_3NH_2(aq) \rightleftharpoons HS^-(aq) + CH_3NH_3^+(aq)$$

Conjugate Acid–Base Pairs

In any acid–base equilibrium, both the forward reaction (to the right) and the reverse reaction (to the left) involve proton transfer. For example, consider the reaction of an acid HX with water:

$$HX(aq) + H_2O(l) \rightleftharpoons X^-(aq) + H_3O^+(aq) \qquad [16.6]$$

In the forward reaction, HX donates a proton to H_2O. Therefore, HX is the Brønsted–Lowry acid and H_2O is the Brønsted–Lowry base. In the reverse reaction, the H_3O^+ ion donates a proton to the X^- ion, so H_3O^+ is the acid and X^- is the base. When the acid HX donates a proton, it leaves behind a substance, X^-, that can act as a base. Likewise, when H_2O acts as a base, it generates H_3O^+, which can act as an acid.

An acid and a base such as HX and X$^-$ that differ only in the presence or absence of a proton are called a **conjugate acid–base pair.*** Every acid has a **conjugate base**, formed by removing a proton from the acid. For example, OH$^-$ is the conjugate base of H$_2$O, and X$^-$ is the conjugate base of HX. Every base has a **conjugate acid**, formed by adding a proton to the base. Thus, H$_3$O$^+$ is the conjugate acid of H$_2$O, and HX is the conjugate acid of X$^-$.

In any acid–base (proton-transfer) reaction, we can identify two sets of conjugate acid–base pairs. For example, consider the reaction between nitrous acid and water:

remove H$^+$

$$HNO_2(aq) + H_2O(l) \rightleftharpoons NO_2^-(aq) + H_3O^+(aq)$$ [16.7]

Acid   Base   Conjugate   Conjugate
                        base   acid

add H$^+$

Likewise, for the reaction between NH$_3$ and H$_2$O (Equation 16.5), we have

add H$^+$

$$NH_3(aq) + H_2O(l) \rightleftharpoons NH_4^+(aq) + OH^-(aq)$$ [16.8]

Base   Acid   Conjugate   Conjugate
                        acid   base

remove H$^+$

SAMPLE EXERCISE 16.1 | Identifying Conjugate Acids and Bases

(a) What is the conjugate base of HClO$_4$, H$_2$S, PH$_4^+$, HCO$_3^-$? **(b)** What is the conjugate acid of CN$^-$, SO$_4^{2-}$, H$_2$O, HCO$_3^-$?

SOLUTION

Analyze We are asked to give the conjugate base for several acids and the conjugate acid for several bases.

Plan The conjugate base of a substance is simply the parent substance minus one proton, and the conjugate acid of a substance is the parent substance plus one proton.

Solve
(a) HClO$_4$ less one proton H$^+$ is ClO$_4^-$. The other conjugate bases are HS$^-$, PH$_3$, and CO$_3^{2-}$.
(b) CN$^-$ plus one proton H$^+$ is HCN. The other conjugate acids are HSO$_4^-$, H$_3$O$^+$, and H$_2$CO$_3$. Notice that the hydrogen carbonate ion (HCO$_3^-$) is amphiprotic. It can act as either an acid or a base.

PRACTICE EXERCISE
Write the formula for the conjugate acid of each of the following: HSO$_3^-$, F$^-$, PO$_4^{3-}$, CO.
Answers: H$_2$SO$_3$, HF, HPO$_4^{2-}$, HCO$^+$

Once you become proficient at identifying conjugate acid–base pairs it is not difficult to write equations for reactions involving Brønsted–Lowry acids and bases (proton-transfer reactions).

*The word *conjugate* means "joined together as a pair."

SAMPLE EXERCISE 16.2 Writing Equations for Proton-Transfer Reactions

The hydrogen sulfite ion (HSO_3^-) is amphiprotic. Write an equation for the reaction of HSO_3^- with water (a) in which the ion acts as an acid and (b) in which the ion acts as a base. In both cases identify the conjugate acid–base pairs.

SOLUTION

Analyze and Plan We are asked to write two equations representing reactions between HSO_3^- and water, one in which HSO_3^- should donate a proton to water, thereby acting as a Brønsted–Lowry acid, and one in which HSO_3^- should accept a proton from water, thereby acting as a base. We are also asked to identify the conjugate pairs in each equation.

Solve

(a)
$$HSO_3^-(aq) + H_2O(l) \rightleftharpoons SO_3^{2-}(aq) + H_3O^+(aq)$$

The conjugate pairs in this equation are HSO_3^- (acid) and SO_3^{2-} (conjugate base), and H_2O (base) and H_3O^+ (conjugate acid).

(b)
$$HSO_3^-(aq) + H_2O(l) \rightleftharpoons H_2SO_3(aq) + OH^-(aq)$$

The conjugate pairs in this equation are H_2O (acid) and OH^- (conjugate base), and HSO_3^- (base) and H_2SO_3 (conjugate acid).

PRACTICE EXERCISE

When lithium oxide (Li_2O) is dissolved in water, the solution turns basic from the reaction of the oxide ion (O^{2-}) with water. Write the equation for this reaction and identify the conjugate acid–base pairs.

Answer: $O^{2-}(aq) + H_2O(l) \longrightarrow OH^-(aq) + OH^-(aq)$. The OH^- is both the conjugate acid of O^{2-} and the conjugate base of H_2O.

Relative Strengths of Acids and Bases

Some acids are better proton donors than others, and some bases are better proton acceptors than others. If we arrange acids in order of their ability to donate a proton, we find that the more easily a substance gives up a proton, the less easily its conjugate base accepts a proton. Similarly, the more easily a base accepts a proton, the less easily its conjugate acid gives up a proton. In other words, *the stronger an acid, the weaker its conjugate base*, and *the stronger a base, the weaker its conjugate acid*. Thus, if we know something about the strength of an acid (its ability to donate protons), we also know something about the strength of its conjugate base (its ability to accept protons).

The inverse relationship between the strengths of acids and their conjugate bases is illustrated in ▶ FIGURE 16.3. Here we have grouped acids and bases into three broad categories based on their behavior in water:

1. A *strong acid* completely transfers its protons to water, leaving no undissociated molecules in solution. ∞ (Section 4.3) Its conjugate base has a negligible tendency to be protonated (to accept protons) in aqueous solution. (*The conjugate base of a strong acid shows negligible basicity*.)

2. A *weak acid* only partially dissociates in aqueous solution and therefore exists in the solution as a mixture of the acid and its conjugate base. The conjugate base of a weak acid shows a slight ability to remove protons from water. (*The conjugate base of a weak acid is a weak base*.)

3. A substance with *negligible acidity* contains hydrogen but does not demonstrate any acidic behavior in water. Its conjugate base is a strong base, reacting completely with water, abstracting protons to form OH^- ions. (*The conjugate base of a substance with negligible acidity is a strong base*.)

The ions $H^+(aq)$ and $OH^-(aq)$ are, respectively, the strongest possible acid and strongest possible base that can exist at equilibrium in aqueous solution. Stronger acids react with water to produce $H^+(aq)$ ions, and stronger bases react with water to produce $OH^-(aq)$ ions. This effect is known as the *leveling effect*.

GO FIGURE

If O^{2-} ions are added to water, what reaction, if any, occurs?

▲ **FIGURE 16.3 Relative strengths of select conjugate acid–base pairs.** The two members of each pair are listed opposite each other in the two columns.

GIVE IT SOME THOUGHT

Given that $HClO_4$ is a strong acid, how would you classify the basicity of ClO_4^-?

We can think of proton-transfer reactions as being governed by the relative abilities of two bases to abstract protons. For example, consider the proton transfer that occurs when an acid HX dissolves in water:

$$HX(aq) + H_2O(l) \rightleftharpoons H_3O^+(aq) + X^-(aq) \qquad [16.9]$$

If H_2O (the base in the forward reaction) is a stronger base than X^- (the conjugate base of HX), H_2O abstracts the proton from HX to produce H_3O^+ and X^-. As a result, the equilibrium lies to the right. This describes the behavior of a strong acid in water. For example, when HCl dissolves in water, the solution consists almost entirely of H_3O^+ and Cl^- ions with a negligible concentration of HCl molecules:

$$HCl(g) + H_2O(l) \longrightarrow H_3O^+(aq) + Cl^-(aq) \qquad [16.10]$$

H_2O is a stronger base than Cl^- (Figure 16.3), so H_2O acquires the proton to become the hydronium ion.

When X^- is a stronger base than H_2O, the equilibrium lies to the left. This situation occurs when HX is a weak acid. For example, an aqueous solution of acetic acid consists mainly of CH_3COOH molecules with only a relatively few H_3O^+ and CH_3COO^- ions:

$$CH_3COOH(aq) + H_2O(l) \rightleftharpoons H_3O^+(aq) + CH_3COO^-(aq) \qquad [16.11]$$

The CH_3COO^- ion is a stronger base than H_2O (Figure 16.3) and therefore abstracts the proton from H_3O^+.

From these examples, we conclude that *in every acid–base reaction, equilibrium favors transfer of the proton from the stronger acid to the stronger base to form the weaker acid and the weaker base.*

For the following proton-transfer reaction use Figure 16.3 to predict whether the equilibrium lies to the left ($K_c < 1$) or to the right ($K_c > 1$):

$$HSO_4^-(aq) + CO_3^{2-}(aq) \rightleftharpoons SO_4^{2-}(aq) + HCO_3^-(aq)$$

SOLUTION

Analyze We are asked to predict whether an equilibrium lies to the right, favoring products, or to the left, favoring reactants.

Plan This is a proton-transfer reaction, and the position of the equilibrium will favor the proton going to the stronger of two bases. The two bases in the equation are CO_3^{2-}, the base in the forward reaction, and SO_4^{2-}, the conjugate base of HSO_4^-. We can find the relative positions of these two bases in Figure 16.3 to determine which is the stronger base.

Solve The CO_3^{2-} ion appears lower in the right-hand column in Figure 16.3 and is therefore a stronger base than SO_4^{2-}. CO_3^{2-}, therefore, will get the proton preferentially to become HCO_3^-, while SO_4^{2-} will remain mostly unprotonated. The resulting equilibrium lies to the right, favoring products (that is, $K_c > 1$):

$$\underset{\text{Acid}}{HSO_4^-(aq)} + \underset{\text{Base}}{CO_3^{2-}(aq)} \rightleftharpoons \underset{\text{Conjugate base}}{SO_4^{2-}(aq)} + \underset{\text{Conjugate acid}}{HCO_3^-(aq)} \qquad K_c > 1$$

Comment Of the two acids HSO_4^- and HCO_3^-, the stronger one (HSO_4^-) gives up a proton more readily, and the weaker one (HCO_3^-) tends to retain its proton. Thus, the equilibrium favors the direction in which the proton moves from the stronger acid and becomes bonded to the stronger base.

PRACTICE EXERCISE

For each reaction, use Figure 16.3 to predict whether the equilibrium lies to the left or to the right:
(a) $HPO_4^{2-}(aq) + H_2O(l) \rightleftharpoons H_2PO_4^-(aq) + OH^-(aq)$
(b) $NH_4^+(aq) + OH^-(aq) \rightleftharpoons NH_3(aq) + H_2O(l)$
Answers: (a) left, (b) right

16.3 | THE AUTOIONIZATION OF WATER

One of the most important chemical properties of water is its ability to act as either a Brønsted-Lowry acid or a Brønsted-Lowry base. In the presence of an acid, it acts as a proton acceptor; in the presence of a base, it acts as a proton donor. In fact, one water molecule can donate a proton to another water molecule:

$$H_2O(l) + H_2O(l) \rightleftharpoons OH^-(aq) + H_3O^+(aq)$$

We call this process the **autoionization** of water.

Because the forward and reverse reactions in Equation 16.12 are extremely rapid no water molecule remains ionized for long. At room temperature only about two out of every 10^9 water molecules are ionized at any given instant. Thus, pure water consists almost entirely of H_2O molecules and is an extremely poor conductor of electricity. Nevertheless, the autoionization of water is very important, as we will soon see.

Acidic solution   **Neutral solution**   **Basic solution**
$[H^+] > [OH^-]$ $[H^+] = [OH^-]$ $[H^+] < [OH^-]$
$[H^+][OH^-] = 1.0 \times 10^{-14}$ $[H^+][OH^-] = 1.0 \times 10^{-14}$ $[H^+][OH^-] = 1.0 \times 10^{-14}$

▲ **FIGURE 16.4** Relative concentrations of H^+ and OH^- in aqueous solutions at 25 °C.

The Ion Product of Water

The equilibrium-constant expression for the autoionization of water is

$$K_c = [H_3O^+][OH^-] \tag{16.13}$$

The term $[H_2O]$ is excluded from the equilibrium-constant expression because we exclude the concentrations of pure solids and liquids. ∞ (Section 15.4) Because this expression refers specifically to the autoionization of water, we use the symbol K_w to denote the equilibrium constant, which we call the **ion-product constant** for water. At 25 °C, K_w equals 1.0×10^{-14}. Thus, we have

$$K_w = [H_3O^+][OH^-] = 1.0 \times 10^{-14} \quad (\text{at } 25\,°C) \tag{16.14}$$

Because we use $H^+(aq)$ and $H_3O^+(aq)$ interchangeably to represent the hydrated proton, the autoionization reaction for water can also be written as

$$H_2O(l) \rightleftharpoons H^+(aq) + OH^-(aq) \tag{16.15}$$

Likewise, the expression for K_w can be written in terms of either H_3O^+ or H^+, and K_w has the same value in either case:

$$K_w = [H_3O^+][OH^-] = [H^+][OH^-] = 1.0 \times 10^{-14} \quad (\text{at } 25\,°C) \tag{16.16}$$

This equilibrium-constant expression and the value of K_w at 25 °C are extremely important, and you should commit them to memory.

A solution in which $[H^+] = [OH^-]$ is said to be *neutral*. In most solutions, however, the H^+ and OH^- concentrations are not equal. As the concentration of one of these ions increases, the concentration of the other must decrease, so that the product of their concentrations always equals 1.0×10^{-14} (▲ **FIGURE 16.4**).

SAMPLE EXERCISE 16.4 Calculating $[H^+]$ for Pure Water

Calculate the values of $[H^+]$ and $[OH^-]$ in a neutral solution at 25 °C.

SOLUTION

Analyze We are asked to determine the concentrations of H^+ and OH^- ions in a neutral solution at 25 °C.

Plan We will use Equation 16.16 and the fact that, by definition, $[H^+] = [OH^-]$ in a neutral solution.

Solve We will represent the concentration of H^+ and OH^- in neutral solution with x. This gives

$$[H^+][OH^-] = (x)(x) = 1.0 \times 10^{-14}$$
$$x^2 = 1.0 \times 10^{-14}$$
$$x = 1.0 \times 10^{-7}\,M = [H^+] = [OH^-]$$

In an acid solution $[H^+]$ is greater than 1.0×10^{-7} *M*; in a basic solution $[H^+]$ is less than 1.0×10^{-7} *M*.

What makes Equation 16.16 particularly useful is that it is applicable both to pure water and to any aqueous solution. Although the equilibrium between $H^+(aq)$ and $OH^-(aq)$ as well as other ionic equilibria are affected somewhat by the presence of additional ions in solution, it is customary to ignore these ionic effects except in work requiring exceptional accuracy. Thus, Equation 16.16 is taken to be valid for any dilute aqueous solution and can be used to calculate either $[H^+]$ (if $[OH^-]$ is known) or $[OH^-]$ (if $[H^+]$ is known).

SAMPLE EXERCISE 16.5 | **Calculating [H$^+$] from [OH$^-$]**

Calculate the concentration of $H^+(aq)$ in **(a)** a solution in which $[OH^-]$ is 0.010 M, **(b)** a solution in which $[OH^-]$ is $1.8 \times 10^{-9}\ M$. *Note:* In this problem and all that follow, we assume, unless stated otherwise, that the temperature is 25 °C.

SOLUTION

Analyze We are asked to calculate the $[H^+]$ concentration in an aqueous solution where the hydroxide concentration is known.

Plan We can use the equilibrium-constant expression for the auto-ionization of water and the value of K_w to solve for each unknown concentration.

Solve

(a) Using Equation 16.16, we have

$$[H^+][OH^-] = 1.0 \times 10^{-14}$$

$$[H^+] = \frac{(1.0 \times 10^{-14})}{[OH^-]} = \frac{1.0 \times 10^{-14}}{0.010} = 1.0 \times 10^{-12}\ M$$

This solution is basic because

$$[OH^-] > [H^+]$$

(b) In this instance

$$[H^+] = \frac{(1.0 \times 10^{-14})}{[OH^-]} = \frac{1.0 \times 10^{-14}}{1.8 \times 10^{-9}} = 5.6 \times 10^{-6}\ M$$

This solution is acidic because

$$[H^+] > [OH^-]$$

PRACTICE EXERCISE

Calculate the concentration of $OH^-(aq)$ in a solution in which **(a)** $[H^+] = 2 \times 10^{-6}\ M$; **(b)** $[H^+] = [OH^-]$; **(c)** $[H^+] = 100 \times [OH^-]$.
Answers: **(a)** $5 \times 10^{-9}\ M$, **(b)** $1.0 \times 10^{-7}\ M$, **(c)** $1.0 \times 10^{-8}\ M$

16.4 | THE pH SCALE

The molar concentration of $H^+(aq)$ in an aqueous solution is usually very small. For convenience, we therefore usually express $[H^+]$ in terms of **pH**, which is the negative logarithm in base 10 of $[H^+]$:*

$$pH = -\log[H^+] \qquad [16.17]$$

If you need to review the use of logarithms, see Appendix A.

We can use Equation 16.17 to calculate the pH of a neutral solution at 25 °C (that is, one in which $[H^+] = 1.0 \times 10^{-7}\ M$):

$$pH = -\log(1.0 \times 10^{-7}) = -(-7.00) = 7.00$$

The pH of a neutral solution is 7.00 at 25 °C. Notice that the pH is reported with two decimal places. We do so because only the numbers to the right of the decimal point are the significant

---

*Because $[H^+]$ and $[H_3O^+]$ are used interchangeably, you might see pH defined as $-\log[H_3O^+]$.

TABLE 16.1 • Relationships among (H^+), (OH^-), and pH at 25 °C			
Solution Type	$[H^+]$ (M)	$[OH^-]$ (M)	pH
Acidic	$>1.0 \times 10^{-7}$	$<1.0 \times 10^{-7}$	<7.00
Neutral	1.0×10^{-7}	1.0×10^{-7}	7.00
Basic	$<1.0 \times 10^{-7}$	$>1.0 \times 10^{-7}$	>7.00

figures in a logarithm. Because our original value for the concentration ($1.0 \times 10^{-7}\ M$) has two significant figures, the corresponding pH has two decimal places (7.00).

What happens to the pH of a solution as we make the solution more and more acidic, so that $[H^+]$ increases? Because of the negative sign in the logarithm term of Equation 16.17, *the pH decreases as $[H^+]$ increases.* For example, the pH of a neutral solution ($[H^+] = 1.0 \times 10^{-7}\ M$) is 7.00, but when we add sufficient acid to make $[H^+] = 1.0 \times 10^{-3}\ M$ the pH is

$$pH = -\log(1.0 \times 10^{-3}) = -(-3.00) = 3.00$$

At 25 °C the pH of an acidic solution is less than 7.00.

We can also calculate the pH of a basic solution, one in which $[OH^-] > 1.0 \times 10^{-7}\ M$. Suppose $[OH^-] = 2.0 \times 10^{-3}\ M$. We can use Equation 16.16 to calculate $[H^+]$ for this solution and Equation 16.17 to calculate the pH:

$$[H^+] = \frac{K_w}{[OH^-]} = \frac{1.0 \times 10^{-14}}{2.0 \times 10^{-3}} = 5.0 \times 10^{-12}\ M$$

$$pH = -\log(5.0 \times 10^{-12}) = 11.30$$

At 25 °C the pH of a basic solution is greater than 7.00. The relationships among $[H^+]$, $[OH^-]$, and pH are summarized in ▲ TABLE 16.1.

 GIVE IT SOME THOUGHT

Is it possible for a solution to have a negative pH? If so, would that pH signify a basic or acidic solution?

You might think that when $[H^+]$ is very small, as is often the case, it would be unimportant. Nothing is further from the truth. If $[H^+]$ is part of a kinetic rate law, for example, changing its concentration changes the rate. ∞ (Section 14.3) Thus, if the rate law is first order in $[H^+]$, doubling the H^+ concentration doubles the rate even if the change is merely from $1 \times 10^{-7}\ M$ to $2 \times 10^{-7}\ M$. In biological systems, many reactions involve proton transfers and have rates that depend on $[H^+]$. Because the speeds of these reactions are crucial, the pH of biological fluids must be maintained within narrow limits. For example, human blood has a normal pH range of 7.35 to 7.45. Illness and even death can result if the pH varies much from this narrow range.

SAMPLE EXERCISE 16.6 Calculating pH from $[H^+]$

Calculate the pH values for the two solutions of Sample Exercise 16.5.

SOLUTION

Analyze We are asked to determine the pH of aqueous solutions for which we have already calculated $[H^+]$.

Plan We can calculate pH using its defining equation, Equation 16.17.

Solve
(a) In the first instance we found $[H^+]$ to be $1.0 \times 10^{-12}\ M$, so that

$$pH = -\log(1.0 \times 10^{-12}) = -(-12.00) = 12.00$$

Because 1.0×10^{-12} has two significant figures, the pH has two decimal places, 12.00.

(b) For the second solution, $[H^+] = 5.6 \times 10^{-6} M$. Before performing the calculation, it is helpful to estimate the pH. To do so, we note that $[H^+]$ lies between 1×10^{-6} and 1×10^{-5}. Thus, we expect the pH to lie between 6.0 and 5.0. We use Equation 16.17 to calculate the pH:

$$pH = -\log(5.6 \times 10^{-6}) = 5.25$$

Check After calculating a pH, it is useful to compare it to your estimate. In this case the pH, as we predicted, falls between 6 and 5. Had the calculated pH and the estimate not agreed, we should have reconsidered our calculation or estimate or both.

PRACTICE EXERCISE

(a) In a sample of lemon juice, $[H^+] = 3.8 \times 10^{-4} M$. What is the pH? **(b)** A commonly available window-cleaning solution has $[OH^-] = 1.9 \times 10^{-6} M$. What is the pH?

Answers: **(a)** 3.42, **(b)** $[H^+] = 5.3 \times 10^{-9} M$, so pH = 8.28

pOH and Other "p" Scales

The negative logarithm is a convenient way of expressing the magnitudes of other small quantities. We use the convention that the negative logarithm of a quantity is labeled "p" (quantity). Thus, we can express the concentration of OH^- as pOH:

$$pOH = -\log[OH^-] \qquad [16.18]$$

Likewise, pK_w equals $-\log K_w$.

By taking the negative logarithm of both sides of the equilibrium-constant expression for water, $K_w = [H^+][OH^-]$, we obtain

$$-\log[H^+] + (-\log[OH^-]) = -\log K_w \qquad [16.19]$$

from which we obtain the useful expression

$$pH + pOH = 14.00 \quad \text{(at 25 °C)} \qquad [16.20]$$

The pH and pOH values characteristic of a number of familiar solutions are shown in ▶ FIGURE 16.5. Notice that a change in $[H^+]$ by a factor of 10 causes the pH to change by 1. Thus, the concentration of $H^+(aq)$ in a solution of pH 6 is 10 times the $H^+(aq)$ concentration in a solution of pH 7.

 GIVE IT SOME THOUGHT

If the pOH for a solution is 3.00, what is the pH? Is the solution acidic or basic?

SAMPLE EXERCISE 16.7 | **Calculating [H⁺] from pOH**

A sample of freshly pressed apple juice has a pOH of 10.24. Calculate $[H^+]$.

SOLUTION

Analyze We need to calculate $[H^+]$ from pOH.

Plan We will first use Equation 16.20, pH + pOH = 14.00, to calculate pH from pOH. Then we will use Equation 16.17 to determine the concentration of H^+.

Solve From Equation 16.20, we have

$$pH = 14.00 - pOH$$
$$pH = 14.00 - 10.24 = 3.76$$

Next we use Equation 16.17:

$$pH = -\log[H^+] = 3.76$$

Thus,

$$\log[H^+] = -3.76$$

To find $[H^+]$, we need to determine the *antilogarithm* of -3.76. Scientific calculators have an antilogarithm function (sometimes labeled INV log or 10^x) that allows us to perform the calculation:

$$[H^+] = \text{antilog}(-3.76) = 10^{-3.76} = 1.7 \times 10^{-4} M$$

Comment The number of significant figures in $[H^+]$ is two because the number of decimal places in the pH is two.

Check Because the pH is between 3.0 and 4.0, we know that $[H^+]$ will be between $1.0 \times 10^{-3}\,M$ and $1.0 \times 10^{-4}\,M$. Our calculated $[H^+]$ falls within this estimated range.

PRACTICE EXERCISE
A solution formed by dissolving an antacid tablet has a pH of 9.18. Calculate $[OH^-]$.
Answer: $[OH^-] = 1.5 \times 10^{-5}$

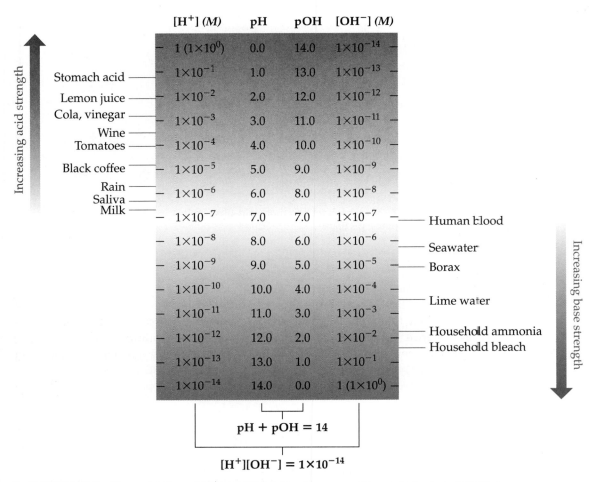

	$[H^+]$ (M)	pH	pOH	$[OH^-]$ (M)	
	$1\,(1 \times 10^0)$	0.0	14.0	1×10^{-14}	
Stomach acid	1×10^{-1}	1.0	13.0	1×10^{-13}	
Lemon juice	1×10^{-2}	2.0	12.0	1×10^{-12}	
Cola, vinegar	1×10^{-3}	3.0	11.0	1×10^{-11}	
Wine / Tomatoes	1×10^{-4}	4.0	10.0	1×10^{-10}	
Black coffee	1×10^{-5}	5.0	9.0	1×10^{-9}	
Rain / Saliva / Milk	1×10^{-6}	6.0	8.0	1×10^{-8}	
	1×10^{-7}	7.0	7.0	1×10^{-7}	Human blood
	1×10^{-8}	8.0	6.0	1×10^{-6}	Seawater
	1×10^{-9}	9.0	5.0	1×10^{-5}	Borax
	1×10^{-10}	10.0	4.0	1×10^{-4}	Lime water
	1×10^{-11}	11.0	3.0	1×10^{-3}	
	1×10^{-12}	12.0	2.0	1×10^{-2}	Household ammonia
	1×10^{-13}	13.0	1.0	1×10^{-1}	Household bleach
	1×10^{-14}	14.0	0.0	$1\,(1 \times 10^0)$	

Increasing acid strength

Increasing base strength

$$pH + pOH = 14$$

$$[H^+][OH^-] = 1 \times 10^{-14}$$

▲ **FIGURE 16.5** **Concentrations of H^+ and pH values of some common substances at 25 °C.**

Measuring pH

The pH of a solution can be measured with a *pH meter* (▶ **FIGURE 16.6**). A complete understanding of how this important device works requires a knowledge of electrochemistry, a subject we take up in Chapter 20. In brief, a pH meter consists of a pair of electrodes connected to a meter capable of measuring small voltages, on the order of millivolts. A voltage, which varies with pH, is generated when the electrodes are placed in a solution. This voltage is read by the meter, which is calibrated to give pH.

Although less precise, acid–base indicators can be used to measure pH. An acid–base indicator is a colored substance that can exist in either an acid or a base form. The two forms have different colors. Thus, the indicator has one color at lower pH and another at higher pH. If you know the pH at which the indicator turns from one form to the other, you can determine whether a solution has a higher or lower pH than this value. Litmus, for example, changes color in the vicinity of pH 7. The color change, however, is not very sharp. Red litmus indicates a pH of about 5 or lower, and blue litmus indicates a pH of about 8 or higher.

▲ **FIGURE 16.6** **A digital pH meter.** The device is a millivoltmeter, and the electrodes immersed in a solution produce a voltage that depends on the pH of the solution.

△ GO FIGURE

Which of these indicators is best suited to distinguish between a solution that is slightly acidic and one that is slightly basic?

Methyl red

Bromthymol blue

Phenolphthalein

▲ FIGURE 16.8 **Solutions containing three common acid–base indicators at various pH values.**

△ GO FIGURE

If a colorless solution turns pink when we add phenolphthalein, what can we conclude about the pH of the solution?

▲ FIGURE 16.7 **pH ranges for common acid–base indicators.** Most indicators have a useful range of about 2 pH units.

Some common indicators are listed in ▲ FIGURE 16.7. The chart tells us, for instance, that methyl red changes color over the pH interval from about 4.5 to 6.0. Below pH 4.5 it is in the acid form, which is red. In the interval between 4.5 and 6.0, it is gradually converted to its basic form, which is yellow. Once the pH rises above 6 the conversion is complete, and the solution is yellow. This color change, along with that of the indicators bromthymol blue and phenolphthalein, is shown in ◀ FIGURE 16.8. Paper tape impregnated with several indicators is widely used for determining approximate pH values.

16.5 | STRONG ACIDS AND BASES

The chemistry of an aqueous solution often depends critically on pH. It is therefore important to examine how pH relates to acid and base concentrations. The simplest cases are those involving strong acids and strong bases. Strong acids and bases are *strong electrolytes*, existing in aqueous solution entirely as ions. There are relatively few common strong acids and bases (see Table 4.2).

Strong Acids

The seven most common strong acids include six monoprotic acids (HCl, HBr, HI, HNO_3, $HClO_3$, and $HClO_4$), and one diprotic acid (H_2SO_4). Nitric acid (HNO_3) exemplifies the behavior of the monoprotic strong acids. For all practical purposes, an aqueous solution of HNO_3 consists entirely of H_3O^+ and NO_3^- ions:

$$HNO_3(aq) + H_2O(l) \longrightarrow H_3O^+(aq) + NO_3^-(aq) \quad \text{(complete ionization)} \quad [16.21]$$

We have not used equilibrium arrows for this equation because the reaction lies entirely to the right. ∞ (Section 4.1) As noted in Section 16.3, we use $H_3O^+(aq)$ and $H^+(aq)$ interchangeably to represent the hydrated proton in water. Thus, we can simplify this acid ionization equation to

$$HNO_3(aq) \longrightarrow H^+(aq) + NO_3^-(aq)$$

In an aqueous solution of a strong acid, the acid is normally the only significant source of H^+ ions.* As a result, calculating the pH of a solution of a strong monoprotic acid is straightforward because $[H^+]$ equals the original concentration of acid. In a 0.20 M solution of $HNO_3(aq)$, for example, $[H^+] = [NO_3^-] = 0.20$ M. The situation with the diprotic acid H_2SO_4 is more complex, as we will see in Section 16.6.

SAMPLE EXERCISE 16.8 | **Calculating the pH of a Strong Acid**

What is the pH of a 0.040 M solution of $HClO_4$?

SOLUTION

Analyze and Plan Because $HClO_4$ is a strong acid, it is completely ionized, giving $[H^+] = [ClO_4^-] = 0.040$ M.

Solve

$$pH = -\log(0.040) = 1.40.$$

Check Because $[H^+]$ lies between 1×10^{-2} and 1×10^{-1}, the pH will be between 2.0 and 1.0. Our calculated pH falls within the estimated range. Furthermore, because the concentration has two significant figures, the pH has two decimal places.

PRACTICE EXERCISE

An aqueous solution of HNO_3 has a pH of 2.34. What is the concentration of the acid?

Answer: 0.0046 M

Strong Bases

The most common soluble strong bases are the ionic hydroxides of the alkali metals, such as NaOH, KOH, and the ionic hydroxides heavier alkaline earth metals, such as $Sr(OH)_2$. These compounds completely dissociate into ions in aqueous solution. Thus, a solution labeled 0.30 M NaOH consists of 0.30 M $Na^+(aq)$ and 0.30 M $OH^-(aq)$; there is essentially no undissociated NaOH.

 GIVE IT SOME THOUGHT

Which solution has the higher pH, a 0.001 M solution of NaOH or a 0.001 M solution of $Ba(OH)_2$?

SAMPLE EXERCISE 16.9 | **Calculating the pH of a Strong Base**

What is the pH of **(a)** a 0.028 M solution of NaOH, **(b)** a 0.0011 M solution of $Ca(OH)_2$?

SOLUTION

Analyze We are asked to calculate the pH of two solutions of strong bases.

Plan We can calculate each pH by either of two equivalent methods. First, we could use Equation 16.16 to calculate $[H^+]$ and then use Equation 16.17 to calculate the pH. Alternatively, we could use $[OH^-]$ to calculate pOH and then use Equation 16.20 to calculate the pH.

Solve
(a) NaOH dissociates in water to give one OH^- ion per formula unit. Therefore, the OH^- concentration for the solution in (a) equals the stated concentration of NaOH, namely 0.028 M.

Method 1:

$$[H^+] = \frac{1.0 \times 10^{-14}}{0.028} = 3.57 \times 10^{-13} \, M \qquad pH = -\log(3.57 \times 10^{-13}) = 12.45$$

Method 2:

$$pOH = -\log(0.028) = 1.55 \qquad pH = 14.00 - pOH = 12.45$$

---

*If the concentration of the acid is 10^{-6} M or less, we also need to consider H^+ ions that result from H_2O autoionization. Normally, the concentration of H^+ from H_2O is so small that it can be neglected.

(b) $Ca(OH)_2$ is a strong base that dissociates in water to give two OH^- ions per formula unit. Thus, the concentration of $OH^-(aq)$ for the solution in part (b) is $2 \times (0.0011 \, M) = 0.0022 \, M$.

Method 1:

$$[H^+] = \frac{1.0 \times 10^{-14}}{0.0022} = 4.55 \times 10^{-12} \, M \qquad pH = -\log(4.55 \times 10^{-12}) = 11.34$$

Method 2:

$$pOH = -\log(0.0022) = 2.66 \qquad pH = 14.00 - pOH = 11.34$$

PRACTICE EXERCISE

What is the concentration of a solution of **(a)** KOH for which the pH is 11.89, **(b)** $Ca(OH)_2$ for which the pH is 11.68?

Answers: **(a)** $7.8 \times 10^{-3} \, M$, **(b)** $2.4 \times 10^{-3} \, M$

Although all of the alkali metal hydroxides are strong electrolytes, LiOH, RbOH, and CsOH are not commonly encountered in the laboratory. The hydroxides of the heavier alkaline earth metals—$Ca(OH)_2$, $Sr(OH)_2$, and $Ba(OH)_2$—are also strong electrolytes. They have limited solubility, however, so they are used only when high solubility is not critical.

Strongly basic solutions are also created by certain substances that react with water to form $OH^-(aq)$. The most common of these contain the oxide ion. Ionic metal oxides, especially Na_2O and CaO, are often used in industry when a strong base is needed. The O^{2-} reacts with water to form OH^-, leaving virtually no O^{2-} in the solution:

$$O^{2-}(aq) + H_2O(l) \longrightarrow 2 \, OH^-(aq) \qquad [16.22]$$

Thus, a solution formed by dissolving 0.010 mol of $Na_2O(s)$ in enough water to form 1.0 L of solution has $[OH^-] = 0.020 \, M$ and a pH of 12.30.

 GIVE IT SOME THOUGHT

The CH_3^- ion is the conjugate base of CH_4, and CH_4 shows no evidence of being an acid in water. What happens when CH_3^- is added to water?

16.6 | WEAK ACIDS

Most acidic substances are weak acids and therefore only partially ionized in aqueous solution (▶ FIGURE 16.9). We can use the equilibrium constant for the ionization reaction to express the extent to which a weak acid ionizes. If we represent a general weak acid as HA, we can write the equation for its ionization in either of the following ways, depending on whether the hydrated proton is represented as $H_3O^+(aq)$ or $H^+(aq)$:

$$HA(aq) + H_2O(l) \rightleftharpoons H_3O^+(aq) + A^-(aq) \qquad [16.23]$$

or

$$HA(aq) \rightleftharpoons H^+(aq) + A^-(aq) \qquad [16.24]$$

Because H_2O is the solvent, it is omitted from the equilibrium-constant expression. ∞ (Section 15.4) Thus, we can write the equilibrium-constant expression as either

$$K_c = \frac{[H_3O^+][A^-]}{[HA]} \quad \text{or} \quad K_c = \frac{[H^+][A^-]}{[HA]}$$

As we did for the ion-product constant for the autoionization of water, we change the subscript on this equilibrium constant to indicate the type of equation to which it corresponds:

$$K_a = \frac{[H_3O^+][A^-]}{[HA]} \quad \text{or} \quad K_a = \frac{[H^+][A^-]}{[HA]} \qquad [16.25]$$

HA(aq) + H₂O(l) →
A⁻(aq) + H₃O⁺(aq)

HA(aq) + H₂O(l) ⇌
A⁻(aq) + H₃O⁺(aq)

Strong acid
HA molecules
completely dissociate

Weak acid
HA molecules
partially dissociate

▲ **FIGURE 16.9** Species present in a solution of a strong acid and a weak acid.

The subscript a denotes that K_a is an equilibrium constant for the ionization of an acid, so K_a is called the **acid-dissociation constant**.

▼ **TABLE 16.2** shows the structural formulas, conjugate bases, and K_a values for a number of weak acids. Appendix D provides a more complete list. Many weak acids are organic compounds composed entirely of carbon, hydrogen, and oxygen. These compounds usually contain some hydrogen atoms bonded to carbon atoms and some bonded to oxygen atoms. In almost all cases, the hydrogen atoms bonded to carbon do not ionize in water; instead, the acidic behavior of these compounds is due to the hydrogen atoms attached to oxygen atoms.

TABLE 16.2 • Some Weak Acids in Water at 25 °C

Acid	Structural Formula*	Conjugate Base	K_a
Chlorous ($HClO_2$)	H—O—Cl—O	ClO_2^-	1.0×10^{-2}
Hydrofluoric (HF)	H—F	F^-	6.8×10^{-4}
Nitrous (HNO_2)	H—O—N=O	NO_2^-	4.5×10^{-4}
Benzoic (C_6H_5COOH)	H—O—C(=O)—C₆H₅	$C_6H_5COO^-$	6.3×10^{-5}
Acetic (CH_3COOH)	H—O—C(=O)—CH₃	CH_3COO^-	1.8×10^{-5}
Hypochlorous (HOCl)	H—O—Cl	OCl^-	3.0×10^{-5}
Hydrocyanic (HCN)	H—C≡N	CN^-	4.9×10^{-10}
Phenol (HOC_6H_5)	H—O—C₆H₅	$C_6H_5O^-$	1.3×10^{-10}

*The proton that ionizes is shown in red.

The magnitude of K_a indicates the tendency of the acid to ionize in water: *The larger the value of K_a, the stronger the acid.* Chlorous acid ($HClO_2$), for example, is the strongest acid in Table 16.2, and phenol (HOC_6H_5) is the weakest. For most weak acids K_a values range from 10^{-2} to 10^{-10}.

 GIVE IT SOME THOUGHT

Based on the entries in Table 16.2, which element is most commonly bonded to the acidic hydrogen?

Calculating K_a from pH

In order to calculate either the K_a value for a weak acid or the pH of its solutions, we will use many of the skills for solving equilibrium problems developed in Section 15.5. In many cases the small magnitude of K_a allows us to use approximations to simplify the problem. In doing these calculations, it is important to realize that proton-transfer reactions are generally very rapid. As a result, the measured or calculated pH for a weak acid always represents an equilibrium condition.

SAMPLE EXERCISE 16.10 **Calculating K_a from Measured pH**

A student prepared a 0.10 M solution of formic acid (HCOOH) and found its pH at 25 °C to be 2.38. Calculate K_a for formic acid at this temperature.

SOLUTION

Analyze We are given the molar concentration of an aqueous solution of weak acid and the pH of the solution, and we are asked to determine the value of K_a for the acid.

Plan Although we are dealing specifically with the ionization of a weak acid, this problem is very similar to the equilibrium problems we encountered in Chapter 15. We can solve this problem using the method first outlined in Sample Exercise 15.9, starting with the chemical reaction and a tabulation of initial and equilibrium concentrations.

Solve The first step in solving any equilibrium problem is to write the equation for the equilibrium reaction. The ionization of formic acid can be written as

$$HCOOH(aq) \rightleftharpoons H^+(aq) + HCOO^-(aq)$$

The equilibrium-constant expression is

$$K_a = \frac{[H^+][HCOO^-]}{[HCOOH]}$$

From the measured pH, we can calculate $[H^+]$:

$$pH = -\log[H^+] = 2.38$$
$$\log[H^+] = -2.38$$
$$[H^+] = 10^{-2.38} = 4.2 \times 10^{-3} \, M$$

To determine the concentrations of the species involved in the equilibrium, we imagine that the solution is initially 0.10 M in HCOOH molecules. We then consider the ionization of the acid into H^+ and $HCOO^-$. For each HCOOH molecule that ionizes, one H^+ ion and one $HCOO^-$ ion are produced in solution. Because the pH measurement indicates that $[H^+] = 4.2 \times 10^{-3} \, M$ at equilibrium, we can construct the following table:

	$HCOOH(aq)$ $\rightleftharpoons$	$H^+(aq)$ +	$HCOO^-(aq)$
Initial	0.10 M	0	0
Change	$-4.2 \times 10^{-3} \, M$	$+4.2 \times 10^{-3} \, M$	$+4.2 \times 10^{-3} \, M$
Equilibrium	$(0.10 - 4.2 \times 10^{-3}) \, M$	$4.2 \times 10^{-3} \, M$	$4.2 \times 10^{-3} \, M$

Notice that we have neglected the very small concentration of $H^+(aq)$ due to H_2O autoionization. Notice also that the amount of HCOOH that ionizes is very small compared with the initial concentration of the acid. To the number of significant figures we are using, the subtraction yields 0.10 M:

$$(0.10 - 4.2 \times 10^{-3}) \, M \simeq 0.10 \, M$$

We can now insert the equilibrium concentrations into the expression for K_a:

$$K_a = \frac{(4.2 \times 10^{-3})(4.2 \times 10^{-3})}{0.10} = 1.8 \times 10^{-4}$$

Check The magnitude of our answer is reasonable because K_a for a weak acid is usually between 10^{-2} and 10^{-10}.

PRACTICE EXERCISE

Niacin, one of the B vitamins, has the molecular structure

A 0.020 M solution of niacin has a pH of 3.26. What is the acid-dissociation constant for niacin?

Answer: 1.5×10^{-5}

Percent Ionization

We have seen that the magnitude of K_a indicates the strength of a weak acid. Another measure of acid strength is **percent ionization**, defined as

$$\text{Percent ionization} = \frac{\text{concentration ionized}}{\text{original concentration}} \times 100\% \qquad [16.26]$$

The stronger the acid, the greater the percent ionization.

For any acid, the concentration of acid that ionizes equals the concentration of $H^+(aq)$ that forms, assuming that H_2O autoionization is negligible. Thus, the percent ionization for an acid HA is also given by

$$\text{Percent ionization} = \frac{[H^+]_{\text{equilibrium}}}{[HA]_{\text{initial}}} \times 100\% \qquad [16.27]$$

For example, a 0.035 M solution of HNO_2 contains $3.7 \times 10^{-3} M\, H^+(aq)$ and its percent ionization is

$$\text{Percent ionization} = \frac{[H^+]_{\text{equilibrium}}}{[HNO_2]_{\text{initial}}} \times 100\% = \frac{3.7 \times 10^{-3}\, M}{0.035\, M} \times 100\% = 11\%$$

SAMPLE EXERCISE 16.11 **Calculating Percent Ionization**

As calculated in Sample Exercise 16.10, a 0.10 M solution of formic acid (HCOOH) contains $4.2 \times 10^{-3} M\, H^+(aq)$. Calculate the percentage of the acid that is ionized.

SOLUTION

Analyze We are given the molar concentration of an aqueous solution of weak acid and the equilibrium concentration of $H^+(aq)$ and asked to determine the percent ionization of the acid.

Plan The percent ionization is given by Equation 16.27.

Solve

$$\text{Percent ionization} = \frac{[H^+]_{\text{equilibrium}}}{[HCOOH]_{\text{initial}}} \times 100\% = \frac{4.2 \times 10^{-3}\, M}{0.10\, M} \times 100\% = 4.2\%$$

PRACTICE EXERCISE

A 0.020 M solution of niacin has a pH of 3.26. Calculate the percent ionization of the niacin.

Answer: 2.7%

Using K_a to Calculate pH

Knowing the value of K_a and the initial concentration of a weak acid, we can calculate the concentration of $H^+(aq)$ in a solution of the acid. Let's calculate the pH at 25 °C of a 0.30 M solution of acetic acid (CH_3COOH), the weak acid responsible for the characteristic odor and acidity of vinegar.

1. Our first step is to write the ionization equilibrium:

$$CH_3COOH(aq) \rightleftharpoons H^+(aq) + CH_3COO^-(aq) \qquad [16.28]$$

Notice that the hydrogen that ionizes is the one attached to an oxygen atom.

2. The second step is to write the equilibrium-constant expression and the value for the equilibrium constant. Taking $K_a = 1.8 \times 10^{-5}$ from Table 16.2, we write

$$K_a = \frac{[H^+][CH_3COO^-]}{[CH_3COOH]} = 1.8 \times 10^{-5} \qquad [16.29]$$

3. The third step is to express the concentrations involved in the equilibrium reaction. This can be done with a little accounting, as described in Sample Exercise 16.10. Because we want to find the equilibrium value for $[H^+]$, let's call this quantity x. The concentration of acetic acid before any of it ionizes is 0.30 M. The chemical equation tells us that for each molecule of CH_3COOH that ionizes, one $H^+(aq)$ and one $CH_3COO^-(aq)$ are formed. Consequently, if x moles per liter of $H^+(aq)$ form at equilibrium, x moles per liter of $CH_3COO^-(aq)$ must also form and x moles per liter of CH_3COOH must be ionized:

$$CH_3COOH(aq) \rightleftharpoons H^+(aq) + CH_3COO^-(aq)$$

	CH_3COOH	H^+	CH_3COO^-
Initial	0.30 M	0	0
Change	$-x\,M$	$+x\,M$	$+x\,M$
Equilibrium	$(0.30 - x)\,M$	$x\,M$	$x\,M$

4. The fourth step is to substitute the equilibrium concentrations into the equilibrium-constant expression and solve for x:

$$K_a = \frac{[H^+][CH_3COO^-]}{[CH_3COOH]} = \frac{(x)(x)}{0.30 - x} = 1.8 \times 10^{-5} \qquad [16.30]$$

This expression leads to a quadratic equation in x, which we can solve by using either an equation-solving calculator or the quadratic formula. We can simplify the problem, however, by noting that the value of K_a is quite small. As a result, we anticipate that the equilibrium lies far to the left and that x is much smaller than the initial concentration of acetic acid. Thus, we *assume* that x is negligible relative to 0.30, so that $0.30 - x$ is essentially equal to 0.30. We can (and should!) check the validity of this assumption when we finish the problem. By using this assumption, Equation 16.30 becomes

$$K_a = \frac{x^2}{0.30} = 1.8 \times 10^{-5}$$

Solving for x, we have

$$x^2 = (0.30)(1.8 \times 10^{-5}) = 5.4 \times 10^{-6}$$
$$x = \sqrt{5.4 \times 10^{-6}} = 2.3 \times 10^{-3}$$
$$[H^+] = x = 2.3 \times 10^{-3}\,M$$
$$pH = -\log(2.3 \times 10^{-3}) = 2.64$$

Now we check the validity of our simplifying assumption that $0.30 - x \approx 0.30$. The value of x we determined is so small that, for this number of significant figures, the assumption is entirely valid. We are thus satisfied that the assumption was a reasonable one to make. Because x represents the moles per liter of acetic acid that ionize, we see that, in this particular case, less than 1% of the acetic acid molecules ionize:

$$\text{Percent ionization of } CH_3COOH = \frac{0.0023\ M}{0.30\ M} \times 100\% = 0.77\%$$

As a general rule, if x is more than about 5% of the initial concentration value, it is better to use the quadratic formula. You should always check the validity of any simplifying assumptions after you have finished solving a problem.

 GIVE IT SOME THOUGHT

Why can we generally assume that the equilibrium concentration of a weak acid equals its initial concentration?

Finally, we can compare the pH value of this weak acid with the pH of a solution of a strong acid of the same concentration. The pH of the 0.30 M acetic acid is 2.64, but the pH of a 0.30 M solution of a strong acid such as HCl is $-\log(0.30) = 0.52$. As expected, the pH of a solution of a weak acid is higher than that of a solution of a strong acid of the same molarity. (Remember, the higher the pH value, the *less* acidic the solution.)

SAMPLE EXERCISE 16.12   Using K_a to Calculate pH

Calculate the pH of a 0.20 M solution of HCN. (Refer to Table 16.2 or Appendix D for the value of K_a.)

SOLUTION

Analyze We are given the molarity of a weak acid and are asked for the pH. From Table 16.2, K_a for HCN is 4.9×10^{-10}.

Plan We proceed as in the example just worked in the text, writing the chemical equation and constructing a table of initial and equilibrium concentrations in which the equilibrium concentration of H^+ is our unknown.

Solve Writing both the chemical equation for the ionization reaction that forms $H^+(aq)$ and the equilibrium-constant (K_a) expression for the reaction:

$$HCN(aq) \rightleftharpoons H^+(aq) + CN^-(aq)$$

$$K_a = \frac{[H^+][CN^-]}{[HCN]} = 4.9 \times 10^{-10}$$

Next, we tabulate the concentrations of the species involved in the equilibrium reaction, letting $x = [H^+]$ at equilibrium:

	$HCN(aq)$	$\rightleftharpoons$	$H^+(aq)$	$+$	$CN^-(aq)$
Initial	0.20 M		0		0
Change	$-x\ M$		$+x\ M$		$+x\ M$
Equilibrium	$(0.20 - x)\ M$		$x\ M$		$x\ M$

Substituting the equilibrium concentrations into the equilibrium-constant expression yields

$$K_a = \frac{(x)(x)}{0.20 - x} = 4.9 \times 10^{-10}$$

We next make the simplifying approximation that x, the amount of acid that dissociates, is small compared with the initial concentration of acid, $0.20 - x \simeq 0.20$. Thus,

$$\frac{x^2}{0.20} = 4.9 \times 10^{-10}$$

Solving for x, we have

$$x^2 = (0.20)(4.9 \times 10^{-10}) = 0.98 \times 10^{-10}$$

$$x = \sqrt{0.98 \times 10^{-10}} = 9.9 \times 10^{-6}\ M = [H^+]$$

A concentration of $9.9 \times 10^{-6}\ M$ is much smaller than 5% of 0.20, the initial HCN concentration. Our simplifying approximation is therefore appropriate. We now calculate the pH of the solution:

$$pH = -\log[H^+] = -\log(9.9 \times 10^{-6}) = 5.00$$

PRACTICE EXERCISE

The K_a for niacin (Practice Exercise 16.10) is 1.5×10^{-5}. What is the pH of a 0.010 M solution of niacin?

Answer: 3.41

Reaction proceeds more rapidly in strong acid, leading to formation of larger H_2 bubbles and rapid disappearance of metal

Reaction complete in strong acid

H_2 bubbles show reaction still in progress in weak acid

Reaction eventually goes to completion in both acids

$1\ M\ \text{HCl}(aq)$
$[H^+] = 1\ M$

$1\ M\ \text{CH}_3\text{COOH}(aq)$
$[H^+] = 0.004\ M$

▲ **FIGURE 16.10** **Rates of the same reaction run in a weak acid and a strong acid.** The bubbles are H_2 gas, which along with metal cations, is produced when a metal is oxidized by an acid (Section 4.4).

The properties of an acid solution that relate directly to the concentration of $H^+(aq)$, such as electrical conductivity and rate of reaction with an active metal, are less evident for a solution of a weak acid than for a solution of a strong acid of the same concentration. ▲ FIGURE 16.10 presents an experiment that demonstrates this difference with $1\ M\ \text{CH}_3\text{COOH}$ and $1\ M\ \text{HCl}$. The $1\ M\ \text{CH}_3\text{COOH}$ contains only $0.004\ M\ H^+(aq)$, whereas the $1\ M\ \text{HCl}$ solution contains $1\ M\ H^+(aq)$. As a result, the reaction rate with the metal is much faster in the HCl solution.

As the concentration of a weak acid increases, the equilibrium concentration of $H^+(aq)$ increases, as expected. However, as shown in ▼ FIGURE 16.11, *the percent ionization decreases as the concentration increases.* Thus, the concentration of $H^+(aq)$ is not directly proportional to the concentration of the weak acid. For example, doubling the concentration of a weak acid does not double the concentration of $H^+(aq)$.

◢ **GO FIGURE**

Is the trend observed in this graph consistent with Le Châtelier's principle? Explain.

CH$_3$COOH molecules less prone to dissociate as concentration increases

▲ **FIGURE 16.11** **Effect of concentration on percent ionization in an acetic acid solution.**

| **SAMPLE EXERCISE 16.13** | Using K_a to Calculate Percent Ionization |

Calculate the percentage of HF molecules ionized in (a) a 0.10 M HF solution, (b) a 0.010 M HF solution.

SOLUTION

Analyze We are asked to calculate the percent ionization of two HF solutions of different concentration. From Appendix D, we find $K_a = 6.8 \times 10^{-4}$.

Plan We approach this problem as we have previous equilibrium problems. We begin by writing the chemical equation for the equilibrium and tabulating the known and unknown concentrations of all species. We then substitute the equilibrium concentrations into the equilibrium-constant expression and solve for the unknown concentration, that of H^+.

Solve

(a) The equilibrium reaction and equilibrium concentrations are as follows:

	$HF(aq)$	$\rightleftharpoons$	$H^+(aq)$	$+$	$F^-(aq)$
Initial	0.10 M		0		0
Change	$-x\,M$		$+x\,M$		$+x\,M$
Equilibrium	$(0.10 - x)\,M$		$x\,M$		$x\,M$

The equilibrium-constant expression is

$$K_a = \frac{[H^+][F^-]}{[HF]} = \frac{(x)(x)}{0.10 - x} = 6.8 \times 10^{-4}$$

When we try solving this equation using the approximation $0.10 - x \simeq 0.10$ (that is, by neglecting the concentration of acid that ionizes), we obtain

$$x = 8.2 \times 10^{-3}\,M$$

Because this value is greater than 5% of 0.10 M, however, we should work the problem without the approximation. Rearranging our equation and writing it in standard quadratic form, we have

$$x^2 = (0.10 - x)(6.8 \times 10^{-4})$$
$$= 6.8 \times 10^{-5} - (6.8 \times 10^{-4})x$$
$$x^2 + (6.8 \times 10^{-4})x - 6.8 \times 10^{-5} = 0$$

Substituting these values in the standard quadratic formula gives

$$x = \frac{-6.8 \times 10^{-4} \pm \sqrt{(6.8 \times 10^{-4})^2 - 4(-6.8 \times 10^{-5})}}{2}$$
$$= \frac{-6.8 \times 10^{-4} \pm 1.6 \times 10^{-2}}{2}$$

Of the two solutions, only the one that gives a positive value for x is chemically reasonable. Thus,

$$x = [H^+] = [F^-] = 7.9 \times 10^{-3}\,M$$

From our result, we can calculate the percent of molecules ionized:

$$\text{Percent ionization of HF} = \frac{\text{concentration ionized}}{\text{original concentration}} \times 100\%$$
$$= \frac{7.9 \times 10^{-3}\,M}{0.10\,M} \times 100\% = 7.9\%$$

(b) Proceeding similarly for the 0.010 M solution, we have

$$\frac{x^2}{0.010 - x} = 6.8 \times 10^{-4}$$

Solving the resultant quadratic expression, we obtain

$$x = [H^+] = [F^-] = 2.3 \times 10^{-3}\,M$$

The percentage of molecules ionized is

$$\frac{0.0023\,M}{0.010\,M} \times 100\% = 23\%$$

Comment Notice that if we do not use the quadratic formula, we calculate 8.2% ionization for (a) and 26% ionization for (b). Notice also that in diluting the solution by a factor of 10, the percentage of molecules ionized increases by a factor of 3. This result is in accord with what we see in Figure 16.11. It is also what we expect from Le Châtelier's principle. ∞ (Section 15.7) There are more "particles" or reaction components on the right side of the equation than on the left. Dilution causes the reaction to shift in the direction of the larger number of particles (toward the product side) because this counters the effect of the decreasing concentration of particles.

PRACTICE EXERCISE

In Practice Exercise 16.11, we found that the percent ionization of niacin ($K_a = 1.5 \times 10^{-5}$) in a 0.020 M solution is 2.7%. Calculate the percentage of niacin molecules ionized in a solution that is (a) 0.010 M, (b) $1.0 \times 10^{-3}\,M$.

Answers: (a) 3.9%, (b) 12%

Citric acid

▲ **FIGURE 16.12** **The structure of the polyprotic acid, citric acid.**

Polyprotic Acids

Many acids have more than one ionizable H atom. These acids are known as **polyprotic acids**. For example, with sulfurous acid (H_2SO_3) we have the successive ionizations

$$H_2SO_3(aq) \rightleftharpoons H^-(aq) + HSO_3^-(aq) \qquad K_{a1} = 1.7 \times 10^{-2} \qquad [16.31]$$

$$HSO_3^-(aq) \rightleftharpoons H^-(aq) + SO_3^{2-}(aq) \qquad K_{a2} = 6.4 \times 10^{-8} \qquad [16.32]$$

Note that the acid-dissociation constants are labeled K_{a1} and K_{a2}. The numbers on the constants refer to the particular proton of the acid that is ionizing. Thus, K_{a2} always refers to the equilibrium involving removal of the second proton of a polyprotic acid.

Note that K_{a2} for sulfurous acid is much smaller than K_{a1}. Because of electrostatic attractions, we would expect a positively charged proton to be lost more readily from the neutral H_2SO_3 molecule than from the negatively charged HSO_3^- ion. This observation is general: *It is always easier to remove the first proton from a polyprotic acid than to remove the second.* Similarly, for an acid with three ionizable protons, it is easier to remove the second proton than the third. Thus, the K_a values become successively smaller as successive protons are removed.

▲ GIVE IT SOME THOUGHT

What is meant by the symbol K_{a3} for H_3PO_4?

The acid-dissociation constants for common polyprotic acids are listed in ▼ TABLE 16.3, and Appendix D provides a more complete list. The structure of citric acid illustrates the presence of multiple ionizable protons ◄ FIGURE 16.12.

Notice in Table 16.3 that in most cases the K_a values for successive losses of protons differ by a factor of at least 10^3. Notice also that the value of K_{a1} for sulfuric acid is listed simply as "large." Sulfuric acid is a strong acid with respect to the removal of the first proton. Thus, the reaction for the first ionization step lies completely to the right:

$$H_2SO_4(aq) \longrightarrow H^+(aq) + HSO_4^-(aq) \quad \text{(complete ionization)}$$

However, HSO_4^- is a weak acid for which $K_{a2} = 1.2 \times 10^{-2}$.

For many polyprotic acids K_{a1} is much larger than subsequent dissociation constants, in which case the $H^+(aq)$ in the solution comes almost entirely from the first ionization reaction. As long as successive K_a values differ by a factor of 10^3 or more, it is possible to obtain a satisfactory estimate of the pH of polyprotic acid solutions by treating the acids as if they were monoprotic, considering only K_{a1}.

TABLE 16.3 • **Acid-Dissociation Constants of Some Common Polyprotic Acids**

Name	Formula	K_{a1}	K_{a2}	K_{a3}
Ascorbic	$H_2C_6H_6O_6$	8.0×10^{-5}	1.6×10^{-12}	
Carbonic	H_2CO_3	4.3×10^{-7}	5.6×10^{-11}	
Citric	$H_3C_6H_5O_7$	7.4×10^{-4}	1.7×10^{-5}	4.0×10^{-7}
Oxalic	$H_2C_2O_4$	5.9×10^{-2}	6.4×10^{-5}	
Phosphoric	H_3PO_4	7.5×10^{-3}	6.2×10^{-8}	4.2×10^{-13}
Sulfurous	H_2SO_3	1.7×10^{-2}	6.4×10^{-8}	
Sulfuric	H_2SO_4	Large	1.2×10^{-2}	
Tartaric	$H_2C_4H_4O_6$	1.0×10^{-3}	4.6×10^{-5}	

SAMPLE EXERCISE 16.14 | Calculating the pH of a Polyprotic Acid Solution

The solubility of CO_2 in water at 25 °C and 0.1 atm is 0.0037 M. The common practice is to assume that all the dissolved CO_2 is in the form of carbonic acid (H_2CO_3), which is produced in the reaction

$$CO_2(aq) + H_2O(l) \rightleftharpoons H_2CO_3(aq)$$

What is the pH of a 0.0037 M solution of H_2CO_3?

SOLUTION

Analyze We are asked to determine the pH of a 0.0037 M solution of a polyprotic acid.

Plan H_2CO_3 is a diprotic acid; the two acid-dissociation constants, K_{a1} and K_{a2} (Table 16.3), differ by more than a factor of 10^3. Consequently, the pH can be determined by considering only K_{a1}, thereby treating the acid as if it were a monoprotic acid.

Solve Proceeding as in Sample Exercises 16.12 and 16.13, we can write the equilibrium reaction and equilibrium concentrations as

	$H_2CO_3(aq)$ $\rightleftharpoons$	$H^+(aq)$ +	$HCO_3^-(aq)$
Initial	0.0037 M	0	0
Change	$-x$ M	$+x$ M	$+x$ M
Equilibrium	$(0.0037 - x)$ M	x M	x M

The equilibrium-constant expression is

$$K_{a1} = \frac{[H^+][HCO_3^-]}{[H_2CO_3]} = \frac{(x)(x)}{0.0037 - x} = 4.3 \times 10^{-7}$$

Solving this equation using an equation-solving calculator, we get

$$x = 4.0 \times 10^{-5} M$$

Alternatively, because K_{a1} is small, we can make the simplifying approximation that x is small, so that

$$0.0037 - x \simeq 0.0037$$

Thus,

$$\frac{(x)(x)}{0.0037} = 4.3 \times 10^{-7}$$

Solving for x, we have

$$x^2 = (0.0037)(4.3 \times 10^{-7}) = 1.6 \times 10^{-9}$$

$$x = [H^+] = [HCO_3^-] = \sqrt{1.6 \times 10^{-9}} = 4.0 \times 10^{-5} M$$

Because we get the same value (to 2 significant figures) our simplifying assumption was justified. The pH is therefore

$$pH = -\log[H^+] = -\log(4.0 \times 10^{-5}) = 4.40$$

Comment If we were asked for $[CO_3^{2-}]$, we would need to use K_{a2}. Let's illustrate that calculation. Using our calculated values of $[HCO_3^-]$ and $[H^+]$ and setting $[CO_3^{2-}] = y$, we have

	$HCO_3^-(aq)$ $\rightleftharpoons$	$H^+(aq)$ +	$CO_3^{2-}(aq)$
Initial	4.0×10^{-5} M	4.0×10^{-5} M	0
Change	$-y$ M	$+y$ M	$+y$ M
Equilibrium	$(4.0 \times 10^{-5} - y)$ M	$(4.0 \times 10^{-5} + y)$ M	y M

Assuming that y is small relative to 4.0×10^{-5}, we have

$$K_{a2} = \frac{[H^+][CO_3^{2-}]}{[HCO_3^-]} = \frac{(4.0 \times 10^{-5})(y)}{4.0 \times 10^{-5}} = 5.6 \times 10^{-11}$$

$$y = 5.6 \times 10^{-11} M = [CO_3^{2-}]$$

This value is indeed very small compared with 4.0×10^{-5}, showing that our assumption was justified. It also shows that the ionization of HCO_3^- is negligible relative to that of H_2CO_3, as far as production of H^+ is concerned. However, it is the *only* source of CO_3^{2-}, which has a very low concentration in the solution. Our calculations thus tell us

that in a solution of carbon dioxide in water, most of the CO_2 is in the form of CO_2 or H_2CO_3, only a small fraction ionizes to form H^+ and HCO_3^-, and an even smaller fraction ionizes to give CO_3^{2-}. Notice also that $[CO_3^{2-}]$ is numerically equal to K_{a2}.

PRACTICE EXERCISE

(a) Calculate the pH of a 0.020 M solution of oxalic acid ($H_2C_2O_4$). (See Table 16.3 for K_{a1} and K_{a2}.) (b) Calculate the concentration of oxalate ion, $[C_2O_4^{2-}]$, in this solution.

Answers: (a) pH = 1.80, (b) $[C_2O_4^{2-}] = 6.4 \times 10^{-5} M$

16.7 | WEAK BASES

Many substances behave as weak bases in water. Weak bases react with water, abstracting protons from H_2O, thereby forming the conjugate acid of the base and OH^- ions:

$$B(aq) + H_2O(l) \rightleftharpoons HB^+(aq) + OH^-(aq) \qquad [16.33]$$

The equilibrium-constant expression for this reaction can be written as

$$K_b = \frac{[BH^+][OH^-]}{[B]} \qquad [16.34]$$

Water is the solvent, so it is omitted from the equilibrium-constant expression. The most commonly encountered weak base is ammonia:

$$NH_3(aq) + H_2O(l) \rightleftharpoons NH_4^+(aq) + OH^-(aq) \quad K_b = \frac{[NH_4^+][OH^-]}{[NH_3]} \qquad [16.35]$$

As with K_w and K_a, the subscript b in K_b denotes that the equilibrium constant refers to a particular type of reaction, namely the ionization of a weak base in water. The constant K_b, the **base-dissociation constant**, *always refers to the equilibrium in which a base reacts with H_2O to form the corresponding conjugate acid and OH^-.*

▼ **TABLE 16.4** lists the Lewis structures, conjugate acids, and K_b values for a number of weak bases in water. Appendix D includes a more extensive list. These bases contain one or more lone pairs of electrons because a lone pair is necessary to form the bond with H^+. Notice that in the neutral molecules in Table 16.4, the lone pairs are on nitrogen atoms. The other bases listed are anions derived from weak acids.

TABLE 16.4 • Some Weak Bases in Water at 25 °C

Base	Structural Formula*	Conjugate Acid	K_b
Ammonia (NH_3)	$H-\ddot{N}-H$ with H below	NH_4^+	1.8×10^{-5}
Pyridine (C_5H_5N)	(ring) $N:$	$C_5H_5NH^+$	1.7×10^{-9}
Hydroxylamine ($HONH_2$)	$H-\ddot{N}-\ddot{O}H$ with H below	$HONH_3^+$	1.1×10^{-8}
Methylamine (CH_3NH_2)	$H-\ddot{N}-CH_3$ with H below	$CH_3NH_3^+$	4.4×10^{-4}
Hydrosulfide ion (HS^-)	$[H-\ddot{S}:]^-$	H_2S	1.8×10^{-7}
Carbonate ion (CO_3^{2-})	$\left[\ddot{O} \; C \; \ddot{O} \; \ddot{O} \right]^{2-}$	HCO_3^-	1.8×10^{-4}
Hypochlorite ion (ClO^-)	$[\ddot{Cl}-\ddot{O}:]^-$	$HClO$	3.3×10^{-7}

*The atom that accepts the proton is shown in blue.

SAMPLE EXERCISE 16.15 | Using K_b to Calculate OH⁻

Calculate the concentration of OH⁻ in a 0.15 M solution of NH_3.

SOLUTION

Analyze We are given the concentration of a weak base and asked to determine the concentration of OH⁻.

Plan We will use essentially the same procedure here as used in solving problems involving the ionization of weak acids, that is, write the chemical equation and tabulate initial and equilibrium concentrations.

Solve The ionization reaction and equilibrium-constant expression are

$$NH_3(aq) + H_2O(l) \rightleftharpoons NH_4^+(aq) + OH^-(aq)$$

$$K_b = \frac{[NH_4^+][OH^-]}{[NH_3]} = 1.8 \times 10^{-5}$$

The equilibrium concentrations are (We ignore the concentration of H_2O because it is not involved in the equilibrium-constant expression.)

	$NH_3(aq)$ +	$H_2O(l)$ ⇌	$NH_4^+(aq)$ +	OH⁻
Initial	0.15 M	—	0	0
Change	$-x\,M$	—	$+x\,M$	$+x\,M$
Equilibrium	$(0.15 - x)\,M$	—	$x\,M$	$x\,M$

Inserting these quantities into the equilibrium-constant expression gives

$$K_b = \frac{[NH_4^+][OH^-]}{[NH_3]} = \frac{(x)(x)}{0.15 - x} = 1.8 \times 10^{-5}$$

Because K_b is small, the amount of NH_3 that reacts with water is much smaller than the NH_3 concentration, and so we can neglect x relative to 0.15 M. Then we have

$$\frac{x^2}{0.15} = 1.8 \times 10^{-5}$$

$$x^2 = (0.15)(1.8 \times 10^{-5}) = 2.7 \times 10^{-6}$$

$$x = [NH_4^+] = [OH^-] = \sqrt{2.7 \times 10^{-5}} = 1.6 \times 10^{-3}\,M$$

Check The value obtained for x is only about 1% of the NH_3 concentration, 0.15 M. Therefore, neglecting x relative to 0.15 was justified.

Comment You may be asked to find the pH of a solution of a weak base. Once you have found [OH⁻], you can proceed as in Sample Exercise 16.9, where we calculated the pH of a strong base. In the present sample exercise, we have seen that the 0.15 M solution of NH_3 contains [OH⁻] = $1.5 \times 10^{-3}\,M$. Thus, pOH = $-\log(1.6 \times 10^{-3}) = 2.80$, and pH = $14.00 - 2.80 = 11.20$. The pH of the solution is above 7 because we are dealing with a solution of a base.

PRACTICE EXERCISE

Which of the following compounds should produce the highest pH as a 0.05 M solution: pyridine, methylamine, or nitrous acid?

Answer: methylamine (because it has the larger K_b value of the two amine bases in the list)

Types of Weak Bases

Weak bases fall into two general categories. The first category is neutral substances that have an atom with a nonbonding pair of electrons that can accept a proton. Most of these bases, including all uncharged bases in Table 16.4, contain a nitrogen atom. These substances include ammonia and a related class of compounds called **amines** (▶ FIGURE 16.13). In organic amines, at least one N—H bond in NH_3 is replaced with an N—C bond. Like NH_3, amines can abstract a proton from a water molecule by forming an N—H bond, as shown here for methylamine:

$$H-\overset{\cdot\cdot}{N}-CH_3(aq) + H_2O(l) \rightleftharpoons \left[H-\overset{\overset{\displaystyle H}{|}}{\underset{\underset{\displaystyle H}{|}}{N}}-CH_3 \right]^+ (aq) + OH^-(aq) \qquad [16.36]$$

GO FIGURE

When hydroxylamine acts as a base, which atom accepts the proton?

Ammonia	Methylamine	Hydroxylamine
NH_3	CH_3NH_2	NH_2OH

▲ FIGURE 16.13 Structures of ammonia and two simple amines.

Anions of weak acids make up the second general category of weak bases. In an aqueous solution of sodium hypochlorite (NaClO), for example, NaClO dissociates to Na^+ and ClO^- ions. The Na^+ ion is always a spectator ion in acid–base reactions. ∞ (Section 4.3) The ClO^- ion, however, is the conjugate base of a weak acid, hypochlorous acid. Consequently, the ClO^- ion acts as a weak base in water:

$$ClO^-(aq) + H_2O(l) \rightleftharpoons HClO(aq) + OH^-(aq) \qquad K_b = 3.3 \times 10^{-7} \qquad [16.37]$$

In Figure 16.5 we saw that bleach is quite basic (pH values of 12–13). Common chlorine bleach is typically a 5% NaOCl solution.

SAMPLE EXERCISE 16.16 | **Using pH to Determine the Concentration of a Salt**

A solution made by adding solid sodium hypochlorite (NaClO) to enough water to make 2.00 L of solution has a pH of 10.50. Using the information in Equation 16.37, calculate the number of moles of NaClO added to the water.

SOLUTION

Analyze NaClO is an ionic compound consisting of Na^+ and ClO^- ions. As such, it is a strong electrolyte that completely dissociates in solution into Na^+, a spectator ion, and ClO^- ion, a weak base with $K_b = 3.3 \times 10^{-7}$ (Equation 16.37). Given this information we must calculate the number of moles of NaClO needed to raise the basicity of 2.00-L of water to 10.50.

Plan From the pH, we can determine the equilibrium concentration of OH^-. We can then construct a table of initial and equilibrium concentrations in which the initial concentration of ClO^- is our unknown. We can calculate $[ClO^-]$ using the expression for K_b.

Solve We can calculate $[OH^-]$ by using either Equation 16.16 or Equation 16.20; we will use the latter method here:

$$pOH = 14.00 - pH = 14.00 - 10.50 = 3.50$$
$$[OH^-] = 10^{-3.50} = 3.2 \times 10^{-4}\ M$$

This concentration is high enough that we can assume that Equation 16.37 is the only source of OH^-; that is, we can neglect any OH^- produced by the autoionization of H_2O. We now assume a value of x for the initial concentration of ClO^- and solve the equilibrium problem in the usual way.

	$ClO^-(aq)$	+	$H_2O(l)$	$\rightleftharpoons$	$HClO(aq)$	+	$OH^-(aq)$
Initial	$x\ M$		—		0		0
Change	$-3.2 \times 10^{-4}\ M$		—		$+3.2 \times 10^{-4}\ M$		$+3.2 \times 10^{-4}\ M$
Equilibrium	$(x - 3.2 \times 10^{-4})\ M$		—		$3.2 \times 10^{-4}\ M$		$3.2 \times 10^{-4}\ M$

We now use the expression for the base-dissociation constant to solve for x:

$$K_b = \frac{[HClO][OH^-]}{[ClO^-]} = \frac{(3.2 \times 10^{-4})^2}{x - 3.2 \times 10^{-4}} = 3.3 \times 10^{-7}$$

$$x = \frac{(3.2 \times 10^{-4})^2}{3.3 \times 10^{-7}} + (3.2 \times 10^{-4}) = 0.31\ M$$

We say that the solution is 0.31 M in NaClO even though some of the ClO⁻ ions have reacted with water. Because the solution is 0.31 M in NaClO and the total volume of solution is 2.00 L, 0.62 mol of NaClO is the amount of the salt that was added to the water.

PRACTICE EXERCISE

What is the molarity of an aqueous NH_3 solution that has a pH of 11.17?

Answer: 0.12 M

WHAT'S AHEAD

5.1 THE NATURE OF ENERGY

We begin by considering the nature of *energy* and the forms it takes, notably *kinetic energy* and *potential energy*. We discuss the units used in measuring energy and the fact that energy can be used to do *work* or to transfer *heat*. To study energy changes, we focus on a particular part of the universe, which we call the *system*. Everything else is called the *surroundings*.

5.2 THE FIRST LAW OF THERMODYNAMICS

We then explore the *first law of thermodynamics*: Energy cannot be created or destroyed but can be transformed from one form to another or transferred between systems and surroundings. The energy possessed by a system is called its *internal energy*. Internal energy is a *state function,* a quantity whose value depends only on the current state of a system, not on how the system came to be in that state.

5.3 ENTHALPY

Next, we encounter a state function called *enthalpy* that is useful because the change in enthalpy measures the quantity of heat energy gained or lost by a system in a process occurring under constant pressure.

BIOENERGY. The sugars in sugarcane, produced from CO_2, H_2O, and sunshine via photosynthesis, can be converted into ethanol, which is used as an alternative to gasoline. In certain climates, such as that in Brazil, the sugarcane crop replenishes itself rapidly, making cane-based ethanol a *sustainable* fuel source.

5

5.4 ENTHALPIES OF REACTION

We see that the enthalpy change associated with a chemical reaction is the enthalpies of the products minus the enthalpies of the reactants. This quantity is directly proportional to the amount of reactant consumed in the reaction.

5.5 CALORIMETRY

We next examine *calorimetry,* an experimental technique used to measure heat changes in chemical processes.

5.6 HESS'S LAW

We observe that the enthalpy change for a given reaction can be calculated using appropriate enthalpy changes for related reactions. To do so, we apply *Hess's law*.

5.7 ENTHALPIES OF FORMATION

Then we discuss how to establish standard values for enthalpy changes in chemical reactions and how to use them to calculate enthalpy changes for reactions.

5.8 FOODS AND FUELS

Finally, we examine foods and fuels as sources of energy and discuss some related health and social issues.

THERMO-CHEMISTRY

CHANCES ARE YOU'VE HEARD THE word *energy* today, perhaps in one of your courses, in the news, in conversation, or possibly in all these instances. Our modern society depends on energy for its existence. The issues surrounding energy—its sources, production, distribution, and consumption—pervade a lot of our

conversation, from science to politics to economics to environmental issues. The production of energy is a major factor in the growth of national economies, especially rapidly developing countries such as China, India, and Brazil. The chapter-opening photograph highlights the efforts in Brazil to use their bountiful and fast-growing sugarcane crop as a source of ethanol. A major part of the Brazilian economy has depended on the use of ethanol instead of petroleum-based fuels in transportation and industry.

With the exception of the energy from the Sun, most of the energy used in our daily lives comes from chemical reactions. The combustion of gasoline, the production of electricity from coal, the heating of homes by natural gas, and the use of batteries to power electronic devices are all examples of how chemistry is used to produce energy. In addition, chemical reactions provide the energy that sustains living systems. Plants, such as the sugarcane in the chapter-opening photograph, use solar energy to carry out photosynthesis, allowing them to grow. The plants in turn provide food from which we humans derive the energy needed to move, maintain body temperature, and carry out all other bodily functions. What exactly is energy, though, and what principles are involved in its production, consumption, and transformation from one form to another?

In this chapter we begin to explore energy and its changes. We are motivated not only by the impact of energy on so many aspects of our daily lives but also by the fact that if we are to properly understand chemistry, we must understand the energy changes that accompany chemical reactions.

The study of energy and its transformations is known as **thermodynamics** (Greek: *thérme-*, "heat"; *dy'namis*, "power"). This area of study began during the Industrial Revolution in order to develop the relationships among heat, work, and fuels in steam engines. In this chapter we will examine the relationships between chemical reactions and energy changes that involve heat. This portion of thermodynamics is called **thermochemistry**. We will discuss additional aspects of thermodynamics in Chapter 19.

5.1 | THE NATURE OF ENERGY

The concept of matter has always been easy to grasp because matter can be seen and touched. By contrast, although the concept of energy is a familiar one, it is challenging to deal with in a precise way. **Energy** is commonly defined as *the capacity to do work or transfer heat.* This definition requires us to understand the concepts of work and heat. **Work** is *the energy used to cause an object to move against a force,* and **heat** is *the energy used to cause the temperature of an object to increase* (◀ **FIGURE 5.1**). Let's begin our study of thermochemistry by examining the ways in which matter can possess energy and how that energy can be transferred from one piece of matter to another.

Kinetic Energy and Potential Energy

Objects, whether they are baseballs or molecules, can possess **kinetic energy**, the energy of *motion*. The magnitude of the kinetic energy, E_k, of an object depends on its mass, m, and speed, v:

$$E_k = \tfrac{1}{2} mv^2 \qquad [5.1]$$

We see that the kinetic energy of an object increases as its speed increases. For example, a car moving at 55 miles per hour (mph) has greater kinetic energy than it does at 25 mph. For a given speed the kinetic energy increases with increasing mass. Thus, a large truck traveling at 55 mph has greater kinetic energy than a small sedan traveling at the same speed because the truck has the greater mass. In chemistry, we are interested in the kinetic energy of atoms and molecules. Although too small to be seen, these particles have mass and are in motion and, therefore, possess kinetic energy.

All other kinds of energy—the energy stored in a stretched spring, in a weight held above your head, or in a chemical bond, for example—are potential energy. An object has **potential energy** by virtue of its position relative to other objects. Potential energy is, in essence, the "stored" energy that arises from the attractions and repulsions an object experiences in relation to other objects.

We are all familiar with instances in which potential energy is converted into kinetic energy. For example, think of a cyclist poised at the top of a hill (▶ **FIGURE 5.2**). Because of the attractive force of gravity, the potential energy of the cyclist and her bicycle is greater at the top of the hill than at the bottom. As a result, the bicycle easily moves down the hill with increasing speed. As it does so, the potential energy initially stored in it is converted into kinetic energy. The potential energy decreases as the bicycle rolls down the hill, but its kinetic energy increases as the speed increases (Equation 5.1).

We will soon see that this interconversion of energy, with one form decreasing while the other increases, is the first cornerstone of thermodynamics.

Gravitational forces play a negligible role in the ways that atoms and molecules interact with one another. Forces that arise from electrical charges are more important when dealing with atoms and molecules. One of the most important forms of potential energy in chemistry is *electrostatic potential energy*, E_{el}, which arises from the interactions between charged particles. This energy is proportional to the electrical charges on the

▲ **GO FIGURE**

Why is a pitcher able to throw a baseball faster than he could throw a bowling ball?

Work done by pitcher on ball to make ball move

(a)

Heat added by burner to water makes water temperature rise

(b)

▲ **FIGURE 5.1 Work and heat, two forms of energy.** (a) *Work* is energy used to cause an object to move. (b) *Heat* is energy used to cause the temperature of an object to increase.

GO FIGURE

Suppose the bicyclist is coasting (not pedaling) at constant speed on a flat road and begins to go up a hill. If she does not start pedaling, what happens to her speed? Why?

High potential energy, zero kinetic energy

Decreasing potential energy, increasing kinetic energy

◄ FIGURE 5.2 **Potential energy and kinetic energy.** The potential energy initially stored in the motionless bicycle at the top of the hill is converted to kinetic energy as the bicycle moves down the hill and loses potential energy.

two interacting objects, Q_1 and Q_2, and inversely proportional to the distance, d, separating them:

$$E_{el} = \frac{\kappa Q_1 Q_2}{d} \qquad [5.2]$$

Here κ is simply a constant of proportionality, 8.99×10^9 J-m/C². [C is the coulomb, a unit of electrical charge ∞ (Section 2.2), and J is the joule, a unit of energy we will discuss soon.] At the molecular level, the electrical charges Q_1 and Q_2 are typically on the order of magnitude of the charge of the electron (1.60×10^{-19} C).

Equation 5.2 shows that the electrostatic potential energy goes to zero as d becomes infinite; in other words, the zero of electrostatic potential energy is defined as infinite separation of the charged particles. ▼ **FIGURE 5.3** illustrates how E_{el} behaves for

GO FIGURE

A positively charged particle and a negatively charged particle are initially far apart. What happens to their electrostatic potential energy as they are brought closer together?

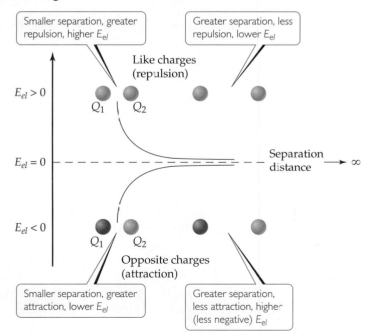

Smaller separation, greater repulsion, higher E_{el}

Greater separation, less repulsion, lower E_{el}

Like charges (repulsion)

$E_{el} > 0$

Q_1 Q_2

$E_{el} = 0$

Separation distance   ∞

$E_{el} < 0$

Q_1 Q_2

Opposite charges (attraction)

Smaller separation, greater attraction, lower E_{el}

Greater separation, less attraction, higher (less negative) E_{el}

◄ FIGURE 5.3 **Electrostatic potential energy.** At finite separation distances for two charged particles, E_{el} is positive for like charges and negative for opposite charges. As the particles move farther apart, their electrostatic potential energy approaches zero.

charges of the same and different sign. When Q_1 and Q_2 have the same sign (for example, both positive), the two charged particles repel each other, and a repulsive force pushes them apart. In this case, E_{el} is positive, and the potential energy decreases as the particles move farther and farther apart. When Q_1 and Q_2 have opposite signs, the particles attract each other, and an attractive force pulls them toward each other. In this case, E_{el} is negative, and the potential energy increases (becomes less negative) as the particles move apart.

These trends in electrostatic potential energy are used often in chemistry, as we will see later in the text.

One of our goals in chemistry is to relate the energy changes seen in the macroscopic world to the kinetic or potential energy of substances at the molecular level. Many substances—fuels, for example—release *chemical energy* when they react, energy due to the potential energy stored in the arrangements of their atoms. The energy a substance possesses because of its temperature (its *thermal energy*) is associated with the kinetic energy of the molecules in the substance.

GIVE IT SOME THOUGHT

When the cyclist and bicycle in Figure 5.2 come to a stop at the bottom of the hill, (a) is the potential energy the same as it was at the top of the hill? (b) Is the kinetic energy the same as it was at the top of the hill?

Units of Energy

The SI unit for energy is the **joule** (pronounced "jool"), J, in honor of James Joule (1818–1889), a British scientist who investigated work and heat: $1 \text{ J} = 1 \text{ kg-m}^2/\text{s}^2$. Equation 5.1 shows that a mass of 2 kg moving at a speed of 1 m/s possesses a kinetic energy of 1 J:

$$E_k = \tfrac{1}{2}\, mv^2 = \tfrac{1}{2}\, (2 \text{ kg})(1 \text{ m/s})^2 = 1 \text{ kg-m}^2/\text{s}^2 = 1 \text{ J}$$

Because a joule is not a large amount of energy, we often use *kilojoules* (kJ) in discussing the energies associated with chemical reactions.

Traditionally, energy changes accompanying chemical reactions have been expressed in calories, a non–SI unit still widely used in chemistry, biology, and biochemistry. A **calorie** (cal) was originally defined as the amount of energy required to raise the temperature of 1 g of water from 14.5 °C to 15.5 °C. A calorie is now defined in terms of the joule:

$$1 \text{ cal} = 4.184 \text{ J (exactly)}$$

A related energy unit used in nutrition is the nutritional *Calorie* (note the capital C): $1 \text{ Cal} = 1000 \text{ cal} = 1 \text{ kcal}$.

System and Surroundings

When analyzing energy changes, we need to focus on a limited and well-defined part of the universe to keep track of the energy changes that occur. The portion we single out for study is called the **system**; everything else is called the **surroundings**. When we study the energy change that accompanies a chemical reaction in the laboratory, the reactants and products constitute the system. The container and everything beyond it are considered the surroundings.

Systems may be open, closed, or isolated. An *open* system is one in which matter and energy can be exchanged with the surroundings. An uncovered pot of boiling water on a stove, such as in Figure 5.1(b), is an open system: Heat comes into the system from the stove, and water is released to the surroundings as steam.

The systems we can most readily study in thermochemistry are called *closed systems*—systems that can exchange energy but not matter with their surroundings. For example, consider a mixture of hydrogen gas, H_2, and oxygen gas, O_2, in a cylinder fitted with a piston (◄ **FIGURE 5.4**). The system is just the hydrogen and oxygen; the cylinder,

GO FIGURE

If the piston is pulled upward so that it sits halfway between the position shown and the top of the cylinder, is the system still closed?

Energy can enter or leave system as heat or as work done on piston

Matter can not enter or leave system

Surroundings = cylinder, piston, and everything beyond

System = $H_2(g)$ and $O_2(g)$

▲ **FIGURE 5.4   A closed system.**

piston, and everything beyond them (including us) are the surroundings. If the gases react to form water, energy is liberated:

$$2\ H_2(g)\ +\ O_2(g)\ \longrightarrow\ 2\ H_2O(g)\ +\ energy$$

Although the chemical form of the hydrogen and oxygen atoms in the system is changed by this reaction, the system has not lost or gained mass, which means it has not exchanged any matter with its surroundings. However, it can exchange energy with its surroundings in the form of *work* and *heat*.

An *isolated* system is one in which neither energy nor matter can be exchanged with the surroundings. An insulated thermos containing hot coffee approximates an isolated system. We know, however, that the coffee eventually cools, so it is not perfectly isolated.

 GIVE IT SOME THOUGHT

Is a human being an isolated, closed, or open system?

Transferring Energy: Work and Heat

Figure 5.1 illustrates the two ways we experience energy changes in our everyday lives—in the form of work and in the form of heat. In Figure 5.1(a) work is done as energy is transferred from the pitcher's arm to the ball, directing it toward the plate at high speed. In Figure 5.1(b) energy is transferred in the form of heat. Causing the motion of an object against a force and causing a temperature change are the two general ways that energy can be transferred into or out of a system.

A **force** is any push or pull exerted on an object. We define work, *w*, as the energy transferred when a force moves an object. The magnitude of this work equals the product of the force, *F*, and the distance, *d*, the object moves:

$$w = F \times d \qquad\qquad [5.3]$$

We perform work, for example, when we lift an object against the force of gravity. If we define the object as the system, then we—as part of the surroundings—are performing work on that system, transferring energy to it.

The other way in which energy is transferred is as heat. *Heat* is the energy transferred from a hotter object to a colder one. A combustion reaction, such as the burning of natural gas illustrated in Figure 5.1(b), releases the chemical energy stored in the molecules of the fuel. ∞ (Section 3.2) If we define the substances involved in the reaction as the system and everything else as the surroundings, we find that the released energy causes the temperature of the system to increase. Energy in the form of heat is then transferred from the hotter system to the cooler surroundings.

SAMPLE EXERCISE 5.1 | **Describing and Calculating Energy Changes**

A bowler lifts a 5.4-kg (12-lb) bowling ball from ground level to a height of 1.6 m (5.2 ft) and then drops it. **(a)** What happens to the potential energy of the ball as it is raised? **(b)** What quantity of work, in J, is used to raise the ball? **(c)** After the ball is dropped, it gains kinetic energy. If all the work done in part (b) has been converted to kinetic energy by the time the ball strikes the ground, what is the ball's speed just before it hits the ground? (Note: The force due to gravity is $F = m \times g$, where m is the mass of the object and g is the gravitational constant; $g = 9.8\ m/s^2$.)

SOLUTION

Analyze We need to relate the potential energy of the bowling ball to its position relative to the ground. We then need to establish the relationship between work and the change in the ball's potential energy. Finally, we need to connect the change in potential energy when the ball is dropped with the kinetic energy attained by the ball.

Plan We can calculate the work done in lifting the ball by using Equation 5.3: $w = F \times d$. The kinetic energy of the ball just before it hits the ground equals its initial potential energy. We can use the kinetic energy and Equation 5.1 to calculate the speed, *v*, just before impact.

Solve

(a) Because the ball is raised above the ground, its potential energy relative to the ground increases.

(b) The ball has a mass of 5.4 kg and is lifted 1.6 m. To calculate the work performed to raise the ball, we use Equation 5.3 and $F = m \times g$ for the force that is due to gravity:

$$w = F \times d = m \times g \times d = (5.4 \text{ kg})(9.8 \text{ m/s}^2)(1.6 \text{ m}) = 85 \text{ kg-m}^2/\text{s}^2 = 85 \text{ J}$$

Thus, the bowler has done 85 J of work to lift the ball to a height of 1.6 m.

(c) When the ball is dropped, its potential energy is converted to kinetic energy. We assume that the kinetic energy just before the ball hits the ground is equal to the work done in part (b), 85 J:

$$E_k = \tfrac{1}{2} mv^2 = 85 \text{ J} = 85 \text{ kg-m}^2/\text{s}^2$$

We can now solve this equation for v:

$$v^2 = \left(\frac{2E_k}{m}\right) = \left(\frac{2(85 \text{ kg-m}^2/\text{s}^2)}{5.4 \text{ kg}}\right) = 31.5 \text{ m}^2/\text{s}^2$$

$$v = \sqrt{31.5 \text{ m}^2/\text{s}^2} = 5.6 \text{ m/s}$$

Check Work must be done in (b) to increase the potential energy of the ball, which is in accord with our experience. The units are appropriate in (b) and (c). The work is in units of J and the speed in units of m/s. In (c) we carry an additional digit in the intermediate calculation involving the square root, but we report the final value to only two significant figures, as appropriate.

Comment A speed of 1 m/s is roughly 2 mph, so the bowling ball has a speed greater than 10 mph just before impact.

PRACTICE EXERCISE

What is the kinetic energy, in J, of **(a)** an Ar atom moving at a speed of 650 m/s, **(b)** a mole of Ar atoms moving at 650 m/s? (*Hint*: 1 amu $= 1.66 \times 10^{-27}$ kg.)

Answers: **(a)** 1.4×10^{-20} J, **(b)** 8.4×10^3 J

5.2 | THE FIRST LAW OF THERMODYNAMICS

We have seen that the potential energy of a system can be converted into kinetic energy, and vice versa. We have also seen that energy can be transferred back and forth between a system and its surroundings in the forms of work and heat. All of these conversions and transfers proceed in accord with one of the most important observations in science: Energy can be neither created nor destroyed. Any energy that is lost by a system must be gained by the surroundings, and vice versa. This important observation—that *energy is conserved*—is known as the **first law of thermodynamics**. To apply this law quantitatively, let's first define the energy of a system more precisely.

Internal Energy

We will use the first law of thermodynamics to analyze energy changes in chemical systems. In order to do so, we must consider all the sources of kinetic and potential energy in the system we are studying. We define the **internal energy**, *E*, of a system as the sum of *all* the kinetic and potential energies of the components of the system. For the system in Figure 5.4, for example, the internal energy includes not only the motions and interactions of the H_2 and O_2 molecules but also the motions and interactions of the nuclei and electrons. We generally do not know the numerical value of a system's internal energy. In thermodynamics, we are mainly concerned with the *change* in *E* (and, as we shall see, changes in other quantities as well) that accompanies a change in the system.

Imagine that we start with a system with an initial internal energy E_{initial}. The system then undergoes a change, which might involve work being done or heat being transferred. After the change, the final internal energy of the system is E_{final}. We define

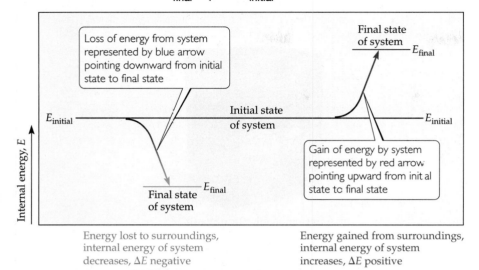

GO FIGURE

What is the value of ΔE if E_{final} equals $E_{initial}$?

Loss of energy from system represented by blue arrow pointing downward from initial state to final state

Final state of system E_{final}

Initial state of system

$E_{initial}$

$E_{initial}$

Gain of energy by system represented by red arrow pointing upward from initial state to final state

Final state of system E_{final}

Internal energy, E

Energy lost to surroundings, internal energy of system decreases, ΔE negative

Energy gained from surroundings, internal energy of system increases, ΔE positive

◄ **FIGURE 5.5   Changes in internal energy.**

the *change* in internal energy, denoted ΔE (read "delta E"),* as the difference between E_{final} and $E_{initial}$:

$$\Delta E = E_{final} - E_{initial} \qquad [5.4]$$

We generally can't determine the actual values of E_{final} and $E_{initial}$ for any system of practical interest. Nevertheless, one of the beautiful aspects of the first law of thermodynamics is that we need only the value of ΔE in order to apply the law. We can often determine the value of ΔE even though we don't know the specific values of E_{final} and $E_{initial}$.

Thermodynamic quantities such as ΔE have three parts: (1) a number and (2) a unit, which together give the magnitude of the change, and (3) a sign that gives the direction. A *positive* value of ΔE results when $E_{final} > E_{initial}$, indicating that the system has gained energy from its surroundings. A *negative* value of ΔE results when $E_{final} < E_{initial}$, indicating that the system has lost energy to its surroundings. Notice that we are taking the point of view of the system rather than that of the surroundings in discussing the energy changes. We need to remember, however, that any increase in the energy of the system is accompanied by a decrease in the energy of the surroundings, and vice versa. These features of energy changes are summarized in ▲ **FIGURE 5.5**.

In a chemical reaction, the initial state of the system refers to the reactants and the final state refers to the products. In the reaction

$$2\,H_2(g) + O_2(g) \longrightarrow 2\,H_2O(l)$$

for instance, the initial state is the $2\,H_2(g) + O_2(g)$ and the final state is the $2\,H_2O(l)$. When hydrogen and oxygen form water at a given temperature, the system loses energy to the surroundings. Because energy is lost from the system, the internal energy of the products (final state) is less than that of the reactants (initial state), and ΔE for the process is negative. Thus, the *energy diagram* in ▶ **FIGURE 5.6** shows that the internal energy of the mixture of H_2 and O_2 is greater than that of the H_2O produced in the reaction.

Relating ΔE to Heat and Work

As we noted in Section 5.1, a system may exchange energy with its surroundings in two general ways: as heat or as work. The internal energy of a system changes in magnitude as heat is added to or removed from the system or as work is done on or by the system. If we think of internal energy as the system's bank account of energy, we see that deposits or withdrawals can be made either in increments of heat or in increments of

GO FIGURE

The internal energy for Mg(s) and $Cl_2(g)$ is greater than that of $MgCl_2(s)$. Sketch an energy diagram that represents the reaction $MgCl_2(s) \longrightarrow Mg(s) + Cl_2(g)$.

Initial state $H_2(g), O_2(g)$

$\Delta E < 0$

Final state $H_2O(l)$

Internal energy, E

$E_{initial}$ greater than E_{final}, energy released from system to surrounding during reaction, $\Delta E < 0$

▲ **FIGURE 5.6   Energy diagram for the reaction $2\,H_2(g) + O_2(g) \longrightarrow 2\,H_2O(l)$.**

*The symbol Δ is commonly used to denote *change*. For example, a change in height, h, can be represented by Δh.

◢ GO FIGURE

Suppose a system receives a "deposit" of work from the surroundings and loses a "withdrawal" of heat to the surroundings. Can we determine the sign of ΔE for this process?

System is interior of vault

► **FIGURE 5.7 Sign conventions for heat and work.** Heat, q, gained by a system and work, w, done on a system are both positive quantities, corresponding to "deposits" of internal energy into the system. Conversely, heat transferred from the system to the surroundings and work done by the system on the surroundings are both "withdrawals" of internal energy from the system.

Energy deposited into system
$\Delta E > 0$

Energy withdrawn from system
$\Delta E < 0$

work. Deposits increase the energy of the system (positive ΔE), whereas withdrawals decrease the energy of the system (negative ΔE).

We can use these ideas to write a useful algebraic expression of the first law of thermodynamics. When a system undergoes any chemical or physical change, the accompanying change in internal energy, ΔE, is the sum of the heat added to or liberated from the system, q, and the work done on or by the system, w:

$$\Delta E = q + w \qquad [5.5]$$

When heat is added to a system or work is done on a system, its internal energy increases. Therefore, when heat is transferred to the system from the surroundings, q has a positive value. Adding heat to the system is like making a deposit to the energy account—the energy of the system increases (▲ **FIGURE 5.7**). Likewise, when work is done on the system by the surroundings, w has a positive value. Conversely, both the heat lost by the system to the surroundings and the work done by the system on the surroundings have negative values; that is, they lower the internal energy of the system. They are energy withdrawals and lower the amount of energy in the system's account.

The sign conventions for q, w, and ΔE are summarized in ▼ **TABLE 5.1**. Notice that any energy entering the system as either heat or work carries a positive sign.

TABLE 5.1 ▪ Sign Conventions for q, w, and ΔE		
For q	+ means system *gains* heat	− means system *loses* heat
For w	+ means work done *on* system	− means work done *by* system
For ΔE	+ means *net gain* of energy by system	− means *net loss* of energy by system

SAMPLE EXERCISE 5.2 | Relating Heat and Work to Changes of Internal Energy

Gases A(g) and B(g) are confined in a cylinder-and-piston arrangement like that in Figure 5.4 and react to form a solid product C(s): A(g) + B(g) $\longrightarrow$ C(s). As the reaction occurs, the system loses 1150 J of heat to the surroundings. The piston moves downward as the gases react to form a solid. As the volume of the gas decreases under the constant pressure of the atmosphere, the surroundings do 480 J of work on the system. What is the change in the internal energy of the system?

SOLUTION

Analyze The question asks us to determine ΔE, given information about q and w.

Plan We first determine the signs of q and w (Table 5.1) and then use Equation 5.5, $\Delta E = q + w$, to calculate ΔE.

Solve Heat is transferred from the system to the surroundings, and work is done on the system by the surroundings, so q is negative and w is positive: $q = -1150$ J and $w = 480$ kJ. Thus,

$$\Delta E = q + w = (-1150 \text{ J}) + (480 \text{ J}) = -670 \text{ J}$$

The negative value of ΔE tells us that a net quantity of 670 J of energy has been transferred from the system to the surroundings.

Comment You can think of this change as a decrease of 670 J in the net value of the system's energy bank account (hence, the negative sign); 1150 J is withdrawn in the form of heat while 480 J is deposited in the form of work. Notice that as the volume of the gases decreases, work is being done *on* the system *by* the surroundings, resulting in a deposit of energy.

PRACTICE EXERCISE

Calculate the change in the internal energy for a process in which a system absorbs 140 J of heat from the surroundings and does 85 J of work on the surroundings.

Answer: +55 J

Endothermic and Exothermic Processes

Because transfer of heat to and from the system is central to our discussion in this chapter, we have some special terminology to indicate the direction of transfer. When a process occurs in which the system absorbs heat, the process is called **endothermic** (*endo-* means "into"). During an endothermic process, such as the melting of ice, heat flows *into* the system from its surroundings [▶ FIGURE 5.8(a)]. If we, as part of the surroundings, touch a container in which ice is melting, the container feels cold to us because heat has passed from our hand to the container.

A process in which the system loses heat is called **exothermic** (*exo-* means "out of"). During an exothermic process, such as the combustion of gasoline, heat *exits* or flows *out* of the system into the surroundings [Figure 5.8(b)].

 GIVE IT SOME THOUGHT

When $H_2(g)$ and $O_2(g)$ react to form $H_2O(l)$, heat is released to the surroundings. Consider the reverse reaction, namely, the formation of $H_2(g)$ and $O_2(g)$ from $H_2O(l)$: 2 $H_2O(l)$ $\longrightarrow$ 2 $H_2(g)$ + $O_2(g)$. Is this reaction exothermic or endothermic? (*Hint:* Refer to Figure 5.6)

State Functions

Although we usually have no way of knowing the precise value of the internal energy of a system, E, it does have a fixed value for a given set of conditions. The conditions that influence internal energy include the temperature and pressure. Furthermore, the internal energy of a system is proportional to the total quantity of matter in the system because energy is an extensive property. ∞ (Section 1.3)

Suppose we define our system as 50 g of water at 25 °C (▶ FIGURE 5.9). The system could have reached this state by cooling 50 g of water from 100 °C to 25 °C or by melting 50 g of ice and subsequently warming the water to 25 °C. The internal energy of

▶ FIGURE 5.8 **Endothermic and exothermic reactions.** (a) When ammonium thiocyanate and barium hydroxide octahydrate are mixed at room temperature, the temperature drops. (b) The reaction of powdered aluminum with Fe_2O_3 (the thermite reaction) proceeds vigorously, releasing heat and forming Al_2O_3 and molten iron.

System: reactants + products

Surroundings: solvent, initially at room temperature

Heat flows from surroundings into system (endothermic reaction), temperature of surroundings drops, thermometer reads temperature well below room temperature

(a)

System: reactants

Surroundings: air around reactants

Heat flows (violently) from system into surroundings (exothermic reaction), temperature of surroundings increases

(b)

▶ FIGURE 5.9 **Internal energy, *E*, a state function.** Any state function depends only on the present state of the system and not on the path by which the system arrived at that state.

50 g
$H_2O(l)$
100 °C

Initially hot water cools to water at 25 °C; once this temperature is reached, system has internal energy *E*

50 g
$H_2O(l)$
25 °C

Ice warms up to water at 25 °C; once this temperature is reached, system has internal energy *E*

50 g
$H_2O(s)$
0 °C

the water at 25 °C is the same in either case. Internal energy is an example of a **state function**, a property of a system that is determined by specifying the system's condition, or state (in terms of temperature, pressure, and so forth). *The value of a state function depends only on the present state of the system, not on the path the system took to reach that state.* Because *E* is a state function, ΔE depends only on the initial and final states of the system, not on how the change occurs.

An analogy may help you understand the difference between quantities that are state functions and those that are not. Suppose you drive from Chicago, which is 596 ft above sea level, to Denver, which is 5280 ft above sea level. No matter which route you take, the altitude change is 4684 ft. The distance you travel, however, depends on your route. Altitude is analogous to a state function because the change in altitude is independent of the path taken. Distance traveled is not a state function.

Some thermodynamic quantities, such as *E*, are state functions. Other quantities, such as *q* and *w*, are not. This means that, although $\Delta E = q + w$ does not depend on how the change occurs, the specific amounts of heat and work produced depend on the way in which the change occurs, analogous to the choice of travel route between Chicago and Denver. Nevertheless, if changing the path by which a system goes from an initial state to a final state increases the value of *q*, that path change will also decrease the value of *w* by exactly the same amount. The result is that ΔE is the same for the two paths.

We can illustrate this principle using a flashlight battery as our system. As the battery is discharged, its internal energy decreases as the energy stored in the battery is released to the surroundings. In ▶ FIGURE 5.10, we consider two possible ways of discharging the battery at constant temperature. If a wire shorts out the battery, no work is accomplished because nothing is moved against a force. All the energy lost from the battery is in the form of heat. (The wire gets warmer and releases heat to the surroundings.) If the battery is used to make a motor turn, the discharge produces work. Some heat is released, but not as much as when the battery is shorted out. We see that the magnitudes of q and w must be different for these two cases. If the initial and final states of the battery are identical in the two cases, however, then $\Delta E = q + w$ must be the same in both cases because ΔE is a state function. Remember: ΔE depends only on the initial and final states of the system, not on the specific path taken from the initial to the final state.

 GIVE IT SOME THOUGHT

In what ways is the balance in your checkbook a state function?

5.3 | ENTHALPY

The chemical and physical changes that occur around us, such as photosynthesis in the leaves of a plant, evaporation of water from a lake, or a reaction in an open beaker in a laboratory, occur under the essentially constant pressure of Earth's atmosphere.* These changes can result in the release or absorption of heat and can be accompanied by work done by or on the system. In exploring these changes, we have a number of experimental means to measure the flow of heat into and out of the system, and we therefore focus much of our discussion on what we can learn from the heat flow. (Of course, in order to apply the first law of thermodynamics to these processes, we still need to account for any work that accompanies the process.)

A system that consists of a gas confined to a container can be characterized by several different properties. Among the most important are the *pressure* of the gas, P, and the *volume* of the container, V. Like internal energy E, both P and V are state functions—they depend only on the current state of the system and not on the path taken to that state.

We can combine these three state functions—E, P, and V—to define a new state function called **enthalpy** (from the Greek *enthalpein*, "to warm"). This new function is particularly useful for discussing heat flow in processes that occur under constant (or nearly constant) pressure. Enthalpy, which we denote by the symbol H, is defined as the internal energy plus the product of the pressure and volume of the system:

$$H = E + PV \tag{5.6}$$

 GIVE IT SOME THOUGHT

Given the definition of enthalpy in Equation 5.6, why must H be a state function?

You might be asking yourself why it is convenient to define a new function H. To answer that question, recall from Equation 5.5 that ΔE involves not only the heat q added to or removed from the system but also the work w done by or on the system. Most commonly, the only kind of work produced by chemical or physical changes open to the atmosphere is the mechanical work associated with a change in volume. For example, when the reaction of zinc metal with hydrochloric acid solution,

$$Zn(s) + 2\,H^+(aq) \longrightarrow Zn^{2+}(aq) + H_2(g) \tag{5.7}$$

*You are probably familiar with the notion of atmospheric pressure from a previous course in chemistry. We will discuss it in detail in Chapter 10. Here we need realize only that the atmosphere exerts a pressure on the surface of Earth that is nearly constant.

GO FIGURE

If the battery is defined as the system, what is the sign on w in part (b)?

Energy lost as both heat and work

Energy lost only as heat

(a)   (b)

Charged battery

Heat

Heat   Work ΔE Energy lost by battery

Discharged battery

▲ **FIGURE 5.10 Internal energy is a state function, but heat and work are not.** (a) A battery shorted out by a wire loses energy to the surroundings only as heat; no work is performed. (b) A battery discharged through a motor loses energy as work (to make the fan turn) and also loses some energy as heat. The value of ΔE is the same for both processes even though the values of q and w in (a) are different from those in (b).

GO FIGURE

If the amount of zinc used in the reaction is increased, will more work be done by the system? Is there additional information you need in order to answer this question?

Increase in volume means system does pressure-volume work

Piston

H₂ gas plus original atmosphere

Zn(s)

HCl(aq)   Zn(s)   HCl(aq)

$$Zn(s) + 2\,H^+(aq) \longrightarrow Zn^{2+}(aq) + H_2(g)$$

▲ **FIGURE 5.11**   A system that does work on its surroundings.

is run at constant pressure in the apparatus illustrated in ▲ **FIGURE 5.11**, the piston moves up or down to maintain a constant pressure in the vessel. If we assume for simplicity that the piston has no mass, the pressure in the apparatus is the same as atmospheric pressure. As the reaction proceeds, H₂ gas forms, and the piston rises. The gas within the flask is thus doing work on the surroundings by lifting the piston against the force of atmospheric pressure.

The work involved in the expansion or compression of gases is called **pressure-volume work** (or *P-V* work). When pressure is constant in a process, as in our preceding example, the sign and magnitude of the pressure-volume work are given by

$$w = -P\,\Delta V \qquad\qquad [5.8]$$

where *P* is pressure and $\Delta V = V_{final} - V_{initial}$ is the change in volume of the system. The negative sign in Equation 5.8 is necessary to conform to the sign conventions of Table 5.1. The pressure *P* is always either a positive number or zero. If the volume of the system expands, then ΔV is positive as well. Because the expanding system does work on the surroundings, *w* is negative—energy leaves the system as work. Notice that if the gas is compressed, ΔV is negative (the volume decreases), and Equation 5.8 indicates that *w* is positive, meaning work is done on the system by the surroundings. The "A Closer Look" box discusses pressure-volume work in detail, but all you need to keep in mind for now is Equation 5.8, which applies to processes occurring at constant pressure.

 GIVE IT SOME THOUGHT

If a system does not change its volume during the course of a process, does it do pressure-volume work?

Let's now return to our discussion of enthalpy. When a change occurs at constant pressure, the change in enthalpy, ΔH, is given by the relationship

$$\Delta H = \Delta(E + PV)$$
$$= \Delta E + P\Delta V \quad \text{(constant pressure)} \qquad [5.9]$$

That is, the change in enthalpy equals the change in internal energy plus the product of the constant pressure times the change in volume.

Recall that $\Delta E = q + w$ (Equation 5.5) and that the work involved in the expansion or compression of a gas is $w = -P\,\Delta V$ (at constant pressure). Substituting $-w$ for $P\,\Delta V$ and $q + w$ for ΔE into Equation 5.9, we have

$$\Delta H = \Delta E + P\,\Delta V = (q_P + w) - w = q_P \qquad [5.10]$$

The subscript P on q indicates that the process occurs at constant pressure. Thus, *the change in enthalpy equals the heat q_P gained or lost at constant pressure.* Because q_P is something we can either measure or readily calculate and because so many physical and chemical changes of interest to us occur at constant pressure, enthalpy is a more useful function for most reactions than is internal energy. In addition, for most reactions the difference in ΔH and ΔE is small because $P\,\Delta V$ is small.

When ΔH is positive (that is, when q_P is positive), the system has gained heat from the surroundings (Table 5.1), which means the process is endothermic. When ΔH is negative, the system has released heat to the surroundings, which means the process is exothermic. To continue the bank analogy of Figure 5.7, under constant pressure an endothermic process deposits energy in the system in the form of heat and an exothermic process withdraws energy in the form of heat (▶ **FIGURE 5.12**).

Because H is a state function, ΔH (which equals q_P) depends only on the initial and final states of the system, not on how the change occurs. At first glance this statement might seem to contradict our discussion in Section 5.2, in which we said that q is *not* a state function. There is no contradiction, however, because the relationship between ΔH and q_P has the special limitations that only *P-V* work is involved and that the pressure is constant.

 GIVE IT SOME THOUGHT

What common laboratory measuring device will we likely always use in experiments that measure enthalpy changes?

Constant pressure maintained in system

$\Delta H > 0$
(Endothermic)

Heat gain

(a)

$\Delta H < 0$
(Exothermic)

Heat loss

(b)

ΔH is amount of heat that flows into or out of system under constant pressure

▲ **FIGURE 5.12 Endothermic and exothermic processes.** (a) An endothermic process ($\Delta H > 0$) deposits heat into the system. (b) An exothermic process ($\Delta H < 0$) withdraws heat from the system.

SAMPLE EXERCISE 5.3 Determining the Sign of ΔH

Indicate the sign of the enthalpy change, ΔH, in these processes carried out under atmospheric pressure and indicate whether each process is endothermic or exothermic: **(a)** An ice cube melts; **(b)** 1 g of butane (C_4H_{10}) is combusted in sufficient oxygen to give complete combustion to CO_2 and H_2O.

SOLUTION

Analyze Our goal is to determine whether ΔH is positive or negative for each process. Because each process occurs at constant pressure, the enthalpy change equals the quantity of heat absorbed or released, $\Delta H = q_P$.

Plan We must predict whether heat is absorbed or released by the system in each process. Processes in which heat is absorbed are endothermic and have a positive sign for ΔH; those in which heat is released are exothermic and have a negative sign for ΔH.

Solve In (a) the water that makes up the ice cube is the system. The ice cube absorbs heat from the surroundings as it melts, so ΔH is positive and the process is endothermic. In (b) the system is the 1 g of butane and the oxygen required to combust it. The combustion of butane in oxygen gives off heat, so ΔH is negative and the process is exothermic.

PRACTICE EXERCISE

Molten gold poured into a mold solidifies at atmospheric pressure. With the gold defined as the system, is the solidification an exothermic or endothermic process?

Answer: In order to solidify, the gold must cool to below its melting temperature. It cools by transferring heat to its surroundings. The air around the sample would feel hot because heat is transferred to it from the molten gold, meaning the process is exothermic.

You may notice that solidification of a liquid is the reverse of the melting we analyzed in the exercise. As we will see, reversing the direction of a process changes the sign of the heat transferred.

A CLOSER LOOK

ENERGY, ENTHALPY, AND *P-V* WORK

In chemistry we are interested mainly in two types of work: electrical work and mechanical work done by expanding gases. We focus here on the latter, called pressure-volume, or *P-V*, work. Expanding gases in the cylinder of an automobile engine do *P-V* work on the piston; this work eventually turns the wheels. Expanding gases from an open reaction vessel do *P-V* work on the atmosphere. This work accomplishes nothing in a practical sense, but we must keep track of all work, useful or not, when monitoring energy changes in a system.

Let's consider a gas confined to a cylinder with a movable piston of cross-sectional area A (▼ **FIGURE 5.13**). A downward force F acts on the piston. The *pressure*, P, on the gas is the force per area: $P = F/A$. We assume that the piston is massless and that the only pressure acting on it is the *atmospheric pressure* that is due to Earth's atmosphere, which we assume to be constant.

System does work $w = -P\Delta V$ on surroundings as gas expands, pushing piston up distance Δh

$P = F/A$ $P = F/A$

Δh ΔV

Volume change

Gas enclosed in cylinder

Initial state   Cross-sectional area $= A$ Final state

▲ **FIGURE 5.13 Pressure-volume work.** The amount of work done by the system on the surroundings is $w = -P\Delta V$.

Suppose the gas expands and the piston moves a distance Δh. From Equation 5.3, the magnitude of the work done by the system is

$$\text{Magnitude of work} = \text{force} \times \text{distance} = F \times \Delta h \quad [5.11]$$

We can rearrange the definition of pressure, $P = F/A$, to $F = P \times A$. The volume change, ΔV, resulting from the movement of the piston is the product of the cross-sectional area of the piston and the distance it moves: $\Delta V = A \times \Delta h$. Substituting into Equation 5.11 gives

$$\text{Magnitude of work} = F \times \Delta h = P \times A \times \Delta h$$
$$= P \times \Delta V$$

Because the system (the confined gas) does work on the surroundings, the work is a negative quantity:

$$w = -P\,\Delta V \quad [5.12]$$

Now, if *P-V* work is the only work that can be done, we can substitute Equation 5.12 into Equation 5.5 to give

$$\Delta E = q + w = q - P\,\Delta V \quad [5.13]$$

When a reaction is carried out in a constant-volume container ($\Delta V = 0$), therefore, the heat transferred equals the change in internal energy:

$$\Delta E = q - P\Delta V = q - P(0) = q_V \quad \text{(constant volume)} \quad [5.14]$$

The subscript V indicates that the volume is constant.

Most reactions are run under constant pressure, so that Equation 5.13 becomes

$$\Delta E = q_P - P\,\Delta V$$
$$q_P = \Delta E + P\,\Delta V \quad \text{(constant pressure)} \quad [5.15]$$

We see from Equation 5.9 that the right side of Equation 5.15 is the enthalpy change under constant-pressure conditions. Thus, $\Delta H = q_P$, as we saw in Equation 5.10.

In summary, the change in internal energy is equal to the heat gained or lost at constant volume, and the change in enthalpy is equal to the heat gained or lost at constant pressure. The difference between ΔE and ΔH is the amount of *P-V* work done by the system when the process occurs at constant pressure, $-P\,\Delta V$. The volume change accompanying many reactions is close to zero, which makes $P\,\Delta V$ and, therefore, the difference between ΔE and ΔH small. Under most circumstances, it is generally satisfactory to use ΔH as the measure of energy changes during most chemical processes.

RELATED EXERCISES: 5.35, 5.36, 5.37, 5.38

5.4 | ENTHALPIES OF REACTION

Because $\Delta H = H_{\text{final}} - H_{\text{initial}}$, the enthalpy change for a chemical reaction is given by

$$\Delta H = H_{\text{products}} - H_{\text{reactants}} \quad [5.16]$$

The enthalpy change that accompanies a reaction is called either the **enthalpy of reaction** or the *heat of reaction* and is sometimes written ΔH_{rxn}, where "rxn" is a commonly used abbreviation for "reaction."

When we give a numerical value for ΔH_{rxn}, we must specify the reaction involved. For example, when 2 mol $H_2(g)$ burn to form 2 mol $H_2O(g)$ at a constant pressure, the system releases 483.6 kJ of heat. We can summarize this information as

$$2\,H_2(g) + O_2(g) \longrightarrow 2\,H_2O(g) \qquad \Delta H = -483.6\,\text{kJ} \quad [5.17]$$

◄ **FIGURE 5.14** **Exothermic reaction of hydrogen with oxygen.** When a mixture of $H_2(g)$ and $O_2(g)$ is ignited to form $H_2O(g)$, the resultant explosion produces a ball of flame. Because the system releases heat to the surroundings, the reaction is exothermic as indicated in the enthalpy diagram.

Explosion and flame indicate system releases heat to surroundings

O_2

H_2O

H_2

$H_2(g) + O_2(g)$

Violent reaction to form $H_2O(g)$

Enthalpy

$2 H_2(g) + O_2(g)$

$\Delta H < 0$ (exothermic)

$2 H_2O(g)$

$$2 H_2(g) + O_2(g) \longrightarrow 2 H_2O(g)$$

The negative sign for ΔH tells us that this reaction is exothermic. Notice that ΔH is reported at the end of the balanced equation, without explicitly specifying the amounts of chemicals involved. In such cases the coefficients in the balanced equation represent the number of moles of reactants and products producing the associated enthalpy change. Balanced chemical equations that show the associated enthalpy change in this way are called *thermochemical equations*.

The exothermic nature of this reaction is also shown in the *enthalpy diagram* in ▲ **FIGURE 5.14**. Notice that the enthalpy of the reactants is greater (more positive) than the enthalpy of the products. Thus, $\Delta H = H_{products} - H_{reactants}$ is negative.

▲ GIVE IT SOME THOUGHT

If the reaction to form water were written $H_2(g) + \frac{1}{2} O_2(g) \longrightarrow H_2O(g)$, would you expect the same value of ΔH as in Equation 5.17? Why or why not?

The reaction of hydrogen with oxygen is highly exothermic and occurs rapidly once it starts. It can occur with explosive violence, as demonstrated by the explosions of the German airship *Hindenburg* in 1937 (▼ **FIGURE 5.15**) and the U.S. space shuttle *Challenger* in 1986.

◄ **FIGURE 5.15** **The burning of the hydrogen-filled airship *Hindenburg*.** This tragedy, in Lakehurst, New Jersey, on May 6, 1937, led to the discontinuation of hydrogen as a buoyant gas in such craft. Modern-day airships are filled with helium, which is not as buoyant as hydrogen but is not flammable.

$$CH_4(g) + 2\,O_2(g)$$

$\Delta H_1 = -890\text{ kJ}$ $\Delta H_2 = 890\text{ kJ}$

$$CO_2(g) + 2\,H_2O(l)$$

Enthalpy →

▲ **FIGURE 5.16 ΔH for a reverse reaction.** Reversing a reaction changes the sign but not the magnitude of the enthalpy change: $\Delta H_2 = -\Delta H_1$.

The following guidelines are helpful when using thermochemical equations and enthalpy diagrams:

1. **Enthalpy is an extensive property.** The magnitude of ΔH is proportional to the amount of reactant consumed in the process. For example, 890 kJ of heat is produced when 1 mol of CH_4 is burned in a constant-pressure system:

$$CH_4(g) + 2\,O_2(g) \longrightarrow CO_2(g) + 2\,H_2O(l) \qquad \Delta H = -890\text{ kJ} \qquad [5.18]$$

Because the combustion of 1 mol of CH_4 with 2 mol of O_2 releases 890 kJ of heat, the combustion of 2 mol of CH_4 with 4 mol of O_2 releases twice as much heat, 1780 kJ.

2. **The enthalpy change for a reaction is equal in magnitude, but opposite in sign, to ΔH for the reverse reaction.** For example, ΔH for the reverse of Equation 5.18 is +890 kJ:

$$CO_2(g) + 2\,H_2O(l) \longrightarrow CH_4(g) + 2\,O_2(g) \qquad \Delta H = +890\text{ kJ} \qquad [5.19]$$

When we reverse a reaction, we reverse the roles of the products and the reactants. From Equation 5.16, we see that reversing the products and reactants leads to the same magnitude of ΔH but a change in sign (◀ **FIGURE 5.16**).

3. **The enthalpy change for a reaction depends on the states of the reactants and products.** If the product in Equation 5.18 were $H_2O(g)$ instead of $H_2O(l)$, ΔH_{rxn} would be −802 kJ instead of −890 kJ. Less heat would be available for transfer to the surroundings because the enthalpy of $H_2O(g)$ is greater than that of $H_2O(l)$. One way to see this is to imagine that the product is initially liquid water. The liquid water must be converted to water vapor, and the conversion of 2 mol $H_2O(l)$ to 2 mol $H_2O(g)$ is an endothermic process that absorbs 88 kJ:

$$2\,H_2O(l) \longrightarrow 2\,H_2O(g) \qquad \Delta H = +88\text{ kJ} \qquad [5.20]$$

Thus, it is important to specify the states of the reactants and products in thermochemical equations. In addition, we will generally assume that the reactants and products are both at the same temperature, 25 °C, unless otherwise indicated.

SAMPLE EXERCISE 5.4   **Relating ΔH to Quantities of Reactants and Products**

How much heat is released when 4.50 g of methane gas is burned in a constant-pressure system? (Use the information given in Equation 5.18.)

SOLUTION

Analyze Our goal is to use a thermochemical equation to calculate the heat produced when a specific amount of methane gas is combusted. According to Equation 5.18, 890 kJ is released by the system when 1 mol CH_4 is burned at constant pressure.

Plan Equation 5.18 provides us with a stoichiometric conversion factor: (1 mol $CH_4 \doteq -890$ kJ). Thus, we can convert moles of CH_4 to kJ of energy. First, however, we must convert grams of CH_4 to moles of CH_4. Thus, the conversion sequence is grams CH_4 (given) → moles CH_4 → kJ (unknown to be found).

Solve By adding the atomic weights of C and 4 H, we have 1 mol $CH_4 = 16.0$ CH_4. We can use the appropriate conversion factors to convert grams of CH_4 to moles of CH_4 to kilojoules:

$$\text{Heat} = (4.50\text{ g }CH_4)\left(\frac{1\text{ mol }CH_4}{16.0\text{ g }CH_4}\right)\left(\frac{-890\text{ kJ}}{1\text{ mol }CH_4}\right) = -250\text{ kJ}$$

The negative sign indicates that the system released 250 kJ into the surroundings.

PRACTICE EXERCISE

Hydrogen peroxide can decompose to water and oxygen by the reaction

$$2\,H_2O_2(l) \longrightarrow 2\,H_2O(l) + O_2(g) \qquad \Delta H = -196\text{ kJ}$$

Calculate the quantity of heat released when 5.00 g of $H_2O_2(l)$ decomposes at constant pressure.
Answer: −14.4 kJ

STRATEGIES IN CHEMISTRY

USING ENTHALPY AS A GUIDE

If you hold a brick in the air and let it go, you know what happens: It falls as the force of gravity pulls it toward Earth. A process that is thermodynamically favored to happen, such as a brick falling to the ground, is called a *spontaneous* process. A spontaneous process can be either fast or slow; the rate at which processes occur is not governed by thermodynamics.

Chemical processes can be thermodynamically favored, or spontaneous, too. By spontaneous, however, we do not mean that the reaction will form products without any intervention. That can be the case, but often some energy must be imparted to get the process started. The enthalpy change in a reaction gives one indication as to whether the reaction is likely to be spontaneous. The combustion of $H_2(g)$ and $O_2(g)$, for example, is highly exothermic:

$$H_2(g) + \tfrac{1}{2} O_2(g) \longrightarrow H_2O(g) \qquad \Delta H = -242 \text{ kJ}$$

Hydrogen gas and oxygen gas can exist together in a volume indefinitely without noticeable reaction occurring. Once the reaction is initiated, however, energy is rapidly transferred from the system (the reactants) to the surroundings as heat. The system thus loses enthalpy by transferring the heat to the surroundings. (Recall that the first law of thermodynamics tells us that the total energy of the system plus the surroundings does not change; energy is conserved.)

Enthalpy change is not the only consideration in the spontaneity of reactions, however, nor is it a foolproof guide. For example, even though ice melting is an endothermic process,

$$H_2O(s) \longrightarrow H_2O(l) \qquad \Delta H = +6.01 \text{ kJ}$$

this process is spontaneous at temperatures above the freezing point of water (0 °C). The reverse process, water freezing, is spontaneous at temperatures below 0 °C. Thus, we know that ice at room temperature melts and water put into a freezer at −20 °C turns into ice. Both processes are spontaneous under different conditions even though they are the reverse of one another. In Chapter 19 we will address the spontaneity of processes more fully. We will see why a process can be spontaneous at one temperature but not at another, as is the case for the conversion of water to ice.

Despite these complicating factors, you should pay attention to the enthalpy changes in reactions. As a general observation, when the enthalpy change is large, it is the dominant factor in determining spontaneity. Thus, reactions for which ΔH is *large* and *negative* tend to be spontaneous. Reactions for which ΔH is *large* and *positive* tend to be spontaneous only in the reverse direction.

RELATED EXERCISES. 5.47, 5.48

In many situations we will find it valuable to know the sign and magnitude of the enthalpy change associated with a given chemical process. As we see in the following sections, ΔH can be either determined directly by experiment or calculated from known enthalpy changes of other reactions.

5.5 | CALORIMETRY

The value of ΔH can be determined experimentally by measuring the heat flow accompanying a reaction at constant pressure. Typically, we can determine the magnitude of the heat flow by measuring the magnitude of the temperature change the heat flow produces. The measurement of heat flow is **calorimetry**; a device used to measure heat flow is a **calorimeter**.

Heat Capacity and Specific Heat

The more heat an object gains, the hotter it gets. All substances change temperature when they are heated, but the magnitude of the temperature change produced by a given quantity of heat varies from substance to substance. The temperature change experienced by an object when it absorbs a certain amount of heat is determined by its **heat capacity**, denoted C. The heat capacity of an object is the amount of heat required to raise its temperature by 1 K (or 1 °C). The greater the heat capacity, the greater the heat required to produce a given increase in temperature.

For pure substances the heat capacity is usually given for a specified amount of the substance. The heat capacity of one mole of a substance is called its **molar heat capacity**, C_m. The heat capacity of one gram of a substance is called its *specific heat capacity,* or merely its **specific heat**. The specific heat, C_s, of a substance can be determined experimentally by

Is the process shown in the figure endothermic or exothermic?

▲ **FIGURE 5.17** **Specific heat of water.**

measuring the temperature change, ΔT, that a known mass m of the substance undergoes when it gains or loses a specific quantity of heat q:

$$\text{Specific heat} = \frac{\text{(quantity of heat transferred)}}{\text{(grams of substance)} \times \text{(temperature change)}}$$

$$C_s = \frac{q}{m \times \Delta T} \qquad [5.21]$$

For example, 209 J is required to increase the temperature of 50.0 g of water by 1.00 K. Thus, the specific heat of water is

$$C_s = \frac{209 \text{ J}}{(50.0 \text{ g})(1.00 \text{ K})} = 4.18 \text{ J/g-K}$$

A temperature change in kelvins is equal in magnitude to the temperature change in degrees Celsius: ΔT in $K = \Delta T$ in °C. ∞ (Section 1.4) Therefore, this specific heat for water can also be reported as 4.18 J/g-°C.

Because the specific heat values for a given substance can vary slightly with temperature, the temperature is often precisely specified. The 4.18 J/g-K value we use here for water, for instance, is for water initially at 14.5 °C (◄ FIGURE 5.17). Water's specific heat at this temperature is used to define the calorie at the value given in Section 5.1: 1 cal = 4.184 J exactly.

When a sample absorbs heat (positive q), its temperature increases (positive ΔT). Rearranging Equation 5.21, we get

$$q = C_s \times m \times \Delta T \qquad [5.22]$$

Thus, we can calculate the quantity of heat a substance gains or loses by using its specific heat together with its measured mass and temperature change.

▼ TABLE 5.2 lists the specific heats of several substances. Notice that the specific heat of liquid water is higher than those of the other substances listed. The high specific heat of water affects Earth's climate because it makes the temperatures of the oceans relatively resistant to change.

GIVE IT SOME THOUGHT

Which substance in Table 5.2 undergoes the greatest temperature change when the same mass of each substance absorbs the same quantity of heat?

TABLE 5.2 • **Specific Heats of Some Substances at 298 K**

Elements		Compounds	
Substance	Specific Heat (J/g-K)	Substance	Specific Heat (J/g-K)
$N_2(g)$	1.04	$H_2O(l)$	4.18
$Al(s)$	0.90	$CH_4(g)$	2.20
$Fe(s)$	0.45	$CO_2(g)$	0.84
$Hg(l)$	0.14	$CaCO_3(s)$	0.82

SAMPLE EXERCISE 5.5 **Relating Heat, Temperature Change, and Heat Capacity**

(a) How much heat is needed to warm 250 g of water (about 1 cup) from 22 °C (about room temperature) to 98 °C (near its boiling point)? **(b)** What is the molar heat capacity of water?

SOLUTION

Analyze In part **(a)** we must find the quantity of heat (q) needed to warm the water, given the mass of water (m), its temperature change (ΔT), and its specific heat (C_s). In part **(b)** we must calculate

the molar heat capacity (heat capacity per mole, C_m) of water from its specific heat (heat capacity per gram).

Plan (a) Given C_s, m, and ΔT, we can calculate the quantity of heat, q, using Equation 5.22. (b) We can use the molar mass of water and dimensional analysis to convert from heat capacity per gram to heat capacity per mole.

Solve

(a) The water undergoes a temperature change of

$$\Delta T = 98\,^\circ\text{C} - 22\,^\circ\text{C} = 76\,^\circ\text{C} = 76\,\text{K}$$

Using Equation 5.22, we have

$$q = C_s \times m \times \Delta T$$
$$= (4.18\,\text{J/g-K})(250\,\text{g})(76\,\text{K}) = 7.9 \times 10^4\,\text{J}$$

(b) The molar heat capacity is the heat capacity of one mole of substance. Using the atomic weights of hydrogen and oxygen, we have

$$1\,\text{mol H}_2\text{O} = 18.0\,\text{g H}_2\text{O}$$

From the specific heat given in part (a), we have

$$C_m = \left(4.18\,\frac{\text{J}}{\text{g-K}}\right)\left(\frac{18.0\,\text{g}}{1\,\text{mol}}\right) = 75.2\,\text{J/mol-K}$$

PRACTICE EXERCISE

(a) Large beds of rocks are used in some solar-heated homes to store heat. Assume that the specific heat of the rocks is 0.82 J/g-K. Calculate the quantity of heat absorbed by 50.0 kg of rocks if their temperature increases by 12.0 °C. (b) What temperature change would these rocks undergo if they emitted 450 kJ of heat?

Answers: (a) 4.9×10^5 J, (b) 11 K decrease = 11 °C decrease

Constant-Pressure Calorimetry

The techniques and equipment employed in calorimetry depend on the nature of the process being studied. For many reactions, such as those occurring in solution, it is easy to control pressure so that ΔH is measured directly. Although the calorimeters used for highly accurate work are precision instruments, a simple "coffee-cup" calorimeter (▶ FIGURE 5.18) is often used in general chemistry laboratories to illustrate the principles of calorimetry. Because the calorimeter is not sealed, the reaction occurs under the essentially constant pressure of the atmosphere.

Imagine adding two aqueous solutions, each containing a reactant, to a coffee-cup calorimeter. Once mixed, the reactants can react to form products. In this case there is no physical boundary between the system and the surroundings. The reactants and products of the reaction are the system, and the water in which they are dissolved is part of the surroundings. (The calorimeter apparatus is also part of the surroundings.) If we assume that the calorimeter is perfectly insulated, then any heat released or absorbed by the reaction will raise or lower the temperature of the water in the solution. Thus, we measure the temperature change of the solution and assume that any changes are due to heat transferred from the reaction to the water (for an exothermic process) or transferred from the water to the reaction (endothermic). In other words, by monitoring the temperature of the solution, we are seeing the flow of heat between the system (the reactants and products in the solution) and the surroundings (the water that forms the bulk of the solution).

For an exothermic reaction, heat is "lost" by the reaction and "gained" by the water in the solution, so the temperature of the solution rises. The opposite occurs for an endothermic reaction: Heat is gained by the reaction and lost by the water in the solution, and the temperature of the solution decreases. The heat gained or lost by the solution, q_{soln}, is therefore equal in magnitude but opposite in sign to the heat absorbed or released by the reaction, q_{rxn}: $q_{\text{soln}} = -q_{\text{rxn}}$. The value of q_{soln} is readily calculated from the mass of the solution, its specific heat, and the temperature change:

$$q_{\text{soln}} = (\text{specific heat of solution}) \times (\text{grams of solution}) \times \Delta T = -q_{\text{rxn}} \quad [5.23]$$

For dilute aqueous solutions we usually assume that the specific heat of the solution is the same as that of water, 4.18 J/g-K.

Equation 5.23 makes it possible to calculate q_{rxn} from the temperature change of the solution in which the reaction occurs. A temperature increase ($\Delta T > 0$) means the reaction is exothermic ($q_{\text{rxn}} < 0$).

△ **GO FIGURE**

Propose a reason for why two Styrofoam® cups are often used instead of just one.

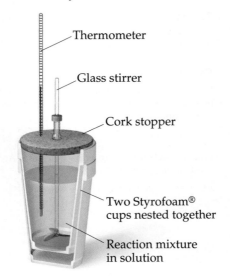

Thermometer

Glass stirrer

Cork stopper

Two Styrofoam® cups nested together

Reaction mixture in solution

▲ **FIGURE 5.18 Coffee-cup calorimeter.** This simple apparatus is used to measure temperature changes of reactions at constant pressure.

SAMPLE EXERCISE 5.6 | **Measuring ΔH Using a Coffee-Cup Calorimeter**

When a student mixes 50 mL of 1.0 M HCl and 50 mL of 1.0 M NaOH in a coffee-cup calorimeter, the temperature of the resultant solution increases from 21.0 °C to 27.5 °C. Calculate the enthalpy change for the reaction in kJ/mol HCl, assuming that the calorimeter loses only a negligible quantity of heat, that the total volume of the solution is 100 mL, that its density is 1.0 g/mL, and that its specific heat is 4.18 J/g-K.

SOLUTION

Analyze Mixing solutions of HCl and NaOH results in an acid–base reaction:

$$HCl(aq) + NaOH(aq) \longrightarrow H_2O(l) + NaCl(aq)$$

We need to calculate the heat produced per mole of HCl, given the temperature increase of the solution, the number of moles of HCl and NaOH involved, and the density and specific heat of the solution.

Plan The total heat produced can be calculated using Equation 5.23. The number of moles of HCl consumed in the reaction must be calculated from the volume and molarity of this substance, and this amount is then used to determine the heat produced per mol HCl.

Solve

Because the total volume of the solution is 100 mL, its mass is	$(100 \text{ mL})(1.0 \text{ g/mL}) = 100 \text{ g}$
The temperature change is	$\Delta T = 27.5 \text{ °C} - 21.0 \text{ °C} = 6.5 \text{ °C} = 6.5 \text{ K}$
Using Equation 5.23, we have	$q_{rxn} = -C_s \times m \times \Delta T$
	$\quad = -(4.18 \text{ J/g-K})(100 \text{ g})(6.5 \text{ K}) = -2.7 \times 10^3 \text{ J} = -2.7 \text{ kJ}$
Because the process occurs at constant pressure,	$\Delta H = q_P = -2.7 \text{ kJ}$
To express the enthalpy change on a molar basis, we use the fact that the number of moles of HCl is given by the product of the volume (50 mL = 0.050 L) and concentration (1.0 M = 1.0 mol/L) of the HCl solution:	$(0.050 \text{ L})(1.0 \text{ mol/L}) = 0.050 \text{ mol}$
Thus, the enthalpy change per mole of HCl is	$\Delta H = -2.7 \text{ kJ}/0.050 \text{ mol} = -54 \text{ kJ/mol}$

Check ΔH is negative (exothermic), which is expected for the reaction of an acid with a base and evidenced by the fact that the reaction causes the temperature of the solution to increase. The magnitude of the molar enthalpy change seems reasonable.

PRACTICE EXERCISE

When 50.0 mL of 0.100 M AgNO₃ and 50.0 mL of 0.100 M HCl are mixed in a constant-pressure calorimeter, the temperature of the mixture increases from 22.30 °C to 23.11 °C. The temperature increase is caused by the following reaction:

$$AgNO_3(aq) + HCl(aq) \longrightarrow AgCl(s) + HNO_3(aq)$$

Calculate ΔH for this reaction in kJ/mol AgNO₃, assuming that the combined solution has a mass of 100.0 g and a specific heat of 4.18 J/g °C.
Answer: −68,000 J/mol = −68 kJ/mol

Bomb Calorimetry (Constant-Volume Calorimetry)

An important type of reaction studied using calorimetry is combustion, in which a compound reacts completely with excess oxygen. ∞ (Section 3.2) Combustion reactions are most accurately studied using a **bomb calorimeter** (▶ FIGURE 5.19). The substance to be studied is placed in a small cup within an insulated sealed vessel called a *bomb*. The bomb, which is designed to withstand high pressures, has an inlet valve for adding oxygen and electrical leads. After the sample has been placed in the bomb, the bomb is sealed and pressurized with oxygen. It is then placed in the calorimeter and covered with an accurately measured quantity of water. The combustion reaction is initiated by passing an electrical current through a fine wire in contact with the sample. When the wire becomes sufficiently hot, the sample ignites.

The heat released when combustion occurs is absorbed by the water and the various components of the calorimeter (which all together make up the surroundings), causing the water temperature to rise. The change in water temperature caused by the reaction is measured very precisely.

To calculate the heat of combustion from the measured temperature increase, we must know the total heat capacity of the calorimeter, C_{cal}. This quantity is determined by combusting a sample that releases a known quantity of heat and measuring the temperature change. For example, combustion of exactly 1 g of benzoic acid, C_6H_5COOH, in a bomb calorimeter produces 26.38 kJ of heat. Suppose 1.000 g of benzoic acid is combusted in a calorimeter, leading to a temperature increase of 4.857 °C. The heat capacity of the calorimeter is then $C_{cal} = 26.38 \text{ kJ}/4.857 \text{ °C} = 5.431 \text{ kJ/°C}$. Once we know C_{cal}, we can measure temperature changes produced by other reactions, and from these we can calculate the heat evolved in the reaction, q_{rxn}:

$$q_{rxn} = -C_{cal} \times \Delta T \qquad [5.24]$$

Measurements made with a bomb calorimeter are generally more precise than those made with a coffee-cup calorimeter.

△ **GO FIGURE**

Why is a stirrer used in calorimeters?

Stirrer

Sample ignition wi:

Thermome

Insulated container

Bomb (reac chamber)

Water

Sample

▲ **FIGURE 5.19** Bomb calorimeter.

SAMPLE EXERCISE 5.7 | Measuring q_{rxn} Using a Bomb Calorimeter

The combustion of methylhydrazine (CH_6N_2), a liquid rocket fuel, produces $N_2(g)$, $CO_2(g)$, and $H_2O(l)$:

$$2 \text{ CH}_6\text{N}_2(l) + 5 \text{ O}_2(g) \longrightarrow 2 \text{ N}_2(g) + 2 \text{ CO}_2(g) + 6 \text{ H}_2\text{O}(l)$$

When 4.00 g of methylhydrazine is combusted in a bomb calorimeter, the temperature of the calorimeter increases from 25.00 °C to 39.50 °C. In a separate experiment the heat capacity of the calorimeter is measured to be 7.794 kJ/°C. Calculate the heat of reaction for the combustion of a mole of CH_6N_2.

SOLUTION

Analyze We are given a temperature change and the total heat capacity of the calorimeter. We are also given the amount of reactant combusted. Our goal is to calculate the enthalpy change per mole for combustion of the reactant.

Plan We will first calculate the heat evolved for the combustion of the 4.00-g sample. We will then convert this heat to a molar quantity.

Solve

For combustion of the 4.00-g sample of methylhydrazine, the temperature change of the calorimeter is

$$\Delta T = (39.50 \text{ °C} - 25.00 \text{ °C}) = 14.50 \text{ °C}$$

We can use ΔT and the value for C_{cal} to calculate the heat of reaction (Equation 5.24):

$$q_{rxn} = -C_{cal} \times \Delta T = -(7.794 \text{ kJ/°C})(14.50 \text{ °C}) = -113.0 \text{ kJ}$$

We can readily convert this value to the heat of reaction for a mole of CH_6N_2:

$$\left(\frac{-113.0 \text{ kJ}}{4.00 \text{ g CH}_6\text{N}_2}\right) \times \left(\frac{46.1 \text{ g CH}_6\text{N}_2}{1 \text{ mol CH}_6\text{N}_2}\right) = -1.30 \times 10^3 \text{ kJ/mol CH}_6\text{N}_2$$

Check The units cancel properly, and the sign of the answer is negative as it should be for an exothermic reaction. The magnitude of the answer seems reasonable.

PRACTICE EXERCISE

A 0.5865-g sample of lactic acid ($HC_3H_5O_3$) is burned in a calorimeter whose heat capacity is 4.812 kJ/°C. The temperature increases from 23.10 °C to 24.95 °C. Calculate the heat of combustion of lactic acid **(a)** per gram and **(b)** per mole.

Answers: **(a)** −15.2 kJ/g, **(b)** −1370 kJ/mol

Because reactions in a bomb calorimeter are carried out at constant volume, the heat transferred corresponds to the change in internal energy, ΔE, rather than the change in enthalpy, ΔH (Equation 5.14). For most reactions, however, the difference between ΔE and ΔH is very small. For the reaction discussed in Sample Exercise 5.7, for example, the difference between ΔE and ΔH is about 1 kJ/mol—a difference of less than 0.1%. It is possible to correct the measured heat changes to obtain ΔH values, and these form the basis of the tables of enthalpy used in the following sections. We need not concern ourselves with how these small corrections are made.

CHEMISTRY AND LIFE

THE REGULATION OF BODY TEMPERATURE

For most of us, being asked the question "Are you running a fever?" was one of our first introductions to medical diagnosis. Indeed, a deviation in body temperature of only a few degrees indicates something amiss. In the laboratory you may have observed how difficult it is to maintain a solution at a constant temperature. Yet our bodies maintain a near-constant temperature in spite of widely varying weather, levels of physical activity, and periods of high metabolic activity (such as after a meal).

Maintaining a near-constant temperature is one of the primary physiological functions of the human body. Normal body temperature generally ranges from 35.8 °C to 37.2 °C (96.5 °F to 99 °F). This very narrow range is essential to proper muscle function and to control of the rates of the biochemical reactions in the body. You will learn more about the effects of temperature on reaction rates in Chapter 14.

The portion of the human brain stem called the *hypothalamus* regulates body temperature—in essence, the hypothalamus acts as a thermostat for the body. When body temperature rises above the normal range, the hypothalamus triggers mechanisms to lower the temperature. It likewise triggers mechanisms to increase the temperature if body temperature drops too low.

To understand how the body's heating and cooling mechanisms operate, we can view the body as a thermodynamic system. The body increases its internal energy content by ingesting foods from the surroundings. The foods, such as glucose ($C_6H_{12}O_6$), are metabolized—a process that is essentially controlled oxidation to CO_2 and H_2O:

$$C_6H_{12}O_6(s) + 6\,O_2(g) \longrightarrow 6\,CO_2(g) + 6\,H_2O(l)$$

$$\Delta H = -2803 \text{ kJ}$$

Roughly 40% of the energy produced is ultimately used to do work in the form of muscle contractions and nerve cell activities. The remainder is released as heat, part of which is used to maintain body temperature. When the body produces too much heat, as in times of heavy physical exertion, it dissipates the excess to the surroundings.

Heat is transferred from the body to its surroundings primarily by *radiation, convection,* and *evaporation.* Radiation is the direct loss of heat from the body to cooler surroundings, much as a hot stovetop radiates heat to its surroundings. Convection is heat loss by virtue of heating air that is in contact with the body. The heated air rises and is replaced with cooler air, and the process continues. Warm clothing, which usually consists of insulating layers of material with "dead air" in between, decreases convective heat loss in cold weather. Evaporative cooling occurs when perspiration is generated at the skin surface by the sweat glands (▶ FIGURE 5.20). Heat is removed from the body as the perspiration evaporates into the surroundings. Perspira-

▲ FIGURE 5.20 **Perspiration!**

tion is predominantly water, so the process is the endothermic conversion of liquid water into water vapor:

$$H_2O(l) \longrightarrow H_2O(g) \qquad \Delta H = +44.0 \text{ kJ}$$

The speed with which evaporative cooling occurs decreases as the atmospheric humidity increases, which is why we feel more sweaty and uncomfortable on hot, humid days.

When the hypothalamus senses that body temperature has risen too high, it increases heat loss from the body in two principal ways. First, it increases blood flow near the skin surface, which allows for increased radiational and convective cooling. The reddish, "flushed" appearance of a hot individual is the result of this increased subsurface blood flow. Second, the hypothalamus stimulates secretion of perspiration from the sweat glands, which increases evaporative cooling. During extreme activity, the amount of liquid secreted as perspiration can be as high as 2 to 4 liters per hour. As a result, the body's water supply must be replenished during these periods. If the body loses too much liquid through perspiration, it will no longer be able to cool itself and blood volume decreases, which can lead to either *heat exhaustion* or the more serious and potentially fatal *heat stroke,* during which the body temperature can rise to as high as 41 °C to 45 °C (106 °F to 113 °F). However, replenishing water without replenishing the electrolytes lost during perspiration can also lead to serious problems, as pointed out in the "Chemistry and Life" box in Section 4.5.

When body temperature drops too low, the hypothalamus decreases blood flow to the skin surface, thereby decreasing heat loss. It also triggers small involuntary contractions of the muscles; the biochemical reactions that generate the energy to do this work also generate heat for the body. When these contractions get large enough—as when the body feels a chill—a *shiver* results. If the body is unable to maintain a temperature above 35 °C (95 °F), the very dangerous condition called *hypothermia* can result.

The ability of the human body to maintain its temperature by "tuning" the amount of heat it transfers to and from its surroundings is truly remarkable. If you take courses in human anatomy and physiology, you will see many other applications of thermochemistry and thermodynamics to the ways in which the human body works.

5.6 | HESS'S LAW

It is often possible to calculate the ΔH for a reaction from the tabulated ΔH values of other reactions. Thus, it is not necessary to make calorimetric measurements for all reactions.

Because enthalpy is a state function, the enthalpy change, ΔH, associated with any chemical process depends only on the amount of matter that undergoes change and on the nature of the initial state of the reactants and the final state of the products. This means that whether a particular reaction is carried out in one step or in a series of steps, the sum of the enthalpy changes associated with the individual steps must be the same as the enthalpy change associated with the one-step process. As an example, combustion of methane gas, $CH_4(g)$, to form $CO_2(g)$ and $H_2O(l)$ can be thought of as occurring in one step, as represented on the left in ▶ **FIGURE 5.21**, or in two steps, as represented on the right in Figure 5.21: (1) combustion of $CH_4(g)$ to form $CO_2(g)$ and $H_2O(g)$ and (2) condensation of $H_2O(g)$ to form $H_2O(l)$. The enthalpy change for the overall process is the sum of the enthalpy changes for these two steps:

$$CH_4(g) + 2\,O_2(g) \longrightarrow CO_2(g) + 2\,H_2O(g) \qquad \Delta H = -802 \text{ kJ}$$

(Add) $\qquad\qquad 2\,H_2O(g) \longrightarrow 2\,H_2O(l) \qquad\qquad\qquad \Delta H = -\ 88 \text{ kJ}$

$$CH_4(g) + 2\,O_2(g) + 2\,H_2O(g) \longrightarrow CO_2(g) + 2\,H_2O(l) + 2\,H_2O(g)$$

$$\Delta H = -890 \text{ kJ}$$

The net equation is

$$CH_4(g) + 2\,O_2(g) \longrightarrow CO_2(g) + 2\,H_2O(l) \qquad \Delta H = -890 \text{ kJ}$$

Hess's law states that *if a reaction is carried out in a series of steps, ΔH for the overall reaction equals the sum of the enthalpy changes for the individual steps.* The overall enthalpy change for the process is independent of the number of steps and independent of the path by which the reaction is carried out. This law is a consequence of the fact that enthalpy is a state function. We can therefore calculate ΔH for any process as long as we find a route for which ΔH is known for each step. This means that a relatively small number of experimental measurements can be used to calculate ΔH for a vast number of reactions.

Hess's law provides a useful means of calculating energy changes that are difficult to measure directly. For instance, it is impossible to measure directly the enthalpy for the combustion of carbon to form carbon monoxide. Combustion of 1 mol of carbon with 0.5 mol of O_2 produces both CO and CO_2, leaving some carbon unreacted. However, solid carbon and carbon monoxide can both be completely burned in O_2 to produce CO_2. We can therefore use the enthalpy changes of these reactions to calculate the heat of combustion of carbon.

 GIVE IT SOME THOUGHT

What effect do these changes have on ΔH for a reaction:
a. reversing the reaction,
b. multiplying the coefficients of the equation for the reaction by 2?

What process corresponds to the -88 kJ enthalpy change?

▲ **FIGURE 5.21   Enthalpy diagram for combustion of 1 mol of methane.** The enthalpy change of the one-step reaction equals the sum of the enthalpy changes of the reaction run in two steps: -890 kJ $= -802$ kJ $+ (-88$ kJ$)$.

| **SAMPLE EXERCISE 5.8** | Using Hess's Law to Calculate ΔH |

The enthalpy of reaction for the combustion of C to CO_2 is -393.5 kJ/mol C, and the enthalpy for the combustion of CO to CO_2 is -283.0 kJ/mol CO:

(1) $\qquad\qquad C(s) + O_2(g) \longrightarrow CO_2(g) \qquad \Delta H = -393.5 \text{ kJ}$

(2) $\qquad\qquad CO(g) + \frac{1}{2}O_2(g) \longrightarrow CO_2(g) \qquad \Delta H = -283.0 \text{ kJ}$

Using these data, calculate the enthalpy for the combustion of C to CO:

(3) $\qquad\qquad C(s) + \frac{1}{2}O_2(g) \longrightarrow CO(g) \qquad \Delta H = ?$

SOLUTION

Analyze We are given two thermochemical equations, and our goal is to combine them in such a way as to obtain the third equation and its enthalpy change.

Plan We will use Hess's law. In doing so, we first note the numbers of moles of substances among the reactants and products in the target equation, (3). We then manipulate equations (1) and (2) to give the same number of moles of these substances, so that when the resulting equations are added, we obtain the target equation. At the same time, we keep track of the enthalpy changes, which we add.

Solve To use equations (1) and (2), we arrange them so that $C(s)$ is on the reactant side and $CO(g)$ is on the product side of the arrow, as in the target reaction, equation (3). Because equation (1) has $C(s)$ as a reactant, we can use that equation just as it is. We need to turn equation (2) around, however, so that $CO(g)$ is a product. Remember that when reactions are turned around, the sign of ΔH is reversed. We arrange the two equations so that they can be added to give the desired equation:

$$C(s) + O_2(g) \longrightarrow CO_2(g) \qquad\qquad \Delta H = -393.5 \text{ kJ}$$
$$\underline{CO_2(g) \longrightarrow CO(g) + \tfrac{1}{2}O_2(g) \qquad\qquad -\Delta H = 283.0 \text{ kJ}}$$
$$C(s) + \tfrac{1}{2}O_2(g) \longrightarrow CO(g) \qquad\qquad \Delta H = -110.5 \text{ kJ}$$

When we add the two equations, $CO_2(g)$ appears on both sides of the arrow and therefore cancels out. Likewise, $\tfrac{1}{2}O_2(g)$ is eliminated from each side.

PRACTICE EXERCISE

Carbon occurs in two forms, graphite and diamond. The enthalpy of the combustion of graphite is -393.5 kJ/mol, and that of diamond is -395.4 kJ/mol:

$$C(graphite) + O_2(g) \longrightarrow CO_2(g) \qquad \Delta H = -393.5 \text{ kJ}$$
$$C(diamond) + O_2(g) \longrightarrow CO_2(g) \qquad \Delta H = -395.4 \text{ kJ}$$

Calculate ΔH for the conversion of graphite to diamond:

$$C(graphite) \longrightarrow C(diamond) \qquad \Delta H = \text{?}$$

Answer: $+1.9$ kJ

SAMPLE EXERCISE 5.9 **Using Three Equations with Hess's Law to Calculate ΔH**

Calculate ΔH for the reaction

$$2\,C(s) + H_2(g) \longrightarrow C_2H_2(g)$$

given the following chemical equations and their respective enthalpy changes:

$$C_2H_2(g) + \tfrac{5}{2}O_2(g) \longrightarrow 2\,CO_2(g) + H_2O(l) \qquad \Delta H = -1299.6 \text{ kJ}$$
$$C(s) + O_2(g) \longrightarrow CO_2(g) \qquad\qquad\qquad\quad \Delta H = -393.5 \text{ kJ}$$
$$H_2(g) + \tfrac{1}{2}O_2(g) \longrightarrow H_2O(l) \qquad\qquad\qquad\quad \Delta H = -285.8 \text{ kJ}$$

SOLUTION

Analyze We are given a chemical equation and asked to calculate its ΔH using three chemical equations and their associated enthalpy changes.

Plan We will use Hess's law, summing the three equations or their reverses and multiplying each by an appropriate coefficient so that they add to give the net equation for the reaction of interest. At the same time, we keep track of the ΔH values, reversing their signs if the reactions are reversed and multiplying them by whatever coefficient is employed in the equation.

Solve Because the target equation has C_2H_2 as a product, we turn the first equation around; the sign of ΔH is therefore changed. The desired equation has $2\,C(s)$ as a reactant, so we multiply the second equation and its ΔH by 2. Because the target equation has H_2 as a reactant, we keep the third equation as it is. We then add the three equations and their enthalpy changes in accordance with Hess's law:

$$2\,CO_2(g) + H_2O(l) \longrightarrow C_2H_2(g) + \tfrac{5}{2}O_2(g) \qquad \Delta H = 1299.6 \text{ kJ}$$
$$2\,C(s) + 2\,O_2(g) \longrightarrow 2\,CO_2(g) \qquad\qquad\qquad\quad \Delta H = -787.0 \text{ kJ}$$
$$\underline{H_2(g) + \tfrac{1}{2}O_2(g) \longrightarrow H_2O(l) \qquad\qquad\qquad\quad \Delta H = -285.8 \text{ kJ}}$$
$$2\,C(s) + H_2(g) \longrightarrow C_2H_2(g) \qquad\qquad\qquad\quad \Delta H = 226.8 \text{ kJ}$$

When the equations are added, there are $2\ CO_2$, $\frac{5}{2}\ O_2$, and H_2O on both sides of the arrow. These are canceled in writing the net equation.

Check The procedure must be correct because we obtained the correct net equation. In cases like this you should go back over the numerical manipulations of the ΔH values to ensure that you did not make an inadvertent error with signs.

PRACTICE EXERCISE

Calculate ΔH for the reaction

$$NO(g) + O(g) \longrightarrow NO_2(g)$$

given the following information:

$$NO(g) + O_3(g) \longrightarrow NO_2(g) + O_2(g) \qquad \Delta H = -198.9 \text{ kJ}$$
$$O_3(g) \longrightarrow \tfrac{3}{2} O_2(g) \qquad \Delta H = -142.3 \text{ kJ}$$
$$O_2(g) \longrightarrow 2\ O(g) \qquad \Delta H = 495.0 \text{ kJ}$$

Answer: -304.1 kJ

The key point of these examples is that H is a state function, so *for a particular set of reactants and products, ΔH is the same whether the reaction takes place in one step or in a series of steps.* We reinforce this point by giving one more example of an enthalpy diagram and Hess's law. Again we use combustion of methane to form CO_2 and H_2O, our reaction from Figure 5.21. This time we envision a different two-step path, with the initial formation of CO, which is then combusted to CO_2 (▶ **FIGURE 5.22**). Even though the two-step path is different from that in Figure 5.21, the overall reaction again has $\Delta H_1 = -890$ kJ. Because H is a state function, both paths *must* produce the same value of ΔH. In Figure 5.22, that means $\Delta H_1 = \Delta H_2 + \Delta H_3$. We will soon see that breaking up reactions in this way allows us to derive the enthalpy changes for reactions that are hard to carry out in the laboratory.

5.7 | ENTHALPIES OF FORMATION

We can use the methods just discussed to calculate enthalpy changes for a great many reactions from tabulated ΔH values. For example, extensive tables exist of *enthalpies of vaporization* (ΔH for converting liquids to gases), *enthalpies of fusion* (ΔH for melting solids), *enthalpies of combustion* (ΔH for combusting a substance in oxygen), and so forth. A particularly important process used for tabulating thermochemical data is the formation of a compound from its constituent elements. The enthalpy change associated with this process is called the **enthalpy of formation** (or *heat of formation*), ΔH_f, where the subscript f indicates that the substance has been *formed* from its constituent elements.

The magnitude of any enthalpy change depends on the temperature, pressure, and state (gas, liquid, or solid crystalline form) of the reactants and products. To compare enthalpies of different reactions, we must define a set of conditions, called a *standard state,* at which most enthalpies are tabulated. The standard state of a substance is its pure form at atmospheric pressure (1 atm) and the temperature of interest, which we usually choose to be 298 K (25 °C).* The **standard enthalpy change** of a reaction is defined as the enthalpy change when all reactants and products are in their standard states. We denote a standard enthalpy change as $\Delta H°$, where the superscript ° indicates standard-state conditions.

The **standard enthalpy of formation** of a compound, $\Delta H_f°$, is the change in enthalpy for the reaction that forms one mole of the compound from its elements with all substances in their standard states:

If: elements (in standard state) $\longrightarrow$ compound (1 mol in standard state)
Then: $\Delta H = \Delta H_f°$

△ **GO FIGURE**

Suppose the overall reaction were modified to produce $2\ H_2O(g)$ rather than $2\ H_2O(l)$. Would any of the values of ΔH in the diagram stay the same?

▲ **FIGURE 5.22 Enthalpy diagram illustrating Hess's law.** The net reaction is the same as in Figure 5.21, but here we imagine different reactions in our two-step version. As long as we can write a series of equations that add up to the equation we need, and as long as we know a value for ΔH for all intermediate reactions, we can calculate the overall ΔH.

---

*The definition of the standard state for gases has been changed to 1 bar (1 atm = 1.013 bar), a slightly lower pressure than 1 atm. For most purposes, this change makes very little difference in the standard enthalpy changes.

TABLE 5.3 • Standard Enthalpies of Formation, ΔH_f°, at 298 K

Substance	Formula	ΔH_f° (kJ/mol)	Substance	Formula	ΔH_f° (kJ/mol)
Acetylene	$C_2H_2(g)$	226.7	Hydrogen chloride	$HCl(g)$	−92.30
Ammonia	$NH_3(g)$	−46.19	Hydrogen fluoride	$HF(g)$	−268.60
Benzene	$C_6H_6(l)$	49.0	Hydrogen iodide	$HI(g)$	25.9
Calcium carbonate	$CaCO_3(s)$	−1207.1	Methane	$CH_4(g)$	−74.80
Calcium oxide	$CaO(s)$	−635.5	Methanol	$CH_3OH(l)$	−238.6
Carbon dioxide	$CO_2(g)$	−393.5	Propane	$C_3H_8(g)$	−103.85
Carbon monoxide	$CO(g)$	−110.5	Silver chloride	$AgCl(s)$	−127.0
Diamond	$C(s)$	1.88	Sodium bicarbonate	$NaHCO_3(s)$	−947.7
Ethane	$C_2H_6(g)$	−84.68	Sodium carbonate	$Na_2CO_3(s)$	−1130.9
Ethanol	$C_2H_5OH(l)$	−277.7	Sodium chloride	$NaCl(s)$	−410.9
Ethylene	$C_2H_4(g)$	52.30	Sucrose	$C_{12}H_{22}O_{11}(s)$	−2221
Glucose	$C_6H_{12}O_6(s)$	−1273	Water	$H_2O(l)$	−285.8
Hydrogen bromide	$HBr(g)$	−36.23	Water vapor	$H_2O(g)$	−241.8

We usually report ΔH_f° values at 298 K. If an element exists in more than one form under standard conditions, the most stable form of the element is usually used for the formation reaction. For example, the standard enthalpy of formation for ethanol, C_2H_5OH, is the enthalpy change for the reaction

$$2\,C(graphite) + 3\,H_2(g) + \tfrac{1}{2}O_2(g) \longrightarrow C_2H_5OH(l) \quad \Delta H_f^{\circ} = -277.7 \text{ kJ} \qquad [5.25]$$

The elemental source of oxygen is O_2, not O or O_3, because O_2 is the stable form of oxygen at 298 K and atmospheric pressure. Similarly, the elemental source of carbon is graphite and not diamond because graphite is the more stable (lower-energy) form at 298 K and atmospheric pressure (see Practice Exercise 5.8). Likewise, the most stable form of hydrogen under standard conditions is $H_2(g)$, so this is used as the source of hydrogen in Equation 5.25.

The stoichiometry of formation reactions always indicates that one mole of the desired substance is produced, as in Equation 5.25. As a result, standard enthalpies of formation are reported in kJ/mol of the substance being formed. Some values are given in ▲ **TABLE 5.3**, and a more extensive table is provided in Appendix C.

By definition, *the standard enthalpy of formation of the most stable form of any element is zero* because there is no formation reaction needed when the element is already in its standard state. Thus, the values of ΔH_f° for C(graphite), $H_2(g)$, $O_2(g)$, and the standard states of other elements are zero by definition.

 GIVE IT SOME THOUGHT

Ozone, $O_3(g)$, is a form of elemental oxygen produced during electrical discharge. Is ΔH_f° for $O_3(g)$ necessarily zero?

SAMPLE EXERCISE 5.10   **Equations Associated with Enthalpies of Formation**

For which of these reactions at 25 °C does the enthalpy change represent a standard enthalpy of formation? For each that does not, what changes are needed to make it an equation whose ΔH is an enthalpy of formation?

(a) $2\,Na(s) + \tfrac{1}{2}O_2(g) \longrightarrow Na_2O(s)$

(b) $2\,K(l) + Cl_2(g) \longrightarrow 2\,KCl(s)$

(c) $C_6H_{12}O_6(s) \longrightarrow 6\,C(diamond) + 6\,H_2(g) + 3\,O_2(g)$

SOLUTION

Analyze The standard enthalpy of formation is represented by a reaction in which each reactant is an element in its standard state and the product is one mole of the compound.

Plan We need to examine each equation to determine (1) whether the reaction is one in which one mole of substance is formed from the elements, and (2) whether the reactant elements are in their standard states.

Solve In (a) 1 mol Na_2O is formed from the elements sodium and oxygen in their proper states, solid Na and O_2 gas, respectively. Therefore, the enthalpy change for reaction (a) corresponds to a standard enthalpy of formation.

In (b) potassium is given as a liquid. It must be changed to the solid form, its standard state at room temperature. Furthermore, two moles of product are formed, so the enthalpy change for the reaction as written is twice the standard enthalpy of formation of $KCl(s)$. The equation for the formation reaction of 1 mol of $KCl(s)$ is

$$K(s) + \tfrac{1}{2}Cl_2(g) \longrightarrow KCl(s)$$

Reaction (c) does not form a substance from its elements. Instead, a substance decomposes to its elements, so this reaction must be reversed. Next, the element carbon is given as diamond, whereas graphite is the standard state of carbon at room temperature and 1 atm pressure. The equation that correctly represents the enthalpy of formation of glucose from its elements is

$$6\,C(graphite) + 6\,H_2(g) + 3\,O_2(g) \longrightarrow C_6H_{12}O_6(s)$$

PRACTICE EXERCISE

Write the equation corresponding to the standard enthalpy of formation of liquid carbon tetrachloride (CCl_4).

Answer: $C(graphite) + 2\,Cl_2(g) \longrightarrow CCl_4(l)$

Using Enthalpies of Formation to Calculate Enthalpies of Reaction

We can use Hess's law and tabulations of ΔH_f° values, such as those in Table 5.3 and Appendix C, to calculate the standard enthalpy change for any reaction for which we know the ΔH_f° values for all reactants and products. For example, consider the combustion of propane gas, $C_3H_8(g)$, to $CO_2(g)$ and $H_2O(l)$ under standard conditions:

$$C_3H_8(g) + 5\,O_2(g) \longrightarrow 3\,CO_2(g) + 4\,H_2O(l)$$

We can write this equation as the sum of three formation equations:

$C_3H_8(g) \longrightarrow 3\,C(s) + 4\,H_2(g)$	$\Delta H_1 = -\Delta H_f^\circ\,[C_3H_8(g)]$	[5.26]
$3\,C(s) + 3\,O_2(g) \longrightarrow 3\,CO_2(g)$	$\Delta H_2 = 3\Delta H_f^\circ\,[CO_2(g)]$	[5.27]
$4\,H_2(g) + 2\,O_2(g) \longrightarrow 4\,H_2O(l)$	$\Delta H_3 = 4\Delta H_f^\circ\,[H_2O(l)]$	[5.28]
$C_3H_8(g) + 5\,O_2(g) \longrightarrow 3\,CO_2(g) + 4\,H_2O(l)$	$\Delta H_{rxn}^\circ = \Delta H_1 + \Delta H_2 + \Delta H_3$	[5.29]

(Note that it is sometimes useful to add subscripts to the enthalpy changes, as we have done here, to keep track of the associations between reactions and their ΔH values.)

Notice that we have used Hess's law to write the standard enthalpy change for Equation 5.29 as the sum of the enthalpy changes for Equations 5.26 through 5.28. We can use values from Table 5.3 to calculate ΔH_{rxn}°:

$$\begin{aligned}
\Delta H_{rxn}^\circ &= \Delta H_1 + \Delta H_2 + \Delta H_3 \\
&= -\Delta H_f^\circ\,[C_3H_8(g)] + 3\Delta H_f^\circ\,[CO_2(g)] + 4\Delta H_f^\circ\,[H_2O(l)] \\
&= -(-103.85\text{ kJ}) + 3(-393.5\text{ kJ}) + 4(-285.8\text{ kJ}) = -2220\text{ kJ} \quad [5.30]
\end{aligned}$$

▶ **FIGURE 5.23**, an enthalpy diagram for Equation 5.29, shows our propane combustion reaction broken down to the three reactions. Several aspects of this calculation depend on the guidelines we discussed in Section 5.4.

1. **Decomposition.** Equation 5.26 is the reverse of the formation reaction for $C_3H_8(g)$, so the enthalpy change for this decomposition reaction is the negative of the ΔH_f° value for the propane formation reaction: $-\Delta H_f^\circ\,[C_3H_8(g)]$.

▲ **FIGURE 5.23** **Enthalpy diagram for propane combustion.**

2. **Formation of CO_2.** Equation 5.27 is the formation reaction for 3 mol of $CO_2(g)$. Because enthalpy is an extensive property, the enthalpy change for this step is $3\Delta H_f^{\circ}\,[CO_2(g)]$.

3. **Formation of H_2O.** The enthalpy change for Equation 5.28, formation of 4 mol of H_2O, is $4\Delta H_f^{\circ}\,[H_2O(l)]$. The reaction specifies that $H_2O(l)$ is produced, so be careful to use the value of ΔH_f° for $H_2O(l)$ and not the value for $H_2O(g)$.

Note that in this analysis we assume that the stoichiometric coefficients in the balanced equation represent moles. For Equation 5.29, therefore, $\Delta H_{rxn}^{\circ} = -2220$ kJ represents the enthalpy change for the reaction of 1 mol C_3H_8 and 5 mol O_2 to form 3 mol CO_2 and 4 mol H_2O. The product of the number of moles and the enthalpy change in kJ/mol has the units kJ: (number of moles) $\times$ (ΔH_f° in kJ/mol) = kJ. We therefore report ΔH_{rxn}° in kJ.

We can break down any reaction into formation reactions as we have done here. When we do, we obtain the general result that the standard enthalpy change of a reaction is the sum of the standard enthalpies of formation of the products minus the standard enthalpies of formation of the reactants:

$$\Delta H_{rxn}^{\circ} = \Sigma n\Delta H_f^{\circ}(\text{products}) - \Sigma m\Delta H_f^{\circ}(\text{reactants}) \qquad [5.31]$$

The symbol Σ (sigma) means "the sum of," and n and m are the stoichiometric coefficients of the relevant chemical equation. The first term on the right in Equation 5.31 represents the formation reactions of the products, which are written in the "forward" direction in the chemical equation, that is, elements reacting to form products. This term is analogous to Equations 5.27 and 5.28. The second term on the right in Equation 5.31 represents the reverse of the formation reactions of the reactants, analogous to Equation 5.26, which is why this term is preceded by a minus sign.

SAMPLE EXERCISE 5.11 Calculating an Enthalpy of Reaction from Enthalpies of Formation

(a) Calculate the standard enthalpy change for the combustion of 1 mol of benzene, $C_6H_6(l)$, to $CO_2(g)$ and $H_2O(l)$. (b) Compare the quantity of heat produced by combustion of 1.00 g propane with that produced by 1.00 g benzene.

SOLUTION

Analyze (a) We are given a reaction [combustion of $C_6H_6(l)$ to form $CO_2(g)$ and $H_2O(l)$] and asked to calculate its standard enthalpy change, $\Delta H°$. (b) We then need to compare the quantity of heat produced by combustion of 1.00 g C_6H_6 with that produced by 1.00 g C_3H_8, whose combustion was treated previously in the text. (See Equations 5.29 and 5.30.)

Plan (a) We need to write the balanced equation for the combustion of C_6H_6. We then look up $\Delta H_f°$ values in Appendix C or in Table 5.3 and apply Equation 5.31 to calculate the enthalpy change for the reaction. (b) We use the molar mass of C_6H_6 to change the enthalpy change per mole to that per gram. We similarly use the molar mass of C_3H_8 and the enthalpy change per mole calculated in the text previously to calculate the enthalpy change per gram of that substance.

Solve

(a) We know that a combustion reaction involves $O_2(g)$ as a reactant. Thus, the balanced equation for the combustion reaction of 1 mol $C_6H_6(l)$ is

We can calculate $\Delta H°$ for this reaction by using Equation 5.31 and data in Table 5.3. Remember to multiply the $\Delta H_f°$ value for each substance in the reaction by that substance's stoichiometric coefficient. Recall also that $\Delta H_f° = 0$ for any element in its most stable form under standard conditions, so $\Delta H_f°[O_2(g)] = 0$:

$$C_6H_6(l) + \tfrac{15}{2} O_2(g) \longrightarrow 6 CO_2(g) + 3 H_2O(l)$$

$$\Delta H_{rxn}° = [6\Delta H_f°(CO_2) + 3\Delta H_f°(H_2O)] - [\Delta H_f°(C_6H_6) + \tfrac{15}{2} \Delta H_f°(O_2)]$$
$$= [6(-393.5 \text{ kJ}) + 3(-285.8 \text{ kJ})] - [(49.0 \text{ kJ}) + \tfrac{15}{2}(0 \text{ kJ})]$$
$$= (-2361 - 857.4 - 49.0) \text{ kJ}$$
$$= -3267 \text{ kJ}$$

(b) From the example worked in the text, $\Delta H° = -2220$ kJ for the combustion of 1 mol of propane. In part (a) of this exercise we determined that $\Delta H° = -3267$ kJ for the combustion of 1 mol benzene. To determine the heat of combustion per gram of each substance, we use the molar masses to convert moles to grams:

$C_3H_8(g)$: $(-2220 \text{ kJ/mol})(1 \text{ mol}/44.1 \text{ g}) = -50.3 \text{ kJ/g}$
$C_6H_6(l)$: $(-3267 \text{ kJ/mol})(1 \text{ mol}/78.1 \text{ g}) = -41.8 \text{ kJ/g}$

Comment Both propane and benzene are hydrocarbons. As a rule, the energy obtained from the combustion of a gram of hydrocarbon is between 40 and 50 kJ.

PRACTICE EXERCISE
Use Table 5.3 to calculate the enthalpy change for the combustion of 1 mol of ethanol:

$$C_2H_5OH(l) + 3 O_2(g) \longrightarrow 2 CO_2(g) + 3 H_2O(l)$$

Answer: −1367 kJ

SAMPLE EXERCISE 5.12 Calculating an Enthalpy of Formation Using an Enthalpy of Reaction

The standard enthalpy change for the reaction $CaCO_3(s) \longrightarrow CaO(s) + CO_2(g)$ is 178.1 kJ. Use Table 5.3 to calculate the standard enthalpy of formation of $CaCO_3(s)$.

SOLUTION

Analyze Our goal is to obtain $\Delta H_f°[CaCO_3(s)]$.

Plan We begin by writing the expression for the standard enthalpy change for the reaction:

$$\Delta H_{rxn}° = \Delta H_f°[CaO(s)] + \Delta H_f°[CO_2(g)] - \Delta H_f°[CaCO_3(s)]$$

Solve Inserting the given $\Delta H_{rxn}°$ and the known $\Delta H_f°$ values from Table 5.3 or Appendix C, we have

$$178.1 = -635.5 \text{ kJ} - 393.5 \text{ kJ} - \Delta H_f°[CaCO_3(s)]$$

Solving for $\Delta H_f°[CaCO_3(s)]$ gives

$$\Delta H_f°[CaCO_3(s)] = -1207.1 \text{ kJ/mol}$$

Check We expect the enthalpy of formation of a stable solid such as calcium carbonate to be negative, as obtained.

PRACTICE EXERCISE
Given the following standard enthalpy change, use the standard enthalpies of formation in Table 5.3 to calculate the standard enthalpy of formation of $CuO(s)$:

$$CuO(s) + H_2(g) \longrightarrow Cu(s) + H_2O(l) \qquad \Delta H° = -129.7 \text{ kJ}$$

Answer: −156.1 kJ/mol

5.8 | FOODS AND FUELS

Most chemical reactions used for the production of heat are combustion reactions. The energy released when one gram of any substance is combusted is the **fuel value** of the substance. The fuel value of any food or fuel can be measured by calorimetry.

Foods

Most of the energy our bodies need comes from carbohydrates and fats. The carbohydrates known as starches are decomposed in the intestines into glucose, $C_6H_{12}O_6$. Glucose is soluble in blood, and in the human body it is known as blood sugar. It is transported by the blood to cells where it reacts with O_2 in a series of steps, eventually producing $CO_2(g)$, $H_2O(l)$, and energy:

$$C_6H_{12}O_6(s) + 6\,O_2(g) \longrightarrow 6\,CO_2(g) + 6\,H_2O(l) \qquad \Delta H^\circ = -2803 \text{ kJ}$$

Because carbohydrates break down rapidly, their energy is quickly supplied to the body. However, the body stores only a very small amount of carbohydrates. The average fuel value of carbohydrates is 17 kJ/g (4 kcal/g).*

Like carbohydrates, fats produce CO_2 and H_2O when metabolized. The reaction of tristearin, $C_{57}H_{110}O_6$, a typical fat, is

$$2\,C_{57}H_{110}O_6(s) + 163\,O_2(g) \longrightarrow 114\,CO_2(g) + 110\,H_2O(l) \quad \Delta H^\circ = -75,520 \text{ kJ}$$

The body uses the chemical energy from foods to maintain body temperature (see the "Chemistry and Life" box in Section 5.5), to contract muscles, and to construct and repair tissues. Any excess energy is stored as fats. Fats are well suited to serve as the body's energy reserve for at least two reasons: (1) They are insoluble in water, which facilitates storage in the body, and (2) they produce more energy per gram than either proteins or carbohydrates, which makes them efficient energy sources on a mass basis. The average fuel value of fats is 38 kJ/g (9 kcal/g).

The combustion of carbohydrates and fats in a bomb calorimeter gives the same products as when they are metabolized in the body. The metabolism of proteins produces less energy than combustion in a calorimeter because the products are different. Proteins contain nitrogen, which is released in the bomb calorimeter as N_2. In the body this nitrogen ends up mainly as urea, $(NH_2)_2CO$. Proteins are used by the body mainly as building materials for organ walls, skin, hair, muscle, and so forth. On average, the metabolism of proteins produces 17 kJ/g (4 kcal/g), the same as for carbohydrates.

Fuel values for some common foods are shown in ▼ TABLE 5.4. Labels on packaged foods show the amounts of carbohydrate, fat, and protein contained in an average serving, as well as the amount of energy supplied by a serving (◄ FIGURE 5.24).

GO FIGURE

Which value would change most if this label were for skim milk instead of whole milk: grams of fat, grams of total carbohydrate, or grams of protein?

▲ **FIGURE 5.24** **Nutrition label for whole milk.**

TABLE 5.4 • Compositions and Fuel Values of Some Common Foods

	Approximate Composition (% by mass)			Fuel Value	
	Carbohydrate	Fat	Protein	kJ/g	kcal/g (Cal/g)
Carbohydrate	100	—	—	17	4
Fat	—	100	—	38	9
Protein	—	—	100	17	4
Apples	13	0.5	0.4	2.5	0.59
Beer[†]	1.2	—	0.3	1.8	0.42
Bread	52	3	9	12	2.8
Cheese	4	37	28	20	4.7
Eggs	0.7	10	13	6.0	1.4
Fudge	81	11	2	18	4.4
Green beans	7.0	—	1.9	1.5	0.38
Hamburger	—	30	22	15	3.6
Milk (whole)	5.0	4.0	3.3	3.0	0.74
Peanuts	22	39	26	23	5.5

[†]Beer typically contains 3.5% ethanol, which has fuel value.

*Although fuel values represent the heat *released* in a combustion reaction, fuel values are reported as positive numbers.

The amount of energy our bodies require varies considerably, depending on such factors as weight, age, and muscular activity. About 100 kJ per kilogram of body mass per day is required to keep the body functioning at a minimal level. An average 70-kg (154-lb) person expends about 800 kJ/hr when doing light work, and strenuous activity often requires 2000 kJ/hr or more. When the fuel value, or caloric content, of the food we ingest exceeds the energy we expend, our body stores the surplus as fat.

 GIVE IT SOME THOUGHT

Which releases the greatest amount of energy per gram when metabolized: carbohydrates, proteins, or fats?

SAMPLE EXERCISE 5.13 **Comparing Fuel Values**

Celery contains carbohydrates in the form of starch and cellulose, which have essentially the same fuel values when combusted in a bomb calorimeter. When we eat celery, however, our bodies receive fuel value from the starch only. What can we conclude about the difference between starch and cellulose as foods?

SOLUTION

If cellulose does not provide fuel value, we must conclude that it is not converted in the body into CO_2 and H_2O, as starch is. A slight but critical difference in the structures of starch and cellulose explains why only starch is broken down into glucose in the body. Cellulose passes through without undergoing significant chemical change. It serves as fiber, or roughage, in the diet but provides no caloric value.

PRACTICE EXERCISE

The nutrition label on a bottle of canola oil indicates that 10 g of the oil has a fuel value of 86 kcal. A similar label on a bottle of pancake syrup indicates that 60 mL (about 60 g) has a fuel value of 200 kcal. Account for the difference.

Answer: The oil has a fuel value of 8.6 kcal/g, whereas the syrup has a fuel value of about 3.3 kcal/g. The higher fuel value for the canola oil arises because the oil is essentially pure fat, whereas the syrup is a solution of sugars (carbohydrates) in water. The oil has a higher fuel value per gram; in addition, the syrup is diluted by water.

SAMPLE EXERCISE 5.14 **Estimating the Fuel Value of a Food from Its Composition**

(a) A 28-g (1-oz) serving of a popular breakfast cereal served with 120 mL of skim milk provides 8 g protein, 26 g carbohydrates, and 2 g fat. Using the average fuel values of these substances, estimate the fuel value (caloric content) of this serving. **(b)** A person of average weight uses about 100 Cal/mi when running or jogging. How many servings of this cereal provide the fuel value requirements to run 3 mi?

SOLUTION

(a) Analyze The fuel value of the serving will be the sum of the fuel values of the protein, carbohydrates, and fat.

Plan We are given the masses of the protein, carbohydrates, and fat contained in a serving. We can use the data in Table 5.4 to convert these masses to their fuel values, which we can sum to get the total fuel value.

Solve

$$(8 \text{ g protein})\left(\frac{17 \text{ kJ}}{1 \text{ g protein}}\right) + (26 \text{ g carbohydrate})\left(\frac{17 \text{ kJ}}{1 \text{ g carbohydrate}}\right) +$$

$$(2 \text{ g fat})\left(\frac{38 \text{ kJ}}{1 \text{ g fat}}\right) = 650 \text{ kJ (to two significant figures)}$$

This corresponds to 160 kcal:

$$(650 \text{ kJ})\left(\frac{1 \text{ kcal}}{4.18 \text{ kJ}}\right) = 160 \text{ kcal}$$

Recall that the dietary Calorie is equivalent to 1 kcal. Thus, the serving provides 160 Cal.

(b) Analyze Here we are faced with the reverse problem, calculating the quantity of food that provides a specific fuel value.

Plan The problem statement provides a conversion factor between Calories and miles. The answer to part (a) provides us with a conversion factor between servings and Calories.

Solve We can use these factors in a straightforward dimensional analysis to determine the number of servings needed, rounded to the nearest whole number:

$$\text{Servings} = (3 \text{ mi})\left(\frac{100 \text{ Cal}}{1 \text{ mi}}\right)\left(\frac{1 \text{ serving}}{160 \text{ Cal}}\right) = 2 \text{ servings}$$

PRACTICE EXERCISE

(a) Dry red beans contain 62% carbohydrate, 22% protein, and 1.5% fat. Estimate the fuel value of these beans. **(b)** During a very light activity, such as reading or watching television, the average adult expends about 7 kJ/min. How many minutes of such activity can be sustained by the energy provided by a serving of chicken noodle soup containing 13 g protein, 15 g carbohydrate, and 5 g fat?
Answers: **(a)** 15 kJ/g, **(b)** 100 min

Fuels

During the complete combustion of fuels, carbon is converted to CO_2 and hydrogen is converted to H_2O, both of which have large negative enthalpies of formation. Consequently, the greater the percentage of carbon and hydrogen in a fuel, the higher its fuel value. In ▼ TABLE 5.5, for example, compare the compositions and fuel values of bituminous coal and wood. The coal has a higher fuel value because of its greater carbon content.

In 2008 the United States consumed 1.05×10^{17} kJ of energy. This value corresponds to an average daily energy consumption per person of 9.4×10^5 kJ, roughly 100 times greater than the per capita food-energy needs. Although the population of the United States is only about 4.5% of the world's population, the United States accounts for nearly 20% of the world's total energy consumption. ◄ FIGURE 5.25 illustrates the sources of this energy.

Coal, petroleum, and natural gas, which are the world's major sources of energy, are known as **fossil fuels.** All have formed over millions of years from the decomposition of plants and animals and are being depleted far more rapidly than they are being formed.

Natural gas consists of gaseous hydrocarbons, compounds of hydrogen and carbon. It contains primarily methane (CH_4), with small amounts of ethane (C_2H_6), propane (C_3H_8), and butane (C_4H_{10}). We determined the fuel value of propane in Sample Exercise 5.11. **Petroleum** is a liquid composed of hundreds of compounds, most of which are hydrocarbons, with the remainder being chiefly organic compounds containing sulfur, nitrogen, or oxygen. **Coal,** which is solid, contains hydrocarbons of high molecular weight as well as compounds containing sulfur, oxygen, or nitrogen. Coal is the most abundant

▲ FIGURE 5.25 Energy consumption in the United States. In 2008 the United States consumed a total of 1.05×10^{17} kJ of energy.

Nuclear (8.5%)
Renewable energy (7.4%)
Petroleum (37.6%)
Coal (22.6%)
Natural gas (24.0%)

TABLE 5.5 • Fuel Values and Compositions of Some Common Fuels

	Approximate Elemental Composition (mass %)			
	C	**H**	**O**	**Fuel Value (kJ/g)**
Wood (pine)	50	6	44	18
Anthracite coal (Pennsylvania)	82	1	2	31
Bituminous coal (Pennsylvania)	77	5	7	32
Charcoal	100	0	0	34
Crude oil (Texas)	85	12	0	45
Gasoline	85	15	0	48
Natural gas	70	23	0	49
Hydrogen	0	100	0	142

fossil fuel; current reserves are projected to last for well over 100 years at current consumption rates. However, the use of coal presents a number of problems.

Coal is a complex mixture of substances, and it contains components that cause air pollution. When coal is combusted, the sulfur it contains is converted mainly to sulfur dioxide, SO_2, a troublesome air pollutant. Because coal is a solid, recovery from its underground deposits is expensive and often dangerous. Furthermore, coal deposits are not always close to locations of high-energy use, so there are often substantial shipping costs.

Fossil fuels release energy in combustion reactions, which ideally produce only CO_2 and H_2O. The production of CO_2 has become a major issue that involves science and public policy because of concerns that increasing concentrations of atmospheric CO_2 are causing global climate changes. In December 2009 the United Nations held a Climate Change Conference in Copenhagen, Denmark, that attracted about 15,000 participants from nearly 200 countries, including many government leaders. Much of the discussion at this conference involved the impact of atmospheric CO_2 and ways in which alternative energy sources could be implemented. We will discuss the environmental aspects of atmospheric CO_2 in Chapter 18.

 GIVE IT SOME THOUGHT

Much current research is directed toward using hydrogen gas, $H_2(g)$, as a fuel. What intrinsic advantage does hydrogen as a fuel have with respect to the current climate-change debate?

Other Energy Sources

Nuclear energy is the energy released in either the splitting or the fusion (combining) of atomic nuclei. Nuclear power is currently used to produce about 21% of the electric power in the United States and makes up about 8.5% of the total U.S. energy production (Figure 5.25). Nuclear energy is, in principle, free of the polluting emissions that are a major problem with fossil fuels. However, nuclear power plants produce radioactive waste products, and their use has therefore been controversial. We will discuss issues related to the production of nuclear energy in Chapter 21.

Fossil fuels and nuclear energy are *nonrenewable* sources of energy—they are limited resources that we are consuming at a much greater rate than they can be regenerated. Eventually these fuels will be expended, although estimates vary greatly as to when this will occur. Because nonrenewable energy sources will eventually be used up, a great deal of research is being conducted on **renewable energy sources**, sources that are essentially inexhaustible. Renewable energy sources include *solar energy* from the Sun, *wind energy* harnessed by windmills, *geothermal energy* from the heat stored inside Earth, *hydroelectric energy* from flowing rivers, and *biomass energy* from crops and biological waste matter. Currently, renewable sources provide about 7.4% of the U.S. annual energy consumption, with hydroelectric and biomass sources the major contributors.

Fulfilling our future energy needs will depend on developing technology to harness solar energy with greater efficiency. Solar energy is the world's largest energy source. On a clear day about 1 kJ of solar energy reaches each square meter of Earth's surface every second. The average solar energy falling on only 0.1% of U.S. land area is equivalent to all the energy this nation currently uses. Harnessing this energy is difficult because it is dilute (that is, distributed over a wide area) and varies with time of day and weather conditions. The effective use of solar energy will depend on the development of some means of storing and distributing it. Any practical means for doing this will almost certainly involve an endothermic chemical process that can be later reversed to release heat. One such reaction is

$$CH_4(g) + H_2O(g) + \text{heat} \longleftrightarrow CO(g) + 3\,H_2(g)$$

This reaction proceeds in the forward direction at high temperatures, which can be obtained in a solar furnace. The CO and H_2 formed in the reaction could then be stored and allowed to react later, with the heat released being put to useful work.

CHEMISTRY PUT TO WORK

The Scientific and Political Challenges of Biofuels

One of the biggest challenges facing us in the twenty-first century is production of abundant sources of energy, both food and fuels. World population more than doubled from 1960 to 2000, from about 3 billion to more than 6 billion people. It continues to grow at a rate of about 750 million per decade—at the end of 2009, the global population was about 6.8 billion people. A growing world population puts greater demands on the global food supply, especially in Asia and Africa, which together make up more than 75% of the world population.

A growing population also increases demands on the production of fuels for transportation, industry, electricity, heating, and cooling. Further, many of the most populous nations, such as China and India, have seen dramatic increases in the quality of life among their citizens. As these countries have modernized, their per capita consumption of energy—for automobiles, new industries, modern housing, and technology advances—has increased significantly. In China, for instance, per capita energy consumption roughly doubled between 1990 and 2010 (although it is still less than 20% of U.S. per capita energy consumption).

Global fuel energy consumption in 2009 was more than 5×10^{17} kJ, a staggeringly large number that is projected to grow to more than 7×10^{17} kJ by 2030. More than 80% of current energy requirements comes from combustion of nonrenewable fossil fuels, especially petroleum. Depletion has generally increased the cost of petroleum-based fuels. In addition, the exploration of new petroleum sources often involves environmentally sensitive regions, such as the Arctic National Wildlife Refuge. Thus, increasing the supplies of petroleum becomes a major political and economic issue.

Global dependence on petroleum is in large part because it provides liquid fuels, such as gasoline, that are critical to supplying transportation needs. One of the most promising—but controversial—alternatives to petroleum-based fuels is *biofuels,* liquid fuels derived from biological matter. The most common approach to producing biofuels is to transform plant sugars and other carbohydrates into combustible liquids. The energy stored in the carbohydrates produced in photosynthesis (Equation 5.32) is higher than the energy in H_2O and CO_2; thus, photosynthesis is a way to "store" solar energy in plants.

The most commonly produced biofuel is *bioethanol,* which is ethanol (C_2H_5OH) made from fermentation of plant carbohydrates. The fuel value of ethanol is about two-thirds that of gasoline and is therefore comparable to that of coal (Table 5.5). The United States and Brazil dominate bioethanol production, together supplying 85% of the world's total.

In the United States, nearly all the bioethanol currently produced is made from yellow feed corn (▶ FIGURE 5.26). Glucose ($C_6H_{12}O_6$) in the corn is converted to ethanol and CO_2:

$$C_6H_{12}O_6(s) \longrightarrow 2\,C_2H_5OH(l) + 2\,CO_2(g) \qquad \Delta H = 15.8 \text{ KJ}$$

Notice that this reaction is *anaerobic*—it does not involve $O_2(g)$—and that the enthalpy change is positive and much smaller in magnitude than for most combustion reactions. Other carbohydrates can be converted to ethanol in similar fashion.

Producing bioethanol from corn is controversial for two main reasons. First, growing and transporting corn are both energy-intensive processes, and growing it requires the use of fertilizers. It is estimated that the *energy return* on corn-based bioethanol is only 34%—that is, for each 1.00 J of energy expended to produce the corn, 1.34 J of energy is produced in the form of bioethanol. Second, the use of corn as a starting material for making bioethanol competes with its use as an important component of the food chain (the so-called "food versus fuel" debate). In particular, the diversion of corn crops to bioethanol production has led to higher prices for food, including beef (corn is used as feed for cattle). Much current research focuses on the formation of bioethanol from *cellulosic* plants, plants that contain the complex carbohydrate cellulose. Cellulose is not readily metabolized (Sample Exercise 5.13) and so does not compete with the food supply. However, the chemistry for converting cellulose to ethanol is much more complex than that for converting corn. Cellulosic bioethanol could be produced from very fast growing nonfood plants, such as prairie grasses and switchgrass, which readily renew themselves without the use of fertilizers.

As shown in the chapter-opening photograph, the Brazilian bioethanol industry uses sugarcane as its feedstock. Sugarcane grows much faster than corn and without the need for fertilizers or tending. Because of these differences, the energy return for sugarcane is much higher than the energy return for corn. It is estimated that for each 1.0 J of energy expended in growing and processing sugarcane, 8.0 J of energy is produced as bioethanol. Because the climate in Brazil is ideal for growing cane, the Brazilian government started investing in the 1970s in ways to utilize sugarcane as a major fuel source.

Other biofuels that are also becoming a major part of the world economy include *biodiesel,* a substitute for petroleum-derived diesel fuel. Biodiesel is typically produced from crops that have a high oil content, such as soybeans and canola. It can also be produced from animal fats and waste vegetable oil from the food and restaurant industry.

Biofuels are combusted in the presence of $O_2(g)$ to produce $CO_2(g)$, $H_2O(g)$, and energy in the form of heat, much as hydrocarbon fuels do. Because $CO_2(g)$ is a product, the use of biofuels is part of the international debate about carbon dioxide and climate change. We will discuss this issue further in Chapter 18.

RELATED EXERCISES:
5.89, 5.90, 5.111, 5.119

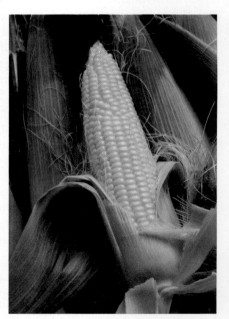

▲ FIGURE 5.26 **Corn, a source of food and bioethanol.** The sugars in the kernels of feed corn can be used as food or as a feedstock for fermentation to ethanol.

Plants utilize solar energy in *photosynthesis,* the reaction in which the energy of sunlight is used to convert CO_2 and H_2O into carbohydrates and O_2. One common photosynthetic reaction produces the sugar glucose:

$$6\,CO_2(g) + 6\,H_2O(l) + \text{sunlight} \longrightarrow C_6H_{12}O_6(s) + 6\,O_2(g) \qquad [5.32]$$

In essence, photosynthesis is the reverse of combustion in that CO_2 and H_2O are consumed and O_2 and an organic molecule are produced. Photosynthesis is an important part of Earth's ecosystem because it replenishes atmospheric O_2, produces an energy-rich molecule that can be used as fuel, and consumes some atmospheric CO_2.

Perhaps the most direct way to use the Sun's energy is to convert it directly into electricity in photovoltaic devices, sometimes called *solar cells.* The efficiencies of such devices have increased dramatically during the past few years. Photovoltaics are vital to the generation of power for space vehicles, such as the International Space Station research facility currently orbiting Earth. Technological advances have led to solar panels that last longer and produce electricity with greater efficiency at steadily decreasing unit cost. Indeed, the future of solar energy is, like the Sun itself, very bright.

SAMPLE INTEGRATIVE EXERCISE | Putting Concepts Together

Trinitroglycerin, $C_3H_5N_3O_9$ (usually referred to simply as nitroglycerin), has been widely used as an explosive. Alfred Nobel used it to make dynamite in 1866. Rather surprisingly, it also is used as a medication, to relieve angina (chest pains resulting from partially blocked arteries to the heart) by dilating the blood vessels. At 1 atm pressure and 25 °C, the enthalpy of decomposition of trinitroglycerin to form nitrogen gas, carbon dioxide gas, liquid water, and oxygen gas is -1541.4 kJ/mol. **(a)** Write a balanced chemical equation for the decomposition of trinitroglycerin. **(b)** Calculate the standard heat of formation of trinitroglycerin. **(c)** A standard dose of trinitroglycerin for relief of angina is 0.60 mg. If the sample is eventually oxidized in the body (not explosively, though!) to nitrogen gas, carbon dioxide gas, and liquid water, what number of calories is released? **(d)** One common form of trinitroglycerin melts at about 3 °C. From this information and the formula for the substance, would you expect it to be a molecular or ionic compound? Explain. **(e)** Describe the various conversions of forms of energy when trinitroglycerin is used as an explosive to break rockfaces in highway construction.

SOLUTION

(a) The general form of the equation we must balance is

$$C_3H_5N_3O_9(l) \longrightarrow N_2(g) + CO_2(g) + H_2O(l) + O_2(g)$$

We go about balancing in the usual way. To obtain an even number of nitrogen atoms on the left, we multiply the formula for $C_3H_5N_3O_9$ by 2, which gives us 3 mol of N_2, 6 mol of CO_2 and 5 mol of H_2O. Everything is balanced except for oxygen. We have an odd number of oxygen atoms on the right. We can balance the oxygen by adding $\frac{1}{2}$ mol of O_2 on the right:

$$2\,C_3H_5N_3O_9(l) \longrightarrow 3\,N_2(g) + 6\,CO_2(g) + 5\,H_2O(l) + \tfrac{1}{2}\,O_2(g)$$

We multiply through by 2 to convert all coefficients to whole numbers:

$$4\,C_3H_5N_3O_9(l) \longrightarrow 6\,N_2(g) + 12\,CO_2(g) + 10\,H_2O(l) + O_2(g)$$

(At the temperature of the explosion, water is a gas. The rapid expansion of the gaseous products creates the force of an explosion.)

(b) The heat of formation is the enthalpy change in the balanced chemical equation:

$$3\,C(s) + \tfrac{3}{2}\,N_2(g) + \tfrac{5}{2}\,H_2(g) + \tfrac{9}{2}\,O_2(g) \longrightarrow C_3H_5N_3O_9(l) \qquad \Delta H_f^\circ = ?$$

We can obtain the value of ΔH_f° by using the equation for the heat of decomposition of trinitroglycerin:

$$4\,C_3H_5N_3O_9(l) \longrightarrow 6\,N_2(g) + 12\,CO_2(g) + 10\,H_2O(l) + O_2(g)$$

The enthalpy change in this reaction is $4(-1541.4\text{ kJ}) = -6165.6$ kJ. [We need to multiply by 4 because there are 4 mol of $C_3H_5N_3O_9(l)$ in the balanced equation.] This enthalpy change is given by the sum of the heats of formation of the products minus the heats of formation of the reactants, each multiplied by its coefficient in the balanced equation:

$$-6165.6\text{ kJ} = \left\{ 6\Delta H_f^\circ[N_2(g)] + 12\Delta H_f^\circ[CO_2(g)] + 10\Delta H_f^\circ[H_2O(l)] + \Delta H_f^\circ[O_2(g)] \right\}$$

$$-4\Delta H_f^\circ\,[C_3H_5N_3O_9(l)]$$

The ΔH_f° values for $N_2(g)$ and $O_2(g)$ are zero, by definition. We look up the values for $H_2O(l)$ and $CO_2(g)$ in Table 5.3 and find that

$$-6165.6 \text{ kJ} = 12(-393.5 \text{ kJ}) + 10(-285.8 \text{ kJ}) - 4\Delta H_f^\circ[C_3H_5N_3O_9(l)]$$

$$\Delta H_f^\circ[C_3H_5N_3O_9(l)] = -353.6 \text{ kJ/mol}$$

(c) We know that on oxidation 1 mol of $C_3H_5N_3O_9(l)$ yields 1541.4 kJ. We need to calculate the number of moles of $C_3H_5N_3O_9(l)$ in 0.60 mg:

$$(0.60 \times 10^{-3} \text{ g } C_3H_5N_3O_9)\left(\frac{1 \text{ mol } C_3H_5N_3O_9}{227 \text{ g } C_3H_5N_3O_9}\right)\left(\frac{1541.4 \text{ kJ}}{1 \text{ mol } C_3H_5N_3O_9}\right) = 4.1 \times 10^{-3} \text{ kJ}$$

$$= 4.1 \text{ J}$$

(d) Because trinitroglycerin melts below room temperature, we expect that it is a molecular compound. With few exceptions, ionic substances are generally hard, crystalline materials that melt at high temperatures. ∞ (Sections 2.6 and 2.7) Also, the molecular formula suggests that it is likely to be a molecular substance. All the elements of which it is composed are nonmetals.

(e) The energy stored in trinitroglycerin is chemical potential energy. When the substance reacts explosively, it forms substances such as carbon dioxide, water, and nitrogen gas, which are of lower potential energy. In the course of the chemical transformation, energy is released in the form of heat; the gaseous reaction products are very hot. This very high heat energy is transferred to the surroundings; the gases expand against the surroundings, which may be solid materials. Work is done in moving the solid materials and imparting kinetic energy to them. For example, a chunk of rock might be impelled upward. It has been given kinetic energy by transfer of energy from the hot, expanding gases. As the rock rises, its kinetic energy is transformed into potential energy. Eventually, it again acquires kinetic energy as it falls to Earth. When it strikes Earth, its kinetic energy is converted largely to thermal energy, though some work may be done on the surroundings as well.

CHAPTER SUMMARY AND KEY TERMS

INTRODUCTION AND SECTION 5.1   **Thermodynamics** is the study of energy and its transformations. In this chapter we have focused on **thermochemistry**, the transformations of energy—especially heat—during chemical reactions.

An object can possess energy in two forms: (1) **kinetic energy** is the energy due to the motion of the object, and (2) **potential energy** is the energy that an object possesses by virtue of its position relative to other objects. An electron in motion near a proton, for example, has kinetic energy because of its motion and potential energy because of its electrostatic attraction to the proton. The SI unit of energy is the **joule** (J): $1 \text{ J} = 1 \text{ kg-m}^2/\text{s}^2$. Another common energy unit is the **calorie** (cal), which was originally defined as the quantity of energy necessary to increase the temperature of 1 g of water by 1 °C: 1 cal = 4.184 J.

When we study thermodynamic properties, we define a specific amount of matter as the **system**. Everything outside the system is the **surroundings**. When we study a chemical reaction, the system is generally the reactants and products. A closed system can exchange energy, but not matter, with the surroundings. Energy can be transferred between the system and the surroundings as work or heat. **Work** is the energy expended to move an object against a **force**. **Heat** is the energy that is transferred from a hotter object to a colder one. **Energy** is the capacity to do work or to transfer heat.

SECTION 5.2   The **internal energy** of a system is the sum of all the kinetic and potential energies of its component parts. The internal energy of a system can change because of energy transferred between the system and the surroundings. According to the **first law of thermodynamics**, the change in the internal energy of a system, ΔE, is the sum of the heat, q, transferred into or out of the system and the work, w, done on or by the system: $\Delta E = q + w$. Both q and w have a sign that indicates the direction of energy transfer. When heat is transferred from the surroundings to the system, $q > 0$. Likewise, when the surroundings do work on the system, $w > 0$. In an **endothermic** process the system absorbs heat from the surroundings; in an **exothermic** process the system releases heat to the surroundings.

The internal energy, E, is a **state function**. The value of any state function depends only on the state or condition of the system and not on the details of how it came to be in that state. The heat, q, and the work, w, are not state functions; their values depend on the particular way by which a system changes its state.

SECTIONS 5.3 AND 5.4   When a gas is produced or consumed in a chemical reaction occurring at constant pressure, the system may perform **pressure-volume (P-V) work** against the prevailing pressure of the surroundings. For this reason, we define a new state function called **enthalpy**, H, which is related to energy: $H = E + PV$. In systems where only pressure-volume work is involved, the change in the enthalpy of a system, ΔH, equals the heat gained or lost by the system at constant pressure: $\Delta H = q_p$ (the subscript p denotes constant pressure). For an endothermic process, $\Delta H > 0$; for an exothermic process, $\Delta H < 0$.

In a chemical process, the **enthalpy of reaction** is the enthalpy of the products minus the enthalpy of the reactants: $\Delta H_{rxn} = H(\text{products}) - H(\text{reactants})$. Enthalpies of reaction follow some simple rules: (1) The enthalpy of reaction is proportional to the amount of reactant that reacts. (2) Reversing a reaction changes the sign of ΔH. (3) The enthalpy of reaction depends on the physical states of the reactants and products.

SECTION 5.5   The amount of heat transferred between the system and the surroundings is measured experimentally by **calorimetry**. A **calorimeter** measures the temperature change accompanying a process. The temperature change of a calorimeter depends on its **heat**

capacity, the amount of heat required to raise its temperature by 1 K. The heat capacity for one mole of a pure substance is called its **molar heat capacity**; for one gram of the substance, we use the term **specific heat**. Water has a very high specific heat, 4.18 J/g-K. The amount of heat, q, absorbed by a substance is the product of its specific heat (C_s), its mass, and its temperature change: $q = C_s \times m \times \Delta T$.

If a calorimetry experiment is carried out under a constant pressure, the heat transferred provides a direct measure of the enthalpy change of the reaction. Constant-volume calorimetry is carried out in a vessel of fixed volume called a **bomb calorimeter**. Bomb calorimeters are used to measure the heat evolved in combustion reactions. The heat transferred under constant-volume conditions is equal to ΔE. Corrections can be applied to ΔE values to yield enthalpies of combustion.

SECTION 5.6 Because enthalpy is a state function, ΔH depends only on the initial and final states of the system. Thus, the enthalpy change of a process is the same whether the process is carried out in one step or in a series of steps. **Hess's law** states that if a reaction is carried out in a series of steps, ΔH for the reaction will be equal to the sum of the enthalpy changes for the steps. We can therefore calculate ΔH for any process, as long as we can write the process as a series of steps for which ΔH is known.

SECTION 5.7 The **enthalpy of formation**, ΔH_f, of a substance is the enthalpy change for the reaction in which the substance is formed from its constituent elements. The **standard enthalpy change** of a reaction, $\Delta H°$, is the enthalpy change when all reactants and products are at 1 atm pressure and a specific temperature, usually 298 K (25 °C). Combining these ideas, the **standard enthalpy of formation**, $\Delta H_f°$, of a substance is the change in enthalpy for the reaction that forms one mole of the substance from its elements in their most stable form with all reactants and products at 1 atm pressure and usually 298 K. For any element in its most stable state at 298 K and 1 atm pressure, $\Delta H_f° = 0$. The standard enthalpy change for any reaction can be readily calculated from the standard enthalpies of formation of the reactants and products in the reaction:

$$\Delta H_{rxn}° = \Sigma n \Delta H_f°(\text{products}) - \Sigma m \Delta H_f°(\text{reactants})$$

SECTION 5.8 The **fuel value** of a substance is the heat released when one gram of the substance is combusted. Different types of foods have different fuel values and differing abilities to be stored in the body. The most common fuels are hydrocarbons that are found as **fossil fuels**, such as **natural gas, petroleum**, and **coal**. Coal is the most abundant fossil fuel, but the sulfur present in most coals causes air pollution. **Renewable energy sources** include solar energy, wind energy, biomass, and hydroelectric energy. Nuclear power does not utilize fossil fuels but does create controversial waste-disposal problems. The challenge of providing energy for the world has significant political and social implications in the areas of food supply and the environment.

KEY SKILLS

- Interconvert energy units. (Section 5.1)
- Distinguish between the system and the surroundings in thermodynamics. (Section 5.1)
- State the first law of thermodynamics. (Section 5.2)
- Understand the concept of a state function and be able to give examples. (Section 5.2)
- Express the relationships among the quantities q, w, ΔE, and ΔH. Learn their sign conventions, including how the signs of q and ΔH relate to whether a process is exothermic or endothermic. (Sections 5.2 and 5.3)
- Use thermochemical equations to relate the amount of heat energy transferred in reactions at constant pressure (ΔH) to the amount of substance involved in the reaction. (Section 5.4)
- Calculate the heat transferred in a process from temperature measurements together with heat capacities or specific heats (calorimetry). (Section 5.5)
- Use Hess's law to determine enthalpy changes for reactions. (Section 5.6)
- Use standard enthalpies of formation to calculate $\Delta H°$ for reactions. (Section 5.7)

KEY EQUATIONS

- $E_k = \frac{1}{2}mv^2$ [5.1]   Kinetic energy
- $\Delta E = E_{\text{final}} - E_{\text{initial}}$ [5.4]   The change in internal energy
- $\Delta E = q + w$ [5.5]   Relates the change in internal energy to heat and work (the first law of thermodynamics)
- $w = -P\,\Delta V$ [5.8]   The work done by an expanding gas at constant pressure
- $\Delta H = \Delta E + P\,\Delta V = q_P$ [5.10]   Enthalpy change at constant pressure
- $q = C_s \times m \times \Delta T$ [5.22]   Heat gained or lost based on specific heat, mass, and temperature change
- $\Delta H_{rxn}° = \Sigma n \Delta H_f°(\text{products}) - \Sigma m \Delta H_f°(\text{reactants})$ [5.31]   Standard enthalpy change of a reaction

EXERCISES

VISUALIZING CONCEPTS

5.1 Imagine a book that is falling from a shelf. At a particular moment during its fall, the book has a kinetic energy of 24 J and a potential energy with respect to the floor of 47 J. **(a)** How does the book's kinetic energy and its potential energy change as it continues to fall? **(b)** What is its total kinetic energy at the instant just before it strikes the floor? **(c)** If a heavier book fell from the same shelf, would it have the same kinetic energy when it strikes the floor? [Section 5.1]

5.2 The accompanying photo shows a pipevine swallowtail caterpillar climbing up a twig. **(a)** As the caterpillar climbs, its potential energy is increasing. What source of energy has been used to effect this change in potential energy? **(b)** If the caterpillar is the system, can you predict the sign of q as the caterpillar climbs? **(c)** Does the caterpillar do work in climbing the twig? Explain. **(d)** Does the amount of work done in climbing a 12-inch section of the twig depend on the speed of the caterpillar's climb? **(e)** Does the change in potential energy depend on the caterpillar's speed of climb? [Section 5.1]

5.3 Consider the accompanying energy diagram. **(a)** Does this diagram represent an increase or decrease in the internal energy of the system? **(b)** What sign is given to ΔE for this process? **(c)** If there is no work associated with the process, is it exothermic or endothermic? [Section 5.2]

5.4 The contents of the closed box in each of the following illustrations represent a system, and the arrows show the changes to the system during some process. The lengths of the arrows represent the relative magnitudes of q and w. **(a)** Which of these processes is endothermic? **(b)** For which of these processes, if any, is $\Delta E < 0$? **(c)** For which process, if any, does the system experience a net gain in internal energy? [Section 5.2]

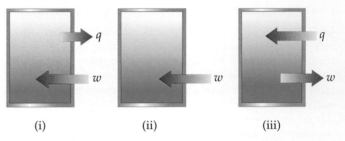

(i)   (ii)   (iii)

5.5 Imagine that you are climbing a mountain. **(a)** Is the distance you travel to the top a state function? Why or why not? **(b)** Is the change in elevation between your base camp and the peak a state function? Why or why not? [Section 5.2]

5.6 The diagram shows four states of a system, each with different internal energy, E. **(a)** Which of the states of the system has the greatest internal energy? **(b)** In terms of the ΔE values, write two expressions for the difference in internal energy between State A and State B. **(c)** Write an expression for the difference in energy between State C and State D. **(d)** Suppose there is another state of the system, State E, and that its energy relative to State A is $\Delta E = \Delta E_1 + \Delta E_4$. Where would State E be on the diagram? [Section 5.2]

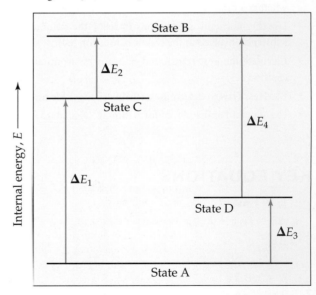

5.7 You may have noticed that when you compress the air in a bicycle pump, the body of the pump gets warmer. **(a)** Assuming the pump and the air in it comprise the system, what is the sign of w when you compress the air? **(b)** What is the sign of q for this process? **(c)** Based on your answers to parts (a) and (b), can you determine the sign of ΔE for compressing the air in the pump? If not, what would you expect for the sign of ΔE? What is your reasoning? [Section 5.2]

5.8 In the accompanying cylinder diagram a chemical process occurs at constant temperature and pressure. **(a)** Is the sign of w indicated by this change positive or negative? **(b)** If the process is endothermic, does the internal energy of the system within the cylinder increase or decrease during the change and is ΔE positive or negative? [Sections 5.2 and 5.3]

5.9 Imagine a container placed in a tub of water, as depicted in the accompanying diagram. **(a)** If the contents of the container are the system and heat is able to flow through the container walls, what qualitative changes will occur in the temperatures of the system and in its surroundings? What is the sign of q associated with each change? From the system's perspective, is the process exothermic or endothermic? **(b)** If neither the volume nor the pressure of the system changes during the process, how is the change in internal energy related to the change in enthalpy? [Sections 5.2 and 5.3]

5.10 The gas-phase reaction shown, between N_2 and O_2, was run in an apparatus designed to maintain a constant pressure. **(a)** Write a balanced chemical equation for the reaction depicted and predict whether w is positive, negative, or zero. **(b)** Using data from Appendix C, determine ΔH for the formation of one mole of the product. Why is this enthalpy change called the enthalpy of formation of the involved product? [Sections 5.3 and 5.7]

5.11 Consider the two diagrams that follow. **(a)** Based on (i), write an equation showing how ΔH_A is related to ΔH_B and ΔH_C. How do both diagram (i) and your equation relate to the fact that enthalpy is a state function? **(b)** Based on (ii), write an equation relating ΔH_Z to the other enthalpy changes in the diagram. **(c)** How do these diagrams relate to Hess's law? [Section 5.6]

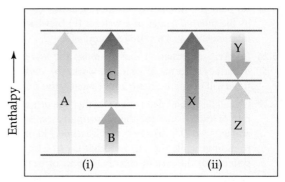

5.12 Consider the conversion of compound A into compound B: A $\longrightarrow$ B. For both compounds A and B, $\Delta H_f^\circ > 0$. **(a)** Sketch an enthalpy diagram for the reaction that is analogous to Figure 5.23. **(b)** Suppose the overall reaction is exothermic. What can you conclude? [Section 5.7]

THE NATURE OF ENERGY (section 5.1)

5.13 In what two ways can an object possess energy? How do these two ways differ from one another?

5.14 Suppose you toss a tennis ball upward. **(a)** Does the kinetic energy of the ball increase or decrease as it moves higher? **(b)** What happens to the potential energy of the ball as it moves higher? **(c)** If the same amount of energy were imparted to a ball the same size as a tennis ball but of twice the mass, how high would it go in comparison to the tennis ball? Explain your answers.

5.15 **(a)** Calculate the kinetic energy in joules of a 1200-kg automobile moving at 18 m/s. **(b)** Convert this energy to calories. **(c)** What happens to this energy when the automobile brakes to a stop?

5.16 **(a)** A baseball weighs 5.13 oz. What is the kinetic energy in joules of this baseball when it is thrown by a major-league pitcher at 95.0 mph? **(b)** By what factor will the kinetic energy change if the speed of the baseball is decreased to 55.0 mph? **(c)** What happens to the kinetic energy when the baseball is caught by the catcher? **(d)** What careful experimental measurement could (in principle) be made to confirm your answer to (c)?

5.17 The use of the British thermal unit (Btu) is common in much engineering work. A Btu is the amount of heat required to raise the temperature of 1 lb of water by 1 °F. Calculate the number of joules in a Btu.

5.18 A watt is a measure of power (the rate of energy change) equal to 1 J/s. **(a)** Calculate the number of joules in a kilowatt-hour. **(b)** An adult person radiates heat to the surroundings at about the same rate as a 100-watt electric incandescent lightbulb. What is the total amount of energy in kcal radiated to the surroundings by an adult in 24 hours?

5.19 **(a)** What is meant by the term *system* in thermodynamics? **(b)** What is a *closed system*? **(c)** What do we call the part of the universe that is not part of the system?

5.20 In a thermodynamic study a scientist focuses on the properties of a solution in an apparatus as illustrated. A solution is continuously flowing into the apparatus at the top and out at the bottom, such that the amount of solution in the apparatus is constant with time. **(a)** Is the solution in the apparatus a closed system, open system, or isolated system? Explain your choice. **(b)** If it is not a closed system, what could be done to make it a closed system?

5.21 **(a)** What is work? **(b)** How do we determine the amount of work done, given the force associated with the work?

5.22 **(a)** What is heat? **(b)** Under what conditions is heat transferred from one object to another?

5.23 Identify the force present and explain whether work is being performed in the following cases: **(a)** You lift a pencil off the top of a desk. **(b)** A spring is compressed to half its normal length.

5.24 Identify the force present and explain whether work is done when **(a)** a positively charged particle moves in a circle at a fixed distance from a negatively charged particle; **(b)** an iron nail is pulled off a magnet.

THE FIRST LAW OF THERMODYNAMICS (section 5.2)

5.25 **(a)** State the first law of thermodynamics. **(b)** What is meant by the *internal energy* of a system? **(c)** By what means can the internal energy of a closed system increase?

5.26 **(a)** Write an equation that expresses the first law of thermodynamics in terms of heat and work. **(b)** Under what conditions will the quantities q and w be negative numbers?

5.27 Calculate ΔE and determine whether the process is endothermic or exothermic for the following cases: **(a)** $q = 0.763$ kJ and $w = -840$ J; **(b)** a system releases 66.1 kJ of heat to its surroundings while the surroundings do 44.0 kJ of work on the system; **(c)** the system absorbs 7.25 kJ of heat from the surroundings while its volume remains constant (assume that only *P-V* work can be done).

5.28 For the following processes, calculate the change in internal energy of the system and determine whether the process is endothermic or exothermic: **(a)** A balloon is cooled by removing 0.655 kJ of heat. It shrinks on cooling, and the atmosphere does 382 J of work on the balloon. **(b)** A 100.0-g bar of gold is heated from 25 °C to 50 °C during which it absorbs 322 J of heat. Assume the volume of the gold bar remains constant. **(c)** The surroundings do 1.44 kJ of work compressing gas in a perfectly insulated cylinder.

5.29 A gas is confined to a cylinder fitted with a piston and an electrical heater, as shown here:

Suppose that current is supplied to the heater so that 100 J of energy is added. Consider two different situations. In case (1) the piston is allowed to move as the energy is added. In case (2) the piston is fixed so that it cannot move. **(a)** In which case does the gas have the higher temperature after addition of the electrical energy? Explain. **(b)** What can you say about the values of q and w in each case? **(c)** What can you say about the relative values of ΔE for the system (the gas in the cylinder) in the two cases?

5.30 Consider a system consisting of two oppositely charged spheres hanging by strings and separated by a distance r_1, as shown in the accompanying illustration. Suppose they are separated to a larger distance r_2, by moving them apart along a track. **(a)** What change, if any, has occurred in the potential energy of the system? **(b)** What effect, if any, does this process have on the value of ΔE? **(c)** What can you say about q and w for this process?

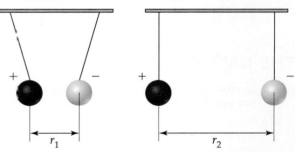

5.31 **(a)** What is meant by the term *state function*? **(b)** Give an example of a quantity that is a state function and one that is not. **(c)** Is the volume of the system a state function? Why or why not?

5.32 Indicate which of the following is independent of the path by which a change occurs: **(a)** the change in potential energy when a book is transferred from table to shelf, **(b)** the heat evolved when a cube of sugar is oxidized to $CO_2(g)$ and $H_2O(g)$, **(c)** the work accomplished in burning a gallon of gasoline.

ENTHALPY (sections 5.3 and 5.4)

5.33 (a) Why is the change in enthalpy usually easier to measure than the change in internal energy? (b) H is a state function, but q is not a state function. Explain. (c) For a given process at constant pressure, ΔH is positive. Is the process endothermic or exothermic?

5.34 (a) Under what condition will the enthalpy change of a process equal the amount of heat transferred into or out of the system? (b) During a constant-pressure process, the system releases heat to the surroundings. Does the enthalpy of the system increase or decrease during the process? (c) In a constant-pressure process, $\Delta H = 0$. What can you conclude about ΔE, q, and w?

5.35 You are given ΔH for a process that occurs at constant pressure. What additional information do you need to determine ΔE for the process?

5.36 Suppose that the gas-phase reaction $2\,NO(g) + O_2(g) \longrightarrow 2\,NO_2(g)$ were carried out in a constant-volume container at constant temperature. Would the measured heat change represent ΔH or ΔE? If there is a difference, which quantity is larger for this reaction? Explain.

5.37 A gas is confined to a cylinder under constant atmospheric pressure, as illustrated in Figure 5.4. When the gas undergoes a particular chemical reaction, it absorbs 824 J of heat from its surroundings and has 0.65 kJ of P-V work done on it by its surroundings. What are the values of ΔH and ΔE for this process?

5.38 A gas is confined to a cylinder under constant atmospheric pressure, as illustrated in Figure 5.4. When 0.49 kJ of heat is added to the gas, it expands and does 214 J of work on the surroundings. What are the values of ΔH and ΔE for this process?

5.39 The complete combustion of ethanol, $C_2H_5OH(l)$, to form $H_2O(g)$ and $CO_2(g)$ at constant pressure releases 1235 kJ of heat per mole of C_2H_5OH. (a) Write a balanced thermochemical equation for this reaction. (b) Draw an enthalpy diagram for the reaction.

5.40 The decomposition of *slaked lime*, $Ca(OH)_2(s)$, into *lime*, $CaO(s)$, and $H_2O(g)$ at constant pressure requires the addition of 109 kJ of heat per mole of $Ca(OH)_2$. (a) Write a balanced thermochemical equation for the reaction. (b) Draw an enthalpy diagram for the reaction.

5.41 Ozone, $O_3(g)$, is a form of elemental oxygen that is important in the absorption of ultraviolet radiation in the stratosphere. It decomposes to $O_2(g)$ at room temperature and pressure according to the following reaction:

$$2\,O_3(g) \longrightarrow 3\,O_2(g) \qquad \Delta H = -284.6\ kJ$$

(a) What is the enthalpy change for this reaction per mole of $O_3(g)$? (b) Which has the higher enthalpy under these conditions, $2\,O_3(g)$ or $3\,O_2(g)$?

5.42 Without referring to tables, predict which of the following has the higher enthalpy in each case: (a) 1 mol $CO_2(s)$ or 1 mol $CO_2(g)$ at the same temperature, (b) 2 mol of hydrogen atoms or 1 mol of H_2, (c) 1 mol $H_2(g)$ and 0.5 mol $O_2(g)$ at 25 °C or 1 mol $H_2O(g)$ at 25 °C, (d) 1 mol $N_2(g)$ at 100 °C or 1 mol $N_2(g)$ at 300 °C.

5.43 Consider the following reaction:

$$2\,Mg(s) + O_2(g) \longrightarrow 2\,MgO(s) \qquad \Delta H = -1204\ kJ$$

(a) Is this reaction exothermic or endothermic? (b) Calculate the amount of heat transferred when 3.55 g of $Mg(s)$ reacts at constant pressure. (c) How many grams of MgO are produced during an enthalpy change of −234 kJ? (d) How many kilojoules of heat are absorbed when 40.3 g of $MgO(s)$ is decomposed into $Mg(s)$ and $O_2(g)$ at constant pressure?

5.44 Consider the following reaction:

$$2\,CH_3OH(g) \longrightarrow 2\,CH_4(g) + O_2(g) \qquad \Delta H = +252.8\ kJ$$

(a) Is this reaction exothermic or endothermic? (b) Calculate the amount of heat transferred when 24.0 g of $CH_3OH(g)$ is decomposed by this reaction at constant pressure. (c) For a given sample of CH_3OH, the enthalpy change during the reaction is 82.1 kJ. How many grams of methane gas are produced? (d) How many kilojoules of heat are released when 38.5 g of $CH_4(g)$ reacts completely with $O_2(g)$ to form $CH_3OH(g)$ at constant pressure?

5.45 When solutions containing silver ions and chloride ions are mixed, silver chloride precipitates:

$$Ag^+(aq) + Cl^-(aq) \longrightarrow AgCl(s) \qquad \Delta H = -65.5\ kJ$$

(a) Calculate ΔH for production of 0.450 mol of AgCl by this reaction. (b) Calculate ΔH for the production of 9.00 g of AgCl. (c) Calculate ΔH when 9.25×10^{-4} mol of AgCl dissolves in water.

5.46 At one time, a common means of forming small quantities of oxygen gas in the laboratory was to heat $KClO_3$:

$$2\,KClO_3(s) \longrightarrow 2\,KCl(s) + 3\,O_2(g) \qquad \Delta H = -89.4\ kJ$$

For this reaction, calculate ΔH for the formation of (a) 1.36 mol of O_2 and (b) 10.4 g of KCl. (c) The decomposition of $KClO_3$ proceeds spontaneously when it is heated. Do you think that the reverse reaction, the formation of $KClO_3$ from KCl and O_2, is likely to be feasible under ordinary conditions? Explain your answer.

5.47 Consider the combustion of liquid methanol, $CH_3OH(l)$:

$$CH_3OH(l) + \tfrac{3}{2}O_2(g) \longrightarrow CO_2(g) + 2\,H_2O(l)$$
$$\Delta H = -726.5\ kJ$$

(a) What is the enthalpy change for the reverse reaction? (b) Balance the forward reaction with whole-number coefficients. What is ΔH for the reaction represented by this equation? (c) Which is more likely to be thermodynamically favored, the forward reaction or the reverse reaction? (d) If the reaction were written to produce $H_2O(g)$ instead of $H_2O(l)$, would you expect the magnitude of ΔH to increase, decrease, or stay the same? Explain.

5.48 Consider the decomposition of liquid benzene, $C_6H_6(l)$, to gaseous acetylene, $C_2H_2(g)$:

$$C_6H_6(l) \longrightarrow 3\,C_2H_2(g) \qquad \Delta H = +630\ kJ$$

(a) What is the enthalpy change for the reverse reaction? (b) What is ΔH for the formation of 1 mol of acetylene? (c) Which is more likely to be thermodynamically favored, the forward reaction or the reverse reaction? (d) If $C_6H_6(g)$ were consumed instead of $C_6H_6(l)$, would you expect the magnitude of ΔH to increase, decrease, or stay the same? Explain.

CALORIMETRY (section 5.5)

5.49 (a) What are the units of molar heat capacity? (b) What are the units of specific heat? (c) If you know the specific heat of copper, what additional information do you need to calculate the heat capacity of a particular piece of copper pipe?

5.50 Two solid objects, A and B, are placed in boiling water and allowed to come to temperature there. Each is then lifted out and placed in separate beakers containing 1000 g water at 10.0 °C. Object A increases the water temperature by 3.50 °C; B increases the water temperature by 2.60 °C. (a) Which object has the larger heat capacity? (b) What can you say about the specific heats of A and B?

5.51 (a) What is the specific heat of liquid water? (b) What is the molar heat capacity of liquid water? (c) What is the heat capacity of 185 g of liquid water? (d) How many kJ of heat are needed to raise the temperature of 10.00 kg of liquid water from 24.6 °C to 46.2 °C?

5.52 (a) Which substance in Table 5.2 requires the smallest amount of energy to increase the temperature of 50.0 g of that substance by 10 K? (b) Calculate the energy needed for this temperature change.

5.53 The specific heat of *octane*, $C_8H_{18}(l)$, is 2.22 J/g-K. (a) How many J of heat are needed to raise the temperature of 80.0 g of octane from 10.0 °C to 25.0 °C? (b) Which will require more heat, increasing the temperature of 1 mol of $C_8H_{18}(l)$ by a certain amount or increasing the temperature of 1 mol of $H_2O(l)$ by the same amount?

5.54 Consider the data about gold metal in Exercise 5.28(b). (a) Based on the data, calculate the specific heat of $Au(s)$. (b) Suppose that the same amount of heat is added to two 10.0-g blocks of metal, both initially at the same temperature. One block is gold metal and one is iron metal. Which block will have the greater rise in temperature after the addition of the heat? (c) What is the molar heat capacity of $Au(s)$?

5.55 When a 6.50-g sample of solid sodium hydroxide dissolves in 100.0 g of water in a coffee-cup calorimeter (Figure 5.18), the temperature rises from 21.6 °C to 37.8 °C. Calculate ΔH (in kJ/mol NaOH) for the solution process

$$NaOH(s) \longrightarrow Na^+(aq) + OH^-(aq)$$

Assume that the specific heat of the solution is the same as that of pure water.

5.56 (a) When a 4.25-g sample of solid ammonium nitrate dissolves in 60.0 g of water in a coffee-cup calorimeter (Figure 5.18), the temperature drops from 22.0 °C to 16.9 °C. Calculate ΔH (in kJ/mol NH$_4$NO$_3$) for the solution process

$$NH_4NO_3(s) \longrightarrow NH_4^+(aq) + NO_3^-(aq)$$

Assume that the specific heat of the solution is the same as that of pure water. (b) Is this process endothermic or exothermic?

5.57 A 2.200-g sample of quinone ($C_6H_4O_2$) is burned in a bomb calorimeter whose total heat capacity is 7.854 kJ/°C. The temperature of the calorimeter increases from 23.44 °C to 30.57 °C. What is the heat of combustion per gram of quinone? Per mole of quinone?

5.58 A 1.800-g sample of phenol (C_6H_5OH) was burned in a bomb calorimeter whose total heat capacity is 11.66 kJ/°C. The temperature of the calorimeter plus contents increased from 21.36 °C to 26.37 °C. (a) Write a balanced chemical equation for the bomb calorimeter reaction. (b) What is the heat of combustion per gram of phenol? Per mole of phenol?

5.59 Under constant-volume conditions, the heat of combustion of glucose ($C_6H_{12}O_6$) is 15.57 kJ/g. A 3.500-g sample of glucose is burned in a bomb calorimeter. The temperature of the calorimeter increased from 20.94 °C to 24.72 °C. (a) What is the total heat capacity of the calorimeter? (b) If the size of the glucose sample had been exactly twice as large, what would the temperature change of the calorimeter have been?

5.60 Under constant-volume conditions, the heat of combustion of benzoic acid (C_6H_5COOH) is 26.38 kJ/g. A 2.760-g sample of benzoic acid is burned in a bomb calorimeter. The temperature of the calorimeter increases from 21.60 °C to 29.93 °C. (a) What is the total heat capacity of the calorimeter? (b) A 1.440-g sample of a new organic substance is combusted in the same calorimeter. The temperature of the calorimeter increases from 22.14 °C to 27.09 °C. What is the heat of combustion per gram of the new substance? (c) Suppose that in changing samples, a portion of the water in the calorimeter were lost. In what way, if any, would this change the heat capacity of the calorimeter?

HESS'S LAW (section 5.6)

5.61 What is the connection between Hess's law and the fact that H is a state function?

5.62 Consider the following hypothetical reactions:

$$A \longrightarrow B \qquad \Delta H = +30 \text{ kJ}$$
$$B \longrightarrow C \qquad \Delta H = +60 \text{ kJ}$$

(a) Use Hess's law to calculate the enthalpy change for the reaction $A \longrightarrow C$. (b) Construct an enthalpy diagram for substances A, B, and C, and show how Hess's law applies.

5.63 Calculate the enthalpy change for the reaction

$$P_4O_6(s) + 2 O_2(g) \longrightarrow P_4O_{10}(s)$$

given the following enthalpies of reaction:

$$P_4(s) + 3 O_2(g) \longrightarrow P_4O_6(s) \qquad \Delta H = -1640.1 \text{ kJ}$$
$$P_4(s) + 5 O_2(g) \longrightarrow P_4O_{10}(s) \qquad \Delta H = -2940.1 \text{ kJ}$$

5.64 From the enthalpies of reaction

$$2 C(s) + O_2(g) \longrightarrow 2 CO(g) \qquad \Delta H = -221.0 \text{ kJ}$$
$$2 C(s) + O_2(g) + 4 H_2(g) \longrightarrow 2 CH_3OH(g) \qquad \Delta H = -402.4 \text{ kJ}$$

calculate ΔH for the reaction

$$CO(g) + 2 H_2(g) \longrightarrow CH_3OH(g)$$

5.65 From the enthalpies of reaction

$$H_2(g) + F_2(g) \longrightarrow 2 HF(g) \qquad \Delta H = -537 \text{ kJ}$$
$$C(s) + 2 F_2(g) \longrightarrow CF_4(g) \qquad \Delta H = -680 \text{ kJ}$$
$$2 C(s) + 2 H_2(g) \longrightarrow C_2H_4(g) \qquad \Delta H = +52.3 \text{ kJ}$$

calculate ΔH for the reaction of ethylene with F_2:

$$C_2H_4(g) + 6 F_2(g) \longrightarrow 2 CF_4(g) + 4 HF(g)$$

5.66 Given the data

$$N_2(g) + O_2(g) \longrightarrow 2\,NO(g) \qquad \Delta H = +180.7 \text{ kJ}$$
$$2\,NO(g) + O_2(g) \longrightarrow 2\,NO_2(g) \qquad \Delta H = -113.1 \text{ kJ}$$
$$2\,N_2O(g) \longrightarrow 2\,N_2(g) + O_2(g) \qquad \Delta H = -163.2 \text{ kJ}$$

use Hess's law to calculate ΔH for the reaction

$$N_2O(g) + NO_2(g) \longrightarrow 3\,NO(g)$$

ENTHALPIES OF FORMATION (section 5.7)

5.67 (a) What is meant by the term *standard conditions* with reference to enthalpy changes? (b) What is meant by the term *enthalpy of formation*? (c) What is meant by the term *standard enthalpy of formation*?

5.68 (a) Why are tables of standard enthalpies of formation so useful? (b) What is the value of the standard enthalpy of formation of an element in its most stable form? (c) Write the chemical equation for the reaction whose enthalpy change is the standard enthalpy of formation of sucrose (table sugar), $C_{12}H_{22}O_{11}(s)$, $\Delta H_f^\circ[C_{12}H_{22}O_{11}]$.

5.69 For each of the following compounds, write a balanced thermochemical equation depicting the formation of one mole of the compound from its elements in their standard states and use Appendix C to obtain the value of ΔH_f°: (a) $NO_2(g)$, (b) $SO_3(g)$, (c) $NaBr(s)$, (d) $Pb(NO_3)_2(s)$.

5.70 Write balanced equations that describe the formation of the following compounds from elements in their standard states, and use Appendix C to obtain the values of their standard enthalpies of formation: (a) $H_2O_2(g)$, (b) $CaCO_3(s)$, (c) $POCl_3(l)$, (d) $C_2H_5OH(l)$.

5.71 The following is known as the thermite reaction [Figure 5.8(b)]:

$$2\,Al(s) + Fe_2O_3(s) \longrightarrow Al_2O_3(s) + 2\,Fe(s)$$

This highly exothermic reaction is used for welding massive units, such as propellers for large ships. Using standard enthalpies of formation in Appendix C, calculate ΔH° for this reaction.

5.72 Many portable gas heaters and grills use propane, $C_3H_8(g)$, as a fuel. Using standard enthalpies of formation, calculate the quantity of heat produced when 10.0 g of propane is completely combusted in air under standard conditions.

5.73 Using values from Appendix C, calculate the standard enthalpy change for each of the following reactions:

(a) $2\,SO_2(g) + O_2(g) \longrightarrow 2\,SO_3(g)$

(b) $Mg(OH)_2(s) \longrightarrow MgO(s) + H_2O(l)$

(c) $N_2O_4(g) + 4\,H_2(g) \longrightarrow N_2(g) + 4\,H_2O(g)$

(d) $SiCl_4(l) + 2\,H_2O(l) \longrightarrow SiO_2(s) + 4\,HCl(g)$

5.74 Using values from Appendix C, calculate the value of ΔH° for each of the following reactions:

(a) $CaO(s) + 2\,HCl(g) \longrightarrow CaCl_2(s) + H_2O(g)$

(b) $4\,FeO(s) + O_2(g) \longrightarrow 2\,Fe_2O_3(s)$

(c) $2\,CuO(s) + NO(g) \longrightarrow Cu_2O(s) + NO_2(g)$

(d) $4\,NH_3(g) + O_2(g) \longrightarrow 2\,N_2H_4(g) + 2\,H_2O(l)$

5.75 Complete combustion of 1 mol of acetone (C_3H_6O) liberates 1790 kJ:

$$C_3H_6O(l) + 4\,O_2(g) \longrightarrow 3\,CO_2(g) + 3\,H_2O(l)$$
$$\Delta H^\circ = -1790 \text{ kJ}$$

Using this information together with data from Appendix C, calculate the enthalpy of formation of acetone.

5.76 Calcium carbide (CaC_2) reacts with water to form acetylene (C_2H_2) and $Ca(OH)_2$. From the following enthalpy of reaction data and data in Appendix C, calculate ΔH_f° for $CaC_2(s)$:

$$CaC_2(s) + 2\,H_2O(l) \longrightarrow Ca(OH)_2(s) + C_2H_2(g)$$
$$\Delta H^\circ = -127.2 \text{ kJ}$$

5.77 Gasoline is composed primarily of hydrocarbons, including many with eight carbon atoms, called *octanes*. One of the cleanest-burning octanes is a compound called 2,3,4-trimethylpentane, which has the following structural formula:

$$\begin{array}{ccccc} & CH_3 & CH_3 & CH_3 & \\ & | & | & | & \\ H_3C- & CH- & CH- & CH- & CH_3 \end{array}$$

The complete combustion of one mole of this compound to $CO_2(g)$ and $H_2O(g)$ leads to $\Delta H^\circ = -5064.9$ kJ/mol. (a) Write a balanced equation for the combustion of 1 mol of $C_8H_{18}(l)$. (b) Write a balanced equation for the formation of $C_8H_{18}(l)$ from its elements. (c) By using the information in this problem and data in Table 5.3, calculate ΔH_f° for 2,3,4-trimethylpentane.

5.78 Diethyl ether, $C_4H_{10}O(l)$, a flammable compound that has long been used as a surgical anesthetic, has the structure

$$CH_3-CH_2-O-CH_2-CH_3$$

The complete combustion of 1 mol of $C_4H_{10}O(l)$ to $CO_2(g)$ and $H_2O(l)$ yields $\Delta H^\circ = -2723.7$ kJ. (a) Write a balanced equation for the combustion of 1 mol of $C_4H_{10}O(l)$. (b) Write a balanced equation for the formation of $C_4H_{10}O(l)$ from its elements. (c) By using the information in this problem and data in Table 5.3, calculate ΔH_f° for diethyl ether.

5.79 Ethanol (C_2H_5OH) is currently blended with gasoline as an automobile fuel. (a) Write a balanced equation for the combustion of liquid ethanol in air. (b) Calculate the standard enthalpy change for the reaction, assuming $H_2O(g)$ as a product. (c) Calculate the heat produced per liter of ethanol by combustion of ethanol under constant pressure. Ethanol has a density of 0.789 g/mL. (d) Calculate the mass of CO_2 produced per kJ of heat emitted.

5.80 Methanol (CH_3OH) is used as a fuel in race cars. (a) Write a balanced equation for the combustion of liquid methanol in air. (b) Calculate the standard enthalpy change for the reaction, assuming $H_2O(g)$ as a product. (c) Calculate the heat produced by combustion per liter of methanol. Methanol has a density of 0.791 g/mL. (d) Calculate the mass of CO_2 produced per kJ of heat emitted.

FOODS AND FUELS (section 5.8)

5.81 (a) What is meant by the term *fuel value*? (b) Which is a greater source of energy as food, 5 g of fat or 9 g of carbohydrate? (c) The metabolism of glucose produces $CO_2(g)$ and $H_2O(l)$. How does the human body expel these reaction products?

5.82 (a) Why are fats well suited for energy storage in the human body? (b) A particular chip snack food is composed of 12% protein, 14% fat, and the rest carbohydrate. What percentage of the calorie content of this food is fat? (c) How many grams of protein provide the same fuel value as 25 g of fat?

5.83 (a) A serving of a particular ready-to-serve chicken noodle soup contains 2.5 g fat, 14 g carbohydrate, and 7 g protein. Estimate the number of Calories in a serving. (b) According to its nutrition label, the same soup also contains 690 mg of sodium. Do you think the sodium contributes to the caloric content of the soup?

5.84 A pound of plain M&M® candies contains 96 g fat, 320 g carbohydrate, and 21 g protein. What is the fuel value in kJ in a 42-g (about 1.5 oz) serving? How many Calories does it provide?

5.85 The heat of combustion of fructose, $C_6H_{12}O_6$, is -2812 kJ/mol. If a fresh golden delicious apple weighing 4.23 oz (120 g) contains 16.0 g of fructose, what caloric content does the fructose contribute to the apple?

5.86 The heat of combustion of ethanol, $C_2H_5OH(l)$, is -1367 kJ/mol. A batch of Sauvignon Blanc wine contains 10.6% ethanol by mass. Assuming the density of the wine to be 1.0 g/mL, what is the caloric content due to the alcohol (ethanol) in a 6-oz glass of wine (177 mL)?

5.87 The standard enthalpies of formation of gaseous propyne (C_3H_4), propylene (C_3H_6), and propane (C_3H_8) are $+185.4$, $+20.4$, and -103.8 kJ/mol, respectively. (a) Calculate the heat evolved per mole on combustion of each substance to yield $CO_2(g)$ and $H_2O(g)$. (b) Calculate the heat evolved on combustion of 1 kg of each substance. (c) Which is the most efficient fuel in terms of heat evolved per unit mass?

5.88 It is interesting to compare the "fuel value" of a hydrocarbon in a world where fluorine rather than oxygen is the combustion agent. The enthalpy of formation of $CF_4(g)$ is -679.9 kJ/mol. Which of the following two reactions is the more exothermic?

$$CH_4(g) + 2\,O_2(g) \longrightarrow CO_2(g) + 2\,H_2O(g)$$
$$CH_4(g) + 4\,F_2(g) \longrightarrow CF_4(g) + 4\,HF(g)$$

[5.89] At the end of 2009, global population was about 6.8 billion people. What mass of glucose in kg would be needed to provide 1500 Cal/person/day of nourishment to the global population for one year? Assume that glucose is metabolized entirely to $CO_2(g)$ and $H_2O(l)$ according to the following thermochemical equation:

$$C_6H_{12}O_6(s) + 6\,O_2(g) \longrightarrow 6\,CO_2(g) + 6H_2O(l)$$
$$\Delta H^\circ = -2803 \text{ kJ}$$

[5.90] The automobile fuel called E85 consists of 85% ethanol and 15% gasoline. E85 can be used in so-called "flex-fuel" vehicles (FFVs), which can use gasoline, ethanol, or a mix as fuels. Assume that gasoline consists of a mixture of octanes (different isomers of C_8H_{18}), that the average heat of combustion of $C_8H_{18}(l)$ is 5400 kJ/mol, and that gasoline has an average density of 0.70 g/mL. The density of ethanol is 0.79 g/mL. (a) By using the information given as well as data in Appendix C, compare the energy produced by combustion of 1.0 L of gasoline and of 1.0 L of ethanol. (b) Assume that the density and heat of combustion of E85 can be obtained by using 85% of the values for ethanol and 15% of the values for gasoline. How much energy could be released by the combustion of 1.0 L of E85? (c) How many gallons of E85 would be needed to provide the same energy as 10 gal of gasoline? (d) If gasoline costs $3.10 per gallon in the United States, what is the break-even price per gallon of E85 if the same amount of energy is to be delivered?

ADDITIONAL EXERCISES

5.91 At 20 °C (approximately room temperature) the average velocity of N_2 molecules in air is 1050 mph. (a) What is the average speed in m/s? (b) What is the kinetic energy (in J) of an N_2 molecule moving at this speed? (c) What is the total kinetic energy of 1 mol of N_2 molecules moving at this speed?

5.92 Suppose an Olympic diver who weighs 52.0 kg executes a straight dive from a 10-m platform. At the apex of the dive, the diver is 10.8 m above the surface of the water. (a) What is the potential energy of the diver at the apex of the dive, relative to the surface of the water? (b) Assuming that all the potential energy of the diver is converted into kinetic energy at the surface of the water, at what speed in m/s will the diver enter the water? (c) Does the diver do work on entering the water? Explain.

5.93 The air bags that provide protection in autos in the event of an accident expand because of a rapid chemical reaction. From the viewpoint of the chemical reactants as the system, what do you expect for the signs of q and w in this process?

[5.94] An aluminum can of a soft drink is placed in a freezer. Later, you find that the can is split open and its contents frozen.

Work was done on the can in splitting it open. Where did the energy for this work come from?

[5.95] Consider a system consisting of the following apparatus, in which gas is confined in one flask and there is a vacuum in the other flask. The flasks are separated by a valve that, when opened, connects the two flasks. Assume that the flasks are perfectly insulated and will not allow the flow of heat into or out of the flasks to the surroundings. (a) When the valve is opened, gas flows from the filled flask to the evacuated one. Does that surprise you? (b) Is work performed during the expansion of the gas? Why or why not? (c) Can you determine the value of ΔE for the process? Does the answer surprise you? (We will talk about this system more in Chapter 19.)

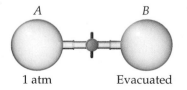

1 atm   Evacuated

[5.96] A sample of gas is contained in a cylinder-and-piston arrangement. It undergoes the change in state shown in the drawing. (a) Assume first that the cylinder and piston are perfect thermal insulators that do not allow heat to be transferred. What is the value of q for the state change? What is the sign of w for the state change? What can be said about ΔE for the state change? (b) Now assume that the cylinder and piston are made up of a thermal conductor such as a metal. During the state change, the cylinder gets warmer to the touch. What is the sign of q for the state change in this case? Describe the difference in the state of the system at the end of the process in the two cases. What can you say about the relative values of ΔE?

[5.97] Limestone stalactites and stalagmites are formed in caves by the following reaction:

$$Ca^{2+}(aq) + 2\,HCO_3^-(aq) \longrightarrow CaCO_3(s) + CO_2(g) + H_2O(l)$$

If 1 mol of $CaCO_3$ forms at 298 K under 1 atm pressure, the reaction performs 2.47 kJ of P-V work, pushing back the atmosphere as the gaseous CO_2 forms. At the same time, 38.95 kJ of heat is absorbed from the environment. What are the values of ΔH and of ΔE for this reaction?

[5.98] Consider the systems shown in Figure 5.10. In one case the battery becomes completely discharged by running the current through a heater and in the other case by running a fan. Both processes occur at constant pressure. In both cases the change in state of the system is the same: The battery goes from being fully charged to being fully discharged. Yet in one case the heat evolved is large, and in the other it is small. Is the enthalpy change the same in the two cases? If not, how can enthalpy be considered a state function? If it is, what can you say about the relationship between enthalpy change and q in this case, as compared with others that we have considered?

5.99 A house is designed to have passive solar energy features. Brickwork incorporated into the interior of the house acts as a heat absorber. Each brick weighs approximately 1.8 kg. The specific heat of the brick is 0.85 J/g-K. How many bricks must be incorporated into the interior of the house to provide the same total heat capacity as 1.7×10^3 gal of water?

[5.100] A coffee-cup calorimeter of the type shown in Figure 5.18 contains 150.0 g of water at 25.1 °C. A 121.0-g block of copper metal is heated to 100.4 °C by putting it in a beaker of boiling water. The specific heat of $Cu(s)$ is 0.385 J/g-K. The Cu is added to the calorimeter, and after a time the contents of the cup reach a constant temperature of 30.1 °C. (a) Determine the amount of heat, in J, lost by the copper block. (b) Determine the amount of heat gained by the water. The specific heat of water is 4.18 J/g-K. (c) The difference between your answers for (a) and (b) is due to heat loss through the Styrofoam® cups and the heat necessary to raise the temperature of the inner wall of the apparatus. The heat capacity of the calorimeter is the amount of heat necessary to raise the temperature of the apparatus (the cups and the stopper) by 1 K. Calculate the heat capacity of the calorimeter in J/K. (d) What would be the final temperature of the system if all the heat lost by the copper block were absorbed by the water in the calorimeter?

[5.101] (a) When a 0.235-g sample of benzoic acid is combusted in a bomb calorimeter (Figure 5.19), the temperature rises 1.642 °C. When a 0.265-g sample of caffeine, $C_8H_{10}O_2N_4$, is burned, the temperature rises 1.525 °C. Using the value 26.38 kJ/g for the heat of combustion of benzoic acid, calculate the heat of combustion per mole of caffeine at constant volume. (b) Assuming that there is an uncertainty of 0.002 °C in each temperature reading and that the masses of samples are measured to 0.001 g, what is the estimated uncertainty in the value calculated for the heat of combustion per mole of caffeine?

5.102 Meals-ready-to-eat (MREs) are military meals that can be heated on a flameless heater. The heat is produced by the following reaction: $Mg(s) + 2\,H_2O(l) \longrightarrow Mg(OH)_2(s) + H_2(g)$. (a) Calculate the standard enthalpy change for this reaction. (b) Calculate the number of grams of Mg needed for this reaction to release enough energy to increase the temperature of 75 mL of water from 21 °C to 79 °C.

5.103 Burning methane in oxygen can produce three different carbon-containing products: soot (very fine particles of graphite), $CO(g)$, and $CO_2(g)$. (a) Write three balanced equations for the reaction of methane gas with oxygen to produce these three products. In each case assume that $H_2O(l)$ is the only other product. (b) Determine the standard enthalpies for the reactions in part (a). (c) Why, when the oxygen supply is adequate, is $CO_2(g)$ the predominant carbon-containing product of the combustion of methane?

5.104 (a) Calculate the standard enthalpy of formation of gaseous diborane (B_2H_6) using the following thermochemical information:

$$4\,B(s) + 3\,O_2(g) \longrightarrow 2\,B_2O_3(s) \qquad \Delta H° = -2509.1 \text{ kJ}$$
$$2\,H_2(g) + O_2(g) \longrightarrow 2\,H_2O(l) \qquad \Delta H° = -571.7 \text{ kJ}$$
$$B_2H_6(g) + 3\,O_2(g) \longrightarrow B_2O_3(s) + 3\,H_2O(l) \quad \Delta H° = -2147.5 \text{ kJ}$$

(b) Pentaborane (B_5H_9) is another boron hydride. What experiment or experiments would you need to perform to yield the data necessary to calculate the heat of formation of $B_5H_9(l)$? Explain by writing out and summing any applicable chemical reactions.

5.105 From the following data for three prospective fuels, calculate which could provide the most energy per unit volume:

Fuel	Density at 20 °C (g/cm³)	Molar Enthalpy of Combustion (kJ/mol)
Nitroethane, $C_2H_5NO_2(l)$	1.052	−1368
Ethanol, $C_2H_5OH(l)$	0.789	−1367
Methylhydrazine, $CH_6N_2(l)$	0.874	−1307

5.106 The hydrocarbons acetylene (C_2H_2) and benzene (C_6H_6) have the same empirical formula. Benzene is an "aromatic" hydrocarbon, one that is unusually stable because of its structure. (a) By using the data in Appendix C, determine the standard enthalpy change for the reaction $3\,C_2H_2(g) \longrightarrow C_6H_6(l)$.

(b) Which has greater enthalpy, 3 mol of acetylene gas or 1 mol of liquid benzene? **(c)** Determine the fuel value in kJ/g for acetylene and benzene.

[**5.107**] Ammonia (NH_3) boils at $-33\ °C$; at this temperature it has a density of $0.81\ g/cm^3$. The enthalpy of formation of $NH_3(g)$ is $-46.2\ kJ/mol$, and the enthalpy of vaporization of $NH_3(l)$ is $23.2\ kJ/mol$. Calculate the enthalpy change when 1 L of liquid NH_3 is burned in air to give $N_2(g)$ and $H_2O(g)$. How does this compare with ΔH for the complete combustion of 1 L of liquid methanol, $CH_3OH(l)$? For $CH_3OH(l)$, the density at 25 °C is $0.792\ g/cm^3$, and $\Delta H_f° = -239\ kJ/mol$.

[**5.108**] Three common hydrocarbons that contain four carbons are listed here, along with their standard enthalpies of formation:

Hydrocarbon	Formula	$\Delta H_f°$ (kJ/mol)
1,3-Butadiene	$C_4H_6(g)$	111.9
1-Butene	$C_4H_8(g)$	1.2
n-Butane	$C_4H_{10}(g)$	−124.7

(a) For each of these substances, calculate the molar enthalpy of combustion to $CO_2(g)$ and $H_2O(l)$. **(b)** Calculate the fuel value in kJ/g for each of these compounds. **(c)** For each hydrocarbon, determine the percentage of hydrogen by mass. **(d)** By comparing your answers for parts (b) and (c), propose a relationship between hydrogen content and fuel value in hydrocarbons.

5.109 A 200-lb man decides to add to his exercise routine by walking up three flights of stairs (45 ft) 20 times per day. He figures that the work required to increase his potential energy in this way will permit him to eat an extra order of French fries, at 245 Cal, without adding to his weight. Is he correct in this assumption?

5.110 The Sun supplies about 1.0 kilowatt of energy for each square meter of surface area ($1.0\ kW/m^2$, where a watt = 1 J/s). Plants produce the equivalent of about 0.20 g of sucrose ($C_{12}H_{22}O_{11}$) per hour per square meter. Assuming that the sucrose is produced as follows, calculate the percentage of sunlight used to produce sucrose.

$$12\ CO_2(g) + 11\ H_2O(l) \longrightarrow C_{12}H_{22}O_{11} + 12\ O_2(g)$$
$$\Delta H = 5645\ kJ$$

[**5.111**] It is estimated that the net amount of carbon dioxide fixed by photosynthesis on the landmass of Earth is $5.5 \times 10^{16}\ g/yr$ of CO_2. Assume that all this carbon is converted into glucose. **(a)** Calculate the energy stored by photosynthesis on land per year in kJ. **(b)** Calculate the average rate of conversion of solar energy into plant energy in MW (1W = 1 J/s). A large nuclear power plant produces about 10^3 MW. The energy of how many such nuclear power plants is equivalent to the solar energy conversion?

INTEGRATIVE EXERCISES

5.112 Consider the combustion of a single molecule of $CH_4(g)$ forming $H_2O(l)$ as a product. **(a)** How much energy, in J, is produced during this reaction? **(b)** A typical X-ray light source has an energy of 8 keV. How does the energy of combustion compare to the energy of the X-ray?

5.113 Consider the following unbalanced oxidation-reduction reactions in aqueous solution:

$$Ag^+(aq) + Li(s) \longrightarrow Ag(s) + Li^+(aq)$$
$$Fe(s) + Na^+(aq) \longrightarrow Fe^{2+}(aq) + Na(s)$$
$$K(s) + H_2O(l) \longrightarrow KOH(aq) + H_2(g)$$

(a) Balance each of the reactions. **(b)** By using data in Appendix C, calculate $\Delta H°$ for each of the reactions. **(c)** Based on the values you obtain for $\Delta H°$, which of the reactions would you expect to be thermodynamically favored? **(d)** Use the activity series to predict which of these reactions should occur. ⚬⚬ (Section 4.4) Are these results in accord with your conclusion in part (c) of this problem?

[**5.114**] Consider the following acid-neutralization reactions involving the strong base NaOH(aq):

$$HNO_3(aq) + NaOH(aq) \longrightarrow NaNO_3(aq) + H_2O(l)$$
$$HCl(aq) + NaOH(aq) \longrightarrow NaCl(aq) + H_2O(l)$$
$$NH_4^+(aq) + NaOH(aq) \longrightarrow NH_3(aq) + Na^+(aq) + H_2O(l)$$

(a) By using data in Appendix C, calculate $\Delta H°$ for each of the reactions. **(b)** As we saw in Section 4.3, nitric acid and hydrochloric acid are strong acids. Write net ionic equations for the neutralization of these acids. **(c)** Compare the values of $\Delta H°$ for the first two reactions. What can you conclude? **(d)** In the third equation $NH_4^+(aq)$ is acting as an acid. Based on the value of $\Delta H°$ for this reaction, do you think it is a strong or a weak acid? Explain.

5.115 Consider two solutions, the first being 50.0 mL of 1.00 M $CuSO_4$ and the second 50.0 mL of 2.00 M KOH. When the two solutions are mixed in a constant-pressure calorimeter, a precipitate forms and the temperature of the mixture rises from 21.5 °C to 27.7 °C. **(a)** Before mixing, how many grams of Cu are present in the solution of $CuSO_4$? **(b)** Predict the identity of the precipitate in the reaction. **(c)** Write complete and net ionic equations for the reaction that occurs when the two solutions are mixed. **(d)** From the calorimetric data, calculate ΔH for the reaction that occurs on mixing. Assume that the calorimeter absorbs only a negligible quantity of heat, that the total volume of the solution is 100.0 mL, and that the specific heat and density of the solution after mixing are the same as that of pure water.

5.116 The precipitation reaction between $AgNO_3(aq)$ and NaCl(aq) proceeds as follows:

$$AgNO_3(aq) + NaCl(aq) \longrightarrow NaNO_3(aq) + AgCl(s)$$

(a) By using Appendix C, calculate $\Delta H°$ for the net ionic equation of this reaction. **(b)** What would you expect for the value of $\Delta H°$ of the overall molecular equation compared to that for the net ionic equation? Explain. **(c)** Use the results from (a) and (b) along with data in Appendix C to determine the value of $\Delta H_f°$ for $AgNO_3(aq)$.

[5.117] A sample of a hydrocarbon is combusted completely in $O_2(g)$ to produce 21.83 g $CO_2(g)$, 4.47 g $H_2O(g)$, and 311 kJ of heat. (a) What is the mass of the hydrocarbon sample that was combusted? (b) What is the empirical formula of the hydrocarbon? (c) Calculate the value of ΔH_f° per empirical-formula unit of the hydrocarbon. (d) Do you think that the hydrocarbon is one of those listed in Appendix C? Explain your answer.

5.118 The methane molecule, CH_4, has the geometry shown in Figure 2.19. Imagine a hypothetical process in which the methane molecule is "expanded," by simultaneously extending all four C—H bonds to infinity. We then have the process

$$CH_4(g) \longrightarrow C(g) + 4 H(g)$$

(a) Compare this process with the reverse of the reaction that represents the standard enthalpy of formation of $CH_4(g)$. (b) Calculate the enthalpy change in each case. Which is the more endothermic process? What accounts for the difference in ΔH° values? (c) Suppose that 3.45 g $CH_4(g)$ reacts with 1.22 g $F_2(g)$, forming $CF_4(g)$ and $HF(g)$ as sole products. What is the limiting reagent in this reaction? If the reaction occurs at constant pressure, what amount of heat is evolved?

5.119 World energy supplies are often measured in the unit of quadrillion British thermal units (10^{12} Btu), generally called a "quad." In 2015, world energy consumption is projected to be 5.31×10^{17} kJ. (a) With reference to Exercise 5.17, how many quads of energy does this quantity represent? (b) Current annual energy consumption in the United States is 99.5 quads. Assume that all this energy is to be generated by burning $CH_4(g)$ in the form of natural gas. If the combustion of the $CH_4(g)$ were complete and 100% efficient, how many moles of $CH_4(g)$ would need to be combusted in order to provide the U.S. energy demand? (c) How many kilograms of $CO_2(g)$ would be generated in the combustion in part (b)? (d) Compare your answer to part (c) with information given in Exercise 5.111. Do you think that photosynthesis is an adequate means to maintain a stable level of CO_2 in the atmosphere?

WHAT'S AHEAD

6.1 THE WAVE NATURE OF LIGHT
We learn that light (radiant energy, or *electromagnetic radiation*) has wavelike properties and is characterized by *wavelength*, *frequency*, and *speed*.

6.2 QUANTIZED ENERGY AND PHOTONS
We recognize that electromagnetic radiation also has particle-like properties and can be described in terms of *photons*, "particles" of light.

6.3 LINE SPECTRA AND THE BOHR MODEL
We examine the light that atoms give off when appropriately stimulated (*line spectra*). Line spectra indicate that electrons exist only at certain energy levels around a nucleus and that energy is involved when an electron moves from one level to another. The Bohr model of the atom pictures the electrons moving only in certain allowed orbits around the nucleus.

6.4 THE WAVE BEHAVIOR OF MATTER
We recognize that matter also has wavelike properties. As a result, it is impossible to determine simultaneously the exact position and the exact motion of an electron in an atom (*Heisenberg's uncertainty principle*).

6.5 QUANTUM MECHANICS AND ATOMIC ORBITALS
We can describe how an electron exists in atoms by treating it as a standing wave. The *wave functions* that mathematically describe the electron's position and energy in an atom are called *atomic*

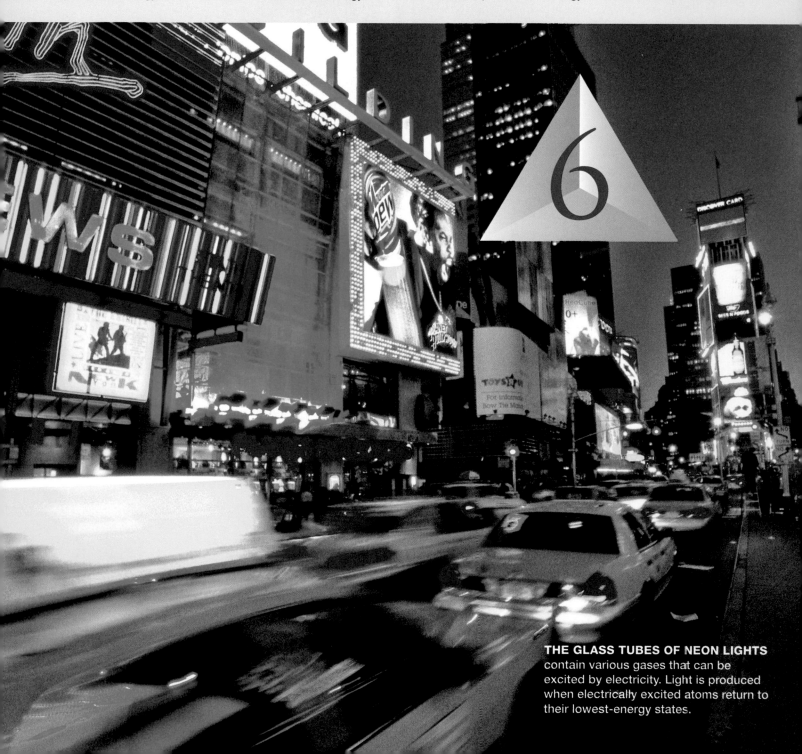

THE GLASS TUBES OF NEON LIGHTS contain various gases that can be excited by electricity. Light is produced when electrically excited atoms return to their lowest-energy states.

orbitals. The orbitals can be described in a shorthand notation using *quantum numbers*.

6.6 REPRESENTATIONS OF ORBITALS
We consider the three-dimensional shapes of orbitals and how they can be represented by graphs of electron density.

6.7 MANY-ELECTRON ATOMS
We recognize that the energy levels for an atom with one electron are altered when the atom contains multiple electrons. Each electron has a quantum-mechanical property called *spin*. The *Pauli exclusion principle* states that no two electrons in an atom can have the same four quantum numbers (three for the orbital

and one for the spin). Therefore, an orbital can hold a maximum of two electrons.

6.8 ELECTRON CONFIGURATIONS
We learn that knowing orbital energies as well as some fundamental characteristics of electrons described by *Hund's rule* allows us to determine how electrons are distributed in an atom (*electron configurations*).

6.9 ELECTRON CONFIGURATIONS AND THE PERIODIC TABLE
We observe that the electron configuration of an atom is related to the location of the element in the periodic table.

ELECTRONIC STRUCTURE OF ATOMS

WHAT HAPPENS WHEN SOMEONE switches on a neon light? Electrons in the neon atoms are excited to a higher energy by electricity. An electron can remain in a higher-energy state for only a very short time, and it emits light when it returns to a lower energy. The resulting glow is explained by one of the most revolutionary discoveries of the twentieth century—the *quantum theory,* which explains much of the behavior of electrons in atoms.

In this chapter we explore the quantum theory and its importance in chemistry. We begin by looking at the nature of light and how our description of light was changed by the quantum theory. We will explore some of the tools used in *quantum mechanics,* the "new" physics that had to be developed to describe atoms correctly. We will then use the quantum theory to describe the arrangements of electrons in atoms— what we call the **electronic structure** of atoms. The electronic structure of an atom refers to the number of electrons in the atom as well as their distribution around the nucleus and their energies. We will see that the quantum description of the electronic structure of atoms helps us to understand the arrangement of the elements in the periodic table—why, for example, helium and neon are both unreactive gases, whereas sodium and potassium are both soft, reactive metals.

▲ FIGURE 6.1 **Water waves.** The movement of a boat through the water forms waves that move away from the boat.

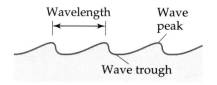

▲ FIGURE 6.2 **Water waves.** The *wavelength* is the distance between two adjacent peaks or two adjacent troughs.

GO FIGURE

If wave (a) has a wavelength of 1.0 m and a frequency of 3.0×10^8 cycles/s, what are the wavelength and frequency of wave (b)?

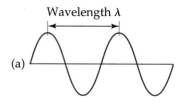

▲ FIGURE 6.3 **Electromagnetic waves.** Like water waves, electromagnetic radiation can be characterized by a wavelength. Notice that the shorter the wavelength, λ, the higher the frequency, ν. The wavelength in (b) is half as long as that in (a), and the frequency of the wave in (b) is therefore twice as great as the frequency in (a).

6.1 | THE WAVE NATURE OF LIGHT

Much of our present understanding of the electronic structure of atoms has come from analysis of the light either emitted or absorbed by substances. To understand electronic structure, therefore, we must first learn about light. The light we see with our eyes, *visible light,* is one type of **electromagnetic radiation**. Because electromagnetic radiation carries energy through space, it is also known as *radiant energy.*

There are many types of electromagnetic radiation in addition to visible light. These different types—radio waves that carry music to our radios, infrared radiation (heat) from a glowing fireplace, X-rays—may seem very different from one another, but they all share certain fundamental characteristics.

All types of electromagnetic radiation move through a vacuum at 3.00×10^8 m/s, the *speed of light.* All have wavelike characteristics similar to those of waves that move through water. Water waves are the result of energy imparted to the water, perhaps by the dropping of a stone or the movement of a boat on the water surface (◀ FIGURE 6.1). This energy is expressed as the up-and-down movements of the water.

A cross section of a water wave (◀ FIGURE 6.2) shows that it is *periodic,* which means that the pattern of peaks and troughs repeats itself at regular intervals. The distance between two adjacent peaks (or between two adjacent troughs) is called the **wavelength**. The number of complete wavelengths, or *cycles,* that pass a given point each second is the **frequency** of the wave.

Just as with water waves, we can assign a frequency and wavelength to electromagnetic waves, as illustrated in ◀ FIGURE 6.3. These and all other wave characteristics of electromagnetic radiation are due to the periodic oscillations in the intensities of the electric and magnetic fields associated with the radiation.

The speed of water waves can vary depending on how they are created—for example, the waves produced by a speedboat travel faster than those produced by a rowboat. In contrast, all electromagnetic radiation moves at the same speed, 3.00×10^8 m/s, the speed of light. As a result, the wavelength and frequency of electromagnetic radiation are always related in a straightforward way. If the wavelength is long, fewer cycles of the wave pass a given point per second, and so the frequency is low. Conversely, for a wave to have a high frequency, it must have a short wavelength. This inverse relationship between the frequency and wavelength of electromagnetic radiation is expressed by the equation

$$c = \lambda\nu \qquad\qquad [6.1]$$

where c is the speed of light, λ (lambda) is wavelength, and ν (nu) is frequency.

Why do different types of electromagnetic radiation have different properties? Their differences are due to their different wavelengths. ▶ FIGURE 6.4 shows the various types of electromagnetic radiation arranged in order of increasing wavelength, a display called the *electromagnetic spectrum.* Notice that the wavelengths span an enormous range. The wavelengths of gamma rays are comparable to the diameters of atomic nuclei, whereas the wavelengths of radio waves can be longer than a football field. Notice also that visible light, which corresponds to wavelengths of about 400 to 750 nm (4×10^{-7} m to 7×10^{-7} m), is an extremely small portion of the electromagnetic spectrum. The unit of length chosen to express wavelength depends on the type of radiation, as shown in ▼ TABLE 6.1.

TABLE 6.1 • Common Wavelength Units for Electromagnetic Radiation			
Unit	**Symbol**	**Length (m)**	**Type of Radiation**
Angstrom	Å	10^{-10}	X-ray
Nanometer	nm	10^{-9}	Ultraviolet, visible
Micrometer	μm	10^{-6}	Infrared
Millimeter	mm	10^{-3}	Microwave
Centimeter	cm	10^{-2}	Microwave
Meter	m	1	Television, radio
Kilometer	km	1000	Radio

GO FIGURE

How do the wavelength and frequency of an X-ray compare with those of the red light from a neon sign?

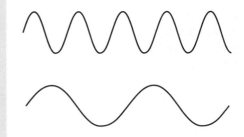

◀ **FIGURE 6.4   The electromagnetic spectrum.** Wavelengths in the spectrum range from very short gamma rays to very long radio waves.

Frequency is expressed in cycles per second, a unit also called a *hertz* (Hz). Because it is understood that cycles are involved, the units of frequency are normally given simply as "per second," which is denoted by s^{-1} or /s. For example, a frequency of 820 kilohertz (kHz), a typical frequency for an AM radio station, could be written as 820 kHz, 820,000 Hz, 820,000 s^{-1}, or 820,000/s.

SAMPLE EXERCISE 6.1   Concepts of Wavelength and Frequency

Two electromagnetic waves are represented in the margin. **(a)** Which wave has the higher frequency? **(b)** If one wave represents visible light and the other represents infrared radiation, which wave is which?

SOLUTION

(a) The lower wave has a longer wavelength (greater distance between peaks). The longer the wavelength, the lower the frequency ($\nu = c/\lambda$). Thus, the lower wave has the lower frequency, and the upper wave has the higher frequency.
(b) The electromagnetic spectrum (Figure 6.4) indicates that infrared radiation has a longer wavelength than visible light. Thus, the lower wave would be the infrared radiation.

PRACTICE EXERCISE

If one of the waves in the margin represents blue light and the other red light, which is which?

Answer: The expanded visible-light portion of Figure 6.4 tells you that red light has a longer wavelength than blue light. The lower wave has the longer wavelength (lower frequency) and would be the red light.

A CLOSER LOOK

THE SPEED OF LIGHT

How do we know that light has a finite speed and does not move infinitely fast?

During the late 1600s, the Danish astronomer Ole Rømer (1644–1710) measured the orbits of several of Jupiter's moons. These moons move much faster than our own—they have orbits of 1–7 days and are eclipsed by Jupiter's shadow at every revolution. Over many months, Rømer measured discrepancies of up to 10 minutes in the times of these orbits. He reasoned that the discrepancies occurred because Jupiter was farther from Earth at different times of the year. Thus, light from the Sun, which reflected off Jupiter and ultimately to his telescope, had farther to travel at different times of the year, implying that light travels at a finite speed. Rømer's data led to the first estimate of the speed of light, 3.5×10^8 m/s.

Since Rømer's time, increasingly sophisticated techniques have been used to measure the speed of light. For example, in 1927, A. A. Michelson (1852–1931) set up a rotating mirror at the top of Mount Wilson in California. The mirror bounced light to the top of Mount San Antonio, 22 miles away, where another mirror bounced the light back to Mount Wilson. Michelson was able to change the speed of the rotating mirror and measure small displacements in the position of the reflected spot. The value for the speed of light (in air) based on this experiment was $2.9980 \pm 0.0002 \times 10^8$ m/s. The main source of error was the distance between the mirrors, which was measured within a fifth of an inch in 22 miles.

By 1975, the measured value was even more precise, $2.99792458 \pm 0.00000004 \times 10^8$ m/s (in vacuum), the error being mostly due to the uncertainty in the length of the meter. In 1983, the meter was redefined based on the distance that light travels in vacuum in one second. As a result, the value for the speed of light became a fixed, exact quantity, $c = 2.99792458 \times 10^8$ m/s.

SAMPLE EXERCISE 6.2   Calculating Frequency from Wavelength

The yellow light given off by a sodium vapor lamp used for public lighting has a wavelength of 589 nm. What is the frequency of this radiation?

SOLUTION

Analyze We are given the wavelength, λ, of the radiation and asked to calculate its frequency, ν.

Plan The relationship between the wavelength and the frequency is given by Equation 6.1. We can solve for ν and use the values of λ and c to obtain a numerical answer. (The speed of light, c, is a fundamental constant whose value is 3.00×10^8 m/s.)

Solve Solving Equation 6.1 for frequency gives $\nu = c/\lambda$. When we insert the values for c and λ, we note that the units of length in these two quantities are different. We can convert the wavelength from nanometers to meters, so the units cancel:

$$\nu = \frac{c}{\lambda} = \left(\frac{3.00 \times 10^8 \text{ m/s}}{589 \text{ nm}}\right)\left(\frac{1 \text{ nm}}{10^{-9} \text{ m}}\right) = 5.09 \times 10^{14} \text{ s}^{-1}$$

Check The high frequency is reasonable because of the short wavelength. The units are proper because frequency has units of "per second," or s^{-1}.

PRACTICE EXERCISE

(a) A laser used in eye surgery to fuse detached retinas produces radiation with a wavelength of 640.0 nm. Calculate the frequency of this radiation. **(b)** An FM radio station broadcasts electromagnetic radiation at a frequency of 103.4 MHz (megahertz; 1 MHz = 10^6 s^{-1}). Calculate the wavelength of this radiation. The speed of light is 2.998×10^8 m/s to four significant digits.

Answers: **(a)** 4.688×10^{14} s^{-1}, **(b)** 2.899 m

 GIVE IT SOME THOUGHT

Our bodies are penetrated by X-rays but not by visible light. Is this because X-rays travel faster than visible light?

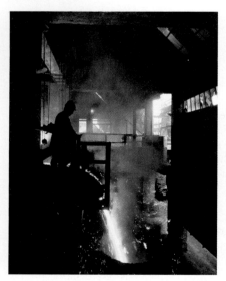

GO FIGURE

Which area in the photograph corresponds to the highest temperature?

▲ **FIGURE 6.5   Color and temperature.** The color and intensity of the light emitted by a hot object, such as this pour of molten steel, depend on the temperature of the object.

6.2 | QUANTIZED ENERGY AND PHOTONS

Although the wave model of light explains many aspects of its behavior, this model cannot explain several phenomena. Three of these are particularly pertinent to our understanding of how electromagnetic radiation and atoms interact: (1) the emission of light from hot objects (referred to as *blackbody radiation* because the objects studied appear black before heating), (2) the emission of electrons from metal surfaces on which light shines (the *photoelectric effect*), and (3) the emission of light from electronically excited gas atoms (*emission spectra*). We examine the first two phenomena here and the third in Section 6.3.

Hot Objects and the Quantization of Energy

When solids are heated, they emit radiation, as seen in the red glow of an electric stove burner or the bright white light of a tungsten lightbulb. The wavelength distribution of the radiation depends on temperature; a red-hot object, for instance, is cooler than a yellowish or white-hot one (◄ **FIGURE 6.5**). During the late 1800s, a number of physicists studied this phenomenon, trying to understand the relationship between the temperature and the intensity and wavelength of the emitted radiation. The prevailing laws of physics could not account for the observations.

In 1900 a German physicist named Max Planck (1858–1947) solved the problem by assuming that energy can be either released or absorbed by atoms only in discrete "chunks" of some minimum size. Planck gave the name **quantum** (meaning "fixed amount") to the smallest quantity of energy that can be emitted or absorbed as electromagnetic radiation. He proposed that the energy, E, of a single quantum equals a constant times the frequency of the radiation:

$$E = h\nu \qquad [6.2]$$

Potential energy of person walking up steps increases in stepwise, quantized manner

Potential energy of person walking up ramp increases in uniform, continuous manner

◀ FIGURE 6.6 **Quantized versus continuous change in energy.**

The constant h is called **Planck's constant** and has a value of 6.626×10^{-34} joule-second (J-s).

According to Planck's theory, matter can emit and absorb energy only in whole-number multiples of $h\nu$, such as $h\nu$, $2h\nu$, $3h\nu$, and so forth. If the quantity of energy emitted by an atom is $3h\nu$, for example, we say that three quanta of energy have been emitted (*quanta* being the plural of *quantum*). Because the energy can be released only in specific amounts, we say that the allowed energies are *quantized*—their values are restricted to certain quantities. Planck's revolutionary proposal that energy is quantized was proved correct, and he was awarded the 1918 Nobel Prize in Physics for his work on the quantum theory.

If the notion of quantized energies seems strange, it might be helpful to draw an analogy by comparing a ramp and a staircase (▲ FIGURE 6.6). As you walk up a ramp, your potential energy increases in a uniform, continuous manner. When you climb a staircase, you can step only *on* individual stairs, not *between* them, so that your potential energy is restricted to certain values and is therefore quantized.

If Planck's quantum theory is correct, why are its effects not obvious in our daily lives? Why do energy changes seem continuous rather than quantized, or "jagged"? Notice that Planck's constant is an extremely small number. Thus, a quantum of energy, $h\nu$, is an extremely small amount. Planck's rules regarding the gain or loss of energy are always the same, whether we are concerned with objects on the scale of our ordinary experience or with microscopic objects. With everyday objects, however, the gain or loss of a single quantum of energy is so small that it goes completely unnoticed. In contrast, when dealing with matter at the atomic level, the impact of quantized energies is far more significant.

 GIVE IT SOME THOUGHT

Calculate the energy (to one significant figure) of one quantum of electromagnetic radiation whose frequency is 5×10^{-3} s^{-1}. Can this radiation produce a burst of energy $E = 5 \times 10^{-36}$ J? Why or why not?

The Photoelectric Effect and Photons

A few years after Planck presented his quantum theory, scientists began to see its applicability to many experimental observations. In 1905, Albert Einstein (1879–1955) used Planck's theory to explain the **photoelectric effect** (▶ FIGURE 6.7). Light shining on a clean metal surface causes the surface to emit electrons. A minimum frequency of light, different for different metals, is required for the emission of electrons. For example, light with a frequency of 4.60×10^{14} s^{-1} or greater causes cesium metal to emit electrons, but light of lower frequency has no effect.

To explain the photoelectric effect, Einstein assumed that the radiant energy striking the metal surface behaves like a stream of tiny energy packets. Each packet, which is like a "particle" of energy, is called a **photon**. Extending Planck's quantum theory,

▲ GO FIGURE

Why is it necessary to carry out this experiment in an evacuated chamber?

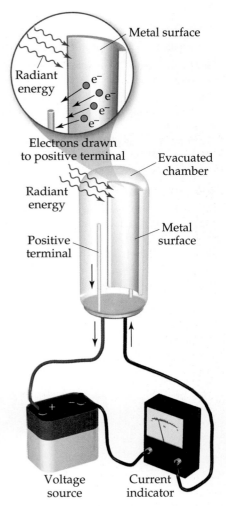

▲ FIGURE 6.7 **The photoelectric effect.**

Einstein deduced that each photon must have an energy equal to Planck's constant times the frequency of the light:

$$\text{Energy of photon} = E = h\nu \qquad [6.3]$$

Thus, radiant energy itself is quantized.

Under the right conditions, photons striking a metal surface can transfer their energy to electrons in the metal. A certain amount of energy—called the *work function*—is required for the electrons to overcome the attractive forces holding them in the metal. If the photons striking the metal have less energy than the work function, the electrons do not acquire sufficient energy to escape from the metal, even if the light beam is intense. If the photons have energy greater than the work function of the particular metal, however, electrons are emitted. The intensity (brightness) of the light is related to the number of photons striking the surface per unit time but not to the energy of each photon. Einstein won the Nobel Prize in Physics in 1921 for his explanation of the photoelectric effect.

To better understand what a photon is, imagine you have a light source that produces radiation of a single wavelength. Further suppose that you could switch the light on and off faster and faster to provide ever-smaller bursts of energy. Einstein's photon theory tells us that you would eventually come to the smallest energy burst, given by $E = h\nu$. This smallest burst consists of a single photon of light.

SAMPLE EXERCISE 6.3 | Energy of a Photon

Calculate the energy of one photon of yellow light that has a wavelength of 589 nm.

SOLUTION

Analyze Our task is to calculate the energy, E, of a photon, given $\lambda = 589$ nm.

Plan We can use Equation 6.1 to convert the wavelength to frequency:

$$\nu = c/\lambda$$

We can then use Equation 6.3 to calculate energy:

$$E = h\nu$$

Solve The frequency, ν, is calculated from the given wavelength, as shown in Sample Exercise 6.2:

$$\nu = c/\lambda = 5.09 \times 10^{14}\ \text{s}^{-1}$$

The value of Planck's constant, h, is given both in the text and in the table of physical constants on the inside back cover of the text, and so we can easily calculate E:

$$E = (6.626 \times 10^{-34}\ \text{J-s})(5.09 \times 10^{14}\ \text{s}^{-1}) = 3.37 \times 10^{-19}\ \text{J}$$

Comment If one photon of radiant energy supplies 3.37×10^{-19} J, then one mole of these photons will supply

$$(6.02 \times 10^{23}\ \text{photons/mol})(3.37 \times 10^{-19}\ \text{J/photon})$$
$$= 2.03 \times 10^{5}\ \text{J/mol}$$

PRACTICE EXERCISE

(a) A laser emits light that has a frequency of $4.69 \times 10^{14}\ \text{s}^{-1}$. What is the energy of one photon of this radiation? (b) If the laser emits a pulse containing 5.0×10^{17} photons of this radiation, what is the total energy of that pulse? (c) If the laser emits 1.3×10^{-2} J of energy during a pulse, how many photons are emitted?

Answers: (a) 3.11×10^{-19} J, (b) 0.16 J, (c) 4.2×10^{16} photons

The idea that the energy of light depends on its frequency helps us understand the diverse effects of different kinds of electromagnetic radiation. For example, because of the high frequency (short wavelength) of X-rays (Figure 6.4), X-ray photons cause tissue damage and even cancer. Thus, signs are normally posted around X-ray equipment warning us of high-energy radiation.

Although Einstein's theory of light as a stream of photons rather than a wave explains the photoelectric effect and a great many other observations, it also poses a dilemma. Is light a wave, or is it particle-like? The only way to resolve this dilemma is to adopt what might seem to be a bizarre position: We must consider that light possesses both wave-like and particle-like characteristics and, depending on the situation, will behave more like waves or more like particles. We will soon see that this dual nature of light is also a characteristic trait of matter.

▲ GIVE IT SOME THOUGHT

Which has more energy, a photon of infrared light or a photon of ultraviolet light?

6.3 | LINE SPECTRA AND THE BOHR MODEL

The work of Planck and Einstein paved the way for understanding how electrons are arranged in atoms. In 1913, the Danish physicist Niels Bohr (▶ FIGURE 6.8) offered a theoretical explanation of *line spectra,* another phenomenon that had puzzled scientists during the nineteenth century.

Line Spectra

A particular source of radiant energy may emit a single wavelength, as in the light from a laser. Radiation composed of a single wavelength is *monochromatic*. However, most common radiation sources, including lightbulbs and stars, produce radiation containing many different wavelengths and is *polychromatic*. A **spectrum** is produced when radiation from such sources is separated into its component wavelengths, as shown in ▶ FIGURE 6.9. The resulting spectrum consists of a continuous range of colors—violet merges into indigo, indigo into blue, and so forth, with no blank spots. This rainbow of colors, containing light of all wavelengths, is called a **continuous spectrum**. The most familiar example of a continuous spectrum is the rainbow produced when raindrops or mist acts as a prism for sunlight.

Not all radiation sources produce a continuous spectrum. When a high voltage is applied to tubes that contain different gases under reduced pressure, the gases emit different colors of light (▶ FIGURE 6.10). The light emitted by neon gas is the familiar red-orange glow of many "neon" lights, whereas sodium vapor emits the yellow light characteristic of some modern streetlights. When light coming from such tubes is passed through a prism, only a few wavelengths are present in the resultant spectra (▼ FIGURE 6.11). Each colored line in such spectra represents light of one wavelength. A spectrum containing radiation of only specific wavelengths is called a **line spectrum**.

When scientists first detected the line spectrum of hydrogen in the mid-1800s, they were fascinated by its simplicity. At that time, only four lines at wavelengths of 410 nm (violet), 434 nm (blue), 486 nm (blue-green), and 656 nm (red) were observed (Figure 6.11). In 1885, a Swiss schoolteacher named Johann Balmer showed that the wavelengths of these four lines fit an intriguingly simple formula that relates the wavelengths to integers. Later, additional lines were found in the ultraviolet and infrared regions of hydrogen's line spectrum. Soon Balmer's equation was extended to a more general one, called the *Rydberg equation,* which allows us to calculate the wavelengths of all the spectral lines of hydrogen:

$$\frac{1}{\lambda} = (R_H)\left(\frac{1}{n_1^2} - \frac{1}{n_2^2}\right) \qquad [6.4]$$

In this formula λ is the wavelength of a spectral line, R_H is the *Rydberg constant* $(1.096776 \times 10^7 \text{ m}^{-1})$, and n_1 and n_2 are positive integers, with n_2 being larger

▲ FIGURE 6.8 **Quantum giants.** Niels Bohr (right) with Albert Einstein. Bohr (1885–1962) made major contributions to the quantum theory and was awarded the Nobel Prize in Physics in 1922.

▲ FIGURE 6.9 **Creating a spectrum.** A continuous visible spectrum is produced when a narrow beam of white light is passed through a prism. The white light could be sunlight or light from an incandescent lamp.

Hydrogen (H)   Neon (Ne)

▲ FIGURE 6.10 **Atomic emission of hydrogen and neon.** Different gases emit light of different characteristic colors when an electric current is passed through them.

▲ FIGURE 6.11 **Line spectra of hydrogen and neon.**

than n_1. How could the remarkable simplicity of this equation be explained? It took nearly 30 more years to answer this question.

Bohr's Model

To explain the line spectrum of hydrogen, Bohr assumed that electrons in hydrogen atoms move in circular orbits around the nucleus, but this assumption posed a problem. According to classical physics, a charged particle (such as an electron) moving in a circular path should continuously lose energy. As an electron loses energy, therefore, it should spiral into the positively charged nucleus. This behavior, however, does not happen—hydrogen atoms are stable. So how can we explain this apparent violation of the laws of physics? Bohr approached this problem in much the same way that Planck had approached the problem of the nature of the radiation emitted by hot objects: He assumed that the prevailing laws of physics were inadequate to describe all aspects of atoms. Furthermore, he adopted Planck's idea that energies are quantized.

Bohr based his model on three postulates:

1. Only orbits of certain radii, corresponding to certain specific energies, are permitted for the electron in a hydrogen atom.
2. An electron in a permitted orbit is in an "allowed" energy state. An electron in an allowed energy state does not radiate energy and, therefore, does not spiral into the nucleus.
3. Energy is emitted or absorbed by the electron only as the electron changes from one allowed energy state to another. This energy is emitted or absorbed as a photon that has energy $E = h\nu$.

▲ GIVE IT SOME THOUGHT

Before reading further about Bohr's model, speculate as to how it explains the fact that hydrogen gas emits a line spectrum (Figure 6.11) rather than a continuous spectrum.

The Energy States of the Hydrogen Atom

Starting with his three postulates and using classical equations for motion and for interacting electrical charges, Bohr calculated the energies corresponding to the allowed orbits for the electron in the hydrogen atom. Ultimately, the calculated energies fit the formula

$$E = (-hcR_H)\left(\frac{1}{n^2}\right) = (-2.18 \times 10^{-18} \text{ J})\left(\frac{1}{n^2}\right) \qquad [6.5]$$

where h, c, and R_H are Planck's constant, the speed of light, and the Rydberg constant, respectively. The integer n, which can have whole-number values of $1, 2, 3, \ldots \infty$, is called the *principal quantum number*. Each orbit corresponds to a different value of n, and the radius of the orbit gets larger as n increases. Thus, the first allowed orbit (the one closest to the nucleus) has $n = 1$, the next allowed orbit (the one second closest to the nucleus) has $n = 2$, and so forth. The electron in the hydrogen atom can be in any allowed orbit, and Equation 6.5 tells us the energy the electron has in each allowed orbit.

Note that the energies of the electron given by Equation 6.5 are negative for all values of n. The lower (more negative) the energy is, the more stable the atom is. The energy is lowest (most negative) for $n = 1$. As n gets larger, the energy becomes less negative and therefore increases. We can liken the situation to a ladder in which the rungs are numbered from the bottom. The higher one climbs (the greater the value of n), the higher the energy. The lowest-energy state ($n = 1$, analogous to the bottom rung) is called the **ground state** of the atom. When the electron is in a higher-energy state ($n = 2$ or higher), the atom is said to be in an **excited state**. ◄ FIGURE 6.12 shows the energy of the electron in a hydrogen atom for several values of n.

▲ GO FIGURE

If the transition of an electron from the $n = 3$ state to the $n = 2$ state results in emission of visible light, is the transition from the $n = 2$ state to the $n = 1$ state more likely to result in the emission of infrared or ultraviolet radiation?

▲ **FIGURE 6.12** **Energy states in the hydrogen atom.** Only states for $n = 1$ through $n = 4$ and $n = \infty$ are shown. Energy is released or absorbed when an electron moves from one energy state to another.

What happens to the orbit radius and the energy as n becomes infinitely large? The radius increases as n^2, so when $n = \infty$ the electron is completely separated from the nucleus, and the energy of the electron is zero:

$$E = (-2.18 \times 10^{-18} \text{ J})\left(\frac{1}{\infty^2}\right) = 0$$

The state in which the electron is removed from the nucleus is called the reference, or zero-energy, state of the hydrogen atom.

In his third postulate, Bohr assumed that the electron can "jump" from one allowed orbit to another by either absorbing or emitting photons whose radiant energy corresponds exactly to the energy difference between the two orbits. The electron must absorb energy in order to move to a higher-energy state (higher value of n). Conversely, radiant energy is emitted when the electron jumps to a lower-energy state (lower value of n).

If the electron jumps from an initial state of energy E_i to a final state of energy E_f, the change in energy is

$$\Delta E = E_f - E_i = E_{\text{photon}} = h\nu \qquad [6.6]$$

Bohr's model of the hydrogen atom states, therefore, that only the specific frequencies of light that satisfy Equation 6.6 can be absorbed or emitted by the atom.

Substituting the energy expression in Equation 6.5 into Equation 6.6 and recalling that $\nu = c/\lambda$, we have

$$\Delta E = h\nu = \frac{hc}{\lambda} = (-2.18 \times 10^{-18} \text{ J})\left(\frac{1}{n_f^2} - \frac{1}{n_i^2}\right) \qquad [6.7]$$

where n_i and n_f are the principal quantum numbers of the initial and final states of the atom, respectively. If n_f is smaller than n_i, the electron moves closer to the nucleus and ΔE is a negative number, indicating that the atom releases energy. For example, if the electron moves from $n_i = 3$ to $n_f = 1$, we have

$$\Delta E = (-2.18 \times 10^{-18} \text{ J})\left(\frac{1}{1^2} - \frac{1}{3^2}\right) = (-2.18 \times 10^{-18} \text{ J})\left(\frac{8}{9}\right) = -1.94 \times 10^{-18} \text{ J}$$

Knowing the energy of the emitted photon, we can calculate either its frequency or its wavelength. For the wavelength, we have

$$\lambda = \frac{c}{\nu} = \frac{hc}{\Delta E} = \frac{(6.626 \times 10^{-34} \text{ J-s})(3.00 \times 10^8 \text{ m/s})}{1.94 \times 10^{-18} \text{ J}} = 1.02 \times 10^{-7} \text{ m}$$

We have not included the negative sign of the energy in this calculation because wavelength and frequency are always reported as positive quantities. The direction of energy flow is indicated by saying that a photon of wavelength 1.02×10^{-7} m has been *emitted*.

If we solve Equation 6.7 for $1/\lambda$ and replace $(-2.18 \times 10^{-18} \text{ J})$ by its equivalent, hcR_H from Equation 6.5, we find that Equation 6.7 derived from Bohr's theory corresponds to the Rydberg equation, Equation 6.4, which was obtained using experimental data:

$$\frac{1}{\lambda} = \frac{-hcR_H}{hc}\left(\frac{1}{n_f^2} - \frac{1}{n_i^2}\right) = R_H\left(\frac{1}{n_i^2} - \frac{1}{n_f^2}\right)$$

Thus, the existence of discrete spectral lines can be attributed to the quantized jumps of electrons between energy levels.

▲ GIVE IT SOME THOUGHT

As the electron in a hydrogen atom jumps from the $n = 3$ orbit to the $n = 7$ orbit, does it absorb energy or emit energy?

SAMPLE EXERCISE 6.4 | Electronic Transitions in the Hydrogen Atom

Using Figure 6.12, predict which of these electronic transitions produces the spectral line having the longest wavelength: $n = 2$ to $n = 1$, $n = 3$ to $n = 2$, or $n = 4$ to $n = 3$.

SOLUTION

The wavelength increases as frequency decreases ($\lambda = c/\nu$). Hence, the longest wavelength will be associated with the lowest frequency. According to Planck's equation, $E = h\nu$, the lowest frequency is associated with the lowest energy. In Figure 6.12 the energy levels (horizontal lines) that are closest together represents the smallest energy change. Thus, the $n = 4$ to $n = 3$ transition produces the longest wavelength (lowest frequency) line.

PRACTICE EXERCISE

Indicate whether each of the following electronic transitions emits energy or requires the absorption of energy: **(a)** $n = 3$ to $n = 1$; **(b)** $n = 2$ to $n = 4$.

Answers: **(a)** emits energy, **(b)** requires absorption of energy

---

Limitations of the Bohr Model

Although the Bohr model explains the line spectrum of the hydrogen atom, it cannot explain the spectra of other atoms, except in a crude way. Bohr also avoided the problem of why the negatively charged electron would not just fall into the positively charged nucleus by simply assuming it would not happen. Furthermore, there is a problem with describing an electron merely as a small particle circling the nucleus. As we will see in Section 6.4, the electron exhibits wavelike properties, a fact that any acceptable model of electronic structure must accommodate. As it turns out, the Bohr model was only an important step along the way toward the development of a more comprehensive model. What is most significant about Bohr's model is that it introduces two important ideas that are also incorporated into our current model:

1. *Electrons exist only in certain discrete energy levels, which are described by quantum numbers.*

2. *Energy is involved in the transition of an electron from one level to another.*

We will now start to develop the successor to the Bohr model, which requires that we take a closer look at the behavior of matter.

6.4 | THE WAVE BEHAVIOR OF MATTER

In the years following the development of Bohr's model for the hydrogen atom, the dual nature of radiant energy became a familiar concept. Depending on the experimental circumstances, radiation appears to have either a wave-like or a particle-like (photon) character. Louis de Broglie (1892–1987), who was working on his Ph.D. thesis in physics at the Sorbonne in Paris, boldly extended this idea. If radiant energy could, under appropriate conditions, behave as though it were a stream of particles (photons), could matter, under appropriate conditions, possibly show the properties of a wave?

De Broglie suggested that an electron moving about the nucleus of an atom behaves like a wave and therefore has a wavelength. He proposed that the wavelength of the electron, or of any other particle, depends on its mass, m, and on its velocity, v:

$$\lambda = \frac{h}{mv} \qquad [6.8]$$

(where h is Planck's constant). The quantity mv for any object is called its **momentum**. De Broglie used the term **matter waves** to describe the wave characteristics of material particles.

Because de Broglie's hypothesis is applicable to all matter, any object of mass m and velocity v would give rise to a characteristic matter wave. However, Equation 6.8 indicates that the wavelength associated with an object of ordinary size, such as a golf ball, is so tiny as to be completely unobservable. This is not so for an electron because its mass is so small, as we see in Sample Exercise 6.5.

SAMPLE EXERCISE 6.5   **Matter Waves**

What is the wavelength of an electron moving with a speed of 5.97×10^6 m/s? The mass of the electron is 9.11×10^{-31} kg.

SOLUTION

Analyze We are given the mass, m, and velocity, v, of the electron, and we must calculate its de Broglie wavelength, λ.

Plan The wavelength of a moving particle is given by Equation 6.8, so λ is calculated by inserting the known quantities h, m, and v. In doing so, however, we must pay attention to units.

Solve Using the value of Planck's constant, $h = 6.626 \times 10^{-34}$ J-s

we have the following:

$$\lambda = \frac{h}{mv}$$

$$= \frac{(6.626 \times 10^{-34} \text{ J-s})}{(9.11 \times 10^{-31} \text{ kg})(5.97 \times 10^6 \text{ m/s})}\left(\frac{1 \text{ kg-m}^2/\text{s}^2}{1 \text{ J}}\right)$$

$$= 1.22 \times 10^{-10} \text{ m} = 0.122 \text{ nm} = 1.22 \text{ Å}$$

Comment By comparing this value with the wavelengths of electromagnetic radiation shown in Figure 6.4, we see that the wavelength of this electron is about the same as that of X-rays.

PRACTICE EXERCISE

Calculate the velocity of a neutron whose de Broglie wavelength is 500 pm. The mass of a neutron is given in the table inside the back cover of the text.

Answer: 7.92×10^2 m/s

A few years after de Broglie published his theory, the wave properties of the electron were demonstrated experimentally. When X-rays pass through a crystal, an interference pattern results that is characteristic of the wavelike properties of electromagnetic radiation. This phenomenon is called X-ray *diffraction*. As electrons pass through a crystal, they are similarly diffracted. Thus, a stream of moving electrons exhibits the same kinds of wave behavior as X-rays and all other types of electromagnetic radiation.

The technique of electron diffraction has been highly developed. In the electron microscope, for instance, the wave characteristics of electrons are used to obtain images at the atomic scale. This microscope is an important tool for studying surface phenomena at very high magnifications (▶ **FIGURE 6.13**). Electron microscopes can magnify objects by 3,000,000 times (×), far more than can be done with visible light (1000×), because the wavelength of the electrons is so much smaller than the wavelengths of visible light.

▲ **FIGURE 6.13**   **Electrons as waves.** The white dots in this transmission electron micrograph indicate the tops of columns of atoms.

⚠️ **GIVE IT SOME THOUGHT**

A baseball pitcher throws a fastball that moves at 95 miles per hour. Does that moving baseball generate matter waves? If so, can we observe them?

The Uncertainty Principle

The discovery of the wave properties of matter raised some new and interesting questions. Consider, for example, a ball rolling down a ramp. Using the equations of classical physics, we can calculate, with great accuracy, the ball's position, direction of motion, and speed at any instant. Can we do the same for an electron, which exhibits wave properties? A wave extends in space and its location is not precisely defined. We might therefore anticipate that it is impossible to determine exactly where an electron is located at a specific instant.

The German physicist Werner Heisenberg (▶ **FIGURE 6.14**) proposed that the dual nature of matter places a fundamental limitation on how precisely we can know both the location and

◀ **FIGURE 6.14**   **Werner Heisenberg (1901–1976).** During his postdoctoral assistantship with Niels Bohr, Heisenberg formulated his famous uncertainty principle. At 32 he was one of the youngest scientists to receive a Nobel Prize.

the momentum of an object at a given instant. The limitation becomes important only when we deal with matter at the subatomic level (that is, with masses as small as that of an electron). Heisenberg's principle is called the **uncertainty principle**. When applied to the electrons in an atom, this principle states that it is impossible for us to know simultaneously both the exact momentum of the electron and its exact location in space.

Heisenberg mathematically related the uncertainty in position, Δx, and the uncertainty in momentum, $\Delta(mv)$, to a quantity involving Planck's constant:

$$\Delta x \cdot \Delta(mv) \geq \frac{h}{4\pi} \qquad [6.9]$$

A brief calculation illustrates the dramatic implications of the uncertainty principle. The electron has a mass of 9.11×10^{-31} kg and moves at an average speed of about 5×10^6 m/s in a hydrogen atom. Let's assume that we know the speed to an uncertainty of 1% [that is, an uncertainty of $(0.01)(5 \times 10^6$ m/s$) = 5 \times 10^4$ m/s] and that this is the only important source of uncertainty in the momentum, so that $\Delta(mv) = m\,\Delta v$. We can use Equation 6.9 to calculate the uncertainty in the position of the electron:

$$\Delta x \geq \frac{h}{4\pi m \Delta v} = \left(\frac{6.626 \times 10^{-34} \text{ J-s}}{4\pi(9.11 \times 10^{-31} \text{ kg})(5 \times 10^4 \text{ m/s})} \right) = 1 \times 10^{-9} \text{ m}$$

Because the diameter of a hydrogen atom is about 1×10^{-10} m, the uncertainty in the position of the electron in the atom is an order of magnitude greater than the size of the atom. Thus, we have essentially no idea where the electron is located in the atom. On the other hand, if we were to repeat the calculation with an object of ordinary mass, such as a tennis ball, the uncertainty would be so small that it would be inconsequential. In that case, m is large and Δx is out of the realm of measurement and therefore of no practical consequence.

De Broglie's hypothesis and Heisenberg's uncertainty principle set the stage for a new and more broadly applicable theory of atomic structure. In this approach, any attempt to define precisely the instantaneous location and momentum of the electron is abandoned. The wave nature of the electron is recognized, and its behavior is described in terms appropriate to waves. The result is a model that precisely describes the energy of the electron while describing its location not precisely but rather in terms of probabilities.

A CLOSER LOOK

MEASUREMENT AND THE UNCERTAINTY PRINCIPLE

Whenever any measurement is made, some uncertainty exists. Our experience with objects of ordinary dimensions, such as balls or trains or laboratory equipment, indicates that using more precise instruments can decrease the uncertainty of a measurement. In fact, we might expect that the uncertainty in a measurement can be made indefinitely small. However, the uncertainty principle states that there is an actual limit to the accuracy of measurements. This limit is not a restriction on how well instruments can be made; rather, it is inherent in nature. This limit has no practical consequences when dealing with ordinary-sized objects, but its implications are enormous when dealing with subatomic particles, such as electrons.

To measure an object, we must disturb it, at least a little, with our measuring device. Imagine using a flashlight to locate a large rubber ball in a dark room. You see the ball when the light from the flashlight bounces off the ball and strikes your eyes. When a beam of photons strikes an object of this size, it does not alter its position or momentum to any practical extent. Imagine, however, that you wish to locate an electron by similarly bouncing light off it into some detector. Objects can be located to an accuracy no greater than the wavelength of the radiation used. Thus, if we want an accurate position measurement for an electron, we must use a short wavelength. This means that photons of high energy must be employed. The more energy the photons have, the more momentum they impart to the electron when they strike it, which changes the electron's motion in an unpredictable way. The attempt to measure accurately the electron's position introduces considerable uncertainty in its momentum; the act of measuring the electron's position at one moment makes our knowledge of its future position inaccurate.

Suppose, then, that we use photons of longer wavelength. Because these photons have lower energy, the momentum of the electron is not so appreciably changed during measurement, but its position will be correspondingly less accurately known. This is the essence of the uncertainty principle: *There is an uncertainty in simultaneously knowing either the position or the momentum of the electron that cannot be reduced beyond a certain minimum level.* The more accurately one is known, the less accurately the other is known. Although we can never know the exact position and momentum of the electron, we can talk about the probability of its being at certain locations in space. In Section 6.5 we introduce a model of the atom that provides the probability of finding electrons of specific energies at certain positions in atoms.

RELATED EXERCISES: 6.47 and 6.48

What is the principal reason we must consider the uncertainty principle when discussing electrons and other subatomic particles but not when discussing our macroscopic world?

6.5 | QUANTUM MECHANICS AND ATOMIC ORBITALS

In 1926 the Austrian physicist Erwin Schrödinger (1887–1961) proposed an equation, now known as Schrödinger's wave equation, that incorporates both the wave-like behavior of the electron and its particle-like behavior. His work opened a new approach to dealing with subatomic particles, an approach known as *quantum mechanics* or *wave mechanics*. The application of Schrödinger's equation requires advanced calculus, and so we will not be concerned with its details. We will, however, qualitatively consider the results Schrödinger obtained because they give us a powerful new way to view electronic structure. Let's begin by examining the electronic structure of the simplest atom, hydrogen.

Schrödinger treated the electron in a hydrogen atom like the wave on a plucked guitar string (▼ FIGURE 6.15). Because such waves do not travel in space, they are called *standing waves*. Just as the plucked guitar string produces a standing wave that has a fundamental frequency and higher overtones (harmonics), the electron exhibits a lowest-energy standing wave and higher-energy ones. Furthermore, just as the overtones of the guitar string have *nodes,* points where the amplitude of the wave is zero, so do the waves characteristic of the electron.

Solving Schrödinger's equation for the hydrogen atom leads to a series of mathematical functions called **wave functions** that describe the electron in an atom. These wave functions are usually represented by the symbol ψ (lowercase Greek letter *psi*). Although the wave function has no direct physical meaning, the square of the wave function, ψ^2, provides information about the electron's location when it is in an allowed energy state.

For the hydrogen atom, the allowed energies are the same as those predicted by the Bohr model. However, the Bohr model assumes that the electron is in a circular orbit of some particular radius about the nucleus. In the quantum mechanical model, the electron's location cannot be described so simply.

According to the uncertainty principle, if we know the momentum of the electron with high accuracy, our simultaneous knowledge of its location is very uncertain. Thus, we cannot hope to specify the exact location of an individual electron around the

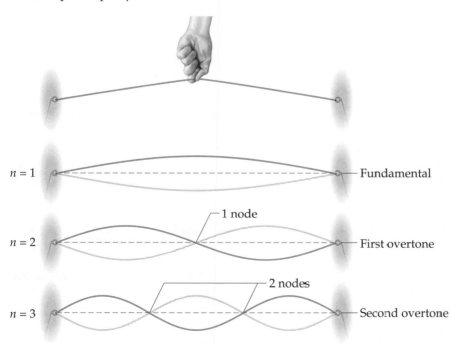

◀ FIGURE 6.15 **Standing waves in a vibrating string.**

GO FIGURE

Where in the figure is the region of highest electron density?

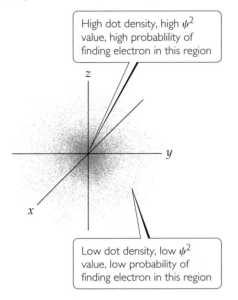

High dot density, high ψ^2 value, high probability of finding electron in this region

Low dot density, low ψ^2 value, low probability of finding electron in this region

▲ **FIGURE 6.16 Electron-density distribution.** This rendering represents the probability, ψ^2, of finding the electron in a hydrogen atom in its ground state. The origin of the coordinate system is at the nucleus.

nucleus. Rather, we must be content with a kind of statistical knowledge. We therefore speak of the *probability* that the electron will be in a certain region of space at a given instant. As it turns out, the square of the wave function, ψ^2, at a given point in space represents the probability that the electron will be found at that location. For this reason, ψ^2 is called either the **probability density** or the **electron density**.

One way of representing the probability of finding the electron in various regions of an atom is shown in ◄ **FIGURE 6.16**, where the density of the dots represents the probability of finding the electron. The regions with a high density of dots correspond to relatively large values for ψ^2 and are therefore regions where there is a high probability of finding the electron. Based on this representation, we often describe atoms as consisting of a nucleus surrounded by an electron cloud.

Orbitals and Quantum Numbers

The solution to Schrödinger's equation for the hydrogen atom yields a set of wave functions called **orbitals**. Each orbital has a characteristic shape and energy. For example, the lowest-energy orbital in the hydrogen atom has the spherical shape illustrated in Figure 6.16 and an energy of -2.18×10^{-18} J. Note that an *orbital* (quantum mechanical model, which describes electrons in terms of probabilities, visualized as "electron clouds") is not the same as an *orbit* (Bohr model, which visualizes the electron moving in a physical orbit, like a planet around a star). The quantum mechanical model does not refer to orbits because the motion of the electron in an atom cannot be precisely determined (Heisenberg uncertainty principle).

The Bohr model introduced a single quantum number, n, to describe an orbit. The quantum mechanical model uses three quantum numbers, n, l, and m_l, which result naturally from the mathematics used, to describe an orbital.

1. The *principal quantum number, n,* can have positive integral values 1, 2, 3, ... As n increases, the orbital becomes larger, and the electron spends more time farther from the nucleus. An increase in n also means that the electron has a higher energy and is therefore less tightly bound to the nucleus. For the hydrogen atom, $E_n = -(2.18 \times 10^{-18} \text{ J})(1/n^2)$, as in the Bohr model.

2. The second quantum number—the *angular momentum quantum number, l*—can have integral values from 0 to $(n - 1)$ for each value of n. This quantum number defines the shape of the orbital. The value of l for a particular orbital is generally designated by the letters s, p, d, and f,* corresponding to l values of 0, 1, 2, and 3:

Value of l	0	1	2	3
Letter used	s	p	d	f

3. The *magnetic quantum number, m_l,* can have integral values between $-l$ and l, including zero. This quantum number describes the orientation of the orbital in space, as we discuss in Section 6.6.

Notice that because the value of n can be any positive integer, an infinite number of orbitals for the hydrogen atom are possible. At any given instant, however, the electron in a hydrogen atom is described by only one of these orbitals—we say that the electron *occupies* a certain orbital. The remaining orbitals are *unoccupied* for that particular state of the hydrogen atom.

 GIVE IT SOME THOUGHT

What is the difference between an *orbit* in the Bohr model of the hydrogen atom and an *orbital* in the quantum mechanical model?

The collection of orbitals with the same value of n is called an **electron shell**. All the orbitals that have $n = 3$, for example, are said to be in the third shell. The set of

*The letters come from the words *sharp, principal, diffuse,* and *fundamental,* which were used to describe certain features of spectra before quantum mechanics was developed.

TABLE 6.2 • Relationship among Values of n, l, and m_l through n = 4

n	Possible Values of l	Subshell Designation	Possible Values of m_l	Number of Orbitals in Subshell	Total Number of Orbitals in Shell
1	0	1s	0	1	1
2	0	2s	0	1	
	1	2p	1, 0, −1	3	4
3	0	3s	0	1	
	1	3p	1, 0, −1	3	
	2	3d	2, 1, 0, −1, −2	5	9
4	0	4s	0	1	
	1	4p	1, 0, −1	3	
	2	4d	2, 1, 0, −1, −2	5	
	3	4f	3, 2, 1, 0, −1, −2, −3	7	16

orbitals that have the same n and l values is called a **subshell**. Each subshell is designated by a number (the value of n) and a letter (s, p, d, or f, corresponding to the value of l). For example, the orbitals that have $n = 3$ and $l = 2$ are called $3d$ orbitals and are in the $3d$ subshell.

▲ TABLE 6.2 summarizes the possible values of l and m_l for values of n through $n = 4$. The restrictions on possible values give rise to the following very important observations:

1. The shell with principal quantum number n consists of exactly n subshells. Each subshell corresponds to a different allowed value of l from 0 to $(n − 1)$. Thus, the first shell ($n = 1$) consists of only one subshell, the $1s$ ($l = 0$); the second shell ($n = 2$) consists of two subshells, the $2s$ ($l = 0$) and $2p$ ($l = 1$); the third shell consists of three subshells, $3s$, $3p$, and $3d$, and so forth.

2. Each subshell consists of a specific number of orbitals. Each orbital corresponds to a different allowed value of m_l. For a given value of l, there are $(2l + 1)$ allowed values of m_l, ranging from $−l$ to $+l$. Thus, each s ($l = 0$) subshell consists of one orbital; each p ($l = 1$) subshell consists of three orbitals; each d ($l = 2$) subshell consists of five orbitals, and so forth.

3. The total number of orbitals in a shell is n^2, where n is the principal quantum number of the shell. The resulting number of orbitals for the shells—1, 4, 9, 16—are related to a pattern seen in the periodic table: We see that the number of elements in the rows of the periodic table—2, 8, 18, and 32—equals twice these numbers. We will discuss this relationship further in Section 6.9.

▶ FIGURE 6.17 shows the relative energies of the hydrogen atom orbitals through $n = 3$. Each box represents an orbital, and orbitals of the same subshell, such as the three $2p$ orbitals, are grouped together. When the electron occupies the lowest-energy orbital ($1s$), the hydrogen atom is said to be in its *ground state*. When the electron occupies any other orbital, the atom is in an *excited state*. (The electron can be excited to a higher-energy orbital by absorption of a photon of appropriate energy.) At ordinary temperatures, essentially all hydrogen atoms are in the ground state.

▲ **GIVE IT SOME THOUGHT**

Notice in Figure 6.17 that the energy difference between the $n = 1$ and $n = 2$ levels is much greater than the energy difference between the $n = 2$ and $n = 3$ levels. How does Equation 6.5 explain this trend?

▲ **GO FIGURE**

If the fourth shell (the $n = 4$ energy level) were shown, how many subshells would it contain? How would they be labeled?

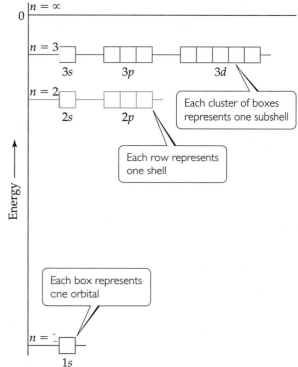

$n = 1$ shell has one orbital
$n = 2$ shell has two subshells composed of four orbitals
$n = 3$ shell has three subshells composed of nine orbitals

▲ **FIGURE 6.17   Energy levels in the hydrogen atom.**

SAMPLE EXERCISE 6.6 | **Subshells of the Hydrogen Atom**

(a) Without referring to Table 6.2, predict the number of subshells in the fourth shell, that is, for $n = 4$. (b) Give the label for each of these subshells. (c) How many orbitals are in each of these subshells?

Analyze and Plan We are given the value of the principal quantum number, n. We need to determine the allowed values of l and m_l for this given value of n and then count the number of orbitals in each subshell.

SOLUTION

There are four subshells in the fourth shell, corresponding to the four possible values of l (0, 1, 2, and 3).

These subshells are labeled 4s, 4p, 4d, and 4f. The number given in the designation of a subshell is the principal quantum number, n; the letter designates the value of the angular momentum quantum number, l: for $l = 0$, s; for $l = 1$, p; for $l = 2$, d; for $l = 3$, f.

There is one 4s orbital (when $l = 0$, there is only one possible value of m_l: 0). There are three 4p orbitals (when $l = 1$, there are three possible values of m_l: 1, 0, −1). There are five 4d orbitals (when $l = 2$, there are five allowed values of m_l: 2, 1, 0, −1, −2). There are seven 4f orbitals (when $l = 3$, there are seven permitted values of m_l: 3, 2, 1, 0, −1, −2, −3).

PRACTICE EXERCISE

(a) What is the designation for the subshell with $n = 5$ and $l = 1$? (b) How many orbitals are in this subshell? (c) Indicate the values of m_l for each of these orbitals.

Answers: (a) 5p; (b) 3; (c) 1, 0, −1

6.6 | REPRESENTATIONS OF ORBITALS

So far we have emphasized orbital energies, but the wave function also provides information about an electron's probable location in space. Let's examine the ways in which we can picture orbitals because their shapes help us visualize how the electron density is distributed around the nucleus.

The s Orbitals

We have already seen one representation of the lowest-energy orbital of the hydrogen atom, the 1s (Figure 6.16). The first thing we notice about the electron density for the 1s orbital is that it is *spherically symmetric*—in other words, the electron density at a given distance from the nucleus is the same regardless of the direction in which we proceed from the nucleus. All of the other s orbitals (2s, 3s, 4s, and so forth) are also spherically symmetric and centered on the nucleus.

Recall that the l quantum number for the s orbitals is 0; therefore, the m_l quantum number must be 0. Thus, for each value of n, there is only one s orbital.

So how do s orbitals differ as the value of n changes? One way to address this question is to look at the **radial probability function**, also called the *radial probability density*, which is defined as the probability that we will find the electron at a specific distance from the nucleus.

▶ **FIGURE 6.18** shows the radial probability density for the 1s, 2s, and 3s orbitals of hydrogen as a function of r, the distance from the nucleus. Three features of these graphs are noteworthy: the number of peaks, the number of points at which the probability function goes to zero (called **nodes**), and how spread out the distribution is, which gives a sense of the size of the orbital.

For the 1s orbital, we see that the probability rises rapidly as we move away from the nucleus, maximizing at about 0.5 Å. Thus, when the electron occupies the 1s orbital, it is *most likely* to be found this distance from the nucleus.* Notice also that in the 1s orbital the probability of finding the electron at a distance greater than about 3 Å from the nucleus is essentially zero.

---

*In the quantum mechanical model, the most probable distance at which to find the electron in the 1s orbital is actually 0.529 Å, the same as the radius of the orbit predicted by Bohr for $n = 1$. The distance 0.529 Å is often called the Bohr radius.

How many maxima would you expect to find in the radial probability function for the 4s orbital of the hydrogen atom? How many nodes would you expect in this function?

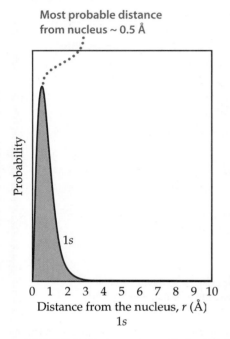

Most probable distance from nucleus ~ 0.5 Å

Probability

1s

Distance from the nucleus, r (Å)

1s

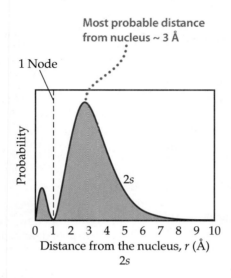

Most probable distance from nucleus ~ 3 Å

1 Node

Probability

2s

Distance from the nucleus, r (Å)

2s

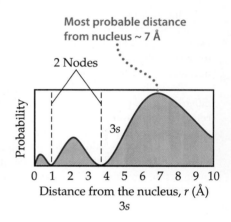

Most probable distance from nucleus ~ 7 Å

2 Nodes

Probability

3s

Distance from the nucleus, r (Å)

3s

▲ **FIGURE 6.18 Radial probability distributions for the 1s, 2s, and 3s orbitals of hydrogen.** These graphs of the radial probability function plot probability of finding the electron as a function of distance from the nucleus. As n increases, the most likely distance at which to find the electron (the highest peak) moves farther from the nucleus.

Comparing the radial probability distributions for the 1s, 2s, and 3s orbitals reveals three trends:

1. *The number of peaks increases with increasing* n, *with the outermost peak being larger than inner ones.*

2. *The number of nodes increases with increasing* n.

3. *The electron density becomes more spread out with increasing* n.

One widely used method of representing orbital *shape* is to draw a boundary surface that encloses some substantial portion, say 90%, of the electron density for the orbital. This type of drawing is called a *contour representation,* and the contour representations for the s orbitals are spheres (▼ **FIGURE 6.19**). All the orbitals have the same shape, but they differ in size, becoming larger as n increases, reflecting the fact that the electron density becomes more spread out as n increases. Although the details of how

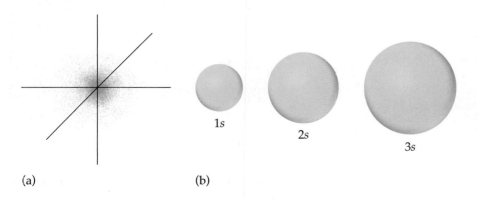

1s

2s

3s

(a)   (b)

◀ **FIGURE 6.19 Comparison of the 1s, 2s, and 3s orbitals.** (a) Electron-density distribution of a 1s orbital. (b) Contour representations of the 1s, 2s, and 3s orbitals. Each sphere is centered on the atom's nucleus and encloses the volume in which there is a 90% probability of finding the electron.

A CLOSER LOOK

PROBABILITY DENSITY AND RADIAL PROBABILITY FUNCTIONS

According to quantum mechanics, we must describe the position of the electron in the hydrogen atom in terms of probabilities. The information about the probability is contained in the wave functions, ψ, obtained from Schrödinger's equation. The square of the wave function, ψ^2, called either the probability density or the electron density, as noted earlier, gives the probability that the electron is at any *point* in space. Because *s* orbitals are spherically symmetric, the value of ψ for an *s* electron depends only on its distance from the nucleus, r. Thus, the probability density can be written as $[\psi(r)]^2$, where $\psi(r)$ is the value of ψ at r. This function $[\psi(r)]^2$ gives the probability density for any point located a distance r from the nucleus.

The radial probability function, which we used in Figure 6.18, differs from the probability density. The radial probability function equals the *total* probability of finding the electron at all the points at any distance r from the nucleus. In other words, to calculate this function, we need to "add up" the probability densities $[\psi(r)]^2$ over all points located a distance r from the nucleus. ▶ FIGURE 6.20 compares the probability density at a point ($[\psi(r)]^2$) with the radial probability function.

Let's examine the difference between probability density and radial probability function more closely. ▶ FIGURE 6.21 shows plots of $[\psi(r)]^2$ as a function of r for the 1*s*, 2*s*, and 3*s* orbitals of the

$4\pi r^2[\psi(r)]^2$ is radial probability function = sum of all $[\psi(r)]^2$ having any given value of r

$[\psi(r)]^2$ is probability density at any given point

▲ FIGURE 6.20 **Comparing probability density $[\psi(r)]^2$ and radial probability function $4\pi r^2[\psi(r)]^2$.**

electron density varies within a given contour representation are lost in these representations, this is not a serious disadvantage. For qualitative discussions, the most important features of orbitals are shape and relative size, which are adequately displayed by contour representations.

The *p* Orbitals

The distribution of electron density for a 2*p* orbital is shown in ▶ FIGURE 6.22(a). The electron density is not distributed spherically as in an *s* orbital. Instead, the density is concentrated in two regions on either side of the nucleus, separated by a node at the nucleus. We say that this dumbbell-shaped orbital has two *lobes*. Recall that we are making no statement of how the electron is moving within the orbital. Figure 6.22(a) portrays only the *averaged* distribution of the electron density in a 2*p* orbital.

Beginning with the $n = 2$ shell, each shell has three *p* orbitals. Recall that the l quantum number for *p* orbitals is 1. Therefore, the magnetic quantum number m_l can have three possible values: -1, 0, and $+1$. Thus, there are three 2*p* orbitals, three 3*p* orbitals, and so forth, corresponding to the three possible values of m_l. Each set of *p* orbitals has the dumbbell shapes shown in Figure 6.22(a) for the 2*p* orbitals. For each value of n, the three *p* orbitals have the same size and shape but differ from one another in spatial orientation. We usually represent *p* orbitals by drawing the shape and orientation of their wave functions, as shown in Figure 6.22(b). It is convenient to label these as the p_x, p_y, and p_z orbitals. The letter subscript indicates the Cartesian axis along which the orbital is oriented.* Like *s* orbitals, *p* orbitals increase in size as we move from 2*p* to 3*p* to 4*p*, and so forth.

---

*We cannot make a simple correspondence between the subscripts (x, y, and z) and the allowed m_l values (1, 0, and -1). To explain why this is so is beyond the scope of an introductory text.

hydrogen atom. You will notice that these plots look distinctly differ-ent from the radial probability functions shown in Figure 6.18.

As shown in Figure 6.20, the collection of points a distance r from the nucleus is the surface of a sphere of radius r. The probabil-ity density at each point on that spherical surface is $[\psi(r)]^2$. To add up all the individual probability densities requires calculus and so is beyond the scope of this text. However, the result of that calculation tells us that the radial probability function is the probability density, $[\psi(r)]^2$, multiplied by the surface area of the sphere, $4\pi r^2$:

$$\text{Radial probability function} = 4\pi r^2 [\psi(r)]^2$$

Thus, the plots of radial probability function in Figure 6.18 are equal to the plots of $[\psi(r)]^2$ in Figure 6.21 multiplied by $4\pi r^2$. The fact that $4\pi r^2$ increases rapidly as we move away from the nucleus makes the two sets of plots look very different from each other. For example, the plot of $[\psi(r)]^2$ for the 3s orbital in Figure 6.21 shows that the function generally gets smaller the farther we go from the nucleus. But when we multiply by $4\pi r^2$, we see peaks that get larger and larger as we move away from the nucleus (Figure 6.18).

The radial probability functions in Figure 6.18 provide us with the more useful information because they tell us the probability of finding the electron at *all* points a distance r from the nucleus, not just one particular point.

RELATED EXERCISES: 6.50, 6.59, 6.60, and 6.91

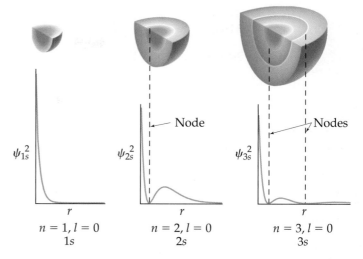

▲ **FIGURE 6.21**   **Probability density $[\psi(r)]^2$ in the 1s, 2s, and 3s orbitals of hydrogen.**

⚠ **GO FIGURE**

(a) Note on the left that the color is deep pink in the interior of each lobe but fades to pale pink at the edges. What does this change in color repre-sent? (b) What label is applied to the 2p orbital aligned along the x axis?

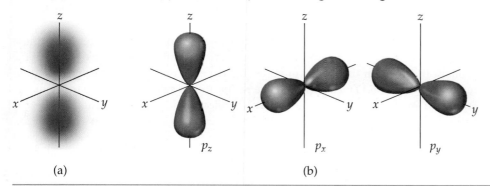

(a)   (b)

◀ **FIGURE 6.22**   **The p orbitals.**
(a) Electron-density distribution of a 2p orbital.
(b) Contour representations of the three p orbitals. The subscript on the orbital label indicates the axis along which the orbital lies.

The *d* and *f* Orbitals

When n is 3 or greater, we encounter the d orbitals (for which $l = 2$). There are five $3d$ orbitals, five $4d$ orbitals, and so forth because in each shell there are five possible values for the m_l quantum number: $-2, -1, 0, 1,$ and 2. The different d orbitals in a given shell have different shapes and orientations in space, as shown in ▶ **FIGURE 6.23**. Four of the d-orbital contour representations have a "four-leaf clover" shape, and each lies primarily in a plane. The d_{xy}, d_{xz}, and d_{yz} lie in the xy, xz, and yz planes, respectively, with the lobes oriented *between* the axes. The lobes of the $d_{x^2-y^2}$ orbital also lie in the xy plane, but the lobes lie *along* the x and y axes. The d_{z^2} orbital looks very different from the other four: It has two lobes along the z axis and a "doughnut" in the xy plane. Even though the d_{z^2} orbital looks different from the other d orbitals, it has the same energy as the other four

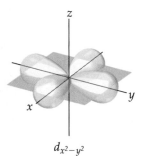

$d_{x^2-y^2}$ d_{z^2}

▲ **FIGURE 6.23 Contour representations of the five *d* orbitals.**

d orbitals. The representations in Figure 6.23 are commonly used for all *d* orbitals, regardless of principal quantum number.

When *n* is 4 or greater, there are seven equivalent *f* orbitals (for which *l* = 3). The shapes of the *f* orbitals are even more complicated than those of the *d* orbitals and are not presented here. As you will see in the next section, however, you must be aware of *f* orbitals as we consider the electronic structure of atoms in the lower part of the periodic table.

In many instances later in the text you will find that knowing the number and shapes of atomic orbitals will help you understand chemistry at the molecular level. You will therefore find it useful to memorize the shapes of the *s*, *p*, and *d* orbitals shown in Figures 6.19, 6.22, and 6.23.

6.7 | MANY-ELECTRON ATOMS

One of our goals in this chapter has been to determine the electronic structures of atoms. So far, we have seen that quantum mechanics leads to an elegant description of the hydrogen atom. This atom, however, has only one electron. How does our description change when we consider an atom with two or more electrons (a *many-electron atom*)? To describe such an atom, we must consider the nature of orbitals and their relative energies as well as how the electrons populate the available orbitals.

Orbitals and Their Energies

We can describe the electronic structure of a many-electron atom in terms of orbitals like those of the hydrogen atom. Thus, we continue to designate orbitals as 1s, $2p_x$, and so forth. Further, these orbitals have the same general shapes as the corresponding hydrogen orbitals.

Although the shapes of the orbitals of a many-electron atom are the same as those for hydrogen, the presence of more than one electron greatly changes the energies of the orbitals. In hydrogen the energy of an orbital depends only on its principal quantum number, *n* (Figure 6.17). For instance, the 3s, 3p, and 3d subshells all have the same energy. In a many-electron atom, however, the electron–electron repulsions cause the various subshells in a given shell to be at different energies, as shown in ◀ **FIGURE 6.24.**

To explain this fact, we must consider the forces between the electrons and how these forces are affected by the shapes of the orbitals. We will, however, forgo this analysis until Chapter 7.

The important idea is this: *In a many-electron atom, for a given value of n, the energy of an orbital increases with increasing value of l.* For example, notice in Figure 6.24 that the *n* = 3 orbitals increase in energy in the order 3s < 3p < 3d. Notice also that all orbitals of a given subshell (such as the five 3d orbitals) have the same energy as one another. Orbitals with the same energy are said to be **degenerate**.

Figure 6.24 is a *qualitative* energy-level diagram; the exact energies of the orbitals and their spacings differ from one atom to another.

GO FIGURE

Not all of the orbitals in the *n* = 4 shell are shown in this figure. Which subshells are missing?

▲ **FIGURE 6.24 General energy ordering of orbitals for a many-electron atom.**

▲ **GIVE IT SOME THOUGHT**

a. How may orbitals have the principal quantum number *n* = 3?
b. In a many-electron atom, what are the relative energies of these orbitals?

Electron Spin and the Pauli Exclusion Principle

We have now seen that we can use hydrogen-like orbitals to describe many-electron atoms. What, however, determines which orbitals the electrons occupy? That is, how do the electrons of a many-electron atom populate the available orbitals? To answer this question, we must consider an additional property of the electron.

When scientists studied the line spectra of many-electron atoms in great detail, they noticed a very puzzling feature: Lines that were originally thought to be single were actually closely spaced pairs. This meant, in essence, that there were twice as many energy levels as there were "supposed" to be. In 1925 the Dutch physicists George Uhlenbeck and Samuel Goudsmit proposed a solution to this dilemma. They postulated that electrons have an intrinsic property, called **electron spin**, that causes each electron to behave as if it were a tiny sphere spinning on its own axis.

By now it probably does not surprise you to learn that electron spin is quantized. This observation led to the assignment of a new quantum number for the electron, in addition to n, l, and m_l, which we have already discussed. This new quantum number, the **spin magnetic quantum number**, is denoted m_s (the subscript s stands for *spin*). Two possible values are allowed for m_s, $+\frac{1}{2}$ or $-\frac{1}{2}$, which was first interpreted as indicating the two opposite directions in which the electron can spin. A spinning charge produces a magnetic field. The two opposite directions of spin therefore produce oppositely directed magnetic fields (▶ FIGURE 6.25).* These two opposite magnetic fields lead to the splitting of spectral lines into closely spaced pairs.

Electron spin is crucial for understanding the electronic structures of atoms. In 1925 the Austrian-born physicist Wolfgang Pauli (1900–1958) discovered the principle that governs the arrangements of electrons in many-electron atoms. The **Pauli exclusion principle** states that *no two electrons in an atom can have the same set of four quantum numbers* n, l, m_l, *and* m_s. For a given orbital, the values of n, l, and m_l are fixed. Thus, if we

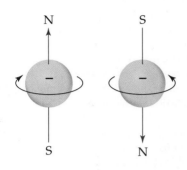

▲ **FIGURE 6.25   Electron spin.** The electron behaves as if it were spinning about an axis, thereby generating a magnetic field whose direction depends on the direction of spin. The two directions for the magnetic field correspond to the two possible values for the spin quantum number, m_s.

A CLOSER LOOK

EXPERIMENTAL EVIDENCE FOR ELECTRON SPIN

Even before electron spin had been proposed, there was experimental evidence that electrons had an additional property that needed explanation. In 1921, Otto Stern and Walter Gerlach succeeded in separating a beam of electrically neutral atoms into two groups by passing them through a nonhomogeneous magnetic field (▶ FIGURE 6.26).

Let's assume they used a beam of hydrogen atoms (in actuality, they used silver atoms, which contain just one unpaired electron). We would normally expect electrically neutral atoms to be unaffected by a magnetic field. However, the magnetic field arising from the electron's spin interacts with the magnet's field, deflecting the atom from its straight-line path. As shown in Figure 6.26, the magnetic field splits the beam in two, suggesting that there are two (and only two) equivalent values for the electron's magnetic field. The Stern–Gerlach experiment could be readily interpreted once it was realized that there are exactly two values for the spin of the electron. These values produce equal magnetic fields that are opposite in direction.

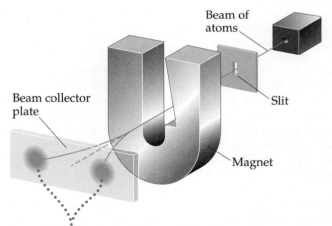

Atoms having unpaired electron with spin quantum number $m_s = +1/2$ deflect in one direction; those having unpaired electron with $m_s = -1/2$ deflect in opposite direction

▲ **FIGURE 6.26   The Stern–Gerlach experiment.**

---

*As we discussed earlier, the electron has both particle-like and wave-like properties. Thus, the picture of an electron as a spinning charged sphere is, strictly speaking, just a useful pictorial representation that helps us understand the two directions of magnetic field that an electron can possess.

CHEMISTRY AND LIFE

NUCLEAR SPIN AND MAGNETIC RESONANCE IMAGING

A major challenge facing medical diagnosis is seeing inside the human body. Until recently, this was accomplished primarily by using X-rays to image human bones, muscles, and organs. However, there are several drawbacks to using X-rays for medical imaging. First, X-rays do not give well-resolved images of overlapping physiological structures. Moreover, because damaged or diseased tissue often yields the same image as healthy tissue, X-rays frequently fail to detect illness or injuries. Finally, X-rays are high-energy radiation that can cause physiological harm, even in low doses.

During the 1980s, a technique called *magnetic resonance imaging* (MRI) moved to the forefront of medical imaging technology. The foundation of MRI is a phenomenon called nuclear magnetic resonance (NMR), which was discovered in the mid-1940s. Today NMR has become one of the most important spectroscopic methods used in chemistry. It is based on the observation that, like electrons, the nuclei of many elements possess an intrinsic spin. Like electron spin, nuclear spin is quantized. For example, the nucleus of ^{1}H has two possible magnetic nuclear spin quantum numbers, $+\frac{1}{2}$ and $-\frac{1}{2}$. The hydrogen nucleus is the most common one studied by NMR.

A spinning hydrogen nucleus acts like a tiny magnet. In the absence of external effects, the two spin states have the same energy. However, when the nuclei are placed in an external magnetic field, they can align either parallel or opposed (antiparallel) to the field, depending on their spin. The parallel alignment is lower in energy than the antiparallel one by a certain amount, ΔE (▶ FIGURE 6.27). If the nuclei are irradiated with photons having energy equal to ΔE, the spin of the nuclei can be "flipped," that is, excited from the parallel to the antiparallel alignment. Detection of the flipping of nuclei between the two spin states leads to an NMR spectrum. The radiation used in an NMR experiment is in the radiofrequency range, typically 100 to 900 MHz, which is far less energetic per photon than X-rays.

Because hydrogen is a major constituent of aqueous body fluids and fatty tissue, the hydrogen nucleus is the most convenient one for study by MRI. In MRI a person's body is placed in a strong magnetic field. By irradiating the body with pulses of radiofrequency radiation and using sophisticated detection techniques, medical technicians can image tissue at specific depths in the body, giving pictures with spectacular detail (▶ FIGURE 6.28). The ability to sample at different depths allows the technicians to construct a three-dimensional picture of the body.

MRI has none of the disadvantages of X-rays. Diseased tissue appears very different from healthy tissue, resolving overlapping structures at different depths in the body is much easier, and the radio frequency radiation is not harmful to humans in the doses used. The technique has had such a profound influence on the modern practice of medicine that Paul Lauterbur, a chemist, and Peter Mansfield, a physicist, were awarded the 2003 Nobel Prize in Physiology or

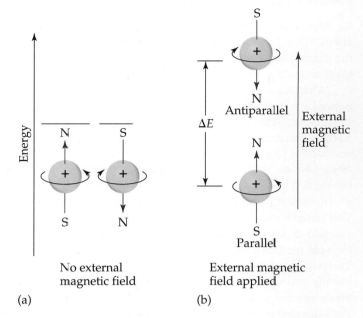

▲ **FIGURE 6.27** **Nuclear spin.** Like electron spin, nuclear spin generates a small magnetic field and has two allowed values. (a) In the absence of an external magnetic field, the two spin states have the same energy. (b) When an external magnetic field is applied, the spin state in which the spin direction is parallel to the direction of the external field is lower in energy than the spin state in which the spin direction is antiparallel to the field direction. The energy difference, ΔE, is in the radio frequency portion of the electromagnetic spectrum

▲ **FIGURE 6.28** **MRI image.** This image of a human head, obtained using magnetic resonance imaging, shows a normal brain, airways, and facial tissues.

Medicine for their discoveries concerning MRI. The major drawback of this technique is expense: The current cost of a new MRI instrument for clinical applications is over $1.5 million.

RELATED EXERCISE: 6.93

want to put more than one electron in an orbital *and* satisfy the Pauli exclusion principle, our only choice is to assign different m_s values to the electrons. Because there are only two such values, we conclude that *an orbital can hold a maximum of two electrons and they must have opposite spins*. This restriction allows us to index the electrons in an atom, giving their quantum numbers and thereby defining the region in space where each electron is most likely to be found. It also provides the key to understanding the structure of the periodic table of the elements.

6.8 | ELECTRON CONFIGURATIONS

Armed with knowledge of the relative energies of orbitals and the Pauli exclusion principle, we are in a position to consider the arrangements of electrons in atoms. The way electrons are distributed among the various orbitals of an atom is called the **electron configuration** of the atom.

The most stable electron configuration—the ground state—is that in which the electrons are in the lowest possible energy states. If there were no restrictions on the possible values for the quantum numbers of the electrons, all the electrons would crowd into the $1s$ orbital because it is the lowest in energy (Figure 6.24) The Pauli exclusion principle tells us, however, that there can be at most two electrons in any single orbital. Thus, *the orbitals are filled in order of increasing energy, with no more than two electrons per orbital.* For example, consider the lithium atom, which has three electrons. (Recall that the number of electrons in a neutral atom equals its atomic number.) The $1s$ orbital can accommodate two of the electrons. The third one goes into the next lowest energy orbital, the $2s$.

We can represent any electron configuration by writing the symbol for the occupied subshell and adding a superscript to indicate the number of electrons in that subshell. For example, for lithium we write $1s^2 2s^1$ (read "$1s$ two, $2s$ one"). We can also show the arrangement of the electrons as

$$\text{Li} \quad \boxed{\uparrow\downarrow} \quad \boxed{\uparrow}$$
$$\qquad\quad 1s \qquad 2s$$

In this representation, which we call an *orbital diagram*, each orbital is denoted by a box and each electron by a half arrow. A half arrow pointing up ($\uparrow$) represents an electron with a positive spin magnetic quantum number ($m_s = +\frac{1}{2}$) and a half arrow pointing down ($\downarrow$) represents an electron with a negative spin magnetic quantum number ($m_s = -\frac{1}{2}$). This pictorial representation of electron spin, which corresponds to the directions of the magnetic fields in Figure 6.25, is quite convenient.

Electrons having opposite spins are said to be *paired* when they are in the same orbital ($\uparrow\downarrow$). An *unpaired electron* is one not accompanied by a partner of opposite spin. In the lithium atom the two electrons in the $1s$ orbital are paired and the electron in the $2s$ orbital is unpaired.

Hund's Rule

Consider now how the electron configurations of the elements change as we move from element to element across the periodic table. Hydrogen has one electron, which occupies the $1s$ orbital in its ground state:

$$\text{H} \quad \boxed{\uparrow} \quad : 1s^1$$
$$\qquad\quad 1s$$

The choice of a spin-up electron here is arbitrary; we could equally well show the ground state with one spin-down electron. It is customary, however, to show unpaired electrons with their spins up.

TABLE 6.3 • Electron Configurations of Several Lighter Elements			
Element	Total Electrons	Orbital Diagram	Electron Configuration

Element	Total Electrons	1s	2s	2p	3s	Electron Configuration
Li	3	⇅	↑	☐ ☐ ☐	☐	$1s^2 2s^1$
Be	4	⇅	⇅	☐ ☐ ☐	☐	$1s^2 2s^2$
B	5	⇅	⇅	↑ ☐ ☐	☐	$1s^2 2s^2 2p^1$
C	6	⇅	⇅	↑ ↑ ☐	☐	$1s^2 2s^2 2p^2$
N	7	⇅	⇅	↑ ↑ ↑	☐	$1s^2 2s^2 2p^3$
Ne	10	⇅	⇅	⇅ ⇅ ⇅	☐	$1s^2 2s^2 2p^6$
Na	11	⇅	⇅	⇅ ⇅ ⇅	↑	$1s^2 2s^2 2p^6 3s^1$

The next element, helium, has two electrons. Because two electrons with opposite spins can occupy the same orbital, both of helium's electrons are in the $1s$ orbital:

$$\text{He} \quad \boxed{\uparrow\downarrow} : 1s^2$$
$$1s$$

The two electrons present in helium complete the filling of the first shell. This arrangement represents a very stable configuration, as is evidenced by the chemical inertness of helium.

The electron configurations of lithium and several elements that follow it in the periodic table are shown in ▲ TABLE 6.3. For the third electron of lithium, the change in principal quantum number from $n = 1$ for the first two electrons to $n = 2$ for the third electron represents a large jump in energy and a corresponding jump in the average distance of the electron from the nucleus. In other words, it represents the start of a new shell occupied with electrons. As you can see by examining the periodic table, lithium starts a new row of the table. It is the first member of the alkali metals (group 1A).

The element that follows lithium is beryllium; its electron configuration is $1s^2 2s^2$ (Table 6.3). Boron, atomic number 5, has the electron configuration $1s^2 2s^2 2p^1$. The fifth electron must be placed in a $2p$ orbital because the $2s$ orbital is filled. Because all the three $2p$ orbitals are of equal energy, it does not matter which $2p$ orbital we place this fifth electron in.

With the next element, carbon, we encounter a new situation. We know that the sixth electron must go into a $2p$ orbital. However, does this new electron go into the $2p$ orbital that already has one electron or into one of the other two $2p$ orbitals? This question is answered by **Hund's rule**, which states that *for degenerate orbitals, the lowest energy is attained when the number of electrons having the same spin is maximized.* This means that electrons occupy orbitals singly to the maximum extent possible and that these single electrons in a given subshell all have the same spin magnetic quantum number. Electrons arranged in this way are said to have *parallel spins.* For a carbon atom to achieve its lowest energy, therefore, the two $2p$ electrons must have the same spin. For this to happen, the electrons must be in different $2p$ orbitals, as shown in Table 6.3. Thus, a carbon atom in its ground state has two unpaired electrons.

Similarly, for nitrogen in its ground state, Hund's rule requires that the three $2p$ electrons singly occupy each of the three $2p$ orbitals. This is the only way that all three electrons can have the same spin. For oxygen and fluorine, we place four and five electrons, respectively, in the 2*p* orbitals. To achieve this, we pair up electrons in the 2*p* orbitals, as we will see in Sample Exercise 6.7.

Hund's rule is based in part on the fact that electrons repel one another. By occupying different orbitals, the electrons remain as far as possible from one another, thus minimizing electron–electron repulsions.

SAMPLE EXERCISE 6.7 | **Orbital Diagrams and Electron Configurations**

Draw the orbital diagram for the electron configuration of oxygen, atomic number 8. How many unpaired electrons does an oxygen atom possess?

SOLUTION

Analyze and Plan Because oxygen has an atomic number of 8, each oxygen atom has 8 electrons. Figure 6.24 shows the ordering of orbitals. The electrons (represented as arrows) are placed in the orbitals (represented as boxes) beginning with the lowest-energy orbital, the 1*s*. Each orbital can hold a maximum of two electrons (the Pauli exclusion principle). Because the 2*p* orbitals are degenerate, we place one electron in each of these orbitals (spin-up) before pairing any electrons (Hund's rule).

Solve Two electrons each go into the 1*s* and 2*s* orbitals with their spins paired. This leaves four electrons for the three degenerate 2*p* orbitals. Following Hund's rule, we put one electron into each 2*p* orbital until all three orbitals have one electron each. The fourth electron is then paired up with one of the three electrons already in a 2*p* orbital, so that the orbital diagram is

$$\boxed{\uparrow\downarrow} \quad \boxed{\uparrow\downarrow} \quad \boxed{\uparrow\downarrow}\boxed{\uparrow}\boxed{\uparrow}$$

$$\text{1}s \qquad \text{2}s \qquad \text{2}p$$

The corresponding electron configuration is written $1s^2 2s^2 2p^4$. The atom has two unpaired electrons.

PRACTICE EXERCISE

(a) Write the electron configuration for phosphorus, element 15. **(b)** How many unpaired electrons does a phosphorus atom possess?

Answers: **(a)** $1s^2 2s^2 2p^6 3s^2 3p^3$, **(b)** three

Condensed Electron Configurations

The filling of the 2*p* subshell is complete at neon (Table 6.3), which has a stable configuration with eight electrons (an *octet*) in the outermost occupied shell. The next element, sodium, atomic number 11, marks the beginning of a new row of the periodic table. Sodium has a single 3*s* electron beyond the stable configuration of neon. We can therefore abbreviate the electron configuration of sodium as

$$\text{Na:} \quad [\text{Ne}]3s^1$$

The symbol [Ne] represents the electron configuration of the ten electrons of neon, $1s^2 2s^2 2p^6$. Writing the electron configuration as $[\text{Ne}]3s^1$ focuses attention on the outermost electron of the atom, which is the one largely responsible for how sodium behaves chemically.

We can generalize what we have just done for the electron configuration of sodium. In writing the *condensed electron configuration* of an element, the electron configuration of the nearest noble-gas element of lower atomic number is represented by its chemical symbol in brackets. For lithium, for example, we write

$$\text{Li:} \quad [\text{He}]2s^1$$

We refer to the electrons represented by the bracketed symbol as the *noble-gas core* of the atom. More usually, these inner-shell electrons are referred to as the **core electrons**. The electrons given after the noble-gas core are called the *outer-shell electrons*. The outer-shell electrons include the electrons involved in chemical bonding, which are called the **valence electrons**. For the elements with atomic number of 30 or less, all of the outer-shell electrons are valence electrons. By comparing the condensed electron configurations of lithium and sodium, we can appreciate why these two elements are so

1A

3
Li
$[He]2s^1$
11
Na
$[Ne]3s^1$
19
K
$[Ar]4s^1$
37
Rb
$[Kr]5s^1$
55
Cs
$[Xe]6s^1$
87
Fr
$[Rn]7s^1$

Alkali
metals

▲ **FIGURE 6.29** **The outer-shell
electron configurations of the alkali
metals (group 1A in the periodic table).**

similar chemically. They have the same type of electron configuration in the outermost occupied shell. Indeed, all the members of the alkali metal group (1A) have a single *s* valence electron beyond a noble-gas configuration (◄ **FIGURE 6.29**).

Transition Metals

The noble-gas element argon ($1s^2 2s^2 2p^6 3s^2 3p^6$) marks the end of the row started by sodium. The element following argon in the periodic table is potassium (K), atomic number 19. In all its chemical properties, potassium is clearly a member of the alkali metal group. The experimental facts about the properties of potassium leave no doubt that the outermost electron of this element occupies an *s* orbital. But this means that the electron with the highest energy has *not* gone into a 3*d* orbital, which we might expect it to do. Because the 4*s* orbital is lower in energy than the 3*d* orbital (Figure 6.24), the condensed electron configuration of potassium is

$$K: \quad [Ar]4s^1$$

Following the complete filling of the 4*s* orbital (this occurs in the calcium atom), the next set of orbitals to be filled is the 3*d*. (You will find it helpful as we go along to refer often to the periodic table on the front inside cover.) Beginning with scandium and extending through zinc, electrons are added to the five 3*d* orbitals until they are completely filled. Thus, the fourth row of the periodic table is ten elements wider than the two previous rows. These ten elements are known as either **transition elements** or **transition metals**. Note the position of these elements in the periodic table.

In writing the electron configurations of the transition elements, we fill orbitals in accordance with Hund's rule—we add them to the 3*d* orbitals singly until all five orbitals have one electron each and then place additional electrons in the 3*d* orbitals with spin pairing until the shell is completely filled. The condensed electron configurations and the corresponding orbital diagram representations of two transition elements are as follows:

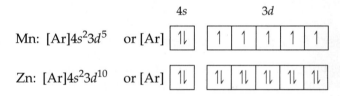

Once all the 3*d* orbitals have been filled with two electrons each, the 4*p* orbitals begin to be occupied until the completed octet of outer electrons ($4s^2 4p^6$) is reached with krypton (Kr), atomic number 36, another of the noble gases. Rubidium (Rb) marks the beginning of the fifth row. Refer again to the periodic table on the front inside cover. Notice that this row is in every respect like the preceding one, except that the value for *n* is greater by 1.

 GIVE IT SOME THOUGHT

Based on the structure of the periodic table, which becomes occupied first, the 6*s* orbital or the 5*d* orbitals?

The Lanthanides and Actinides

The sixth row of the periodic table begins with one electron in the 6*s* orbital of cesium (Cs) and two electrons in the 6*s* orbital of barium (Ba). Notice, however, that the periodic table then has a break, with elements 57–70 placed below the main portion of the table. This break point is where we begin to encounter a new set of orbitals, the 4*f*.

There are seven degenerate 4*f* orbitals, corresponding to the seven allowed values of m_l, ranging from 3 to −3. Thus, it takes 14 electrons to fill the 4*f* orbitals completely. The 14 elements corresponding to the filling of the 4*f* orbitals are known as either the **lanthanide elements** or the **rare earth elements**. These elements are set below the other elements to avoid making the periodic table unduly wide. The properties of the lanthanide elements are all quite similar, and these elements occur together in nature. For many years it was virtually impossible to separate them from one another.

Because the energies of the $4f$ and $5d$ orbitals are very close to each other, the electron configurations of some of the lanthanides involve $5d$ electrons. For example, the elements lanthanum (La), cerium (Ce), and praseodymium (Pr) have the following electron configurations:

$$[Xe]6s^2 5d^1 \qquad [Xe]6s^2 5d^1 4f^1 \qquad [Xe]6s^2 4f^3$$
$$\text{Lanthanum} \qquad \text{Cerium} \qquad \text{Praseodymium}$$

Because La has a single $5d$ electron, it is sometimes placed below yttrium (Y) as the first member of the third series of transition elements; Ce is then placed as the first member of the lanthanides. Based on their chemistry, however, La can be considered the first element in the lanthanide series. Arranged this way, there are fewer apparent exceptions to the regular filling of the $4f$ orbitals among the subsequent members of the series.

After the lanthanide series, the third transition element series is completed by the filling of the $5d$ orbitals, followed by the filling of the $6p$ orbitals. This brings us to radon (Rn), heaviest of the known noble-gas elements.

The final row of the periodic table begins by filling the $7s$ orbitals. The **actinide elements**, of which uranium (U, element 92) and plutonium (Pu, element 94) are the best known, are then built up by completing the $5f$ orbitals. The actinide elements are radioactive, and most of them are not found in nature.

6.9 | ELECTRON CONFIGURATIONS AND THE PERIODIC TABLE

We just saw that the electron configurations of the elements correspond to their locations in the periodic table. Thus, elements in the same column of the table have related outer-shell (valence) electron configurations. As ▶ **TABLE 6.4** shows, for example, all 2A elements have an ns^2 outer configuration, and all 3A elements have an $ns^2 np^1$ outer configuration, with the value of n increasing as we move down each column.

As shown in ▼ **FIGURE 6.30**, the periodic table can be divided into four blocks based on the filling order of orbitals. On the left are *two* blue columns of elements. These elements, known as the alkali metals (group 1A) and alkaline earth metals (group 2A), are those in which the valence s orbitals are being filled. These two columns make up the s block of the periodic table.

On the right is a block of *six* pink columns that comprises the p block, where the valence p orbitals are being filled. The s block and the p block elements together are the **representative elements**, sometimes called the **main-group elements**.

The orange block in Figure 6.30 has *ten* columns containing the transition metals. These are the elements in which the valence d orbitals are being filled and make up the d block.

TABLE 6.4 •
Electron Configurations of Group 2A and 3A Elements

Group 2A

Be	$[He]2s^2$
Mg	$[Ne]3s^2$
Ca	$[Ar]4s^2$
Sr	$[Kr]5s^2$
Ba	$[Xe]6s^2$
Ra	$[Rn]7s^2$

Group 3A

B	$[He]2s^2 2p^1$
Al	$[Ne]3s^2 3p^1$
Ga	$[Ar]3d^{10}4s^2 4p^1$
In	$[Kr]4d^{10}5s^2 5p^1$
Tl	$[Xe]4f^{14}5d^{10}6s^2 6p^1$

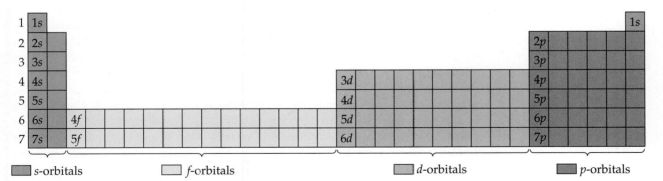

s-orbitals   f-orbitals   d-orbitals   p-orbitals

▲ **FIGURE 6.30 Regions of the periodic table.** The order in which electrons are added to orbitals is read left to right beginning in the top left corner.

The elements in the two tan rows containing *14* columns are the ones in which the valence *f* orbitals are being filled and make up the *f* block. Consequently, these elements are often referred to as the **f-block metals**. In most tables, the *f* block is positioned below the periodic table to save space:

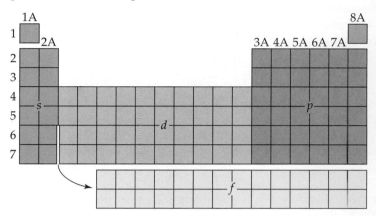

The number of columns in each block corresponds to the maximum number of electrons that can occupy each kind of subshell. Recall that 2, 6, 10, and 14 are the numbers of electrons that can fill the *s*, *p*, *d*, and *f* subshells, respectively. Thus, the *s* block has 2 columns, the *p* block has 6, the *d* block has 10, and the *f* block has 14. Recall also that ls is the first *s* subshell, 2*p* is the first *p* subshell, 3*d* is the first *d* subshell, and 4*f* is the first *f* subshell, as Figure 6.30 shows. Using these facts, you can write the electron configuration of an element based merely on its position in the periodic table.

Let's use the periodic table to write the electron configuration of selenium (Se, element 34). We first locate Se in the table and then move backward from it through the table, from element 34 to 33 to 32 and so forth, until we come to the noble gas that precedes Se. In this case, the noble gas is argon, Ar, element 18. Thus, the noble-gas core for Se is [Ar]. Our next step is to write symbols for the outer electrons. We do this by moving across period 4 from K, the element following Ar, to Se:

Because K is in the fourth period and the *s* block, we begin with the 4*s* electrons, meaning our first two outer electrons are written $4s^2$. We then move into the *d* block, which begins with the 3*d* electrons. (The principal quantum number in the *d* block is always one less than that of the preceding elements in the *s* block, as seen in Figure 6.30.) Traversing the *d* block adds ten electrons, $3d^{10}$. Finally we move into the *p* block, whose principal quantum number is always the same as that of the *s* block. Counting the squares as we move across the *p* block to Se tells us that we need four electrons, $4p^4$. The electron configuration for Se is therefore $[Ar]4s^2 3d^{10} 4p^4$. This configuration can also be written with the subshells arranged in order of increasing principal quantum number: $[Ar]3d^{10}4s^2 4p^3$.

As a check, we add the number of electrons in the [Ar] core, 18, to the number of electrons we added to the 4*s*, 3*d*, and 4*p* subshells. This sum should equal the atomic number of Se, 34: $18 + 2 + 10 + 4 = 34$.

SAMPLE EXERCISE 6.8   Electron Configurations for a Group

What is the characteristic valence electron configuration of the group 7A elements, the halogens?

SOLUTION

Analyze and Plan We first locate the halogens in the periodic table, write the electron configurations for the first two elements, and then determine the general similarity between the configurations.

Solve The first member of the halogen group is fluorine (F, element 9). Moving backward from F, we find that the noble-gas core is [He]. Moving from He to the element of next higher atomic number brings us to Li, element 3. Because Li is in the second period of the s block, we add electrons to the $2s$ subshell. Moving across this block gives $2s^2$. Continuing to move to the right, we enter the p block. Counting the squares to F gives $2p^5$. Thus, the condensed electron configuration for fluorine is

$$\text{F:}\quad [\text{He}]2s^2 2p^5$$

The electron configuration for chlorine, the second halogen, is

$$\text{Cl:}\quad [\text{Ne}]3s^2 3p^5$$

From these two examples, we see that the characteristic valence electron configuration of a halogen is $ns^2 np^5$, where n ranges from 2 in the case of fluorine to 6 in the case of astatine.

PRACTICE EXERCISE

Which family of elements is characterized by an $ns^2 np^2$ electron configuration in the outer-most occupied shell?

Answer: group 4A

SAMPLE EXERCISE 6.9   Electron Configurations from the Periodic Table

(a) Based on its position in the periodic table, write the condensed electron configuration for bismuth, element 83. **(b)** How many unpaired electrons does a bismuth atom have?

SOLUTION

(a) Our first step is to write the noble-gas core. We do this by locating bismuth, element 83, in the periodic table. We then move backward to the nearest noble gas, which is Xe, element 54. Thus, the noble-gas core is [Xe].

   Next, we trace the path in order of increasing atomic numbers from Xe to Bi. Moving from Xe to Cs, element 55, we find ourselves in period 6 of the s block. Knowing the block and the period identifies the subshell in which we begin placing outer electrons, $6s$. As we move through the s block, we add two electrons: $6s^2$.

   As we move beyond the s block, from element 56 to element 57, the curved arrow below the periodic table reminds us that we are entering the f block. The first row of the f block corresponds to the $4f$ subshell. As we move across this block, we add 14 electrons: $4f^{14}$.

   With element 71, we move into the third row of the d block. Because the first row of the d block is $3d$, the second row is $4d$ and the third row is $5d$. Thus, as we move through the ten elements of the d block, from element 71 to element 80, we fill the $5d$ subshell with ten electrons: $5d^{10}$.

   Moving from element 80 to element 81 puts us into the p block in the $6p$ subshell. (Remember that the principal quantum number in the p block is the same as in the s block.) Moving across to Bi requires 3 electrons: $6p^3$. The path we have taken is

Putting the parts together, we obtain the condensed electron configuration: $[\text{Xe}]6s^2 4f^{14} 5d^{10} 6p^3$. This configuration can also be written with the subshells arranged in order of increasing principal quantum number: $[\text{Xe}]4f^{14} 5d^{10} 6s^2 6p^3$.

Finally, we check our result to see if the number of electrons equals the atomic number of Bi, 83: Because Xe has 54 electrons (its atomic number), we have $54 + 2 + 14 + 10 + 3 = 83$. (If we had 14 electrons too few, we would realize that we have missed the f block.)

(b) We see from the condensed electron configuration that the only partially occupied subshell is $6p$. The orbital diagram representation for this subshell is

In accordance with Hund's rule, the three $6p$ electrons occupy the three $6p$ orbitals singly, with their spins parallel. Thus, there are three unpaired electrons in the bismuth atom.

PRACTICE EXERCISE

Use the periodic table to write the condensed electron configuration for **(a)** Co (element 27), **(b)** Te (element 52).

Answers: **(a)** $[\text{Ar}]4s^2 3d^7$ or $[\text{Ar}]3d^7 4s^2$, **(b)** $[\text{Kr}]5s^2 4d^{10} 5p^4$ or $[\text{Kr}]4d^{10} 5s^2 5p^4$

▼ **FIGURE 6.31** gives, for all the elements, the ground-state electron configurations for the valence electrons. You can use this figure to check your answers as you practice writing electron configurations. We have written these configurations with orbitals

▲ **FIGURE 6.31** Valence electron configurations of the elements.

listed in order of increasing principal quantum number. As we saw in Sample Exercise 6.9, the orbitals can also be listed in order of filling, as they would be read off the periodic table.

Figure 6.31 allow us to reexamine the concept of *valence electrons*. Notice, for example, that as we proceed from Cl ($[Ne]3s^23p^5$) to Br ($[Ar]3d^{10}4s^24p^5$) we add a complete subshell of $3d$ electrons to the electrons beyond the [Ar] core. Although the $3d$ electrons are outer-shell electrons, they are not involved in chemical bonding and are therefore not considered valence electrons. Thus, we consider only the $4s$ and $4p$ electrons of Br to be valence electrons. Similarly, if we compare the electron configurations of Ag (element 47) and Au (element 79), we see that Au has a completely full $4f^{14}$ subshell beyond its noble-gas core, but those $4f$ electrons are not involved in bonding. In general, *for representative elements we do not consider the electrons in completely filled d or f subshells to be valence electrons,* and *for transition elements we do not consider the electrons in a completely filled f subshell to be valence electrons.*

Anomalous Electron Configurations

The electron configurations of certain elements appear to violate the rules we have just discussed. For example, Figure 6.31 shows that the electron configuration of chromium (element 24) is $[Ar]3d^54s^1$ rather than the $[Ar]3d^44s^2$ configuration we might expect. Similarly, the configuration of copper (element 29) is $[Ar]3d^{10}4s^1$ instead of $[Ar]3d^94s^2$.

This anomalous behavior is largely a consequence of the closeness of the $3d$ and $4s$ orbital energies. It frequently occurs when there are enough electrons to form precisely half-filled sets of degenerate orbitals (as in chromium) or a completely filled d subshell (as in copper). There are a few similar cases among the heavier transition metals (those with partially filled $4d$ or $5d$ orbitals) and among the f-block metals. Although these minor departures from the expected are interesting, they are not of great chemical significance.

 GIVE IT SOME THOUGHT

The elements Ni, Pd, and Pt are all in the same group. By examining the electron configurations for these elements in Figure 6.31, what can you conclude about the relative energies of the *nd* and (n + 1)s orbitals for this group?

SAMPLE INTEGRATIVE EXERCISE   **Putting Concepts Together**

Boron, atomic number 5, occurs naturally as two isotopes, ^{10}B and ^{11}B, with natural abundances of 19.9% and 80.1%, respectively. (**a**) In what ways do the two isotopes differ from each other? Does the electronic configuration of ^{10}B differ from that of ^{11}B? (**b**) Draw the orbital diagram for an atom of ^{11}B. Which electrons are the valence electrons? (**c**) Indicate three major ways in which the $1s$ electrons in boron differ from its $2s$ electrons. (**d**) Elemental boron reacts with fluorine to form BF_3, a gas. Write a balanced chemical equation for the reaction of solid boron with fluorine gas. (**e**) ΔH_f° for $BF_3(g)$ is -1135.6 kJ/mol. Calculate the standard enthalpy change in the reaction of boron with fluorine. (**f**) When BCl_3, also a gas at room temperature, comes into contact with water, the two react to form hydrochloric acid and boric acid, H_3BO_3, a very weak acid in water. Write a balanced net ionic equation for this reaction.

SOLUTION

(**a**) The two isotopes of boron differ in the number of neutrons in the nucleus. ∞ (Sections 2.3 and 2.4) Each of the isotopes contains five protons, but ^{10}B contains five neutrons, whereas ^{11}B contains six neutrons. The two isotopes of boron have identical electron configurations, $1s^22s^22p^1$, because each has five electrons.

(**b**) The complete orbital diagram is

The valence electrons are the ones in the outermost occupied shell, the $2s^2$ and $2p^1$ electrons. The $1s^2$ electrons constitute the core electrons, which we represent as [He] when we write the condensed electron configuration, $[He]2s^22p^1$.

(c) The 1s and 2s orbitals are both spherical, but they differ in three important respects: First, the 1s orbital is lower in energy than the 2s orbital. Second, the average distance of the 2s electrons from the nucleus is greater than that of the 1s electrons, so the 1s orbital is smaller than the 2s. Third, the 2s orbital has one node, whereas the 1s orbital has no nodes (Figure 6.18).

(d) The balanced chemical equation is

$$2\,B(s) + 3\,F_2(g) \longrightarrow 2\,BF_3(g)$$

(e) $\Delta H° = 2(-1135.6) - [0 + 0] = -2271.2$ kJ. The reaction is strongly exothermic.

(f) $BCl_3(g) + 3\,H_2O(l) \longrightarrow H_3BO_3(aq) + 3\,H^+(aq) + 3\,Cl^-(aq)$. Note that because H_3BO_3 is a very weak acid, its chemical formula is written in molecular form, as discussed in Section 4.3.

CHAPTER SUMMARY AND KEY TERMS

INTRODUCTION AND SECTION 6.1 The **electronic structure** of an atom describes the energies and arrangement of electrons around the atom. Much of what is known about the electronic structure of atoms was obtained by observing the interaction of light with matter. Visible light and other forms of **electromagnetic radiation** (also known as radiant energy) move through a vacuum at the speed of light, $c = 3.00 \times 10^8$ m/s. Electromagnetic radiation has both electric and magnetic components that vary periodically in wavelike fashion. The wave characteristics of radiant energy allow it to be described in terms of **wavelength**, λ, and **frequency**, ν, which are interrelated: $c = \lambda\nu$.

SECTION 6.2 Planck proposed that the minimum amount of radiant energy that an object can gain or lose is related to the frequency of the radiation: $E = h\nu$. This smallest quantity is called a **quantum** of energy. The constant h is called **Planck's constant**: $h = 6.626 \times 10^{-34}$ J-s. In the quantum theory, energy is quantized, meaning that it can have only certain allowed values. Einstein used the quantum theory to explain the **photoelectric effect**, the emission of electrons from metal surfaces when exposed to light. He proposed that light behaves as if it consists of quantized energy packets called **photons**. Each photon carries energy, $E = h\nu$.

SECTION 6.3 Dispersion of radiation into its component wavelengths produces a **spectrum**. If the spectrum contains all wavelengths, it is called a **continuous spectrum**; if it contains only certain specific wavelengths, the spectrum is called a **line spectrum**. The radiation emitted by excited hydrogen atoms forms a line spectrum.

Bohr proposed a model of the hydrogen atom that explains its line spectrum. In this model the energy of the electron in the hydrogen atom depends on the value of a quantum number, n. The value of n must be a positive integer $(1, 2, 3, \ldots)$, and each value of n corresponds to a different specific energy, E_n. The energy of the atom increases as n increases. The lowest energy is achieved for $n = 1$; this is called the **ground state** of the hydrogen atom. Other values of n correspond to **excited states**. Light is emitted when the electron drops from a higher-energy state to a lower-energy state; light is absorbed to excite the electron from a lower energy state to a higher one. The frequency of light emitted or absorbed is such that $h\nu$ equals the difference in energy between two allowed states.

SECTION 6.4 De Broglie proposed that matter, such as electrons, should exhibit wavelike properties. This hypothesis of **matter waves** was proved experimentally by observing the diffraction of electrons. An object has a characteristic wavelength that depends on its **momentum**, mv: $\lambda = h/mv$. Discovery of the wave properties of the electron led to Heisenberg's **uncertainty principle**, which states that

there is an inherent limit to the accuracy with which the position and momentum of a particle can be measured simultaneously.

SECTION 6.5 In the quantum mechanical model of the hydrogen atom, the behavior of the electron is described by mathematical functions called **wave functions**, denoted with the Greek letter ψ. Each allowed wave function has a precisely known energy, but the location of the electron cannot be determined exactly; rather, the probability of it being at a particular point in space is given by the **probability density**, ψ^2. The **electron density** distribution is a map of the probability of finding the electron at all points in space.

The allowed wave functions of the hydrogen atom are called **orbitals**. An orbital is described by a combination of an integer and a letter, corresponding to values of three quantum numbers. The *principal quantum number, n,* is indicated by the integers 1, 2, 3, ... This quantum number relates most directly to the size and energy of the orbital. The *angular momentum quantum number, l,* is indicated by the letters *s, p, d, f,* and so on, corresponding to the values of 0, 1, 2, 3, ... The l quantum number defines the shape of the orbital. For a given value of n, l can have integer values ranging from 0 to $(n - 1)$. The *magnetic quantum number, m_l,* relates to the orientation of the orbital in space. For a given value of l, m_l can have integral values ranging from $-l$ to l, including 0. Subscripts can be used to label the orientations of the orbitals. For example, the three $3p$ orbitals are designated $3p_x$, $3p_y$, and $3p_z$, with the subscripts indicating the axis along which the orbital is oriented.

An **electron shell** is the set of all orbitals with the same value of n, such as $3s$, $3p$, and $3d$. In the hydrogen atom all the orbitals in an electron shell have the same energy. A **subshell** is the set of one or more orbitals with the same n and l values; for example, $3s$, $3p$, and $3d$ are each subshells of the $n = 3$ shell. There is one orbital in an s subshell, three in a p subshell, five in a d subshell, and seven in an f subshell.

SECTION 6.6 Contour representations are useful for visualizing the shapes of the orbitals. Represented this way, s orbitals appear as spheres that increase in size as n increases. The **radial probability function** tells us the probability that the electron will be found at a certain distance from the nucleus. The wave function for each p orbital has two lobes on opposite sides of the nucleus. They are oriented along the x, y, and z axes. Four of the d orbitals appear as shapes with four lobes around the nucleus; the fifth one, the d_{z^2} orbital, is represented as two lobes along the z axis and a "doughnut" in the xy plane. Regions in which the wave function is zero are called **nodes**. There is zero probability that the electron will be found at a node.

SECTION 6.7 In many-electron atoms, different subshells of the same electron shell have different energies. For a given value of n, the energy of the subshells increases as the value of l increases: $ns<np<nd<nf$. Orbitals within the same subshell are **degenerate**, meaning they have the same energy.

Electrons have an intrinsic property called **electron spin**, which is quantized. The **spin magnetic quantum number**, m_s, can have two possible values, $+\frac{1}{2}$ and $-\frac{1}{2}$, which can be envisioned as the two directions of an electron spinning about an axis. The **Pauli exclusion principle** states that no two electrons in an atom can have the same values for n, l, m_l, and m_s. This principle places a limit of two on the number of electrons that can occupy any one atomic orbital. These two electrons differ in their value of m_s.

SECTIONS 6.8 AND 6.9 The **electron configuration** of an atom describes how the electrons are distributed among the orbitals of the atom. The ground-state electron configurations are generally obtained by placing the electrons in the atomic orbitals of lowest possible energy with the restriction that each orbital can hold no more than two electrons. When electrons occupy a subshell with more than one degenerate orbital, such as the $2p$ subshell, **Hund's rule** states that the lowest energy is attained by maximizing the number of electrons with the same electron spin. For example, in the ground-state electron configuration of carbon, the two $2p$ electrons have the same spin and must occupy two different $2p$ orbitals.

Elements in any given group in the periodic table have the same type of electron arrangements in their outermost shells. For example, the electron configurations of the halogens fluorine and chlorine are $[He]2s^22p^5$ and $[Ne]3s^23p^5$, respectively. The outer-shell electrons are those that lie outside the orbitals occupied in the next lowest noble-gas element. The outer-shell electrons that are involved in chemical bonding are the **valence electrons** of an atom; for the elements with atomic number 30 or less, all the outer-shell electrons are valence electrons. The electrons that are not valence electrons are called **core electrons**.

The periodic table is partitioned into different types of elements, based on their electron configurations. Those elements in which the outermost subshell is an s or p subshell are called the **representative** (or **main-group**) **elements**. The alkali metals (group 1A), halogens (group 7A), and noble gases (group 8A) are representative elements. Those elements in which a d subshell is being filled are called the **transition elements** (or **transition metals**). The elements in which the $4f$ subshell is being filled are called the **lanthanide** (or **rare earth**) **elements**. The **actinide elements** are those in which the $5f$ subshell is being filled. The lanthanide and actinide elements are collectively referred to as the **f-block metals**. These elements are shown as two rows of 14 elements below the main part of the periodic table. The structure of the periodic table, summarized in Figure 6.30, allows us to write the electron configuration of an element from its position in the periodic table.

KEY SKILLS

- Calculate the wavelength of electromagnetic radiation given its frequency or its frequency given its wavelength. (Section 6.1)

- Order the common kinds of radiation in the electromagnetic spectrum according to their wavelengths or energy. (Section 6.1)

- Explain what photons are and be able to calculate their energies given either their frequency or wavelength. (Section 6.2)

- Explain how line spectra relate to the idea of quantized energy states of electrons in atoms. (Section 6.3)

- Calculate the wavelength of a moving object. (Section 6.4)

- Explain how the uncertainty principle limits how precisely we can specify the position and the momentum of subatomic particles such as electrons. (Section 6.4)

- Relate the quantum numbers to the number and type of orbitals and recognize the different orbital shapes. (Section 6.5)

- Interpret radial probability function graphs for the orbitals. (Section 6.6)

- Draw an energy-level diagram for the orbitals in a many-electron atom and describe how electrons populate the orbitals in the ground state of an atom, using the Pauli exclusion principle and Hund's rule. (Section 6.8)

- Use the periodic table to write condensed electron configurations and determine the number of unpaired electrons in an atom. (Section 6.9)

KEY EQUATIONS

- $c = \lambda\nu$ [6.1]   light as a wave: c = speed of light (3.00×10^8 m/s), λ = wavelength in meters, ν = frequency in s^{-1}

- $E = h\nu$ [6.2]   light as a particle (photon): E = energy of photon in joules, h = Planck's constant (6.626×10^{-34} J-s), ν = frequency in s^{-1} (same frequency as previous formula)

- $\lambda = h/mv$ [6.8]   matter as a wave: λ = wavelength, h = Planck's constant, m = mass of object in kg, v = speed of object in m/s

- $\Delta x \cdot \Delta(mv) \geq \dfrac{h}{4\pi}$ [6.9]   Heisenberg's uncertainty principle. The uncertainty in position (Δx) and momentum [$\Delta(mv)$] of an object cannot be zero; the smallest value of their product is $h/4\pi$

EXERCISES

VISUALIZING CONCEPTS

6.1 Consider the water wave shown here. **(a)** How could you measure the speed of this wave? **(b)** How would you determine the wavelength of the wave? **(c)** Given the speed and wavelength of the wave, how could you determine the frequency of the wave? **(d)** Suggest an independent experiment to determine the frequency of the wave. [Section 6.1]

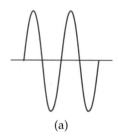

6.2 A popular kitchen appliance produces electromagnetic radiation with a frequency of 2450 MHz. With reference to Figure 6.4, answer the following: **(a)** Estimate the wavelength of this radiation. **(b)** Would the radiation produced by the appliance be visible to the human eye? **(c)** If the radiation is not visible, do photons of this radiation have more or less energy than photons of visible light? **(d)** Propose the identity of the kitchen appliance. [Section 6.1]

6.3 The following diagrams represent two electromagnetic waves. Which wave corresponds to the higher-energy radiation? Explain. [Section 6.2]

       (a)   (b)

6.4 As shown in the accompanying photograph, an electric stove burner on its highest setting exhibits an orange glow. **(a)** When the burner setting is changed to low, the burner continues to produce heat but the orange glow disappears. How can this observation be explained with reference to one of the fundamental observations that led to the notion of quanta? **(b)** Suppose that the energy provided to the burner could be increased beyond the highest setting of the stove. What would we expect to observe with regard to visible light emitted by the burner? [Section 6.2]

6.5 The familiar phenomenon of a rainbow results from the diffraction of sunlight through raindrops. **(a)** Does the wavelength of light increase or decrease as we proceed outward from the innermost band of the rainbow? **(b)** Does the frequency of light increase or decrease as we proceed outward? **(c)** Suppose that instead of sunlight, the visible light from a hydrogen discharge tube (Figure 6.10) was used as the light source. What do you think the resulting "hydrogen discharge rainbow" would look like? [Section 6.3]

6.6 A certain quantum mechanical system has the energy levels shown in the diagram below. The energy levels are indexed by a single quantum number n that is an integer. **(a)** As drawn, which quantum numbers are involved in the transition that requires the most energy? **(b)** Which quantum numbers are involved in the transition that requires the least energy? **(c)** Based on the drawing, put the following in order of increasing wavelength of the light absorbed or emitted during the transition: (*i*) $n = 1$ to $n = 2$; (*ii*) $n = 3$ to $n = 2$; (*iii*) $n = 2$ to $n = 4$; (*iv*) $n = 3$ to $n = 1$. [Section 6.3]

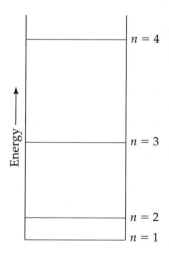

6.7 Consider a fictitious one-dimensional system with one electron. The wave function for the electron, drawn at the top of the next page, is $\psi(x) = \sin x$ from $x = 0$ to $x = 2\pi$. **(a)** Sketch the probability density, $\psi^2(x)$, from $x = 0$ to $x = 2\pi$. **(b)** At what value or values of x will there be the greatest probability of finding the electron? **(c)** What is the probability that the electron will be found at $x = \pi$? What is such a point in a wave function called? [Section 6.5]

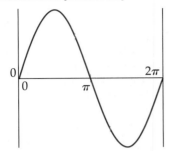

6.8 The contour representation of one of the orbitals for the $n = 3$ shell of a hydrogen atom is shown below. **(a)** What is the quantum number l for this orbital? **(b)** How do we label this orbital? **(c)** How would you modify this sketch to show the analogous orbital for the $n = 4$ shell? [Section 6.6]

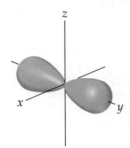

6.9 The drawing below shows part of the orbital diagram for an element. **(a)** As drawn, the drawing is *incorrect*. Why? **(b)** How would you correct the drawing without changing the number of electrons? **(c)** To which group in the periodic table does the element belong? [Section 6.8]

6.10 State where in the periodic table these elements appear:
(a) elements with the valence-shell electron configuration ns^2np^5
(b) elements that have three unpaired p electrons
(c) an element whose valence electrons are $4s^24p^1$
(d) the d-block elements

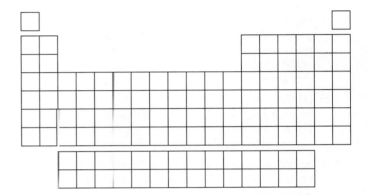

THE WAVE NATURE OF LIGHT (section 6.1)

6.11 What are the basic SI units for **(a)** the wavelength of light, **(b)** the frequency of light, **(c)** the speed of light?

6.12 **(a)** What is the relationship between the wavelength and the frequency of radiant energy? **(b)** Ozone in the upper atmosphere absorbs energy in the 210–230-nm range of the spectrum. In what region of the electromagnetic spectrum does this radiation occur?

6.13 Label each of the following statements as true or false. For those that are false, correct the statement. **(a)** Visible light is a form of electromagnetic radiation. **(b)** Ultraviolet light has longer wavelengths than visible light. **(c)** X-rays travel faster than microwaves. **(d)** Electromagnetic radiation and sound waves travel at the same speed.

6.14 Determine which of the following statements are false and correct them. **(a)** The frequency of radiation increases as the wavelength increases. **(b)** Electromagnetic radiation travels through a vacuum at a constant speed, regardless of wavelength. **(c)** Infrared light has higher frequencies than visible light. **(d)** The glow from a fireplace, the energy within a microwave oven, and a foghorn blast are all forms of electromagnetic radiation.

6.15 Arrange the following kinds of electromagnetic radiation in order of increasing wavelength: infrared, green light, red light, radio waves, X-rays, ultraviolet light.

6.16 List the following types of electromagnetic radiation in order of increasing wavelength: **(a)** the gamma rays produced by a radioactive nuclide used in medical imaging; **(b)** radiation from an FM radio station at 93.1 MHz on the dial; **(c)** a radio signal from an AM radio station at 680 kHz on the dial; **(d)** the yellow light from sodium vapor streetlights; **(e)** the red light of a light-emitting diode, such as in a calculator display.

6.17 **(a)** What is the frequency of radiation that has a wavelength of 10 μm, about the size of a bacterium? **(b)** What is the wavelength of radiation that has a frequency of 5.50×10^{14} s^{-1}? **(c)** Would the radiations in part (a) or part (b) be visible to the human eye? **(d)** What distance does electromagnetic radiation travel in 50.0 μs?

6.18 **(a)** What is the frequency of radiation whose wavelength is 5.0×10^{-5} m? **(b)** What is the wavelength of radiation that has a frequency of 2.5×10^8 s^{-1}? **(c)** Would the radiations in part (a) or part (b) be detected by an X-ray detector? **(d)** What distance does electromagnetic radiation travel in 10.5 fs?

6.19 An argon ion laser emits light at 532 nm. What is the frequency of this radiation? Using Figure 6.4, predict the color associated with this wavelength.

6.20 It is possible to convert radiant energy into electrical energy using photovoltaic cells. Assuming equal efficiency of conversion, would infrared or ultraviolet radiation yield more electrical energy on a per-photon basis?

QUANTIZED ENERGY AND PHOTONS (section 6.2)

6.21 If human height were quantized in one-foot increments, what would happen to the height of a child as she grows up?

6.22 Einstein's 1905 paper on the photoelectric effect was the first important application of Planck's quantum hypothesis. Describe Planck's original hypothesis, and explain how Einstein made use of it in his theory of the photoelectric effect.

6.23 (a) Calculate the energy of a photon of electromagnetic radiation whose frequency is $6.75 \times 10^{12} \text{ s}^{-1}$. (b) Calculate the energy of a photon of radiation whose wavelength is 322 nm. (c) What wavelength of radiation has photons of energy 2.87×10^{-18} J?

6.24 (a) A red laser pointer emits light with a wavelength of 650 nm. What is the frequency of this light? (b) What is the energy of one of these photons? (c) The laser pointer emits light because electrons in the material are excited (by a battery) from their ground state to an upper excited state. When the electrons return to the ground state, they lose the excess energy in the form of 650 nm photons. What is the energy gap between the ground state and excited state in the laser material?

6.25 (a) Calculate and compare the energy of a photon of wavelength 3.3 μm with that of wavelength 0.154 nm. (b) Use Figure 6.4 to identify the region of the electromagnetic spectrum to which each belongs.

6.26 An AM radio station broadcasts at 1010 kHz, and its FM partner broadcasts at 98.3 MHz. Calculate and compare the energy of the photons emitted by these two radio stations.

6.27 One type of sunburn occurs on exposure to UV light of wavelength in the vicinity of 325 nm. (a) What is the energy of a photon of this wavelength? (b) What is the energy of a mole of these photons? (c) How many photons are in a 1.00 mJ burst of this radiation? (d) These UV photons can break chemical bonds in your skin to cause sunburn—a form of radiation damage. If the 325-nm radiation provides exactly the energy to break an average chemical bond in the skin, estimate the average energy of these bonds in kJ/mol.

6.28 The energy from radiation can be used to cause the rupture of chemical bonds. A minimum energy of 941 kJ/mol is required to break the nitrogen–nitrogen bond in N_2. What is the longest wavelength of radiation that possesses the necessary energy to break the bond? What type of electromagnetic radiation is this?

6.29 A diode laser emits at a wavelength of 987 nm. (a) In what portion of the electromagnetic spectrum is this radiation found? (b) All of its output energy is absorbed in a detector that measures a total energy of 0.52 J over a period of 32 s. How many photons per second are being emitted by the laser?

6.30 A stellar object is emitting radiation at 3.55 mm. (a) What type of electromagnetic spectrum is this radiation? (b) If a detector is capturing 3.2×10^8 photons per second at this wavelength, what is the total energy of the photons detected in one hour?

6.31 Molybdenum metal must absorb radiation with a minimum frequency of $1.09 \times 10^{15} \text{ s}^{-1}$ before it can eject an electron from its surface via the photoelectric effect. (a) What is the minimum energy needed to eject an electron? (b) What wavelength of radiation will provide a photon of this energy? (c) If molybdenum is irradiated with light of wavelength of 120 nm, what is the maximum possible kinetic energy of the emitted electrons?

6.32 Sodium metal requires a photon with a minimum energy of 4.41×10^{-19} J to emit electrons. (a) What is the minimum frequency of light necessary to emit electrons from sodium via the photoelectric effect? (b) What is the wavelength of this light? (c) If sodium is irradiated with light of 405 nm, what is the maximum possible kinetic energy of the emitted electrons? (d) What is the maximum number of electrons that can be freed by a burst of light whose total energy is 1.00 μJ?

BOHR'S MODEL; MATTER WAVES (sections 6.3 and 6.4)

6.33 Explain how the existence of line spectra is consistent with Bohr's theory of quantized energies for the electron in the hydrogen atom.

6.34 (a) In terms of the Bohr theory of the hydrogen atom, what process is occurring when excited hydrogen atoms emit radiant energy of certain wavelengths and only those wavelengths? (b) Does a hydrogen atom "expand" or "contract" as it moves from its ground state to an excited state?

6.35 Is energy emitted or absorbed when the following electronic transitions occur in hydrogen: (a) from $n = 4$ to $n = 2$, (b) from an orbit of radius 2.12 Å to one of radius 8.46 Å, (c) an electron adds to the H^+ ion and ends up in the $n = 3$ shell?

6.36 Indicate whether energy is emitted or absorbed when the following electronic transitions occur in hydrogen: (a) from $n = 2$ to $n = 6$, (b) from an orbit of radius 4.76 Å to one of radius 0.529 Å, (c) from the $n = 6$ to the $n = 9$ state.

6.37 (a) Using Equation 6.5, calculate the energy of an electron in the hydrogen atom when $n = 2$ and when $n = 6$. Calculate the wavelength of the radiation released when an electron moves from $n = 6$ to $n = 2$. (b) Is this line in the visible region of the electromagnetic spectrum? If so, what color is it?

6.38 (a) Calculate the energies of an electron in the hydrogen atom for $n = 1$ and for $n = \infty$. How much energy does it require to move the electron out of the atom completely (from $n = 1$ to $n = \infty$), according to Bohr? Put your answer in kJ/mol. (b) The energy for the process $H + \text{energy} \rightarrow H^+ + e^-$ is called the ionization energy of hydrogen. The experimentally determined value for the ionization energy of hydrogen is 1310 kJ/mol. How does this compare to your calculation?

6.39 The visible emission lines observed by Balmer all involved $n_f = 2$. (a) Explain why only the lines with $n_f = 2$ were observed in the visible region of the electromagnetic spectrum. (b) Calculate the wavelengths of the first three lines in the Balmer series—those for which $n_i = 3$, 4, and 5—and identify these lines in the emission spectrum shown in Figure 6.11.

6.40 The Lyman series of emission lines of the hydrogen atom are those for which $n_f = 1$. (a) Determine the region of the electromagnetic spectrum in which the lines of the Lyman series are observed. (b) Calculate the wavelengths of the first three lines in the Lyman series—those for which $n_i = 2$, 3, and 4.

6.41 One of the emission lines of the hydrogen atom has a wavelength of 93.8 nm. (a) In what region of the electromagnetic spectrum is this emission found? (b) Determine the initial and final values of n associated with this emission.

6.42 The hydrogen atom can absorb light of wavelength 2626 nm. **(a)** In what region of the electromagnetic spectrum is this absorption found? **(b)** Determine the initial and final values of n associated with this absorption.

6.43 Use the de Broglie relationship to determine the wavelengths of the following objects: **(a)** an 85-kg person skiing at 50 km/hr, **(b)** a 10.0-g bullet fired at 250 m/s, **(c)** a lithium atom moving at 2.5×10^5 m/s, **(d)** an ozone (O_3) molecule in the upper atmosphere moving at 550 m/s.

6.44 Among the elementary subatomic particles of physics is the muon, which decays within a few nanoseconds after formation. The muon has a rest mass 206.8 times that of an electron. Calculate the de Broglie wavelength associated with a muon traveling at a velocity of 8.85×10^5 cm/s.

6.45 Neutron diffraction is an important technique for determining the structures of molecules. Calculate the velocity of a neutron needed to achieve a wavelength of 0.955 Å. (Refer to the inside cover for the mass of the neutron).

6.46 The electron microscope has been widely used to obtain highly magnified images of biological and other types of materials. When an electron is accelerated through a particular potential field, it attains a speed of 8.95×10^6 m/s. What is the characteristic wavelength of this electron? Is the wavelength comparable to the size of atoms?

6.47 Using Heisenberg's uncertainty principle, calculate the uncertainty in the position of **(a)** a 1.50-mg mosquito moving at a speed of 1.40 m/s if the speed is known to within ± 0.01 m/s; **(b)** a proton moving at a speed of $(5.00 \pm 0.01) \times 10^4$ m/s. (The mass of a proton is given in the table of fundamental constants in the inside cover of the text.)

6.48 Calculate the uncertainty in the position of **(a)** an electron moving at a speed of $(3.00 \pm 0.01) \times 10^5$ m/s, **(b)** a neutron moving at this same speed. (The masses of an electron and a neutron are given in the table of fundamental constants in the inside cover of the text.) **(c)** What are the implications of these calculations to our model of the atom?

QUANTUM MECHANICS AND ATOMIC ORBITALS (sections 6.5 and 6.6)

6.49 **(a)** Why does the Bohr model of the hydrogen atom violate the uncertainty principle? **(b)** In what way is the description of the electron using a wave function consistent with de Broglie's hypothesis? **(c)** What is meant by the term *probability density*? Given the wave function, how do we find the probability density at a certain point in space?

6.50 **(a)** According to the Bohr model, an electron in the ground state of a hydrogen atom orbits the nucleus at a specific radius of 0.53 Å. In the quantum mechanical description of the hydrogen atom, the most probable distance of the electron from the nucleus is 0.53 Å. Why are these two statements different? **(b)** Why is the use of Schrödinger's wave equation to describe the location of a particle very different from the description obtained from classical physics? **(c)** In the quantum mechanical description of an electron, what is the physical significance of the square of the wave function, ψ^2?

6.51 **(a)** For $n = 4$, what are the possible values of l? **(b)** For $l = 2$, what are the possible values of m_l? **(c)** If m_l is 2, what are the possible values for l?

6.52 How many possible values for l and m_l are there when **(a)** $n = 3$; **(b)** $n = 5$?

6.53 Give the numerical values of n and l corresponding to each of the following orbital designations: **(a)** $3p$, **(b)** $2s$, **(c)** $4f$, **(d)** $5d$.

6.54 Give the values for n, l, and m_l for **(a)** each orbital in the $2p$ subshell, **(b)** each orbital in the $5d$ subshell.

6.55 Which of the following represent impossible combinations of n and l: **(a)** $1p$, **(b)** $4s$, **(c)** $5f$, **(d)** $2d$?

6.56 For the table that follows, write which orbital goes with the quantum numbers. Don't worry about x, y, z subscripts. If the quantum numbers are not allowed, write "not allowed."

n	l	m_l	Orbital
2	1	-1	$2p$ (example)
1	0	0	
3	-3	2	
3	2	-2	
2	0	-1	
0	0	0	
4	2	1	
5	3	0	

6.57 Sketch the shape and orientation of the following types of orbitals: **(a)** s, **(b)** p_z, **(c)** d_{xy}.

6.58 Sketch the shape and orientation of the following types of orbitals: **(a)** p_x, **(b)** d_{z^2}, **(c)** $d_{x^2-y^2}$.

6.59 **(a)** What are the similarities and differences between the $1s$ and $2s$ orbitals of the hydrogen atom? **(b)** In what sense does a $2p$ orbital have directional character? Compare the "directional" characteristics of the p_x and $d_{x^2-y^2}$ orbitals. (That is, in what direction or region of space is the electron density concentrated?) **(c)** What can you say about the average distance from the nucleus of an electron in a $2s$ orbital as compared with a $3s$ orbital? **(d)** For the hydrogen atom, list the following orbitals in order of increasing energy (that is, most stable ones first): $4f$, $6s$, $3d$, $1s$, $2p$.

6.60 **(a)** With reference to Figure 6.18, what is the relationship between the number of nodes in an s orbital and the value of the principal quantum number? **(b)** Identify the number of nodes; that is, identify places where the electron density is zero, in the $2p_x$ orbital; in the $3s$ orbital. **(c)** What information is obtained from the radial probability functions in Figure 6.18? **(d)** For the hydrogen atom, list the following orbitals in order of increasing energy: $3s$, $2s$, $2p$, $5s$, $4d$.

MANY-ELECTRON ATOMS AND ELECTRON CONFIGURATIONS (sections 6.7–6.9)

6.61 For a given value of the principal quantum number, n, how do the energies of the s, p, d, and f subshells vary for **(a)** hydrogen, **(b)** a many-electron atom?

6.62 **(a)** The average distance from the nucleus of a $3s$ electron in a chlorine atom is smaller than that for a $3p$ electron. In light of this fact, which orbital is higher in energy? **(b)** Would you expect

it to require more or less energy to remove a $3s$ electron from the chlorine atom, as compared with a $2p$ electron? Explain.

6.63 **(a)** What experimental evidence is there for the electron having a "spin"? **(b)** Draw an energy-level diagram that shows the relative energetic positions of a $1s$ orbital and a $2s$ orbital. Put two electrons in the 1s orbital. **(c)** Draw an arrow showing the excitation of an electron from the 1s to the 2s orbital.

6.64 **(a)** State the Pauli exclusion principle in your own words. **(b)** The Pauli exclusion principle is, in an important sense, the key to understanding the periodic table. Explain.

6.65 What is the maximum number of electrons that can occupy each of the following subshells: **(a)** 3p, **(b)** 5d, **(c)** 2s, **(d)** 4f ?

6.66 What is the maximum number of electrons in an atom that can have the following quantum numbers: **(a)** $n = 2$, $m_s = -\frac{1}{2}$, **(b)** $n = 5$, $l = 3$; **(c)** $n = 4$, $l = 3$, $m_l = -3$; **(d)** $n = 4, l = 0, m_l = 0$?

6.67 **(a)** What are "valence electrons"? **(b)** What are "core electrons"? **(c)** What does each box in an orbital diagram represent? **(d)** What quantity is represented by the half arrows in an orbital diagram?

6.68 For each element, indicate the number of valence electrons, core electrons, and unpaired electrons in the ground state: **(a)** carbon, **(b)** phosphorus, **(c)** neon.

6.69 Write the condensed electron configurations for the following atoms, using the appropriate noble-gas core abbreviations: **(a)** Cs, **(b)** Ni, **(c)** Se, **(d)** Cd, **(e)** U, **(f)** Pb.

6.70 Write the condensed electron configurations for the following atoms and indicate how many unpaired electrons each has: **(a)** Mg, **(b)** Ge, **(c)** Br, **(d)** V, **(e)** Y, **(f)** Lu.

6.71 Identify the specific element that corresponds to each of the following electron configurations and indicate the number of unpaired electrons for each: **(a)** $1s^2 2s^2$, **(b)** $1s^2 2s^2 2p^4$, **(c)** $[Ar]4s^1 3d^5$, **(d)** $[Kr]5s^2 4d^{10} 5p^4$.

6.72 Identify the group of elements that corresponds to each of the following generalized electron configurations and indicate the number of unpaired electrons for each:
(a) [noble gas] $ns^2 np^5$
(b) [noble gas] $ns^2 (n-1)d^2$
(c) [noble gas] $ns^2 (n-1)d^{10} np^1$
(d) [noble gas] $ns^2 (n-2)f^6$

6.73 What is wrong with the following electron configurations for atoms in their ground states? **(a)** $1s^2 2s^2 3s^1$, **(b)** $[Ne]2s^2 2p^3$, **(c)** $[Ne]3s^2 3d^5$.

6.74 The following electron configurations represent excited states. Identify the element, and write its ground-state condensed electron configuration. **(a)** $1s^2 2s^2 3p^2 4p^1$, **(b)** $[Ar]3d^{10} 4s^1 4p^4 5s^1$, **(c)** $[Kr]4d^6 5s^2 5p^1$.

ADDITIONAL EXERCISES

6.75 Consider the two waves shown here, which we will consider to represent two electromagnetic radiations:
(a) What is the wavelength of wave A? Of wave B?
(b) What is the frequency of wave A? Of wave B?
(c) Identify the regions of the electromagnetic spectrum to which waves A and B belong.

6.76 If you put 120 volts of electricity through a pickle, the pickle will smoke and start glowing orange-yellow. The light is emitted because sodium ions in the pickle become excited; their return to the ground state results in light emission. **(a)** The wavelength of this emitted light is 589 nm. Calculate its frequency. **(b)** What is the energy of 0.10 mole of these photons? **(c)** Calculate the energy gap between the excited and ground states for the sodium ion. **(d)** If you soaked the pickle for a long time in a different salt solution, such as strontium chloride, would you still observe 589-nm light emission? Why or why not?

6.77 Certain elements emit light of a specific wavelength when they are burned. Historically, chemists used such emission wavelengths to determine whether specific elements were present in a sample. Characteristic wavelengths for some of the elements are given in the following table:

Ag	328.1 nm	Fe	372.0 nm
Au	267.6 nm	K	404.7 nm
Ba	455.4 nm	Mg	285.2 nm
Ca	422.7 nm	Na	589.6 nm
Cu	324.8 nm	Ni	341.5 nm

(a) Determine which elements emit radiation in the visible part of the spectrum. **(b)** Which element emits photons of highest energy? Of lowest energy? **(c)** When burned, a sample of an unknown substance is found to emit light of frequency 6.59×10^{14} s^{-1}. Which of these elements is probably in the sample?

6.78 In June 2004, the Cassini–Huygens spacecraft began orbiting Saturn and transmitting images to Earth. The closest distance between Saturn and Earth is 746 million miles. What is the minimum amount of time it takes for the transmitted signals to travel from the spacecraft to Earth?

6.79 The rays of the Sun that cause tanning and burning are in the ultraviolet portion of the electromagnetic spectrum. These rays are categorized by wavelength. So-called UV-A radiation has wavelengths in the range of 320–380 nm, whereas UV-B radiation has wavelengths in the range of 290–320 nm. **(a)** Calculate the frequency of light that has a wavelength of 320 nm. **(b)** Calculate the energy of a mole of 320-nm photons. **(c)** Which are more energetic, photons of UV-A radiation or photons of UV-B radiation? **(d)** The UV-B radiation from the Sun is considered a greater cause of sunburn in humans than is UV-A radiation. Is this observation consistent with your answer to part (c)?

6.80 The watt is the derived SI unit of power, the measure of energy per unit time: 1 W = 1 J-s. A semiconductor laser in a CD player has an output wavelength of 780 nm and a power level of 0.10 mW. How many photons strike the CD surface during the playing of a CD 69 minutes in length?

6.81 Carotenoids are yellow, orange, and red pigments synthesized by plants. The observed color of an object is not the color of light it absorbs but rather the complementary color, as described by a color wheel such as the one shown here. On this wheel, complementary colors are across from each other. **(a)** Based on this wheel, what color is absorbed most strongly if a plant is orange? **(b)** If a particular carotenoid absorbs photons at 455 nm, what is the energy of the photon?

6.82 A photocell is a device used to measure the intensity of light. In a certain experiment, when light of wavelength 630 nm is directed onto the photocell, electrons are emitted at the rate of 2.6×10^{-12} C/s (coulombs per second). Assume that each photon that impinges on the photocell emits one electron. How many photons per second are striking the photocell? How much energy per second is the photocell absorbing?

6.83 In an experiment to study the photoelectric effect, a scientist measures the kinetic energy of ejected electrons as a function of the frequency of radiation hitting a metal surface. She obtains the following plot. The point labeled "ν_0" corresponds to light with a wavelength of 680 nm. (a) What is the value of ν_0 in s^{-1}? (b) What is the value of the work function of the metal in units of kJ/mol of ejected electrons? (c) What happens when the metal is irradiated with light of frequency less than ν_0? (d) Note that when the frequency of the light is greater than ν_0, the plot shows a straight line with a nonzero slope. Why is this the case? (e) Can you determine the slope of the line segment discussed in part (d)? Explain.

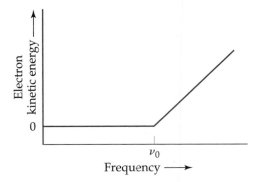

6.84 The human retina has three types of receptor cones, each sensitive to a different range of wavelengths of visible light, as shown in this figure (the colors are merely to differentiate the three curves from one another; they do not indicate the actual colors represented by each curve):

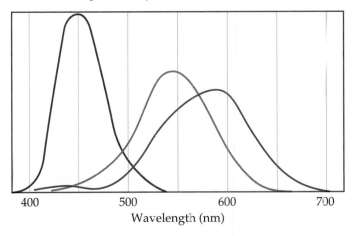

(a) Estimate the energies of photons with wavelengths at the maximum for each type of cone. (b) The color of the sky is due to scattering of solar light by the molecules of the atmosphere. Lord Rayleigh was one of the first to study scattering of this kind. He showed that the amount of scattering for very small particles such as molecules is inversely proportional to the fourth power of the wavelength. Estimate the ratio of the scattering efficiency of light at the wavelength of the maximum for the "blue" cones, as compared with that for the "green" cones. (c) Explain why the sky appears blue even though all wavelengths of solar light are scattered by the atmosphere.

6.85 The series of emission lines of the hydrogen atom for which $n_f = 3$ is called the *Paschen series*. (a) Determine the region of the electromagnetic spectrum in which the lines of the Paschen series are observed. (b) Calculate the wavelengths of the first three lines in the Paschen series—those for which $n_i = 4, 5,$ and 6.

6.86 When the spectrum of light from the Sun is examined in high resolution in an experiment similar to that illustrated in Figure 6.9, dark lines are evident. These are called Fraunhofer lines, after the scientist who studied them extensively in the early nineteenth century. Altogether, about 25,000 lines have been identified in the solar spectrum between 2950 Å and 10,000 Å. The Fraunhofer lines are attributed to absorption of certain wavelengths of the Sun's "white" light by gaseous elements in the Sun's atmosphere. (a) Describe the process that causes absorption of specific wavelengths of light from the solar spectrum. (b) To determine which Fraunhofer lines belonged to a given element, say neon, what experiments could a scientist conduct here on Earth?

[6.87] Bohr's model can be used for hydrogen-like ions—ions that have only one electron, such as He^+ and Li^{2+}. (a) Why is the Bohr model applicable to He^+ ions but not to neutral He atoms? (b) The ground-state energies of H, He^+, and Li^{2+} are tabulated as follows:

Atom or ion	H	He^+	Li^{2+}
Ground-state energy	-2.18×10^{-18} J	-8.72×10^{-18} J	-1.96×10^{-17} J

By examining these numbers, propose a relationship between the ground-state energy of hydrogen-like systems and the nuclear charge, Z. (c) Use the relationship you derive in part (b) to predict the ground-state energy of the C^{5+} ion.

[6.88] An electron is accelerated through an electric potential to a kinetic energy of 18.6 keV. What is its characteristic wavelength? [*Hint:* Recall that the kinetic energy of a moving object is $E = \frac{1}{2}mv^2$, where m is the mass of the object and v is the speed of the object.]

6.89 In the television series *Star Trek,* the transporter beam is a device used to "beam down" people from the *Starship Enterprise* to another location, such as the surface of a planet. The writers of the show put a "Heisenberg compensator" into the transporter beam mechanism. Explain why such a compensator (which is entirely fictional) would be necessary to get around Heisenberg's uncertainty principle.

6.90 Which of the quantum numbers governs (a) the shape of an orbital, (b) the energy of an orbital, (c) the spin properties of the electron, (d) the spatial orientation of the orbital?

[6.91] Consider the discussion of radial probability functions in "A Closer Look" in Section 6.6. (a) What is the difference between the probability density as a function of r and the radial probability function as a function of r? (b) What is the significance of the term $4\pi r^2$ in the radial probability functions for the *s* orbitals? (c) Based on Figures 6.18 and 6.21, make sketches of what you think the probability density as a function of r and the radial probability function would look like for the 4*s* orbital of the hydrogen atom.

[6.92] For orbitals that are symmetric but not spherical, the contour representations (as in Figures 6.22 and 6.23) suggest where nodal planes exist (that is, where the electron density is zero). For example, the p_x orbital has a node wherever $x = 0$. This equation is satisfied by all points on the yz plane, so this plane is called a nodal plane of the p_x orbital. (a) Determine the nodal plane of the p_z orbital. (b) What are the two nodal planes of the d_{xy} orbital? (c) What are the two nodal planes of the $d_{x^2-y^2}$ orbital?

[6.93] The "Chemistry and Life" box in Section 6.7 described the techniques called NMR and MRI. (a) Instruments for obtaining MRI data are typically labeled with a frequency, such as 600 MHz. Why do you suppose this label is relevant to the experiment? (b) What is the value of ΔE in Figure 6.27 that would correspond to the absorption of a photon of radiation with frequency 450 MHz? (c) In general, the stronger the magnetic field, the greater the information obtained from an NMR or MRI experiment. Why do you suppose this is the case?

6.94 Suppose that the spin quantum number, m_s, could have *three* allowed values instead of two. How would this affect the number of elements in the first four rows of the periodic table?

6.95 Using the periodic table as a guide, write the condensed electron configuration and determine the number of unpaired electrons for the ground state of (a) Si, (b) Zn, (c) Zr, (d) Sn, (e) Ba, (f) Tl.

6.96 Scientists have speculated that element 126 might have a moderate stability, allowing it to be synthesized and characterized. Predict what the condensed electron configuration of this element might be.

INTEGRATIVE EXERCISES

6.97 Microwave ovens use microwave radiation to heat food. The energy of the microwaves is absorbed by water molecules in food and then transferred to other components of the food. (a) Suppose that the microwave radiation has a wavelength of 11.2 cm. How many photons are required to heat 200 mL of coffee from 23 °C to 60 °C? (b) Suppose the microwave's power is 900 W (1 Watt = 1 joule-second). How long would you have to heat the coffee in part (a)?

6.98 The stratospheric ozone (O_3) layer helps to protect us from harmful ultraviolet radiation. It does so by absorbing ultraviolet light and falling apart into an O_2 molecule and an oxygen atom, a process known as photodissociation.

$$O_3(g) \longrightarrow O_2(g) + O(g)$$

Use the data in Appendix C to calculate the enthalpy change for this reaction. What is the maximum wavelength a photon can have if it is to possess sufficient energy to cause this dissociation? In what portion of the spectrum does this wavelength occur?

6.99 The discovery of hafnium, element number 72, provided a controversial episode in chemistry. G. Urbain, a French chemist, claimed in 1911 to have isolated an element number 72 from a sample of rare earth (elements 58–71) compounds. However, Niels Bohr believed that hafnium was more likely to be found along with zirconium than with the rare earths. D. Coster and G. von Hevesy, working in Bohr's laboratory in Copenhagen, showed in 1922 that element 72 was present in a sample of Norwegian zircon, an ore of zirconium. (The name hafnium comes from the Latin name for Copenhagen, *Hafnia*). (a) How would you use electron configuration arguments to justify Bohr's prediction? (b) Zirconium, hafnium's neighbor in group 4B, can be produced as a metal by reduction of solid $ZrCl_4$ with molten sodium metal. Write a balanced chemical equation for the reaction. Is this an oxidation-reduction reaction? If yes, what is reduced and what is oxidized? (c) Solid zirconium dioxide, ZrO_2, is reacted with chlorine gas in the presence of carbon. The products of the reaction are $ZrCl_4$ and two gases, CO_2 and CO in the ratio 1:2. Write a balanced chemical equation for the reaction. Starting with a 55.4-g sample of ZrO_2, calculate the mass of $ZrCl_4$ formed, assuming that ZrO_2 is the limiting reagent and assuming 100% yield. (d) Using their electron configurations, account for the fact that Zr and Hf form chlorides MCl_4 and oxides MO_2.

6.100 (a) Account for formation of the following series of oxides in terms of the electron configurations of the elements and the discussion of ionic compounds in Section 2.7: K_2O, CaO, Sc_2O_3, TiO_2, V_2O_5, CrO_3. (b) Name these oxides. (c) Consider the metal oxides whose enthalpies of formation (in kJ mol^{-1}) are listed here.

Oxide	$K_2O(s)$	$CaO(s)$	$TiO_2(s)$	$V_2O_5(s)$
ΔH_f°	-363.2	-635.1	-938.7	-1550.6

Calculate the enthalpy changes in the following general reaction for each case:

$$M_nO_m(s) + H_2(g) \longrightarrow nM(s) + mH_2O(g)$$

(You will need to write the balanced equation for each case and then compute ΔH°.) (d) Based on the data given, estimate a value of ΔH_f° for $Sc_2O_3(s)$.

6.101 The first 25 years of the twentieth century were momentous for the rapid pace of change in scientists' understanding of the nature of matter. (a) How did Rutherford's experiments on the scattering of α particles by a gold foil set the stage for Bohr's theory of the hydrogen atom? (b) In what ways is de Broglie's hypothesis, as it applies to electrons, consistent with J. J. Thomson's conclusion that the electron has mass? In what sense is it consistent with proposals preceding Thomson's work that the cathode rays are a wave phenomenon?

[**6.102**] The two most common isotopes of uranium are ^{235}U and ^{238}U. (a) Compare the number of protons, the number of electrons, and the number of neutrons in atoms of these two isotopes. (b) Using the periodic table in the front inside cover, write the electron configuration for a U atom. (c) Compare your answer to part (b) to the electron configuration given in Figure 6.31. How can you explain any differences between these two electron configurations? (d) ^{238}U undergoes radioactive decay to ^{234}Th. How many protons, electrons, and neutrons are gained or lost by the ^{238}U atom during this process? (e) Examine the electron configuration for Th in Figure 6.31. Are you surprised by what you find? Explain.

6.103 Imagine sunlight falling on three square areas. One is an inert black material. The second is a photovoltaic cell surface, which converts radiant energy into electricity. The third is an area on a green tree leaf. Draw diagrams that show the energy conversions in each case, using Figure 5.9 as a model. How are these three examples related to the idea of sustainable energy sources?

WHAT'S AHEAD

7.1 DEVELOPMENT OF THE PERIODIC TABLE
We begin our discussion with a brief history of the periodic table.

7.2 EFFECTIVE NUCLEAR CHARGE
We next explore the many properties of atoms that depend on the net attraction of the outer electrons to the nucleus and on the average distance of those electrons from the nucleus. The net positive charge of the nucleus experienced by the outer electrons is called the *effective nuclear charge*.

7.3 SIZES OF ATOMS AND IONS
We explore the relative sizes of atoms and ions, both of which follow trends that are related to their placement in the periodic table.

7.4 IONIZATION ENERGY
We next encounter the *ionization energy* required to remove one or more electrons from an atom. The periodic trends in ionization energy depend on variations in effective nuclear charge and atomic radii.

Light-emitting diodes, LEDs.

PERIODIC PROPERTIES OF THE ELEMENTS

THE BRILLIANT COLORS OF light-emitting diodes (LEDs) arise from the composition of the materials from which they are made. The LEDs shown here are compounds of gallium and aluminum mixed with nitrogen, phosphorus, and arsenic. GaN, GaP, and GaAs can make solid solutions with each other and with AlN, AlP, and AlAs; the composition of each solid solution dictates the wavelength of light emitted by a given LED. Because these elements are in groups 3A and 5A, we say that LEDs are composed of "3-5" materials.

As we saw in Chapter 6, the periodic nature of the periodic table arises from repeating patterns in the electron configurations of the elements. Elements in the same column contain the same number of electrons in their **valence orbitals**, which are the occupied orbitals that hold the electrons involved in bonding. For example, O ($[He]2s^2 2p^4$) and S ($[Ne]3s^2 3p^4$) are both in group 6A. The similarity of the electron distribution in their valence s and p orbitals leads to similarities in the properties of these two elements. When we compare elemental O and elemental S, however, it is apparent that they exhibit differences as well, not the least of which is that at room temperature oxygen is a colorless gas but sulfur is a yellow solid. One major difference between O and S atoms is that the outermost electrons of O are in the second shell, whereas those of S are in the third shell. Thus, electron configurations can be used to explain differences as well as similarities in the properties of elements.

In this chapter we explore how some of the important properties of elements change as we move across a row or down a column of the periodic table. In many cases the trends in a row or column allow us to predict the physical and chemical properties of the elements.

7.1 | DEVELOPMENT OF THE PERIODIC TABLE

The discovery of chemical elements has been ongoing since ancient times (▼ **FIGURE 7.1**). Certain elements, such as gold (Au), appear in nature in elemental form and were thus discovered thousands of years ago. In contrast, some elements, such as technetium (Tc), are radioactive and intrinsically unstable. We know about them only because of technology developed during the twentieth century.

The majority of elements readily form compounds and, consequently, are not found in nature in their elemental form. For centuries, therefore, scientists were unaware of their existence. During the early nineteenth century, advances in chemistry made it easier to isolate elements from their compounds. As a result, the number of known elements more than doubled from 31 in 1800 to 63 by 1865.

As the number of known elements increased, scientists began classifying them. In 1869, Dmitri Mendeleev in Russia and Lothar Meyer in Germany published nearly identical classification schemes. Both scientists noted that similar chemical and physical properties recur periodically when the elements are arranged in order of increasing atomic weight. Scientists at that time had no knowledge of atomic numbers. Atomic weights, however, generally increase with increasing atomic number, so both Mendeleev and Meyer fortuitously arranged the elements in proper sequence. Although Mendeleev and Meyer came to essentially the same conclusion about the periodicity of elemental properties, Mendeleev is given credit for advancing his ideas more vigorously and stimulating new work. His insistence that elements with similar characteristics be listed in the same column forced him to leave blank spaces in his table. For example, both gallium (Ga) and germanium (Ge) were unknown to Mendeleev. He boldly predicted their

GO FIGURE

Which row of the periodic table contains the most recently discovered elements? Can you suggest a reason?

▶ **FIGURE 7.1** Discovering the elements.

TABLE 7.1 • Comparison of the Properties of Eka-Silicon Predicted by Mendeleev with the Observed Properties of Germanium

Property	Mendeleev's Predictions for Eka-Silicon (made in 1871)	Observed Properties of Germanium (discovered in 1886)
Atomic weight	72	72.59
Density (g/cm^3)	5.5	5.35
Specific heat (J/g-K)	0.305	0.309
Melting point (°C)	High	947
Color	Dark gray	Grayish white
Formula of oxide	XO_2	GeO_2
Density of oxide (g/cm^3)	4.7	4.70
Formula of chloride	XCl_4	$GeCl_4$
Boiling point of chloride (°C)	A little under 100	84

existence and properties, referring to them as *eka-aluminum* ("under" aluminum) and *eka-silicon* ("under" silicon), respectively, after the elements under which they appeared in his table. When these elements were discovered, their properties closely matched those predicted by Mendeleev, as shown in ▲ TABLE 7.1.

In 1913, two years after Rutherford proposed the nuclear model of the atom ∞ (Section 2.2), English physicist Henry Moseley (1887–1915) developed the concept of atomic numbers. Bombarding different elements with high-energy electrons, Moseley found that each element produced X-rays of a unique frequency and that the frequency generally increased as the atomic mass increased. He arranged the X-ray frequencies in order by assigning a unique whole number, called an *atomic number,* to each element. Moseley correctly identified the atomic number as the number of protons in the nucleus of the atom. ∞ (Section 2.3)

The concept of atomic number clarified some problems in the periodic table of Moseley's day, which was based on atomic weights. For example, the atomic weight of Ar (atomic number 18) is greater than that of K (atomic number 19), yet the chemical and physical properties of Ar are much more like those of Ne and Kr than like those of Na and Rb. However, when the elements are arranged in order of increasing atomic number, rather than increasing atomic weight, Ar and K appear in their correct places in the table. Moseley's studies also made it possible to identify "holes" in the periodic table, which led to the discovery of previously unknown elements.

 GIVE IT SOME THOUGHT

Arranging the elements by atomic weight leads to an order slightly different from that in a modern periodic table, where the arrangement is by atomic number. Why does this happen? Looking at the periodic table on the inside front cover, can you find an example other than Ar and K where the order of the elements would be different if the elements were arranged in order of increasing atomic weight?

7.2 | EFFECTIVE NUCLEAR CHARGE

Many properties of atoms depend on electron configuration and on how strongly the outer electrons in the atoms are attracted to the nucleus. Coulomb's law tells us that the strength of the interaction between two electrical charges depends on the magnitudes of the charges and on the distance between them. ∞ (Section 2.3) Thus, the attractive force between an electron and the nucleus depends on the magnitude of the nuclear charge and on the average distance between the nucleus and the electron. The force increases as the nuclear charge increases and decreases as the electron moves farther from the nucleus.

Sodium nucleus
contains 11 protons (11$^+$)

e$^-$ — Valence electron (3s)

10$^-$

Each of the 11 electrons is attracted to positively charged nucleus

Sodium atoms contains 10 core electrons (10$^-$) that screen the 3s valence electron

▲ **FIGURE 7.2 Effective nuclear charge.** The effective nuclear charge experienced by the valence electron in a sodium atom depends mostly on the 11+ charge of the nucleus and the 10− charge of the core electrons.

In a many-electron atom, each electron is simultaneously attracted to the nucleus and repelled by the other electrons. In general, there are so many electron–electron repulsions that we cannot analyze the situation exactly. We can, however, estimate the attractive force between any one electron and the nucleus by considering how the electron interacts with the *average* environment created by the nucleus and the other electrons in the atom. We treat each electron as though it were moving in the net electric field created by the nucleus and the electron density of the other electrons. We view this net electric field as if it results from a single positive charge located at the nucleus, called the **effective nuclear charge**, Z_{eff}. The effective nuclear charge acting on an electron in an atom is smaller than the *actual* nuclear charge ($Z_{eff} < Z$) because the effective nuclear charge includes the effect of the other electrons in the atom.

In any many-electron atom, the inner electrons partially *screen* outer electrons from the attraction of the nucleus, and the relationship between Z_{eff} and the number of protons in the nucleus Z is

$$Z_{eff} = Z - S \qquad [7.1]$$

where S is a positive number called the *screening constant*. It represents the portion of the nuclear charge that is screened from a valence electron by the other electrons in the atom. Because core electrons are most effective at screening a valence electron from the nucleus, *the value of S is usually close to the number of core electrons in an atom.* (Electrons in the same valence shell do not screen one another very effectively, but they do affect the value of S slightly; see "A Closer Look: Effective Nuclear Charge.")

Let's look at the Na atom to see what to expect for the magnitude of Z_{eff}. Sodium has the electron configuration [Ne]3s^1. The nuclear charge is $Z = 11+$, and there are 10 core electrons (1s^{2}2s^{2}2p^6). We therefore expect S to equal 10 and the 3s electron to experience an effective nuclear charge of $Z_{eff} = 11 - 10 = 1+$ (◄ **FIGURE 7.2**). The situation is more complicated, however, because the 3s electron has a small probability of being closer to the nucleus, in the region occupied by the core electrons. ∞ (Section 6.6) Thus, there is a probability that this electron experiences a greater attraction than our simple $S = 10$ model suggests. This greater attraction turns out to increase the value of Z_{eff} for the 3s electron in Na from our expected $Z_{eff} = 1+$ to $Z_{eff} = 2.5+$. In other words, the fact that the 3s electron spends some small amount of time close to the nucleus changes the value of S in Equation 7.1 from 10 to 8.5.

The notion of effective nuclear charge also explains an important effect we noted in Section 6.7: For a many-electron atom, the energies of orbitals with the same n value increase with increasing l value. For example, in the carbon atom, electron configuration 1s^{2}2s^{2}2p^2, the energy of the 2p orbital ($l = 1$) is higher than that of the 2s orbital ($l = 0$) even though both orbitals are in the $n = 2$ shell (Figure 6.24). This difference in energies is due to the radial probability functions for the orbitals (◄ **FIGURE 7.3**). The greater attraction between the 2s electron and the nucleus

▲ **GO FIGURE**

Which orbital has more electron density near the nucleus, 2s or 2p?

No peak here tells you 2p electron stays far from the nucleus

This peak tells you the 2s electron spends some time close to nucleus

▲ **FIGURE 7.3 2s and 2p radial probability functions.**

leads to a lower energy for the 2s orbital than for the 2p orbital. The same reasoning explains the general trend in orbital energies ($ns < np < nd$) in many-electron atoms.

Finally, let's examine trends in valence-electron Z_{eff} values. *The effective nuclear charge increases from left to right across any period of the periodic table.* Although the number of core electrons stays the same across the period, the number of protons increases. The valence electrons added to counterbalance the increasing nuclear charge screen one another ineffectively. Thus, Z_{eff} increases steadily. For example, the core electrons of lithium ($1s^2 2s^1$) screen the $2s$ valence electron from the 3+ nucleus fairly efficiently. Consequently, the valence electron experiences an effective nuclear charge of roughly $3 - 2 = 1+$. For beryllium ($1s^2 2s^2$) the effective nuclear charge experienced by each valence electron is larger because here the $1s$ electrons screen a 4+ nucleus, and each $2s$ electron only partially screens the other. Consequently, the effective nuclear charge experienced by each $2s$ electron is about $4 - 2 = 2+$.

A CLOSER LOOK

EFFECTIVE NUCLEAR CHARGE

To get a sense of how effective nuclear charge varies as both nuclear charge and number of electrons increase, consider ▼ FIGURE 7.4. Although the details of how the Z_{eff} values in the graph were calculated are beyond the scope of our discussion, the trends are instructive.

The effective nuclear charge felt by the outermost electrons is smaller than that felt by inner electrons because of screening by the inner electrons. In addition, the effective nuclear charge felt by the outermost electrons does not increase as steeply with increasing atomic number because the valence electrons make a small but nonnegligible contribution to the screening constant S. The most striking feature associated with the Z_{eff} value for the outermost electrons is the sharp drop between the last period 2 element (Ne) and the first period 3 element (Na). This drop reflects the fact that the core electrons are much more effective than the valence electrons at screening the nuclear charge.

Because Z_{eff} can be used to understand many physically measurable quantities, it is desirable to have a simple method for estimating it. The value of Z in Equation 7.1 is known exactly, so the challenge boils down to estimating the value of S. In the text, we estimated S by assuming that each core electron contributes 1.00 to S and the outer electrons contribute nothing. A more accurate approach was developed by John Slater, however, and we can use his approach if we limit ourselves to elements that do not have electrons in d or f subshells.

Electrons for which the principal quantum number n is larger than the value of n for the electron of interest contribute 0 to the value of S. Electrons with the same value of n as the electron of interest contribute 0.35 to the value of S. Electrons for which n is 1 less than n for the electron of interest contribute 0.85, while those with even smaller values of n contribute 1.00. For example, consider fluorine, which has the ground-state electron configuration $1s^2 2s^2 2p^5$. For a valence electron in fluorine, Slater's rules tell us that $S = (0.35 \times 6) + (0.85 \times 2) = 3.8$. (Slater's rules ignore the contribution of an electron to itself in screening; therefore, we consider only six $n = 2$ electrons, not all seven). Thus, $Z_{eff} = Z - S = 9 - 3.8 = 5.2+$.

Values of Z_{eff} estimated using the simple method outlined in the text, as well as those estimated with Slater's rules, are plotted in Figure 7.4. While neither of these methods exactly replicate the values of Z_{eff} obtained from more sophisticated calculations, both methods effectively capture the periodic variation in Z_{eff}. While Slater's approach is more accurate, the method outlined in the text does a reasonably good job of estimating Z_{eff} despite its simplicity. For our purposes, therefore, we can assume that the screening constant S in Equation 7.1 is roughly equal to the number of core electrons.

▲ **FIGURE 7.4** **Variations in effective nuclear charge for period 2 and period 3 elements.** Moving from one element to the next in the periodic table, the increase in Z_{eff} felt by the innermost (1s) electrons (red circles) closely tracks the increase in nuclear charge Z (black line) because these electrons are not screened. The results of several methods to calculate Z_{eff} for valence electrons are shown in other colors.

RELATED EXERCISES: 7.11, 7.12, 7.13, 7.14, 7.34, 7.35, 7.84, 7.85

Going down a column, the effective nuclear charge experienced by valence electrons changes far less than it does across a period. For example, we would expect the effective nuclear charge experienced by the valence electrons in lithium and sodium to be about the same, roughly $3 - 2 = 1+$ for lithium and $11 - 10 = 1+$ for sodium. In fact, however, effective nuclear charge increases slightly as we go down a column because the more diffuse core electron cloud is less able to screen the valence electrons from the nuclear charge. In the case of the alkali metals, Z_{eff} increases from 1.3+ for lithium, to 2.5+ for sodium, to 3.5+ for potassium.

 GIVE IT SOME THOUGHT

Which would you expect to experience a greater effective nuclear charge, a 2*p* electron of a Ne atom or a 3*s* electron of a Na atom?

7.3 | SIZES OF ATOMS AND IONS

We often think of atoms as hard, spherical objects. According to the quantum mechanical model, however, atoms do not have sharply defined boundaries at which the electron distribution becomes zero. ∞ (Section 6.5) Nevertheless, we can define atomic size in several ways, based on the distances between atoms in various situations.

Imagine a collection of argon atoms in the gas phase. When two of these atoms collide with each other, they ricochet apart like colliding billiard balls. This ricocheting happens because the electron clouds of the colliding atoms cannot penetrate each other to any significant extent. The shortest distance separating the two nuclei during such collisions is twice the radii of the atoms. We call this radius the *nonbonding atomic radius* or the *van der Waals* radius (◄ FIGURE 7.5).

In molecules, an attractive interaction exists between any two adjacent atoms in the molecule, leading to a chemical bond between the atoms. We discuss bonding in Chapter 8. For now, we only need to realize that this attractive interaction brings the two atoms closer together than they would be in a nonbonding collision where the atoms ricochet apart. We can define an atomic radius based on the distance separating the nuclei when two atoms are bonded to each other, shown as distance *d* in Figure 7.5. The **bonding atomic radius** for any atom in a molecule is equal to half of the nucleus-to-nucleus distance *d*. Note from Figure 7.5 that the bonding atomic radius (also known as the *covalent radius*) is shorter than the nonbonding atomic radius. Unless otherwise noted, we mean the bonding atomic radius when we speak of the "size" of an atom.

Scientists have developed a variety of techniques for measuring the distances separating nuclei in molecules. From observations of these distances in many molecules, each element can be assigned a bonding atomic radius. For example, in the I_2 molecule, the distance separating the nuclei is observed to be 2.66 Å, which means the bonding atomic radius of an iodine atom is (2.66 Å)/2 = 1.33 Å.* Similarly, the distance separating adjacent carbon nuclei in diamond (a three-dimensional solid network of carbon atoms) is 1.54 Å; thus, the bonding atomic radius of carbon is 0.77 Å. The bonding atomic radii of other elements can be similarly defined (► FIGURE 7.6). (For helium and neon, the bonding atomic radii must be estimated because there are no known compounds of these elements.)

Knowing atomic radii allows us to estimate bond lengths in molecules. For example, the Cl—Cl bond length in Cl_2 is 1.99 Å, so a bonding atomic radius of 0.99 Å is assigned to Cl. In CCl_4 the measured length of the C—Cl bond is 1.77 Å, very close to the sum (0.77 + 0.99 Å) of the bonding atomic radii of C and Cl.

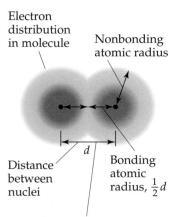

Electron distribution in molecule

Nonbonding atomic radius

Distance between nuclei

d

Bonding atomic radius, $\frac{1}{2}d$

Nuclei cannot get any closer to each other because of electron–electron repulsion

▲ FIGURE 7.5 **Distinction between nonbonding and bonding atomic radii within a molecule.**

---

*Remember: The angstrom (1 Å = 10^{-10} m) is a convenient metric unit for atomic measurements of length. It is not an SI unit. The most commonly used SI unit for atomic measurements is the picometer (1 pm = 10^{-12} m; 1 Å = 100 pm).

GO FIGURE

Which part of the periodic table (top/bottom, left/right) has the elements with the largest atoms?

◄ **FIGURE 7.6   Trends in bonding atomic radii for periods 1 through 5.**

SAMPLE EXERCISE 7.1   Bond Lengths in a Molecule

Natural gas used in home heating and cooking is odorless. Because natural gas leaks pose the danger of explosion or suffocation, various smelly substances are added to the gas to allow detection of a leak. One such substance is methyl mercaptan, CH_3SH. Use Figure 7.6 to predict the lengths of the C—S, C—H, and S—H bonds in this molecule.

SOLUTION

Analyze and Plan We are given three bonds and told to use Figure 7.6 for bonding atomic radii. We will assume that each bond length is the sum of the bonding atomic radii of the two atoms involved.

Solve

$$C-S \text{ bond length} = \text{bonding atomic radius of } C + \text{bonding atomic radius of } S$$

$$= 0.77 \text{Å} + 1.02 \text{ Å} = 1.79 \text{Å}$$

$$C-H \text{ bond length} = 0.77 \text{Å} + 0.37 \text{ Å} = 1.14 \text{Å}$$

$$S-H \text{ bond length} = 1.02 \text{Å} + 0.37 \text{ Å} = 1.39 \text{Å}$$

Check The experimentally determined bond lengths are C—S = 1.82 Å, C—H = 1.10 Å, and S—H = 1.33 Å. (In general, the lengths of bonds involving hydrogen show larger deviations from the values predicted from bonding atomic radii than do bonds involving larger atoms.)

Comment Notice that our estimated bond lengths are close but not exact matches to the measured bond lengths. Bonding atomic radii must be used with some caution in estimating bond lengths.

PRACTICE EXERCISE

Using Figure 7.6, predict which is longer, the P—Br bond in PBr_3 or the As—Cl bond in $AsCl_3$.

Answer: P—Br

Methyl mercaptan

S	
C	
H	

Periodic Trends in Atomic Radii

Figure 7.6 shows two interesting trends:

1. Within each group, bonding atomic radius tends to increase from top to bottom. This trend results primarily from the increase in the principal quantum number (n) of the outer electrons. As we go down a column, the outer electrons have a greater probability of being farther from the nucleus, causing the atomic radius to increase.

2. Within each period, bonding atomic radius tends to decrease from left to right. The major factor influencing this trend is the increase in effective nuclear charge Z_{eff} across a period. The increasing effective nuclear charge steadily draws the valence electrons closer to the nucleus, causing the bonding atomic radius to decrease.

 GIVE IT SOME THOUGHT

In Section 7.2 we said that Z_{eff} generally increases when you move down a column of the periodic table, whereas in Chapter 6 we saw that the "size" of an orbital increases as the principal quantum number n increases. With respect to atomic radii, do these trends work together or against each other? Which effect is larger?

SAMPLE EXERCISE 7.2 | **Atomic Radii**

Referring to a periodic table, arrange (as much as possible) the atoms $_{15}P$, $_{16}S$, $_{33}As$, and $_{34}Se$ in order of increasing size. (Atomic numbers are given to help you locate the atoms quickly in the table.)

SOLUTION

Analyze and Plan We are given the chemical symbols for four elements and told to use their relative positions in the periodic table to predict the relative size of their atomic radii. We can use the two periodic trends just described to help with this problem.

Solve P and S are in the same period, with S to the right of P. Therefore, we expect the radius of S to be smaller than that of P because radii decrease as we move across a period. Likewise, the radius of Se is expected to be smaller than that of As. As is directly below P. and Se is directly below S. We expect, therefore, the radius of P to be smaller than that of As and the radius of S to be smaller than that of Se. Thus, so far we can say S < P, P < As, S < Se, Se < As. We can therefore conclude that S has the smallest radius and As has the largest radius and so can write S < ? < ? < As.

Our two periodic trends for atomic size do not supply enough information to allow us to determine whether P or Se (represented by the two question marks) has the larger radius, however. Going from P to Se in the periodic table, we move down (radius tends to increase) and to the right (radius tends to decrease). In Figure 7.6 we see that the radius of Se is greater than that of P. If you examine the figure carefully, you will discover that for the s- and p-block elements the increase in radius moving down a column tends to be the greater effect. There are exceptions, however.

Check From Figure 7.6, we have S (1.02 Å) < P (1.06 Å) < Se (1.16 Å) < As (1.19 Å).

Comment Note that the trends we have just discussed are for the s- and p-block elements. Figure 7.6 shows that the transition elements do not show a regular decrease moving across a period.

PRACTICE EXERCISE

Arrange $_{11}Na$, $_4Be$, and $_{12}Mg$ in order of increasing atomic radius.
Answer: Be < Mg < Na

Periodic Trends in Ionic Radii

Just as bonding atomic radii can be determined from interatomic distances in molecules, ionic radii can be determined from interatomic distances in ionic compounds. Like the size of an atom, the size of an ion depends on its nuclear charge, the number of electrons it possesses, and the orbitals in which the valence electrons reside. When a cation is formed from a neutral atom, electrons are removed from the occupied atomic orbitals that are the most spatially extended from the nucleus. Also, the number of electron–electron repulsions is reduced. Therefore, *cations are smaller than their parent atoms* (▶ FIGURE 7.7). The opposite is true of anions. When electrons are added to an atom to form an anion, the increased electron–electron repulsions cause the electrons to spread out more in space. Thus, *anions are larger than their parent atoms.*

⬛ GO FIGURE

How do cations of the same charge change in radius as you move down a column in the periodic table?

Group 1A	Group 2A	Group 3A	Group 6A	Group 7A
Li^+ 0.90	Be^{2+} 0.59	B^{3+} 0.41	O^{2-} 1.26	F^- 1.19
Li 1.34	Be 0.90	B 0.82	O 0.73	F 0.71
Na^+ 1.16	Mg^{2+} 0.86	Al^{3+} 0.68	S^{2-} 1.70	Cl^- 1.67
Na 1.54	Mg 1.30	Al 1.18	S 1.02	Cl 0.99
K^+ 1.52	Ca^{2+} 1.14	Ga^{3+} 0.76	Se^{2-} 1.84	Br^- 1.82
K 1.96	Ca 1.24	Ga 1.26	Se 1.16	Br 1.14
Rb^+ 1.66	Sr^{2+} 1.32	In^{3+} 0.94	Te^{2-} 2.07	I^- 2.06
Rb 2.11	Sr 1.92	In 1.44	Te 1.35	I 1.33

⬤ = cation   ⬤ = anion   ⬤ = neutral atom

▲ **FIGURE 7.7   Cation and anion size.** Radii, in angstroms, of atoms and their ions for five groups of representative elements.

For ions carrying the same charge, ionic radius increases as we move down a column in the periodic table (Figure 7.7). In other words, as the principal quantum number of the outermost occupied orbital of an ion increases, the radius of the ion increases.

SAMPLE EXERCISE 7.3   Atomic and Ionic Radii

Arrange Mg^{2+}, Ca^{2+}, and Ca in order of decreasing radius.

SOLUTION

Cations are smaller than their parent atoms, and so Ca^{2+} < Ca. Because Ca is below Mg in group 2A, Ca^{2+} is larger than Mg^{2+}. Consequently, Ca > Ca^{2+} > Mg^{2+}.

PRACTICE EXERCISE

Which of the following atoms and ions is largest: S^{2-}, S, O^{2-}?

Answer: S^{2-}

An **isoelectronic series** is a group of ions all containing the same number of electrons. For example, each ion in the isoelectronic series O^{2-}, F^-, Na^+, Mg^{2+}, Al^{3+} has 10 electrons. In any isoelectronic series we can list the members in order of increasing atomic number; therefore, nuclear charge increases as we move through the series. Because the number of electrons remains constant, ionic radius decreases with increasing nuclear charge as the electrons are more strongly attracted to the nucleus:

$$\text{— Increasing nuclear charge } \longrightarrow$$

O^{2-}	F^-	Na^+	Mg^{2+}	Al^{3+}
1.26 Å	1.19 Å	1.16 Å	0.86 Å	0.68 Å

$$\text{— Decreasing ionic radius } \longrightarrow$$

Notice the positions and atomic numbers of these elements in the periodic table. The nonmetal anions precede the noble gas Ne in the table. The metal cations follow Ne. Oxygen, the largest ion in this isoelectronic series, has the lowest atomic number, 8. Aluminum, the smallest of these ions, has the highest atomic number, 13.

CHEMISTRY PUT TO WORK

Ion Movement Powers Electronics

Ionic size plays a major role in determining the properties of devices that rely on movement of ions. "Lithium ion" batteries are everywhere—cell phones, iPods, laptop computers—and so let's see how a lithium ion battery works.

A fully charged battery spontaneously produces an electric current and, therefore, power when its positive and negative electrodes are connected in an electrical circuit. The positive electrode is called the anode, and the negative electrode is called the cathode. The materials used for the electrodes in lithium ion batteries are under intense development. Currently the anode material is graphite, a form of carbon, and the cathode is most frequently $LiCoO_2$, lithium cobalt oxide (▶ FIGURE 7.8). Between anode and cathode is a *separator*, a solid material that allows lithium ions, but not electrons, to pass through.

When the battery is being charged by an external source, lithium ions migrate from the cathode to the anode where they insert between the layers of carbon atoms. Lithium ions are smaller and lighter than most other elements, which means that many can fit between the layers. When the battery discharges and its electrodes are properly connected, it is energetically favorable for the lithium ions to move from anode to cathode. In order to maintain charge balance, electrons simultaneously migrate from anode to cathode through an external circuit, thereby producing electricity.

At the cathode, lithium ions then insert in the oxide material. Again, the small size of lithium ions is an advantage. For every lithium ion that inserts into the lithium cobalt oxide cathode, a Co^{4+} ion is reduced to a Co^{3+} by an electron that has traveled through the external circuit.

The ion migration and the changes in structure that result when lithium ions enter and leave the electrode materials are complicated.

Teams all over the world are trying to discover new cathode and anode materials that will easily accept and release lithium ions without falling apart over many repeated cycles. New separator materials that allow for faster lithium ion passage are also under development. Some research groups are looking at using sodium ions instead of lithium ions because sodium is far more abundant on Earth than lithium; new materials that allow sodium ion insertion and release are therefore under development. In the next decade we expect great advances in battery technology based on chemistry.

RELATED EXERCISE: 7.91

▲ FIGURE 7.8 **Schematic of a lithium ion battery.**

Arrange the ions K^+, Cl^-, Ca^{2+}, and S^{2-} in order of decreasing size.

SOLUTION

This is an isoelectronic series, with all ions having 18 electrons. In such a series, size decreases as nuclear charge (atomic number) increases. The atomic numbers of the ions are S 16, Cl 17, K 19, Ca 20. Thus, the ions decrease in size in the order $S^{2-} > Cl^- > K^+ > Ca^{2+}$.

PRACTICE EXERCISE

In the isoelectronic series Rb^+, Sr^{2+}, Y^{3+}, which ion is largest?
Answer: Rb^+

7.4 | IONIZATION ENERGY

The ease with which electrons can be removed from an atom or ion has a major impact on chemical behavior. The **ionization energy** of an atom or ion is the minimum energy required to remove an electron from the ground state of the isolated gaseous atom or ion. The *first ionization energy*, I_1, is the energy needed to remove the first electron from a neutral atom. For example, the first ionization energy for the sodium atom is the energy required for the process

$$Na(g) \longrightarrow Na^+(g) + e^- \qquad [7.2]$$

The *second ionization energy*, I_2, is the energy needed to remove the second electron, and so forth, for successive removals of additional electrons. Thus, I_2 for the sodium atom is the energy associated with the process

$$Na^+(g) \longrightarrow Na^{2+}(g) + e^- \qquad [7.3]$$

The greater the ionization energy, the more difficult it is to remove an electron.

Variations in Successive Ionization Energies

Notice in ▼ **TABLE 7.2** that ionization energies for a given element increase as successive electrons are removed: $I_1 < I_2 < I_3$, and so forth. This trend exists because with each successive removal, an electron is being pulled away from an increasingly more positive ion, requiring increasingly more energy.

 GIVE IT SOME THOUGHT

Light can be used to ionize atoms and ions. Which of the two processes shown in Equations 7.2 and 7.3 requires shorter-wavelength radiation?

A second important feature shown in Table 7.2 is the sharp increase in ionization energy that occurs when an inner-shell electron is removed. For example, consider silicon, $1s^2 2s^2 2p^6 3s^2 3p^2$. The ionization energies increase steadily from 786 kJ/mol to

TABLE 7.2 • Successive Values of Ionization Energies, *I,* for the Elements Sodium through Argon (kJ/mol)

Element	I_1	I_2	I_3	I_4	I_5	I_6	I_7
Na	496	4562	(inner-shell electrons)				
Mg	738	1451	7733				
Al	578	1817	2745	11,577			
Si	786	1577	3232	4356	16,091		
P	1012	1907	2914	4964	6274	21,267	
S	1000	2252	3357	4556	7004	8496	27,107
Cl	1251	2298	3822	5159	6542	9362	11,018
Ar	1521	2666	3931	5771	7238	8781	11,995

4356 kJ/mol for the four electrons in the $3s$ and $3p$ subshells. Removal of the fifth electron, which comes from the $2p$ subshell, requires a great deal more energy: 16,091 kJ/mol. The large increase occurs because the $2p$ electron is much more likely to be found close to the nucleus than are the four $n = 3$ electrons and, therefore, the $2p$ electron experiences a much greater effective nuclear charge than do the $3s$ and $3p$ electrons.

 GIVE IT SOME THOUGHT

Which would you expect to be greater, I_1 for a boron atom or I_2 for a carbon atom?

Every element exhibits a large increase in ionization energy when one of its inner electrons is removed. This observation supports the idea that only the outermost electrons are involved in the sharing and transfer of electrons that give rise to chemical bonding and reactions. The inner electrons are too tightly bound to the nucleus to be lost from the atom or even shared with another atom.

SAMPLE EXERCISE 7.5 | **Trends in Ionization Energy**

Three elements are indicated in the periodic table in the margin. Which one has the largest second ionization energy?

SOLUTION

Analyze and Plan The locations of the elements in the periodic table allow us to predict the electron configurations. The greatest ionization energies involve removal of core electrons. Thus, we should look first for an element with only one electron in the outermost occupied shell.

Solve The red box represents Na, which has one valence electron. The second ionization energy of this element is associated, therefore, with the removal of a core electron. The other elements indicated, S (green) and Ca (blue), have two or more valence electrons. Thus, Na should have the largest second ionization energy.

Check A chemistry handbook gives these I_2 values: Ca 1145 kJ/mol, S 2252 kJ/mol, Na 4562 kJ/mol.

PRACTICE EXERCISE

Which has the greater third ionization energy, Ca or S?

Answer: Ca

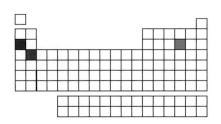

Periodic Trends in First Ionization Energies

▶ FIGURE 7.9 shows, for the first 54 elements, the trends we observe in first ionization energy as we move from one element to another in the periodic table. The important trends are as follows:

1. I_1 generally increases as we move across a period. The alkali metals show the lowest ionization energy in each period, and the noble gases show the highest. There are slight irregularities in this trend that we will discuss shortly.

2. I_1 generally decreases as we move down any column in the periodic table. For example, the ionization energies of the noble gases follow the order He > Ne > Ar > Kr > Xe.

3. The s- and p-block elements show a larger range of I_1 values than do the transition-metal elements. Generally, the ionization energies of the transition metals increase slowly from left to right in a period. The f-block metals (not shown in Figure 7.9) also show only a small variation in the values of I_1.

In general, smaller atoms have higher ionization energies. The same factors that influence atomic size also influence ionization energies. The energy needed to remove an electron from the outermost occupied shell depends on both the effective nuclear charge and the average distance of the electron from the nucleus. Either increasing the effective nuclear charge or decreasing the distance from the nucleus increases the attraction

GO FIGURE

Which has a larger first ionization energy, Ar or As? Why?

▲ FIGURE 7.9   **Trends in first ionization energies of the elements.**

between the electron and the nucleus. As this attraction increases, it becomes more difficult to remove the electron and, thus, the ionization energy increases. As we move across a period, there is both an increase in effective nuclear charge and a decrease in atomic radius, causing the ionization energy to increase. As we move down a column, the atomic radius increases while the effective nuclear charge increases rather gradually. Thus, the attraction between the nucleus and the electron decreases, causing the ionization energy to decrease.

The irregularities in a given period are subtle but still readily explained. For example, the decrease in ionization energy from beryllium ($[He]2s^2$) to boron ($[He]2s^2 2p^1$), shown in Figure 7.9, occurs because the third valence electron of B must occupy the $2p$ subshell, which is empty for Be. Recall that the $2p$ subshell is at a higher energy than the $2s$ subshell (Figure 6.24). The decrease in ionization energy when moving from nitrogen ($[He]2s^2 2p^3$) to oxygen ($[He]2s^2 2p^4$) is because of the repulsion of paired electrons in the p^4 configuration (▶ FIGURE 7.10). Remember that according to Hund's rule, each electron in the p^3 configuration resides in a different p orbital, which minimizes the electron–electron repulsion among the three $2p$ electrons. ∞ (Section 6.8)

GO FIGURE

Explain why it is easier to remove a 2p electron from an oxygen atom than from a nitrogen atom.

▲ FIGURE 7.10   **2p orbital filling in nitrogen and oxygen.**

SAMPLE EXERCISE 7.6   Periodic Trends in Ionization Energy

Referring to a periodic table, arrange the atoms Ne, Na, P, Ar, K in order of increasing first ionization energy.

SOLUTION

Analyze and Plan   We are given the chemical symbols for five elements. To rank them according to increasing first ionization energy, we need to locate each element in the periodic table. We can then use their relative positions and the trends in first ionization energies to predict their order.

Solve Ionization energy increases as we move left to right across a period and decreases as we move down a group. Because Na, P, and Ar are in the same period, we expect I_1 to vary in the order Na < P < Ar. Because Ne is above Ar in group 8A, we expect Ar < Ne. Similarly, K is directly below Na in group 1A, and so we expect K < Na.

From these observations, we conclude that the ionization energies follow the order

$$K < Na < P < Ar < Ne$$

Check The values shown in Figure 7.9 confirm this prediction.

PRACTICE EXERCISE
Which has the lowest first ionization energy, B, Al, C, or Si? Which has the highest?
Answer: Al lowest, C highest

Electron Configurations of Ions

When electrons are removed from an atom to form a cation, they are always removed first from the occupied orbitals having the largest principal quantum number, n. For example, when one electron is removed from a lithium atom ($1s^2 2s^1$), it is the $2s^1$ electron:

$$\text{Li } (1s^2 2s^1) \Rightarrow \text{Li}^+ (1s^2) + e^-$$

Likewise, when two electrons are removed from Fe ($[\text{Ar}]3d^6 4s^2$), the $4s^2$ electrons are the ones removed:

$$\text{Fe } ([\text{Ar}]3d^6 4s^2) \Rightarrow \text{Fe}^{2+} ([\text{Ar}]3d^6) + 2e^-$$

If an additional electron is removed, forming Fe^{3+}, it comes from a $3d$ orbital because all the orbitals with $n = 4$ are empty:

$$\text{Fe}^{2+} ([\text{Ar}]3d^6) \Rightarrow \text{Fe}^{3+} ([\text{Ar}]3d^5) + e^-$$

It may seem odd that $4s$ electrons are removed before $3d$ electrons in forming transition-metal cations. After all, in writing electron configurations, we added the $4s$ electrons before the $3d$ ones. In writing electron configurations for atoms, however, we are going through an imaginary process in which we move through the periodic table from one element to another. In doing so, we are adding both an electron to an orbital and a proton to the nucleus to change the identity of the element. In ionization, we do not reverse this process because no protons are being removed.

If there is more than one occupied subshell for a given value of n, the electrons are first removed from the orbital with the highest value of l. For example, a tin atom loses its $5p$ electrons before it loses its $5s$ electrons:

$$\text{Sn } ([\text{Kr}]4d^{10}5s^2 5p^2) \Rightarrow \text{Sn}^{2+} ([\text{Kr}]4d^{10}5s^2) + 2e^- \Rightarrow \text{Sn}^{4+} ([\text{Kr}]4d^{10}) + 4e^-$$

Electrons added to an atom to form an anion are added to the empty or partially filled orbital having the lowest value of n. For example, an electron added to a fluorine atom to form the F^- ion goes into the one remaining vacancy in the $2p$ subshell:

$$\text{F } (1s^2 2s^2 2p^5) + e^- \Rightarrow \text{F}^- (1s^2 2s^2 2p^6)$$

 GIVE IT SOME THOUGHT
Do Cr^{3+} and V^{2+} have the same or different electron configurations?

SAMPLE EXERCISE 7.7 Electron Configurations of Ions

Write the electron configuration for (a) Ca^{2+}, (b) Co^{3+}, and (c) S^{2-}.

SOLUTION

Analyze and Plan We are asked to write electron configurations for three ions. To do so, we first write the electron configuration of each parent atom, then remove or add electrons to form the ions. Electrons are first removed from the orbitals having the highest value of n. They are added to the empty or partially filled orbitals having the lowest value of n.

Solve

(a) Calcium (atomic number 20) has the electron configuration $[Ar]4s^2$. To form a 2+ ion, the two outer electrons must be removed, giving an ion that is isoelectronic with Ar:

$$Ca^{2+}: [Ar]$$

(b) Cobalt (atomic number 27) has the electron configuration $[Ar]3d^74s^2$. To form a 3+ ion, three electrons must be removed. As discussed in the text, the $4s$ electrons are removed before the $3d$ electrons. Consequently, the electron configuration for Co^{3+} is

$$Co^{3+}: [Ar]3d^6$$

(c) Sulfur (atomic number 16) has the electron configuration $[Ne]3s^23p^4$. To form a 2− ion, two electrons must be added. There is room for two additional electrons in the $3p$ orbitals. Thus, the S^{2-} electron configuration is

$$S^{2-}: [Ne]3s^2\,3p^6 = [Ar]$$

Comment Remember that many of the common ions of the s- and p-block elements, such as Ca^{2+} and S^{2-}, have the same number of electrons as the closest noble gas. ∞ (Section 2.7)

PRACTICE EXERCISE
Write the electron configuration for **(a)** Ga^{3+}, **(b)** Cr^{3+}, and **(c)** Br^-.
Answers: **(a)** $[Ar]3d^{10}$, **(b)** $[Ar]3d^3$, **(c)** $[Ar]3d^{10}4s^24p^6 = [Kr]$

7.5 | ELECTRON AFFINITIES

The first ionization energy of an atom is a measure of the energy change associated with removing an electron from the atom to form a cation. For example, the first ionization energy of $Cl(g)$, 1251 kJ/mol, is the energy change associated with the process

$$\text{Ionization energy: } Cl(g) \longrightarrow Cl^+(g) + e^- \quad \Delta E = 1251 \text{ kJ/mol} \qquad [7.4]$$
$$[Ne]3s^23p^5 \quad [Ne]3s^23p^4$$

The positive ionization energy means that energy must be put into the atom to remove the electron.

Most atoms can also gain electrons to form anions. The energy change that occurs when an electron is added to a gaseous atom is called the **electron affinity** because it measures the attraction, or *affinity,* of the atom for the added electron. For most atoms, energy is released when an electron is added. For example, the addition of an electron to a chlorine atom is accompanied by an energy change of −349 kJ/mol, the negative sign indicating that energy is released during the process. We therefore say that the electron affinity of Cl is −349 kJ/mol.*

$$\text{Electron affinity: } Cl(g) + e^- \longrightarrow Cl^-(g) \quad \Delta E = -349 \text{ kJ/mol} \qquad [7.5]$$
$$[Ne]3s^23p^5 \quad [Ne]3s^23p^6$$

It is important to understand the difference between ionization energy and electron affinity: Ionization energy measures the ease with which an atom *loses* an electron, whereas electron affinity measures the ease with which an atom *gains* an electron.

The greater the attraction between an atom and an added electron, the more negative the atom's electron affinity. For some elements, such as the noble gases, the electron affinity has a positive value, meaning that the anion is higher in energy than are the separated atom and electron:

$$Ar(g) + e^- \longrightarrow Ar^-(g) \quad \Delta E > 0 \qquad [7.6]$$
$$[Ne]3s^23p^6 \quad [Ne]3s^23p^64s^1$$

---

*Two sign conventions are used for electron affinity. In most introductory texts, including this one, the thermodynamic sign convention is used: A negative sign indicates that addition of an electron is an exothermic process, as in the electron affinity for chlorine, −349 kJ/mol. Historically, however, electron affinity has been defined as the energy released when an electron is added to a gaseous atom or ion. Because 349 kJ/mol is released when an electron is added to $Cl(g)$, the electron affinity by this convention would be +349 kJ/mol.

GO FIGURE

Which of the groups shown here has the most negative electron affinities? Why does this make sense?

1A							8A
H −73	2A	3A 4A 5A 6A 7A					**He** > 0
Li −60	**Be** > 0	**B** −27	**C** −122	**N** > 0	**O** −141	**F** −328	**Ne** > 0
Na −53	**Mg** > 0	**Al** −43	**Si** −134	**P** −72	**S** −200	**Cl** −349	**Ar** > 0
K −48	**Ca** −2	**Ga** −30	**Ge** −119	**As** −78	**Se** −195	**Br** −325	**Kr** > 0
Rb −47	**Sr** −5	**In** −30	**Sn** −107	**Sb** −103	**Te** −190	**I** −295	**Xe** > 0

▲ **FIGURE 7.11** **Electron affinity in kJ/mol for selected *s*- and *p*-block elements.**

The fact that the electron affinity is positive means that an electron will not attach itself to an Ar atom; the Ar⁻ ion is unstable and does not form.

◄ **FIGURE 7.11** shows the electron affinities for the *s*- and *p*-block elements of the first five periods. Notice that the trends are not as evident as they are for ionization energy. The halogens, which are one electron shy of a filled *p* subshell, have the most-negative electron affinities. By gaining an electron, a halogen atom forms a stable anion that has a noble-gas configuration (Equation 7.5). The addition of an electron to a noble gas, however, requires that the electron reside in a higher-energy subshell that is empty in the atom (Equation 7.6). Because occupying a higher-energy subshell is energetically unfavorable, the electron affinity is highly positive. The electron affinities of Be and Mg are positive for the same reason; the added electron would reside in a previously empty *p* subshell that is higher in energy.

The electron affinities of the group 5A elements are also interesting. Because these elements have half-filled *p* subshells, the added electron must be put in an orbital that is already occupied, resulting in larger electron–electron repulsions. Consequently, these elements have electron affinities that are either positive (N) or less negative than the electron affinities of their neighbors to the left (P, As, Sb). Recall that in Section 7.4 we saw a discontinuity in the trends for first ionization energy for the same reason.

Electron affinities do not change greatly as we move down a group (Figure 7.11). For F, for instance, the added electron goes into a 2*p* orbital, for Cl a 3*p* orbital, for Br a 4*p* orbital, and so forth. As we proceed from F to I, therefore, the average distance between the added electron and the nucleus steadily increases, causing the electron–nucleus attraction to decrease. However, the orbital that holds the outermost electron is increasingly spread out, so that as we proceed from F to I, the electron–electron repulsions are also reduced. As a result, the reduction in the electron–nucleus attraction is counterbalanced by the reduction in electron–electron repulsions.

 GIVE IT SOME THOUGHT

What is the relationship between the value for the first ionization energy of a Cl⁻(*g*) ion and the electron affinity of Cl(*g*)?

7.6 | METALS, NONMETALS, AND METALLOIDS

Atomic radii, ionization energies, and electron affinities are properties of individual atoms. With the exception of the noble gases, however, none of the elements exist in nature as individual atoms. To get a broader understanding of the properties of elements, we must also examine periodic trends in properties that involve large collections of atoms.

The elements can be broadly grouped as metals, nonmetals, and metalloids (► **FIGURE 7.12**). ∞ (Section 2.5) Some of the distinguishing properties of metals and nonmetals are summarized in ▼ **TABLE 7.3**.

In the following sections, we explore some common patterns of reactivity across the periodic table. We will examine reactivity for nonmetals and metals in more depth in later chapters.

TABLE 7.3 • Characteristic Properties of Metals and Nonmetals

Metals	Nonmetals
Have a shiny luster; various colors, although most are silvery	Do not have a luster; various colors
Solids are malleable and ductile	Solids are usually brittle; some are hard, some are soft
Good conductors of heat and electricity	Poor conductors of heat and electricity
Most metal oxides are ionic solids that are basic	Most nonmetal oxides are molecular substances that form acidic solutions
Tend to form cations in aqueous solution	Tend to form anions or oxyanions in aqueous solution

Notice that germanium, Ge, is a metalloid but tin, Sn, is a metal. What changes in atomic properties do you think are important in explaining this difference?

Increasing metallic character ←

1A 1																	8A 18
1 **H**	2A 2											3A 13	4A 14	5A 15	6A 16	7A 17	2 **He**
3 **Li**	4 **Be**											5 **B**	6 **C**	7 **N**	8 **O**	9 **F**	10 **Ne**
11 **Na**	12 **Mg**	3B 3	4B 4	5B 5	6B 6	7B 7	8	8B 9	10	1B 11	2B 12	13 **Al**	14 **Si**	15 **P**	16 **S**	17 **Cl**	18 **Ar**
19 **K**	20 **Ca**	21 **Sc**	22 **Ti**	23 **V**	24 **Cr**	25 **Mn**	26 **Fe**	27 **Co**	28 **Ni**	29 **Cu**	30 **Zn**	31 **Ga**	32 **Ge**	33 **As**	34 **Se**	35 **Br**	36 **Kr**
37 **Rb**	38 **Sr**	39 **Y**	40 **Zr**	41 **Nb**	42 **Mo**	43 **Tc**	44 **Ru**	45 **Rh**	46 **Pd**	47 **Ag**	48 **Cd**	49 **In**	50 **Sn**	51 **Sb**	52 **Te**	53 **I**	54 **Xe**
55 **Cs**	56 **Ba**	71 **Lu**	72 **Hf**	73 **Ta**	74 **W**	75 **Re**	76 **Os**	77 **Ir**	78 **Pt**	79 **Au**	80 **Hg**	81 **Tl**	82 **Pb**	83 **Bi**	84 **Po**	85 **At**	86 **Rn**
87 **Fr**	88 **Ra**	103 **Lr**	104 **Rf**	105 **Db**	106 **Sg**	107 **Bh**	108 **Hs**	109 **Mt**	110 **Ds**	111 **Rg**	112 **Cp**	113	114	115	116	117	118

↓ Increasing metallic character

	57 **La**	58 **Ce**	59 **Pr**	60 **Nd**	61 **Pm**	62 **Sm**	63 **Eu**	64 **Gd**	65 **Tb**	66 **Dy**	67 **Ho**	68 **Er**	69 **Tm**	70 **Yb**
	89 **Ac**	90 **Th**	91 **Pa**	92 **U**	93 **Np**	94 **Pu**	95 **Am**	96 **Cm**	97 **Bk**	98 **Cf**	99 **Es**	100 **Fm**	101 **Md**	102 **No**

☐ Metals
☐ Metalloids
☐ Nonmetals

▲ **FIGURE 7.12**   **Metals, metalloids, and nonmetals.**

The more an element exhibits the physical and chemical properties of metals, the greater its **metallic character**. As indicated in Figure 7.12, metallic character generally increases as we proceed down a group of the periodic table and decreases as we proceed right across a period. Let's now examine the close relationships that exist between electron configurations and the properties of metals, nonmetals, and metalloids.

Metals

Most metallic elements exhibit the shiny luster we associate with metals (▶ **FIGURE 7.13**). Metals conduct heat and electricity. In general they are malleable (can be pounded into thin sheets) and ductile (can be drawn into wires). All are solids at room temperature except mercury (melting point $= -39\ °C$), which is a liquid at room temperature. Two metals melt at slightly above room temperature, cesium at $28.4\ °C$ and gallium at $29.8\ °C$. At the other extreme, many metals melt at very high temperatures. For example, chromium melts at $1900\ °C$.

Metals tend to have low ionization energies (Figure 7.9) *and therefore tend to form cations relatively easily.* As a result, metals are oxidized (lose electrons) when they undergo chemical reactions. Among the fundamental atomic properties (radius, electron configuration, electron affinity, and so forth), first ionization energy is the best indicator of whether an element behaves as a metal or a nonmetal.

▶ **FIGURE 7.14** shows the oxidation states of representative ions of metals and nonmetals. As noted in Section 2.7, the charge on any alkali metal ion in a compound is always 1+, and that on any alkaline earth metal is always 2+. For atoms belonging to either of these groups, the outer s electrons are easily lost, yielding a noble-gas electron configuration. For metals belonging to groups with partially occupied p orbitals (groups 3A–7A), cations are formed either by losing only the outer p electrons (such as Sn^{2+}) or the outer s and p electrons (such as Sn^{4+}). The charge on transition-metal ions does not follow an obvious pattern. One characteristic of the transition metals is their ability to form more than one cation. For example, iron is 2+ in some compounds and 3+ in others.

▲ **FIGURE 7.13**   **Metals are shiny and malleable.**

Describe a general relationship between trends in metallic character and trends in ionization energy.

GO FIGURE

The red stepped line divides metals from nonmetals. How are common oxidation states divided by this line?

1A																7A	8A
H^+	2A											3A	4A	5A	6A	H^-	N O B L E G A S E S
Li^+														N^{3-}	O^{2-}	F^-	
Na^+	Mg^{2+}				Transition metals							Al^{3+}		P^{3-}	S^{2-}	Cl^-	
K^+	Ca^{2+}	Sc^{3+}	Ti^{4+}	V^{5+} V^{4+}	Cr^{3+}	Mn^{2+} Mn^{4+}	Fe^{2+} Fe^{3+}	Co^{2+} Co^{3+}	Ni^{2+}	Cu^+ Cu^{2+}	Zn^{2+}				Se^{2-}	Br^-	
Rb^+	Sr^{2+}								Pd^{2+}	Ag^+	Cd^{2+}	Sn^{2+} Sn^{4+}	Sb^{3+} Sb^{5+}	Te^{2-}		I^-	
Cs^+	Ba^{2+}								Pt^{2+}	Au^+ Au^{3+}	Hg_2^{2+} Hg^{2+}	Pb^{2+} Pb^{4+}	Bi^{3+} Bi^{5+}				

▲ **FIGURE 7.14   Representative oxidation states of the elements.** Note that hydrogen has both positive and negative oxidation numbers, +1 and −1.

Compounds made up of a metal and a nonmetal tend to be ionic substances. For example, most metal oxides and halides are ionic solids. To illustrate, the reaction between nickel metal and oxygen produces nickel oxide, an ionic solid containing Ni^{2+} and O^{2-} ions:

$$2\ Ni(s) + O_2(g) \longrightarrow 2\ NiO(s) \qquad [7.7]$$

The oxides are particularly important because of the great abundance of oxygen in our environment.

Most metal oxides are basic. Those that dissolve in water react to form metal hydroxides, as in the following examples:

$$\text{Metal oxide} + \text{water} \longrightarrow \text{metal hydroxide}$$

$$Na_2O(s) + H_2O(l) \longrightarrow 2\ NaOH(aq) \qquad [7.8]$$

$$CaO(s) + H_2O(l) \longrightarrow Ca(OH)_2(aq) \qquad [7.9]$$

The basicity of metal oxides is due to the oxide ion, which reacts with water:

$$O^{2-}(aq) + H_2O(l) \longrightarrow 2\ OH^-(aq) \qquad [7.10]$$

Even metal oxides that are insoluble in water demonstrate their basicity by reacting with acids to form a salt plus water, as illustrated in ▼ **FIGURE 7.15**:

$$\text{Metal oxide} + \text{acid} \longrightarrow \text{salt} + \text{water}$$

$$NiO(s) + 2\ HNO_3(aq) \longrightarrow Ni(NO_3)_2(aq) + H_2O(l) \qquad [7.11]$$

► **FIGURE 7.15   Metal oxides react with acids.** NiO does not dissolve in water but does react with nitric acid (HNO_3) to give a green solution of $Ni(NO_3)_2$.

Nickle oxide (NiO), nitric acid (HNO_3), and water

NiO is insoluble in water but reacts with HNO_3 to give a green solution of the salt $Ni(NO_3)_2$

SAMPLE EXERCISE 7.8 **Metal Oxides**

(a) Would you expect scandium oxide to be a solid, liquid, or gas at room temperature?
(b) Write the balanced chemical equation for the reaction of scandium oxide with nitric acid.

SOLUTION

Analyze and Plan We are asked about one physical property of scandium oxide—its state at room temperature—and one chemical property—how it reacts with nitric acid.

Solve

(a) Because scandium oxide is the oxide of a metal, we expect it to be an ionic solid. Indeed it is, with the very high melting point of 2485 °C.

(b) In compounds, scandium has a 3+ charge, Sc^{3+}, and the oxide ion is O^{2-}. Consequently, the formula of scandium oxide is Sc_2O_3. Metal oxides tend to be basic and, therefore, to react with acids to form a salt plus water. In this case the salt is scandium nitrate, $Sc(NO_3)_3$:

$$Sc_2O_3(s) + 6\,HNO_3(aq) \longrightarrow 2\,Sc(NO_3)_3(aq) + 3\,H_2O(l)$$

PRACTICE EXERCISE

Write the balanced chemical equation for the reaction between copper(II) oxide and sulfuric acid.

Answer: $CuO(s) + H_2SO_4(aq) \longrightarrow CuSO_4(aq) + H_2O(l)$

Nonmetals

Nonmetals can be solid, liquid, or gas. They are not lustrous and generally are poor conductors of heat and electricity. Their melting points are generally lower than those of metals (although diamond, a form of carbon, is an exception and melts at 3570 °C). Under ordinary conditions, seven nonmetals exist as diatomic molecules. Five of these are gases (H_2, N_2, O_2, F_2, and Cl_2), one is a liquid (Br_2), and one is a volatile solid (I_2). Excluding the noble gases, the remaining nonmetals are solids that can be either hard, such as diamond, or soft, such as sulfur (▶ **FIGURE 7.16**).

Because of their relatively large, negative electron affinities, nonmetals tend to gain electrons when they react with metals. For example, the reaction of aluminum with bromine produces the ionic compound aluminum bromide:

$$2\,Al(s) + 3\,Br_2(l) \longrightarrow 2\,AlBr_3(s) \qquad [7.12]$$

A nonmetal typically will gain enough electrons to fill its outermost occupied p subshell, giving a noble-gas electron configuration. For example, the bromine atom gains one electron to fill its $4p$ subshell:

$$Br\,([Ar]4s^23d^{10}4p^5) + e^- \Longrightarrow Br^-\,([Ar]4s^23d^{10}4p^6)$$

Compounds composed entirely of nonmetals are typically molecular substances that tend to be gases, liquids, or low-melting solids at room temperature. Examples include the common hydrocarbons we use for fuel (methane, CH_4; propane, C_3H_8; octane, C_8H_{18}) and the gases HCl, NH_3, and H_2S. Many drugs are molecules composed of C, H, N, O, and other nonmetals. For example, the molecular formula for the drug Celebrex is $C_{17}H_{14}F_3N_3O_2S$. *Most nonmetal oxides are acidic,* which means that those that dissolve in water form acids:

$$\text{Nonmetal oxide} + \text{water} \longrightarrow \text{acid}$$

$$CO_2(g) + H_2O(l) \longrightarrow H_2CO_3(aq) \qquad [7.13]$$

$$P_4O_{10}(s) + 6\,H_2O(l) \longrightarrow 4\,H_3PO_4(aq) \qquad [7.14]$$

The reaction of carbon dioxide with water (▶ **FIGURE 7.17**) accounts for the acidity of carbonated water and, to some extent, rainwater. Because sulfur is present in oil and coal, combustion of these common fuels produces sulfur dioxide and sulfur trioxide. These

▲ **FIGURE 7.16** **Sulfur, known to the medieval world as "brimstone," is a nonmetal.**

▲ **FIGURE 7.17** **The reaction of CO_2 with water containing a bromthymol blue indicator.** Initially, the blue color tells us the water is slightly basic. When a piece of solid carbon dioxide ("dry ice") is added, the color changes to yellow, indicating an acidic solution. The mist is water droplets condensed from the air by the cold CO_2 gas.

substances dissolve in water to produce *acid rain*, a major pollutant in many parts of the world. Like acids, most nonmetal oxides dissolve in basic solutions to form a salt plus water:

$$\text{Nonmetal oxide} + \text{base} \longrightarrow \text{salt} + \text{water}$$

$$CO_2(g) + 2\,NaOH(aq) \longrightarrow Na_2CO_3(aq) + H_2O(l) \qquad [7.15]$$

 GIVE IT SOME THOUGHT

A compound ACl_3 (A is an element) has a melting point of -112 °C. Would you expect the compound to be molecular or ionic? If you were told that A is either scandium or phosphorus, which do you think is the more likely choice?

SAMPLE EXERCISE 7.9   **Nonmetal Oxides**

Write the balanced chemical equation for the reaction of solid selenium dioxide, $SeO_2(s)$, with **(a)** water, **(b)** aqueous sodium hydroxide.

SOLUTION

Analyze and Plan We note that selenium is a nonmetal. We therefore need to write chemical equations for the reaction of a nonmetal oxide with water and with a base, NaOH. Nonmetal oxides are acidic, reacting with water to form an acid and with bases to form a salt and water.

Solve

(a) The reaction between selenium dioxide and water is like that between carbon dioxide and water (Equation 7.13):

$$SeO_2(s) + H_2O(l) \longrightarrow H_2SeO_3(aq)$$

(It does not matter that SeO_2 is a solid and CO_2 is a gas under ambient conditions; the point is that both are water-soluble nonmetal oxides.)

(b) The reaction with sodium hydroxide is like the reaction in Equation 7.15:

$$SeO_2(s) + 2\,NaOH(aq) \longrightarrow Na_2SeO_3(aq) + H_2O(l)$$

PRACTICE EXERCISE

Write the balanced chemical equation for the reaction of solid tetraphosphorus hexoxide with water.

Answer: $P_4O_6(s) + 6\,H_2O(l) \longrightarrow 4\,H_3PO_3(aq)$

Metalloids

Metalloids have properties intermediate between those of metals and those of nonmetals. They may have some characteristic metallic properties but lack others. For example, the metalloid silicon *looks* like a metal (◄ **FIGURE 7.18**), but it is brittle rather than malleable and does not conduct heat or electricity nearly as well as metals do. Compounds of metalloids can have characteristics of the compounds of metals or nonmetals.

Several metalloids, most notably silicon, are electrical semiconductors and are the principal elements used in integrated circuits and computer chips. One of the reasons metalloids can be used for integrated circuits is that their electrical conductivity is intermediate between that of metals and that of nonmetals. Very pure silicon is an electrical insulator, but its conductivity can be dramatically increased with the addition of specific impurities called *dopants*. This modification provides a mechanism for controlling the electrical conductivity by controlling the chemical composition. We will return to this point in Chapter 12.

▲ **FIGURE 7.18 Elemental silicon.** Although it looks metallic, silicon, a metalloid, is brittle and a poor thermal and electrical conductor.

7.7 | TRENDS FOR GROUP 1A AND GROUP 2A METALS

As we have seen, elements in a given group possess general similarities. However, trends also exist within each group. In this section we use the periodic table and our knowledge of electron configurations to examine the chemistry of the **alkali metals** and **alkaline earth metals**.

TABLE 7.4 • Some Properties of the Alkali Metals

Element	Electron Configuration	Melting Point (°C)	Density (g/cm³)	Atomic Radius (Å)	I_1 (kJ/mol)
Lithium	$[He]2s^1$	181	0.53	1.34	520
Sodium	$[Ne]3s^1$	98	0.97	1.54	496
Potassium	$[Ar]4s^1$	63	0.86	1.96	419
Rubidium	$[Kr]5s^1$	39	1.53	2.11	403
Cesium	$[Xe]6s^1$	28	1.88	2.25	376

Group 1A: The Alkali Metals

The alkali metals are soft metallic solids (▶ **FIGURE 7.19**). All have characteristic metallic properties, such as a silvery, metallic luster and high thermal and electrical conductivity. The name *alkali* comes from an Arabic word meaning "ashes." Many compounds of sodium and potassium, two alkali metals, were isolated from wood ashes by early chemists.

As ▲ **TABLE 7.4** shows, the alkali metals have low densities and melting points, and these properties vary in a fairly regular way with increasing atomic number. We see the usual trends as we move down the group, such as increasing atomic radius and decreasing first ionization energy. The alkali metal of any given period has the lowest I_1 value in the period (Figure 7.9), which reflects the relative ease with which its outer *s* electron can be removed. As a result, the alkali metals are all very reactive, readily losing one electron to form ions carrying a 1+ charge. ∞ (Section 2.7)

The alkali metals exist in nature only as compounds. Sodium and potassium are relatively abundant in Earth's crust, in seawater, and in biological systems, usually as the cations of ionic compounds. All alkali metals combine directly with most nonmetals. For example, they react with hydrogen to form hydrides and with sulfur to form sulfides:

$$2\,M(s) \;+\; H_2(g) \longrightarrow 2\,MH(s) \qquad [7.16]$$

$$2\,M(s) \;+\; S(s) \longrightarrow M_2S(s) \qquad [7.17]$$

where M represents any alkali metal. In hydrides of the alkali metals (LiH, NaH, and so forth), hydrogen is present as H^-, the **hydride ion**. A hydrogen atom that has *gained* an electron, this ion is distinct from the hydrogen ion, H^+, formed when a hydrogen atom *loses* its electron.

The alkali metals react vigorously with water, producing hydrogen gas and a solution of an alkali metal hydroxide:

$$2\,M(s) \;+\; 2\,H_2O(l) \longrightarrow 2\,MOH(aq) \;+\; H_2(g) \qquad [7.18]$$

These reactions are very exothermic. In many cases enough heat is generated to ignite the H_2, producing a fire or sometimes even an explosion (▼ **FIGURE 7.20**). The reaction is most violent for the heavier alkali metals, in keeping with their lower ionization energies.

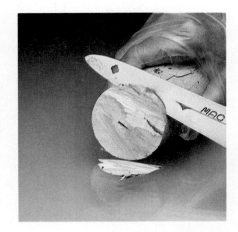

▲ **FIGURE 7.19   Sodium, like the other alkali metals, is soft enough to be cut with a knife.**

Li

Na

K

◀ **FIGURE 7.20   The alkali metals react vigorously with water.**

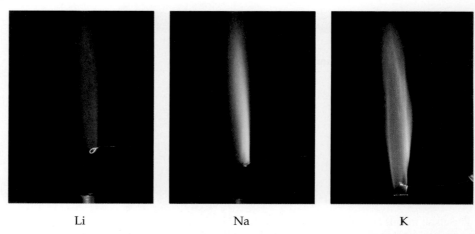

Li   Na   K

▲ **FIGURE 7.21**   **Placed in a flame, ions of each alkali metal emit light of a characteristic wavelength.**

GO FIGURE

If we had potassium vapor lamps, what color would they be?

▲ **FIGURE 7.22**   **The characteristic yellow light in a sodium lamp is the result of electrons in the high-energy 3p orbital falling back to the lower-energy 3s orbital.** The energy gap corresponds to the energy of yellow light.

The reactions between the alkali metals and oxygen are complex. Metal oxides, which contain the O^{2-} ion, are usually formed:

$$4\,Li(s) + O_2(g) \longrightarrow 2\,Li_2O(s) \underset{\text{lithium oxide}}{} \qquad [7.19]$$

When dissolved in water, Li_2O and other soluble metal oxides form hydroxide ions from the reaction of O^{2-} ions with H_2O (Equation 7.10). In contrast, the other alkali metals react with oxygen to form metal *peroxides*, which contain the O_2^{2-} ion:

$$2\,Na(s) + O_2(g) \longrightarrow Na_2O_2(s) \underset{\text{sodium peroxide}}{} \qquad [7.20]$$

Potassium, rubidium, and cesium also form compounds that contain the O_2^- ion, which we call the *superoxide ion*. For example, potassium forms potassium superoxide, KO_2:

$$K(s) + O_2(g) \longrightarrow KO_2(s) \underset{\text{potassium superoxide}}{} \qquad [7.21]$$

Be aware that the reactions in Equations 7.20 and 7.21 are somewhat surprising; in most cases, the reaction of oxygen with a metal forms the metal oxide.

As is evident from Equations 7.18 through 7.21, the alkali metals are extremely reactive toward water and oxygen. Because of this, the metals are usually stored submerged in a liquid hydrocarbon, such as mineral oil or kerosene.

Although alkali metal ions are colorless, each emits a characteristic color when placed in a flame (▲ **FIGURE 7.21**). The ions are reduced to gaseous metal atoms in the flame. The high temperature excites the valence electron from the ground state to a higher-energy orbital, causing the atom to be in an excited state. The atom then emits energy in the form of visible light as the electron falls back into the lower-energy orbital and the atom returns to its ground state. The light emitted is at a specific wavelength for each element, just as we saw earlier for line spectra of hydrogen and sodium ∞ (Section 6.3). The characteristic yellow emission of sodium at 589 nm is the basis for sodium vapor lamps (◄ **FIGURE 7.22**).

GIVE IT SOME THOUGHT

Cesium tends to be the most reactive of the stable alkali metals (francium, Fr, is radioactive and has not been extensively studied). What *atomic* property of Cs is most responsible for its high reactivity?

| SAMPLE EXERCISE 7.10 | Reactions of an Alkali Metal |

Write a balanced equation for the reaction of cesium metal with (a) $Cl_2(g)$, (b) $H_2O(l)$, (c) $H_2(g)$.

SOLUTION

Analyze and Plan Because cesium is an alkali metal, we expect its chemistry to be dominated by oxidation of the metal to Cs^+ ions. Further, we recognize that Cs is far down the periodic table, which means it is among the most active of all metals and probably reacts with all three substances.

Solve The reaction between Cs and Cl_2 is a simple combination reaction between a metal and a nonmetal, forming the ionic compound CsCl:

$$2\ Cs(s) + Cl_2(g) \longrightarrow 2\ CsCl(s)$$

From Equations 7.18 and 7.16, we predict the reactions of cesium with water and hydrogen to proceed as follows:

$$2\ Cs(s) + 2\ H_2O(l) \longrightarrow 2\ CsOH(aq) + H_2(g)$$
$$2\ Cs(s) + H_2(g) \longrightarrow 2\ CsH(s)$$

All three reactions are redox reactions where cesium forms a Cs^+ ion. The Cl^-, OH^-, and H^- are all 1– ions, which means the products have 1:1 stoichiometry with Cs^+.

PRACTICE EXERCISE

Write a balanced equation for the reaction between potassium metal and elemental sulfur.

Answer: $2\ K(s) + S(s) \longrightarrow K_2S(s)$

CHEMISTRY AND LIFE

THE IMPROBABLE DEVELOPMENT OF LITHIUM DRUGS

Alkali metal ions tend to play an unexciting role in most chemical reactions. As noted in Section 4.2, all salts of the alkali metal ions are soluble in water, and the ions are spectators in most aqueous reactions (except for those involving the alkali metals in their elemental form, such as in Equations 7.16 through 7.21). However, these ions play an important role in human physiology. Sodium and potassium ions, for example, are major components of blood plasma and intracellular fluid, respectively, with average concentrations of 0.1 M. These electrolytes serve as vital charge carriers in normal cellular function. In contrast, the lithium ion has no known function in normal human physiology. Since the discovery of lithium in 1817, however, people have believed that salts of the element possessed almost mystical healing powers. There were even claims that lithium ions were an ingredient in ancient "fountain of youth" formulas. In 1927, C. L. Grigg began marketing a soft drink that contained lithium. The original unwieldy name of the beverage was "Bib-Label Lithiated Lemon-Lime Soda," which was soon changed to the simpler and more familiar name 7UP® (▶ FIGURE 7.23).

Because of concerns of the Food and Drug Administration, lithium was removed from 7UP® during the early 1950s. At nearly the same time, psychiatrists discovered that the lithium ion has a remarkable therapeutic effect on the mental disorder called *bipolar affective disorder*, or *manic-depressive illness*. Over 1 million Americans suffer from this psychosis, undergoing severe mood swings from deep depression to a manic euphoria. The lithium ion smoothes these mood swings, allowing the bipolar patient to function more effectively in daily life.

The antipsychotic action of Li^+ was discovered by accident in the 1940s by Australian psychiatrist John Cade as he was researching the use of uric acid—a component of urine—to treat manic-depressive illness. He administered the acid to manic laboratory animals in the form of its most soluble salt, lithium urate, and found that many of the manic symptoms seemed to disappear. Later studies showed that uric acid has no role in the therapeutic effects observed; rather, the Li^+ ions were responsible. Because lithium overdose can cause severe side effects in humans, including kidney failure and death, lithium salts were not approved as antipsychotic drugs for humans until 1970. Today Li^+ is usually administered orally in the form of Li_2CO_3, which is the active ingredient in prescription drugs such as Eskalith®. Lithium drugs are effective for about 70% of bipolar patients who take it.

In this age of sophisticated drug design and biotechnology, the simple lithium ion is still the most effective treatment of this destructive psychological disorder. Remarkably, in spite of intensive research, scientists still do not fully understand the biochemical action of lithium that leads to its therapeutic effects. Because of its similarity to Na^+, Li^+ is incorporated into blood plasma, where it can affect the behavior of nerve and muscle cells. Because Li^+ has a smaller radius than Na^+ (Figure 7.7), the way Li^+ interacts with molecules in human cells is different from the way Na^+ interacts with the molecules. Other studies indicate that Li^+ alters the function of certain neurotransmitters, which might lead to its effectiveness as an antipsychotic drug.

▲ FIGURE 7.23 **Lithium no more.** The soft drink 7UP® originally contained a lithium salt that was claimed to give the beverage healthful benefits, including "an abundance of energy, enthusiasm, a clear complexion, lustrous hair, and shining eyes!" The lithium was removed from the beverage in the early 1950s, about the time that the antipsychotic action of Li^+ was discovered.

TABLE 7.5 • Some Properties of the Alkaline Earth Metals

Element	Electron Configuration	Melting Point (°C)	Density (g/cm³)	Atomic Radius (Å)	I_1 (kJ/mol)
Beryllium	$[He]2s^2$	1287	1.85	0.90	899
Magnesium	$[Ne]3s^2$	650	1.74	1.30	738
Calcium	$[Ar]4s^2$	842	1.55	1.74	590
Strontium	$[Kr]5s^2$	777	2.63	1.92	549
Barium	$[Xe]6s^2$	727	3.51	1.98	503

▲ FIGURE 7.24 **Elemental calcium reacts with water.**

Group 2A: The Alkaline Earth Metals

Like the alkali metals, the alkaline earth metals are all solids at room temperature and have typical metallic properties (▲ TABLE 7.5). Compared with the alkali metals, the alkaline earth metals are harder and more dense and melt at higher temperatures.

The first ionization energies of the alkaline earth metals are low but not as low as those of the alkali metals. Consequently, the alkaline earth metals are less reactive than their alkali metal neighbors. As noted in Section 7.4, the ease with which the elements lose electrons decreases as we move across a period and increases as we move down a group. Thus, beryllium and magnesium, the lightest alkaline earth metals, are the least reactive.

The trend of increasing reactivity within the group is shown by the way the alkaline earth metals behave in the presence of water. Beryllium does not react with either water or steam, even when heated red-hot. Magnesium reacts slowly with liquid water and more readily with steam:

$$Mg(s) + H_2O(g) \longrightarrow MgO(s) + H_2(g) \qquad [7.22]$$

Calcium and the elements below it react readily with water at room temperature (although more slowly than the alkali metals adjacent to them in the periodic table). The reaction between calcium and water (◄ FIGURE 7.24), for example, is

$$Ca(s) + 2\,H_2O(l) \longrightarrow Ca(OH)_2(aq) + H_2(g) \qquad [7.23]$$

Equations 7.22 and 7.23 illustrate the dominant pattern in the reactivity of the alkaline earth elements: They tend to lose their two outer s electrons and form 2+ ions. For example, magnesium reacts with chlorine at room temperature to form $MgCl_2$ and burns with dazzling brilliance in air to give MgO:

$$Mg(s) + Cl_2(g) \longrightarrow MgCl_2(s) \qquad [7.24]$$
$$2\,Mg(s) + O_2(g) \longrightarrow 2\,MgO(s) \qquad [7.25]$$

In the presence of O_2, magnesium metal is protected by a thin coating of water-insoluble MgO. Thus, even though Mg is high in the activity series ∞ (Section 4.4), it can be incorporated into lightweight structural alloys used in, for example, automobile wheels. The heavier alkaline earth metals (Ca, Sr, and Ba) are even more reactive toward nonmetals than is magnesium.

The heavier alkaline earth ions give off characteristic colors when heated in a hot flame. Strontium salts produce the brilliant red color in fireworks, and barium salts produce the green color.

Like their neighbors sodium and potassium, magnesium and calcium are relatively abundant on Earth and in seawater and are essential for living organisms as cations in ionic compounds. Calcium is particularly important for growth and maintenance of bones and teeth.

GIVE IT SOME THOUGHT

Calcium carbonate, $CaCO_3$, is often used as a dietary calcium supplement for bone health. Although $CaCO_3(s)$ is insoluble in water (Table 4.1), it can be taken orally to allow for the delivery of $Ca^{2+}(aq)$ ions to the musculoskeletal system. Why is this the case? [*Hint:* Recall the reactions of metal carbonates discussed in Section 4.3.]

7.8 | TRENDS FOR SELECTED NONMETALS

Hydrogen

Because hydrogen has the electron configuration $1s^1$, its usual position in the periodic table is above the alkali metals. However, hydrogen does not truly belong to any particular group. Unlike the alkali metals, it is a nonmetal that occurs as a colorless diatomic gas, $H_2(g)$, under most conditions.

Owing to the complete absence of nuclear screening of its sole electron, the ionization energy of hydrogen, 1312 kJ/mol, is more than double that of any of the alkali metals. In fact, hydrogen's ionization energy is comparable to the I_1 values of other nonmetals, such as oxygen and chlorine. As a result, hydrogen does not lose its valence electron as easily as do the alkali metals. Instead, hydrogen shares its electron with nonmetals and thereby forms molecular compounds. Reactions between hydrogen and another nonmetal can be quite exothermic, as evidenced by the combustion reaction between hydrogen and oxygen to form water:

$$2\,H_2(g) + O_2(g) \longrightarrow 2\,H_2O(l) \qquad \Delta H° = -571.7\text{ kJ} \qquad [7.26]$$

We saw in Equation 7.16 that hydrogen reacts with active metals to form solid metal hydrides that contain the hydride ion, H^-. The fact that hydrogen can gain an electron further illustrates that it is not truly an alkali metal. In fact, in terms of chemical reactivity, hydrogen has more in common with the halogens than with the alkali metals.

In addition to its ability to form covalent bonds and metal hydrides, probably the most important characteristic of hydrogen is its ability to lose its electron to form a cation. Indeed, the aqueous chemistry of hydrogen is dominated by the $H^+(aq)$ ion. ∞ (Section 4.1)

Group 6A: The Oxygen Group

As we proceed down group 6A, there is a change from nonmetallic to metallic character (Figure 7.12). Oxygen, sulfur, and selenium are typical nonmetals. Tellurium is a metalloid, and polonium, which is radioactive and quite rare, is a metal. Oxygen is a colorless gas at room temperature; all of the other members of group 6A are solids. Some of the physical properties of the group 6A elements are given in ▼ TABLE 7.6.

As we saw in Section 2.6, oxygen is encountered in two molecular forms, O_2 and O_3. Because O_2 is the more common form, people generally mean it when they say "oxygen," although the name *dioxygen* is more descriptive. The O_3 form is **ozone**. The two forms of oxygen are examples of *allotropes*, defined as different forms of the same element in the same state. (In this case both forms are gases.) About 21% of dry air consists of O_2 molecules. Ozone is present in very small amounts in the upper atmosphere and in polluted air. It is also formed from O_2 in electrical discharges, such as in lightning storms:

$$3\,O_2(g) \longrightarrow 2\,O_3(g) \qquad \Delta H° = 284.6\text{ kJ} \qquad [7.27]$$

This reaction is strongly endothermic, telling us that O_3 is less stable than O_2.

Although both O_2 and O_3 are colorless and therefore do not absorb visible light, O_3 absorbs certain wavelengths of ultraviolet light that O_2 does not. Because of this difference, the presence of ozone in the upper atmosphere is beneficial, filtering out harmful

TABLE 7.6 • Some Properties of the Group 6A Elements

Element	Electron Configuration	Melting Point (°C)	Density	Atomic Radius (Å)	I_1 (kJ/mol)
Oxygen	$[He]2s^2 2p^4$	−218	1.43 g/L	0.73	1314
Sulfur	$[Ne]3s^2 3p^4$	115	1.96 g/cm³	1.02	1000
Selenium	$[Ar]3d^{10}4s^2 4p^4$	221	4.82 g/cm³	1.16	941
Tellurium	$[Kr]4d^{10}5s^2 5p^4$	450	6.24 g/cm³	1.35	869
Polonium	$[Xe]4f^{14}5d^{10}6s^2 6p^4$	254	9.20 g/cm³	—	812

UV light. Ozone and oxygen also have different chemical properties. Ozone, which has a pungent odor, is a powerful oxidizing agent. Because of this property, ozone is sometimes added to water to kill bacteria or used in low levels to help to purify air. However, the reactivity of ozone also makes its presence in polluted air near Earth's surface detrimental to human health.

Oxygen has a great tendency to attract electrons from other elements (to *oxidize* them). Oxygen in combination with a metal is almost always present as the oxide ion, O^{2-}. This ion has a noble-gas configuration and is particularly stable. As shown in Equation 7.26, the formation of nonmetal oxides is also often very exothermic and thus energetically favorable.

In our discussion of the alkali metals, we noted two less common oxygen anions— the peroxide (O_2^{2-}) ion and the superoxide (O_2^-) ion. Compounds of these ions often react to produce an oxide and O_2:

$$2\,H_2O_2(aq) \longrightarrow 2\,H_2O(l) + O_2(g) \qquad \Delta H^\circ = -196.1\,\text{kJ} \qquad [7.28]$$

For this reason, bottles of aqueous hydrogen peroxide are topped with caps that are able to release the $O_2(g)$ produced before the pressure inside becomes too great (◀ FIGURE 7.25).

▲ **FIGURE 7.25 Hydrogen peroxide solution in bottle with venting cap.**

▲ **FIGURE 7.26 Elemental sulfur exists as the S_8 molecule.** At room temperature, this is the most common allotropic form of sulfur.

GIVE IT SOME THOUGHT

Hydrogen peroxide is light sensitive and so is stored in brown bottles because its O—O bond is relatively weak. If we assume that the brown bottle absorbs all visible wavelengths of light ∞∞(Section 6.1), how might you estimate the energy of the O—O bond in hydrogen peroxide?

After oxygen, the most important member of group 6A is sulfur. This element exists in several allotropic forms, the most common and stable of which is the yellow solid having the molecular formula S_8. This molecule consists of an eight-membered ring of sulfur atoms (◀ FIGURE 7.26). Even though solid sulfur consists of S_8 rings, we usually write it simply as S(s) in chemical equations to simplify the stoichiometric coefficients.

Like oxygen, sulfur has a tendency to gain electrons from other elements to form sulfides, which contain the S^{2-} ion. In fact, most sulfur in nature is present as metal sulfides. Sulfur is below oxygen in the periodic table, and the tendency of sulfur to form sulfide anions is not as great as that of oxygen to form oxide ions. As a result, the chemistry of sulfur is more complex than that of oxygen. In fact, sulfur and its compounds (including those in coal and petroleum) can be burned in oxygen. The main product is sulfur dioxide, a major air pollutant:

$$S(s) + O_2(g) \longrightarrow SO_2(g) \qquad [7.29]$$

Below sulfur in group 6A is selenium, Se. This relatively rare element is essential for life in trace quantities, although it is toxic at high doses. There are many allotropes of Se, including several eight-membered ring structures that resemble the S_8 ring.

The next element in the group is tellurium, Te. Its elemental structure is even more complex than that of Se, consisting of long, twisted chains of Te—Te bonds. Both Se and Te favor the −2 oxidation state, as do O and S.

From O to S to Se to Te, the elements form larger and larger molecules and become increasingly metallic. The thermal stability of group 6A compounds with hydrogen decreases down the column: $H_2O > H_2S > H_2Se > H_2Te$, with H_2O, water, being the most stable of the series.

Group 7A: The Halogens

Some of the properties of the group 7A elements, the **halogens**, are given in ▶ TABLE 7.7. Astatine, which is both extremely rare and radioactive, is omitted because many of its properties are not yet known.

Unlike the group 6A elements, all the halogens are typical nonmetals. Their melting and boiling points increase with increasing atomic number. Fluorine and chlorine are gases at room temperature, bromine is a liquid, and iodine is a solid. Each element consists of diatomic molecules: F_2, Cl_2, Br_2, and I_2 (▶ FIGURE 7.27).

◀ **FIGURE 7.27** **The elemental halogens exist as diatomic molecules.**

TABLE 7.7 • **Some Properties of the Halogens**

Element	Electron Configuration	Melting Point (°C)	Density	Atomic Radius (Å)	I_1 (kJ/mol)
Fluorine	$[He]2s^2 2p^5$	−220	1.69 g/L	0.71	1681
Chlorine	$[Ne]3s^2 3p^5$	−102	3.12 g/L	0.99	1251
Bromine	$[Ar]3d^{10}4s^2 4p^5$	−7.3	3.12 g/cm³	1.14	1140
Iodine	$[Kr]4d^{10}5s^2 5p^5$	114	4.94 g/cm³	1.33	1008

 GIVE IT SOME THOUGHT

The halogens do not exist as X_8 molecules like sulfur and selenium do. Can you speculate why?

The halogens have highly negative electron affinities (Figure 7.11). Thus, it is not surprising that the chemistry of the halogens is dominated by their tendency to gain electrons from other elements to form halide ions, X^-. (In many equations X is used to indicate any one of the halogen elements.) Fluorine and chlorine are more reactive than bromine and iodine. In fact, fluorine removes electrons from almost any substance with which it comes into contact, including water, and usually does so very exothermically, as in the following examples:

$$2\,H_2O(l) + 2\,F_2(g) \longrightarrow 4\,HF(aq) + O_2(g) \qquad \Delta H = -758.9\,\text{kJ} \qquad [7.30]$$

$$SiO_2(s) + 2\,F_2(g) \longrightarrow SiF_4(g) + O_2(g) \qquad \Delta H = -704.0\,\text{kJ} \qquad [7.31]$$

As a result, fluorine gas is difficult and dangerous to use in the laboratory, requiring specialized equipment.

Chlorine is the most industrially useful of the halogens. In 2008, total production was 21 billion pounds, making it one of the top ten most produced chemicals in the United States ∞ (Section 1.1). Unlike fluorine, chlorine reacts slowly with water to form relatively stable aqueous solutions of HCl and HOCl (hypochlorous acid):

$$Cl_2(g) + H_2O(l) \longrightarrow HCl(aq) + HOCl(aq) \qquad [7.32]$$

Chlorine is often added to drinking water and swimming pools, where the $HOCl(aq)$ that is generated serves as a disinfectant.

The halogens react directly with most metals to form ionic halides. The halogens also react with hydrogen to form gaseous hydrogen halide compounds:

$$H_2(g) + X_2 \longrightarrow 2\,HX(g) \qquad\qquad [7.33]$$

These compounds are all very soluble in water and dissolve to form the hydrohalic acids. As we discussed in Section 4.3, HCl(*aq*), HBr(*aq*), and HI(*aq*) are strong acids, whereas HF(*aq*) is a weak acid.

 GIVE IT SOME THOUGHT

Can you use data in Table 7.7 to provide estimates for the atomic radius and first ionization energy of an astatine atom?

Group 8A: The Noble Gases

The group 8A elements, known as the **noble gases**, are all nonmetals that are gases at room temperature. They are all *monatomic* (that is, they consist of single atoms rather than molecules). Some physical properties of the noble-gas elements are listed in ▼ TABLE 7.8. The high radioactivity of radon (Rn, atomic number 86) has limited the study of its reaction chemistry and some of its properties.

The noble gases have completely filled *s* and *p* subshells. All elements of group 8A have large first ionization energies, and we see the expected decrease as we move down the column. Because the noble gases possess such stable electron configurations, they are exceptionally unreactive. In fact, until the early 1960s the elements were called the *inert gases* because they were thought to be incapable of forming chemical compounds. In 1962, Neil Bartlett at the University of British Columbia reasoned that the ionization energy of Xe might be low enough to allow it to form compounds. In order for this to happen, Xe would have to react with a substance with an extremely high ability to remove electrons from other substances, such as fluorine. Bartlett synthesized the first noble-gas compound by combining Xe with the fluorine-containing compound PtF_6. Xenon also reacts directly with $F_2(g)$ to form the molecular compounds XeF_2, XeF_4, and XeF_6. Krypton has a higher I_1 value than xenon and is therefore less reactive. In fact, only a single stable compound of krypton is known, KrF_2. In 2000, Finnish scientists reported the first neutral molecule that contains argon, the HArF molecule, which is stable only at low temperatures.

TABLE 7.8 • Some Properties of the Noble Gases

Element	Electron Configuration	Boiling Point (K)	Density (g/L)	Atomic Radius* (Å)	I_1 (kJ/mol)
Helium	$1s^2$	4.2	0.18	0.32	2372
Neon	$[He]2s^22p^6$	27.1	0.90	0.69	2081
Argon	$[Ne]3s^23p^6$	87.3	1.78	0.97	1521
Krypton	$[Ar]3d^{10}4s^24p^6$	120	3.75	1.10	1351
Xenon	$[Kr]4d^{10}5s^25p^6$	165	5.90	1.30	1170
Radon	$[Xe]4f^{14}5d^{10}6s^26p^6$	211	9.73	1.45	1037

*Only the heaviest of the noble-gas elements form chemical compounds. Thus, the atomic radii for the lighter noble-gas elements are estimated values.

SAMPLE INTEGRATIVE EXERCISE   Putting Concepts Together

The element bismuth (Bi, atomic number 83) is the heaviest member of group 5A. A salt of the element, bismuth subsalicylate, is the active ingredient in Pepto-Bismol®, an over-the-counter medication for gastric distress.

(a) The bonding atomic radii of thallium (Tl) and lead (Pb) are 1.48 Å and 1.47 Å, respectively. Using these values and those in Figure 7.6, predict the bonding atomic radius of the element bismuth (Bi). Explain your answer.

(b) What accounts for the general increase in atomic radius going down the group 5A elements?

(c) Another major use of bismuth has been as an ingredient in low-melting metal alloys, such as those used in fire sprinkler systems and in typesetting. The element itself is a brittle white crystalline solid. How do these characteristics fit with the fact that bismuth is in the same periodic group with such nonmetallic elements as nitrogen and phosphorus?

(d) Bi_2O_3 is a basic oxide. Write a balanced chemical equation for its reaction with dilute nitric acid. If 6.77 g of Bi_2O_3 is dissolved in dilute acidic solution to make 0.500 L of solution, what is the molarity of the solution of Bi^{3+} ion?

(e) ^{209}Bi is the heaviest stable isotope of any element. How many protons and neutrons are present in this nucleus?

(f) The density of Bi at 25 °C is 9.808 g/cm^3. How many Bi atoms are present in a cube of the element that is 5.00 cm on each edge? How many moles of the element are present?

SOLUTION

(a) Note that there is a gradual decrease in radius of the elements in groups 3A–5A as we proceed across the fifth period, that is, in the series In–Sn–Sb. Therefore, it is reasonable to expect a decrease of about 0.02 Å as we move from Pb to Bi, leading to an estimate of 1.45 Å. The tabulated value is 1.46 Å.

(b) The general increase in radius with increasing atomic number in the group 5A elements occurs because additional shells of electrons are being added, with corresponding increases in nuclear charge. The core electrons in each case largely screen the outermost electrons from the nucleus, so the effective nuclear charge does not vary greatly as we go to higher atomic numbers. However, the principal quantum number, n, of the outermost electrons steadily increases, with a corresponding increase in orbital radius.

(c) The contrast between the properties of bismuth and those of nitrogen and phosphorus illustrates the general rule that there is a trend toward increased metallic character as we move down in a given group. Bismuth, in fact, is a metal. The increased metallic character occurs because the outermost electrons are more readily lost in bonding, a trend that is consistent with its lower ionization energy.

(d) Following the procedures described in Section 4.2 for writing molecular and net ionic equations, we have the following:

Molecular equation: $Bi_2O_3(s) + 6\ HNO_3(aq) \longrightarrow 2\ Bi(NO_3)_3(aq) + 3\ H_2O(l)$

Net ionic equation: $Bi_2O_3(s) + 6\ H^+(aq) \longrightarrow 2\ Bi^{3+}(aq) + 3\ H_2O(l)$

In the net ionic equation, nitric acid is a strong acid and $Bi(NO_3)_3$ is a soluble salt, so we need show only the reaction of the solid with the hydrogen ion forming the $Bi^{3+}(aq)$ ion and water. To calculate the concentration of the solution, we proceed as follows (Section 4.5):

$$\frac{6.77\ g\ Bi_2O_3}{0.500\ L\ soln} \times \frac{1\ mol\ Bi_2O_3}{466.0\ g\ Bi_2O_3} \times \frac{2\ mol\ Bi^{3+}}{1\ mol\ Bi_2O_3} = \frac{0.0581\ mol\ Bi^{3+}}{L\ soln} = 0.0581\ M$$

(e) We can proceed as in Section 2.3. Bismuth is element 83; there are therefore 83 protons in the nucleus. Because the atomic mass number is 209, there are $209 - 83 = 126$ neutrons in the nucleus.

(f) We proceed as in Sections 1.4 and 3.4: The volume of the cube is $(5.00)^3\ cm^3 = 125\ cm^3$. Then we have

$$125\ cm^3\ Bi \times \frac{9.808\ g\ Bi}{1\ cm^3} \times \frac{1\ mol\ Bi}{209.0\ g\ Bi} = 5.87\ mol\ Bi$$

$$5.87\ mol\ Bi \times \frac{6.022 \times 10^{23}\ atom\ Bi}{1\ mol\ Bi} = 3.53 \times 10^{24}\ atoms\ Bi$$

CHAPTER SUMMARY AND KEY TERMS

INTRODUCTION AND SECTION 7.1 The periodic table was first developed by Mendeleev and Meyer on the basis of the similarity in chemical and physical properties exhibited by certain elements. Moseley established that each element has a unique atomic number, which added more order to the periodic table. We now recognize that elements in the same column of the periodic table have the same number of electrons in their **valence orbitals**. This similarity in valence electronic structure leads to the similarities among elements in the same group. The differences among elements in the same group arise because their valence orbitals are in different shells.

SECTION 7.2 Many properties of atoms are due to the average distance of the outer electrons from the nucleus and to the **effective nuclear charge** experienced by these electrons. The core electrons are very effective in screening the outer electrons from the full charge of the nucleus, whereas electrons in the same shell do not screen each other effectively. As a result, the effective nuclear charge experienced by valence electrons increases as we move left to right across a period.

SECTION 7.3 The size of an atom can be gauged by its **bonding atomic radius,** based on measurements of the distances separating atoms in their chemical compounds. In general, atomic radii increase as we go down a column in the periodic table and decrease as we proceed left to right across a row.

Cations are smaller than their parent atoms; anions are larger than their parent atoms. For ions of the same charge, size increases going down a column of the periodic table. An **isoelectronic series** is a series of ions that has the same number of electrons. For such a series, size decreases with increasing nuclear charge as the electrons are attracted more strongly to the nucleus.

SECTION 7.4 The first **ionization energy** of an atom is the minimum energy needed to remove an electron from the atom in the gas phase, forming a cation. The second ionization energy is the energy needed to remove a second electron, and so forth. Ionization energies show a sharp increase after all the valence electrons have been removed because of the much higher effective nuclear charge experienced by the core electrons. The first ionization energies of the elements show periodic trends that are opposite those seen for atomic radii, with smaller atoms having higher first ionization energies. Thus, first ionization energies decrease as we go down a column and increase as we proceed left to right across a row.

We can write electron configurations for ions by first writing the electron configuration of the neutral atom and then removing or adding the appropriate number of electrons. Electrons are removed first from the orbitals with the largest value of n. If there are two valence orbitals with the same value of n (such as $4s$ and $4p$), then the electrons are lost first from the orbital with a higher value of l (in this case, $4p$). Electrons are added to orbitals in the reverse order.

SECTION 7.5 The **electron affinity** of an element is the energy change upon adding an electron to an atom in the gas phase, forming an anion. A negative electron affinity means that the anion is stable; a positive electron affinity means that the anion is not stable relative to the separated atom and electron, in which case its exact value cannot be measured. In general, electron affinities become more negative as we proceed from left to right across the periodic table. The halogens have the most-negative electron affinities. The electron affinities of the noble gases are positive because the added electron would have to occupy a new, higher-energy subshell.

SECTION 7.6 The elements can be categorized as metals, non-metals, and metalloids. Most elements are metals; they occupy the left side and the middle of the periodic table. Nonmetals appear in the upper-right section of the table. Metalloids occupy a narrow band between the metals and nonmetals. The tendency of an element to exhibit the properties of metals, called the **metallic character,** increases as we proceed down a column and decreases as we proceed from left to right across a row.

Metals have a characteristic luster, and they are good conductors of heat and electricity. When metals react with nonmetals, the metal atoms are oxidized to cations and ionic substances are generally formed. Most metal oxides are basic; they react with acids to form salts and water.

Nonmetals lack metallic luster and are generally poor conductors of heat and electricity. Several are gases at room temperature. Compounds composed entirely of nonmetals are generally molecular. Nonmetals usually form anions in their reactions with metals. Nonmetal oxides are acidic; they react with bases to form salts and water. Metalloids have properties that are intermediate between those of metals and nonmetals.

SECTION 7.7 The periodic properties of the elements can help us understand the properties of groups of the representative elements. The **alkali metals** (group 1A) are soft metals with low densities and low melting points. They have the lowest ionization energies of the elements. As a result, they are very reactive toward nonmetals, easily losing their outer s electron to form $1+$ ions. The **alkaline earth metals** (group 2A) are harder and more dense and have higher melting points than the alkali metals. They are also very reactive toward nonmetals, although not as reactive as the alkali metals. The alkaline earth metals readily lose their two outer s electrons to form $2+$ ions. Both alkali and alkaline earth metals react with hydrogen to form ionic substances that contain the **hydride ion,** H^-.

SECTION 7.8 Hydrogen is a nonmetal with properties that are distinct from any of the groups of the periodic table. It forms molecular compounds with other nonmetals, such as oxygen and the halogens.

Oxygen and sulfur are the most important elements in group 6A. Oxygen is usually found as a diatomic molecule, O_2. **Ozone,** O_3, is an important allotrope of oxygen. Oxygen has a strong tendency to gain electrons from other elements, thus oxidizing them. In combination with metals, oxygen is usually found as the oxide ion, O^{2-}, although salts of the peroxide ion, O_2^{2-}, and superoxide ion, O_2^-, are sometimes formed. Elemental sulfur is most commonly found as S_8 molecules. In combination with metals, it is most often found as the sulfide ion, S^{2-}.

The **halogens** (group 7A) are nonmetals that exist as diatomic molecules. The halogens have the most negative electron affinities of the elements. Thus, their chemistry is dominated by a tendency to form $1-$ ions, especially in reactions with metals.

The **noble gases** (group 8A) are nonmetals that exist as monatomic gases. They are very unreactive because they have completely filled s and p subshells. Only the heaviest noble gases are known to form compounds, and they do so only with very active nonmetals, such as fluorine.

KEY SKILLS

- Understand the meaning of effective nuclear charge, Z_{eff}, and how Z_{eff} depends on nuclear charge and electron configuration. (Section 7.2)

- Use the periodic table to predict the trends in atomic radii, ionic radii, ionization energy, and electron affinity. (Sections 7.2, 7.3, 7.4, and 7.5)

- Explain how the radius of an atom changes upon losing electrons to form a cation or gaining electrons to form an anion. (Section 7.3)

- Be able to write the electron configurations of ions. (Section 7.3)

- Explain how the ionization energy changes as we remove successive electrons. Recognize the jump in ionization energy that occurs when the ionization corresponds to removing a core electron. (Section 7.4)

- Understand how irregularities in the periodic trends for electron affinity can be related to electron configuration. (Section 7.5)

• Recognize the differences in chemical and physical properties of metals and nonmetals, including the basicity of metal oxides and the acidity of nonmetal oxides. (Section 7.6)

• Understand how the atomic properties, such as ionization energy and electron configuration, are related to the chemical reactivity and physical properties of the alkali and alkaline earth metals (groups 1A and 2A). (Section 7.7)

• Be able to write balanced equations for the reactions of the group 1A and 2A metals with water, oxygen, hydrogen, and the halogens. (Sections 7.7 and 7.8)

• Understand and recognize the unique characteristics of hydrogen. (Section 7.7)

• Understand how the atomic properties (such as ionization energy, electron configuration, and electron affinity) of group 6A, 7A, and 8A elements are related to their chemical reactivity and physical properties. (Section 7.8)

KEY EQUATIONS

• $Z_{eff} = Z - S$ [7.1]   Estimating effective nuclear charge

EXERCISES

VISUALIZING CONCEPTS

7.1 We can draw an analogy between the attraction of an electron to a nucleus and seeing a lightbulb—in essence, the more nuclear charge the electron "sees," the greater the attraction. **(a)** Within this analogy, discuss how the screening by core electrons is analogous to putting a frosted-glass lampshade between the lightbulb and your eyes, as shown in the illustration. **(b)** Explain how we could mimic moving to the right in a row of the periodic table by changing the wattage of the lightbulb. **(c)** How would you change the wattage of the bulb and/or the frosted glass to mimic the effect of moving down a column of the periodic table? [Section 7.2]

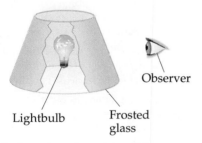

Observer

Lightbulb   Frosted glass

7.2 If you look up the radius of the sulfur atom in this book, you will find just one number: 1.02 Å. However, if you look deeper into the chemical literature, you can find another number for the radius of a sulfur atom: the nonbonding radius of 1.80 Å. This is a very large difference! Explain. [Section 7.3]

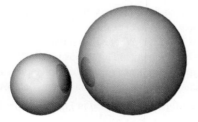

7.3 Consider the A_2X_4 molecule depicted here, where A and X are elements. The A—A bond length in this molecule is d_1, and the four A—X bond lengths are each d_2. **(a)** In terms of d_1 and d_2, how could you define the bonding atomic radii of atoms A and X? **(b)** In terms of d_1 and d_2, what would you predict for the X—X bond length of an X_2 molecule? [Section 7.3]

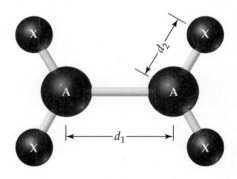

7.4 Make a simple sketch of the shape of the main part of the periodic table, as shown. **(a)** Ignoring H and He, write a single straight arrow from the element with the smallest bonding atomic radius to the element with the largest. **(b)** Ignoring H and He, write a single straight arrow from the element with the smallest first ionization energy to the element with the largest. **(c)** What significant observation can you make from the arrows you drew in parts (a) and (b)? [Sections 7.3 and 7.4]

7.5 In the chemical process called *electron transfer*, an electron is transferred from one atom or molecule to another. (We will talk about electron transfer extensively in Chapter 20.) A simple electron transfer reaction is

$$A(g) + A(g) \longrightarrow A^+(g) + A^-(g)$$

In terms of the ionization energy and electron affinity of atom A, what is the energy change for this reaction? For a representative nonmetal such as chlorine, is this process exothermic? For a representative metal such as sodium, is this process exothermic? [Sections 7.4 and 7.5]

7.6 An element X reacts with $F_2(g)$ to form the molecular product shown here. **(a)** Write a balanced equation for this reaction (do not worry about the phases for X and the product). **(b)** Do you think that X is a metal or nonmetal? Explain. [Section 7.6]

PERIODIC TABLE; EFFECTIVE NUCLEAR CHARGE (sections 7.1 and 7.2)

7.7 Explain the structure of the periodic table—two columns on the left, a block of ten for the transition metals, a block of six on the right, and a pair of 14-member rows below, with reference to the orbitals we discussed in Chapter 6.

7.8 The prefix *eka-* comes from the Sanskrit word for "one." Mendeleev used this prefix to indicate that the unknown element was one place away from the known element that followed the prefix. For example, *eka-silicon*, which we now call germanium, is one element below silicon. Mendeleev also predicted the existence of *eka-manganese*, which was not experimentally confirmed until 1937 because this element is radioactive and does not occur in nature. Based on the periodic table shown in Figure 7.1, what do we now call the element Mendeleev called *eka-manganese*?

7.9 You might have expected that the elements would have been discovered in order of their relative abundance in the Earth's crust (Figure 1.6), but this is not the case. Suggest a general reason.

7.10 **(a)** Moseley's experiments on X-rays emitted from atoms led to the concept of atomic numbers. Where exactly do these X-rays come from? Draw an energy-level diagram to explain. **(b)** Why are chemical and physical properties of the elements more closely related to atomic number than they are to atomic weight?

7.11 **(a)** What is meant by the term *effective nuclear charge*? **(b)** How does the effective nuclear charge experienced by the valence electrons of an atom vary going from left to right across a period of the periodic table?

7.12 **(a)** How is the concept of effective nuclear charge used to simplify the numerous electron–electron repulsions in a many-electron atom? **(b)** Which experiences a greater effective nuclear charge in a Be atom, the $1s$ electrons or the $2s$ electrons? Explain.

7.13 Detailed calculations show that the value of Z_{eff} for the outermost electrons in Na and K atoms is 2.51+ and 3.49+, respectively. **(a)** What value do you estimate for Z_{eff} experienced by the outermost electron in both Na and K by assuming core electrons contribute 1.00 and valence electrons contribute 0.00 to the screening constant? **(b)** What values do you estimate for Z_{eff} using Slater's rules? **(c)** Which approach gives a more accurate estimate of Z_{eff}? **(d)** Does either method of approximation account for the gradual increase in Z_{eff} that occurs upon moving down a group? **(e)** Predict Z_{eff} for the outermost electrons in the Rb atom based on the calculations for Na and K.

7.14 Detailed calculations show that the value of Z_{eff} for the outermost electrons in Si and Cl atoms is 4.29+ and 6.12+, respectively. **(a)** What value do you estimate for Z_{eff} experienced by the outermost electron in both Si and Cl by assuming core electrons contribute 1.00 and valence electrons contribute 0.00 to the screening constant? **(b)** What values do you estimate for Z_{eff} using Slater's rules? **(c)** Which approach gives a more accurate estimate of Z_{eff}? **(d)** Which method of approximation more accurately accounts for the steady increase in Z_{eff} that occurs upon moving left to right across a period? **(e)** Predict Z_{eff} for a valence electron in P, phosphorus, based on the calculations for Si and Cl.

7.15 Which will experience the greater effective nuclear charge, the electrons in the $n = 3$ shell in Ar or the $n = 3$ shell in Kr? Which will be closer to the nucleus? Explain.

7.16 Arrange the following atoms in order of increasing effective nuclear charge experienced by the electrons in the $n = 3$ electron shell: K, Mg, P, Rh, and Ti. Explain the basis for your order.

ATOMIC AND IONIC RADII (section 7.3)

7.17 **(a)** Because an exact outer boundary cannot be measured or even calculated for an atom, how are atomic radii determined? **(b)** What is the difference between a bonding radius and a nonbonding radius? **(c)** For a given element, which one is larger? **(d)** If a free atom reacts to become part of a molecule, would you say that the atom gets smaller or larger?

7.18 **(a)** Why does the quantum mechanical description of many-electron atoms make it difficult to define a precise atomic radius? **(b)** When nonbonded atoms come up against one another, what determines how closely the nuclear centers can approach?

7.19 Tungsten has the highest melting point of any metal in the periodic table: 3422 °C. The distance between W atoms in tungsten metal is 2.74 Å. **(a)** What is the atomic radius of a tungsten atom in this environment? (This radius is called the *metallic radius.*) **(b)** If you put tungsten metal under high pressure, predict what would happen to the distance between W atoms.

7.20 Based on the radii presented in Figure 7.6, predict the distance between Si atoms in solid silicon. How does this compare to the distance between the C atoms in diamond, which has the same structure as solid silicon?

7.21 Estimate the As—I bond length from the data in Figure 7.6, and compare your value to the experimental As—I bond length in arsenic triiodide, AsI_3, 2.55 Å.

7.22 The experimental Bi—I bond length in bismuth triiodide, BiI_3, is 2.81 Å. Based on this value and data in Figure 7.6, predict the atomic radius of Bi.

7.23 How do the sizes of atoms change as we move **(a)** from left to right across a row in the periodic table, **(b)** from top to bottom in a group in the periodic table? **(c)** Arrange the following atoms in order of increasing atomic radius: O, Si, I, Ge.

7.24 **(a)** Among the nonmetallic elements, the change in atomic radius in moving one place left or right in a row is smaller than the change in moving one row up or down. Explain these observations. **(b)** Arrange the following atoms in order of increasing atomic radius: Si, Al, Ge, Ga.

7.25 Using only the periodic table, arrange each set of atoms in order from largest to smallest: **(a)** K, Li, Cs; **(b)** Pb, Sn, Si; **(c)** F, O, N.

7.26 Using only the periodic table, arrange each set of atoms in order of increasing radius: **(a)** Ba, Ca, Na; **(b)** Sn, Sb, As; **(c)** Al, Be, Si.

7.27 True or False: **(a)** Cations are larger than their corresponding neutral atoms. **(b)** Li^+ is smaller than Li. **(c)** Cl^- is bigger than I^-.

7.28 Explain the following variations in atomic or ionic radii: **(a)** $I^- > I > I^+$, **(b)** $Ca^{2+} > Mg^{2+} > Be^{2+}$, **(c)** $Fe > Fe^{2+} > Fe^{3+}$.

7.29 In the reaction

Reactants   Products

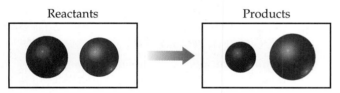

which sphere represents a metal and which represents a nonmetal? Explain your answer.

7.30 Which of these spheres represents F, which represents Br, and which represents Br^-?

7.31 **(a)** What is an isoelectronic series? **(b)** Which neutral atom is isoelectronic with each of the following ions: Ga^{3+}, Zr^{4+}, Mn^{7+}, I^-, Pb^{2+}?

7.32 Identify at least two ions that have the following ground-state electron configurations: **(a)** [Ar]; **(b)** $[Ar]3d^5$; **(c)** $[Kr]5s^24d^{10}$.

7.33 Some ions do not have a corresponding neutral atom that has the same electron configuration. For each of the following ions, identify the neutral atom that has the same number of electrons and determine if this atom has the same electron configuration. If such an atom does not exist, explain why. **(a)** Cl^-, **(b)** Sc^{3+}, **(c)** Fe^{2-}, **(d)** Zn^{2+}, **(e)** Sn^{4+}.

7.34 Consider the isoelectronic ions F^- and Na^+. **(a)** Which ion is smaller? **(b)** Using Equation 7.1 and assuming that core electrons contribute 1.00 and valence electrons contribute 0.00 to the screening constant, S, calculate Z_{eff} for the $2p$ electrons in both ions. **(c)** Repeat this calculation using Slater's rules to estimate the screening constant, S. **(d)** For isoelectronic ions, how are effective nuclear charge and ionic radius related?

7.35 Consider the isoelectronic ions Cl^- and K^+. **(a)** Which ion is smaller? **(b)** Using Equation 7.1 and assuming that core electrons contribute 1.00 and valence electrons contribute nothing to the screening constant, S, calculate Z_{eff} for these two ions. **(c)** Repeat this calculation using Slater's rules to estimate the screening constant, S. **(d)** For isoelectronic ions, how are effective nuclear charge and ionic radius related?

7.36 Consider S, Cl, and K and their most common ions. **(a)** List the atoms in order of increasing size. **(b)** List the ions in order of increasing size. **(c)** Explain any differences in the orders of the atomic and ionic sizes.

7.37 For each of the following sets of atoms and ions, arrange the members in order of increasing size: **(a)** Se^{2-}, Te^{2-}, Se; **(b)** Co^{3+}, Fe^{2+}, Fe^{3+}; **(c)** Ca, Ti^{4+}, Sc^{3+}; **(d)** Be^{2+}, Na^+, Ne.

7.38 In the ionic compounds LiF, NaCl, KBr, and RbI, the measured cation–anion distances are 2.01 Å (Li–F), 2.82 Å (Na–Cl), 3.30 Å (K–Br), and 3.67 Å (Rb–I), respectively. **(a)** Predict the cation–anion distance using the values of ionic radii given in Figure 7.7. **(b)** Calculate the difference between the experimentally measured ion–ion distances and the ones predicted from Figure 7.7. Assuming we have an accuracy of 0.04 Å in the measurement, would you say that the two sets of ion–ion distances are the same or not? **(c)** What estimates of the cation–anion distance would you obtain for these four compounds using *bonding atomic radii*? Are these estimates as accurate as the estimates using ionic radii?

IONIZATION ENERGIES; ELECTRON AFFINITIES (sections 7.4 and 7.5)

7.39 Write equations that show the processes that describe the first, second, and third ionization energies of an aluminum atom. Which process would require the least amount of energy?

7.40 Write equations that show the process for **(a)** the first two ionization energies of lead and **(b)** the fourth ionization energy of zirconium.

7.41 Identify each statement as true or false. If it is false, rewrite it so that it is true: **(a)** Ionization energies are always negative quantitites. **(b)** Oxygen has a larger first ionization energy than fluorine. **(c)** The second ionization energy of an atom is always greater than its first ionization energy.

7.42 **(a)** Why does Li have a larger first ionization energy than Na? **(b)** The difference between the third and fourth ionization energies of scandium is much larger than the difference between the third and fourth ionization energies of titanium. Why? **(c)** Why does Li have a much larger second ionization energy than Be?

7.43 **(a)** What is the general relationship between the size of an atom and its first ionization energy? **(b)** Which element in the periodic table has the largest ionization energy? Which has the smallest?

7.44 **(a)** What is the trend in first ionization energies as one proceeds down the group 7A elements? Explain how this trend relates to the variation in atomic radii. **(b)** What is the trend in first ionization energies as one moves across the fourth period from K to Kr? How does this trend compare with the trend in atomic radii?

7.45 Based on their positions in the periodic table, predict which atom of the following pairs will have the smaller first ionization energy: **(a)** Cl, Ar; **(b)** Be, Ca; **(c)** K, Co; **(d)** S, Ge; **(e)** Sn, Te.

7.46 For each of the following pairs, indicate which element has the smaller first ionization energy: **(a)** Ti, Ba; **(b)** Ag, Cu; **(c)** Ge, Cl; **(d)** Pb, Sb. (In each case use electron configuration and effective nuclear charge to explain your answer.)

7.47 Write the electron configurations for the following ions: **(a)** Fe^{2+}, **(b)** Hg^{2+}, **(c)** Mn^{2+}, **(d)** Pt^{2+}, **(e)** P^{3-}.

7.48 Write electron configurations for the following ions, and determine which have noble-gas configurations: **(a)** Cr^{3+}, **(b)** N^{3-}, **(c)** Sc^{3+}, **(d)** Cu^{2+}, **(e)** Tl^{+}, **(f)** Au^{+}.

7.49 Find three examples of ions in the periodic table that have an electron configuration of nd^8 ($n = 3, 4, 5...$).

7.50 Find three atoms in the periodic table whose ions have an electron configuration of nd^6 ($n = 3, 4, 5...$).

7.51 The first ionization energy and electron affinity of Ar are both positive values. **(a)** What is the significance of the positive value in each case? **(b)** What are the units of electron affinity?

7.52 If the electron affinity for an element is a negative number, does it mean that the anion of the element is more stable than the neutral atom? Explain.

7.53 Although the electron affinity of bromine is a negative quantity, it is positive for Kr. Use the electron configurations of the two elements to explain the difference.

7.54 What is the relationship between the ionization energy of an anion with a 1− charge such as F^- and the electron affinity of the neutral atom, F?

7.55 Consider the first ionization energy of neon and the electron affinity of fluorine. **(a)** Write equations, including electron configurations, for each process. **(b)** These two quantities will have opposite signs. Which will be positive, and which will be negative? **(c)** Would you expect the **magnitudes** of these two quantities to be equal? If not, which one would you expect to be larger? Explain your answer.

7.56 Write an equation for the process that corresponds to the electron affinity of the Mg^+ ion. Also write the electron configurations of the species involved. What is the magnitude of the energy change in the process? [*Hint:* The answer is in Table 7.2.]

PROPERTIES OF METALS AND NONMETALS (section 7.6)

7.57 How are metallic character and first ionization energy related?

[7.58] It is possible to define *metallic character* as we do in this book and base it on the reactivity of the element and the ease with which it loses electrons. Alternatively, one could measure how well electricity is conducted by each of the elements to determine how "metallic" the elements are. On the basis of conductivity, there is not much of a trend in the periodic table: Silver is the most conductive metal, and manganese the least. Look up the first ionization energies of silver and manganese; which of these two elements would you call more metallic based on the way we define it in this book?

7.59 Discussing this chapter, a classmate says, "An element that commonly forms a cation is a metal." Do you agree or disagree? Explain your answer.

7.60 Discussing this chapter, a classmate says, "Since elements that form cations are metals and elements that form anions are nonmetals, elements that do not form ions are metalloids." Do you agree or disagree? Explain your answer.

7.61 Predict whether each of the following oxides is ionic or molecular: SnO_2, Al_2O_3, CO_2, Li_2O, Fe_2O_3, H_2O. Explain the reasons for your choices.

7.62 Some metal oxides, such as Sc_2O_3, do not react with pure water, but they do react when the solution becomes either acidic or basic. Do you expect Sc_2O_3 to react when the solution becomes acidic or when it becomes basic? Write a balanced chemical equation to support your answer.

7.63 **(a)** What is meant by the terms *acidic oxide* and *basic oxide*? **(b)** How can we predict whether an oxide will be acidic or basic based on its composition?

7.64 Arrange the following oxides in order of increasing acidity: CO_2, CaO, Al_2O_3, SO_3, SiO_2, and P_2O_5.

7.65 Chlorine reacts with oxygen to form Cl_2O_7. **(a)** What is the name of this product (see Table 2.6)? **(b)** Write a balanced equation for the formation of $Cl_2O_7(l)$ from the elements. **(c)** Under usual conditions, Cl_2O_7 is a colorless liquid with a boiling point of 81 °C. Is this boiling point expected or surprising? **(d)** Would you expect Cl_2O_7 to be more reactive toward $H^+(aq)$ or $OH^-(aq)$? Explain. **(e)** If the oxygen in Cl_2O_7 is considered to have the −2 oxidation state, what is the oxidation state of the Cl? What is the electron configuration of Cl in this oxidation state?

[7.66] An element X reacts with oxygen to form XO_2 and with chlorine to form XCl_4. XO_2 is a white solid that melts at high temperatures (above 1000 °C). Under usual conditions, XCl_4 is a colorless liquid with a boiling point of 58 °C. **(a)** XCl_4 reacts with water to form XO_2 and another product. What is the likely identity of the other product? **(b)** Do you think that element X is a metal, nonmetal, or metalloid? Explain. **(c)** By using a sourcebook such as the *CRC Handbook of Chemistry and Physics,* try to determine the identity of element X.

7.67 Write balanced equations for the following reactions: **(a)** barium oxide with water, **(b)** iron(II) oxide with perchloric acid, **(c)** sulfur trioxide with water, **(d)** carbon dioxide with aqueous sodium hydroxide.

7.68 Write balanced equations for the following reactions: **(a)** potassium oxide with water, **(b)** diphosphorus trioxide with water, **(c)** chromium(III) oxide with dilute hydrochloric acid, **(d)** selenium dioxide with aqueous potassium hydroxide.

GROUP TRENDS IN METALS AND NONMETALS (sections 7.7 and 7.8)

7.69 Does the reactivity of a metal correlate with its first ionization energy? Explain.

7.70 Silver and rubidium both form +1 ions, but silver is far less reactive. Suggest an explanation, taking into account the ground-state electron configurations of these elements and atomic radii.

7.71 (a) Why is calcium generally more reactive than magnesium? (b) Why is calcium generally less reactive than potassium?

7.72 (a) One of the alkali metals reacts with oxygen to form a solid white substance. When this substance is dissolved in water, the solution gives a positive test for hydrogen peroxide, H_2O_2. When the solution is tested in a burner flame, a lilac-purple flame is produced. What is the likely identity of the metal? (b) Write a balanced chemical equation for reaction of the white substance with water.

7.73 Write a balanced equation for the reaction that occurs in each of the following cases: (a) Potassium metal burns in an atmosphere of chlorine gas. (b) Strontium oxide is added to water. (c) A fresh surface of lithium metal is exposed to oxygen gas. (d) Sodium metal is reacted with molten sulfur.

7.74 Write a balanced equation for the reaction that occurs in each of the following cases: (a) Cesium is added to water. (b) Strontium is added to water. (c) Sodium reacts with oxygen. (d) Calcium reacts with iodine.

7.75 (a) As described in Section 7.7, the alkali metals react with hydrogen to form hydrides and react with halogens—for example, fluorine—to form halides. Compare the roles of hydrogen and the halogen in these reactions. How are the forms of hydrogen and halogen in the products alike? (b) Write balanced equations for the reaction of fluorine with calcium and for the reaction of hydrogen with calcium. What are the similarities among the products of these reactions?

7.76 The interior of the planets Jupiter and Saturn are believed to contain *metallic hydrogen*: hydrogen that is put under such tremendous pressure that it no longer exists as H_2 molecules, but instead exists as an extended metallic solid. Predict what properties metallic hydrogen might have compared to "normal" hydrogen in terms of first ionization energy, atomic size, and reactivity.

7.77 Compare the elements bromine and chlorine with respect to the following properties: (a) electron configuration, (b) most common ionic charge, (c) first ionization energy, (d) reactivity toward water, (e) electron affinity, (f) atomic radius. Account for the differences between the two elements.

7.78 Little is known about the properties of astatine, At, because of its rarity and high radioactivity. Nevertheless, it is possible for us to make many predictions about its properties. (a) Do you expect the element to be a gas, liquid, or solid at room temperature? Explain. (b) Would you expect At to be a metal, nonmetal, or metalloid? Explain. (c) What is the chemical formula of the compound it forms with Na?

7.79 Until the early 1960s the group 8A elements were called the inert gases; before that they were called the rare gases. The term *rare gases* was dropped after it was discovered that argon accounts for roughly 1% of Earth's atmosphere. (a) Why was the term *inert gases* dropped? (b) What discovery triggered this change in name? (c) What name is applied to the group now?

7.80 (a) Why does xenon react with fluorine, whereas neon does not? (b) Using reference sources such as the *CRC Handbook of Chemistry and Physics* or online sources, look up the bond lengths of Xe—F bonds in several molecules. How do these numbers compare to the radii of the elements?

7.81 Write a balanced equation for the reaction that occurs in each of the following cases: (a) Ozone decomposes to dioxygen. (b) Xenon reacts with fluorine. (Write three different equations.) (c) Sulfur reacts with hydrogen gas. (d) Fluorine reacts with water.

7.82 Write a balanced equation for the reaction that occurs in each of the following cases: (a) Chlorine reacts with water. (b) Barium metal is heated in an atmosphere of hydrogen gas. (c) Lithium reacts with sulfur. (d) Fluorine reacts with magnesium metal.

ADDITIONAL EXERCISES

7.83 Consider the stable elements through lead ($Z = 82$). In how many instances are the atomic weights of the elements in the reverse order relative to the atomic numbers of the elements? What is the explanation for these cases?

[7.84] We saw in Chapter 6 that the probability of finding an electron in three-dimensional space depends on what orbital it is in. Look back at Figures 6.19 and 6.22, which show the radial probability distribution functions for the *s* orbitals and contour plots of the 2*p* orbitals, respectively. (a) Which orbitals, 2*s* or 2*p*, have more electron density at the nucleus? (b) How would you modify Slater's rules to adjust for the difference in electronic penetration of the nucleus for the 2*s* and 2*p* orbitals?

7.85 (a) If the core electrons were totally effective at screening the valence electrons and the valence electrons provided no screening for each other, what would be the effective nuclear charge acting on the 3*s* and 3*p* valence electrons in P? (b) Repeat these calculations using Slater's rules. (c) Detailed calculations indicate that the effective nuclear charge is 5.6+ for the 3*s* electrons and 4.9+ for the 3*p* electrons. Why are the values for the 3*s* and 3*p* electrons different? (d) If you remove a single electron from a P atom, which orbital will it come from? Explain.

7.86 The size of an atomic nucleus is on the order of 10^{-15} m. If two protons were able to make a bond, what would you predict the bond length to be?

7.87 As we move across a period of the periodic table, why do the sizes of the transition elements change more gradually than those of the representative elements?

7.88 In the series of group 5A hydrides, of general formula MH_3, the measured bond distances are P—H, 1.419 Å; As—H, 1.519 Å; Sb—H, 1.707 Å. **(a)** Compare these values with those estimated by use of the atomic radii in Figure 7.6. **(b)** Explain the steady increase in M—H bond distance in this series in terms of the electronic configurations of the M atoms.

7.89 Elements in group 7A in the periodic table are the halogens; elements in group 6A are called the chalcogens. **(a)** What is the most common oxidation state of the chalcogens compared to the halogens? Can you suggest an explanation for the difference? **(b)** For each of the following periodic properties, state whether the halogens or the chalcogens have larger values: atomic radii; ionic radii of the most common oxidation state; first ionization energy; second ionization energy.

7.90 Note from the following table that the increase in atomic radius in moving from Zr to Hf is smaller than in moving from Y to La. Suggest an explanation for this effect.

Atomic Radii (Å)

Sc	1.44	Ti	1.36
Y	1.62	Zr	1.48
La	1.69	Hf	1.50

[7.91] **(a)** Which ion is smaller, Co^{3+} or Co^{4+}? **(b)** In a lithium ion battery that is discharging to power a device, for every Li^+ that inserts into the lithium cobalt oxide electrode, a Co^{4+} ion must be reduced to a Co^{3+} ion in order to balance charge. Using the *CRC Handbook of Chemistry and Physics* or other standard reference, find the ionic radii of Li^+, Co^{3+}, and Co^{4+}. Order these ions from smallest to largest. **(c)** Will the lithium cobalt electrode expand or contract as lithium ions are inserted? **(d)** Lithium is not nearly as abundant as sodium. If sodium ion batteries were developed that function as lithium ion ones, do you think "sodium cobalt oxide" would still work as the electrode material? Explain. **(e)** If you don't think cobalt would work as the redox-active partner ion in the sodium version of the electrode, suggest an alternative metal ion and explain your reasoning.

[7.92] The ionic substance strontium oxide, SrO, forms from the reaction of strontium metal with molecular oxygen. The arrangement of the ions in solid SrO is analogous to that in solid NaCl (Figure 2.21):

(a) Write a balanced equation for the formation of SrO(s) from its elements. **(b)** Based on the ionic radii in Figure 7.7, predict the length of the side of the cube in the figure (the distance from the center of an atom at one corner to the center of an atom at a neighboring corner). **(c)** The density of SrO is 5.10 g/cm³. Given your answer to part (b), how many formula units of SrO are contained in the cube shown here?

7.93 Explain the variation in ionization energies of carbon, as displayed in this graph:

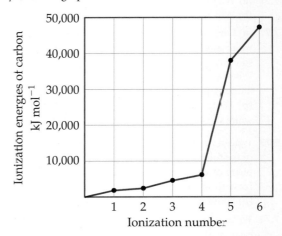

7.94 Group 4A elements have much more negative electron affinities than their neighbors in groups 3A and 5A (see Figure 7.11). Suggest an explanation.

7.95 **(a)** Use orbital diagrams to illustrate what happens when an oxygen atom gains two electrons. **(b)** Why does O^{3-} not exist?

[7.96] Use electron configurations to explain the following observations: **(a)** The first ionization energy of phosphorus is greater than that of sulfur. **(b)** The electron affinity of nitrogen is lower (less negative) than those of both carbon and oxygen. **(c)** The second ionization energy of oxygen is greater than the first ionization energy of fluorine. **(d)** The third ionization energy of manganese is greater than those of both chromium and iron.

7.97 The electron affinities, in kJ/mol, for the group 1B and group 2B metals are

Cu	Zn
−119	> 0
Ag	**Cd**
−126	> 0
Au	**Hg**
−223	> 0

(a) Why are the electron affinities of the group 2B elements greater than zero? **(b)** Why do the electron affinities of the group 1B elements become more negative as we move down the group? [*Hint:* Examine the trends in the electron affinity of other groups as we proceed down the periodic table.]

7.98 Hydrogen is an unusual element because it behaves in some ways like the alkali metal elements and in other ways like nonmetals. Its properties can be explained in part by its electron configuration and by the values for its ionization energy and electron affinity. **(a)** Explain why the electron affinity of hydrogen is much closer to the values for the alkali elements than for the halogens. **(b)** Is the following statement true? "Hydrogen has the smallest bonding atomic radius of any element that forms chemical compounds." If not, correct it. If it is, explain in terms of electron configurations. (c) Explain why the ionization energy of hydrogen is closer to the values for the halogens than for the alkali metals. (d) The hydride ion is H^-. Write out the process corresponding to the first ionization energy of hydride. (e) How does the process you wrote in part (d) compare to the process for the electron affinity of elemental hydrogen?

[7.99] The first ionization energy of the oxygen molecule is the energy required for the following process:

$$O_2(g) \longrightarrow O_2^+(g) + e^-$$

The energy needed for this process is 1175 kJ/mol, very similar to the first ionization energy of Xe. Would you expect O_2 to react with F_2? If so, suggest a product or products of this reaction.

7.100 The elements of group 4A—carbon, silicon, germanium, tin, and lead—go from nonmetal through metalloid to metal as we go down the column. (a) Predict the order of melting temperature from highest to lowest in this group and justify your logic. (b) Using the *CRC Handbook of Chemistry and Physics* or other resource, look up the melting points of these elements. How accurate was your prediction?

7.101 Zinc in its 2+ oxidation state is an essential metal ion for life. Zn^{2+} is found bound to many proteins that are involved in biological processes, but unfortunately Zn^{2+} is hard to detect by common chemical methods. Therefore, scientists who are interested in studying Zn^{2+}-containing proteins will frequently substitute Cd^{2+} for Zn^{2+}, since Cd^{2+} is easier to detect. (a) On the basis of the properties of the elements and ions discussed in this chapter and their positions in the periodic table, describe the pros and cons of using Cd^{2+} as a Zn^{2+} substitute. (b) Proteins that speed up (catalyze) chemical reactions are called *enzymes*. Many enzymes are required for proper metabolic reactions in the body. One problem with using Cd^{2+} to replace Zn^{2+} in enzymes is that Cd^{2+} substitution can decrease or even eliminate enzymatic activity. Can you suggest a different metal ion that might replace Zn^{2+} in enzymes instead of Cd^{2+}? Justify your answer.

INTEGRATIVE EXERCISES

[7.105] Moseley established the concept of atomic number by studying X-rays emitted by the elements. The X-rays emitted by some of the elements have the following wavelengths:

Element	Wavelength (Å)
Ne	14.610
Ca	3.358
Zn	1.435
Zr	0.786
Sn	0.491

(a) Calculate the frequency, ν, of the X-rays emitted by each of the elements, in Hz. (b) Using the appropriate graphing program on your computer, plot the square root of ν versus the atomic number of the element. What do you observe about the plot? (c) Explain how the plot in part (b) allowed Moseley to predict the existence of undiscovered elements. (d) Use the result from part (b) to predict the X-ray wavelength emitted by iron. (e) A particular element emits X-rays with a wavelength of 0.980 Å. What element do you think it is?

[7.102] A historian discovers a nineteenth-century notebook in which some observations, dated 1822, were recorded on a substance thought to be a new element. Here are some of the data recorded in the notebook: "Ductile, silver-white, metallic looking. Softer than lead. Unaffected by water. Stable in air. Melting point: 153 °C. Density: 7.3 g/cm³. Electrical conductivity: 20% that of copper. Hardness: About 1% as hard as iron. When 4.20 g of the unknown is heated in an excess of oxygen, 5.08 g of a white solid is formed. The solid could be sublimed by heating to over 800 °C." (a) Using information in the text and the *CRC Handbook of Chemistry and Physics,* and making allowances for possible variations in numbers from current values, identify the element reported. (b) Write a balanced chemical equation for the reaction with oxygen. (c) Judging from Figure 7.1, might this nineteenth-century investigator have been the first to discover a new element?

7.103 In April 2010, a research team reported that they had made Element 117. The report has yet to be confirmed. Write out Element 117's ground-state electron configuration, and estimate values for its first ionization energy, electron affinity, atomic size, and common oxidation state based on its position in the periodic table.

7.104 We will see in Chapter 12 that semiconductors are materials that conduct electricity better than nonmetals but not as well as metals. The only two elements in the periodic table that are technologically useful semiconductors are silicon and germanium. Integrated circuits in computer chips today are based on silicon. Compound semiconductors are also used in the electronics industry. Examples are gallium arsenide, GaAs; gallium phosphide, GaP; cadmium sulfide, CdS; cadium selenide, CdSe. (a) What is the relationship between the compound semiconductors' compositions and the positions of their elements on the periodic table relative to Si and Ge? (b) Workers in the semiconductor industry refer to "II-VI" and "III-V" materials, using Roman numerals; can you identify which compound semiconductors are II-VI and which are III-V? (c) Suggest other compositions of compound semiconductors based on the positions of their elements in the periodic table.

[7.106] (a) Write the electron configuration for Li, and estimate the effective nuclear charge experienced by the valence electron. (b) The energy of an electron in a one-electron atom or ion equals $(-2.18 \times 10^{-18} \text{ J})\left(\dfrac{Z^2}{n^2}\right)$ where Z is the nuclear charge and n is the principal quantum number of the electron. Estimate the first ionization energy of Li. (c) Compare the result of your calculation with the value reported in Table 7.4 and explain the difference. (d) What value of the effective nuclear charge gives the proper value for the ionization energy? Does this agree with your explanation in (c)?

[7.107] One way to measure ionization energies is ultraviolet photoelectron spectroscopy (UPS, or just PES), a technique based on the photoelectric effect. ∞∞ (Section 6.2) In PES, monochromatic light is directed onto a sample, causing electrons to be emitted. The kinetic energy of the emitted electrons is measured. The difference between the energy of the photons and the kinetic energy of the electrons corresponds to the energy needed to remove the electrons (that is, the ionization energy). Suppose that a PES experiment is performed in which mercury vapor is irradiated with ultraviolet light of wavelength 58.4 nm. (a) What is the energy of a photon of this light in eV? **(b)** Write an equation that shows the process corresponding to the first ionization energy of Hg. **(c)** The kinetic energy of the emitted electrons is measured to be 10.75 eV. What is the first ionization energy of Hg in kJ/mol? **(d)** Using Figure 7.9, determine which of the halogen elements has a first ionization energy closest to that of mercury.

7.108 Mercury in the environment can exist in oxidation states 0, +1, and +2. One major question in environmental chemistry research is how to best measure the oxidation state of mercury in natural systems; this is made more complicated by the fact that mercury can be reduced or oxidized on surfaces differently than it would be if it were free in solution. XPS, X-ray photoelectron spectroscopy, is a technique related to PES (see Exercise 7.107), but instead of using ultraviolet light to eject valence electrons, X-rays are used to eject core electrons. The energies of the core electrons are different for different oxidation states of the element. In one set of experiments, researchers examined mercury contamination of minerals in water. They measured the XPS signals that corresponded to electrons ejected from mercury's $4f$ orbitals at 105 eV, from an X-ray source that provided 1253.6 eV of energy. The oxygen on the mineral surface gave emitted electron energies at 531 eV, corresponding to the $1s$ orbital of oxygen. Overall the researchers concluded that oxidation states were +2 for Hg and −2 for O. **(a)** Calculate the wavelength of the X-rays used in this experiment. **(b)** Compare the energies of the $4f$ electrons in mercury and the $1s$ electrons in oxygen from these data to the first ionization energies of mercury and oxygen from the data in this chapter. **(c)** Write out the ground-state electron configurations for Hg^{2+} and O^{2-}; which electrons are the valence electrons in each case? **(d)** Use Slater's rules to estimate Z_{eff} for the $4f$ and valence electrons of Hg^{2+} and O^{2-}; assume for this purpose that all the inner electrons with $(n - 3)$ or less screen a full +1.

7.109 Consider the gas-phase transfer of an electron from a sodium atom to a chlorine atom:

$$Na(g) + Cl(g) \longrightarrow Na^+(g) + Cl^-(g)$$

(a) Write this reaction as the sum of two reactions, one that relates to an ionization energy and one that relates to an electron affinity. **(b)** Use the result from part (a), data in this chapter, and Hess's law to calculate the enthalpy of the preceding reaction. Is the reaction exothermic or endothermic? **(c)** The reaction between sodium metal and chlorine gas is highly exothermic and produces NaCl(s), whose structure was discussed in Section 2.7. Comment on this observation relative to the calculated enthalpy for the aforementioned gas-phase reaction.

[7.110] When magnesium metal is burned in air (Figure 3.6), two products are produced. One is magnesium oxide, MgO. The other is the product of the reaction of Mg with molecular nitrogen, magnesium nitride. When water is added to magnesium nitride, it reacts to form magnesium oxide and ammonia gas. **(a)** Based on the charge of the nitride ion (Table 2.5), predict the formula of magnesium nitride. **(b)** Write a balanced equation for the reaction of magnesium nitride with water. What is the driving force for this reaction? **(c)** In an experiment a piece of magnesium ribbon is burned in air in a crucible. The mass of the mixture of MgO and magnesium nitride after burning is 0.470 g. Water is added to the crucible, further reaction occurs, and the crucible is heated to dryness until the final product is 0.486 g of MgO. What was the mass percentage of magnesium nitride in the mixture obtained after the initial burning? **(d)** Magnesium nitride can also be formed by reaction of the metal with ammonia at high temperature. Write a balanced equation for this reaction. If a 6.3-g Mg ribbon reacts with 2.57 g $NH_3(g)$ and the reaction goes to completion, which component is the limiting reactant? What mass of $H_2(g)$ is formed in the reaction? **(e)** The standard enthalpy of formation of solid magnesium nitride is -461.08 kJ/mol. Calculate the standard enthalpy change for the reaction between magnesium metal and ammonia gas.

7.111 **(a)** The measured Bi — Br bond length in bismuth tribromide, $BiBr_3$, is 2.63 Å. Based on this value and the data in Figure 7.7, predict the atomic radius of Bi. **(b)** Bismuth tribromide is soluble in acidic solution. It is formed by treating solid bismuth(III) oxide with aqueous hydrobromic acid. Write a balanced chemical equation for this reaction. **(c)** While bismuth(III) oxide is soluble in acidic solutions, it is insoluble in basic solutions such as $NaOH(aq)$. Based on these properties, is bismuth characterized as a metallic, metalloid, or nonmetallic element? **(d)** Treating bismuth with fluorine gas forms BiF_5. Use the electron configuration of Bi to explain the formation of a compound with this formulation. **(e)** While it is possible to form BiF_5 in the manner just described, pentahalides of bismuth are not known for the other halogens. Explain why the pentahalide might form with fluorine but not with the other halogens. How does the behavior of bismuth relate to the fact that xenon reacts with fluorine to form compounds but not with the other halogens?

7.112 Potassium superoxide, KO_2, is often used in oxygen masks (such as those used by firefighters) because KO_2 reacts with CO_2 to release molecular oxygen. Experiments indicate that 2 mol of $KO_2(s)$ react with each mole of $CO_2(g)$. **(a)** The products of the reaction are $K_2CO_3(s)$ and $O_2(g)$. Write a balanced equation for the reaction between $KO_2(s)$ and $CO_2(g)$. **(b)** Indicate the oxidation number for each atom involved in the reaction in part (a). What elements are being oxidized and reduced? **(c)** What mass of $KO_2(s)$ is needed to consume 18.0 g $CO_2(g)$? What mass of $O_2(g)$ is produced during this reaction?

WHAT'S AHEAD

8.1 LEWIS SYMBOLS AND THE OCTET RULE
We begin with descriptions of the three main types of chemical bonds: *ionic, covalent,* and *metallic*. In evaluating bonding, *Lewis symbols* provide a useful shorthand for keeping track of valence electrons.

8.2 IONIC BONDING
We observe that in ionic substances the atoms are held together by the electrostatic attractions between ions of opposite charge. We discuss the energetics of forming ionic substances and describe the *lattice energy* of these substances.

8.3 COVALENT BONDING
We examine the bonding in molecular substances in which atoms bond by sharing one or more electron pairs. In general, the electrons are shared in such a way that each atom attains an *octet* of electrons.

8.4 BOND POLARITY AND ELECTRONEGATIVITY
We define *electronegativity* as the ability of an atom in a compound to attract electrons to itself. In general, electron pairs are shared unequally between atoms with different electro-negativities, leading to *polar covalent bonds*.

CHEMICAL BONDING AS ART. The *Atomium* is a 110-m-high steel sculpture commissioned for the 1958 World's Fair in Brussels. The nine spheres represent atoms, and the connecting rods evoke the chemical bonds holding them together. One sphere sits in the center of a cube formed by the other eight, a common arrangement of the atoms in metallic elements, such as iron.

BASIC CONCEPTS OF CHEMICAL BONDING

WHENEVER TWO ATOMS OR IONS are strongly held together, we say there is a **chemical bond** between them. There are three general types of chemical bonds: *ionic, covalent, and metallic* (▶ **FIGURE 8.1**). We can get a glimpse of these three types of bonds by thinking about the simple act of using a stainless-steel spoon to add table salt to a glass of water. Table salt is sodium chloride, NaCl, which consists of sodium ions, Na^+, and chloride ions, Cl^-. The structure is held together by **ionic bonds,** which are due to the attractions between oppositely charged ions. The water consists mainly of H_2O molecules. The hydrogen and oxygen atoms are bonded to one another through **covalent bonds**, in which molecules are formed by the sharing of electrons between atoms. The spoon consists mainly of iron metal, in which Fe atoms are connected to one another via **metallic bonds**, which are formed by electrons that are relatively free to move through the metal. These different substances—NaCl, H_2O, and Fe metal—behave as they do because of the ways in which their constituent atoms are connected to one another.

What determines the type of bonding in any substance? How do the characteristics of these bonds give rise to different physical and chemical properties? The keys to answering the first question are found in the electronic structure of the atoms involved, discussed in Chapters 6 and 7. In this chapter and the next, we examine the relationship between the electronic structure of atoms and the ionic and covalent chemical bonds they form. We will discuss metallic bonding in greater detail in Chapter 12.

Which of these three bond types do you expect to see in CO₂(g)?

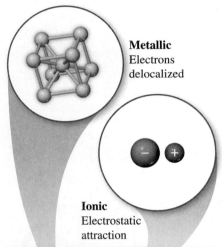

Metallic
Electrons delocalized

Ionic
Electrostatic attraction

Covalent
Electrons shared

▲ **FIGURE 8.1 Ionic, covalent, and metallic bonds.** Different types of interactions between atoms lead to different types of chemical bonds.

8.1 | LEWIS SYMBOLS AND THE OCTET RULE

The electrons involved in chemical bonding are the *valence electrons,* which, for most atoms, are those in the outermost occupied shell. ∞ (Section 6.8) The American chemist G. N. Lewis (1875–1946) suggested a simple way of showing the valence electrons in an atom and tracking them during bond formation, using what are now known as either *Lewis electron-dot symbols* or simply Lewis symbols.

The **Lewis symbol** for an element consists of the element's chemical symbol plus a dot for each valence electron. Sulfur, for example, has the electron configuration $[Ne]3s^2 3p^4$ and therefore six valence electrons. Its Lewis symbol is

$$\cdot\ddot{\underset{\cdot\cdot}{S}}\cdot$$

The dots are placed on the four sides of the symbol—top, bottom, left, and right—and each side can accommodate up to two electrons. All four sides are equivalent, which means that the choice of on which sides to place two electrons rather than one electron is arbitrary. In general, we spread out the dots as much as possible. In the Lewis symbol for S, for instance, we prefer the dot arrangement shown rather the arrangement having two electrons on three of the sides and none on the fourth.

The electron configurations and Lewis symbols for the main-group elements of periods 2 and 3 are shown in ▼ TABLE 8.1. Notice that the number of valence electrons in any representative element is the same as the element's group number. For example, the Lewis symbols for oxygen and sulfur, members of group 6A, both show six dots.

▲ **GIVE IT SOME THOUGHT**

Are all these Lewis symbols for Cl correct?

$$:\ddot{\underset{\cdot\cdot}{Cl}}\cdot \quad :\ddot{Cl}: \quad :\ddot{\underset{\cdot}{Cl}}\cdot$$

The Octet Rule

Atoms often gain, lose, or share electrons to achieve the same number of electrons as the noble gas closest to them in the periodic table. The noble gases have very stable electron arrangements, as evidenced by their high ionization energies, low affinity for additional electrons, and general lack of chemical reactivity. ∞ (Section 7.8) Because all the noble gases except He have eight valence electrons, many atoms undergoing reactions end up with eight valence electrons. This observation has led to a guideline known as the **octet rule**: *Atoms tend to gain, lose, or share electrons until they are surrounded by eight valence electrons.*

An octet of electrons consists of full *s* and *p* subshells in an atom. In a Lewis symbol, an octet is shown as four pairs of valence electrons arranged around the element symbol, as in the Lewis symbols for Ne and Ar in Table 8.1. There are exceptions to the octet rule, but it provides a useful framework for introducing many important concepts of bonding.

TABLE 8.1 • Lewis Symbols						
Group	Element	Electron Configuration	Lewis Symbol	Element	Electron Configuration	Lewis Symbol
1A	Li	$[He]2s^1$	Li·	Na	$[Ne]3s^1$	Na·
2A	Be	$[He]2s^2$	·Be·	Mg	$[Ne]3s^2$	·Mg·
3A	B	$[He]2s^2 2p^1$	·Ḃ·	Al	$[Ne]3s^2 3p^1$	·Ȧl·
4A	C	$[He]2s^2 2p^2$	·Ċ·	Si	$[Ne]3s^2 3p^2$	·Ṡi·
5A	N	$[He]2s^2 2p^3$	·N̈·	P	$[Ne]3s^2 3p^3$	·P̈·
6A	O	$[He]2s^2 2p^4$	:Ö:	S	$[Ne]3s^2 3p^4$	:S̈·
7A	F	$[He]2s^2 2p^5$	·F̈:	Cl	$[Ne]3s^2 3p^5$	·Cl̈:
8A	Ne	$[He]2s^2 2p^6$	:N̈e:	Ar	$[Ne]3s^2 3p^6$	: Är:

⚠ **GO FIGURE**

Do you expect a similar reaction between potassium metal and elemental bromine?

Electrons transfer
from Na(s) to Cl₂(g),
forming Na⁺ and Cl⁻

NaCl(s) forms

Highly exothermic reaction
forming sodium chloride, an ionic
compound composed of sodium
ions, Na⁺, and chloride ions, Cl⁻

▲ **FIGURE 8.2** **Reaction of sodium metal with chlorine gas to form the ionic compound sodium chloride.**

8.2 | IONIC BONDING

Ionic substances generally result from the interaction of metals on the left side of the periodic table with nonmetals on the right side (excluding the noble gases, group 8A). For example, when sodium metal, Na(s), is brought into contact with chlorine gas, $Cl_2(g)$, a violent reaction ensues (▲ **FIGURE 8.2**). The product of this very exothermic reaction is sodium chloride, NaCl(s):

$$Na(s) + \tfrac{1}{2}Cl_2(g) \longrightarrow NaCl(s) \qquad \Delta H_f^\circ = -410.9 \text{ kJ} \qquad [8.1]$$

Sodium chloride is composed of Na^+ and Cl^- ions arranged in a three-dimensional array (▶ **FIGURE 8.3**).

The formation of Na^+ from Na and Cl^- from Cl_2 indicates that an electron has been lost by a sodium atom and gained by a chlorine atom—we can envision an *electron transfer* from the Na atom to the Cl atom. Two of the atomic properties discussed in Chapter 7 give us an indication of how readily electron transfer occurs: ionization energy, which indicates how easily an electron can be removed from an atom, and electron affinity, which measures how much an atom wants to gain an electron. ∞ (Sections 7.4 and 7.5) Electron transfer to form oppositely charged ions occurs when one atom readily gives up an electron (low ionization energy) and another atom readily gains an electron (high electron affinity). Thus, NaCl is a typical ionic compound because it consists of a metal of low ionization energy and a nonmetal of high electron affinity. Using Lewis electron-dot symbols (and showing a chlorine atom rather than the Cl_2 molecule), we can represent this reaction as

$$Na\cdot + \cdot\ddot{\underset{..}{Cl}}: \longrightarrow Na^+ + [:\ddot{\underset{..}{Cl}}:]^- \qquad [8.2]$$

The arrow indicates the transfer of an electron from the Na atom to the Cl atom. Each ion has an octet of electrons, the Na^+ octet being the $2s^2 2p^6$ electrons that lie below the single 3s valence electron of the Na atom. We have put a bracket around the chloride ion to emphasize that all eight electrons are located on it.

⚠ **GO FIGURE**

If no color key were provided, is there a way for you to guess whether the green spheres represent Na^+ or Cl^-? If so, what information would you use?

 = Na^+ = Cl^-

Each Na^+ ion
surrounded by
six Cl^- ions

Each Cl^- ion
surrounded by
six Na^+ ions

▲ **FIGURE 8.3** **The crystal structure of sodium chloride.**

GIVE IT SOME THOUGHT

Describe the electron transfers that occur in the formation of calcium fluoride from elemental calcium and elemental fluorine.

Ionic substances possess several characteristic properties. They are usually brittle substances with high melting points. They are usually crystalline. Furthermore, ionic crystals often can be cleaved; that is, they break apart along smooth, flat surfaces. These characteristics result from electrostatic forces that maintain the ions in a rigid, well-defined, three-dimensional arrangement such as that shown in Figure 8.3.

Energetics of Ionic Bond Formation

The formation of sodium chloride from sodium and chlorine is *very* exothermic, as indicated by the large negative enthalpy of formation value given in Equation 8.1, $\Delta H_f^\circ = -410.9$ kJ. Appendix C shows that the heat of formation of other ionic substances is also quite negative. What factors make the formation of ionic compounds so exothermic?

In Equation 8.2 we represented the formation of NaCl as the transfer of an electron from Na to Cl. Recall from Section 7.4 that the loss of electrons from an atom is always an endothermic process. Removing an electron from $Na(g)$ to form $Na^+(g)$, for instance, requires 496 kJ/mol. Recall from Section 7.5 that when a nonmetal gains an electron, the process is generally exothermic, as seen from the negative electron affinities of the elements. Adding an electron to $Cl(g)$, for example, releases 349 kJ/mol. From the magnitudes of these energies, we can see that the transfer of an electron from a Na atom to a Cl atom would not be exothermic—the overall process would be an endothermic process that requires $496 - 349 = 147$ kJ/mol. This endothermic process corresponds to the formation of sodium and chloride ions that are infinitely far apart—in other words, the positive energy change assumes that the ions do not interact with each other, which is quite different from the situation in ionic solids.

 GIVE IT SOME THOUGHT

Consider the trends in ionization energies of the alkali metals and electron affinities of the halogens shown in Figures 7.9 and 7.11. For which pair is electron transfer from the alkali metal atom to the halogen atom most likely to be an exothermic process?

The principal reason ionic compounds are stable is the attraction between ions of opposite charge. This attraction draws the ions together, releasing energy and causing the ions to form a solid array, or lattice, such as that shown in Figure 8.3. A measure of how much stabilization results from arranging oppositely charged ions in an ionic solid is given by the **lattice energy**, which is *the energy required to completely separate one mole of a solid ionic compound into its gaseous ions.*

To envision this process for NaCl, imagine that the structure in Figure 8.3 expands from within, so that the distances between the ions increase until the ions are very far apart. This process requires 788 kJ/mol, which is the value of the lattice energy:

$$NaCl(s) \longrightarrow Na^+(g) + Cl^-(g) \qquad \Delta H_{\text{lattice}} = +788 \text{ kJ/mol} \qquad [8.3]$$

Notice that this process is highly endothermic. The reverse process—the coming together of $Na^+(g)$ and $Cl^-(g)$ to form $NaCl(s)$—is therefore highly exothermic ($\Delta H = -788$ kJ/mol).

▶ **TABLE 8.2** lists the lattice energies for a number of ionic compounds. The large positive values indicate that the ions are strongly attracted to one another in ionic solids. The energy released by the attraction between ions of unlike charge more than makes up for the endothermic nature of ionization energies, making the formation of ionic compounds an exothermic process. The strong attractions also cause most ionic materials to be hard and brittle with high melting points—for example, NaCl melts at 801 °C.

Compound	Lattice Energy (kJ/mol)	Compound	Lattice Energy (kJ/mol)
LiF	1030	$MgCl_2$	2326
LiCl	834	$SrCl_2$	2127
LiI	730		
NaF	910	MgO	3795
NaCl	788	CaO	3414
NaBr	732	SrO	3217
NaI	682		
KF	808	ScN	7547
KCl	701		
KBr	671		
CsCl	657		
CsI	600		

TABLE 8.2 • Lattice Energies for Some Ionic Compounds

The magnitude of the lattice energy of an ionic solid depends on the charges of the ions, their sizes, and their arrangement in the solid. We saw in Section 5.1 that the potential energy of two interacting charged particles is given by

$$E_{el} = \frac{\kappa Q_1 Q_2}{d} \qquad [8.4]$$

In this equation Q_1 and Q_2 are the charges on the particles, d is the distance between their centers, and κ is a constant, 8.99×10^9 J-m/C^2. Equation 8.4 indicates that the attractive interaction between two oppositely charged ions increases as the magnitudes of their charges increase and as the distance between their centers decreases. Thus, *for a given arrangement of ions, the lattice energy increases as the charges on the ions increase and as their radii decrease.* The magnitude of lattice energies depends predominantly on the ionic charges because ionic radii vary over only a limited range.

SAMPLE EXERCISE 8.1 **Magnitudes of Lattice Energies**

Without consulting Table 8.2, arrange the ionic compounds NaF, CsI, and CaO in order of increasing lattice energy.

SOLUTION

Analyze From the formulas for three ionic compounds, we must determine their relative lattice energies.

Plan We need to determine the charges and relative sizes of the ions in the compounds. We then use Equation 8.4 qualitatively to determine the relative energies, knowing that (a) the larger the ionic charges, the greater the energy and (b) the farther apart the ions are, the lower the energy.

Solve NaF consists of Na$^+$ and F$^-$ ions, CsI of Cs$^+$ and I$^-$ ions, and CaO of Ca^{2+} and O^{2-} ions. Because the product $Q_1 Q_2$ appears in the numerator of Equation 8.4, the lattice energy increases dramatically when the charges increase. Thus, we expect the lattice energy of CaO, which has 2+ and 2− ions, to be the greatest of the three.

The ionic charges are the same in NaF and CsI. As a result, the difference in their lattice energies depends on the difference in the distance between ions in the lattice. Because ionic size increases as we go down a group in the periodic table ∞ (Section 7.3), we know that Cs$^+$ is larger than Na$^+$ and I$^-$ is larger than F$^-$. Therefore, the distance between Na$^+$ and F$^-$ ions in NaF is less than the distance between the Cs$^+$ and I$^-$ ions in CsI. As a result, the lattice energy of NaF should be greater than that of CsI. In order of increasing energy, therefore, we have CsI < NaF < CaO.

Check Table 8.2 confirms our predicted order is correct.

PRACTICE EXERCISE

Which substance do you expect to have the greatest lattice energy, MgF_2, CaF_2, or ZrO_2?
Answer: ZrO_2

GO FIGURE

Using this figure, can you place an upper and lower limit on the lattice energy of KF?

► **FIGURE 8.4   Periodic trends in lattice energy as a function of cation or anion radius.**

Because lattice energy decreases as distance between ions increases, lattice energies follow trends that parallel those in ionic radius shown in Figure 7.6. In particular, because ionic radius increases as we go down a group of the periodic table, we find that, for a given type of ionic compound, lattice energy decreases as we go down a group. ▲ **FIGURE 8.4** illustrates this trend for the alkali chlorides MCl (M = Li, Na, K, Rb, Cs) and the sodium halides NaX (X = F, Cl, Br, I).

Electron Configurations of Ions of the *s*- and *p*-Block Elements

The energetics of ionic bond formation helps explain why many ions tend to have noble-gas electron configurations. For example, sodium readily loses one electron to form Na^+, which has the same electron configuration as Ne:

$$Na \qquad 1s^2 2s^2 2p^6 3s^1 = [Ne]3s^1$$

$$Na^+ \qquad 1s^2 2s^2 2p^6 \quad = [Ne]$$

Even though lattice energy increases with increasing ionic charge, we never find ionic compounds that contain Na^{2+} ions. The second electron removed would have to come from an inner shell of the sodium atom, and removing electrons from an inner shell requires a very large amount of energy. ∞ (Section 7.4) The increase in lattice energy is not enough to compensate for the energy needed to remove an inner-shell electron. Thus, sodium and the other group 1A metals are found in ionic substances only as 1+ ions.

Similarly, adding electrons to nonmetals is either exothermic or only slightly endothermic as long as the electrons are added to the valence shell. Thus, a Cl atom easily adds an electron to form Cl^-, which has the same electron configuration as Ar:

$$Cl \qquad 1s^2 2s^2 2p^6 3s^2 3p^5 = [Ne]3s^2 3p^5$$

$$Cl^- \qquad 1s^2 2s^2 2p^6 3s^2 3p^6 = [Ne]3s^2 3p^6 = [Ar]$$

To form a Cl^{2-} ion, the second electron would have to be added to the next higher shell of the Cl atom, an addition that is energetically very unfavorable. Therefore, we never observe Cl^{2-} ions in ionic compounds. We thus expect ionic compounds of the representative metals from groups 1A, 2A, and 3A to contain 1+, 2+, and 3+ cations, respectively, and usually expect ionic compounds of the representative nonmetals of groups 5A, 6A, and 7A to contain 3−, 2−, and 1− anions, respectively.

A CLOSER LOOK

CALCULATION OF LATTICE ENERGIES: THE BORN–HABER CYCLE

Lattice energies cannot be determined directly by experiment. They can, however, be calculated by envisioning the formation of an ionic compound as occurring in a series of well-defined steps. We can then use Hess's law ∞∞ (Section 5.6) to combine the steps in a way that gives the lattice energy for the compound. By so doing, we construct a **Born–Haber cycle**, a thermochemical cycle named after the German scientists Max Born (1882–1970) and Fritz Haber (1868–1934), who introduced it to analyze the factors contributing to the stability of ionic compounds.

In the Born–Haber cycle for NaCl, we consider the formation of NaCl(s) from Na(s) and $Cl_2(g)$ by two routes, as shown in ▶ FIGURE 8.5. The enthalpy change for the direct route (red arrow) is the heat of formation of NaCl(s):

$$Na(s) + \tfrac{1}{2} Cl_2(g) \longrightarrow NaCl(s) \quad \Delta H^\circ_f[NaCl(s)] = -411 \text{ kJ} \quad [8.5]$$

The indirect route has five steps (green arrows in Figure 8.5). First, we generate Na(g) atoms by vaporizing Na(s). Then we form Cl(g) atoms by breaking the bonds in Cl_2 molecules. The enthalpy changes are (Appendix C):

$$Na(s) \longrightarrow Na(g) \quad \Delta H^\circ_f[Na(g)] = 108 \text{ kJ} \quad [8.6]$$

$$\tfrac{1}{2} Cl_2(g) \longrightarrow Cl(g) \quad \Delta H^\circ_f[Cl(g)] = 122 \text{ kJ} \quad [8.7]$$

Note that both processes are endothermic.

In the next two steps we remove the electron from Na(g) to form $Na^+(g)$ and then add the electron to Cl(g) to form $Cl^-(g)$. The enthalpy changes for these processes equal the first ionization energy of Na, $I_1(Na)$, and the electron affinity of Cl, denoted $E(Cl)$, respectively: ∞∞ (Sections 7.4, 7.5)

$$Na(g) \longrightarrow Na^+(g) + e^- \quad \Delta H = I_1(Na) = 496 \text{ kJ} \quad [8.8]$$

$$Cl(g) + e^- \longrightarrow Cl^-(g) \quad \Delta H = E(Cl) = -349 \text{ kJ} \quad [8.9]$$

Finally, we combine the $Na^+(g)$ and $Cl^-(g)$ to form NaCl(s). Because forming solid NaCl is the reverse of breaking the solid into its gaseous ions, the enthalpy change for solid formation is the negative of the lattice energy, the quantity we want to determine:

$$Na^+(g) + Cl^-(g) \longrightarrow NaCl(s) \quad \Delta H = -\Delta H_{lattice} = ? \quad [8.10]$$

▲ **FIGURE 8.5 Born–Haber cycle for formation of NaCl.** This Hess's law representation shows the energetic relationships in the formation of the ionic solid from its elements.

The result of the five-step pathway is formation of NaCl(s) from Na(s) and $\tfrac{1}{2} Cl_2(g)$. Thus, from Hess's law we know that the sum of the enthalpy changes for the five steps equals the enthalpy change for the direct reaction (Equation 8.5):

$$\Delta H^\circ_f[NaCl(s)] = \Delta H^\circ_f[Na(g)] + \Delta H^\circ_f[Cl(g)]$$
$$+ I_1(Na) + E(Cl) - \Delta H_{lattice}$$
$$-411 \text{ kJ} = 108 \text{ kJ} + 122 \text{ kJ} + 496 \text{ kJ} - 349 \text{ kJ} - \Delta H_{lattice}$$

Solving for $\Delta H_{lattice}$:

$$\Delta H_{lattice} = 108 \text{ kJ} + 122 \text{ kJ} + 496 \text{ kJ} - 349 \text{ kJ} + 411 \text{ kJ}$$
$$= 788 \text{ kJ}$$

Thus, the lattice energy of NaCl is 788 kJ/mol.

RELATED EXERCISES: 8.28, 8.29, 8.30, 8.83, 8.102, 8.103

SAMPLE EXERCISE 8.2 Charges on Ions

Predict the ion generally formed by (**a**) Sr, (**b**) S, (**c**) Al.

SOLUTION

Analyze We must decide how many electrons are most likely to be gained or lost by atoms of Sr, S, and Al.

Plan In each case we can use the element's position in the periodic table to predict whether the element forms a cation or an anion. We can then use its electron configuration to determine the most likely ion formed.

Solve (**a**) Strontium is a metal in group 2A and therefore forms a cation. Its electron configuration is $[Kr]5s^2$, and so we expect that the two valence electrons can be lost easily to give an Sr^{2+} ion. (**b**) Sulfur is a nonmetal in group 6A and will thus tend to be found as an anion. Its electron configuration ($[Ne]3s^23p^4$) is two electrons short of a noble-gas configuration. Thus, we expect that sulfur will form S^{2-} ions. (**c**) Aluminum is a metal in group 3A. We therefore expect it to form Al^{3+} ions.

Check The ionic charges we predict here are confirmed in Tables 2.4 and 2.5.

PRACTICE EXERCISE
Predict the charges on the ions formed when magnesium reacts with nitrogen.
Answer: Mg^{2+} and N^{3-}

Transition-Metal Ions

Because ionization energies increase rapidly for each successive electron removed, the lattice energies of ionic compounds are generally large enough to compensate for the loss of up to only three electrons from atoms. Thus, we find cations with charges of 1+, 2+, or 3+ in ionic compounds. Most transition metals, however, have more than three electrons beyond a noble-gas core. Silver, for example, has a $[Kr]4d^{10}5s^1$ electron configuration. Metals of group 1B (Cu, Ag, Au) often occur as 1+ ions (as in CuBr and AgCl). In forming Ag^+, the 5s electron is lost, leaving a completely filled 4d subshell. As in this example, transition metals generally do not form ions that have a noble-gas configuration. The octet rule, although useful, is clearly limited in scope.

Recall from Section 7.4 that when a positive ion forms from an atom, electrons are always lost first from the subshell having the largest value of *n*. Thus, *in forming ions, transition metals lose the valence-shell s electrons first, then as many d electrons as required to reach the charge of the ion.* For instance, in forming Fe^{2+} from Fe, which has the electron configuration $[Ar]3d^64s^2$, the two 4s electrons are lost, leading to an $[Ar]3d^6$ configuration. Removal of an additional electron gives Fe^{3+}, whose electron configuration is $[Ar]3d^5$.

GIVE IT SOME THOUGHT
Which element forms a 3+ ion that has the electron configuration $[Kr]4d^6$?

8.3 | COVALENT BONDING

The vast majority of chemical substances do not have the characteristics of ionic materials. Most of the substances with which we come into daily contact—such as water—tend to be gases, liquids, or solids with low melting points. Many, such as gasoline, vaporize readily. Many are pliable in their solid forms—for example, plastic bags and paraffin.

For the very large class of substances that do not behave like ionic substances, we need a different model for the bonding between atoms. G. N. Lewis reasoned that atoms might acquire a noble-gas electron configuration by sharing electrons with other atoms. A chemical bond formed by sharing a pair of electrons is a *covalent bond*.

The hydrogen molecule, H_2, provides the simplest example of a covalent bond. When two hydrogen atoms are close to each other, the two positively charged nuclei repel each other, the two negatively charged electrons repel each other, and the nuclei and electrons attract each other, as shown in ◀ FIGURE 8.6(a). Because the molecule is stable, we know that the attractive forces must overcome the repulsive ones. Let's take a closer look at the attractive forces that hold this molecule together.

By using quantum mechanical methods analogous to those used for atoms in Section 6.5, we can calculate the distribution of electron density in molecules. Such a calculation for H_2 shows that the attractions between the nuclei and the electrons cause electron density to concentrate between the nuclei, as shown in Figure 8.6(b). As a result, the overall electrostatic interactions are attractive. Thus, the atoms in H_2 are held together principally because the two positive nuclei are attracted to the concentration of negative charge between them. In essence, the shared pair of electrons in any covalent bond acts as a kind of "glue" to bind atoms together.

GO FIGURE

What would happen to the magnitudes of the attractions and repulsions represented in (a) if the nuclei were farther apart?

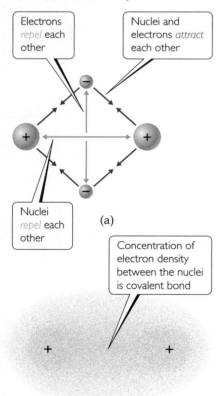

▲ **FIGURE 8.6 The covalent bond in H_2.**
(a) The attractions and repulsions among electrons and nuclei in the hydrogen molecule. (b) Electron distribution in the H_2 molecule.

⚠ GIVE IT SOME THOUGHT

Ionizing an H_2 molecule to H_2^+ changes the strength of the bond. Based on the description of covalent bonding given previously, do you expect the H—H bond in H_2^+ to be weaker or stronger than the H—H bond in H_2?

Lewis Structures

The formation of covalent bonds can be represented with Lewis symbols. The formation of the H_2 molecule from two H atoms, for example, can be represented as

$$H\cdot\ +\ \cdot H \longrightarrow \boxed{H\!:\!H}$$

In forming the covalent bond, each hydrogen atom acquires a second electron, achieving the stable, two-electron, noble-gas electron configuration of helium.

Formation of a covalent bond between two Cl atoms to give a Cl_2 molecule can be represented in a similar way:

$$:\!\overset{..}{\underset{..}{Cl}}\!\cdot\ +\ \cdot\overset{..}{\underset{..}{Cl}}\!: \longrightarrow \boxed{:\!\overset{..}{\underset{..}{Cl}}\!:\!\overset{..}{\underset{..}{Cl}}\!:}$$

By sharing the bonding electron pair, each chlorine atom has eight electrons (an octet) in its valence shell, thus achieving the noble-gas electron configuration of argon.

The structures shown here for H_2 and Cl_2 are called either **Lewis structures** or *Lewis electron-dot structures*. In writing Lewis structures, we usually show each shared electron pair as a line and any unshared electron pairs as dots. Written this way, the Lewis structures for H_2 and Cl_2 are

$$H\!-\!H \qquad\qquad :\!\overset{..}{\underset{..}{Cl}}\!-\!\overset{..}{\underset{..}{Cl}}\!:$$

For nonmetals, the number of valence electrons in a neutral atom is the same as the group number. Therefore, one might predict that 7A elements, such as F, would form one covalent bond to achieve an octet; 6A elements, such as O, would form two covalent bonds; 5A elements, such as N, would form three; and 4A elements, such as C, would form four. These predictions are borne out in many compounds, as in, for example, the compounds with hydrogen of the nonmetals of the second row of the periodic table:

$$H\!-\!\overset{..}{\underset{..}{F}}\!: \qquad H\!-\!\overset{..}{\underset{..}{\underset{\displaystyle H}{O}}}\!: \qquad H\!-\!\overset{..}{\underset{\displaystyle H}{N}}\!-\!H \qquad H\!-\!\overset{\displaystyle H}{\underset{\displaystyle H}{C}}\!-\!H$$

SAMPLE EXERCISE 8.3 | **Lewis Structure of a Compound**

Given the Lewis symbols for nitrogen and fluorine in Table 8.1, predict the formula of the stable binary compound (a compound composed of two elements) formed when nitrogen reacts with fluorine and draw its Lewis structure.

SOLUTION

Analyze The Lewis symbols for nitrogen and fluorine reveal that nitrogen has five valence electrons and fluorine has seven.

Plan We need to find a combination of the two elements that results in an octet of electrons around each atom. Nitrogen requires three additional electrons to complete its octet, and fluorine requires one. Sharing a pair of electrons between one N atom and one F atom will result in an octet of electrons for fluorine but not for nitrogen. We therefore need to figure out a way to get two more electrons for the N atom.

Solve Nitrogen must share a pair of electrons with three fluorine atoms to complete its octet. Thus, the binary compound these two elements form must be NF_3:

$$\cdot\overset{\displaystyle\cdot}{N}\!\cdot\ +\ 3\ \cdot\overset{..}{\underset{..}{F}}\!: \longrightarrow :\!\overset{..}{\underset{..}{F}}\!:\!\overset{\displaystyle\cdot\cdot}{N}\!:\!\overset{..}{\underset{..}{F}}\!: \longrightarrow :\!\overset{..}{\underset{..}{F}}\!-\!\overset{..}{\underset{\displaystyle :\!\overset{..}{\underset{..}{F}}\!:}{N}}\!-\!\overset{..}{\underset{..}{F}}\!:$$
$$\overset{..}{\underset{..}{F}}:$$

Check The Lewis structure in the center shows that each atom is surrounded by an octet of electrons. Once you are accustomed to thinking of each line in a Lewis structure as representing *two* electrons, you can just as easily use the structure on the right to check for octets.

PRACTICE EXERCISE

Compare the Lewis symbol for neon with the Lewis structure for methane, CH_4. In what important way are the electron arrangements about neon and carbon alike? In what important way are they different?

Answer: Both atoms have an octet of electrons. However, the electrons about neon are unshared electron pairs, whereas those about carbon are shared with four hydrogen atoms.

Multiple Bonds

A shared electron pair constitutes a single covalent bond, generally referred to simply as a **single bond**. In many molecules, atoms attain complete octets by sharing more than one pair of electrons. When two electron pairs are shared, two lines are drawn in the Lewis structure, representing a **double bond**. In carbon dioxide, for example, bonding occurs between carbon, with four valence electrons, and oxygen, with six:

$$:\ddot{O}: + \cdot\dot{C}\cdot + :\ddot{O}: \longrightarrow \ddot{O}::C::\ddot{O} \quad \text{(or } \ddot{O}{=}C{=}\ddot{O})$$

As the diagram shows, each oxygen atom acquires an octet by sharing two electron pairs with carbon. Carbon acquires an octet by sharing two electron pairs with each of the two oxygen atoms; each double bond involves four electrons.

A **triple bond** corresponds to the sharing of three pairs of electrons, such as in the N_2 molecule:

$$:\dot{N}\cdot + \cdot\dot{N}: \longrightarrow :N{:::}N: \quad \text{(or } :N{\equiv}N:)$$

Because each nitrogen atom has five valence electrons, three electron pairs must be shared to achieve the octet configuration.

The properties of N_2 are in complete accord with its Lewis structure. Nitrogen is a diatomic gas with exceptionally low reactivity that results from the very stable nitrogen–nitrogen bond. The nitrogen atoms are separated by only 1.10 Å. The short separation distance between the two N atoms is a result of the triple bond between the atoms. From studies of the structures of many different substances in which nitrogen atoms share one or two electron pairs, we have learned that the average distance between bonded nitrogen atoms varies with the number of shared electron pairs:

N—N	N=N	N≡N
1.47 Å	1.24 Å	1.10 Å

As a general rule, the length of the bond between two atoms decreases as the number of shared electron pairs increases.

> ▲ **GIVE IT SOME THOUGHT**
>
> The C—O bond length in carbon monoxide, CO, is 1.13 Å, whereas the C—O bond length in CO_2 is 1.24 Å. Without drawing a Lewis structure, do you think that CO contains a single, double, or triple bond?

8.4 | BOND POLARITY AND ELECTRONEGATIVITY

When two identical atoms bond, as in Cl_2 or H_2, the electron pairs must be shared equally. When two atoms from opposites sides of the periodic table bond, such as NaCl, there is relatively little sharing of electrons, which means that NaCl is best described as composed of Na^+ and Cl^- ions. The $3s$ electron of the Na atom is, in effect, transferred completely to chlorine. The bonds that are found in most substances fall somewhere between these extremes.

Bond polarity is a measure of how equally or unequally the electrons in any covalent bond are shared. A **nonpolar covalent bond** is one in which the electrons are shared equally, as in Cl_2 and N_2. In a **polar covalent bond**, one of the atoms exerts a greater attraction for the bonding electrons than the other. If the difference in relative ability to attract electrons is large enough, an ionic bond is formed.

Electronegativity

We use a quantity called electronegativity to estimate whether a given bond is nonpolar covalent, polar covalent, or ionic. **Electronegativity** is defined as the ability of an atom *in a molecule* to attract electrons to itself. The greater an atom's electronegativity, the greater its ability to attract electrons to itself. The electronegativity of an atom in a molecule is related to the atom's ionization energy and electron affinity, which are properties of isolated atoms. An atom with a very negative electron affinity and a high ionization energy both attracts electrons from other atoms and resists having its electrons attracted away; it is highly electronegative.

Electronegativity values can be based on a variety of properties, not just ionization energy and electron affinity. The American chemist Linus Pauling (1901–1994) developed the first and most widely used electronegativity scale, which is based on thermochemical data. As ▼ **FIGURE 8.7** shows, there is generally an increase in electronegativity from left to right across a period—that is, from the most metallic to the most nonmetallic elements. With some exceptions (especially in the transition metals), electronegativity decreases with increasing atomic number in a group. This is what we expect because we know that ionization energies decrease with increasing atomic number in a group and electron affinities do not change very much.

You do not need to memorize electronegativity values. Instead, you should know the periodic trends so that you can predict which of two elements is more electronegative.

 GIVE IT SOME THOUGHT

How does the *electronegativity* of an element differ from its *electron affinity*?

 GO FIGURE

For the group 6A elements, what is the trend in electronegativity with increasing atomic number?

◀ **FIGURE 8.7 Electronegativity values based on Pauling's thermochemical data.**

Electronegativity and Bond Polarity

We can use the difference in electronegativity between two atoms to gauge the polarity of the bond the atoms form. Consider these three fluorine-containing compounds:

	F_2	HF	LiF
Electronegativity difference	$4.0 - 4.0 = 0$	$4.0 - 2.1 = 1.9$	$4.0 - 1.0 = 3.0$
Type of bond	Nonpolar covalent	Polar covalent	Ionic

In F_2 the electrons are shared equally between the fluorine atoms and, thus, the co-valent bond is *nonpolar*. A nonpolar covalent bond results when the electronegativities of the bonded atoms are equal.

In HF the fluorine atom has a greater electronegativity than the hydrogen atom, with the result that the electrons are shared unequally—the bond is *polar*. In general, a polar covalent bond results when the atoms differ in electronegativity. In HF the more electronegative fluorine atom attracts electron density away from the less electronegative hydrogen atom, leaving a partial positive charge on the hydrogen atom and a partial negative charge on the fluorine atom. We can represent this charge distribution as

$$\overset{\delta+}{H} - \overset{\delta-}{F}$$

The $\delta+$ and $\delta-$ (read "delta plus" and "delta minus") symbolize the partial positive and negative charges, respectively.

In LiF the electronegativity difference is very large, meaning that the electron density is shifted far toward F. The resultant bond is therefore most accurately described as *ionic*.

The shift of electron density toward the more electronegative atom in a bond can be seen in the results of calculations of electron density distributions. For the three species in our example, the calculated electron density distributions are shown in ▼ FIGURE 8.8. You can see that in F_2 the distribution is symmetrical, in HF the electron density is clearly shifted toward fluorine, and in LiF the shift is even greater. These examples illustrate, therefore, that *the greater the difference in electronegativity between two atoms, the more polar their bond.*

F_2 HF LiF

▲ **FIGURE 8.8 Electron density distribution.** This computer-generated rendering shows the calculated electron-density distribution on the surface of the F_2, HF, and LiF molecules.

◢ GIVE IT SOME THOUGHT

Based on differences in electronegativity, how would you characterize the bonding in sulfur dioxide, SO_2? Do you expect the bonds between S and O to be nonpolar, polar covalent, or ionic?

SAMPLE EXERCISE 8.4 Bond Polarity

In each case, which bond is more polar: **(a)** B—Cl or C—Cl, **(b)** P—F or P—Cl ? Indicate in each case which atom has the partial negative charge.

SOLUTION

Analyze We are asked to determine relative bond polarities, given nothing but the atoms involved in the bonds.

Plan Because we are not asked for quantitative answers, we can use the periodic table and our knowledge of electronegativity trends to answer the question.

Solve
(a) The chlorine atom is common to both bonds. Therefore, the analysis reduces to a comparison of the electronegativities of B and C. Because boron is to the left of carbon in the periodic table, we predict that boron has the lower electronegativity. Chlorine, being on the right side of the table, has a higher electronegativity. The more polar bond will be the one between the atoms having the lowest electronegativity (boron) and the highest electronegativity (chlorine). Consequently, the B—Cl bond is more polar; the chlorine atom carries the partial negative charge because it has a higher electronegativity.

(b) In this example phosphorus is common to both bonds, and the analysis reduces to a comparison of the electronegativities of F and Cl. Because fluorine is above chlorine in the periodic table, it should be more electronegative and will form the more polar bond with P. The higher electronegativity of fluorine means that it will carry the partial negative charge.

Check
(a) Using Figure 8.7: The difference in the electronegativities of chlorine and boron is $3.0 - 2.0 = 1.0$; the difference between chlorine and carbon is $3.0 - 2.5 = 0.5$. Hence, the B—Cl bond is more polar, as we had predicted.

(b) Using Figure 8.7: The difference in the electronegativities of chlorine and phosphorus is $3.0 - 2.1 = 0.9$; the difference between fluorine and phosphorus is $4.0 - 2.1 = 1.9$. Hence, the P—F bond is more polar, as we had predicted.

PRACTICE EXERCISE
Which of the following bonds is most polar: S—Cl, S—Br, Se—Cl, cr Se—Br ?
Answer: Se—Cl

Dipole Moments

The difference in electronegativity between H and F leads to a polar covalent bond in the HF molecule. As a consequence, there is a concentration of negative charge on the more electronegative F atom, leaving the less electronegative H atom at the positive end of the molecule. A molecule such as HF, in which the centers of positive and negative charge do not coincide, is a **polar molecule**. Thus, we describe both bonds and entire molecules as being polar and nonpolar.

We can indicate the polarity of the HF molecule in two ways:

$$\overset{\delta-}{H} - \overset{\delta-}{F} \quad or \quad \overset{\longmapsto}{H-F}$$

In the notation on the right, the arrow denotes the shift in electron density toward the fluorine atom. The crossed end of the arrow can be thought of as a plus sign designating the positive end of the molecule.

Polarity helps determine many properties we observe at the macroscopic level in the laboratory and in everyday life. Polar molecules align themselves with respect to one another, with the negative end of one molecule and the positive end of another attracting each other. Polar molecules are likewise attracted to ions. The negative end of a polar molecule is attracted to a positive ion, and the positive end is attracted to a negative ion. These interactions account for many properties of liquids, solids, and solutions, as you will see in Chapters 11, 12, and 13.

How can we quantify the polarity of a molecule? Whenever two electrical charges of equal magnitude but opposite sign are separated by a distance, a **dipole** is established. The quantitative measure of the magnitude of a dipole is called its **dipole moment**, denoted μ. If two equal and opposite charges $Q+$ and $Q-$ are separated by a distance r, as in ▶ FIGURE 8.9, the magnitude of the dipole moment is the product of Q and r:

$$\mu = Qr \qquad [8.11]$$

▲ **GO FIGURE**

If the charged particles are moved closer together, does μ increase, decrease, or stay the same?

Dipole moment $\mu = Qr$

▲ **FIGURE 8.9   Dipole and dipole moment.** When charges of equal magnitude and opposite sign $Q+$ and $Q-$ are separated by a distance r, a dipole is produced.

This expression tells us that dipole moment increases as the magnitude of Q increases and as r increases. For a nonpolar molecule, such as F_2, the dipole moment is zero because there is no charge separation.

▲ GIVE IT SOME THOUGHT

Chlorine monofluoride, ClF, and iodine monofluoride, IF, are *interhalogen* compounds—compounds that contain bonds between different halogen elements. Which of these molecules has the larger dipole moment?

Dipole moments are usually reported in *debyes* (D), a unit that equals 3.34×10^{-30} coulomb-meters (C-m). For molecules, we usually measure charge in units of the electronic charge e, 1.60×10^{-19} C, and distance in angstroms. This means we need to convert units whenever we want to report a dipole moment in debyes. Suppose that two charges $1+$ and $1-$ (in units of e) are separated by 1.00 Å. The dipole moment produced is

$$\mu = Qr = (1.60 \times 10^{-19}\,\text{C})(1.00\,\text{Å})\left(\frac{10^{-10}\,\text{m}}{1\,\text{Å}}\right)\left(\frac{1\,\text{D}}{3.34 \times 10^{-30}\,\text{C-m}}\right) = 4.79\,\text{D}$$

Measurement of the dipole moments can provide us with valuable information about the charge distributions in molecules, as illustrated in Sample Exercise 8.5.

SAMPLE EXERCISE 8.5 | Dipole Moments of Diatomic Molecules

The bond length in the HCl molecule is 1.27 Å. **(a)** Calculate the dipole moment, in debyes, that results if the charges on the H and Cl atoms were $1+$ and $1-$, respectively. **(b)** The experimentally measured dipole moment of $HCl(g)$ is 1.08 D. What magnitude of charge, in units of e, on the H and Cl atoms leads to this dipole moment?

SOLUTION

Analyze and Plan We are asked in (a) to calculate the dipole moment of HCl that would result if there were a full charge transferred from H to Cl. We can use Equation 8.11 to obtain this result. In (b), we are given the actual dipole moment for the molecule and will use that value to calculate the actual partial charges on the H and Cl atoms.

Solve:

(a) The charge on each atom is the electronic charge, $e = 1.60 \times 10^{-19}$ C. The separation is 1.27 Å. The dipole moment is therefore

$$\mu = Qr = (1.60 \times 10^{-19}\,\text{C})(1.27\,\text{Å})\left(\frac{10^{-10}\,\text{m}}{1\,\text{Å}}\right)\left(\frac{1\,\text{D}}{3.34 \times 10^{-30}\,\text{C-m}}\right) = 6.08\,\text{D}$$

(b) We know the value of μ, 1.08 D, and the value of r, 1.27 Å. We want to calculate the value of Q:

$$Q = \frac{\mu}{r} = \frac{(1.08\,\text{D})\left(\dfrac{3.34 \times 10^{-30}\,\text{C-m}}{1\,\text{D}}\right)}{(1.27\,\text{Å})\left(\dfrac{10^{-10}\,\text{m}}{1\,\text{Å}}\right)} = 2.84 \times 10^{-20}\,\text{C}$$

We can readily convert this charge to units of e:

$$\text{Charge in } e = (2.84 \times 10^{-20}\,\text{C})\left(\frac{1\,e}{1.60 \times 10^{-19}\,\text{C}}\right) = 0.178e$$

Thus, the experimental dipole moment indicates that the charge separation in the HCl molecule is

$$\overset{0.178+}{\text{H}} \quad - \quad \overset{0.178-}{\text{Cl}}$$

Because the experimental dipole moment is less than that calculated in part (a), the charges on the atoms are much less than a full electronic charge. We could have anticipated this because the H—Cl bond is polar covalent rather than ionic.

PRACTICE EXERCISE

The dipole moment of chlorine monofluoride, $ClF(g)$, is 0.88 D. The bond length of the molecule is 1.63 Å. **(a)** Which atom is expected to have the partial negative charge? **(b)** What is the charge on that atom in units of e?

Answers: **(a)** F, **(b)** $0.11-$

TABLE 8.3 • Bond Lengths, Electronegativity Differences, and Dipole Moments of the Hydrogen Halides

Compound	Bond Length (Å)	Electronegativity Difference	Dipole Moment (D)
HF	0.92	1.9	1.82
HCl	1.27	0.9	1.08
HBr	1.41	0.7	0.82
HI	1.61	0.4	0.44

▲ **TABLE 8.3** presents the bond lengths and dipole moments of the hydrogen halides. Notice that as we proceed from HF to HI, the electronegativity difference decreases and the bond length increases. The first effect decreases the amount of charge separated and causes the dipole moment to decrease from HF to HI, even though the bond length is increasing. Calculations identical to those used in Sample Exercise 8.5 show that the charges on the atoms decrease from 0.41+ and 0.41− in HF to 0.057+ and 0.057− in HI. We can visualize the varying degree of electronic charge shift in these substances from computer-generated renderings based on calculations of electron distribution, as shown in ▼ **FIGURE 8.10**. For these molecules, the change in the electronegativity difference has a greater effect on the dipole moment than does the change in bond length.

GIVE IT SOME THOUGHT

The bond between carbon and hydrogen is one of the most important types of bonds in chemistry. The length of a H—C bond is approximately 1.1 Å. Based on this distance and differences in electronegativity, do you expect the dipole moment of an individual H—C bond to be larger or smaller than that of the H—I bond?

Before leaving this section, let's return to the LiF molecule in Figure 8.8. Under standard conditions, LiF exists as an ionic solid with an arrangement of atoms analogous to the sodium chloride structure shown in Figure 8.3. However, it is possible to generate LiF *molecules* by vaporizing the ionic solid at high temperature. The molecules have a dipole moment of 6.28 D and a bond distance of 1.53 Å. From these values we can calculate the charge on lithium and fluorine to be 0.857+ and 0.857−, respectively. This bond is extremely polar, and the presence of such large charges strongly favors the formation of an extended ionic lattice in which each lithium ion is surrounded by fluoride ions and vice versa.

GO FIGURE

How do you interpret the fact that there is no red in the HBr and HI representations?

HF   HCl   HBr   HI

▲ **FIGURE 8.10 Charge separation in the hydrogen halides.** In HF, the strongly electronegative F pulls much of the electron density away from H. In HI, the I, being much less electronegative than F, does not attract the shared electrons as strongly and, consequently, there is far less polarization of the bond.

Differentiating Ionic and Covalent Bonding

To understand the interactions responsible for chemical bonding, it is advantageous to treat ionic and covalent bonding separately. That is the approach taken in this chapter, as well as in most other undergraduate-level chemistry texts. In reality, however, there is a continuum between the extremes of ionic and covalent bonding. This lack of a well-defined separation between the two types of bonding may seem unsettling or confusing at first.

The simple models of ionic and covalent bonding presented in this chapter go a long way toward understanding and predicting the structures and properties of chemical compounds. When covalent bonding is dominant, more often than not we expect compounds to exist as molecules,* having all the properties we associate with molecular substances, such as relatively low melting and boiling points and nonelectrolyte behavior when dissolved in water. When ionic bonding is dominant, we expect the compounds to be brittle, high-melting solids with extended lattice structures and exhibiting strong electrolyte behavior when dissolved in water.

There are, of course, exceptions to these general characterizations, some of which we examine later in the book. Nonetheless, the ability to quickly categorize the predominant bonding interactions in a substance as covalent or ionic imparts considerable insight into the properties of that substance. The question then becomes the best way to recognize which type of bonding dominates.

The simplest approach is to assume that the interaction between a metal and a nonmetal is ionic and that between two nonmetals is covalent. While this classification scheme is reasonably predictive, there are far too many exceptions to use it blindly. For example, tin is a metal and chlorine is a nonmetal, but $SnCl_4$ is a molecular substance that exists as a colorless liquid at room temperature. It freezes at $-33\ °C$ and boils at $114\ °C$. Clearly this substance does not have the characteristics of an ionic substance. A more sophisticated approach is to use the difference in electronegativity as the main criterion for determining whether ionic or covalent bonding will be dominant. This approach correctly predicts the bonding in $SnCl_4$ to be polar covalent based on an electronegativity difference of 1.2 and at the same time correctly predicts the bonding in NaCl to be predominantly ionic based on an electronegativity difference of 2.1.

Evaluating bonding based on electronegativity difference is a useful system, but it has one shortcoming. The electronegativity values given in Figure 8.7 do not take into account changes in bonding that accompany changes in the oxidation state of the metal. For example, Figure 8.7 gives the electronegativity difference between manganese and oxygen as $3.5 - 1.5 = 2.0$, which falls in the range where the bonding is normally considered ionic (the electronegativity difference for NaCl is $3.0 - 0.9 = 2.1$). Therefore, it is not surprising to learn that manganese(II) oxide, MnO, is a green solid that melts at $1842\ °C$ and has the same crystal structure as NaCl.

However, the bonding between manganese and oxygen is not always ionic. Manganese(VII) oxide, Mn_2O_7, is a green liquid that freezes at $5.9\ °C$, which indicates that covalent rather than ionic bonding dominates. The change in the oxidation state of manganese is responsible for the change in bonding. In general, as the oxidation state of a metal increases, so does the degree of covalent bonding. When the oxidation state of the metal is highly positive (roughly speaking, +4 or larger), we should expect significant covalency in the bonds it forms with nonmetals. Thus, with metals in high oxidation states we find molecular substances, such as Mn_2O_7, or polyatomic ions, such as MnO_4^- and CrO_4^{2-}, rather than ionic compounds.

 GIVE IT SOME THOUGHT

You have a yellow solid that melts at 41 °C and boils at 131 °C and a green solid that melts at 2320 °C. If you are told that one of them is Cr_2O_3 and the other is OsO_4, which one do you expect to be the yellow solid?

---

*There are some exceptions to this statement, such as network solids, including diamond, silicon, and germanium, where an extended structure is formed even though the bonding is clearly covalent. These examples are discussed in Section 12.7.

8.5 | DRAWING LEWIS STRUCTURES

Lewis structures can help us understand the bonding in many compounds and are frequently used when discussing the properties of molecules. For this reason, drawing Lewis structures is an important skill that you should practice. To do so, you should use the following procedure.

1. **Sum the valence electrons from all atoms.** (Use the periodic table to help you determine the number of valence electrons in each atom.) For an anion, add one electron to the total for each negative charge. For a cation, subtract one electron from the total for each positive charge. Do not worry about keeping track of which electrons come from which atoms. Only the total number is important.

2. **Write the symbols for the atoms, show which atoms are attached to which, and connect them with a single bond** (*a dash, representing* **two** *electrons*). Chemical formulas are often written in the order in which the atoms are connected in the molecule or ion. The formula HCN, for example, tells you that the carbon atom is bonded to the H and to the N. In many polyatomic molecules and ions, the central atom is usually written first, as in CO_3^{2-} and SF_4. Remember that the central atom is generally less electronegative than the atoms surrounding it. In other cases, you may need more information before you can draw the Lewis structure.

3. **Complete the octets around all the atoms bonded to the central atom.** Remember, however, that a hydrogen atom has only a single pair of electrons around it.

4. **Place any leftover electrons on the central atom,** even if doing so results in more than an octet of electrons around the atom.

5. **If there are not enough electrons to give the central atom an octet, try multiple bonds.** Use one or more of the unshared pairs of electrons on the atoms bonded to the central atom to form double or triple bonds.

SAMPLE EXERCISE 8.6   Drawing a Lewis Structure

Draw the Lewis structure for phosphorus trichloride, PCl_3.

SOLUTION

Analyze and Plan We are asked to draw a Lewis structure from a molecular formula. Our plan is to follow the five-step procedure just described.

Solve

First, we sum the valence electrons. Phosphorus (group 5A) has five valence electrons, and each chlorine (group 7A) has seven. The total number of valence electrons is therefore

$$5 + (3 \times 7) = 26$$

Second, we arrange the atoms to show which atom is connected to which, and we draw a single bond between them. There are various ways the atoms might be arranged. In binary compounds, however, the first element in the chemical formula is generally surrounded by the remaining atoms. Thus, we begin with a skeleton structure that shows a single bond between the P atom and each Cl atom:

$$\text{Cl}-\text{P}-\text{Cl}$$
$$|$$
$$\text{Cl}$$

(It is not crucial that the Cl atoms be left of, right of, and below the P atom—any structure that shows each of the three Cl atoms bonded to P will work.)

Third, we complete the octets on the atoms bonded to the central atom. Placing octets around each Cl atom accounts for 24 electrons (remember, each line in our structure represents *two* electrons):

$$:\ddot{\text{Cl}}-\text{P}-\ddot{\text{Cl}}:$$
$$|$$
$$:\ddot{\text{Cl}}:$$

Fourth, recalling that our total number of electrons is 26, we place the remaining two electrons on the central atom, completing the octet around it:

$$:\ddot{\text{Cl}}-\ddot{\text{P}}-\ddot{\text{Cl}}:$$
$$|$$
$$:\ddot{\text{Cl}}:$$

This structure gives each atom an octet, so we stop at this point. (In checking for octets, remember to count both electrons in a single bond twice, once for each atom in the bond.)

PRACTICE EXERCISE

(a) How many valence electrons should appear in the Lewis structure for CH_2Cl_2?

(b) Draw the Lewis structure.

Answers: (a) 20, (b)

$$:\ddot{\underset{..}{Cl}}-\overset{\overset{\displaystyle H}{|}}{\underset{\underset{\displaystyle H}{|}}{C}}-\ddot{\underset{..}{Cl}}:$$

SAMPLE EXERCISE 8.7 Lewis Structure with a Multiple Bond

Draw the Lewis structure for HCN.

SOLUTION

Hydrogen has one valence electron, carbon (group 4A) has four, and nitrogen (group 5A) has five. The total number of valence electrons is, therefore, $1 + 4 + 5 = 10$. In principle, there are different ways in which we might choose to arrange the atoms. Because hydrogen can accommodate only one electron pair, it always has only one single bond associated with it. Therefore, C—H—N is an impossible arrangement. The remaining two possibilities are H—C—N and H—N—C. The first is the arrangement found experimentally. You might have guessed this because (a) the formula is written with the atoms in this order and (b) carbon is less electronegative than nitrogen. Thus, we begin with the skeleton structure

$$H-C-N$$

The two bonds account for four electrons. The H atom can have only two electrons associated with it, and so we will not add any more electrons to it. If we place the remaining six electrons around N to give it an octet, we do not achieve an octet on C:

$$H-C-\ddot{\underset{..}{N}}:$$

We therefore try a double bond between C and N, using one of the unshared pairs we placed on N. Again we end up with fewer than eight electrons on C, and so we next try a triple bond. This structure gives an octet around both C and N:

$$H-C\overset{\frown}{\underset{\smile}{=}}\ddot{\underset{..}{N}}: \longrightarrow H-C\equiv N:$$

The octet rule is satisfied for the C and N atoms, and the H atom has two electrons around it. This is a correct Lewis structure.

PRACTICE EXERCISE

Draw the Lewis structure for (a) NO^+ ion, (b) C_2H_4.

Answers: (a) $[:N\equiv O:]^+$, (b)

$$\underset{\displaystyle H}{\overset{\displaystyle H}{}}\!\diagdown\!\!C=C\!\!\diagup\!\overset{\displaystyle H}{\underset{\displaystyle H}{}}$$

SAMPLE EXERCISE 8.8 Lewis Structure for a Polyatomic Ion

Draw the Lewis structure for the BrO_3^- ion.

SOLUTION

Bromine (group 7A) has seven valence electrons, and oxygen (group 6A) has six. We must add one more electron to our sum to account for the 1− charge of the ion. The total number of valence electrons is, therefore, $7 + (3 \times 6) + 1 = 26$. For oxyanions—$BrO_3^-$, SO_4^{2-}, NO_3^-, CO_3^{2-}, and so forth—the oxygen atoms surround the central nonmetal atom. After following this format and then putting in the single bonds and distributing the unshared electron pairs, we have

$$\left[:\ddot{\underset{..}{O}}-\overset{\textstyle}{\underset{\underset{\displaystyle :\ddot{\underset{..}{O}}:}{|}}{Br}}-\ddot{\underset{..}{O}}: \right]^-$$

Notice that the Lewis structure for an ion is written in brackets and the charge is shown outside the brackets at the upper right.

PRACTICE EXERCISE
Draw the Lewis structure for (a) ClO_2^-, (b) PO_4^{3-}.

Answers: (a) $\left[:\ddot{O}-\ddot{C}l-\ddot{O}:\right]^-$ **(b)** $\left[\begin{array}{c} :\ddot{O}: \\ | \\ :\ddot{O}-P-\ddot{O}: \\ | \\ :\ddot{O}: \end{array}\right]^{3-}$

Formal Charge and Alternative Lewis Structures

When we draw a Lewis structure, we are describing how the electrons are distributed in a molecule or polyatomic ion. In some instances we can draw more than one Lewis structure and have all of them obey the octet rule. All these structures can be thought of as contributing to the *actual* arrangement of the electrons in the molecule, but not all of them will contribute to the same extent. How do we decide which of several Lewis structures is the most important? One approach is to do some "bookkeeping" of the valence electrons to determine the *formal charge* of each atom in each Lewis structure. The **formal charge** of any atom in a molecule is the charge the atom would have if all the atoms in the molecule had the same electronegativity (that is, if each bonding electron pair in the molecule were shared equally between its two atoms).

To calculate the formal charge on any atom in a Lewis structure, we assign electrons to the atom as follows:

1. *All* unshared (nonbonding) electrons are assigned to the atom on which they are found.

2. For any bond—single, double, or triple—*half* of the bonding electrons are assigned to each atom in the bond.

The formal charge of each atom is calculated *by subtracting the number of electrons assigned to the atom from the number of valence electrons in the neutral atom.*

Let's practice by calculating the formal charges in the cyanide ion, CN^-, which has the Lewis structure

$$[:C\equiv N:]^-$$

For the C atom, there are two nonbonding electrons and three electrons from the six in the triple bond ($\frac{1}{2} \times 6 = 3$) for a total of five. The number of valence electrons on a neutral C atom is four. Thus, the formal charge on C is $4 - 5 = -1$. For N, there are two nonbonding electrons and three electrons from the triple bond. Because the number of valence electrons on a neutral N atom is five, its formal charge is $5 - 5 = 0$:

$$[:\overset{-1}{C}\equiv\overset{0}{N}:]^-$$

Notice that the sum of the formal charges equals the overall charge on the ion, $1-$. The formal charges on a neutral molecule must add to zero, whereas those on an ion add to give the charge on the ion.

If we can draw several Lewis structures for a molecule, the concept of formal charge can help us decide which is the most important, which we shall call the *dominant* Lewis structure. One Lewis structure for CO_2, for instance, has two double bonds, as we saw on page 298. However, we can also satisfy the octet rule by drawing a Lewis structure having one single bond and one triple bond. Calculating formal charges in these structures, we have

	$\ddot{O}=C=\ddot{O}$			$:\ddot{O}-C\equiv O:$		
Valence electrons:	6	4	6	6	4	6
−(Electrons assigned to atom):	6	4	6	7	4	5
Formal charge:	0	0	0	−1	0	+1

Note that in both cases the formal charges add up to zero, as they must because CO_2 is a neutral molecule. So, which is the more correct structure? As a general rule, when more than one Lewis structure is possible, we will use the following guidelines to choose the dominant one:

1. The dominant Lewis structure is generally the one in which the atoms bear formal charges closest to zero.

2. A Lewis structure in which any negative charges reside on the more electronegative atoms is generally more dominant than one that has negative charges on the less electronegative atoms.

Thus, the first Lewis structure of CO_2 is the dominant one because the atoms carry no formal charges and so satisfy the first guideline. The other Lewis structure shown (and the similar one that has a triple bond to the left O and a single bond to the right O) do contribute to the actual structure but to a much smaller extent.

Although the concept of formal charge helps us to arrange alternative Lewis structures in order of importance, it is important that you remember that *formal charges do not represent real charges on atoms*. These charges are just a bookkeeping convention. The actual charge distributions in molecules and ions are determined not by formal charges but by a number of other factors, including electronegativity differences between atoms.

 GIVE IT SOME THOUGHT

Suppose a Lewis structure for a neutral fluorine-containing molecule results in a formal charge on the fluorine atom of +1. What conclusion would you draw?

SAMPLE EXERCISE 8.9 | **Lewis Structures and Formal Charges**

Three possible Lewis structures for the thiocyanate ion, NCS^-, are

$$[:\ddot{N}-C\equiv S:]^- \qquad [\ddot{N}=C=\ddot{S}]^- \qquad [:N\equiv C-\ddot{\ddot{S}}:]^-$$

(a) Determine the formal charges in each structure. (b) Based on the formal charges, which Lewis structure is the dominant one?

SOLUTION

(a) Neutral N, C, and S atoms have five, four, and six valence electrons, respectively. We can determine the formal charges in the three structures by using the rules we just discussed:

$$\begin{array}{ccc} -2 \quad 0 \quad +1 & -1 \quad 0 \quad 0 & 0 \quad 0 \quad -1 \\ [:\ddot{N}-C\equiv S:]^- & [\ddot{N}=C=\ddot{S}]^- & [:N\equiv C-\ddot{\ddot{S}}:]^- \end{array}$$

As they must, the formal charges in all three structures sum to $1-$, the overall charge of the ion. (b) The dominant Lewis structure generally produces formal charges of the smallest magnitude (guideline 1). That rules out the left structure as the dominant one. Further, as discussed in Section 8.4, N is more electronegative than C or S. Therefore, we expect any negative formal charge to reside on the N atom (guideline 2). For these two reasons, the middle Lewis structure is the dominant one for NCS^-.

PRACTICE EXERCISE

The cyanate ion, NCO^-, has three possible Lewis structures. (a) Draw these three structures and assign formal charges in each. (b) Which Lewis structure is dominant?

$$\begin{array}{ccc} -2 \quad 0 \quad +1 & -1 \quad 0 \quad 0 & 0 \quad 0 \quad -1 \\ \textbf{\textit{Answers:}}\ (a)\ [:\ddot{N}-C\equiv O:]^- & [\ddot{N}=C=\ddot{O}]^- & [:N\equiv C-\ddot{\ddot{O}}:]^- \\ (i) & (ii) & (iii) \end{array}$$

(b) Structure (iii), which places a negative charge on oxygen, the most electronegative element in the ion, is the dominant Lewis structure.

A CLOSER LOOK

OXIDATION NUMBERS, FORMAL CHARGES, AND ACTUAL PARTIAL CHARGES

In Chapter 4 we introduced the rules for assigning *oxidation numbers* to atoms. The concept of electronegativity is the basis of these numbers. An atom's oxidation number is the charge the atom would have if its bonds were completely ionic. That is, in determining oxidation number, all shared electrons are counted with the more electronegative atom. For example, consider the Lewis structure of HCl in ▼ FIGURE 8.11(a). To assign oxidation numbers, both electrons in the covalent bond between the atoms are assigned to the more electronegative Cl atom. This procedure gives Cl eight valence electrons, one more than in the neutral atom. Thus, its oxidation number is −1. Hydrogen has no valence electrons when they are counted this way, giving it an oxidation number of +1.

To assign formal charges in this molecule, we ignore electronegativity and assign the electrons in bonds equally to the two bonded atoms. In the case of HCl, we divide the bonding pair of electrons equally between H and Cl, as in Figure 8.11(b). In this case Cl has seven assigned electrons, the same as that of the neutral Cl atom, and H has one assigned electron. Thus, the formal charges of both Cl and H in this compound are 0.

Neither oxidation number nor formal charge gives an accurate depiction of the actual charges on atoms because oxidation numbers overstate the role of electronegativity and formal charges ignore it.

It seems reasonable that electrons in covalent bonds should be apportioned according to the relative electronegativities of the bonded atoms. From Figure 8.7 we see that Cl has an electronegativity of 3.0, while that of H is 2.1. The more electronegative Cl atom might therefore be expected to have roughly $3.0/(3.0 + 2.1) = 0.59$ of the electrical charge in the bonding pair, whereas the H atom has $2.1/(3.0 + 2.1) = 0.41$ of the charge. Because the bond consists of two electrons, the Cl atom's share is $0.59 \times 2e = 1.18e$, or $0.18e$ more than the neutral Cl atom. This gives rise to a partial negative charge of 0.18− on Cl and a partial positive charge of 0.18+ on H. (Notice again that we place the plus and minus signs *before* the magnitude in writing oxidation numbers and formal charges but *after* the magnitude in writing actual charges.)

The dipole moment of HCl gives an experimental measure of the partial charge on each atom. In Sample Exercise 8.5 we saw that the dipole moment of HCl indicates a partial charge of 0.178+ on H and 0.178− on Cl, in remarkably good agreement with our simple approximation based on electronegativities. Although our approximation method provides "ballpark" numbers for the magnitude of charge on atoms, the relationship between electronegativities and charge separation is generally more complicated. As we have already seen, computer programs employing quantum mechanical principles have been developed to obtain more accurate estimates of the partial charges on atoms, even in complex molecules. A computer-graphical representation of the charge distribution in HCl is shown in Figure 8.11(c).

RELATED EXERCISES 8.8, 8.49, 8.50, 8.51, 8.52, 8.86, 8.87, 8.90, and 8.91

(a)

(b)

(c)

◀ FIGURE 8.11 **Oxidation number, formal charge, and electron density distribution for the HCl molecule.**

8.6 | RESONANCE STRUCTURES

We sometimes encounter molecules and ions in which the experimentally determined arrangement of atoms is not adequately described by a single dominant Lewis structure. Consider ozone, O_3, which is a bent molecule with two equal O—O bond lengths (▶ FIGURE 8.12). Because each oxygen atom contributes 6 valence electrons, the ozone molecule has 18 valence electrons. This means the Lewis structure must have one O—O single bond and one O=O double bond to attain an octet about each atom:

However, this single structure cannot by itself be dominant because it requires that one O—O bond be different from the other, contrary to the observed structure—we would expect the O=O double bond to be shorter than the O—O single bond. ∞ (Section 8.3) In drawing the Lewis structure, however, we could just as easily have put the O=O bond on the left:

GO FIGURE

What feature of this structure suggests that the two outer O atoms are in some way equivalent to each other?

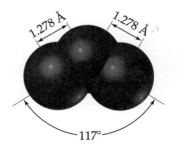

1.278 Å   1.278 Å

117°

▲ FIGURE 8.12 **Molecular structure of ozone.**

Is the electron density consistent with equal weights for the two resonance structures for O_3? Explain.

Primary color   Primary color

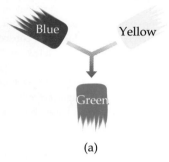

(a)

Resonance   Resonance
structure   structure

Ozone molecule

(b)

▲ **FIGURE 8.13 Resonance.** Describing a molecule as a blend of different resonance structures is similar to describing a paint color as a blend of primary colors. (a) Green paint is a blend of blue and yellow. We cannot describe green as a single primary color. (b) The ozone molecule is a blend of two resonance structures. We cannot describe the ozone molecule in terms of a single Lewis structure.

There is no reason for one of these Lewis structures to be dominant because they are equally valid representations of the molecule. The placement of the atoms in these two alternative but completely equivalent Lewis structures is the same, but the placement of the electrons is different. Lewis structures of this sort are called **resonance structures.** To describe the structure of ozone properly, we write both resonance structures and use a double-headed arrow to indicate that the real molecule is described by an average of the two:

To understand why certain molecules require more than one resonance structure, we can draw an analogy to mixing paint (◄ **FIGURE 8.13**). Blue and yellow are both primary colors of paint pigment. An equal blend of blue and yellow pigments produces green pigment. We cannot describe green paint in terms of a single primary color, yet it still has its own identity. Green paint does not oscillate between its two primary colors: It is not blue part of the time and yellow the rest of the time. Similarly, molecules such as ozone cannot be described as oscillating between the two individual Lewis structures shown previously—there are two equivalent dominant Lewis structures that contribute equally to the actual structure of the molecule.

The actual arrangement of the electrons in molecules such as O_3 must be considered as a blend of two (or more) Lewis structures. By analogy to the green paint, the molecule has its own identity separate from the individual resonance structures. For example, the ozone molecule always has two equivalent O—O bonds whose lengths are intermediate between the lengths of an oxygen–oxygen single bond and an oxygen–oxygen double bond. Another way of looking at it is to say that the rules for drawing Lewis structures do not allow us to have a single dominant structure for the ozone molecule. For example, there are no rules for drawing half-bonds. We can get around this limitation by drawing two equivalent Lewis structures that, when averaged, amount to something very much like what is observed experimentally.

⚠ **GIVE IT SOME THOUGHT**

The O—O bonds in ozone are often described as "one-and-a-half" bonds. Is this description consistent with the idea of resonance?

As an additional example of resonance structures, consider the nitrate ion, NO_3^-, for which three equivalent Lewis structures can be drawn:

Notice that the arrangement of atoms is the same in each structure—only the placement of electrons differs. In writing resonance structures, the same atoms must be bonded to each other in all structures, so that the only differences are in the arrangements of electrons. All three NO_3^- Lewis structures are equally dominant and taken together adequately describe the ion, in which all three N—O bond lengths are the same.

⚠ **GIVE IT SOME THOUGHT**

In the same sense that we describe the O—O bonds in O_3 as "one-and-a-half" bonds, how would you describe the N—O bonds in NO_3^- ?

In some instances, all the possible Lewis structures for a species may not be equivalent to one another. Instead, one or more may be dominant. We will encounter examples of this as we proceed.

SAMPLE EXERCISE 8.10   Resonance Structures

Which is predicted to have the shorter sulfur–oxygen bonds, SO_3 or $SC_3{}^{2-}$?

SOLUTION

The sulfur atom has six valence electrons, as does oxygen. Thus, SO_3 contains 24 valence electrons. In writing the Lewis structure, we see that three equivalent resonance structures can be drawn:

As with $NO_3{}^-$, the actual structure of SO_3 is an equal blend of all three. Thus, each S—O bond length should be about one-third of the way between the length of a single bond and the length of a double bond. That is, they should be shorter than single bonds but not as short as double bonds.

The $SO_3{}^{2-}$ ion has 26 electrons, which leads to a dominant Lewis structure in which all the S—O bonds are single:

Our analysis of the Lewis structures leads us to conclude that SO_3 should have the shorter S—O bonds and $SO_3{}^{2-}$ the longer ones. This conclusion is correct: The experimentally measured S—O bond lengths are 1.42 Å in SO_3 and 1.51 Å in $SO_3{}^{2-}$.

PRACTICE EXERCISE

Draw two equivalent resonance structures for the formate ion, $HCO_2{}^-$.

Answer:

Resonance in Benzene

Resonance is an important concept in describing the bonding in organic molecules, particularly *aromatic* organic molecules, a category that includes the hydrocarbon *benzene*, C_6H_6. The six C atoms are bonded in a hexagonal ring, and one H atom is bonded to each C atom. We can write two equivalent dominant Lewis structures for benzene, each of which satisfies the octet rule. These two structures are in resonance:

Note that the double bonds are in different places in the two structures. Each of these resonance structures shows three carbon–carbon single bonds and three carbon–carbon double bonds. However, experimental data show that all six C—C bonds are of equal length, 1.40 Å, intermediate between the typical bond lengths for a C—C single bond (1.54 Å) and a C═C double bond (1.34 Å). Each of the C—C bonds in benzene can be thought of as a blend of a single bond and a double bond (▶ FIGURE 8.14).

Benzene is commonly represented by omitting the hydrogen atoms and showing only the carbon–carbon framework with the vertices unlabeled. In this convention, the resonance in the molecule is represented either by two structures separated by a double-headed arrow or by a shorthand notation in which we draw a hexagon with a circle inside:

The shorthand notation reminds us that benzene is a blend of two resonance structures—it emphasizes that the C═C double bonds cannot be assigned to specific edges of the hexagon. Chemists use both representations of benzene interchangeably.

GO FIGURE

What is the significance of the dashed bonds in this ball-and-stick model?

▲ **FIGURE 8.14   Benzene, an "aromatic" organic compound.** The benzene molecule is a regular hexagon of carbon atoms with a hydrogen atom bonded to each one. The dashed lines represent the blending of two equivalent resonance structures, leading to C—C bonds that are intermediate between single and double bonds.

The bonding arrangement in benzene confers special stability to the molecule. As a result, millions of organic compounds contain the six-membered ring characteristic of benzene. Many of these compounds are important in biochemistry, in pharmaceuticals, and in the production of modern materials.

▲ GIVE IT SOME THOUGHT

Each Lewis structure of benzene has three C=C double bonds. Another hydrocarbon containing three C=C double bonds is *hexatriene*, C_6H_8. A Lewis structure of hexatriene is

$$\underset{\overset{|}{H}}{\overset{\overset{H}{|}}{C}}=\underset{\overset{|}{H}}{\overset{\overset{H}{|}}{C}}-\underset{}{\overset{\overset{H}{|}}{C}}=\underset{}{\overset{\overset{H}{|}}{C}}-\underset{}{\overset{\overset{H}{|}}{C}}=\underset{\overset{|}{H}}{\overset{\overset{H}{|}}{C}}$$

Do you expect hexatriene to have multiple resonance structures? If not, why is this molecule different from benzene with respect to resonance?

8.7 | EXCEPTIONS TO THE OCTET RULE

The octet rule is so simple and useful in introducing the basic concepts of bonding that you might assume it is always obeyed. In Section 8.2, however, we noted its limitation in dealing with ionic compounds of the transition metals. The rule also fails in many situations involving covalent bonding. These exceptions to the octet rule are of three main types:

1. Molecules and polyatomic ions containing an odd number of electrons
2. Molecules and polyatomic ions in which an atom has fewer than an octet of valence electrons
3. Molecules and polyatomic ions in which an atom has more than an octet of valence electrons

Odd Number of Electrons

In the vast majority of molecules and polyatomic ions, the total number of valence electrons is even, and complete pairing of electrons occurs. However, in a few molecules and polyatomic ions, such as ClO_2, NO, NO_2, and O_2^-, the number of valence electrons is odd. Complete pairing of these electrons is impossible, and an octet around each atom cannot be achieved. For example, NO contains $5 + 6 = 11$ valence electrons. The two most important Lewis structures for this molecule are

$$\ddot{\text{N}}{=}\ddot{\text{O}} \quad \text{and} \quad \dot{\text{N}}{=}\ddot{\text{O}}$$

▲ GIVE IT SOME THOUGHT

Which of the Lewis structures for NO is dominant based on analysis of the formal charges?

Less than an Octet of Valence Electrons

A second type of exception occurs when there are fewer than eight valence electrons around an atom in a molecule or polyatomic ion. This situation is also relatively rare (with the exception of hydrogen and helium as we have already discussed), most often encountered in compounds of boron and beryllium. As an example, let's consider boron trifluoride, BF_3. If we follow the first four steps of our procedure for drawing Lewis structures, we obtain the structure which has only six electrons around the boron atom. The formal charge is zero on both B and F, and we could complete the octet around boron by forming a double bond (step 5). In so doing, we see that there are three equivalent resonance structures (the formal charges are shown in red):

Each of these structures forces a fluorine atom to share additional electrons with the boron atom, which is inconsistent with the high electronegativity of fluorine. In fact, the formal charges tell us that this is an unfavorable situation. In each structure, the F atom involved in the $B{=}F$ double bond has a formal charge of $+1$, while the less electronegative B atom has a formal charge of -1. Thus, the resonance structures containing a $B{=}F$ double bond are less important than the one in which there are fewer than an octet of valence electrons around boron:

We usually represent BF_3 solely by the dominant resonance structure, in which there are only six valence electrons around boron. The chemical behavior of BF_3 is consistent with this representation. In particular, BF_3 reacts energetically with molecules having an unshared pair of electrons that can be used to form a bond with boron, as, for example, in the reaction

In the stable compound NH_3BF_3, boron has an octet of valence electrons.

More than an Octet of Valence Electrons

The third and largest class of exceptions consists of molecules or polyatomic ions in which there are more than eight electrons in the valence shell of an atom. When we draw the Lewis structure for PF_5, for example, we are forced to place ten electrons around the central phosphorus atom:

Molecules and ions with more than an octet of electrons around the central atom are often called *hypervalent*. Other examples of hypervalent species are SF_4, AsF_6^-, and ICl_4^-. The corresponding molecules with a second-period atom as the central atom, such as NCl_5 and OF_4, do *not* exist.

Hypervalent molecules are formed only for central atoms from period 3 and below in the periodic table. The principal reason for their formation is the relatively larger size of the central atom. For example, a P atom is large enough that five F (or even five Cl) atoms can be bonded to it without being too crowded. By contrast, an N atom is too small to accommodate five atoms bonded to it. Because size is a factor, hypervalent molecules occur most often when the central atom is bonded to the smallest and most electronegative atoms—F, Cl, and O.

The notion of a valence shell containing more than an octet of electrons is also consistent with the presence of unfilled nd orbitals in atoms from period 3 and below. By comparison, elements of the second period have only the $2s$ and $2p$ valence orbitals available for bonding. Detailed analyses of the bonding in molecules such as PF_5 and SF_6 suggest that the presence of unfilled $3d$ orbitals in P and S has a relatively minor impact on the formation of hypervalent molecules, and the general current belief is that the increased size of third-period atoms is the more important factor.

SAMPLE EXERCISE 8.11 **Lewis Structure for an Ion with More than an Octet of Electrons**

Draw the Lewis structure for ICl_4^-.

SOLUTION

Iodine (group 7A) has seven valence electrons. Each chlorine atom (group 7A) also has seven. An extra electron is added to account for the 1− charge of the ion. Therefore, the total number of valence electrons is

$$7 + (4 \times 7) + 1 = 36$$

The I atom is the central atom in the ion. Putting eight electrons around each Cl atom (including a pair of electrons between I and each Cl to represent the single bond between these atoms) requires $8 \times 4 = 32$ electrons.

We are thus left with $36 - 32 = 4$ electrons to be placed on the larger iodine:

Iodine has 12 valence electrons around it, four more than needed for an octet.

PRACTICE EXERCISE

(a) Which of the following atoms is never found with more than an octet of valence electrons around it: S, C, P, Br? (b) Draw the Lewis structure for XeF_2.

Answers: (a) C, (b) $:\!\ddot{\text{F}}\!-\!\ddot{\text{X}}\text{e}\!-\!\ddot{\text{F}}\!:$

Finally, there are Lewis structures where you might have to choose between satisfying the octet rule and obtaining the most favorable formal charges by using more than an octet of electrons. For example, consider these Lewis structures for the phosphate ion, PO_4^{3-}:

The formal charges on the atoms are shown in red. In the left structure, the P atom obeys the octet rule. In the right structure, however, the P atom has five electron pairs, leading to smaller formal charges on the atoms. (You should be able to see that there are three additional resonance structures for the Lewis structure on the right.)

Chemists are still debating which of these two structures is dominant for PO_4^{3-}. Recent theoretical calculations based on quantum mechanics suggest to some researchers that the left structure is the dominant one. Other researchers claim that the bond lengths in the ion are more consistent with the right structure being dominant. This disagreement is a convenient reminder that, in general, multiple Lewis structures can contribute to the actual electron distribution in an atom or molecule.

8.8 | STRENGTHS OF COVALENT BONDS

The stability of a molecule is related to the strengths of its covalent bonds. The strength of a covalent bond between two atoms is determined by the energy required to break the bond. It is easiest to relate bond strength to the enthalpy change in reactions in which bonds are broken. ∞ (Section 5.4) The **bond enthalpy** is the enthalpy change, ΔH, for the breaking of a particular bond in one mole of a gaseous substance. For example, the bond enthalpy for the bond in Cl_2 is the enthalpy change when 1 mol of $Cl_2(g)$ dissociates into chlorine atoms:

$$:\ddot{C}l\!-\!\ddot{C}l\!:(g) \longrightarrow 2\;:\ddot{C}l\!\cdot(g)$$

We use the letter D followed by the bond in question to represent bond enthalpies. Thus, for example, $D(Cl\!-\!Cl)$ is the bond enthalpy for the Cl_2 bond, and $D(H\!-\!Br)$ is the bond enthalpy for the HBr bond.

It is relatively simple to assign bond enthalpies to the bond in a diatomic molecule because in these cases the bond enthalpy is just the energy required to break the molecule into its atoms. However, many important bonds, such as the $C\!-\!H$ bond, exist only in polyatomic molecules. For these bonds, we usually use *average* bond enthalpies. For example, the enthalpy change for the following process in which a methane molecule is decomposed into its five atoms (a process called *atomization*) can be used to define an average bond enthalpy for the $C\!-\!H$ bond, $D(C\!-\!H)$:

$$\underset{\displaystyle H}{\overset{\displaystyle H}{H\!-\!\underset{|}{\overset{|}{C}}\!-\!H}}(g) \longrightarrow \cdot\dot{C}\cdot(g) \;+\; 4\,H\!\cdot(g) \qquad \Delta H = 1660 \text{ kJ}$$

Because there are four equivalent $C\!-\!H$ bonds in methane, the enthalpy of atomization is equal to the sum of the bond enthalpies of the four $C\!-\!H$ bonds. Therefore, the average $C\!-\!H$ bond enthalpy for CH_4 is $D(C\!-\!H) = (1660/4) \text{ kJ/mol} = 415 \text{ kJ/mol}$.

The bond enthalpy for a given pair of atoms, say $C\!-\!H$, depends on the rest of the molecule containing the atom pair. However, the variation from one molecule to another is generally small, which supports the idea that bonding electron pairs are localized between atoms. If we consider $C\!-\!H$ bond enthalpies in many different compounds, we find that the average bond enthalpy is 413 kJ/mol, close to the 415 kJ/mol we just calculated from CH_4.

▲ **GIVE IT SOME THOUGHT**

How can you use the enthalpy of atomization of the hydrocarbon ethane, $C_2H_6(g)$, along with the value $D(C\!-\!H) = 413$ kJ/mol to estimate the value for $D(C\!-\!C)$?

▶ **TABLE 8.4** lists average bond enthalpies for a number of atom pairs. *The bond enthalpy is always a positive quantity*; energy is always required to break chemical bonds. Conversely, energy is *always* released when a bond forms between two gaseous atoms or molecular fragments. The greater the bond enthalpy, the stronger the bond. Further, a molecule with strong chemical bonds generally has less tendency to undergo chemical change than does one with weak bonds. For example, N_2, which has a very strong $N\!\equiv\!N$ triple bond, is very unreactive, whereas hydrazine, N_2H_4, which has an $N\!-\!N$ single bond, is highly reactive.

▲ **GIVE IT SOME THOUGHT**

Based on bond enthalpies, which do you expect to be more reactive, oxygen, O_2, or hydrogen peroxide, H_2O_2?

TABLE 8.4 • Average Bond Enthalpies (kJ/mol)							
Single Bonds							
C—H	413	N—H	391	O—H	463	F—F	155
C—C	348	N—N	163	O—O	146		
C—N	293	N—O	201	O—F	190	Cl—F	253
C—O	358	N—F	272	O—Cl	203	Cl—Cl	242
C—F	485	N—Cl	200	O—I	234		
C—Cl	328	N—Br	243			Br—F	237
C—Br	276			S—H	339	Br—Cl	218
C—I	240	H—H	436	S—F	327	Br—Br	193
C—S	259	H—F	567	S—Cl	253		
		H—Cl	431	S—Br	218	I—Cl	208
Si—H	323	H—Br	366	S—S	266	I—Br	175
Si—Si	226	H—I	299			I—I	151
Si—C	301						
Si—O	368						
Si—Cl	464						
Multiple Bonds							
C=C	614	N=N	418	O_2	495		
C≡C	839	N≡N	941				
C=N	615	N=O	607	S=O	523		
C≡N	891			S=S	418		
C=O	799						
C≡O	1072						

Bond Enthalpies and the Enthalpies of Reactions

We can use average bond enthalpies to estimate the enthalpies of reactions in which bonds are broken and new bonds are formed. This procedure allows us to estimate quickly whether a given reaction will be endothermic ($\Delta H > 0$) or exothermic ($\Delta H < 0$) even if we do not know ΔH_f° for all the species involved.

Our strategy for estimating reaction enthalpies is a straightforward application of Hess's law. ∞ (Section 5.6) We use the fact that breaking bonds is always endothermic and forming bonds is always exothermic. We therefore imagine that the reaction occurs in two steps:

1. We supply enough energy to break those bonds in the reactants that are not present in the products. The enthalpy of the system is increased by the sum of the bond enthalpies of the bonds that are broken.

2. We form the bonds in the products that were not present in the reactants. This step releases energy and therefore lowers the enthalpy of the system by the sum of the bond enthalpies of the bonds that are formed.

The enthalpy of the reaction, ΔH_{rxn}, is estimated as the sum of the bond enthalpies of the bonds broken minus the sum of the bond enthalpies of the bonds formed:

$$\Delta H_{rxn} = \Sigma(\text{bond enthalpies of bonds broken}) -$$
$$\Sigma(\text{bond enthalpies of bonds formed}) \quad [8.12]$$

Consider, for example, the gas-phase reaction between methane, CH_4, and chlorine to produce methyl chloride, CH_3Cl, and hydrogen chloride, HCl:

$$H—CH_3(g) + Cl—Cl(g) \longrightarrow Cl—CH_3(g) + H—Cl(g) \quad \Delta H_{rxn} = ? \quad [8.13]$$

GO FIGURE:

Is this reaction exothermic or endothermic?

◀ **FIGURE 8.15   Using bond enthalpies to calculate ΔH_{rxn}.** Average bond enthalpies are used to estimate ΔH_{rxn} for the reaction in Equation 8.13.

Our two-step procedure is outlined in ▲ **FIGURE 8.15.** We note that the following bonds are broken and made:

Bonds broken: 1 mol C—H, 1 mol Cl—Cl

Bonds made: 1 mol C—Cl, 1 mol H—Cl

We first supply enough energy to break the C—H and Cl—Cl bonds, which raises the enthalpy of the system (indicated as $\Delta H_1 > 0$ in Figure 8.15). We then form the C—Cl and H—Cl bonds, which release energy and lower the enthalpy of the system ($\Delta H_2 < 0$). We then use Equation 8.12 and data from Table 8.4 to estimate the enthalpy of the reaction:

$$\Delta H_{rxn} = [D(C-H) + D(Cl-Cl)] - [D(Cl-Cl) + D(H-Cl)]$$

$$= (413 \text{ kJ} + 242 \text{ kJ}) - (328 \text{ kJ} + 431 \text{ kJ}) = -104 \text{ kJ}$$

The reaction is exothermic because the bonds in the products (especially the H—Cl bond) are stronger than the bonds in the reactants (especially the Cl—Cl bond).

We usually use bond enthalpies to estimate ΔH_{rxn} only if we do not have the needed ΔH_f° values readily available. For the preceding reaction, we cannot calculate ΔH_{rxn} from ΔH_f° values and Hess's law because ΔH_f° for $CH_3Cl(g)$ is not given in Appendix C. If we obtain the value of ΔH_f° for $CH_3Cl(g)$ from another source and use Equation 5.31,

$$\Delta H_{rxn}^\circ = \Sigma n\Delta H_f^\circ(\text{products}) - \Sigma m\Delta H_f^\circ(\text{reactants})$$

we find that $\Delta H_{rxn} = -99.8 \text{ kJ}$ for the reaction in Equation 8.13. Thus, the use of average bond enthalpies provides a reasonably accurate estimate of the actual reaction enthalpy change.

It is important to remember that bond enthalpies are derived for *gaseous* molecules and that they are often *averaged* values. Nonetheless, average bond enthalpies are useful for estimating reaction enthalpies quickly, especially for gas-phase reactions.

TABLE 8.5 • Average Bond Lengths for Some Single, Double, and Triple Bonds

Bond	Bond Length (Å)	Bond	Bond Length (Å)
C—C	1.54	N—N	1.47
C=C	1.34	N=N	1.24
C≡C	1.20	N≡N	1.10
C—N	1.43	N—O	1.36
C=N	1.38	N=O	1.22
C≡N	1.16		
		O—O	1.48
C—O	1.43	O=O	1.21
C=O	1.23		
C≡O	1.13		

SAMPLE EXERCISE 8.12 Using Average Bond Enthalpies

Using data from Table 8.4, estimate ΔH for the reaction

$$2\ \text{H}-\overset{\overset{\displaystyle H}{|}}{\underset{\underset{\displaystyle H}{|}}{C}}-\overset{\overset{\displaystyle H}{|}}{\underset{\underset{\displaystyle H}{|}}{C}}-\text{H}(g) + 7\ O_2(g) \longrightarrow 4\ O=C=O(g) + 6\ \text{H}-O-\text{H}(g)$$

SOLUTION

Analyze We are asked to estimate the enthalpy change for a chemical reaction by using average bond enthalpies for the bonds broken and formed.

Plan In the reactants, we must break twelve C—H bonds and two C—C bonds in the two molecules of C_2H_6 and seven O_2 bonds in the seven O_2 molecules. In the products, we form eight C=O bonds (two in each CO_2) and twelve O—H bonds (two in each H_2O).

Solve Using Equation 8.12 and data from Table 8.4, we have

$$\Delta H = [12D(C-H) + 2D(C-C) + 7D(O_2)] - [8D(C=O) + 12D(O-H)]$$
$$= [12(413\ \text{kJ}) + 2(348\ \text{kJ}) + 7(495\ \text{kJ})] - [8(799\ \text{kJ}) + 12(463\ \text{kJ})]$$
$$= 9117\ \text{kJ} - 11948\ \text{kJ}$$
$$= -2831\ \text{kJ}$$

Check This estimate can be compared with the value of −2856 kJ calculated from more accurate thermochemical data; the agreement is good.

PRACTICE EXERCISE

Using Table 8.4, estimate ΔH for the reaction

$$\text{H}-\overset{}{\underset{\underset{\displaystyle H}{|}}{N}}-\overset{}{\underset{\underset{\displaystyle H}{|}}{N}}-\text{H}(g) \longrightarrow N\equiv N(g) + 2\ \text{H}-\text{H}(g)$$

Answer: −86 kJ

Bond Enthalpy and Bond Length

Just as we can define an average bond enthalpy, we can also define an average bond length for a number of common bonds (▲ TABLE 8.5). Of particular interest is the relationship, in any atom pair, among bond enthalpy, bond length, and number of bonds between the atoms. For example, we can use data in Tables 8.4 and 8.5 to compare the bond lengths and bond enthalpies of carbon–carbon single, double, and triple bonds:

C—C	C=C	C≡C
1.54 Å	1.34 Å	1.20 Å
348 kJ/mol	614 kJ/mol	839 kJ/mol

CHEMISTRY PUT TO WORK

Explosives and Alfred Nobel

Enormous amounts of energy can be stored in chemical bonds. Perhaps the most graphic illustration of this fact is seen in certain molecular substances used as explosives. Our discussion of bond enthalpies allows us to examine more closely some of the properties of such explosive substances.

A useful explosive substance must (1) decompose very exothermically, (2) have gaseous products so that a tremendous gas pressure accompanies the decomposition, (3) decompose very rapidly, and (4) be stable enough so that it can be detonated predictably. The combination of the first three effects leads to the violent evolution of heat and gases.

To give the most exothermic reaction, an explosive should have weak chemical bonds and should decompose into molecules that have very strong bonds. Table 8.4 tells us that $N\equiv N$, $C\equiv O$, and $C=O$ bonds are among the strongest. Not surprisingly, explosives are usually designed to produce the gaseous products $N_2(g)$, $CO(g)$, and $CO_2(g)$. Water vapor is nearly always produced as well.

Many common explosives are organic molecules that contain nitro (NO_2) or nitrate (NO_3) groups attached to a carbon skeleton. The Lewis structures of two of the most familiar explosives, nitroglycerin and trinitrotoluene (TNT), are shown here (resonance structures are not shown for clarity). TNT contains the six-membered ring characteristic of benzene.

Nitroglycerin

Trinitrotoluene (TNT)

Nitroglycerin is a pale yellow, oily liquid. It is highly *shock-sensitive*. Merely shaking the liquid can cause its explosive decomposition into nitrogen, carbon dioxide, water, and oxygen gases:

$$4\,C_3H_5N_3O_9(l) \longrightarrow 6\,N_2(g) + 12\,CO_2(g) + 10\,H_2O(g) + O_2(g)$$

The large bond enthalpies of N_2 (941 kJ/mol), CO_2 (2 × 799 kJ/mol), and H_2O (2 × 463 kJ/mol) make this reaction enormously exothermic. Nitroglycerin is an exceptionally unstable explosive because it is in nearly perfect *explosive balance*: With the exception of a small amount of $O_2(g)$ produced, the only products are N_2, CO_2, and H_2O. Note also that, unlike combustion reactions ∞ (Section 3.2), explosions are entirely self-contained. No other reagent, such as $O_2(g)$, is needed for the explosive decomposition.

Because nitroglycerin is so unstable, it is difficult to use as a controllable explosive. The Swedish inventor Alfred Nobel (▼ FIGURE 8.16) found that mixing nitroglycerin with an absorbent solid material such as diatomaceous earth or cellulose gives a solid explosive (*dynamite*) that is much safer than liquid nitroglycerin.

RELATED EXERCISES: 8.98 and 8.99

▲ FIGURE 8.16 **Alfred Nobel (1833–1896), Swedish inventor of dynamite.** By many accounts Nobel's discovery that nitroglycerin could be made more stable by absorbing it onto cellulose was an accident. This discovery made Nobel a wealthy man. He was also a complex and lonely man, however, who never married, was frequently ill, and suffered from chronic depression. He had invented the most powerful military explosive to date, but he strongly supported international peace movements. His will stated that his fortune be used to establish prizes awarding those who "have conferred the greatest benefit on mankind," including the promotion of peace and "fraternity between nations." The Nobel Prize is probably the most coveted award that a scientist, writer, or peace advocate can receive.

As the number of bonds between the carbon atoms increases, the bond length decreases and the bond enthalpy increases. That is, the carbon atoms are held more closely and more tightly together. In general, *as the number of bonds between two atoms increases, the bond grows shorter and stronger.* This trend is illustrated in ▶ FIGURE 8.17 for N—N single, double, and triple bonds.

◢ **GO FIGURE**

The line segments in the graph both have negative slopes. Why does this make sense?

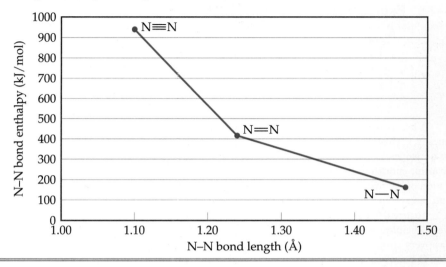

▶ **FIGURE 8.17 Bond strength versus bond length for N—N bonds.**

SAMPLE INTEGRATIVE EXERCISE | **Putting Concepts Together**

Phosgene, a substance used in poisonous gas warfare during World War I, is so named because it was first prepared by the action of sunlight on a mixture of carbon monoxide and chlorine gases. Its name comes from the Greek words *phos* (light) and *genes* (born of). Phosgene has the following elemental composition:12.14% C, 16.17% O, and 71.69% Cl by mass. Its molar mass is 98.9 g/mol. **(a)** Determine the molecular formula of this compound. **(b)** Draw three Lewis structures for the molecule that satisfy the octet rule for each atom. (The Cl and O atoms bond to C.) **(c)** Using formal charges, determine which Lewis structure is the dominant one. **(d)** Using average bond enthalpies, estimate ΔH for the formation of gaseous phosgene from $CO(g)$ and $Cl_2(g)$.

SOLUTION

(a) The empirical formula of phosgene can be determined from its elemental composition. ∞ (Section 3.5) Assuming 100 g of the compound and calculating the number of moles of C, O, and Cl in this sample, we have

$$(12.14 \text{ g C})\left(\frac{1 \text{ mol C}}{12.01 \text{ g C}}\right) = 1.011 \text{ mol C}$$

$$(16.17 \text{ g O})\left(\frac{1 \text{ mol O}}{16.00 \text{ g O}}\right) = 1.011 \text{ mol O}$$

$$(71.69 \text{ g Cl})\left(\frac{1 \text{ mol Cl}}{35.45 \text{ g Cl}}\right) = 2.022 \text{ mol Cl}$$

The ratio of the number of moles of each element, obtained by dividing each number of moles by the smallest quantity, indicates that there is one C and one O for each two Cl in the empirical formula, $COCl_2$.

The molar mass of the empirical formula is $12.01 + 16.00 + 2(35.45) = 98.91$ g/mol, the same as the molar mass of the molecule. Thus, $COCl_2$ is the molecular formula.

(b) Carbon has four valence electrons, oxygen has six, and chlorine has seven, giving $4 + 6 + 2(7) = 24$ electrons for the Lewis structures. Drawing a Lewis structure with all single bonds does not give the central carbon atom an octet. Using multiple bonds, three structures satisfy the octet rule:

(c) Calculating the formal charges on each atom gives

$$:\overset{0}{\underset{}{O}}: \qquad :\overset{-1}{\underset{}{O}}: \qquad :\overset{-1}{\underset{}{O}}:$$

$$:\overset{0}{\underset{}{Cl}}-\overset{}{\underset{}{C}}-\overset{0}{\underset{}{Cl}}: \longleftrightarrow \overset{+1}{\underset{}{Cl}}=\overset{0}{\underset{}{C}}-\overset{0}{\underset{}{Cl}}: \longleftrightarrow :\overset{0}{\underset{}{Cl}}-\overset{0}{\underset{}{C}}=\overset{+1}{\underset{}{Cl}}$$

The first structure is expected to be the dominant one because it has the lowest formal charges on each atom. Indeed, the molecule is usually represented by this single Lewis structure.

(d) Writing the chemical equation in terms of the Lewis structures of the molecules, we have

$$:C\equiv O: \quad + \quad :\ddot{C}l-\ddot{C}l: \quad \longrightarrow \quad :\ddot{C}l-\overset{:O:}{\underset{}{C}}-\ddot{C}l:$$

Thus, the reaction involves breaking a $C\equiv O$ bond and a $Cl-Cl$ bond and forming a $C=O$ bond and two $C-Cl$ bonds. Using bond enthalpies from Table 8.4, we have

$$\Delta H = D(C\equiv O) + D(Cl-Cl) - [D(C=O) + 2D(C-Cl)]$$

$$= 1072 \text{ kJ} + 242 \text{ kJ} - [799 \text{ kJ} + 2(328 \text{ kJ})] = -141 \text{ kJ}$$

Notice that the reaction is exothermic. Nevertheless, energy is needed from sunlight or another source for the reaction to begin, as is the case for the combustion of $H_2(g)$ and $O_2(g)$ to form $H_2O(g)$ (Figure 5.14).

CHAPTER SUMMARY AND KEY TERMS

INTRODUCTION AND SECTION 8.1 In this chapter we have focused on the interactions that lead to the formation of **chemical bonds**. We classify these bonds into three broad groups: **ionic bonds**, which result from the electrostatic forces that exist between ions of opposite charge; **covalent bonds**, which result from the sharing of electrons by two atoms; and **metallic bonds**, which result from a delocalized sharing of electrons in metals. The formation of bonds involves interactions of the outermost electrons of atoms, their valence electrons. The valence electrons of an atom can be represented by electron-dot symbols, called **Lewis symbols**. The tendencies of atoms to gain, lose, or share their valence electrons often follow the **octet rule**, which can be viewed as an attempt by atoms to achieve a noble-gas electron configuration.

SECTION 8.2 Ionic bonding results from the transfer of electrons from one atom to another, leading to the formation of a three-dimensional lattice of charged particles. The stabilities of ionic substances result from the strong electrostatic attractions between an ion and the surrounding ions of opposite charge. The magnitude of these interactions is measured by the **lattice energy**, which is the energy needed to separate an ionic lattice into gaseous ions. Lattice energy increases with increasing charge on the ions and with decreasing distance between the ions. The **Born–Haber cycle** is a useful thermochemical cycle in which we use Hess's law to calculate the lattice energy as the sum of several steps in the formation of an ionic compound.

SECTION 8.3 A covalent bond results from the sharing of electrons. We can represent the electron distribution in molecules by means of **Lewis structures**, which indicate how many valence electrons are involved in forming bonds and how many remain as unshared electron pairs. The octet rule helps determine how many bonds will be formed between two atoms. The sharing of one pair of electrons produces a **single bond**; the sharing of two or three pairs of electrons between two atoms produces **double** or **triple bonds**, respectively. Double and triple bonds are examples of multiple bonding between atoms. The bond length decreases as the number of bonds between the atoms increases.

SECTION 8.4 In covalent bonds, the electrons may not necessarily be shared equally between two atoms. **Bond polarity** helps describe unequal sharing of electrons in a bond. In a **nonpolar covalent bond** the electrons in the bond are shared equally by the two atoms; in a **polar covalent bond** one of the atoms exerts a greater attraction for the electrons than the other.

Electronegativity is a numerical measure of the ability of an atom to compete with other atoms for the electrons shared between them. Fluorine is the most electronegative element, meaning it has the greatest ability to attract electrons from other atoms. Electronegativity values range from 0.7 for Cs to 4.0 for F. Electronegativity generally increases from left to right in a row of the periodic table and decreases going down a column. The difference in the electronegativities of bonded atoms can be used to determine the polarity of a bond. The greater the electronegativity difference, the more polar the bond.

A **polar molecule** is one whose centers of positive and negative charge do not coincide. Thus, a polar molecule has a positive side and a negative side. This separation of charge produces a **dipole,** the magnitude of which is given by the **dipole moment,** which is measured in debyes (D). Dipole moments increase with increasing amount of charge separated and increasing distance of separation. Any diatomic molecule $X-Y$ in which X and Y have different electronegativities is a polar molecule.

Most bonding interactions lie between the extremes of covalent and ionic bonding. While it is generally true that the bonding between a metal and a nonmetal is predominantly ionic, exceptions to this guideline are not uncommon when the difference in electronegativity of the atoms is relatively small or when the oxidation state of the metal becomes large.

SECTIONS 8.5 AND 8.6 If we know which atoms are connected to one another, we can draw Lewis structures for molecules and ions by a simple procedure. Once we do so, we can determine the **formal charge** of each atom in a Lewis structure, which is the charge that the atom would have if all atoms had the same electronegativity. In general, the dominant Lewis structure will have low formal charges with any negative formal charges residing on more electronegative atoms.

Sometimes a single dominant Lewis structure is inadequate to represent a particular molecule (or ion). In such situations, we describe the molecule by using two or more **resonance structures** for the molecule. The molecule is envisioned as a blend of these multiple resonance structures. Resonance structures are important in describing the bonding in molecules such as ozone, O_3, and the organic molecule benzene, C_6H_6.

SECTION 8.7   The octet rule is not obeyed in all cases. Exceptions occur when (a) a molecule has an odd number of electrons, (b) it is not possible to complete an octet around an atom without forcing an unfavorable distribution of electrons, or (c) a large atom is surrounded by a sufficiently large number of small electronegative atoms that it has more than an octet of electrons around it. Lewis structures with more than an octet of electrons are observed for atoms in the third row and beyond in the periodic table.

SECTION 8.8   The strength of a covalent bond is measured by its **bond enthalpy**, which is the molar enthalpy change upon breaking a particular bond. Average bond enthalpies can be determined for a wide variety of covalent bonds. The strengths of covalent bonds increase with the number of electron pairs shared between two atoms. We can use bond enthalpies to estimate the enthalpy change during chemical reactions in which bonds are broken and new bonds formed. The average bond length between two atoms decreases as the number of bonds between the atoms increases, consistent with the bond being stronger as the number of bonds increases.

KEY SKILLS

- Write Lewis symbols for atoms and ions. (Section 8.1)

- Understand lattice energy and be able to arrange compounds in order of increasing lattice energy based on the charges and sizes of the ions involved. (Section 8.2)

- Use atomic electron configurations and the octet rule to write Lewis structures for molecules to determine their electron distribution. (Section 8.3)

- Use electronegativity differences to identify nonpolar covalent, polar covalent, and ionic bonds. (Section 8.4)

- Calculate charge separation in diatomic molecules based on the experimentally measured dipole moment and bond distance. (Section 8.4)

- Calculate formal charges from Lewis structures and use those formal charges to identify the dominant Lewis structure for a molecule or ion. (Section 8.5)

- Recognize molecules where resonance structures are needed to describe the bonding. (Section 8.6)

- Recognize exceptions to the octet rule and draw accurate Lewis structures even when the octet rule is not obeyed. (Section 8.7)

- Understand the relationship between bond type (single, double, and triple), bond strength (or enthalpy), and bond length. (Section 8.8)

- Use bond enthalpies to estimate enthalpy changes for reactions involving gas-phase reactants and products. (Section 8.8)

KEY EQUATIONS

- $E_{el} = \dfrac{\kappa Q_1 Q_2}{d}$ [8.4]   The potential energy of two interacting charges

- $\mu = Qr$ [8.11]   The dipole moment of two charges of equal magnitude but opposite sign, separated by a distance r

- $\Delta H_{rxn} = \Sigma(\text{bond enthalpies of bonds broken}) - \Sigma(\text{bond enthalpies of bonds formed})$ [8.12]   The enthalpy change as a function of bond enthalpies for reactions involving gas-phase molecules

EXERCISES

VISUALIZING CONCEPTS

8.1 For each of these Lewis symbols, indicate the group in the periodic table in which the element X belongs: [Section 8.1]

(a) $\cdot\overset{\displaystyle\cdot}{X}\cdot$ (b) $\cdot X\cdot$ (c) $:\overset{\displaystyle\cdot}{X}\cdot$

8.2 Illustrated are four ions—A, B, X, and Y— showing their relative ionic radii. The ions shown in red carry positive charges: a

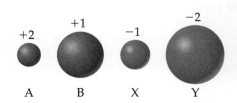

2+ charge for A and a 1+ charge for B. Ions shown in blue carry negative charges: a 1− charge for X and a 2− charge for Y. **(a)** Which combinations of these ions produce ionic compounds where there is a 1:1 ratio of cations and anions? **(b)** Among the combinations in part (a), which leads to the ionic compound having the largest lattice energy? **(c)** Which combination of ions leads to the ionic compound having the smallest lattice energy? [Section 8.2]

8.3 A portion of a two-dimensional "slab" of NaCl(s) is shown here (see Figure 8.3) in which the ions are numbered. **(a)** Of the following types of interactions (identified by color), which are attractive and which are repulsive: "purple-purple," "purple-green," "green-green"? Explain. **(b)** Consider the "green-green" interactions between ions 1 and 3, ions 1 and 5, and ions 3 and 5. Which one or more of these three will result in the interaction of largest magnitude? Which one or more will result in the interaction of the smallest magnitude? **(c)** Consider the "green-green" interactions between ions 1 and 5 and the "green-purple" interactions between ions 1 and 2. Which of these will have the greater magnitude? **(d)** Does your answer to part (c) help explain why NaCl is a stable ionic solid? [Section 8.2]

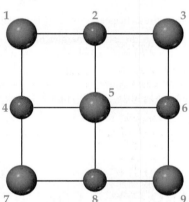

8.4 The orbital diagram that follows shows the valence electrons for a 2+ ion of an element. **(a)** What is the element? **(b)** What is the electron configuration of an atom of this element? [Section 8.2]

4*d*

8.5 In the Lewis structure shown here, A, D, E, Q, X, and Z represent elements in the first two rows of the periodic table (H—Ne). Identify all six elements so that the formal charges of all atoms are zero. [Section 8.3]

$$:\overset{\displaystyle :E:}{\underset{\displaystyle}{}} \quad X$$

:Ä—D—Q—Z

8.6 Incomplete Lewis structures for the nitrous acid molecule, HNO_2, and the nitrite ion, NO_2^-, are shown below. **(a)** Complete each Lewis structure by adding electron pairs as needed. **(b)** Is the formal charge on N the same or different in these two species? **(c)** Would either HNO_2 or NO_2^- be expected to exhibit resonance? **(d)** Would you expect the N═O bond in HNO_2 to be longer, shorter, or the same length as the N—O bonds in NO_2^-? Explain. [Sections 8.5 and 8.6]

H—O—N═O   O—N═O

8.7 The partial Lewis structure that follows is for a hydrocarbon molecule. In the full Lewis structure, each carbon atom satisfies the octet rule, and there are no unshared electron pairs in the molecule. The carbon–carbon bonds are labeled 1, 2, and 3. **(a)** Determine where the hydrogen atoms are in the molecule. **(b)** Rank the carbon–carbon bonds in order of increasing bond length. **(c)** Rank the carbon–carbon bonds in order of increasing bond enthalpy. [Sections 8.3 and 8.8]

$$C\overset{1}{=}C\overset{2}{-}C\overset{3}{\equiv}C$$

8.8 Consider the Lewis structure for the polyatomic oxyanion shown here, where X is an element from the third period (Na—Ar). By changing the overall charge, *n*, from 1− to 2− to 3− we get three different polyatomic ions. For each of these ions **(a)** identify the central atom, X; **(b)** determine the formal charge of the central atom, X; **(c)** draw a Lewis structure that makes the formal charge on the central atom equal to zero. [Sections 8.5, 8.6, and 8.7]

$$\left[\begin{array}{c} :\ddot{O}: \\ | \\ :\ddot{O}-X-\ddot{O}: \\ | \\ :\ddot{O}: \end{array}\right]^{n-}$$

LEWIS SYMBOLS (section 8.1)

8.9 **(a)** What are valence electrons? **(b)** How many valence electrons does a nitrogen atom possess? **(c)** An atom has the electron configuration $1s^2 2s^2 2p^6 3s^2 3p^2$. How many valence electrons does the atom have?

8.10 **(a)** What is the octet rule? **(b)** How many electrons must a sulfur atom gain to achieve an octet in its valence shell? **(c)** If an atom has the electron configuration $1s^2 2s^2 2p^3$, how many electrons must it gain to achieve an octet?

8.11 Write the electron configuration for silicon. Identify the valence electrons in this configuration and the nonvalence electrons. From the standpoint of chemical reactivity, what is the important difference between them?

8.12 **(a)** Write the electron configuration for the element titanium, Ti. How many valence electrons does this atom possess? **(b)** Hafnium, Hf, is also found in group 4B. Write the electron configuration for Hf. **(c)** Ti and Hf behave as though they possess the same number of valence electrons. Which of the subshells in the electron configuration of Hf behave as valence orbitals? Which behave as core orbitals?

8.13 Write the Lewis symbol for atoms of each of the following elements: **(a)** Al, **(b)** Br, **(c)** Ar, **(d)** Sr.

8.14 What is the Lewis symbol for each of the following atoms or ions: **(a)** K, **(b)** As, **(c)** Sn^{2+}, **(d)** N^{3-}?

IONIC BONDING (section 8.2)

8.15 Using Lewis symbols, diagram the reaction between magnesium and oxygen atoms to give the ionic substance MgO.

8.16 Use Lewis symbols to represent the reaction that occurs between Ca and F atoms.

8.17 Predict the chemical formula of the ionic compound formed between the following pairs of elements: (a) Al and F, (b) K and S, (c) Y and O, (d) Mg and N.

8.18 Which ionic compound is expected to form from combining the following pairs of elements: (a) barium and fluorine, (b) cesium and chlorine, (c) lithium and nitrogen, (d) aluminum and oxygen?

8.19 Write the electron configuration for each of the following ions, and determine which ones possess noble-gas configurations: (a) Sr^{2+}, (b) Ti^{2+}, (c) Se^{2-}, (d) Ni^{2+}, (e) Br^-, (f) Mn^{3+}.

8.20 Write electron configurations for the following ions, and determine which have noble-gas configurations: (a) Cd^{2+}, (b) P^{3-}, (c) Zr^{4+}, (d) Ru^{3+}, (e) As^{3-}, (f) Ag^+.

8.21 (a) Define the term *lattice energy*. (b) Which factors govern the magnitude of the lattice energy of an ionic compound?

8.22 NaCl and KF have the same crystal structure. The only difference between the two is the distance that separates cations and anions. (a) The lattice energies of NaCl and KF are given in Table 8.2. Based on the lattice energies, would you expect the Na—Cl or the K—F distance to be longer? (b) Use the ionic radii given in Figure 7.7 to estimate the Na—Cl and K—F distances. Does this estimate agree with the prediction you made based on the lattice energies?

8.23 The ionic substances KF, CaO, and ScN are isoelectronic (they have the same number of electrons). Examine the lattice energies for these substances in Table 8.2, and account for the trends you observe.

8.24 (a) Does the lattice energy of an ionic solid increase or decrease (i) as the charges of the ions increase, (ii) as the sizes of the ions increase? (b) Arrange the following substances not listed in Table 8.2 according to their expected lattice energies, listing them from lowest lattice energy to the highest: MgS, KI, GaN, LiBr.

8.25 The lattice energies of KBr and CsCl are nearly equal (Table 8.2). What can you conclude from this observation?

8.26 Explain the following trends in lattice energy:
(a) NaCl > RbBr > CsBr; (b) BaO > KF; (c) SrO > $SrCl_2$.

8.27 Energy is required to remove two electrons from Ca to form Ca^{2-} and is required to add two electrons to O to form O^{2-}. Why, then, is CaO stable relative to the free elements?

8.28 List the individual steps used in constructing a Born–Haber cycle for the formation of BaI_2 from the elements. Which of the steps would you expect to be exothermic?

8.29 Use data from Appendix C, Figure 7.9, and Figure 7.11 to calculate the lattice energy of RbCl. Is this value greater than or less than the lattice energy of NaCl? Explain.

8.30 (a) Based on the lattice energies of $MgCl_2$ and $SrCl_2$ given in Table 8.2, what is the range of values that you would expect for the lattice energy of $CaCl_2$? (b) Using data from Appendix C, Figure 7.9, and Figure 7.11 and the value of the second ionization energy for Ca, 1145 kJ/mol, calculate the lattice energy of $CaCl_2$.

COVALENT BONDING, ELECTRONEGATIVITY, AND BOND POLARITY (sections 8.3 and 8.4)

8.31 (a) What is meant by the term *covalent bond*? (b) Give three examples of covalent bonding. (c) A substance XY, formed from two different elements, boils at $-33\ °C$. Is XY likely to be a covalent or an ionic substance? Explain.

8.32 Which of these elements are unlikely to form covalent bonds: S, H, K, Ar, Si? Explain your choices.

8.33 Using Lewis symbols and Lewis structures, diagram the formation of $SiCl_4$ from Si and Cl atoms.

8.34 Use Lewis symbols and Lewis structures to diagram the formation of PF_3 from P and F atoms.

8.35 (a) Construct a Lewis structure for O_2 in which each atom achieves an octet of electrons. (b) Explain why it is necessary to form a double bond in the Lewis structure. (c) The bond in O_2 is shorter than the O—O bond in compounds that contain an O—O single bond. Explain this observation.

8.36 (a) Construct a Lewis structure for hydrogen peroxide, H_2O_2, in which each atom achieves an octet of electrons. (b) Do you expect the O—O bond in H_2O_2 to be longer or shorter than the O—O bond in O_2?

8.37 (a) What is meant by the term *electronegativity*? (b) On the Pauling scale what is the range of electronegativity values for the elements? (c) Which element has the greatest electronegativity? (d) Which element has the smallest electronegativity?

8.38 (a) What is the trend in electronegativity going from left to right in a row of the periodic table? (b) How do electronegativity values generally vary going down a column in the periodic table? (c) How do periodic trends in electronegativity relate to those for ionization energy and electron affinity?

8.39 Using only the periodic table as your guide, select the most electronegative atom in each of the following sets: (a) Na, Mg, K, Ca; (b) P, S, As, Se; (c) Be, B, C, Si; (d) Zn, Ge, Ga, As.

8.40 By referring only to the periodic table, select (a) the most electronegative element in group 6A; (b) the least electronegative element in the group Al, Si, P; (c) the most electronegative element in the group Ga, P, Cl, Na; (d) the element in the group K, C, Zn, F that is most likely to form an ionic compound with Ba.

8.41 Which of the following bonds are polar: (a) B—F, (b) Cl—Cl, (c) Se—O, (d) H—I ? Which is the more electronegative atom in each polar bond?

8.42 Arrange the bonds in each of the following sets in order of increasing polarity: (a) C—F, O—F, Be—F; (b) O—Cl, S—Br, C—P; (c) C—S, B—F, N—O.

8.43 (a) From the data in Table 8.3, calculate the effective charges on the H and Br atoms of the HBr molecule in units of the electronic charge, *e*. (b) Compare your answers to part

(a) with those in Sample Exercise 8.5 for the HCl molecule. Can you explain why the values are different?

8.44 The iodine monobromide molecule, IBr, has a bond length of 2.49 Å and a dipole moment of 1.21 D. **(a)** Which atom of the molecule is expected to have a negative charge? Explain. **(b)** Calculate the effective charges on the I and Br atoms in IBr, in units of the electronic charge, e.

8.45 In the following pairs of binary compounds determine which one is a molecular substance and which one is an ionic

substance. Use the appropriate naming convention (for ionic or molecular substances) to assign a name to each compound: **(a)** SiF_4 and LaF_3, **(b)** $FeCl_2$ and $ReCl_6$, **(c)** $PbCl_4$ and RbCl.

8.46 In the following pairs of binary compounds determine which one is a molecular substance and which one is an ionic substance. Use the appropriate naming convention (for ionic or molecular substances) to assign a name to each compound: **(a)** $TiCl_4$ and CaF_2, **(b)** ClF_3 and VF_3, **(c)** $SbCl_5$ and AlF_3.

LEWIS STRUCTURES; RESONANCE STRUCTURES (sections 8.5 and 8.6)

8.47 Draw Lewis structures for the following: **(a)** SiH_4, **(b)** CO, **(c)** SF_2, **(d)** H_2SO_4 (H is bonded to O), **(e)** ClO_2^-, **(f)** NH_2OH.

8.48 Write Lewis structures for the following: **(a)** H_2CO (both H atoms are bonded to C), **(b)** H_2O_2, **(c)** C_2F_6 (contains a C—C bond), **(d)** AsO_3^{3-}, **(e)** H_2SO_3 (H is bonded to O), **(f)** C_2H_2.

8.49 **(a)** When talking about atoms in a Lewis structure, what is meant by the term *formal charge*? **(b)** Does the formal charge of an atom represent the actual charge on that atom? Explain. **(c)** How does the formal charge of an atom in a Lewis structure differ from the oxidation number of the atom?

8.50 **(a)** Write a Lewis structure for the phosphorus trifluoride molecule, PF_3. Is the octet rule satisfied for all the atoms in your structure? **(b)** Determine the oxidation numbers of the P and F atoms. **(c)** Determine the formal charges of the P and F atoms. **(d)** Is the oxidation number for the P atom the same as its formal charge? Explain.

8.51 Write Lewis structures that obey the octet rule for each of the following, and assign oxidation numbers and formal charges to each atom: **(a)** OCS, **(b)** $SOCl_2$ (S is bonded to the two Cl atoms and to the O), **(c)** BrO_3^-, **(d)** $HClO_2$ (H is bonded to O).

8.52 For each of the following molecules or ions of sulfur and oxygen, write a single Lewis structure that obeys the octet rule, and calculate the oxidation numbers and formal charges on all the atoms: **(a)** SO_2, **(b)** SO_3, **(c)** SO_3^{2-}. **(d)** Arrange these molecules/ions in order of increasing S—O bond distance.

8.53 **(a)** Write one or more appropriate Lewis structures for the nitrite ion, NO_2^-. **(b)** With what allotrope of oxygen is it isoelectronic? **(c)** What would you predict for the lengths of the bonds in NO_2^- relative to N—O single bonds and double bonds?

8.54 Consider the formate ion, HCO_2^-, which is the anion formed when formic acid loses an H^+ ion. The H and the two O atoms are bonded to the central C atom. **(a)** Write one or more appropriate Lewis structures for this ion. **(b)** Are resonance structures needed to describe the structure? **(c)** What would you predict for the C—O bond lengths in the formate ion relative to those in CO_2?

8.55 Predict the ordering of the C—O bond lengths in CO, CO_2, and CO_3^{2-}.

8.56 Based on Lewis structures, predict the ordering of N—O bond lengths in NO^+, NO_2^-, and NO_3^-.

8.57 **(a)** Use the concept of resonance to explain why all six C—C bonds in benzene are equal in length. **(b)** Are the C—C bond lengths in benzene shorter than C—C single bonds? Are they shorter than C=C double bonds?

8.58 Mothballs are composed of naphthalene, $C_{10}H_8$, a molecule of which consists of two six-membered rings of carbon fused along an edge, as shown in this incomplete Lewis structure:

(a) Write two complete Lewis structures for naphthalene. **(b)** The observed C—C bond lengths in the molecule are intermediate between C—C single and C=C double bonds. Explain. **(c)** Represent the resonance in naphthalene in a way analogous to that used to represent it in benzene.

EXCEPTIONS TO THE OCTET RULE (section 8.7)

8.59 **(a)** State the octet rule. **(b)** Does the octet rule apply to ionic as well as to covalent compounds? Explain using examples as appropriate.

8.60 Considering the nonmetals, what is the relationship between the group number for an element (carbon, for example, belongs to group 4A; see the periodic table on the inside front cover) and the number of single covalent bonds that element needs to form to conform to the octet rule?

8.61 The chlorine oxides, in which a chlorine atom is bonded to one or more oxygen atoms, are important molecules in the chemistry of the atmosphere. Will any of the chlorine oxides obey the octet rule? Why or why not?

8.62 For elements in the third row of the periodic table and beyond, the octet rule is often not obeyed. What factors are usually cited to explain this fact?

8.63 Draw the Lewis structures for each of the following ions or molecules. Identify those that do not obey the octet rule, and explain why they do not: **(a)** SO_3^{2-}, **(b)** AlH_3, **(c)** N_3^-, **(d)** CH_2Cl_2, **(e)** SbF_5.

8.64 Draw the Lewis structures for each of the following molecules or ions. Which do not obey the octet rule? **(a)** NO, **(b)** BF_3, **(c)** ICl_2^-, **(d)** $OPBr_3$ (the P is the central atom), **(e)** XeF_4.

8.65 In the vapor phase, $BeCl_2$ exists as a discrete molecule. **(a)** Draw the Lewis structure of this molecule, using only single bonds. Does this Lewis structure satisfy the octet rule? **(b)** What other resonance structures are possible that satisfy the octet rule? **(c)** On the basis of the formal charges, which Lewis structure is expected to be dominant for $BeCl_2$?

8.66 **(a)** Describe the molecule xenon trioxide, XeO_3, using four possible Lewis structures, one each with zero, one, two, or three Xe—O double bonds. **(b)** Do any of these resonance structures satisfy the octet rule for every atom in the molecule? **(c)** Do any of the four Lewis structures have multiple resonance structures? If so, how many resonance structures do you find? **(d)** Which of the Lewis structures in (a) yields the most favorable formal charges for the molecule?

8.67 Consider the following statement: "For some molecules and ions, a Lewis structure that satisfies the octet rule does not lead

to the lowest formal charges, and a Lewis structure that leads to the lowest formal charges does not satisfy the octet rule." Illustrate this statement using the hydrogen sulfite ion, HSO_3^-, as an example (the H atom is bonded to one of the O atoms).

8.68 Some chemists believe that satisfaction of the octet rule should be the top criterion for choosing the dominant Lewis structure of a molecule or ion. Other chemists believe that achieving the best formal charges should be the top criterion. Consider the dihydrogen phosphate ion, $H_2PO_4^-$, in which the H atoms are bonded to O atoms. **(a)** What would be the predicted dominant Lewis structure if satisfying the octet rule is the top criterion? **(b)** What would it be if achieving the best formal charges is the top criterion? **(c)** Is there another Lewis structure you can draw that satisfies neither of these criteria?

BOND ENTHALPIES (section 8.8)

8.69 Using Table 8.4, estimate ΔH for each of the following gas-phase reactions:

(a)

(b)

(c) $2\ Cl—N—Cl \longrightarrow N\equiv N + 3\ Cl—Cl$
         $\quad\quad\ \ |$
         $\quad\quad\ Cl$

8.70 Using Table 8.4, estimate ΔH for the following gas-phase reactions:

8.71 Using Table 8.4, estimate ΔH for each of the following reactions:
(a) $2\ CH_4(g) + O_2(g) \longrightarrow 2\ CH_3OH(g)$
(b) $H_2(g) + Br_2(g) \longrightarrow 2\ HBr(g)$
(c) $2\ H_2O_2(g) \longrightarrow 2\ H_2O(g) + O_2(g)$

8.72 Use Table 8.4 to estimate the enthalpy change for each of the following reactions:
(a) $H_2C{=}O(g) + HCl(g) \longrightarrow H_3C—O—Cl(g)$
(b) $H_2O_2(g) + 2\ CO(g) \longrightarrow H_2(g) + 2\ CO_2(g)$
(c) $3\ H_2C{=}CH_2(g) \longrightarrow C_6H_{12}(g)$ (the six carbon atoms form a six-membered ring with two H atoms on each C atom)

8.73 Ammonia is produced directly from nitrogen and hydrogen by using the Haber process. The chemical reaction is
$$N_2(g) + 3\ H_2(g) \longrightarrow 2\ NH_3(g)$$
(a) Use Table 8.4 to estimate the enthalpy change for the reaction. Is it exothermic or endothermic? **(b)** Compare the enthalpy change you calculate in (a) to the true enthalpy change as obtained using ΔH_f° values.

8.74 **(a)** Use bond enthalpies to estimate the enthalpy change for the reaction of hydrogen with ethylene:
$$H_2(g) + C_2H_4(g) \longrightarrow C_2H_6(g)$$
(b) Calculate the standard enthalpy change for this reaction, using heats of formation. Why does this value differ from that calculated in (a)?

8.75 Given the following bond-dissociation energies, calculate the average bond enthalpy for the Ti—Cl bond.

	$\Delta H(kJ/mol)$
$TiCl_4(g) \longrightarrow TiCl_3(g) + Cl(g)$	335
$TiCl_3(g) \longrightarrow TiCl_2(g) + Cl(g)$	423
$TiCl_2(g) \longrightarrow TiCl(g) + Cl(g)$	444
$TiCl(g) \longrightarrow Ti(g) + Cl(g)$	519

[8.76] **(a)** Using average bond enthalpies, predict which of the following reactions will be most exothermic:
(i) $C(g) + 2\ F_2(g) \longrightarrow CF_4(g)$
(ii) $CO(g) + 3\ F_2 \longrightarrow CF_4(g) + OF_2(g)$
(iii) $CO_2(g) + 4\ F_2 \longrightarrow CF_4(g) + 2\ OF_2(g)$
(b) Explain the trend, if any, that exists between reaction exothermicity and the extent to which the carbon atom is bonded to oxygen.

ADDITIONAL EXERCISES

8.77 How many elements in the periodic table are represented by a Lewis symbol with a single dot? Are all these elements in the same group? Explain.

[8.78] From Equation 8.4 and the ionic radii given in Figure 7.7, calculate the potential energy of the following pairs of ions. Assume that the ions are separated by a distance equal to the sum of their ionic radii: (a) Na^+, Br^-; (b) Rb^+, Br^-; (c) Sr^{2+}, S^{2-}.

8.79 (a) Explain the following trend in lattice energy: BeH_2, 3205 kJ/mol; MgH_2, 2791 kJ/mol; CaH_2, 2410 kJ/mol; SrH_2, 2250 kJ/mol; BaH_2, 2121 kJ/mol. (b) The lattice energy of ZnH_2 is 2870 kJ/mol. Based on the data given in part (a), the radius of the Zn^{2+} ion is expected to be closest to that of which group 2A element?

8.80 Based on data in Table 8.2, estimate (within 30 kJ/mol) the lattice energy for (a) LiBr, (b) CsBr, (c) $CaCl_2$.

8.81 An ionic substance of formula MX has a lattice energy of 6×10^3 kJ/mol. Is the charge on the ion M likely to be 1+, 2+ or 3+? Explain your reasoning.

[8.82] From the ionic radii given in Figure 7.7, calculate the potential energy of a Ca^{2+} and O^{2-} ion pair that is just touching (the magnitude of the electronic charge is given on the back inside cover). Calculate the energy of a mole of such pairs. How does this value compare with the lattice energy of CaO (Table 8.2)? Explain the difference.

8.83 Construct a Born–Haber cycle for the formation of the hypothetical compound $NaCl_2$, where the sodium ion has a 2+ charge (the second ionization energy for sodium is given in Table 7.2). (a) How large would the lattice energy need to be for the formation of $NaCl_2$ to be exothermic? (b) If we were to estimate the lattice energy of $NaCl_2$ to be roughly equal to that of $MgCl_2$ (2326 kJ/mol from Table 8.2), what value would you obtain for the standard enthalpy of formation, ΔH_f°, of $NaCl_2$?

8.84 (a) How does a polar molecule differ from a nonpolar one? (b) Atoms X and Y have different electronegativities. Will the diatomic molecule X—Y necessarily be polar? Explain. (c) What factors affect the size of the dipole moment of a diatomic molecule?

8.85 For the following collection of nonmetallic elements, O, P, Te, I, B, (a) which two would form the most polar single bond? (b) Which two would form the longest single bond? (c) Which two would be likely to form a compound of formula XY_2? (d) Which combinations of elements would likely yield a compound of empirical formula X_2Y_3? In each case explain your answer.

8.86 The substance chlorine monoxide, $ClO(g)$, is important in atmospheric processes that lead to depletion of the ozone layer. The ClO molecule has a dipole moment of 1.24 D and the Cl—O bond length is 1.60 Å. (a) Determine the magnitude of the charges on the Cl and O atoms in units of the electronic charge, e. (b) Based on the electronegativities of the elements, which atom would you expect to have a negative charge in the ClO molecule? (c) By using formal charges as a guide, propose the dominant Lewis structure for the molecule. Are the formal charges consistent with your answers to parts (a) and (b)? Can you reconcile any differences you find?

[8.87] Using the electronegativities of Br and Cl, estimate the partial charges on the atoms in the Br—Cl molecule. Using these partial charges and the atomic radii given in Figure 7.7, estimate the dipole moment of the molecule. The measured dipole moment is 0.57 D.

8.88 A major challenge in implementing the "hydrogen economy" is finding a safe, lightweight, and compact way of storing hydrogen for use as a fuel. The hydrides of light metals are attractive for hydrogen storage because they can store a high weight percentage of hydrogen in a small volume. For example, $NaAlH_4$ can release 5.6% of its mass as H_2 upon decomposing to NaH(s), Al(s), and $H_2(g)$. $NaAlH_4$ possesses both covalent bonds, which hold polyatomic anions together, and ionic bonds. (a) Write a balanced equation for the decomposition of $NaAlH_4$. (b) Which element in $NaAlH_4$ is the most electronegative? Which one is the least electronegative? (c) Based on electronegativity differences, what do you think is the identity of the polyatomic anion? Draw a Lewis structure for this ion.

8.89 Although I_3^- is known, F_3^- is not. Using Lewis structures, explain why F_3^- does not form.

8.90 Calculate the formal charge on the indicated atom in each of the following molecules or ions: (a) the central oxygen atom in O_3, (b) phosphorus in PF_6^-, (c) nitrogen in NO_2, (d) iodine in ICl_3, (e) chlorine in $HClO_4$ (hydrogen is bonded to O).

8.91 (a) Determine the formal charge on the chlorine atom in the hypochlorite ion, ClO^-, and the perchlorate ion, ClO_4^-, using resonance structures where the Cl atom has an octet. (b) What are the oxidation numbers of chlorine in ClO^- and in ClO_4^-? (c) Is it uncommon for the formal charge and the oxidation state to be different? Explain. (d) Perchlorate is a much stronger oxidizing agent than hypochlorite. Would you expect there to be any relationship between the oxidizing power of the oxyanion and either the oxidation state or the formal charge of chlorine?

8.92 The following three Lewis structures can be drawn for N_2O:

$$:N\equiv N-\ddot{\underset{..}{O}}: \longleftrightarrow :\ddot{\underset{..}{N}}-N\equiv O: \longleftrightarrow :\ddot{N}=N=\ddot{\underset{..}{O}}:$$

(a) Using formal charges, which of these three resonance forms is likely to be the most important? (b) The N—N bond length in N_2O is 1.12 Å, slightly longer than a typical $N\equiv N$ bond; and the N—O bond length is 1.19 Å, slightly shorter than a typical $N=O$ bond. (See Table 8.5.) Rationalize these observations in terms of the resonance structures shown previously and your conclusion for part (a).

[8.93] (a) Triazine, $C_3H_3N_3$, is like benzene except that in triazine every other C—H group is replaced by a nitrogen atom. Draw the Lewis structure(s) for the triazine molecule. (b) Estimate the carbon–nitrogen bond distances in the ring.

[8.94] Ortho-dichlorobenzene, $C_6H_4Cl_2$, is obtained when two of the adjacent hydrogen atoms in benzene are replaced with Cl atoms. A skeleton of the molecule is shown here. (a) Complete a Lewis structure for the molecule using bonds and electron pairs as needed. (b) Are there any resonance structures for the molecule? If so, sketch them. (c) Are the resonance structures in (a) and (b) equivalent to one another as they are in benzene? If not, explain what makes them different.

8.95 Consider the hypothetical molecule $B-A=B$. How could you use an experimentally determined structure of the molecule to decide whether resonance is important in it?

8.96 An important reaction for the conversion of natural gas to other useful hydrocarbons is the conversion of methane to ethane.

$$2\,CH_4(g) \longrightarrow C_2H_6(g) + H_2(g)$$

In practice, this reaction is carried out in the presence of oxygen, which converts the hydrogen produced to water.

$$2\,CH_4(g) + \tfrac{1}{2}O_2(g) \longrightarrow C_2H_6(g) + H_2O(g)$$

Use Table 8.4 to estimate ΔH for these two reactions. Why is the conversion of methane to ethane more favorable when oxygen is used?

8.97 Two compounds are isomers if they have the same chemical formula but a different arrangement of atoms. Use Table 8.4 to estimate ΔH for each of the following gas-phase isomerization reactions, and indicate which isomer has the lower enthalpy:

(a)

Ethanol   Dimethyl ether

(b)

Ethylene oxide   Acetaldehyde

(c)

Cyclopentene   Pentadiene

(d)

Methyl isocyanide   Acetonitrile

[8.98] With reference to the "Chemistry Put to Work" box on explosives, **(a)** use bond enthalpies to estimate the enthalpy change for the explosion of 1.00 g of nitroglycerin. **(b)** Write a balanced equation for the decomposition of TNT. Assume that, upon explosion, TNT decomposes into $N_2(g)$, $CO_2(g)$, $H_2O(g)$, and $C(s)$.

[8.99] The "plastic" explosive C-4, often used in action movies, contains the molecule *cyclotrimethylenetrinitramine*, which is often called RDX (for Royal Demolition eXplosive):

Cyclotrimethylenetrinitramine (RDX)

(a) Complete the Lewis structure for the molecule by adding unshared electron pairs where they are needed. **(b)** Does the Lewis structure you drew in part (a) have any resonance structures? If so, how many? **(c)** The molecule causes an explosion by decomposing into $CO(g)$, $N_2(g)$, and $H_2O(g)$. Write a balanced equation for the decomposition reaction. **(d)** With reference to Table 8.4, which is the weakest type of bond in the molecule? **(e)** Use average bond enthalpies to estimate the enthalpy change when 5.0 g of RDX decomposes.

8.100 The bond lengths of carbon–carbon, carbon–nitrogen, carbon–oxygen, and nitrogen–nitrogen single, double, and triple bonds are listed in Table 8.5. Plot bond enthalpy (Table 8.4) versus bond length for these bonds (as in Figure 8.17). What do you conclude about the relationship between bond length and bond enthalpy? What do you conclude about the relative strengths of $C-C$, $C-N$, $C-O$, and $N-N$ bonds?

INTEGRATIVE EXERCISES

8.101 The Ti^{2+} ion is isoelectronic with the Ca atom. **(a)** Are there any differences in the electron configurations of Ti^{2+} and Ca? **(b)** With reference to Figure 6.24, comment on the changes in the ordering of the $4s$ and $3d$ subshells in Ca and Ti^{2+}. **(c)** Will Ca and Ti^{2+} have the same number of unpaired electrons? Explain.

[8.102] **(a)** Write the chemical equations that are used in calculating the lattice energy of $SrCl_2(s)$ via a Born–Haber cycle. **(b)** The second ionization energy of $Sr(g)$ is 1064 kJ/mol. Use this fact along with data in Appendix C, Figure 7.9, Figure 7.11, and Table 8.2 to calculate ΔH_f° for $SrCl_2(s)$.

[8.103] The electron affinity of oxygen is −141 kJ/mol, corresponding to the reaction

$$O(g) + e^- \longrightarrow O^-(g)$$

The lattice energy of $K_2O(s)$ is 2238 kJ/mol. Use these data along with data in Appendix C and Figure 7.9 to calculate the "second electron affinity" of oxygen, corresponding to the reaction

$$O^-(g) + e^- \longrightarrow O^{2-}(g)$$

8.104 You and a partner are asked to complete a lab entitled "Oxides of Ruthenium" that is scheduled to extend over two lab periods. The first lab, which is to be completed by your partner, is devoted to carrying out compositional analysis. In the second lab, you are to determine melting points. Upon going to lab you find two unlabeled vials, one containing a soft yellow substance and the other a black powder. You also find the following notes in your partner's notebook—*Compound 1*: 76.0% Ru and 24.0% O (by mass), *Compound 2*: 61.2% Ru and

38.8% O (by mass). **(a)** What is the empirical formula for Compound 1? **(b)** What is the empirical formula for Compound 2? **(c)** Upon determining the melting points of these two compounds, you find that the yellow compound melts at 25 °C, while the black powder does not melt up to the maximum temperature of your apparatus, 1200 °C. What is the identity of the yellow compound? What is the identity of the black compound? Be sure to use the appropriate naming convention depending on whether the compound is better described as a molecular or ionic compound.

[8.105] One scale for electronegativity is based on the concept that the electronegativity of any atom is proportional to the ionization energy of the atom minus its electron affinity: electronegativity = $k(IE - EA)$, where k is a proportionality constant. **(a)** How does this definition explain why the electronegativity of F is greater than that of Cl even though Cl has the greater electron affinity? **(b)** Why are both ionization energy and electron affinity relevant to the notion of electronegativity? **(c)** By using data in Chapter 7, determine the value of k that would lead to an electronegativity of 4.0 for F under this definition. **(d)** Use your result from part (c) to determine the electronegativities of Cl and O using this scale. Do these values follow the trend shown in Figure 8.7?

8.106 The compound chloral hydrate, known in detective stories as knockout drops, is composed of 14.52% C, 1.83% H, 64.30% Cl, and 19.35% O by mass and has a molar mass of 165.4 g/mol. **(a)** What is the empirical formula of this substance? **(b)** What is the molecular formula of this substance? **(c)** Draw the Lewis structure of the molecule, assuming that the Cl atoms bond to a single C atom and that there are a C—C bond and two C—O bonds in the compound.

8.107 Barium azide is 62.04% Ba and 37.96% N. Each azide ion has a net charge of 1−. **(a)** Determine the chemical formula of the azide ion. **(b)** Write three resonance structures for the azide ion. **(c)** Which structure is most important? **(d)** Predict the bond lengths in the ion.

8.108 Acetylene (C_2H_2) and nitrogen (N_2) both contain a triple bond, but they differ greatly in their chemical properties. **(a)** Write the Lewis structures for the two substances. **(b)** By referring to Appendix C, look up the enthalpies of formation of acetylene and nitrogen and compare their reactivities. **(c)** Write balanced chemical equations for the complete oxidation of N_2 to form $N_2O_5(g)$ and of acetylene to form $CO_2(g)$ and $H_2O(g)$. **(d)** Calculate the enthalpy of oxidation per mole of N_2 and C_2H_2 (the enthalpy of formation of $N_2O_5(g)$ is 11.30 kJ/mol). How do these comparative values relate to your response to part (b)? Both N_2 and C_2H_2 possess triple bonds with quite high bond enthalpies (Table 8.4). What aspect of chemical bonding in these molecules or in the oxidation products seems to account for the difference in chemical reactivities?

[8.109] Under special conditions, sulfur reacts with anhydrous liquid ammonia to form a binary compound of sulfur and nitrogen.

The compound is found to consist of 69.6% S and 30.4% N. Measurements of its molecular mass yield a value of 184.3 g mol^{-1}. The compound occasionally detonates on being struck or when heated rapidly. The sulfur and nitrogen atoms of the molecule are joined in a ring. All the bonds in the ring are of the same length. **(a)** Calculate the empirical and molecular formulas for the substance. **(b)** Write Lewis structures for the molecule, based on the information you are given. (*Hint:* You should find a relatively small number of dominant Lewis structures.) **(c)** Predict the bond distances between the atoms in the ring. (*Note:* The S—S distance in the S_8 ring is 2.05 Å.) **(d)** The enthalpy of formation of the compound is estimated to be 480 kJ mol^{-1}. ΔH_f° of $S(g)$ is 222.8 kJ mol^{-1}. Estimate the average bond enthalpy in the compound.

[8.110] A common form of elemental phosphorus is the tetrahedral P_4 molecule, where all four phosphorus atoms are equivalent:

P_4

At room temperature phosphorus is a solid. **(a)** Do you think there are any unshared pairs of electrons in the P_4 molecule? **(b)** How many P—P bonds are there in the molecule? **(c)** Can you draw a Lewis structure for a linear P_4 molecule that satisfies the octet rule? **(d)** Using formal charges, what can you say about the stability of the linear molecule versus that of the tetrahedral molecule?

[8.111] Consider benzene (C_6H_6) in the gas phase. **(a)** Write the reaction for breaking all the bonds in $C_6H_6(g)$, and use data in Appendix C to determine the enthalpy change for this reaction. **(b)** Write a reaction that corresponds to breaking all the carbon–carbon bonds in $C_6H_6(g)$. **(c)** By combining your answers to parts (a) and (b) and using the average bond enthalpy for C—H from Table 8.4, calculate the average bond enthalpy for the carbon–carbon bonds in $C_6H_6(g)$. **(d)** Comment on your answer from part (c) as compared to the values for C—C single bonds and C=C double bonds in Table 8.4.

8.112 Average bond enthalpies are generally defined for gas-phase molecules. Many substances are liquids in their standard state. ∞∞ (Section 5.7) By using appropriate thermochemical data from Appendix C, calculate average bond enthalpies in the liquid state for the following bonds, and compare these values to the gas-phase values given in Table 8.4: **(a)** Br—Br, from $Br_2(l)$; **(b)** C—Cl, from $CCl_4(l)$; **(c)** O—O, from $H_2O_2(l)$ (assume that the O—H bond enthalpy is the same as in the gas phase). **(d)** What can you conclude about the process of breaking bonds in the liquid as compared to the gas phase? Explain the difference in the ΔH values between the two phases.

9.1 MOLECULAR SHAPES
We begin by discussing *molecular shapes* and examining some shapes commonly encountered in molecules.

9.2 THE VSEPR MODEL
We consider how molecular geometries can be predicted using the *valence-shell electron-pair repulsion,* or *VSEPR,* model, which is based on Lewis structures and the repulsions between regions of high electron density.

9.3 MOLECULAR SHAPE AND MOLECULAR POLARITY
Once we know the geometry of a molecule and the types of bonds it contains, we can determine whether the molecule is *polar* or *nonpolar.*

9.4 COVALENT BONDING AND ORBITAL OVERLAP
We recognize that electrons are shared between atoms in a covalent bond. In *valence-bond theory,* the bonding electrons are visualized as originating in atomic orbitals on two atoms. A covalent bond is formed when these orbitals overlap.

THE DRUG SHOWN HERE IS DIAZEPAM, better known as Valium. It is commonly prescribed for a wide range of disorders, including *anxiety, insomnia, seizures, muscle spasms, restless legs syndrome,* and *obsessive-compulsive disorder.* Valium was invented by Leo Sternbach at Hoffmann-LaRoche Pharmaceuticals and first licensed for use in 1960. It was the top-selling pharmaceutical in the United States from 1969 to 1982, with peak sales in 1978 of 2.3 billion tablets! It continues to be an important medication and is on the World Health Organization's Essential Drugs list.

9.5 HYBRID ORBITALS
To account for molecular shape, we consider how the orbitals of one atom mix with one another, or *hybridize,* to create *hybrid orbitals*.

9.6 MULTIPLE BONDS
Atomic orbitals that contribute to covalent bonding in a molecule can overlap in multiple ways to produce *sigma* and *pi* bonds between atoms. Single bonds generally consist of one sigma bond; multiple bonds involve one sigma and one or more pi bonds. We examine the geometric arrangements of these bonds and how they are exemplified in organic compounds.

9.7 MOLECULAR ORBITALS
We examine a more sophisticated treatment of bonding called *molecular orbital theory,* which introduces the concepts of *bonding* and *antibonding molecular orbitals*.

9.8 PERIOD 2 DIATOMIC MOLECULES
We consider how molecular orbital theory is used to construct *energy-level diagrams* for second-row diatomic molecules.

MOLECULAR GEOMETRY AND BONDING THEORIES

WE SAW IN CHAPTER 8 THAT LEWIS STRUCTURES help us understand the compositions of molecules and their covalent bonds. However, Lewis structures do not show one of the most important aspects of molecules—their overall shapes. The shape and size of molecules—sometimes referred to as molecular *architecture*—are defined by the angles and distances between the nuclei of the component atoms.

The shape and size of a molecule of a substance, together with the strength and polarity of its bonds, largely determine the properties of that substance. Some of the most dramatic examples of the important roles of molecular architecture are seen in biochemical reactions. For example, the chapter-opening photograph shows a molecular model of diazepam, better known as Valium. In the body, this relatively simple molecule enters into an extraordinary array of biochemical interactions. Valium works by binding to certain important sites in the central nervous system. Its effectiveness is highly dependent on the shape and size of the molecule as well on the charge distributions within it. Even a small modification to molecular shape or size alters the drug's effectiveness.

One of our goals in this chapter is to develop a sense of the shapes of molecules and how those shapes are governed in large measure by the kinds of bonds that exist between the atoms making up the molecules.

Our first goal is to learn the relationship between two-dimensional Lewis structures and three-dimensional molecular shapes. Armed with this knowledge, we can examine the nature of covalent bonds. The lines used to depict bonds in Lewis structures provide important clues about the orbitals that molecules use in bonding. By examining these orbitals, we can gain a greater understanding of the behavior of molecules. Mastering the material in this chapter will help you in later discussions of the physical and chemical properties of substances.

9.1 | MOLECULAR SHAPES

In Chapter 8 we used Lewis structures to account for the formulas of covalent compounds. ∞ (Section 8.5) Lewis structures, however, do not indicate the shapes of molecules; they simply show the number and types of bonds. For example, the Lewis structure of CCl_4 tells us only that four Cl atoms are bonded to a central C atom:

$$:\overset{\displaystyle ..}{\underset{\displaystyle ..}{Cl}}:$$
$$:\overset{\displaystyle ..}{\underset{\displaystyle ..}{Cl}}-C-\overset{\displaystyle ..}{\underset{\displaystyle ..}{Cl}}:$$
$$:\overset{\displaystyle ..}{\underset{\displaystyle ..}{Cl}}:$$

The Lewis structure is drawn with the atoms all in the same plane. As shown in ▼ FIGURE 9.1, however, the actual arrangement is the Cl atoms at the corners of a *tetrahedron,* a geometric object with four corners and four faces, each an equilateral triangle.

The shape of a molecule is determined by its **bond angles**, the angles made by the lines joining the nuclei of the atoms in the molecule. The bond angles of a molecule, together with the bond lengths ∞ (Section 8.8), define the shape and size of the molecule. In Figure 9.1, you should be able to see that there are six Cl—C—Cl bond angles in CCl_4 and that they all have the same value of 109.5°, the angle size characteristic of a tetrahedron. In addition, all four C—Cl bonds are the same length (1.78 Å). Thus, the shape and size of CCl_4 are completely described by stating that the molecule is tetrahedral with C—Cl bonds of length 1.78 Å.

We begin our discussion of molecular shapes with molecules (and ions) that, like CCl_4, have a single central atom bonded to two or more atoms of the same type. Such molecules have the general formula AB_n in which the central atom A is bonded to n

GO FIGURE

In the space-filling model, what determines the relative sizes of the spheres?

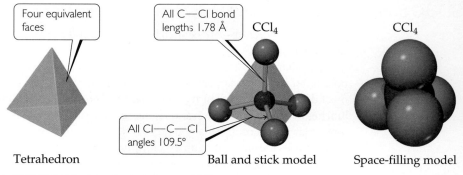

| Four equivalent faces | | All C—Cl bond lengths 1.78 Å | | CCl_4 | | CCl_4 |

All Cl—C—Cl angles 109.5°

Tetrahedron   Ball and stick model   Space-filling model

▲ **FIGURE 9.1** **Tetrahedral shape of CCl_4.**

CO_2	SO_2	SO_3	NF_3	ClF_3
AB_2 linear	AB_2 bent	AB_3 trigonal planar	AB_3 trigonal pyramidal	AB_3 T-shaped

▲ **FIGURE 9.2** Shapes of AB_2 and AB_3 molecules.

B atoms. Both CO_2 and H_2O are AB_2 molecules, for example, whereas SO_3 and NH_3 are AB_3 molecules, and so on.

The number of shapes possible for AB_n molecules depends on the value of n. Those commonly found for AB_2 and AB_3 molecules are shown in ▲ **FIGURE 9.2**. An AB_2 molecule must be either linear (bond angle $= 180°$) or bent (bond angle $\neq 180°$). For AB_3 molecules, the two most common shapes place the B atoms at the corners of an equilateral triangle. If the A atom lies in the same plane as the B atoms, the shape is *trigonal planar*. If the A atom lies above the plane of the B atoms, the shape is *trigonal pyramidal* (a pyramid with an equilateral triangle as its base). Some AB_3 molecules, such as ClF_3, are *T-shaped*, the relatively unusual shape shown in Figure 9.2. The atoms lie in one plane, but the angles between them vary as shown.

Compare Figures 9.1 and 9.2 to notice the difference between NF_3 and CCl_4. The CCl_4 molecule is tetrahedral because the four atoms bonded to the carbon are disposed at the four apexes of a tetrahedron around the central atom. The NF_3 molecule is pyramidal because the three atoms bonded to nitrogen lie at the base of a trigonal pyramid.

The shapes that maximize the separation of outer atoms are shown in ▼ **FIGURE 9.3**. In addition to the shapes we have already seen, this figure shows those encountered when there are five or six atoms surrounding a central atom. The trigonal bipyramid can be thought of as two face-to-face trigonal pyramids; the octahedron is like two face-to-face square pyramids.

◢ GO FIGURE

Which of these molecular shapes do you expect for the SF_6 molecule?

AB_2 linear	AB_3 trigonal planar	AB_4 tetrahedral
180°	120°	109.5°

AB_5 trigonal bipyramidal	AB_6 octahedral
90°, 120°	90°, 90°

◀ **FIGURE 9.3** Shapes allowing maximum distances between atoms in AB_n molecules.

Removal of one corner atom

Removal of a second corner atom

Tetrahedral   Trigonal pyramidal   Bent

▶ **FIGURE 9.4** **Derivatives of the tetrahedral molecular shape.**

Some molecules have shapes other than those shown in Figure 9.3, but we can usually derive the shape of those molecules from Figure 9.3. Neither trigonal pyramidal nor bent is shown in Figure 9.3, for instance, but ▲ **FIGURE 9.4** shows how we can arrive at these shapes by removing atoms from the tetrahedral shape.

Why do so many AB_n molecules have shapes related to those shown in Figure 9.3, and can we predict these shapes? When A is a representative element (one from the *s* block or *p* block of the periodic table), we can answer these questions by using the **valence-shell electron-pair repulsion (VSEPR) model**. Although the name is rather imposing, the model is quite simple. It has useful predictive capabilities, as we will see in Section 9.2.

 GIVE IT SOME THOUGHT

In addition to tetrahedral, another common shape for AB_4 molecules is *square planar*. All five atoms lie in the same plane, with the B atoms at the corners of a square and the A atom at the center of the square. Which shape in Figure 9.3 could lead to a square-planar shape upon removal of one or more atoms?

Two balloons
linear orientation

Three balloons
trigonal-planar orientation

Four balloons
tetrahedral orientation

▲ **FIGURE 9.5** **A balloon analogy for electron domains.**

9.2 | THE VSEPR MODEL

Imagine tying two identical balloons together at their ends. As shown in ◀ **FIGURE 9.5**, the two balloons naturally orient themselves to point away from each other; that is, they try to "get out of each other's way" as much as possible. If we add a third balloon, the balloons orient themselves toward the vertices of an equilateral triangle, and if we add a fourth balloon, they adopt a tetrahedral shape. We see that an optimum geometry exists for each number of balloons.

In some ways, the electrons in molecules behave like these balloons. We have seen that a single covalent bond is formed between two atoms when a pair of electrons occupies the space between the atoms. ∞ (Section 8.3) A **bonding pair** of electrons thus defines a region in which the electrons are most likely to be found. We will refer to such a region as an **electron domain**. Likewise, a **nonbonding pair** (or **lone pair**) of electrons defines an electron domain that is located principally on one atom. For example, the Lewis structure of NH_3 has four electron domains around the central nitrogen atom (three bonding pairs, represented as usual by short lines, and one nonbonding pair, represented by dots):

$$H—\ddot{N}—H$$
$$|$$
$$H$$

Each multiple bond in a molecule also constitutes a single electron domain. Thus, the resonance structure for O_3 has three electron domains around the central oxygen atom (a single bond, a double bond, and a nonbonding pair of electrons):

$$:\ddot{O}—\ddot{O}=\ddot{O}$$

In general, *each nonbonding pair, single bond, or multiple bond produces a single electron domain around the central atom in a molecule.*

GIVE IT SOME THOUGHT

Suppose a particular AB_3 molecule has the resonance structure

$$
\begin{array}{c}
:\!\ddot{B}\!: \\
\parallel \\
:\!\ddot{B}\!-\!A\!-\!\ddot{B}\!:
\end{array}
$$

Does this structure follow the octet rule? How many electron domains are there around the A atom?

The VSEPR model is based on the idea that electron domains are negatively charged and therefore repel one another. Like the balloons in Figure 9.5, electron domains try to stay out of one another's way. *The best arrangement of a given number of electron domains is the one that minimizes the repulsions among them.* In fact, the analogy between electron domains and balloons is so close that the same preferred geometries are found in both cases. Like the balloons in Figure 9.5, two electron domains orient *linearly,* three domains orient in a *trigonal-planar* fashion, and four orient *tetrahedrally.* These arrangements, together with those for five- and six-electron domains, are summarized in ▼ **TABLE 9.1**. If you compare the geometries in Table 9.1 with those in Figure 9.3,

TABLE 9.1 • Electron-Domain Geometries as a Function of Number of Electron Domains

Number of Electron Domains	Arrangement of Electron Domains	Electron-Domain Geometry	Predicted Bond Angles
2		Linear	180°
3		Trigonal planar	120°
4		Tetrahedral	109.5°
5		Trigonal bipyramidal	120° 90°
6		Octahedral	90°

you will see that they are the same. *The shapes of different AB$_n$ molecules or ions depend on the number of electron domains surrounding the central atom.*

The arrangement of electron domains about the central atom of an AB$_n$ molecule or ion is called its **electron-domain geometry**. In contrast, the **molecular geometry** is the arrangement of *only the atoms* in a molecule or ion—any nonbonding pairs in the molecule are *not* part of the description of the molecular geometry.

In determining the shape of any molecule, we first use the VSEPR model to predict the electron-domain geometry. From knowing how many of the domains are due to nonbonding pairs, we can then predict the molecular geometry. When all the electron domains in a molecule arise from bonds, the molecular geometry is identical to the electron-domain geometry. When, however, one or more domains involve nonbonding pairs of electrons, we must remember to ignore those domains when talking about molecular shape.

We can generalize the steps we follow in using the VSEPR model to predict the shapes of molecules or ions:

1. Draw the *Lewis structure* of the molecule or ion, and count the number of electron domains around the central atom. Each nonbonding electron pair, each single bond, each double bond, and each triple bond counts as one electron domain.

2. Determine the *electron-domain geometry* by arranging the electron domains about the central atom so that the repulsions among them are minimized, as shown in Table 9.1.

3. Use the arrangement of the bonded atoms to determine the *molecular geometry*.

▼ **FIGURE 9.6** shows how these steps are applied to predict the geometry of the NH$_3$ molecule. The three bonds and one nonbonding pair in the Lewis structure tell us we have four electron domains. We know from Table 9.1 that the repulsions among four electron domains are minimized when the domains point toward the vertices of a tetrahedron, so the electron-domain geometry of NH$_3$ is tetrahedral. We know from the Lewis structure that one electron domain holds a nonbonding pair of electrons, which occupies one of the four vertices of the tetrahedron. The bonding arrangement is therefore three atoms bonded to a central atom, with the central atom not in the same plane as the three others. This is just the situation we find in the middle molecule of Figure 9.4. Hence, the molecular geometry of NH$_3$ is trigonal pyramidal. Notice that the tetrahedral arrangement of the four electron domains leads us to predict the trigonal-pyramidal molecular geometry.

Because the trigonal-pyramidal molecular geometry is based on a tetrahedral electron-domain geometry, the *ideal bond angles* are 109.5°. As we will soon see, bond angles deviate from ideal values when the surrounding atoms and electron domains are not identical.

▲ GIVE IT SOME THOUGHT

From the standpoint of the VSEPR model, what do nonbonding electron pairs, single bonds, and multiple bonds have in common?

1. Draw Lewis structure

2. Determine electron-domain geometry by counting *all* electron domains, then use Table 9.1 to determine appropriate electron domain geomtry.

3. Determine molecular geometry by counting *only* bonding electron domains to see arrangement of bonded atoms (trigonal pyramidal)

▶ **FIGURE 9.6 Determining the molecular geometry of NH$_3$.**

As one more example, let's determine the shape of the CO_2 molecule. Its Lewis structure reveals two electron domains (each one a double bond) around the central carbon:

$$\ddot{O}=C=\ddot{O}$$

Two electron domains orient in a linear electron-domain geometry (Table 9.1). Because neither domain is a nonbonding pair of electrons, the molecular geometry is also linear, and the $O-C-O$ bond angle is 180°.

▼ TABLE 9.2 summarizes the possible molecular geometries when an AB_n molecule has four or fewer electron domains about A. These geometries are important because they include all the shapes usually seen in molecules or ions that obey the octet rule.

TABLE 9.2 • Electron-Domain and Molecular Geometries for Two, Three, and Four Electron Domains around a Central Atom

Number of Electron Domains	Electron-Domain Geometry	Bonding Domains	Nonbonding Domains	Molecular Geometry	Example
2	Linear	2	0	Linear	$\ddot{O}=C=\ddot{O}$
3	Trigonal planar	3	0	Trigonal planar	
		2	1	Bent	
4	Tetrahedral	4	0	Tetrahedral	
		3	1	Trigonal pyramidal	
		2	2	Bent	

SAMPLE EXERCISE 9.1   **Using the VSEPR Model**

Use the VSEPR model to predict the molecular geometry of (**a**) O_3, (**b**) $SnCl_3^-$.

SOLUTION

Analyze We are given the molecular formulas of a molecule and a polyatomic ion, both conforming to the general formula AB_n and both having a central atom from the p block of the periodic table.

Plan To predict the molecular geometries, we draw their Lewis structures and count electron domains around the central atom to get the electron-domain geometry. We then obtain the molecular geometry from the arrangement of the domains that are due to bonds.

Solve

(**a**) We can draw two resonance structures for O_3:

$$:\ddot{O}-\ddot{O}=\ddot{O} \longleftrightarrow \ddot{O}=\ddot{O}-\ddot{O}:$$

Because of resonance, the bonds between the central O atom and the outer O atoms are of equal length. In both resonance structures the central O atom is bonded to the two outer O atoms and has one nonbonding pair. Thus, there are three electron domains about the central O atoms. (Remember that a double bond counts as a single electron domain.) The arrangement of three electron domains is trigonal planar (Table 9.1). Two of the domains are from bonds, and one is due to a nonbonding pair. So, the molecule has a bent shape with an ideal bond angle of 120° (Table 9.2).

Comment As this example illustrates, when a molecule exhibits resonance, any one of the resonance structures can be used to predict the molecular geometry.

(**b**) The Lewis structure for $SnCl_3^-$ is

$$\left[:\ddot{Cl}-\overset{\underset{|}{:\ddot{Cl}:}}{Sn}-\ddot{Cl}:\right]^-$$

The central Sn atom is bonded to the three Cl atoms and has one nonbonding pair; thus, we have four electron domains, meaning tetrahedral electron-domain geometry (Table 9.1) with one vertex occupied by a nonbonding pair of electrons. Tetrahedral electron-domain geometry with three bonding and one nonbonding domains means the molecular geometry is trigonal pyramidal (Table 9.2).

PRACTICE EXERCISE

Predict the electron-domain and molecular geometries for (**a**) $SeCl_2$, (**b**) CO_3^{2-}.
Answers: (**a**) tetrahedral, bent; (**b**) trigonal planar, trigonal planar

Effect of Nonbonding Electrons and Multiple Bonds on Bond Angles

We can refine the VSEPR model to explain slight distortions from the ideal geometries summarized in Table 9.2. For example, consider methane (CH_4), ammonia (NH_3), and water (H_2O). All three have a tetrahedral electron-domain geometry, but their bond angles differ slightly:

Notice that the bond angles decrease as the number of nonbonding electron pairs increases. A bonding pair of electrons is attracted by both nuclei of the bonded atoms, but a nonbonding pair is attracted primarily by only one nucleus. Because a nonbonding pair experiences less nuclear attraction, its electron domain is spread out more in space than is the electron domain for a bonding pair (▶ FIGURE 9.7). Nonbonding electron pairs therefore take up more space than bonding pairs. As a result, *electron domains for nonbonding electron pairs exert greater repulsive forces on adjacent electron domains and tend to compress bond angles.*

Because multiple bonds contain a higher electronic-charge density than single bonds, multiple bonds also represent enlarged electron domains. Consider the Lewis structure of phosgene:

$$
:\overset{..}{\underset{..}{Cl}}
$$
$$
\overset{\displaystyle |}{C}=\overset{..}{\underset{..}{O}}
$$
$$
:\overset{..}{\underset{..}{Cl}}
$$

Because three electron domains surround the central atom, we might expect a trigonal-planar geometry with 120° bond angles. The double bond, however, seems to act much like a nonbonding pair of electrons, reducing the Cl—C—Cl bond angle to 111.4°:

$$
\begin{array}{c}
Cl \\
111.4°\,C\!=\!O \\
Cl
\end{array}
$$

124.3°

124.3°

In general, *electron domains for multiple bonds exert a greater repulsive force on adjacent electron domains than do electron domains for single bonds.*

 GIVE IT SOME THOUGHT

One resonance structure of the nitrate ion is

$$
\left[\begin{array}{c}
:O: \\
\| \\
N \\
:\overset{..}{\underset{..}{O}}\quad\overset{..}{\underset{..}{O}}:
\end{array}\right]^{-}
$$

The bond angles in this ion are 120°. Is this observation consistent with the preceding discussion of the effect of multiple bonds on bond angles?

Molecules with Expanded Valence Shells

Atoms from period 3 and beyond may be surrounded by more than four electron pairs. ∞ (Section 8.7) Molecules with five or six electron domains around the central atom have molecular geometries based on either a *trigonal-bipyramidal* (five domains) or *octahedral* (six domains) electron-domain geometry (▶ TABLE 9.3).

The most stable electron-domain geometry for five electron domains is the trigonal bipyramid (two trigonal pyramids sharing a base). Unlike the other arrangements we have seen, the electron domains in a trigonal bipyramid can point toward two geometrically distinct types of positions. Two domains point toward *axial positions* and three point toward *equatorial positions* (▶ FIGURE 9.8). Each axial domain makes a 90° angle with any equatorial domain. Each equatorial domain makes a 120° angle with either of the other two equatorial domains and a 90° angle with either axial domain.

Suppose a molecule has five electron domains, and there are one or more nonbonding pairs. Will the domains from the nonbonding pairs occupy axial or equatorial positions? To answer this question, we must determine which location minimizes repulsion between domains. Repulsion between two domains is much greater when they are situated 90° from each other than when they are at 120°. An equatorial domain is 90° from only two other domains (the axial domains), but an axial domain is 90° from *three* other domains (the equatorial domains). Hence, an equatorial domain experiences less repulsion than an axial domain. Because the domains from nonbonding pairs exert larger repulsions than those from bonding pairs, nonbonding domains always occupy the equatorial positions in a trigonal bipyramid.

 GIVE IT SOME THOUGHT

It might seem that a square-planar geometry of four electron domains around a central atom would be more favorable than a tetrahedron. Can you rationalize why the tetrahedron is preferred, based on angles between electron domains?

 GO FIGURE

Why is the volume occupied by the nonbonding electron pair domain larger than the volume occupied by the bonding domain?

Bonding electron pair

Nuclei

Nonbonding pair

Nucleus

▲ **FIGURE 9.7 Relative volumes occupied by bonding and nonbonding electron domains.**

 GO FIGURE

What is the bond angle formed by an axial atom, the central atom, and any equatorial atom?

Axial position

Three equatorial positions form an equilateral triangle

Axial position

▲ **FIGURE 9.8 In a trigonal-bipyramidal geometry, there are two types of positions for the outer atoms.**

TABLE 9.3 • Electron-Domain and Molecular Geometries for Five and Six Electron Domains around a Central Atom

Number of Electron Domains	Electron-Domain Geometry	Bonding Domains	Nonbonding Domains	Molecular Geometry	Example
5	Trigonal bipyramidal	5	0	Trigonal bipyramidal	PCl_5
		4	1	Seesaw	SF_4
		3	2	T-shaped	ClF_3
		2	3	Linear	XeF_2
6	Octahedral	6	0	Octahedral	SF_6
		5	1	Square pyramidal	BrF_5
		4	2	Square planar	XeF_4

The most stable electron-domain geometry for six electron domains is the *octahedron*. An octahedron is a polyhedron with six vertices and eight faces, each an equilateral triangle. An atom with six electron domains around it can be visualized as being at the center of the octahedron with the electron domains pointing toward the six vertices, as shown in Table 9.3. All the bond angles are 90°, and all six vertices are equivalent. Therefore, if an atom has five bonding electron domains and one nonbonding domain, we can put the nonbonding domain at any of the six vertices of the octahedron. The result is always a *square-pyramidal* molecular geometry. When there are two nonbonding electron domains, however, their repulsions are minimized by pointing them toward opposite sides of the octahedron, producing a *square-planar* molecular geometry, as shown in Table 9.3.

SAMPLE EXERCISE 9.2 Molecular Geometries of Molecules with Expanded Valence Shells

Use the VSEPR model to predict the molecular geometry of (a) SF_4, (b) IF_5.

SOLUTION

Analyze The molecules are of the AB_n type with a central *p*-block atom.

Plan We first draw Lewis structures and then use the VSEPR model to determine the electron-domain geometry and molecular geometry.

Solve
(a) The Lewis structure for SF_4 is

The sulfur has five electron domains around it: four from the S—F bonds and one from the nonbonding pair. Each domain points toward a vertex of a trigonal bipyramid. The domain from the nonbonding pair will point toward an equatorial position. The four bonds point toward the remaining four positions, resulting in a molecular geometry that is described as seesaw-shaped:

Comment The experimentally observed structure is shown on the right. We can infer that the nonbonding electron domain occupies an equatorial position, as predicted. The axial and equatorial S—F bonds are slightly bent away from the nonbonding domain, suggesting that the bonding domains are "pushed" by the nonbonding domain, which exerts a greater repulsion (Figure 9.7).

(b) The Lewis structure of IF_5 is

The iodine has six electron domains around it, one of which is nonbonding. The electron-domain geometry is therefore octahedral, with one position occupied by the nonbonding pair, and the molecular geometry is *square pyramidal* (Table 9.3):

Comment Because the nonbonding domain is larger than the bonding domains, we predict that the four F atoms in the base of the pyramid will be tipped up slightly toward the top F atom. Experimentally, we find that the angle between the base atoms and top F atom is 82°, smaller than the ideal 90° angle of an octahedron.

PRACTICE EXERCISE

Predict the electron-domain and molecular geometries of (a) BrF_3, (b) ICl_4^-.
Answers: (a) trigonal bipyramidal, T-shaped; (b) octahedral, square planar

GO FIGURE

Although the electron-domain geometry around the right O is tetrahedral, the C—O—H bond is slightly less than 109.5°. Explain.

Electron-domain geometry tetrahedral, molecular geometry tetrahedral

Electron-domain geometry trigonal planar, molecular geometry trigonal planar

Electron-domain geometry tetrahedral, molecular geometry bent

▲ FIGURE 9.9 **Acetic acid, CH₃COOH.**

Shapes of Larger Molecules

Although the molecules and ions we have considered contain only a single central atom, the VSEPR model can be extended to more complex molecules. For the acetic acid molecule, for example,

$$H-\underset{\underset{H}{|}}{\overset{\overset{H}{|}}{C}}-\overset{\overset{\ddot{:}\ddot{O}:}{||}}{C}-\ddot{\ddot{O}}-H$$

we can use the VSEPR model to predict the geometry about each atom:

	H—C (with H above and below)	:O: C (double bond)	Ö—H
Number of electron domains	4	3	4
Electron-domain geometry	Tetrahedral	Trigonal planar	Tetrahedral
Predicted bond angles	109.5°	120°	109.5°

The left C has four electron domains (all bonding), and so the electron-domain and molecular geometries around that atom are both tetrahedral. The central C has three electron domains (counting the double bond as one domain), making both the electron-domain and the molecular geometries trigonal planar. The O on the right has four electron domains (two bonding, two nonbonding), so its electron-domain geometry is tetrahedral and its molecular geometry is bent. The bond angles about the central C atom and the O atom are expected to deviate slightly from the ideal values of 120° and 109.5° because of the spatial demands of multiple bonds and nonbonding electron pairs.

The structure of the acetic acid molecule is shown in ◄ FIGURE 9.9.

SAMPLE EXERCISE 9.3 **Predicting Bond Angles**

Eyedrops for dry eyes usually contain a water-soluble polymer called *poly(vinyl alcohol)*, which is based on the unstable organic molecule *vinyl alcohol*:

$$H-\ddot{O}-\underset{\underset{H}{|}}{\overset{\overset{H}{|}}{C}}=\underset{}{\overset{\overset{H}{|}}{C}}-H$$

Predict the approximate values for the H—O—C and O—C—C bond angles in vinyl alcohol.

SOLUTION

Analyze We are given a Lewis structure and asked to determine two bond angles.

Plan To predict a bond angle, we determine the number of electron domains surrounding the middle atom in the bond. The ideal angle corresponds to the electron-domain geometry around the atom. The angle will be compressed somewhat by nonbonding electrons or multiple bonds.

Solve In H—O—C, the O atom has four electron domains (two bonding, two nonbonding). The electron-domain geometry around O is therefore tetrahedral, which gives an ideal angle of 109.5°. The H—O—C angle is compressed somewhat by the nonbonding pairs, so we expect this angle to be slightly less than 109.5°.

To predict the O—C—C bond angle, we examine the middle atom in the angle. In the molecule, there are three atoms bonded to this C atom and no nonbonding pairs, and so it has three electron domains about it. The predicted electron-domain geometry is trigonal planar, resulting in an ideal bond angle of 120°. Because of the larger size of the C=C domain, the bond angle should be slightly greater than 120°.

PRACTICE EXERCISE
Predict the H—C—H and C—C—C bond angles in *propyne*:

$$H-\underset{\underset{H}{|}}{\overset{\overset{H}{|}}{C}}-C\equiv C-H$$

Answers: 109.5°, 180°

9.3 | MOLECULAR SHAPE AND MOLECULAR POLARITY

Recall that bond polarity is a measure of how equally the electrons in a bond are shared between the two atoms of the bond. As the difference in electronegativity between the two atoms increases, so does the bond polarity. ∞ (Section 8.4) We saw that the dipole moment of a diatomic molecule is a measure of the amount of charge separation in the molecule.

For a molecule consisting of more than two atoms, *the dipole moment depends on both the polarities of the individual bonds and the geometry of the molecule.* For each bond in the molecule, we consider the **bond dipole**, which is the dipole moment due only to the two atoms in that bond. Consider the linear CO_2 molecule, for example. As shown in ▶ FIGURE 9.10, each C=O bond is polar, and because the C=O bonds are identical, the bond dipoles are equal in magnitude. A plot of the molecule's electron density clearly shows that the individual bonds are polar, but what can we say about the *overall* dipole moment of the molecule?

Bond dipoles and dipole moments are vector quantities; that is, they have both a magnitude and a direction. The dipole moment of a polyatomic molecule is the vector sum of its bond dipoles. Both the magnitudes *and* the directions of the bond dipoles must be considered when summing vectors. The two bond dipoles in CO_2, although equal in magnitude, are opposite in direction. Adding them is the same as adding two numbers that are equal in magnitude but opposite in sign, such as $100 + (-100)$. The bond dipoles, like the numbers, "cancel" each other. Therefore, the dipole moment of CO_2 is zero, even though the individual bonds are polar. The geometry of the molecule dictates that the overall dipole moment be zero, making CO_2 a *nonpolar* molecule.

Now consider H_2O, a bent molecule with two polar bonds (▶ FIGURE 9.11). Again, the two bonds are identical, and the bond dipoles are equal in magnitude. Because the molecule is bent, however, the bond dipoles do not directly oppose each other and therefore do not cancel. Hence, the H_2O molecule has an overall nonzero dipole moment ($\mu = 1.85$ D) and is therefore a *polar* molecule. The oxygen atom carries a partial negative charge, and the hydrogen atoms each have a partial positive charge, as shown in the electron-density model.

▲ **GIVE IT SOME THOUGHT**
The molecule O=C=S is linear and has a Lewis structure analogous to that of CO_2. Would you expect this molecule to have a dipole moment?

▶ FIGURE 9.12 shows some polar and nonpolar molecules, all with polar bonds. The molecules in which the central atom is symmetrically surrounded by identical atoms (BF_3 and CCl_4) are nonpolar. For AB_n molecules in which all the B atoms are the same, certain symmetrical shapes—linear (AB_2), trigonal planar (AB_3), tetrahedral and square planar (AB_4), trigonal bipyramidal (AB_5), and octahedral (AB_6)—must lead to nonpolar molecules even though the individual bonds might be polar.

▲ **GO FIGURE**

Explain how the directions of the red bond dipole arrows relate to the electron density picture.

Equal and oppositely directed bond dipoles

Overall dipole moment = 0

High electron density

Low electron density

▲ **FIGURE 9.10 CO_2, a nonpolar molecule.** The numbers are electronegativity values for these two atoms.

Bond dipoles

Overall dipole moment

▲ **FIGURE 9.11 H_2O, a polar molecule.** The numbers are electronegativity values.

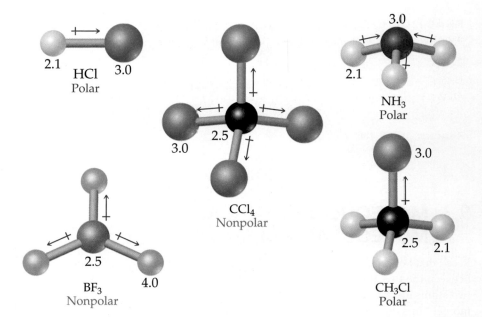

▶ **FIGURE 9.12 Polar and nonpolar molecules containing polar bonds.** The numbers are electronegativity values.

SAMPLE EXERCISE 9.4 **Polarity of Molecules**

Predict whether these molecules are polar or nonpolar: (a) BrCl, (b) SO_2, (c) SF_6.

SOLUTION

Analyze We are given three molecular formulas and asked to predict whether the molecules are polar.

Plan A molecule containing only two atoms is polar if the atoms differ in electronegativity. The polarity of a molecule containing three or more atoms depends on both the molecular geometry and the individual bond polarities. Thus, we must draw a Lewis structure for each molecule containing three or more atoms and determine its molecular geometry. We then use electronegativity values to determine the direction of the bond dipoles. Finally, we see whether the bond dipoles cancel to give a nonpolar molecule or reinforce each other to give a polar one.

Solve

(a) Chlorine is more electronegative than bromine. All diatomic molecules with polar bonds are polar molecules. Consequently, BrCl is polar, with chlorine carrying the partial negative charge:

$$\overset{+\longrightarrow}{Br\!-\!Cl}$$

The measured dipole moment of BrCl is $\mu = 0.57$ D.

(b) Because oxygen is more electronegative than sulfur, SO_2 has polar bonds. Three resonance forms can be written:

$$:\!\ddot{O}\!-\!\ddot{S}\!=\!\ddot{O}\!: \longleftrightarrow :\!\ddot{O}\!=\!\ddot{S}\!-\!\ddot{O}\!: \longleftrightarrow :\!\ddot{O}\!=\!\ddot{S}\!=\!\ddot{O}\!:$$

For each of these, the VSEPR model predicts a bent molecular geometry. Because the molecule is bent, the bond dipoles do not cancel, and the molecule is polar:

Experimentally, the dipole moment of SO_2 is $\mu = 1.63$ D.

(c) Fluorine is more electronegative than sulfur, so the bond dipoles point toward fluorine. For clarity, only one S—F dipole is shown. The six S—F bonds are arranged octahedrally around the central sulfur:

Because the octahedral molecular geometry is symmetrical, the bond dipoles cancel, and the molecule is nonpolar, meaning that $\mu = 0$.

PRACTICE EXERCISE
Determine whether the following molecules are polar or nonpolar: (**a**) NF_3, (**b**) BCl_3.
Answers: (**a**) polar because polar bonds are arranged in a trigonal-pyramidal geometry, (**b**) nonpolar because polar bonds are arranged in a trigonal-planar geometry

9.4 | COVALENT BONDING AND ORBITAL OVERLAP

The VSEPR model provides a simple means for predicting molecular geometries but does not explain why bonds exist between atoms. In developing theories of covalent bonding, chemists have approached the problem from another direction, using quantum mechanics. How can we use atomic orbitals to explain bonding and to account for molecular geometries? The marriage of Lewis's notion of electron-pair bonds and the idea of atomic orbitals leads to a model of chemical bonding, called **valence-bond theory**, in which bonding electron pairs are concentrated in the regions between atoms and nonbonding electron pairs lie in directed regions of space. By extending this approach to include the ways in which atomic orbitals can mix with one another, we obtain an explanatory picture that corresponds to the VSEPR model.

In Lewis theory, covalent bonding occurs when atoms share electrons because the sharing concentrates electron density between the nuclei. In valence-bond theory, we visualize the buildup of electron density between two nuclei as occurring when a valence atomic orbital of one atom shares space, or *overlaps*, with a valence atomic orbital of another atom. The overlap of orbitals allows two electrons of opposite spin to share the space between the nuclei, forming a covalent bond.

The coming together of two H atoms to form H_2 is depicted in ▶ **FIGURE 9.13**. Each atom has a single electron in a $1s$ orbital. As the orbitals overlap, electron density is concentrated between the nuclei. Because the electrons in the overlap region are simultaneously attracted to both nuclei, they hold the atoms together, forming a covalent bond.

The idea of orbital overlap producing a covalent bond applies equally well to other molecules. In HCl, for example, chlorine has the electron configuration $[Ne]3s^23p^5$. All the valence orbitals of chlorine are full except one $3p$ orbital, which contains a single electron. This $3p$ electron pairs with the single $1s$ electron of H to form a covalent bond (Figure 9.13). Because the other two chlorine $3p$ orbitals are already filled with a pair of electrons, they do not participate in the bonding to hydrogen. Likewise, we can explain the covalent bond in Cl_2 in terms of the overlap of the singly occupied $3p$ orbital of one Cl atom with the singly occupied $3p$ orbital of another.

There is always an optimum distance between the two nuclei in any covalent bond. ▶ **FIGURE 9.14** shows how the potential energy of a system consisting of two H atoms changes as the atoms come together to form an H_2 molecule. When the atoms are infinitely far apart, they do not "feel" each other and so the energy approaches zero. As the distance between the atoms decreases, the overlap between their $1s$ orbitals increases. Because of the resultant increase in electron density between the nuclei, the potential energy of the system decreases. That is, the strength of the bond increases, as shown by the decrease in the potential energy of the two-atom system. However, Figure 9.14 also shows that as the atoms come closer together than 0.74 Å, the energy increases sharply. This increase, which becomes significant at short internuclear distances, is due mainly to the electrostatic repulsion between the nuclei. The internuclear distance, or bond length, is the distance that corresponds to the minimum of the potential-energy curve. The potential energy at this minimum corresponds to the bond strength. Thus, the observed bond length is the distance at which the attractive forces between unlike charges (electrons and nuclei) are balanced by the repulsive forces between like charges (electron–electron and nucleus–nucleus).

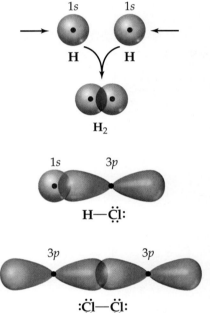

▲ **FIGURE 9.13** **Covalent bonds in H_2, HCl, and Cl_2 result from overlap of atomic orbitals.**

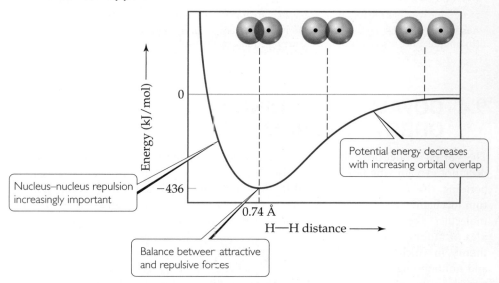

On the left part of the curve the potential energy rises above zero. What causes this to happen?

▲ **FIGURE 9.14**   **Formation of the H₂ molecule as atomic orbitals overlap.**

9.5 | HYBRID ORBITALS

The VSEPR model, simple as it is, does a surprisingly good job at predicting molecular shape, despite the fact that it has no obvious relationship to the filling and shapes of atomic orbitals. For example, based on the shapes and orientations of the $2s$ and $2p$ orbitals on a carbon atom, it is not obvious why a CH_4 molecule should have a tetrahedral geometry. How can we reconcile the notion that covalent bonds are formed from overlap of atomic orbitals with the molecular geometries that come from the VSEPR model?

To begin with, we recall that atomic orbitals are mathematical functions that come from the quantum mechanical model for atomic structure. ∞ (Section 6.5) To explain molecular geometries, we can assume that the atomic orbitals on an atom (usually the central atom) mix to form new orbitals called **hybrid orbitals**. The shape of any hybrid orbital is different from the shapes of the original atomic orbitals. The process of mixing atomic orbitals is a mathematical operation called **hybridization**. The total number of atomic orbitals on an atom remains constant, so the number of hybrid orbitals on an atom equals the number of atomic orbitals that are mixed.

As we examine the common types of hybridization, notice the connection between the type of hybridization and certain of the molecular geometries predicted by the VSEPR model: linear, bent, trigonal planar, and tetrahedral.

sp Hybrid Orbitals

To illustrate the process of hybridization, consider the BeF_2 molecule, which has the Lewis structure

$$:\ddot{\text{F}}\text{—Be—}\ddot{\text{F}}:$$

The VSEPR model correctly predicts that BeF_2 is linear with two identical Be—F bonds. How can we use valence-bond theory to describe the bonding? The electron configuration of F ($1s^2 2s^2 2p^5$) indicates an unpaired electron in a $2p$ orbital. This electron can be paired with an unpaired Be electron to form a polar covalent bond. Which orbitals on the Be atom, however, overlap with those on the F atoms to form the Be—F bonds?

The orbital diagram for a ground-state Be atom is

Because it has no unpaired electrons, the Be atom in its ground state cannot bond with the fluorine atoms. The Be atom could form two bonds, however, by "promoting" one of the $2s$ electrons to a $2p$ orbital:

The Be atom now has two unpaired electrons and can therefore form two polar covalent bonds with F atoms. The two bonds would not be identical, however, because a Be $2s$ orbital would be used to form one of the bonds and a $2p$ orbital would be used to form the other. Therefore, although the promotion of an electron allows two Be—F bonds to form, we still have not explained the structure of BeF_2.

We can solve this dilemma by "mixing" the $2s$ orbital with one $2p$ orbital to generate two new orbitals, as shown in ▼ **FIGURE 9.15**. Like p orbitals, each new orbital has two lobes. Unlike p orbitals, however, one lobe is much larger than the other. The two new orbitals are identical in shape, but their large lobes point in opposite directions. These two new orbitals, which we color-code purple in Figure 9.15, are hybrid orbitals. Because we have hybridized one s and one p orbital, we call each hybrid an sp hybrid orbital. *According to the valence-bond model, a linear arrangement of electron domains implies sp hybridization.*

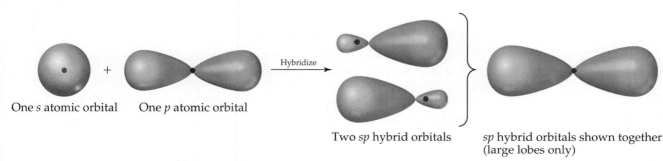

One s atomic orbital   One p atomic orbital   Two sp hybrid orbitals sp hybrid orbitals shown together (large lobes only)

▲ **FIGURE 9.15   Formation of *sp* hybrid orbitals.**

For the Be atom of BeF_2, we write the orbital diagram for the formation of two sp hybrid orbitals as

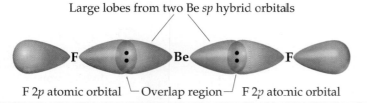

The electrons in the sp hybrid orbitals can form bonds with the two fluorine atoms (▼ **FIGURE 9.16**). Because the sp hybrid orbitals are equivalent but point in opposite

GO FIGURE

Why is it reasonable to take account of only the large lobes of the Be hybrid orbitals in considering the bonding to F?

Large lobes from two Be sp hybrid orbitals

F   Be   F

F $2p$ atomic orbital   Overlap region   F $2p$ atomic orbital

◀ **FIGURE 9.16   Formation of two equivalent Be—F bonds in BeF₂.**

directions, BeF$_2$ has two identical bonds and a linear geometry. The remaining two 2p atomic orbitals of Be remain unhybridized and are vacant. Remember also that each fluorine atom has two other valence p atomic orbitals, each containing one nonbonding electron pair. Those atomic orbitals are omitted from Figure 9.16 to keep the illustration simpler.

 GIVE IT SOME THOUGHT

What is the orientation of the two unhybridized p orbitals on Be with respect to the two Be—F bonds?

sp^2 and sp^3 Hybrid Orbitals

Whenever we mix a certain number of atomic orbitals, we get the same number of hybrid orbitals. Each hybrid orbital is equivalent to the others but points in a different direction. Thus, mixing one 2s and one 2p atomic orbital yields two equivalent sp hybrid orbitals that point in opposite directions (Figure 9.15). Other combinations of atomic orbitals can be hybridized to obtain different geometries. In BF$_3$, for example, mixing the 2s and two of the 2p atomic orbitals yields three equivalent sp^2 (pronounced "s-p-two") hybrid orbitals (▼ **FIGURE 9.17**).

The three sp^2 hybrid orbitals lie in the same plane, 120° apart from one another. They are used to make three equivalent bonds with the three fluorine atoms, leading to the trigonal-planar molecular geometry of BF$_3$. Notice that an unfilled 2p atomic orbital remains unhybridized. This unhybridized orbital will be important when we discuss double bonds in Section 9.6.

 GIVE IT SOME THOUGHT

In an sp^2 hybridized atom, what is the orientation of the unhybridized p atomic orbital relative to the three sp^2 hybrid orbitals?

An s atomic orbital can also mix with all three p atomic orbitals in the same subshell. For example, the carbon atom in CH$_4$ forms four equivalent bonds with the four

GO FIGURE.

How many atomic orbitals contribute to form the three sp^2 hybrid orbitals?

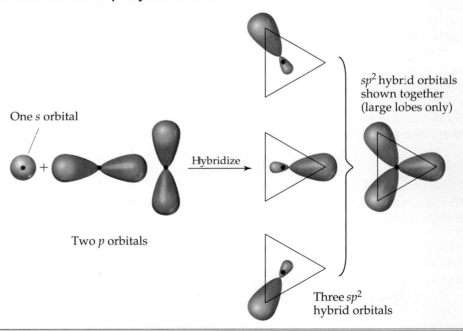

▶ **FIGURE 9.17 Formation of sp^2 hybrid orbitals.**

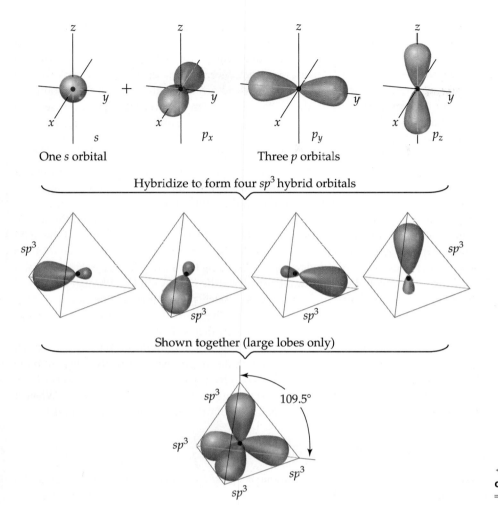

One *s* orbital   Three *p* orbitals

Hybridize to form four sp^3 hybrid orbitals

Shown together (large lobes only)

109.5°

◀ **FIGURE 9.18**   **Formation of sp^3 hybrid orbitals.**

hydrogen atoms. We envision this process as resulting from the mixing of the 2*s* and all three 2*p* atomic orbitals of carbon to create four equivalent sp^3 (pronounced "*s-p-three*") hybrid orbitals. Each sp^3 hybrid orbital has a large lobe that points toward one vertex of a tetrahedron (▲ **FIGURE 9.18**). These hybrid orbitals can be used to form two-electron bonds by overlap with the atomic orbitals of another atom, such as H. Using valence-bond theory, we can describe the bonding in CH_4 as the overlap of four equivalent sp^3 hybrid orbitals on C with the 1*s* orbitals of the four H atoms to form four equivalent bonds.

The idea of hybridization is also used to describe the bonding in molecules containing nonbonding pairs of electrons. In H_2O, for example, the electron-domain geometry around the central O atom is approximately tetrahedral (▶ **FIGURE 9.19**). Thus, the four electron pairs can be envisioned as occupying sp^3 hybrid orbitals. Two of the hybrid orbitals contain nonbonding pairs of electrons, and the other two form bonds with the hydrogen atoms.

So far our discussion of hybridization has extended only to period 2 elements, specifically carbon, nitrogen, and oxygen. The elements of period 3 and beyond introduce a new consideration because in many of their compounds these elements have more than an octet of electrons in the valence shell, as we saw in Section 9.2. How do we analyze the bonding in compounds such as PCl_5, SF_5, or BrF_5? The use of only *s* and *p* orbitals on the central atom limits us to four hybrid orbitals, yet in these compounds the central atom is involved in bonding to five or six other atoms.

For such elements, the number of hybrid orbitals formed could be increased by including valence-shell *d* orbitals. For example, to explain the bonding in SF_6 we could include two sulfur *3d* orbitals

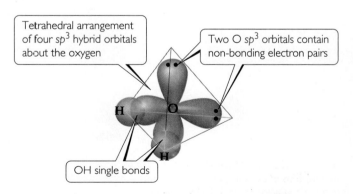

Tetrahedral arrangement of four sp^3 hybrid orbitals about the oxygen

Two O sp^3 orbitals contain non-bonding electron pairs

OH single bonds

▲ **FIGURE 9.19**   **Hybrid orbital description of H_2O.**

in addition to the *3s* and three *3p* orbitals. These six atomic orbitals could make six hybrid orbitals, but there is more involved in hybridization than simply finding a set of orbitals that point in the right directions; we must also consider orbital energies. The sulfur *3d* orbitals lie substantially higher in energy than the *3s* and *3p* orbitals. The amount of energy needed to form the six hybrid orbitals is greater than the amount returned by forming bonds with the six fluorine atoms. Theoretical calculations seem to show that the sulfur *3d* orbitals do not participate to a significant degree in the bonding between sulfur and the six fluorine atoms.

The valence-bond model we have developed for period 2 elements works well for compounds of period 3 elements so long as we have no more than an octet of electrons in the valence-shell orbitals. Thus, for example, it is appropriate to discuss the bonding in PF_3 or H_2Se in terms of hybrid *s* and *p* orbitals on the central atom. However, the model turns out not to be appropriate when there is more than an octet of electrons about the central atom. How then do we account for the bonding in SF_6 and other compounds of the main group elements in which the central atom has more than an octet of valence electrons? To address that question from the viewpoint of bonding theory requires a treatment beyond the scope of a general chemistry text. Fortunately, the VSEPR model, although it does not explain the bonding in such molecules, can accurately predict their geometries.

This discussion points up the important fact that models in science are not reality but rather are our attempts to describe aspects of reality that we have been able to measure, such as bond distances, bond energies, molecular geometries, and so on. A model may work well up to a certain point but not beyond it, as with the idea of hybrid orbitals. The hybrid orbital model for period 2 elements has proven very useful and is an essential part of any modern discussion of bonding and molecular geometry in organic chemistry. When it comes to substances such as SF_6, however, we encounter the limitations of the model.

Hybrid Orbital Summary

Overall, hybrid orbitals provide a convenient model for using valence-bond theory to describe covalent bonds in molecules in which the molecular geometry conforms to the electron-domain geometry predicted by the VSEPR model. The picture of hybrid orbitals has limited predictive value. When we know the electron-domain geometry, however, we can employ hybridization to describe the atomic orbitals used by the central atom in bonding.

The following steps allow us to describe the hybrid orbitals used by an atom in bonding:

1. Draw the *Lewis structure* for the molecule or ion.

2. Use the VSEPR model to determine the electron-domain geometry around the central atom.

3. Specify the *hybrid orbitals* needed to accommodate the electron pairs based on their geometric arrangement (▶ **TABLE 9.4**).

These steps are illustrated in ▼ **FIGURE 9.20**, which shows how the hybridization at N in NH_3 is determined.

▶ FIGURE 9.20 **Hybrid orbital description of bonding in NH₃.** Note the comparison with Figure 9.6. Here we focus on the hybrid orbitals used to make bonds and hold nonbonding electron pairs.

NH_3

1. Draw Lewis structure

2. Determine electron-domain geometry about central atom from VSEPR model and Table 9.1

sp^3 hybridization

3. Using Table 9.4, select sp^3 hybrid orbital set

TABLE 9.4 • Geometric Arrangements Characteristic of Hybrid Orbital Sets

Atomic Orbital Set	Hybrid Orbital Set	Geometry	Examples
s,p	Two sp	180° Linear	BeF_2, $HgCl_2$
s,p,p	Three sp^2	120° Trigonal planar	BF_3, SO_3
s,p,p,p	Four sp^3	109.5° Tetrahedral	CH_4, NH_3, H_2O, NH_4^+

SAMPLE EXERCISE 9.5 **Hybridization**

Indicate the orbital hybridization around the central atom in NH_2^-.

SOLUTION

Analyze We are given the chemical formula for a polyatomic anion and asked to describe the type of hybrid orbitals surrounding the central atom.

Plan To determine the central atom hybrid orbitals, we must know the electron-domain geometry around the atom. Thus, we draw the Lewis structure to determine the number of electron domains around the central atom. The hybridization conforms to the number and geometry of electron domains around the central atom as predicted by the VSEPR model.

Solve The Lewis structure is

$$\left[H : \ddot{N} : H \right]^-$$

Because there are four electron domains around N, the electron-domain geometry is tetrahedral. The hybridization that gives a tetrahedral electron-domain geometry is sp^3 (Table 9.4). Two of the sp^3 hybrid orbitals contain nonbonding pairs of electrons, and the other two are used to make bonds with the hydrogen atoms.

PRACTICE EXERCISE

Predict the electron-domain geometry and hybridization of the central atom in SO_3^{2-}.

Answer: tetrahedral, sp^3

9.6 | MULTIPLE BONDS

In the covalent bonds we have considered thus far, the electron density is concentrated along the line connecting the nuclei (the *internuclear axis*). In other words, the line joining the two nuclei passes through the middle of the overlap region. These bonds are called **sigma (σ) bonds**. The overlap of two s orbitals in H_2, the overlap of an s and a p

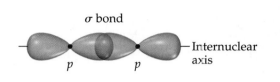

▶ **FIGURE 9.21 Comparison of σ and π bonds.** Note that the two regions of overlap in the π bond, above and below the internuclear axis, constitute a *single* π bond.

orbital in HCl, the overlap of two p orbitals in Cl_2 (all shown in Figure 9.13), and the overlap of a p orbital and an sp hybrid orbital in BeF_2 (Figure 9.16) are all σ bonds.

To describe multiple bonding, we must consider a second kind of bond, this one the result of overlap between two p orbitals oriented perpendicularly to the internuclear axis (▲ **FIGURE 9.21**). This sideways overlap of p orbitals produces a **pi (π) bond**. A π bond is one in which the overlap regions lie above and below the internuclear axis. Unlike in a σ bond, in a π bond the electron density is not concentrated on the internuclear axis. Although it is not evident in Figure 9.21, the sideways orientation of p orbitals in a π bond makes for weaker overlap. As a result, π bonds are generally weaker than σ bonds.

In almost all cases, single bonds are σ bonds. A double bond consists of one σ bond and one π bond, and a triple bond consists of one σ bond and two π bonds:

One σ bond   One σ bond plus   One σ bond plus
                    one π bond   two π bonds

To see how these ideas are used, consider ethylene (C_2H_4), which has a $C=C$ double bond. As illustrated by the ball-and-stick model of ◀ **FIGURE 9.22**, the three bond angles about each carbon are all approximately 120°, suggesting that each carbon atom uses sp^2 hybrid orbitals (Figure 9.17) to form σ bonds with the other carbon and with two hydrogens. Because carbon has four valence electrons, after sp^2 hybridization one electron in each carbon remains in the unhybridized $2p$ orbital, which is directed perpendicular to the plane that contains the three sp^2 hybrid orbitals.

Each sp^2 hybrid orbital on a carbon atom contains one electron. ▶ **FIGURE 9.23** shows how the $C-H$ σ bonds are formed by overlap of sp^2 hybrid orbitals on C with the $1s$ orbitals on each H atom. We use eight electrons to form these four $C-H$ bonds. The $C-C$ σ bond is formed by the overlap of two sp^2 hybrid orbitals, one on each carbon atom, and requires two more electrons. Thus, ten of the 12 valence electrons in the C_2H_4 molecule are used to form five σ bonds.

The remaining two valence electrons reside in the unhybridized $2p$ orbitals, one electron on each carbon. These two orbitals can overlap sideways with each other, as shown in Figure 9.23. The resultant electron density is concentrated above and below the $C-C$ bond axis, which means this is a π bond (Figure 9.21). Thus, the $C=C$ double bond in ethylene consists of one σ bond and one π bond. You should note one point about the carbon p orbitals that form the π bond. It appears from Figure 9.21 that the p orbitals on the two carbons don't overlap sufficiently to form a π bond. The problem is that we can't show the true extent of overlap in the drawing without obscuring other aspects of the figure. Although π bonding of the p orbitals does occur, as pointed out earlier, π bonds are generally weaker than σ bonds.

Although we cannot experimentally observe a π bond directly (all we can observe are the positions of the atoms), the structure of ethylene provides strong support for its presence. First, the $C-C$ bond length in ethylene (1.34 Å) is much shorter than in compounds with $C-C$ single bonds (1.54 Å), consistent with the presence of a stronger $C=C$ double bond. Second, all six atoms in C_2H_4 lie in the same plane. The $2p$ orbitals that make up the π bond can achieve a good overlap only when the two CH_2

▲ **FIGURE 9.22 Trigonal-planar molecular geometry of ethylene.** The double bond is made up of one $C-C$ σ bond and one $C-C$ π bond.

GO FIGURE

Why is it important that the *sp*^{2} hybrid orbitals of the two carbon atoms lie in the same plane?

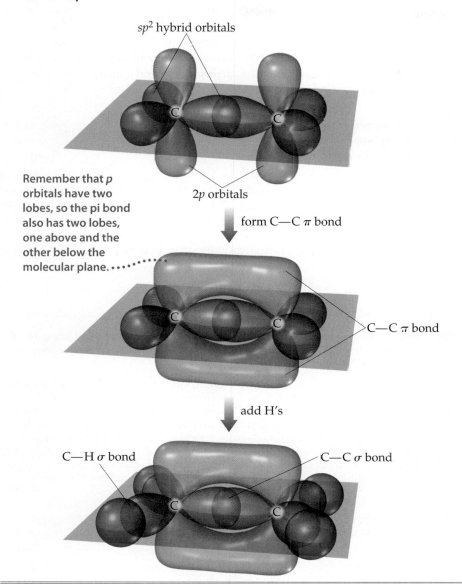

sp^2 hybrid orbitals

Remember that *p* orbitals have two lobes, so the pi bond also has two lobes, one above and the other below the molecular plane.

2*p* orbitals

form C—C π bond

C—C π bond

add H's

C—H σ bond   C—C σ bond

◀ FIGURE 9.23   **The orbital structure of ethylene.**

fragments lie in the same plane. If the π bond were absent, there would be no reason for the two CH$_2$ fragments to lie in the same plane. Because π bonds require that portions of a molecule be planar, they can introduce rigidity into molecules.

▲ GIVE IT SOME THOUGHT

The molecule called *diazine* has the formula N$_2$H$_2$ and the Lewis structure

$$\text{H}-\ddot{\text{N}}=\ddot{\text{N}}-\text{H}$$

Do you expect diazine to be a linear molecule (all four atoms on the same line)? If not, do you expect the molecule to be planar (all four atoms in the same plane)?

Triple bonds can also be explained using hybrid orbitals. Acetylene (C$_2$H$_2$), for example, is a linear molecule containing a triple bond: H—C≡C—H. The linear geometry suggests that each carbon atom uses *sp* hybrid orbitals to form σ bonds with the other

Based on the models of bonding in ethylene and acetylene, which molecule should have the higher carbon–carbon bond energy?

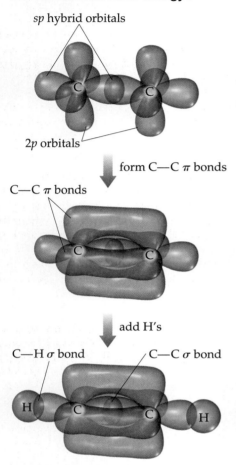

sp hybrid orbitals

2p orbitals

↓ form C—C π bonds

C—C π bonds

↓ add H's

C—H σ bond   C—C σ bond

▲ **FIGURE 9.24** **Formation of two π bonds in acetylene, C_2H_2.**

carbon and one hydrogen. Each carbon atom thus has two unhybridized *2p* orbitals at right angles to each other and to the axis of the *sp* hybrid set (◄ **FIGURE 9.24**). These *p* orbitals overlap to form a pair of π bonds. Thus, the triple bond in acetylene consists of one σ bond and two π bonds.

Although it is possible to make π bonds from *d* orbitals, the only π bonds we will consider are those formed by the overlap of *p* orbitals. These π bonds can form only if unhybridized *p* orbitals are present on the bonded atoms. Therefore, only atoms having *sp* or sp^2 hybridization can form π bonds. Further, double and triple bonds (and hence π bonds) are more common in molecules made up of period 2 atoms, especially C, N, and O. Larger atoms, such as S, P, and Si, form π bonds less readily.

SAMPLE EXERCISE 9.6 Describing σ and π Bonds in a Molecule

Formaldehyde has the Lewis structure

$$\text{H} \atop \text{H}} \text{C}=\ddot{\text{O}}:$$

Describe how the bonds in formaldehyde are formed in terms of overlaps of hybrid and unhybridized orbitals.

SOLUTION

Analyze We are asked to describe the bonding in formaldehyde in terms of hybrid orbitals.

Plan Single bonds are σ bonds, and double bonds consist of one σ bond and one π bond. The ways in which these bonds form can be deduced from the molecular geometry, which we predict using the VSEPR model.

Solve The C atom has three electron domains around it, which suggests a trigonal-planar geometry with bond angles of about 120°. This geometry implies sp^2 hybrid orbitals on C (Table 9.4). These hybrids are used to make the two C—H and one C—O σ bonds to C. There remains an unhybridized *2p* orbital on carbon, perpendicular to the plane of the three sp^2 hybrids.

The O atom also has three electron domains around it, and so we assume it has sp^2 hybridization as well. One of these hybrid orbitals participates in the C—O σ bond, while the other two hold the two nonbonding electron pairs of the O atom. Like the C atom, therefore, the O atom has an unhybridized *2p* orbital that is perpendicular to the plane of the molecule. These two orbitals overlap to form a C—O π bond (▼ **FIGURE 9.25**).

PRACTICE EXERCISE

(a) Predict the bond angles around each carbon atom in acetonitrile:

$$\text{H} \atop \text{H}} \text{H—C—C≡N:}$$

(b) Describe the hybridization at each carbon atom, and **(c)** determine the number of σ and π bonds in the molecule.

Answers: **(a)** approximately 109° around the left C and 180° around the right C; **(b)** sp^3, *sp*; **(c)** five σ bonds and two π bonds

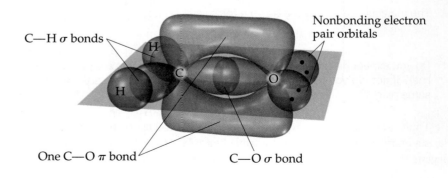

C—H σ bonds   Nonbonding electron pair orbitals

One C—O π bond   C—O σ bond

▶ **FIGURE 9.25** **Formation of σ and π bonds in formaldehyde, H_2CO.**

Resonance Structures, Delocalization, and π Bonding

In the molecules we have discussed thus far in this section, the bonding electrons are *localized*. By this we mean that the σ and π electrons are associated totally with the two atoms that form the bond. In many molecules, however, we cannot adequately describe the bonding as being entirely localized. This situation arises particularly in molecules that have two or more resonance structures involving π bonds.

One molecule that cannot be described with localized π bonds is benzene (C_6H_6), which has two resonance structures: ∞ (Section 8.6)

To describe the bonding in benzene using hybrid orbitals, we first choose a hybridization scheme consistent with the geometry of the molecule. Because each carbon is surrounded by three atoms at 120° angles, the appropriate hybrid set is sp^2. Six localized C—C σ bonds and six localized C—H σ bonds are formed from the sp^2 hybrid orbitals, as shown in ▼ **FIGURE 9.26**(a). This leaves on each carbon a $2p$ orbital oriented perpendicular to the plane of the molecule. The situation is very much like that in ethylene except we now have six carbon $2p$ orbitals arranged in a ring [Figure 9.26(b)]. Each unhybridized $2p$ orbital is occupied by one electron, leaving six electrons to be accounted for by π bonding.

◢ **GO FIGURE**

What are the two kinds of σ bonds found in benzene?

(a) σ bonds   (b) $2p$ atomic orbitals

◀ **FIGURE 9.26** σ and π bond networks in benzene, C_6H_6. (a) The σ bond framework. (b) The π bonds are formed from overlap of the unhybridized $2p$ orbitals on the six carbon atoms.

We could envision using the unhybridized $2p$ orbitals to form three localized π bonds. As shown in ▼ **FIGURE 9.27**, there are two equivalent ways to make these localized bonds, each corresponding to one resonance structure. However, a representation that reflects *both* resonance structures has the six π electrons "smeared out" among all six carbon atoms, as shown on the right in Figure 9.27. Notice how this combined representation corresponds to the circle-in-a-hexagon drawing we often use to represent benzene. This model leads us to predict that all the carbon–carbon bond lengths will be identical, with a bond length between that of a C—C single bond (1.54 Å) and that of a C=C double bond (1.34 Å). This prediction is consistent with the observed carbon–carbon bond length in benzene (1.40 Å).

Localized π bond   Delocalized π bond

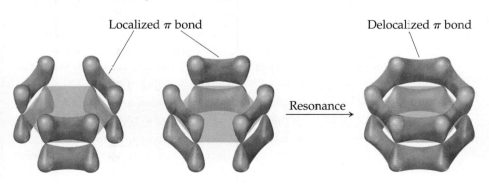

Resonance

◀ **FIGURE 9.27**   Delocalized π bonds in benzene.

Because we cannot describe the π bonds in benzene as individual bonds between neighboring atoms, we say that the π bonds are **delocalized** among the six carbon atoms. Delocalization of the electrons in its π bonds gives benzene a special stability. Delocalization of π bonds is also responsible for the color of many organic molecules. A final important point to remember about delocalized π bonds is the constraint they place on the geometry of a molecule. For optimal overlap of the unhybridized p orbitals, all the atoms involved in a delocalized π bonding network should lie in the same plane. This restriction imparts a certain rigidity to the molecule that is absent in molecules containing only σ bonds (see the "Chemistry and Life" box on vision).

If you take a course in organic chemistry, you will see many examples of how electron delocalization influences the properties of organic molecules.

SAMPLE EXERCISE 9.7 | **Delocalized Bonding**

Describe the bonding in the nitrate ion, NO_3^-. Does this ion have delocalized π bonds?

SOLUTION

Analyze Given the chemical formula for a polyatomic anion, we are asked to describe the bonding and determine whether the ion has delocalized π bonds.

Plan Our first step is to draw Lewis structures. Multiple resonance structures involving the placement of the double bonds in different locations suggest that the π component of the double bonds is delocalized.

Solve In Section 8.6 we saw that NO_3^- has three resonance structures:

$$\left[\begin{array}{c} :\!\ddot{O}\!: \\ \| \\ \underset{:\ddot{O}:\quad:\ddot{O}:}{N} \end{array} \right]^- \longleftrightarrow \left[\begin{array}{c} :\!\ddot{O}\!: \\ | \\ \underset{\ddot{O}:\quad:\ddot{O}}{N} \end{array} \right]^- \longleftrightarrow \left[\begin{array}{c} :\!\ddot{O}\!: \\ | \\ \underset{:\ddot{O}:\quad\ddot{O}:}{N} \end{array} \right]^-$$

In each structure, the electron-domain geometry at nitrogen is trigonal planar, which implies sp^2 hybridization of the N atom. The sp^2 hybrid orbitals are used to construct the three N—O σ bonds present in each resonance structure.

The unhybridized $2p$ orbital on the N atom can be used to make π bonds. For any one of the three resonance structures shown, we might imagine a single localized N—O π bond formed by the overlap of the unhybridized $2p$ orbital on N and a $2p$ orbital on one of the O atoms, as shown in ◀ **FIGURE 9.28**. Because each resonance structure contributes equally to the observed structure of NO_3^-, however, we represent the π bonding as delocalized over the three N—O bonds, as shown in the figure.

PRACTICE EXERCISE

Which of these species have delocalized bonding: SO_3, SO_3^{2-}, H_2CO, O_3, NH_4^+?

Answer: SO_3 and O_3, as indicated by the presence of two or more resonance structures involving π bonding for each of these molecules

---

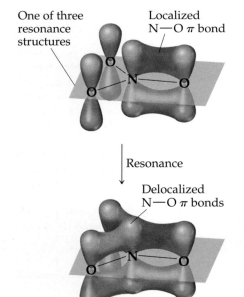

One of three resonance structures

Localized N—O π bond

Resonance

Delocalized N—O π bonds

▲ FIGURE 9.28 **Localized and delocalized π bonds in NO_3^-.**

General Conclusions

On the basis of the examples we have seen, we can draw a few helpful conclusions for using hybrid orbitals to describe molecular structures:

1. Every pair of bonded atoms shares one or more pairs of electrons. The lines we draw in Lewis structures represent two electrons each. In every bond at least one pair of electrons is localized in the space between the atoms in a σ bond. The appropriate set of hybrid orbitals used to form the σ bonds between an atom and its neighbors is determined by the observed geometry of the molecule. The correlation between the set of hybrid orbitals and the geometry about an atom is given in Table 9.4.

2. The electrons in σ bonds are localized in the region between two bonded atoms and do not make a significant contribution to the bonding between any other two atoms.

3. When atoms share more than one pair of electrons, one pair is used to form a σ bond; the additional pairs form π bonds. The centers of charge density in a π bond lie above and below the internuclear axis.

4. Molecules with two or more resonance structures can have π bonds that extend over more than two bonded atoms. Electrons in π bonds that extend over more than two atoms are said to be "delocalized."

CHEMISTRY AND LIFE

THE CHEMISTRY OF VISION

Vision begins when light is focused by the lens of the eye onto the retina, the layer of cells lining the interior of the eyeball. The retina contains *photoreceptor* cells called rods and cones (▼ FIGURE 9.29). The rods are sensitive to dim light and are used in night vision. The cones are sensitive to colors. The tops of the rods and cones contain a molecule called *rhodopsin*, which consists of a protein, *opsin*, bonded to a reddish purple pigment called *retinal*. Structural changes around a double bond in the retinal portion of the molecule trigger a series of chemical reactions that result in vision.

We know that a double bond between two atoms is stronger than a single bond between the same atom, but our recent discussions allow us to appreciate another aspect of double bonds: the rigidity they introduce into molecules.

Imagine rotating one —CH₂ group in ethylene relative to the other —CH₂ group, as in ▶ FIGURE 9.30. This rotation destroys the overlap of *p* orbitals, breaking the π bond, a process that requires

C–C
π bond

90° rotation
around
double bond

▲ FIGURE 9.30   **Rotation about the carbon–carbon double bond in ethylene breaks the π bond.**

considerable energy. Thus, the presence of a double bond restricts bond rotation in a molecule. In contrast, molecules can rotate almost freely around the bond axis in single (σ) bonds because this motion has no effect on the orbital overlap for a σ bond. This rotation allows molecules with single bonds to twist and fold almost as if their atoms were attached by hinges.

Our vision depends on the rigidity of double bonds in retinal. In its normal form, retinal is held rigid by its double bonds. Light entering the eye is absorbed by rhodopsin, and the energy is used to break the π-bond portion of the double bond shown in red in ▼ FIGURE 9.31. The molecule then rotates around this bond, changing its geometry. The retinal then separates from the opsin, triggering the reactions that produce a nerve impulse that the brain interprets as the sensation of vision. It takes as few as five closely spaced molecules reacting in this fashion to produce the sensation of vision. Thus, only five photons of light are necessary to stimulate the eye.

The retinal slowly reverts to its original form and reattaches to the opsin. The slowness of this process helps explain why intense bright light causes temporary blindness. The light causes all the retinal to separate from opsin, leaving no molecules to absorb light.

RELATED EXERCISES: 9.108 and 9.112

▶ FIGURE 9.29
Inside the eye. A color-enhanced scanning electron micrograph of the rods and cones in the retina of the human eye.

Rods
Cones

180° rotation about this bond when light absorbed

Light

Retinal

▲ FIGURE 9.31   **The rhodopsin molecule, the chemical basis of vision.** When rhodopsin absorbs visible light, the π component of the double bond shown in red breaks, allowing rotation that produces a change in molecular geometry before the π bond re-forms.

▲ GIVE IT SOME THOUGHT

When two atoms are bonded by a triple bond, what is the hybridization of the orbitals that make up the σ-bond component of the bond?

9.7 | MOLECULAR ORBITALS

Valence-bond theory and hybrid orbitals allow us to move in a straightforward way from Lewis structures to rationalizing the observed geometries of molecules in terms of atomic orbitals. The valence-bond model, however, does not explain all aspects of bonding. It is not successful, for example, in describing the excited states of molecules, which we must understand to explain how molecules absorb light, giving them color.

Some aspects of bonding are better explained by a more sophisticated model called **molecular orbital theory**. In Chapter 6 we saw that electrons in atoms can be described by wave functions, which we call atomic orbitals. In a similar way, molecular orbital theory describes the electrons in molecules by using specific wave functions called **molecular orbitals (MO)**.

Molecular orbitals have many of the same characteristics as atomic orbitals. For example, an MO can hold a maximum of two electrons (with opposite spins), it has a definite energy, and we can visualize its electron-density distribution by using a contour representation, as we did with atomic orbitals. Unlike atomic orbitals, however, MOs are associated with an entire molecule, not with a single atom.

The Hydrogen Molecule

We begin our study of MO theory with the hydrogen molecule, H_2. *Whenever two atomic orbitals overlap, two molecular orbitals form.* Thus, the overlap of the $1s$ orbitals of two hydrogen atoms to form H_2 produces two MOs (▼ FIGURE 9.32). One MO is formed by adding the wave functions for the two $1s$ orbitals. We refer to this as *constructive combination*. The energy of the resulting MO is lower than the energy of the two atomic orbitals from which it was made. It is called the **bonding molecular orbital**.

The other MO is formed by combining the two atomic orbitals in a way that causes the electron density to be more or less canceled in the central region where the two overlap. We refer to this as *destructive combination*. The process is discussed more fully in the "Closer Look" box later in the chapter; we don't need to concern ourselves with it to understand molecular orbital bond formation. The energy of the resulting MO, referred to as the **antibonding molecular orbital**, is higher than the energy of the atomic orbitals.

As illustrated in Figure 9.32, in the bonding MO electron density is concentrated in the region between the two nuclei. This sausage-shaped MO results from summing the

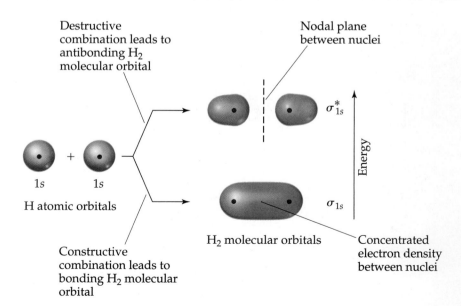

Destructive combination leads to antibonding H_2 molecular orbital

Nodal plane between nuclei

σ_{1s}^*

$1s$ $1s$

H atomic orbitals

Constructive combination leads to bonding H_2 molecular orbital

σ_{1s}

Energy

H_2 molecular orbitals

Concentrated electron density between nuclei

▶ **FIGURE 9.32 The two molecular orbitals of H_2, one a bonding MO and one an antibonding MO.**

two atomic orbitals so that the atomic orbital wave functions combine in the region be-tween the two nuclei. Because an electron in this MO is attracted to both nuclei, the electron is more stable (it has lower energy) than it is in the $1s$ atomic orbital of an iso-lated hydrogen atom. Further, because this bonding MO concentrates electron density between the nuclei, it holds the atoms together in a covalent bond.

By contrast, the antibonding MO has very little electron density between the nuclei. Instead of combining in the region between the nuclei, the atomic orbital wave func-tions cancel each other in this region, leaving the greatest electron density on opposite sides of the two nuclei. Thus, this MO excludes electrons from the very region in which a bond must be formed. Antibonding orbitals invariably have a nodal plane in the re-gion between the nuclei, where the electron density is zero. (The nodal plane is shown as a dashed line in Figure 9.32 and subsequent figures.) An electron in an antibonding MO is repelled from the bonding region and is therefore less stable (it has higher energy) than it is in the $1s$ atomic orbital of a hydrogen atom.

Notice from Figure 9.32 that the electron density in both the bonding MO and the antibonding MO of H_2 is centered about the internuclear axis. MOs of this type are called **sigma (σ) molecular orbitals** (by analogy to σ bonds). The bonding sigma MO of H_2 is labeled σ_{1s}; the subscript indicates that the MO is formed from two $1s$ orbitals. The antibonding sigma MO of H_2 is labeled σ_{1s}^* (read "sigma-star-one-s"); the asterisk denotes that the MO is antibonding.

The relative energies of two $1s$ atomic orbitals and the molecular orbitals formed from them are represented by an **energy-level diagram** (also called a **molecular orbital diagram**). Such diagrams show the interacting atomic orbitals on the left and right and the MOs in the middle, as shown in ▼ **FIGURE 9.33**. Like atomic orbitals, each MO can accommodate two electrons with their spins paired (Pauli exclusion principle). ∞ (Section 6.7)

As the MO diagram for H_2 in Figure 9.33 shows, each H atom brings one electron to the molecule, so there are two electrons in H_2. These two electrons occupy the lower-energy bonding (σ_{1s}) MO, and their spins are paired. Electrons occupying a bonding molecular orbital are called *bonding electrons*. Because the σ_{1s} MO is lower in energy than the $1s$ atomic orbitals, the H_2 molecule is more stable than the two separate H atoms.

By analogy with atomic electron configurations, the electron configurations for molecules can be written with superscripts to indicate electron occupancy. The electron configuration for H_2, then, is σ_{1s}^2.

▲ **GO FIGURE**

By referring to Figure 9.32, determine which molecular orbital in He_2 has a node between the nuclei.

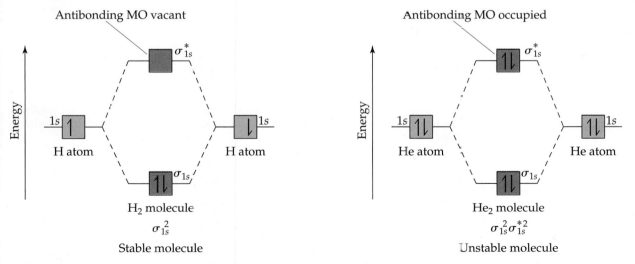

▲ **FIGURE 9.33 Energy-level diagrams and electron configurations for H_2 and He_2.**

Figure 9.33 also shows the energy-level diagram for the hypothetical He$_2$ molecule, which requires four electrons to fill its molecular orbitals. Because only two electrons can go in the σ_{1s} MO, the other two electrons must go in the σ_{1s}^* MO. The electron configuration of He$_2$ is thus $\sigma_{1s}^2 \sigma_{1s}^{*2}$. The energy decrease realized in going from He atomic orbitals to the He bonding MO is offset by the energy increase realized in going from the atomic orbitals to the He antibonding MO.[†] Hence, He$_2$ is an unstable molecule. Molecular orbital theory correctly predicts that hydrogen forms diatomic molecules but helium does not.

Bond Order

In molecular orbital theory, the stability of a covalent bond is related to its **bond order**, defined as half the difference between the number of bonding electrons and the number of antibonding electrons:

$$\text{Bond order} = \tfrac{1}{2}(\text{no. of bonding electrons} - \text{no. of antibonding electrons}) \quad [9.1]$$

We take half the difference because we are used to thinking of bonds as pairs of electrons. *A bond order of 1 represents a single bond, a bond order of 2 represents a double bond, and a bond order of 3 represents a triple bond.* Because MO theory also treats molecules containing an odd number of electrons, bond orders of 1/2 , 3/2, or 5/2 are possible.

Because, as Figure 9.33 shows, H$_2$ has two bonding electrons and zero antibonding electrons, it has a bond order of 1. Because He$_2$ has two bonding electrons and two antibonding electrons, it has a bond order of 0. A bond order of 0 means that no bond exists.

 GIVE IT SOME THOUGHT

Suppose one electron in H$_2$ is excited from the σ_{1s} MO to the σ_{1s}^* MO. Would you expect the H atoms to remain bonded to each other, or would the molecule fall apart?

SAMPLE EXERCISE 9.8 **Bond Order**

What is the bond order of the He$_2^+$ ion? Would you expect this ion to be stable relative to the separated He atom and He$^+$ ion?

SOLUTION

Analyze We will determine the bond order for the He$_2^+$ ion and use it to predict whether the ion is stable.

Plan To determine the bond order, we must determine the number of electrons in the molecule and how these electrons populate the available MOs. The valence electrons of He are in the $1s$ orbital, and the $1s$ orbitals combine to give an MO diagram like that for H$_2$ or He$_2$ (Figure 9.33). If the bond order is greater than 0, we expect a bond to exist, and the ion is stable.

Solve The energy-level diagram for the He$_2^+$ ion is shown in ◀ **FIGURE 9.34**. This ion has three electrons. Two are placed in the bonding orbital and the third in the antibonding orbital. Thus, the bond order is

$$\text{Bond order} = \tfrac{1}{2}(2 - 1) = \tfrac{1}{2}$$

Because the bond order is greater than 0, we predict the He$_2^+$ ion to be stable relative to the separated He and He$^+$. Formation of He$_2^+$ in the gas phase has been demonstrated in laboratory experiments.

PRACTICE EXERCISE

Determine the bond order of the H$_2^-$ ion.
Answer: $\tfrac{1}{2}$

 GO FIGURE

Which electrons in this diagram contribute to the stability of the He$_2^+$ ion?

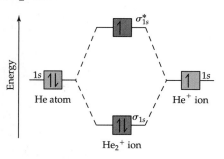

▲ **FIGURE 9.34** Energy-level diagram for the He$_2^+$ ion.

[†]Antibonding MOs are slightly more energetically unfavorable than bonding MOs are energetically favorable. Thus, whenever there is an equal number of electrons in bonding and antibonding orbitals, the energy of the molecule is slightly higher than that for the separated atoms. As a result, no bond is formed.

9.8 | PERIOD 2 DIATOMIC MOLECULES

In considering the MO description of diatomic molecules other than H_2, we will initially restrict our discussion to *homonuclear* diatomic molecules (those composed of two identical atoms) of period 2 elements.

Period 2 atoms have valence $2s$ and $2p$ orbitals, and we need to consider how they interact to form MOs. The following rules summarize some of the guiding principles for the formation of MOs and for how they are populated by electrons:

1. The number of MOs formed equals the number of atomic orbitals combined.

2. Atomic orbitals combine most effectively with other atomic orbitals of similar energy.

3. The effectiveness with which two atomic orbitals combine is proportional to their overlap. That is, as the overlap increases, the energy of the bonding MO is lowered and the energy of the antibonding MO is raised.

4. Each MO can accommodate, at most, two electrons, with their spins paired (Pauli exclusion principle). ∞ (Section 6.7)

5. When MOs of the same energy are populated, one electron enters each orbital (with the same spin) before spin pairing occurs (Hund's rule). ∞ (Section 6.8)

Molecular Orbitals for Li₂ and Be₂

Lithium has the electron configuration $1s^2 2s^1$. When lithium metal is heated above its boiling point (1342 °C), Li_2 molecules are found in the vapor phase. The Lewis structure for Li_2 indicates a Li—Li single bond. We will now use MOs to describe the bonding in Li_2.

▶ FIGURE 9.35 shows that the Li $1s$ and $2s$ atomic orbitals have substantially different energy levels. From this, we can assume that the $1s$ orbital on one Li atom interacts only with the $1s$ orbital on the other atom (rule 2), just as Figure 9.35 indicates. Likewise, the $2s$ orbitals interact only with each other. Notice that combining four atomic orbitals produces four MOs (rule 1).

The Li $1s$ orbitals combine to form σ_{1s} and σ_{1s}^* bonding and antibonding MOs, as they did for H_2. The $2s$ orbitals interact with one another in exactly the same way, producing bonding (σ_{2s}) and antibonding (σ_{2s}^*) MOs. In general, the separation between bonding and antibonding MOs depends on the extent to which the constituent atomic orbitals overlap. Because the Li $2s$ orbitals extend farther from the nucleus than the $1s$ orbitals do, the $2s$ orbitals overlap more effectively. As a result, the energy difference between the σ_{2s} and σ_{2s}^* orbitals is greater than the energy difference between the σ_{1s} and σ_{1s}^* orbitals. The $1s$ orbitals of Li are so much lower in energy than the $2s$ orbitals, however, that the energy of the σ_{1s}^* antibonding MO is much lower than the energy of σ_{2s} bonding MO.

Each Li atom has three electrons, so six electrons must be placed in Li_2 MOs. As shown in Figure 9.35, these electrons occupy the σ_{1s}, σ_{1s}^*, and σ_{2s} MOs, each with two electrons. There are four electrons in bonding orbitals and two in antibonding orbitals, so the bond order is $\frac{1}{2}(4-2)=1$. The molecule has a single bond, in agreement with its Lewis structure.

Because both the σ_{1s} and σ_{1s}^* MOs of Li_2 are completely filled, the $1s$ orbitals contribute almost nothing to the bonding. The single bond in Li_2 is due essentially to the interaction of the valence $2s$ orbitals on the Li atoms. This example illustrates the general rule that *core electrons usually do not contribute significantly to bonding in molecules.* The rule is equivalent to using only the valence electrons when drawing Lewis structures. Thus, we need not consider further the $1s$ orbitals while discussing the other period 2 diatomic molecules.

The MO description of Be_2 follows readily from the energy-level diagram for Li_2. Each Be atom has four electrons ($1s^2 2s^2$), so we must place eight electrons in molecular orbitals. Thus, we completely fill the

GO FIGURE

Why do the 1s orbitals of the Li atoms not contribute to the bonding in Li_2?

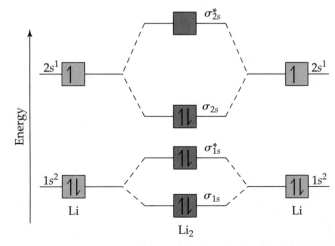

▲ FIGURE 9.35   **Energy-level diagram for the Li₂ molecule.**

σ_{1s}, σ_{1s}^*, σ_{2s}, and σ_{2s}^* MOs. With equal numbers of bonding and antibonding electrons, the bond order is zero; thus, Be$_2$ does not exist.

 GIVE IT SOME THOUGHT

Would you expect Be$_2^+$ to be a stable ion?

Molecular Orbitals from 2*p* Atomic Orbitals

Before we can consider the remaining period 2 diatomic molecules, we must look at the MOs that result from combining 2*p* atomic orbitals. The interactions between *p* orbitals are shown in ▼ **FIGURE 9.36**, where we have arbitrarily chosen the internuclear axis to be the *z*-axis. The $2p_z$ orbitals face each other head to head. Just as with *s* orbitals, we can combine $2p_z$ orbitals in two ways. One combination concentrates electron density between the nuclei and is, therefore, a bonding molecular orbital. The other combination excludes electron density from the bonding region and so is an antibonding molecular orbital. In both MOs the electron density lies along the internuclear axis, so they are σ molecular orbitals: σ_{2p} and σ_{2p}^*.

The other 2*p* orbitals overlap sideways and thus concentrate electron density above and below the internuclear axis. MOs of this type are called **pi (π) molecular orbitals** by

 GO FIGURE

In what types of MOs do we find nodal planes?

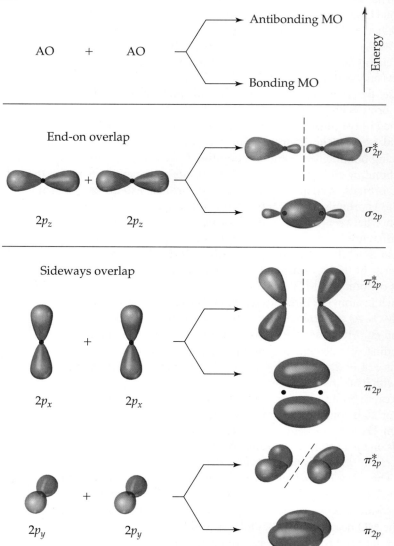

▶ **FIGURE 9.36 Contour representations of the molecular orbitals formed by 2*p* orbitals.**

A CLOSER LOOK

PHASES IN ATOMIC AND MOLECULAR ORBITALS

Our discussion of atomic orbitals in Chapter 6 and molecular orbitals in this chapter highlights some of the most important applications of quantum mechanics in chemistry. In the quantum mechanical treatment of electrons in atoms and molecules, we are mainly interested in determining two characteristics of the electrons—their energies and their distribution in space. Recall that solving Schrödinger's wave equation yields the electron's energy, E, and wave function, ψ, but that ψ does not have a direct physical meaning. ∞ (Section 6.5) The contour representations of atomic and molecular orbitals we have presented thus far are based on ψ^2 (the *probability density*), which gives the probability of finding the electron at a given point in space.

Because probability densities are squares of functions, their values must be nonnegative (zero or positive) at all points in space. However, the functions themselves can have negative values. Consider, for example, the sine function plotted in ▶ FIGURE 9.37. In the top graph, the sine function is negative for x between 0 and $-\pi$ and positive for x between 0 and $+\pi$. We say that the *phase* of the sine function is negative between 0 and $-\pi$ and positive between 0 and $+\pi$. If we square the sine function (bottom graph), we get two peaks that are symmetrical about the origin. Both peaks are positive because squaring a negative number produces a positive number. In other words, *we lose the phase information of the function upon squaring it.*

Like the sine function, the more complicated wave functions for atomic orbitals can also have phases. Consider, for example, the representations of the 1s orbital in ▼ FIGURE 9.38. Note that here we

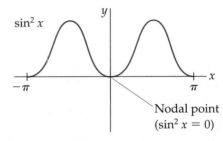

▲ **FIGURE 9.37** **Graphs for a sine function and the same function squared.**

plot this orbital a bit differently from what is shown in Section 6.6. The origin is the point where the nucleus resides, and the wave function for

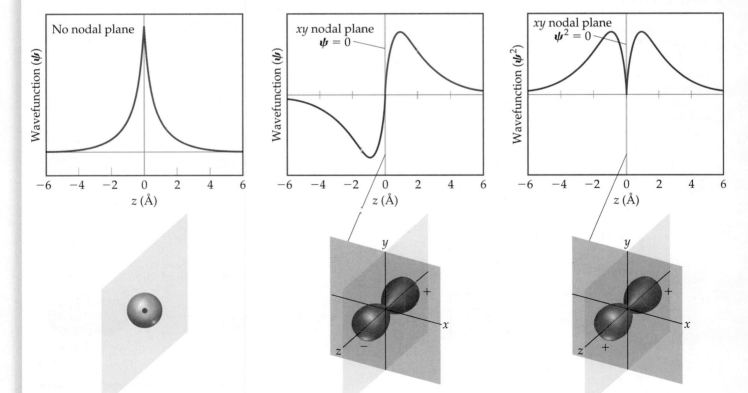

▲ FIGURE 9.38 **Phases in wave functions of *s* and *p* atomic orbitals.**

the 1s orbital extends from the origin out into space. The plot shows the value of ψ for a slice taken along the z-axis. Below the plot is a contour representation of the 1s orbital. Notice that the value of the 1s wave function is always a positive number. Thus, it has only one phase. Notice also that the wave function approaches zero only at a long distance from the nucleus. It therefore has no nodes, as we saw in Figure 6.21.

In the Figure 9.38 graph for the $2p_z$ orbital, the wave function changes sign when it passes through $z = 0$. Notice that the two halves of the wave have the same shape except that one has positive values and the other negative values. Analogously to the sine function, the wave function changes phase when it passes through the origin. Mathematically the $2p_z$ wave function is equal to zero whenever $z = 0$. This corresponds to any point on the xy plane, so we say that the xy plane is a *nodal plane* of the $2p_z$ orbital. The wave function for a p orbital is much like a sine function because it has two equal parts that have opposite phases. Figure 9.38 gives a typical representation used by chemists of the wave function for a p_z orbital.* The plus and minus signs indicate the phases of the orbital. As with the sine function, the origin is a node.

The third graph in Figure 9.38 shows that when we square the wave function of the $2p_z$ orbital, we get two peaks that are symmetrical about the origin. Both peaks are positive because squaring a negative number produces a positive number. Thus, *we lose the phase information of the function upon squaring it* just as we did for the sine function. When we square the wave function for the p_z orbital, we get the probability density for the orbital, which is given as a contour representation in Figure 9.38. This is what we saw in the earlier presentation of p orbitals. ∞ (Section 6.6) For this squared wave function, both lobes have the same phase and therefore the same sign. We use this representation throughout most of this book because it has a simple physical interpretation: The square of the wave function at any point in space represents the electron density at that point.

The lobes of the wave functions for the d orbitals also have different phases. For example, the wave function for a d_{xy} orbital has four lobes, with the phase of each lobe opposite the phase of its nearest neighbors (▶ FIGURE 9.39). The wave functions for the other d orbitals likewise have lobes in which the phase in one lobe is opposite that in an adjacent lobe.

Why do we need to consider the complexity introduced by considering the phase of the wave function? While it is true that the phase is not necessary to visualize the shape of an atomic orbital in an isolated atom, it does become important when we consider overlap of orbitals in molecular orbital theory. Let's use the sine function as an example again. If you add two sine functions having the same phase, they add *constructively,* resulting in increased amplitude:

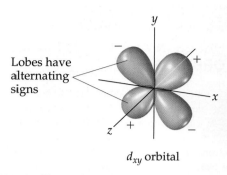

Lobes have alternating signs

d_{xy} orbital

▲ FIGURE 9.39 **Phases in *d* orbitals.**

but if you add two sine functions having opposite phases, they add *destructively* and cancel each other.

The idea of constructive and destructive interactions of wave functions is key to understanding the origin of bonding and antibonding molecular orbitals. For example, the wave function of the σ_{1s} MO of H_2 is generated by adding the wave function for the 1s orbital on one atom to the wave function for the 1s orbital on the other atom, with both orbitals having the same phase. The atomic wave functions overlap *constructively* in this case to increase the electron density between the two atoms (▼ FIGURE 9.40). The wave function of the σ_{1s}^* MO of H_2 is generated by subtracting the wave function for a 1s orbital on one atom from the wave function for a 1s orbital on the other atom. The result is that the atomic orbital wave functions overlap *destructively* to create a region of zero electron density between the two atoms—a node. Notice the similarity between this figure and Figure 9.32. In Figure 9.40 we use plus and minus signs to denote positive and negative phases in the H atomic orbitals. However, chemists may alternatively draw contour representations in different colors to denote the two phases.

When we square the wave function of the σ_{1s}^* MO, we get the electron density representation which we saw earlier, in Figure 9.32. Notice once again that we lose the phase information when we look at the electron density.

RELATED EXERCISES: 9.103, 9.115, 9.117

Destructive addition

1s atomic orbital   1s atomic orbital σ_{1s}^* molecular orbital

Contructive addition

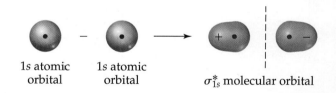

1s atomic orbital   1s atomic orbital σ_{1s} molecular orbital

▲ FIGURE 9.40 **Molecular orbitals from atomic orbital wave functions.**

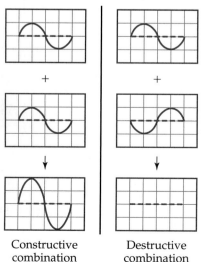

Constructive combination   Destructive combination

---

*The mathematical development of this three-dimensional function (and its square) is beyond the scope of this book and, as is typically done by chemists, we have used lobes that are the same shape as in Figure 6.22.

analogy to π bonds. We get one π bonding MO by combining the $2p_x$ atomic orbitals and another from the $2p_y$ atomic orbitals. These two π_{2p} molecular orbitals have the same energy; in other words, they are degenerate. Likewise, we get two degenerate π_{2p}^* antibonding MOs that are perpendicular to each other like the $2p$ orbitals from which they were made. These π_{2p}^* orbitals have four lobes, pointing away from the two nuclei, as shown in Figure 9.36. The $2p_z$ orbitals on two atoms point directly at each other. Hence, the overlap of two $2p_z$ orbitals is greater than that of two $2p_x$ or $2p_y$ orbitals. From rule 3 we therefore expect the σ_{2p} MO to be lower in energy (more stable) than the π_{2p} MOs. Similarly, the σ_{2p}^* MO should be higher in energy (less stable) than the π_{2p}^* MOs.

Electron Configurations for B$_2$ through Ne$_2$

We can combine our analyses of MOs formed from s orbitals (Figure 9.32) and from p orbitals (Figure 9.36) to construct an energy-level diagram (▼ **FIGURE 9.41**) for homonuclear diatomic molecules of the elements boron through neon, all of which have valence $2s$ and $2p$ atomic orbitals. The following features of the diagram are notable:

1. The $2s$ atomic orbitals are substantially lower in energy than the $2p$ atomic orbitals. ∞ (Section 6.7) Consequently, both MOs formed from the $2s$ orbitals are lower in energy than the lowest-energy MO derived from the $2p$ atomic orbitals.

2. The overlap of the two $2p_z$ orbitals is greater than that of the two $2p_x$ or $2p_y$ orbitals. As a result, the bonding σ_{2p} MO is lower in energy than the π_{2p} MOs, and the antibonding σ_{2p}^* MO is higher in energy than the π_{2p}^* MOs.

3. Both the π_{2p} and π_{2p}^* MOs are *doubly degenerate*; that is, there are two degenerate MOs of each type.

Before we can add electrons to Figure 9.41, we must consider one more effect. We have constructed the diagram assuming no interaction between the $2s$ orbital on one atom and the $2p$ orbitals on the other. In fact, such interactions can and do take place. ▶ **FIGURE 9.42** shows the overlap of a $2s$ orbital on one of the atoms with a $2p$ orbital on the other. These interactions increase the energy difference between the σ_{2s} and σ_{2p} MOs, with the σ_{2s} energy decreasing and the σ_{2p} energy increasing (Figure 9.42). These $2s$–$2p$ interactions can be strong enough that the energetic ordering of the MOs can be altered: For B$_2$, C$_2$, and N$_2$, the σ_{2p} MO is above the π_{2p} MOs in energy. For O$_2$, F$_2$, and Ne$_2$, the σ_{2p} MO is below the π_{2p} MOs.

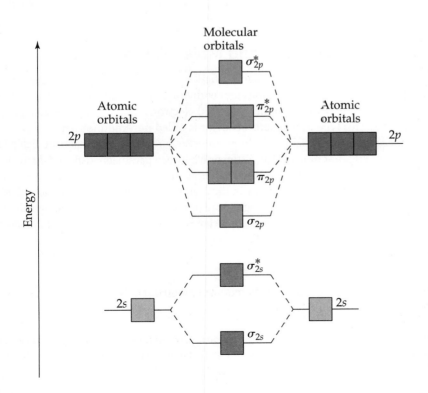

◀ **FIGURE 9.41 Energy-level diagram for MOs of period 2 homonuclear diatomic molecules.** The diagram assumes no interaction between the $2s$ atomic orbital on one atom and the $2p$ atomic orbitals on the other atom, and experiment shows that it fits only for O$_2$, F$_2$, and Ne$_2$.

GO FIGURE

Which molecular orbitals have switched relative energy in the group on the right as compared with the group on the left?

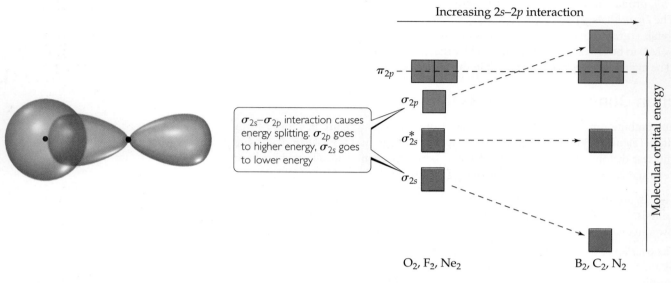

Increasing 2s–2p interaction

σ_{2s}–σ_{2p} interaction causes energy splitting. σ_{2p} goes to higher energy, σ_{2s} goes to lower energy

π_{2p}

σ_{2p}

σ_{2s}^*

σ_{2s}

Molecular orbital energy

O_2, F_2, Ne_2

B_2, C_2, N_2

▲ **FIGURE 9.42** **The effect of interactions between 2s and 2p atomic orbitals.**

Given the energy ordering of the molecular orbitals, it is a simple matter to determine the electron configurations for the diatomic molecules B_2 through Ne_2. For example, a boron atom has three valence electrons. (Remember that we are ignoring the 1s electrons.) Thus, for B_2 we must place six electrons in MOs. Four of them fill the σ_{2s} and σ_{2s}^* MOs, leading to no net bonding. The fifth electron goes in one π_{2p} MO, and the sixth goes in the other π_{2p} MO, with the two electrons having the same spin. Therefore, B_2 has a bond order of 1.

Each time we move one element to the right in period 2, two more electrons must be placed in the diagram of Figure 9.41. For example, on moving to C_2, we have two more electrons than in B_2, and these electrons are placed in the π_{2p} MOs, completely filling them. The electron configurations and bond orders for B_2 through Ne_2 are given in ▶ **FIGURE 9.43**.

Electron Configurations and Molecular Properties

The way a substance behaves in a magnetic field can in some cases provide insight into the arrangements of its electrons. Molecules with one or more unpaired electrons are attracted to a magnetic field. The more unpaired electrons in a species, the stronger the attractive force. This type of magnetic behavior is called **paramagnetism**.

Substances with no unpaired electrons are weakly repelled by a magnetic field. This property is called **diamagnetism**. The distinction between paramagnetism and diamagnetism is nicely illustrated in an older method for measuring magnetic properties (▶ **FIGURE 9.44**). It involves weighing the substance in the presence and absence of a magnetic field. A paramagnetic substance appears to weigh more in the magnetic field; a diamagnetic substance appears to weigh less. The magnetic behaviors observed for the period 2 diatomic molecules agree with the electron configurations shown in Figure 9.43.

◢ GIVE IT SOME THOUGHT

Figure 9.43 indicates that C_2 is diamagnetic. Would that be expected if the σ_{2p} MO were lower in energy than the π_{2p} MOs?

Electron configurations in molecules can also be related to bond distances and bond enthalpies. ∞ (Section 8.8) As bond order increases, bond distances decrease

◢ GO FIGURE

What difference in electron configuration accounts for most of the difference between the bond enthalpy of N_2 and that of F_2?

	Large 2s–2p interaction			Small 2s–2p interaction		
	B_2	**C_2**	**N_2**	**O_2**	**F_2**	**Ne_2**
σ^*_{2p}	☐	☐	☐	☐	☐	⇅
π^*_{2p}	☐ ☐	☐ ☐	☐ ☐	↑ ↑	⇅ ⇅	⇅ ⇅
σ_{2p}	☐	☐	⇅			
π_{2p}	↑ ↑	⇅ ⇅	⇅ ⇅	⇅ ⇅ / ⇅ ⇅	⇅ ⇅	⇅ ⇅
σ_{2p} (small)				⇅	⇅	⇅
σ^*_{2s}	⇅	⇅	⇅	⇅	⇅	⇅
σ_{2s}	⇅	⇅	⇅	⇅	⇅	⇅

	B_2	C_2	N_2	O_2	F_2	Ne_2
Bond order	1	2	3	2	1	0
Bond enthalpy (kJ/mol)	290	620	941	495	155	—
Bond length (Å)	1.59	1.31	1.10	1.21	1.43	—
Magnetic behavior	Paramagnetic	Diamagnetic	Diamagnetic	Paramagnetic	Diamagnetic	—

▲ **FIGURE 9.43** Molecular orbital electron configurations and some experimental data for period 2 diatomic molecules.

Weigh sample in absence of a magnetic field

A diamagnetic sample appears to weigh less in magnetic field (weak effect)

A paramagnetic sample appears to weigh more in magnetic field

— Sample

◀ **FIGURE 9.44** Determining the magnetic properties of a sample.

and bond enthalpies increase. N_2, for example, whose bond order is 3, has a short bond distance and a large bond enthalpy. The N_2 molecule does not react readily with other substances to form nitrogen compounds. The relatively high bond order of the molecule helps explain its exceptional stability. We should also note, however, that molecules with the same bond orders do *not* have the same bond distances and bond enthalpies. Bond order is only one factor influencing these properties. Other factors include nuclear charge and extent of orbital overlap.

Bonding in O_2 provides an interesting test case for molecular orbital theory. The Lewis structure for this molecule shows a double bond and complete pairing of electrons:

$$\ddot{O}=\ddot{O}$$

The short O—O bond distance (1.21 Å) and relatively high bond enthalpy (495 kJ/mol) are in agreement with the presence of a double bond. However, Figure 9.43 tells us that

◢ **GO FIGURE**

What would you expect to see if liquid nitrogen were poured between the poles of the magnet?

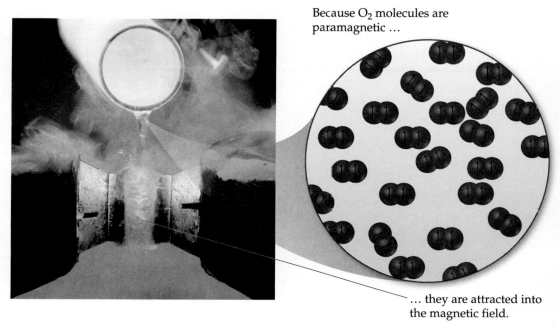

Because O_2 molecules are paramagnetic …

… they are attracted into the magnetic field.

▲ **FIGURE 9.45** **Paramagnetism of O_2.**

the molecule contains two unpaired electrons, a detail not discernible in the Lewis structure. Unpaired electrons mean paramagnetism, and the paramagnetism of O_2 is demonstrated in ▲ **FIGURE 9.45**. The Lewis structure fails to account for this paramagnetism, but molecular orbital theory correctly predicts two unpaired electrons in the $\pi_{2p}^{\star}$ orbital. The MO description also correctly indicates a bond order of 2.

Going from O_2 to F_2, we add two electrons, completely filling the $\pi_{2p}^{\star}$ MOs. Thus, F_2 is expected to be diamagnetic and have an F—F single bond, in accord with its Lewis structure. Finally, the addition of two more electrons to make Ne_2 fills all the bonding and antibonding MOs. Therefore, the bond order of Ne_2 is zero, and the molecule is not expected to exist.

SAMPLE EXERCISE 9.9 **Molecular Orbitals of a Period 2 Diatomic Ion**

For the O_2^{+} ion, predict (a) number of unpaired electrons, (b) bond order, (c) bond enthalpy and bond length.

SOLUTION

Analyze Our task is to predict several properties of the cation O_2^{+}.

Plan We will use the MO description of O_2^{+} to determine the desired properties. We must first determine the number of electrons in O_2^{+} and then draw its MO energy diagram. The unpaired electrons are those without a partner of opposite spin. The bond order is one-half the difference between the number of bonding and antibonding electrons. After calculating the bond order, we can use Figure 9.43 to estimate the bond enthalpy and bond length.

Solve
(a) The O_2^{+} ion has 11 valence electrons, one fewer than O_2. The electron removed from O_2 to form O_2^{+} is one of the two unpaired $\pi_{2p}^{\star}$ electrons (see Figure 9.43). Therefore, O_2^{+} has one unpaired electron.

(b) The molecule has eight bonding electrons (the same as O_2) and three antibonding electrons (one fewer than O_2). Thus, its bond order is

$$\tfrac{1}{2}(8 - 3) = 2\tfrac{1}{2}$$

(c) The bond order of O_2^+ is between that for O_2 (bond order 2) and N_2 (bond order 3). Thus, the bond enthalpy and bond length should be about midway between those for O_2 and N_2, approximately 700 kJ/mol and 1.15 Å. (The experimentally measured values are 625 kJ/mol and 1.123 Å.)

PRACTICE EXERCISE

Predict the magnetic properties and bond orders of **(a)** the peroxide ion, O_2^{2-}; **(b)** the acetylide ion, C_2^{2-}.

Answers: **(a)** diamagnetic, 1; **(b)** diamagnetic, 3

Heteronuclear Diatomic Molecules

The principles we have used in developing an MO description of homonuclear diatomic molecules can be extended to *heteronuclear* diatomic molecules—those in which the two atoms in the molecule are not the same—and we conclude this section with a fascinating heteronuclear diatomic molecule—nitric oxide, NO.

The NO molecule controls several important human physiological functions. Our bodies use it, for example, to relax muscles, kill foreign cells, and reinforce memory. The 1998 Nobel Prize in Physiology or Medicine was awarded to three scientists for their research that uncovered the importance of NO as a "signaling" molecule in the cardiovascular system. NO also functions as a neurotransmitter and is implicated in many other biological pathways. That NO plays such an important role in human metabolism was unsuspected before 1987 because NO has an odd number of electrons and is highly reactive. The molecule has 11 valence electrons, and two possible Lewis structures can be drawn. The Lewis structure with the lower formal charges places the odd electron on the N atom:

Both structures indicate the presence of a double bond, but when compared with the molecules in Figure 9.43, the experimental bond length of NO (1.15 Å) suggests a bond order greater than 2. How do we treat NO using the MO model?

If the atoms in a heteronuclear diatomic molecule do not differ too greatly in electronegativities, their MOs resemble those in homonuclear diatomics, with one important modification: The energy of the atomic orbitals of the more electronegative atom is lower than that of the atomic orbitals of the less electronegative element. In ▶ **FIGURE 9.46**, you see that the 2s and 2p atomic orbitals of oxygen are slightly lower than those of nitrogen because oxygen is more electronegative than nitrogen. The MO energy-level diagram for NO is much like that of a homonuclear diatomic molecule—because the 2s and 2p orbitals on the two atoms interact, the same types of MOs are produced.

There is one other important difference in the MOs of heteronuclear molecules. The MOs are still a mix of atomic orbitals from both atoms, but in general *an MO in a heteronuclear diatomic molecule has a greater contribution from the atomic orbital to which it is closer in energy*. In the case of NO, for example, the σ_{2s} bonding MO is closer in energy to the O 2s atomic orbital than to the N 2s atomic orbital. As a result, the σ_{2s} MO has a slightly greater contribution from O than from N—the orbital is no longer an equal mixture of the two atoms, as was the case for the homonuclear diatomic molecules. Similarly, the σ_{2s}^* antibonding MO is weighted more heavily toward the N atom because that MO is closest in energy to the N 2s atomic orbital.

▲ GO FIGURE

How many valence-shell electrons are there in NO?

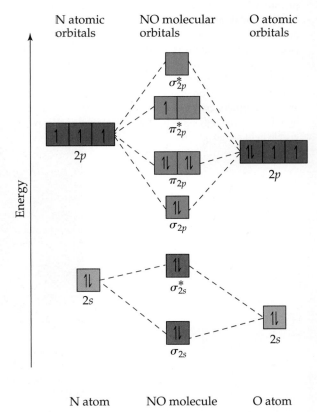

▲ **FIGURE 9.46** **The energy-level diagram for atomic and molecular orbitals in NO.**

CHEMISTRY PUT TO WORK

Orbitals and Energy

Asked to identify the major technological challenge for the twenty-first century, you might say "energy," reasoning that development of sustainable energy sources is crucial to meet the needs of future generations of people on our planet. Currently, the majority of the world, in one way or another, relies on exothermic combustion reactions of oil, coal, or natural gas to provide heat and power. These are all *fossil fuels*—carbon-containing compounds that are the long-term decomposition products of ancient plants and animals.

Fossil fuels are not renewable in the several-hundred-year timeframe in which we need them, but every day our planet receives plenty of energy from the Sun to easily power the world for millions of years. Whereas combustion of fossil fuels releases CO_2 into the atmosphere, solar energy represents a renewable energy source that is potentially less harmful to the environment. One way to utilize solar energy is to convert it into electrical energy via photovoltaic solar cells. The problem with this alternative is that the current efficiency of solar-cell devices is low; only about 10–15% of sunlight is converted into useful energy. Furthermore, the cost of manufacturing solar cells is relatively high.

How does solar energy conversion work? Fundamentally, we need to be able to use photons from the Sun to excite electrons in molecules and materials to different energy levels. The brilliant colors around you—those of your clothes, the photographs in this book, the foods you eat—are due to the selective absorption of light by chemicals. Light excites electrons in molecules. In a molecular orbital picture, we can envision light exciting an electron from a filled molecular orbital to an empty one at higher energy. Because the MOs have definite energies, only light of the proper wavelengths can excite electrons. The situation is analogous to that of atomic line spectra. ∞ (Section 6.3) If the appropriate wavelength for exciting electrons is in the visible portion of the electromagnetic spectrum, the substance appears colored: Certain wavelengths of white light are absorbed; others are not. A green leaf appears green because green light is most strongly reflected by the leaf while other wavelengths of visible light are absorbed.

In discussing light absorption by molecules, we can focus on two MOs. The *highest occupied molecular orbital* (HOMO) is the MO of highest energy that has electrons in it. The *lowest unoccupied molecular orbital* (LUMO) is the MO of lowest energy that does not have electrons in it. In N_2, for example, the HOMO is the σ_{2p} MO and the LUMO is the π_{2p}^* MO (Figure 9.43).

The energy difference between the HOMO and the LUMO—known as the HOMO–LUMO gap—is related to the minimum energy needed to excite an electron in the molecule. Colorless or white substances usually have such a large HOMO–LUMO gap that visible light is not energetic enough to excite an electron to the higher level. The minimum energy needed to excite an electron from the HOMO to the LUMO in N_2 corresponds to light with a wavelength of less than 200 nm, which is far into the ultraviolet part of the spectrum. ∞ (Figure 6.4) As a result, N_2 cannot absorb visible light and is therefore colorless.

The magnitude of the energy gap between filled and empty electronic states is critical for solar energy conversion. Ideally, we want a substance that absorbs as many solar photons as possible and then converts the energy of those photons into a useful form of energy. Titanium dioxide is a readily available material that can be reasonably efficient at converting light directly into electricity. However, TiO_2 is white and absorbs only a small amount of the Sun's radiant energy. Scientists are working to make solar cells in which TiO_2 is mixed with highly colored molecules, whose HOMO–LUMO gaps correspond to visible and near-infrared light. That way, the molecules can absorb more of the solar spectrum. The molecule's HOMO must also be higher in energy than the TiO_2's HOMO so that the excited electrons can flow from the molecules into the TiO_2, thereby generating electricity when the device is illuminated with light and connected to an external circuit.

▼ **FIGURE 9.47** shows a solar cell made from ruthenium-containing molecules, which appear red, mixed with TiO_2 in a paste that is sandwiched between two glass plates. Incoming light excites electrons on the ruthenium-containing molecules from occupied MOs to empty MOs. The electrons are then transferred into the TiO_2 and move through the external circuit, generating enough current to run the small fan.

RELATED EXERCISES: 9.105, 9.116

TiO$_2$ matrix

Incoming light source

Light excites electrons in a ruthenium complex.

Excited electrons flow in external circuit, powering fan

▲ **FIGURE 9.47** **Light into electricity.**

We complete the MO diagram for NO by filling the MOs in Figure 9.46 with the 11 valence electrons. Eight bonding and three antibonding electrons give a bond order of $\frac{1}{2}(8-3) = 2\frac{1}{2}$, which agrees better with experiment than the Lewis structures do. The unpaired electron resides in one of the π_{2p}^* MOs, which are more heavily weighted toward the N atom. (We could have placed this electron in either the left or right π_{2p}^* MO.) Thus, the Lewis structure that places the unpaired electron on nitrogen (the one preferred on the basis of formal charge) is the more accurate description of the true electron distribution in the molecule.

SAMPLE INTEGRATIVE EXERCISE   **Putting Concepts Together**

Elemental sulfur is a yellow solid that consists of S_8 molecules. The structure of the S_8 molecule is a puckered, eight-membered ring (see Figure 7.26). Heating elemental sulfur to high temperatures produces gaseous S_2 molecules:

$$S_8(s) \longrightarrow 4\,S_2(g)$$

(a) The electron configuration of which period 2 element is most similar to that of sulfur? (b) Use the VSEPR model to predict the S—S—S bond angles in S_8 and the hybridization at S in S_8. (c) Use MO theory to predict the sulfur–sulfur bond order in S_2. Do you expect this molecule to be diamagnetic or paramagnetic? (d) Use average bond enthalpies (Table 8.4) to estimate the enthalpy change for this reaction. Is the reaction exothermic or endothermic?

SOLUTION

(a) Sulfur is a group 6A element with an $[Ne]3s^23p^4$ electron configuration. It is expected to be most similar electronically to oxygen (electron configuration, $[He]2s^22p^4$), which is immediately above it in the periodic table.

(b) The Lewis structure of S_8 is

There is a single bond between each pair of S atoms and two nonbonding electron pairs on each S atom. Thus, we see four electron domains around each S atom and expect a tetrahedral electron-domain geometry corresponding to sp^3 hybridization. Because of the nonbonding pairs, we expect the S—S—S angles to be somewhat less than 109.5°, the tetrahedral angle. Experimentally, the S—S—S angle in S_8 is 108°, in good agreement with this prediction. Interestingly, if S_8 were a planar ring, it would have S—S—S angles of 135°. Instead, the S_8 ring puckers to accommodate the smaller angles dictated by sp^3 hybridization.

(c) The MOs of S_2 are analogous to those of O_2, although the MOs for S_2 are constructed from the 3s and 3p atomic orbitals of sulfur. Further, S_2 has the same number of valence electrons as O_2. Thus, by analogy with O_2, we expect S_2 to have a bond order of 2 (a double bond) and to be paramagnetic with two unpaired electrons in the π_{3p}^* molecular orbitals of S_2.

(d) We are considering the reaction in which an S_8 molecule falls apart into four S_2 molecules. From parts (b) and (c), we see that S_8 has S—S single bonds and S_2 has S=S double bonds. During the reaction, therefore, we are breaking eight S—S single bonds and forming four S=S double bonds. We can estimate the enthalpy of the reaction by using Equation 8.12 and the average bond enthalpies in Table 8.4:

$$\Delta H_{rxn} = 8\,D(\text{S—S}) - 4\,D(\text{S=S}) = 8(266\text{ kJ}) - 4(418\text{ kJ}) = +456\text{ kJ}$$

Recall that $D(\text{X—Y})$ represents the X—Y bond enthalpy. Because $\Delta H_{rxn} > 0$, the reaction is endothermic. ∞ (Section 5.4) The very positive value of ΔH_{rxn} suggests that high temperatures are required to cause the reaction to occur.

CHAPTER SUMMARY AND KEY TERMS

INTRODUCTION AND SECTION 9.1 The three-dimensional shapes and sizes of molecules are determined by their **bond angles** and bond lengths. Molecules with a central atom A surrounded by n atoms B, denoted AB_n, adopt a number of different geometric shapes, depending on the value of n and on the particular atoms involved. In the overwhelming majority of cases, these geometries are related to five basic shapes (linear, trigonal pyramidal, tetrahedral, trigonal bipyramidal, and octahedral).

SECTION 9.2 The **valence-shell electron-pair repulsion (VSEPR) model** rationalizes molecular geometries based on the repulsions between **electron domains**, which are regions about a central atom in which electrons are likely to be found. **Bonding pairs** of electrons, which are those involved in making bonds, and **nonbonding pairs** of electrons, also called **lone pairs**, both create electron domains around an atom. According to the VSEPR model, electron domains orient themselves to minimize electrostatic repulsions; that is, they remain as far apart as possible. Electron domains from nonbonding pairs exert slightly greater repulsions than those from bonding pairs, which leads to certain preferred positions for nonbonding pairs and to the departure of bond angles from idealized values. Electron domains from multiple bonds exert slightly greater repulsions than those from single bonds. The arrangement of electron domains around a central atom is called the **electron-domain geometry**; the arrangement of atoms is called the **molecular geometry**.

SECTION 9.3 The dipole moment of a polyatomic molecule depends on the vector sum of the dipole moments associated with the individual bonds, called the **bond dipoles**. Certain molecular shapes, such as linear AB_2 and trigonal planar AB_3, assure that the bond dipoles cancel, producing a nonpolar molecule, which is one whose dipole moment is zero. In other shapes, such as bent AB_2 and trigonal pyramidal AB_3, the bond dipoles do not cancel and the molecule will be polar (that is, it will have a nonzero dipole moment).

SECTION 9.4 **Valence-bond theory** is an extension of Lewis's notion of electron-pair bonds. In valence-bond theory, covalent bonds are formed when atomic orbitals on neighboring atoms overlap one another. The overlap region is one of low energy, or greater stability, for the two electrons because of their simultaneous attraction to two nuclei. The greater the overlap between two orbitals, the stronger will be the bond that is formed.

SECTION 9.5 To extend the ideas of valence-bond theory to polyatomic molecules, we must envision mixing s, p, and sometimes d orbitals to form **hybrid orbitals**. The process of **hybridization** leads to hybrid atomic orbitals that have a large lobe directed to overlap with orbitals on another atom to make a bond. Hybrid orbitals can also accommodate nonbonding pairs. A particular mode of hybridization can be associated with each of three common electron-domain geometries (linear $= sp$; trigonal planar $= sp^2$; tetrahedral $= sp^3$).

SECTION 9.6 Covalent bonds in which the electron density lies along the line connecting the atoms (the internuclear axis) are called **sigma (σ) bonds**. Bonds can also be formed from the sideways overlap of p orbitals. Such a bond is called a **pi (π) bond**. A double bond, such as that in C_2H_4, consists of one σ bond and one π bond; a triple bond,

such as that in C_2H_2, consists of one σ and two π bonds. The formation of a π bond requires that molecules adopt a specific orientation; the two CH_2 groups in C_2H_4, for example, must lie in the same plane. As a result, the presence of π bonds introduces rigidity into molecules. In molecules that have multiple bonds and more than one resonance structure, such as C_6H_6, the π bonds are **delocalized**; that is, the π bonds are spread among several atoms.

SECTION 9.7 **Molecular orbital theory** is another model used to describe the bonding in molecules. In this model the electrons exist in allowed energy states called **molecular orbitals (MOs)**. An MO can extend over all the atoms of a molecule. Like an atomic orbital, a molecular orbital has a definite energy and can hold two electrons of opposite spin. We can think of molecular orbitals as built up by combining atomic orbitals on different atomic centers. In the simplest case, the combination of two atomic orbitals leads to the formation of two MOs, one at lower energy and one at higher energy relative to the energy of the atomic orbitals. The lower-energy MO concentrates charge density in the region between the nuclei and is called a **bonding molecular orbital**. The higher-energy MO excludes electrons from the region between the nuclei and is called an **antibonding molecular orbital**. Occupation of bonding MOs favors bond formation, whereas occupation of antibonding MOs is unfavorable. The bonding and antibonding MOs formed by the combination of s orbitals are **sigma (σ) molecular orbitals**; they lie on the internuclear axis.

The combination of atomic orbitals and the relative energies of the molecular orbitals are shown by an **energy-level (or molecular orbital) diagram**. When the appropriate number of electrons are put into the MOs, we can calculate the **bond order** of a bond, which is half the difference between the number of electrons in bonding MOs and the number of electrons in antibonding MOs. A bond order of 1 corresponds to a single bond, and so forth. Bond orders can be fractional numbers.

SECTION 9.8 Electrons in core orbitals do not contribute to the bonding between atoms, so a molecular orbital description usually needs to consider only electrons in the outermost electron subshells. In order to describe the MOs of period 2 homonuclear diatomic molecules, we need to consider the MOs that can form by the combination of p orbitals. The p orbitals that point directly at one another can form σ bonding and σ^* antibonding MOs. The p orbitals that are oriented perpendicular to the internuclear axis combine to form **pi (π) molecular orbitals**. In diatomic molecules the π molecular orbitals occur as a pair of degenerate (same energy) bonding MOs and a pair of degenerate antibonding MOs. The σ_{2p} bonding MO is expected to be lower in energy than the π_{2p} bonding MOs because of larger orbital overlap of the p orbitals directed along the internuclear axis. However, this ordering is reversed in B_2, C_2, and N_2 because of interaction between the $2s$ and $2p$ atomic orbitals of different atoms.

The molecular orbital description of period 2 diatomic molecules leads to bond orders in accord with the Lewis structures of these molecules. Further, the model predicts correctly that O_2 should exhibit **paramagnetism**, which leads to attraction of a molecule into a magnetic field due to the influence of unpaired electrons. Molecules in which all the electrons are paired exhibit **diamagnetism**, which leads to weak repulsion from a magnetic field.

KEY SKILLS

- Be able to describe the three-dimensional shapes of molecules using the VSEPR model. (Section 9.2)
- Determine whether a molecule is polar or nonpolar based on its geometry and the individual bond dipole moments. (Section 9.3)
- Be able to explain the role of orbital overlap in the formation of covalent bonds. (Section 9.4)
- Be able to specify the hybridization state of atoms in molecules based on observed molecular structures. (Section 9.5)
- Be able to sketch how orbitals overlap to form sigma (σ) and pi (π) bonds. (Section 9.6)
- Be able to explain the existence of delocalized π bonds in molecules such as benzene. (Section 9.6)
- Be able to explain the concept of bonding and antibonding orbitals. (Section 9.7)
- Be able to draw molecular orbital energy-level diagrams and place electrons into them to obtain the bond orders and electron configurations of diatomic molecules using molecular orbital theory. (Sections 9.7 and 9.8)
- Understand the relationships among bond order, bond strength (bond enthalpy), and bond length. (Section 9.8)

KEY EQUATION

- Bond order $= \frac{1}{2}$ (no. of bonding electrons $-$ no. of antibonding electrons)   [9.1]

EXERCISES

VISUALIZING CONCEPTS

9.1 A certain AB_4 molecule has a "seesaw" shape:

From which of the fundamental geometries shown in Figure 9.3 could you remove one or more atoms to create a molecule having this seesaw shape? [Section 9.1]

9.2 (a) If these three balloons are all the same size, what angle is formed between the red one and the green one? (b) If additional air is added to the blue balloon so that it gets larger, what happens to the angle between the red and green balloons? (c) What aspect of the VSEPR model is illustrated by part (b)? [Section 9.2]

9.3 For each molecule (a)-(f), indicate how many different electron-domain geometries are consistent with the molecular geometry shown. [Section 9.2]

(a)   (b)

(c)   (d)

(e)   (f)

9.4 The molecule shown here is *difluoromethane* (CH_2F_2), which is used as a refrigerant called R-32. (a) Based on the structure, how many electron domains surround the C atom in this molecule? (b) Would the molecule have a nonzero dipole moment? (c) If the molecule is polar, in what direction will the overall dipole moment vector point in the molecule? [Sections 9.2 and 9.3]

9.5 The following plot shows the potential energy of two Cl atoms as a function of the distance between them. (**a**) To what does an energy of zero correspond in this diagram? (**b**) According to the valence-bond model, why does the energy decrease as the Cl atoms move from a large separation to a smaller one? (**c**) What is the significance of the Cl—Cl distance at the minimum point in the plot? (**d**) Why does the energy rise at Cl—Cl distances less than that at the minimum point in the plot? (**e**) How can you estimate the bond strength of the Cl—Cl bond from the plot? [Section 9.4]

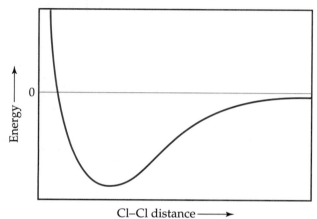

9.6 In the series SiF_4, PF_3, and SF_2, estimate the F—X—F bond angle in each case and explain your rationale. [Section 9.2]

9.7 The orbital diagram that follows presents the final step in the formation of hybrid orbitals by a silicon atom. What type of hybrid orbital is produced in this hybridization? [Section 9.5]

9.8 In the hydrocarbon

H—C=C—C—C≡C—C—H (with H atoms attached as drawn)

(**a**) What is the hybridization at each carbon atom in the molecule? (**b**) How many σ bonds are there in the molecule? (**c**) How many π bonds? (**d**) Identify all the 120° bond angles in the molecule. [Section 9.6]

9.9 For each of these contour representations of molecular orbitals, identify (**a**) the atomic orbitals (s or p) used to construct the MO (**b**) the type of MO (σ or π), (**c**) whether the MO is bonding or antibonding, and (**d**) the locations of nodal planes. [Sections 9.7 and 9.8]

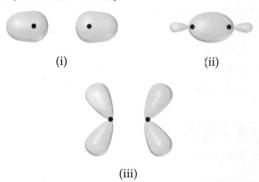

(i)   (ii)

(iii)

9.10 The diagram that follows shows the highest-energy occupied MOs of a neutral molecule CX, where element X is in the same row of the periodic table as C. (**a**) Based on the number of electrons, can you determine the identity of X? (**b**) Would the molecule be diamagnetic or paramagnetic? (**c**) Consider the π_{2p} MOs of the molecule. Would you expect them to have a greater atomic orbital contribution from C, have a greater atomic orbital contribution from X, or be an equal mixture of atomic orbitals from the two atoms? [Section 9.8]

MOLECULAR SHAPES; THE VSEPR MODEL (sections 9.1 and 9.2)

9.11 An AB_2 molecule is described as linear, and the A—B bond length is known. (**a**) Does this information completely describe the geometry of the molecule? (**b**) Can you tell how many nonbonding pairs of electrons are around the A atom from this information?

9.12 (**a**) Methane (CH_4) and the perchlorate ion (ClO_4^-) are both described as tetrahedral. What does this indicate about their bond angles? (**b**) The NH_3 molecule is trigonal pyramidal, while BF_3 is trigonal planar. Which of these molecules is flat?

9.13 How does a trigonal pyramid differ from a tetrahedron so far as molecular geometry is concerned?

9.14 Describe the bond angles to be found in each of the following molecular structures: (**a**) planar trigonal, (**b**) tetrahedral, (**c**) octahedral, (**d**) linear.

9.15 (**a**) What is meant by the term *electron domain*? (**b**) Explain in what way electron domains behave like the balloons in Figure 9.5. Why do they do so?

9.16 What property of the electron causes electron domains to have an effect on molecular shapes?

9.17 (**a**) How does one determine the number of electron domains in a molecule or ion? (**b**) What is the difference between a *bonding electron domain* and a *nonbonding electron domain*?

9.18 Would you expect the nonbonding electron-pair domain in NH_3 to be greater or less in size than for the corresponding one in PH_3? Explain.

9.19 In which of these molecules or ions does the presence of nonbonding electron pairs produce an effect on molecular shape, assuming they are all in the gaseous state? (**a**) SiH_4, (**b**) PF_3, (**c**) HBr, (**d**) HCN, (**e**) SO_2.

9.20 In which of the following molecules can you confidently predict the bond angles about the central atom, and for which would you be a bit uncertain? Explain in each case. (**a**) H_2S, (**b**) BCl_3, (**c**) CH_3I, (**d**) CBr_4, (**e**) $TeBr_4$.

9.21 How many nonbonding electron pairs are there in each of the following molecules: (a) $(CH_3)_2S$, (b) HCN, (c) H_2C_2, (d) CH_3F?

9.22 Describe the characteristic electron-domain geometry of each of the following numbers of electron domains about a central atom: (a) 3, (b) 4, (c) 5, (d) 6.

9.23 What is the difference between the electron-domain geometry and the molecular geometry of a molecule? Use the water molecule as an example in your discussion. Why do we need to make this distinction?

9.24 An AB_3 molecule is described as having a trigonal-bipyramidal electron-domain geometry. How many nonbonding domains are on atom A? Explain.

9.25 Give the electron-domain and molecular geometries of a molecule that has the following electron domains on its central atom: (a) four bonding domains and no nonbonding domains, (b) three bonding domains and two nonbonding domains, (c) five bonding domains and one nonbonding domain, (d) four bonding domains and two nonbonding domains.

9.26 What are the electron-domain and molecular geometries of a molecule that has the following electron domains on its central atom? (a) three bonding domains and no nonbonding domains, (b) three bonding domains and one nonbonding domain, (c) two bonding domains and two nonbonding domains.

9.27 Give the electron-domain and molecular geometries for the following molecules and ions: (a) HCN, (b) SO_3^{2-}, (c) SF_4, (d) PF_6^-, (e) NH_3Cl^+, (f) N_3^-.

9.28 Draw the Lewis structure for each of the following molecules or ions, and predict their electron-domain and molecular geometries: (a) AsF_3, (b) CH_3^+, (c) BrF_3, (d) ClO_3^-, (e) XeF_2, (f) BrO_2^-.

9.29 The figure that follows shows ball-and-stick drawings of three possible shapes of an AF_3 molecule. (a) For each shape, give the electron-domain geometry on which the molecular geometry is based. (b) For each shape, how many nonbonding electron domains are there on atom A? (c) Which of the following elements will lead to an AF_3 molecule with the shape in (ii): Li, B, N, Al, P, Cl? (d) Name an element A that is expected to lead to the AF_3 structure shown in (iii). Explain your reasoning.

(i) (ii) (iii)

9.30 The figure that follows contains ball-and-stick drawings of three possible shapes of an AF_4 molecule. (a) For each shape, give the electron-domain geometry on which the molecular geometry is based. (b) For each shape, how many nonbonding electron domains are there on atom A? (c) Which of the following elements will lead to an AF_4 molecule with the shape in (iii): Be, C, S, Se, Si, Xe? (d) Name an element A that is expected to lead to the AF_4 structure shown in (i).

(i) (ii) (iii)

9.31 Give the approximate values for the indicated bond angles in the following molecules:

(a) H—Ö—Cl—Ö: with angles 1 and 2, and :O: below Cl

(b) H—C—Ö—H with H above and H below C, angles 3 and 4

(c) H—C≡C—H angle 5

(d) H—C—Ö—C—H with :O: double bonded to first C (angle 6), H above and H below second C, angle 7 and 8

9.32 Give approximate values for the indicated bond angles in the following molecules:

(a) H—Ö—N=Ö angles 1 and 2

(b) H—C—C=Ö with H above and below first C (angle 3), angle 4

(c) H—N—Ö—H with H above N (angle 5), angle 6

(d) H—C—C≡N: with H above and below C, angles 7 and 8

9.33 In which of the following AF_n molecules or ions is there more than one F—A—F bond angle: SiF_4, PF_5, SF_4, AsF_3?

9.34 The three species NH_2^-, NH_3, and NH_4^+ have H—N—H bond angles of 105°, 107°, and 109°, respectively. Explain this variation in bond angles.

9.35 (a) Explain why BrF_4^- is square planar, whereas BF_4^- is tetrahedral. (b) How would you expect the H—X—H bond angle to vary in the series H_2O, H_2S, H_2Se? Explain. (*Hint:* The size of an electron pair domain depends in part on the electronegativity of the central atom.)

9.36 (a) Explain why the following ions have different bond angles: ClO_2^- and NO_2^-. Predict the bond angle in each case. (b) Explain why the XeF_2 molecule is linear.

SHAPES AND POLARITY OF POLYATOMIC MOLECULES (section 9.3)

9.37 What is the distinction between a bond dipole and a molecular dipole moment?

9.38 Consider a molecule with formula AX_3. Supposing the A—X bond is polar, how would you expect the dipole moment of the AX_3 molecule to change as the X—A—X bond angle increases from $100°$ to $120°$?

9.39 (a) Does SCl_2 have a dipole moment? If so, in which direction does the net dipole point? (b) Does $BeCl_2$ have a dipole moment? If so, in which direction does the net dipole point?

9.40 (a) The PH_3 molecule is polar. Does this offer experimental proof that the molecule cannot be planar? Explain. (b) It turns out that ozone, O_3, has a small dipole moment. How is this possible, given that all the atoms are the same?

9.41 (a) Consider the AF_3 molecules in Exercise 9.29. Which of these will have a nonzero dipole moment? Explain. (b) Which of the AF_4 molecules in Exercise 9.30 will have a zero dipole moment?

9.42 (a) What conditions must be met if a molecule with polar bonds is nonpolar? (b) What geometries will signify nonpolar molecules for AB_2, AB_3, and AB_4 geometries?

9.43 Predict whether each of the following molecules is polar or nonpolar: (a) IF, (b) CS_2, (c) SO_3, (d) PCl_3, (e) SF_6, (f) IF_5.

9.44 Predict whether each of the following molecules is polar or nonpolar: (a) CCl_4, (b) NH_3, (c) SF_4, (d) XeF_4, (e) CH_3Br, (f) GaH_3.

9.45 Dichloroethylene ($C_2H_2Cl_2$) has three forms (isomers), each of which is a different substance. (a) Draw Lewis structures of the three isomers, all of which have a carbon–carbon double bond. (b) Which of these isomers has a zero dipole moment? (c) How many isomeric forms can chloroethylene, C_2H_3Cl, have? Would they be expected to have dipole moments?

9.46 Dichlorobenzene, $C_6H_4Cl_2$, exists in three forms (isomers) called *ortho*, *meta*, and *para*:

ortho   *meta*   *para*

Which of these has a nonzero dipole moment? Explain.

ORBITAL OVERLAP; HYBRID ORBITALS (sections 9.4 and 9.5)

9.47 (a) What is meant by the term *orbital overlap*? (b) Describe what a chemical bond is in terms of electron density between two atoms.

9.48 Draw sketches illustrating the overlap between the following orbitals on two atoms: (a) the $2s$ orbital on each atom, (b) the $2p_z$ orbital on each atom (assume both atoms are on the z-axis), (c) the $2s$ orbital on one atom and the $2p_z$ orbital on the other atom.

9.49 Consider the bonding in an MgH_2 molecule. (a) Draw a Lewis structure for the molecule, and predict its molecular geometry. (b) What hybridization scheme is used in MgH_2? (c) Sketch one of the two-electron bonds between an Mg hybrid orbital and an H $1s$ atomic orbital.

9.50 How would you expect the extent of overlap of the bonding atomic orbitals to vary in the series IF, ICl, IBr, and I_2? Explain your answer.

9.51 Fill in the blank spaces in the following chart. If the molecule column is blank, find an example that fulfills the conditions of the rest of the row.

Molecule	Electron-Domain Geometry	Hybridization of Central Atom	Dipole Moment? Yes or No
CO_2			
		sp^3	Yes
		sp^3	No
	Trigonal planar		No
SF_4			
	Octahedral		No
		sp^2	Yes
	Trigonal bipyramidal		No
XeF_2			

9.52 Why are there no sp^4 or sp^5 hybrid orbitals?

9.53 (a) Starting with the orbital diagram of a boron atom, describe the steps needed to construct hybrid orbitals appropriate to describe the bonding in BF_3. (b) What is the name given to the hybrid orbitals constructed in (a)? (c) Sketch the large lobes of the hybrid orbitals constructed in part (a). (d) Are any valence atomic orbitals of B left unhybridized? If so, how are they oriented relative to the hybrid orbitals?

9.54 (a) Starting with the orbital diagram of a sulfur atom, describe the steps needed to construct hybrid orbitals appropriate to describe the bonding in SF_2. (b) What is the name given to the hybrid orbitals constructed in (a)? (c) Sketch the large lobes of these hybrid orbitals. (d) Would the hybridization scheme in part (a) be appropriate for SF_4? Explain.

9.55 Indicate the hybridization of the central atom in (a) BCl_3, (b) $AlCl_4^-$, (c) CS_2, (d) GeH_4.

9.56 What is the hybridization of the central atom in (a) $SiCl_4$, (b) HCN, (c) SO_3, (d) $TeCl_2$.

9.57 Shown here are three pairs of hybrid orbitals, with each set at a characteristic angle. For each pair, determine the type of hybridization, if any, that could lead to hybrid orbitals at the specified angle.

9.58 (a) Which geometry and central atom hybridization would you expect in the series BH_4^-, CH_4, NH_4^+? (b) What would you expect for the magnitude and direction of the bond dipoles in this series? (c) Write the formulas for the analogous species of the elements of period 3; would you expect them to have the same hybridization at the central atom?

MULTIPLE BONDS (section 9.6)

9.59 (a) Draw a picture showing how two p orbitals on two different atoms can be combined to make a sigma bond. (b) Sketch a π bond that is constructed from p orbitals. (c) Which is generally stronger, a σ bond or a π bond? Explain. (d) Can two s orbitals combine to form a π bond? Explain.

9.60 (a) If the valence atomic orbitals of an atom are sp hybridized, how many unhybridized p orbitals remain in the valence shell? How many π bonds can the atom form? (b) Imagine that you could hold two atoms that are bonded together, twist them, and not change the bond length. Would it be easier to twist (rotate) around a single σ bond or around a double (σ plus π) bond, or would they be the same? Explain.

9.61 (a) Draw Lewis structures for ethane (C_2H_6), ethylene (C_2H_4), and acetylene (C_2H_2). (b) What is the hybridization of the carbon atoms in each molecule? (c) Predict which molecules, if any, are planar. (d) How many σ and π bonds are there in each molecule? (e) Suppose that silicon could form molecules that are precisely the analogs of ethane, ethylene, and acetylene. How would you describe the bonding about Si in terms of hybrid orbitals? Silicon does not readily form some of the analogous compounds containing π bonds. Why might this be the case?

9.62 The nitrogen atoms in N_2 participate in multiple bonding, whereas those in hydrazine, N_2H_4, do not. (a) Draw Lewis structures for both molecules. (b) What is the hybridization of the nitrogen atoms in each molecule? (c) Which molecule has the stronger N—N bond?

9.63 Propylene, C_3H_6, is a gas that is used to form the important polymer called polypropylene. Its Lewis structure is

(a) What is the total number of valence electrons in the propylene molecule? (b) How many valence electrons are used to make σ bonds in the molecule? (c) How many valence electrons are used to make π bonds in the molecule? (d) How many valence electrons remain in nonbonding pairs in the molecule? (e) What is the hybridization at each carbon atom in the molecule?

9.64 Ethyl acetate, $C_4H_8O_2$, is a fragrant substance used both as a solvent and as an aroma enhancer. Its Lewis structure is

(a) What is the hybridization at each of the carbon atoms of the molecule? (b) What is the total number of valence electrons in ethyl acetate? (c) How many of the valence electrons are used to make σ bonds in the molecule? (d) How many

valence electrons are used to make π bonds? (e) How many valence electrons remain in nonbonding pairs in the molecule?

9.65 Consider the Lewis structure for glycine, the simplest amino acid:

(a) What are the approximate bond angles about each of the two carbon atoms, and what are the hybridizations of the orbitals on each of them? (b) What are the hybridizations of the orbitals on the two oxygens and the nitrogen atom, and what are the approximate bond angles at the nitrogen? (c) What is the total number of σ bonds in the entire molecule, and what is the total number of π bonds?

9.66 Acetylsalicylic acid, better known as aspirin, has the Lewis structure

(a) What are the approximate values of the bond angles labeled 1, 2, and 3? (b) What hybrid orbitals are used about the central atom of each of these angles? (c) How many σ bonds are in the molecule?

9.67 (a) What is the difference between a localized π bond and a delocalized one? (b) How can you determine whether a molecule or ion will exhibit delocalized π bonding? (c) Is the π bond in NO_2^- localized or delocalized?

9.68 (a) Write a single Lewis structure for SO_3, and determine the hybridization at the S atom. (b) Are there other equivalent Lewis structures for the molecule? (c) Would you expect SO_3 to exhibit delocalized π bonding? Explain.

9.69 Predict the molecular geometry of each of the following molecules:

(a) $H-C\equiv C-C\equiv C-C\equiv N$

(b)

(c) $H-N\!=\!N-H$

9.70 What hybridization do you expect for the atom indicated in red in each of the following species? (a) $CH_3CO_2^-$; (b) PH_4^+; (c) AlF_3; (d) $H_2C\!=\!CH-CH_2^+$

MOLECULAR ORBITALS AND SECOND-ROW DIATOMIC MOLECULES (sections 9.7 and 9.8)

9.71 (a) What is the difference between hybrid orbitals and molecular orbitals? (b) How many electrons can be placed into each MO of a molecule? (c) Can antibonding molecular orbitals have electrons in them?

9.72 (a) If you combine two atomic orbitals on two different atoms to make a new orbital, is this a hybrid orbital or a molecular orbital? (b) If you combine two atomic orbitals on *one* atom to make a new orbital, is this a hybrid orbital or a molecular orbital? (c) Does the Pauli exclusion principle (Section 6.7) apply to MOs? Explain.

9.73 Consider the H_2^+ ion. **(a)** Sketch the molecular orbitals of the ion and draw its energy-level diagram. **(b)** How many electrons are there in the H_2^+ ion? **(c)** Draw the electron configuration of the ion in terms of its MOs. **(d)** What is the bond order in H_2^+? **(e)** Suppose that the ion is excited by light so that an electron moves from a lower-energy to a higher-energy MO. Would you expect the excited-state H_2^+ ion to be stable or to fall apart? Explain.

9.74 **(a)** Sketch the molecular orbitals of the H_2^- ion and draw its energy-level diagram. **(b)** Write the electron configuration of the ion in terms of its MOs. **(c)** Calculate the bond order in H_2^-. **(d)** Suppose that the ion is excited by light, so that an electron moves from a lower-energy to a higher-energy molecular orbital. Would you expect the excited-state H_2^- ion to be stable? Explain.

9.75 Draw a picture that shows all three $2p$ orbitals on one atom and all three $2p$ orbitals on another atom. **(a)** Imagine the atoms coming close together to bond. How many σ bonds can the two sets of $2p$ orbitals make with each other? **(b)** How many π bonds can the two sets of $2p$ orbitals make with each other? **(c)** How many antibonding orbitals, and of what type, can be made from the two sets of $2p$ orbitals?

9.76 **(a)** What is the probability of finding an electron on the internuclear axis if the electron occupies a π molecular orbital? **(b)** For a homonuclear diatomic molecule, what similarities and differences are there between the π_{2p} MO made from the $2p_x$ atomic orbitals and the π_{2p} MO made from the $2p_y$ atomic orbitals? **(c)** How do the π_{2p}^* MOs formed from the $2p_x$ and $2p_y$ atomic orbitals differ from the π_{2p} MOs in terms of energies and electron distributions?

9.77 **(a)** What are the relationships among bond order, bond length, and bond energy? **(b)** According to molecular orbital theory, would either Be_2 or Be_2^+ be expected to exist? Explain.

9.78 Explain the following: **(a)** The *peroxide* ion, O_2^{2-}, has a longer bond length than the *superoxide* ion, O_2^-. **(b)** The magnetic properties of B_2 are consistent with the π_{2p} MOs being lower in energy than the σ_{2p} MO. **(c)** The O_2^{2+} ion has a stronger O—O bond than O_2 itself.

9.79 **(a)** What does the term *diamagnetism* mean? **(b)** How does a diamagnetic substance respond to a magnetic field? **(c)** Which of the following ions would you expect to be diamagnetic: N_2^{2-}, O_2^{2-}, Be_2^{2+}, C_2^-?

9.80 **(a)** What does the term *paramagnetism* mean? **(b)** How can one determine experimentally whether a substance is paramagnetic? **(c)** Which of the following ions would you expect to be paramagnetic: O_2^+, N_2^{2-}, Li_2^+, O_2^{2-}? For those ions that are paramagnetic, determine the number of unpaired electrons.

9.81 Using Figures 9.35 and 9.43 as guides, draw the molecular orbital electron configuration for **(a)** B_2^+, **(b)** Li_2^+, **(c)** N_2^+, **(d)** Ne_2^{2+}. In each case indicate whether the addition of an electron to the ion would increase or decrease the bond order of the species.

9.82 If we assume that the energy-level diagrams for homonuclear diatomic molecules shown in Figure 9.43 can be applied to heteronuclear diatomic molecules and ions, predict the bond order and magnetic behavior of **(a)** CO^+, **(b)** NO^-, **(c)** OF^+, **(d)** NeF^+.

9.83 Determine the electron configurations for CN^+, CN, and CN^-. **(a)** Which species has the strongest C—N bond? **(b)** Which species, if any, has unpaired electrons?

9.84 **(a)** The nitric oxide molecule, NO, readily loses one electron to form the NO^+ ion. Why is this consistent with the electronic structure of NO? **(b)** Predict the order of the N—O bond strengths in NO, NO^+, and NO^-, and describe the magnetic properties of each. **(c)** With what neutral homonuclear diatomic molecules are the NO^+ and NO^- ions isoelectronic (same number of electrons)?

[9.85] Consider the molecular orbitals of the P_2 molecule. Assume that the MOs of diatomics from the third row of the periodic table are analogous to those from the second row. **(a)** Which valence atomic orbitals of P are used to construct the MOs of P_2? **(b)** The figure that follows shows a sketch of one of the MOs for P_2. What is the label for this MO? **(c)** For the P_2 molecule, how many electrons occupy the MO in the figure? **(d)** Is P_2 expected to be diamagnetic or paramagnetic? Explain.

[9.86] The iodine bromide molecule, IBr, is an *interhalogen compound*. Assume that the molecular orbitals of IBr are analogous to the homonuclear diatomic molecule F_2. **(a)** Which valence atomic orbitals of I and of Br are used to construct the MOs of IBr? **(b)** What is the bond order of the IBr molecule? **(c)** One of the valence MOs of IBr is sketched here. Why are the atomic orbital contributions to this MO different in size? **(d)** What is the label for the MO? **(e)** For the IBr molecule, how many electrons occupy the MO?

ADDITIONAL EXERCISES

9.87 **(a)** What is the physical basis for the VSEPR model? **(b)** When applying the VSEPR model, we count a double or triple bond as a single electron domain. Why is this justified?

9.88 What is the fundamental basis on which we assign electrons to electron domains in pairs and with their spins paired?

9.89 The molecules SiF_4, SF_4, and XeF_4 have molecular formulas of the type AF_4, but the molecules have different molecular geometries. Predict the shape of each molecule, and explain why the shapes differ.

9.90 Consider the molecule PF_4Cl. **(a)** Draw a Lewis structure for the molecule, and predict its electron-domain geometry. **(b)**

Which would you expect to take up more space, a P—F bond or a P—Cl bond? Explain. **(c)** Predict the molecular geometry of PF_4Cl. How did your answer for part (b) influence your answer here in part (c)? **(d)** Would you expect the molecule to distort from its ideal electron-domain geometry? If so, how would it distort?

[9.91] The vertices of a tetrahedron correspond to four alternating corners of a cube. By using analytical geometry, demonstrate that the angle made by connecting two of the vertices to a point at the center of the cube is 109.5°, the characteristic angle for tetrahedral molecules.

9.92 From their Lewis structures, determine the number of σ and π bonds in each of the following molecules or ions: **(a)** CO_2; **(b)** cyanogen, $(CN)_2$; **(c)** formaldehyde, H_2CO; **(d)** formic acid, HCOOH, which has one H and two O atoms attached to C.

9.93 The lactic acid molecule, $CH_3CH(OH)COOH$, gives sour milk its unpleasant, sour taste. **(a)** Draw the Lewis structure for the molecule, assuming that carbon always forms four bonds in its stable compounds. **(b)** How many π and how many σ bonds are in the molecule? **(c)** Which CO bond is shortest in the molecule? **(d)** What is the hybridization of atomic orbitals around the carbon atom associated with that short bond? **(e)** What are the approximate bond angles around each carbon atom in the molecule?

9.94 The PF_3 molecule has a dipole moment of 1.03 D, but BF_3 has a dipole moment of zero. How can you explain the difference?

9.95 An AB_5 molecule adopts the geometry shown here. **(a)** What is the name of this geometry? **(b)** Do you think there are any non-bonding electron pairs on atom A? Why or why not? **(c)** Suppose the atoms B are halogen atoms. Can you determine uniquely to which group in the periodic table atom A belongs?

9.96 There are two compounds of the formula $Pt(NH_3)_2Cl_2$:

$$\begin{array}{ccc} & NH_3 & & & Cl \\ & | & & & | \\ Cl-&Pt&-Cl & Cl-&Pt&-NH_3 \\ & | & & & | \\ & NH_3 & & & NH_3 \end{array}$$

The compound on the right, *cisplatin,* is used in cancer therapy. The compound on the left, *transplatin,* is ineffective for cancer therapy. Both compounds have a square-planar geometry. **(a)** Which compound has a nonzero dipole moment? **(b)** The reason cisplatin is a good anticancer drug is that it binds tightly to DNA. Cancer cells are rapidly dividing, producing a lot of DNA. Consequently, cisplatin kills cancer cells at a faster rate than normal cells. However, since normal cells also are making DNA, cisplatin also attacks healthy cells, which leads to unpleasant side effects. The way both molecules bind to DNA involves the Cl^- ions leaving the Pt ion, to be replaced by two nitrogens in DNA. Draw a picture in which a long vertical line represents a piece of DNA. Draw the $Pt(NH_3)_2$ fragments of cisplatin and transplatin with the proper shape. Also draw them attaching to your DNA line. Can you explain from your drawing why the shape of the cisplatin causes it to bind to DNA more effectively than transplatin?

[9.97] The O—H bond lengths in the water molecule (H_2O) are 0.96 Å, and the H—O—H angle is 104.5°. The dipole moment of the water molecule is 1.85 D. **(a)** In what directions do the bond dipoles of the O—H bonds point? In what direction does the dipole moment vector of the water molecule point? **(b)** Calculate the magnitude of the bond dipole of the O—H bonds. (*Note:* You will need to use vector addition to do this.) **(c)** Compare your answer from part (b) to the dipole moments of the hydrogen halides (Table 8.3). Is your answer in accord with the relative electronegativity of oxygen?

[9.98] The reaction of three molecules of fluorine gas with a Xe atom produces the substance xenon hexafluoride, XeF_6:

$$Xe(g) + 3\,F_2(g) \longrightarrow XeF_6(s)$$

(a) Draw a Lewis structure for XeF_6. **(b)** If you try to use the VSEPR model to predict the molecular geometry of XeF_6, you run into a problem. What is it? **(c)** What could you do to resolve the difficulty in part (b)? **(d)** The molecule IF_7 has a pentagonal-bipyramidal structure (five equatorial fluorine atoms at the vertices of a regular pentagon and two axial fluorine atoms). Based on the structure of IF_7, suggest a structure for XeF_6.

[9.99] The Lewis structure for allene is

$$\begin{array}{ccc} H & & H \\ \diagdown & & \diagup \\ & C=C=C & \\ \diagup & & \diagdown \\ H & & H \end{array}$$

Make a sketch of the structure of this molecule that is analogous to Figure 9.25. In addition, answer the following three questions: **(a)** Is the molecule planar? **(b)** Does it have a nonzero dipole moment? **(c)** Would the bonding in allene be described as delocalized? Explain.

[9.100] The azide ion, N_3^-, is linear with two N—N bonds of equal length, 1.16 Å. **(a)** Draw a Lewis structure for the azide ion. **(b)** With reference to Table 8.5, is the observed N—N bond length consistent with your Lewis structure? **(c)** What hybridization scheme would you expect at each of the nitrogen atoms in N_3^-? **(d)** Show which hybridized and unhybridized orbitals are involved in the formation of σ and π bonds in N_3^-. **(e)** It is often observed that σ bonds that involve an sp hybrid orbital are shorter than those that involve only sp^2 or sp^3 hybrid orbitals. Can you propose a reason for this? Is this observation applicable to the observed bond lengths in N_3^-?

[9.101] In ozone, O_3, the two oxygen atoms on the ends of the molecule are equivalent to one another. **(a)** What is the best choice of hybridization scheme for the atoms of ozone? **(b)** For one of the resonance forms of ozone, which of the orbitals are used to make bonds and which are used to hold nonbonding pairs of electrons? **(c)** Which of the orbitals can be used to delocalize the π electrons? **(d)** How many electrons are delocalized in the π system of ozone?

9.102 Butadiene, C_4H_6, is a planar molecule that has the following carbon–carbon bond lengths:

$$H_2C\underset{1.34\,\text{Å}}{=\!=\!=}CH\underset{1.48\,\text{Å}}{-\!-\!-}CH\underset{1.34\,\text{Å}}{=\!=\!=}CH_2$$

(a) Predict the bond angles around each of the carbon atoms and sketch the molecule.

(b) Compare the bond lengths to the average bond lengths listed in Table 8.5. Can you explain any differences?

[9.103] The following sketches show the atomic orbital wave functions (with phases) used to construct some of the MOs of a homonuclear diatomic molecule. For each sketch, determine the type of MO that will result from mixing the atomic orbital wave functions as drawn. Use the same labels for the MOs as in the "Closer Look" box on phases.

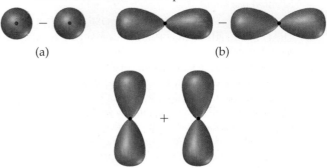

9.104 Write the electron configuration for the first excited state for N_2 —that is, the state with the highest-energy electron moved to the next available energy level. (a) Is the nitrogen in its first excited state diamagnetic or paramagnetic? (b) Is the N—N bond strength in the first excited state stronger or weaker compared to that in the ground state? Explain.

9.105 *Azo dyes* are organic dyes that are used for many applications, such as the coloring of fabrics. Many azo dyes are derivatives of the organic substance *azobenzene*, $C_{12}H_{10}N_2$. A closely related substance is *hydrazobenzene*, $C_{12}H_{12}N_2$. The Lewis structures of these two substances are

Azobenzene   Hydrazobenzene

(Recall the shorthand notation used for benzene.) (a) What is the hybridization at the N atom in each of the substances? (b) How many unhybridized atomic orbitals are there on the N and the C atoms in each of the substances? (c) Predict the N—N—C angles in each of the substances. (d) Azobenzene is said to have greater delocalization of its π electrons than hydrazobenzene. Discuss this statement in light of your answers to (a) and (b). (e) All the atoms of azobenzene lie in one plane, whereas those of hydrazobenzene do not. Is this observation consistent with the statement in part (d)? (f) Azobenzene is an intense red-orange color, whereas hydrazobenzene is nearly colorless. Which molecule would be a better one to use in a solar energy conversion device? (See the "Chemistry Put to Work" box for more information about solar cells.)

[9.106] (a) Using only the valence atomic orbitals of a hydrogen atom and a fluorine atom, and following the model of Figure 9.46, how many MOs would you expect for the HF molecule? (b) How many of the MOs from part (a) would be occupied by electrons? (c) It turns out that the difference in energies between the valence atomic orbitals of H and F are sufficiently different that we can neglect the interaction of the 1s orbital of

hydrogen with the 2s orbital of fluorine. The 1s orbital of hydrogen will mix only with one 2p orbital of fluorine. Draw pictures showing the proper orientation of all three 2p orbitals on F interacting with a 1s orbital on H. Which of the 2p orbitals can actually make a bond with a 1s orbital, assuming that the atoms lie on the z-axis? (d) In the most accepted picture of HF, all the other atomic orbitals on fluorine move over at the same energy into the molecular orbital energy-level diagram for HF. These are called "nonbonding orbitals." Sketch the energy-level diagram for HF using this information and calculate the bond order. (Nonbonding electrons do not contribute to bond order.) (e) Look at the Lewis structure for HF. Where are the nonbonding electrons?

[9.107] Carbon monoxide, CO, is isoelectronic to N_2. (a) Draw a Lewis structure for CO that satisfies the octet rule. (b) Assume that the diagram in Figure 9.46 can be used to describe the MOs of CO. What is the predicted bond order for CO? Is this answer in accord with the Lewis structure you drew in part (a)? (c) Experimentally, it is found that the highest-energy electrons in CO reside in a σ-type MO. Is that observation consistent with Figure 9.46? If not, what modification needs to be made to the diagram? How does this modification relate to Figure 9.43? (d) Would you expect the π_{2p} MOs of CO to have equal atomic orbital contributions from the C and O atoms? If not, which atom would have the greater contribution?

9.108 The energy-level diagram in Figure 9.36 shows that the sideways overlap of a pair of p orbitals produces two molecular orbitals, one bonding and one antibonding. In ethylene there is a pair of electrons in the bonding π orbital between the two carbons. Absorption of a photon of the appropriate wavelength can result in promotion of one of the bonding electrons from the π_{2p} to the π_{2p}^* molecular orbital. (a) What would you expect this electronic transition to do to the carbon–carbon bond order in ethylene? (b) How does this relate to the fact that absorption of a photon of appropriate wavelength can cause ready rotation about the carbon–carbon bond, as described in the "Chemistry and Life" box and shown in Figure 9.30?

INTEGRATIVE EXERCISES

9.109 A compound composed of 2.1% H, 29.8% N, and 68.1% O has a molar mass of approximately 50 g/mol. (a) What is the molecular formula of the compound? (b) What is its Lewis structure if H is bonded to O? (c) What is the geometry of the molecule? (d) What is the hybridization of the orbitals around the N atom? (e) How many σ and how many π bonds are there in the molecule?

9.110 Sulfur tetrafluoride (SF_4) reacts slowly with O_2 to form sulfur tetrafluoride monoxide (OSF_4) according to the following unbalanced reaction:

$$SF_4(g) + O_2(g) \longrightarrow OSF_4(g)$$

The O atom and the four F atoms in OSF_4 are bonded to a central S atom. (a) Balance the equation. (b) Write a Lewis structure of OSF_4 in which the formal charges of all atoms are zero. (c) Use average bond enthalpies (Table 8.4) to estimate the enthalpy of the reaction. Is it endothermic or exothermic? (d) Determine the electron-domain geometry of OSF_4, and write two possible molecular geometries for the molecule based on this electron-domain geometry. (e) Which of the molecular geometries in part (d) is more likely to be observed for the molecule? Explain.

[9.111] The phosphorus trihalides (PX_3) show the following variation in the bond angle X—P—X: PF_3, 96.3°; PCl_3, 100.3°; PBr_3, 101.0°; PI_3, 102.0°. The trend is generally attributed to the change in the electronegativity of the halogen. (a) Assuming that all electron domains are the same size, what value of the X—P—X angle is predicted by the VSEPR model? (b) What is the general trend in the X—P—X angle as the halide electronegativity increases? (c) Using the VSEPR model, explain the observed trend in X—P—X angle as the electronegativity of X changes. (d) Based on your answer to part (c), predict the structure of $PBrCl_4$.

[9.112] The molecule 2-butene, C_4H_8, can undergo a geometric change called *cis-trans isomerization*:

cis-2-butene   *trans*-2-butene

As discussed in the "Chemistry and Life" box on the chemistry of vision, such transformations can be induced by light and are the key to human vision. **(a)** What is the hybridization at the two central carbon atoms of 2-butene? **(b)** The isomerization occurs by rotation about the central C—C bond. With reference to Figure 9.30, explain why the π bond between the two central carbon atoms is destroyed halfway through the rotation from *cis*- to *trans*-2-butene. **(c)** Based on average bond enthalpies (Table 8.4), how much energy per molecule must be supplied to break the C—C π bond? **(d)** What is the longest wavelength of light that will provide photons of sufficient energy to break the C—C π bond and cause the isomerization? **(e)** Is the wavelength in your answer to part (d) in the visible portion of the electromagnetic spectrum? Comment on the importance of this result for human vision.

9.113 **(a)** Compare the bond enthalpies (Table 8.4) of the carbon–carbon single, double, and triple bonds to deduce an average π-bond contribution to the enthalpy. What fraction of a single bond does this quantity represent? **(b)** Make a similar comparison of nitrogen–nitrogen bonds. What do you observe? **(c)** Write Lewis structures of N_2H_4, N_2H_2, and N_2, and determine the hybridization around nitrogen in each case. **(d)** Propose a reason for the large difference in your observations of parts (a) and (b).

9.114 Use average bond enthalpies (Table 8.4) to estimate ΔH for the atomization of benzene, C_6H_6:

$$C_6H_6(g) \longrightarrow 6\,C(g) + 6\,H(g)$$

Compare the value to that obtained by using ΔH_f° data given in Appendix C and Hess's law. To what do you attribute the large discrepancy in the two values?

[9.115] Many compounds of the transition-metal elements contain direct bonds between metal atoms. We will assume that the *z*-axis is defined as the metal–metal bond axis. **(a)** Which of the *3d* orbitals (Figure 6.23) can be used to make a σ bond between metal atoms? **(b)** Sketch the σ_{3d} bonding and σ_{3d}^* antibonding MOs. **(c)** With reference to the "Closer Look" box on the phases of orbitals, explain why a node is generated in the σ_{3d}^* MO. **(d)** Sketch the energy-level diagram for the Sc_2 molecule, assuming that only the *3d* orbital from part (a) is important. **(e)** What is the bond order in Sc_2?

[9.116] The organic molecules shown here are derivatives of benzene in which six-membered rings are "fused" at the edges of the hexagons.

Naphthalene   Anthracene

Tetracene

(a) Determine the empirical formula of benzene and of these three compounds. **(b)** Suppose you are given a sample of one of the compounds. Could combustion analysis be used to determine unambiguously which of the three it is? **(c)** Naphthalene, the active ingredient in mothballs, is a white solid. Write a balanced equation for the combustion of naphthalene to $CO_2(g)$ and $H_2O(g)$. **(d)** Using the Lewis structure for naphthalene and the average bond enthalpies in Table 8.4, estimate the heat of combustion of naphthalene in kJ/mol. **(e)** Would you expect naphthalene, anthracene, and tetracene to have multiple resonance structures? If so, draw the additional resonance structures for naphthalene. **(f)** Benzene, naphthalene, and anthracene are colorless, but tetracene is orange. What does this imply about the relative HOMO–LUMO energy gaps in these molecules? See the "Chemistry Put to Work" box on orbitals and energy.

[9.117] Antibonding molecular orbitals can be used to make bonds to other atoms in a molecule. For example, metal atoms can use appropriate *d* orbitals to overlap with the π_{2p}^* orbitals of the carbon monoxide molecule. This is called *d*–π backbonding. **(a)** Draw a coordinate axis system in which the *y*-axis is vertical in the plane of the paper and the *x*-axis horizontal. Write "M" at the origin to denote a metal atom. **(b)** Now, on the *x*-axis to the right of M, draw the Lewis structure of a CO molecule, with the carbon nearest the M. The CO bond axis should be on the *x*-axis. **(c)** Draw the CO π_{2p}^* orbital, with phases (see the "Closer Look" box on phases) in the plane of the paper. Two lobes should be pointing toward M. **(d)** Now draw the d_{xy} orbital of M, with phases. Can you see how they will overlap with the π_{2p}^* orbital of CO? **(e)** What kind of bond is being made with the orbitals between M and C, σ or π? **(f)** Predict what will happen to the strength of the CO bond in a metal–CO complex compared to CO alone.

9.118 Methyl isocyanate, CH_3NCO, was made infamous in 1984 when an accidental leakage of this compound from a storage tank in Bhopal, India, resulted in the deaths of about 3,800 people and severe and lasting injury to many thousands more. **(a)** Draw a Lewis structure for methyl isocyanate. **(b)** Draw a ball-and-stick model of the structure, including estimates of all the bond angles in the compound. **(c)** Predict all the bond distances in the molecule. **(d)** Do you predict that the molecule will have a dipole moment? Explain.

WHAT'S AHEAD

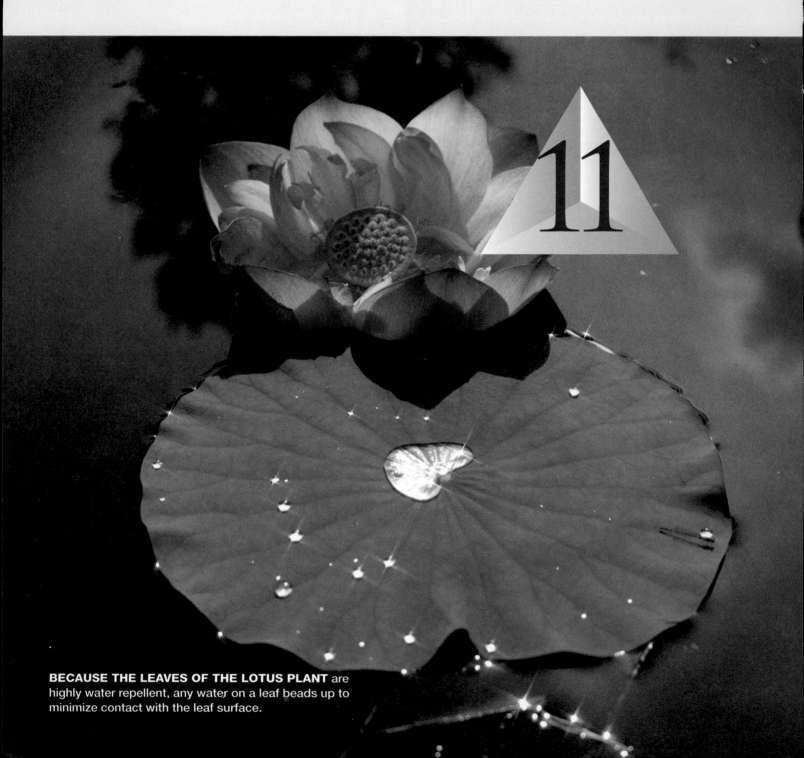

BECAUSE THE LEAVES OF THE LOTUS PLANT are highly water repellent, any water on a leaf beads up to minimize contact with the leaf surface.

LIQUIDS AND INTERMOLECULAR FORCES

THE LOTUS PLANT GROWS in aquatic environments. In order to thrive in such an environment the surface of a lotus leaf is highly water repellent. Scientists call surfaces with this property "superhydrophobic." The superhydrophobic character of the lotus leaf not only allows it to float on water but also causes

any water that falls on the leaf to bead up and roll off. The water drops collect dirt as they roll off, keeping the leaf clean, even in the muddy ponds and lakes where lotus plants tend to grow. Because of its self-cleaning properties, the lotus plant is considered a symbol of purity in many Eastern cultures.

What forces cause the lotus leaf to repel water so efficiently? Although this plant's self-cleaning nature has been known for millennia, the effect was not fully understood until the 1970s when scanning electron microscopy images revealed a rough, one might say mountainous, leaf surface (▶ **FIGURE 11.1**). The rough surface helps minimize contact between water and leaf.

Another important factor contributing to the plant's self-cleaning nature is the contrast between the molecular composition of the leaf and that of the water. The leaf is coated by hydrocarbon molecules that are held together by forces that are different

425

20 μm

▲ FIGURE 11.1 **A microscopic view of a water droplet on the surface of a lotus leaf.**

from those that hold the water molecules together. As a result the water molecules preferentially surround themselves with other water molecules, thereby minimizing their contact with the surface.

The lotus effect has inspired scientists to design superhydrophobic surfaces for applications such as self-cleaning windows and water-repellent clothing. To understand the lotus effect and other phenomena involving liquids and solids, we must understand **intermolecular forces**, the forces that exist *between* molecules. Only by understanding the nature and strength of these forces can we understand how the composition and structure of a substance are related to its physical properties in the liquid or solid state.

11.1 | A MOLECULAR COMPARISON OF GASES, LIQUIDS, AND SOLIDS

As we learned in Chapter 10, the molecules in a gas are widely separated and in a state of constant, chaotic motion. One of the key tenets of kinetic-molecular theory is the assumption that we can neglect the interactions between molecules. ∞ (Section 10.7) The properties of liquids and solids are quite different from gases largely because the intermolecular forces in liquids and solids are much stronger. A comparison of the properties of gases, liquids, and solids is given in ▼ TABLE 11.1.

In liquids the intermolecular attractive forces are strong enough to hold particles close together. Thus, liquids are much denser and far less compressible than gases. Unlike gases, liquids have a definite volume, independent of the size and shape of their container. The attractive forces in liquids are not strong enough, however, to keep the particles from moving past one another. Thus, any liquid can be poured, and assumes the shape of the container it occupies.

In solids the intermolecular attractive forces are strong enough to hold particles close together and to lock them virtually in place. Solids, like liquids, are not very compressible because the particles have little free space between them. Because the particles in a solid or liquid are fairly close together compared with those of a gas, we often refer to solids and liquids as *condensed phases*. We will study solids in Chapter 12. For now it is sufficient to know that the particles of a solid are not free to undergo long-range movement, which makes solids rigid.*

TABLE 11.1 • Some Characteristic Properties of the States of Matter	
Gas	Assumes both volume and shape of its container
	Expands to fill its container
	Is compressible
	Flows readily
	Diffusion within a gas occurs rapidly
Liquid	Assumes shape of portion of container it occupies
	Does not expand to fill its container
	Is virtually incompressible
	Flows readily
	Diffusion within a liquid occurs slowly
Solid	Retains own shape and volume
	Does not expand to fill its container
	Is virtually incompressible
	Does not flow
	Diffusion within a solid occurs extremely slowly

*The atoms in a solid are able to vibrate in place. As the temperature of a solid increases, the vibrational motion increases.

GO FIGURE

For a given substance, do you expect the density of the substance in its liquid state to be closer to the density in the gaseous state or in the solid state?

Strength of intermolecular attractions increasing

Gas

Liquid

Crystalline solid

Chlorine, Cl_2
Particles far apart;
possess complete
freedom of motion

Bromine, Br_2
Particles are closely packed but
randomly oriented; retain freedom
of motion; rapidly change neighbors

Iodine, I_2
Particles are closely packed in
an ordered array; positions
are essentially fixed

▲ **FIGURE 11.2** **Gases, liquids, and solids.** Chlorine, bromine, and iodine are all made up of diatomic molecules as a result of covalent bonding. However, due to differences in the strength of the intermolecular forces, they exist in three different states at room temperature and standard pressure: Cl_2 gaseous, Br_2 liquid, I_2 solid.

▲ **FIGURE 11.2** compares the three states of matter. *The state of a substance depends largely on the balance between the kinetic energies of the particles (atoms, molecules or ions) and the interparticle energies of attraction.* The kinetic energies, which depend on temperature, tend to keep the particles apart and moving. The interparticle attractions tend to draw the particles together. Substances that are gases at room temperature have much weaker interparticle attractions than those that are liquids; substances that are liquids have weaker interparticle attractions than those that are solids. The different states of matter adopted by the halogens at room temperature—iodine is solid, bromine is a liquid, and chlorine is a gas—is a direct consequence of a decrease in the strength of the intermolecular forces as we move from I_2 to Br_2 to Cl_2.

We can change a substance from one state to another by heating or cooling, which changes the average kinetic energy of the particles. NaCl, for example, a solid at room temperature, melts at 1074 K and boils at 1686 K under 1 atm pressure, and Cl_2, a gas at room temperature, liquefies at 239 K and solidifies at 172 K under 1 atm pressure. As the temperature of a gas decreases, the average kinetic energy of its particles decreases, allowing the attractions between the particles to first draw the particles close together, forming a liquid, and then to virtually lock them in place, forming a solid. Increasing the pressure on a gas can also drive transformations from gas to liquid to solid because the increased pressure brings the molecules closer together, thus making intermolecular forces more effective. For example, propane (C_3H_8) is a gas at room temperature and 1 atm pressure, whereas liquefied propane (LP) is a liquid at room temperature because it is stored under much higher pressure.

11.2 | INTERMOLECULAR FORCES

Strong intramolecular attraction (covalent bond)

Weak intermolecular attraction

▲ FIGURE 11.3 **Intermolecular and intramolecular forces.**

The strengths of intermolecular forces in different substances vary over a wide range but are generally much weaker than intramolecular forces—ionic, metallic or covalent bonds (◄ FIGURE 11.3). Less energy, therefore, is required to vaporize a liquid or melt a solid than to break covalent bonds. For example, only 16 kJ/mol is required to overcome the intermolecular attractions in liquid HCl in order to vaporize it. In contrast, the energy required to break the covalent bond in HCl is 431 kJ/mol. Thus, when a molecular substance such as HCl changes from solid to liquid to gas, the molecules remain intact.

Many properties of liquids, including *boiling points,* reflect the strength of the intermolecular forces. A liquid boils when bubbles of its vapor form within the liquid. The molecules of the liquid must overcome their attractive forces in order to separate and form a vapor. The stronger the attractive forces, the higher the temperature at which the liquid boils. Similarly, the *melting points* of solids increase as the strengths of the intermolecular forces increase. As shown in ▼ TABLE 11.2, the melting and boiling points of substances in which the particles are held together by chemical bonds tend to be much higher than those of substances in which the particles are held together by intermolecular forces.

Three types of intermolecular attractions exist between electrically neutral molecules: dispersion forces, dipole–dipole attractions, and hydrogen bonding. The first two are collectively called *van der Waals forces* after Johannes van der Waals, who developed the equation for predicting the deviation of gases from ideal behavior. ∞∞ (Section 10.9) Another kind of attractive force, the ion–dipole force, is important in solutions.

All intermolecular interactions are electrostatic, involving attractions between positive and negative species, much like ionic bonds. ∞∞ (Section 8.2) Why then are intermolecular forces so much weaker than ionic bonds? Recall from Equation 8.4 that electrostatic interactions get stronger as the magnitude of the charges increases and weaker as the distance between charges increases. The charges responsible for intermolecular forces are generally much smaller than the charges in ionic compounds. For example, from its dipole moment it is possible to estimate charges of +0.178 and −0.178 for the hydrogen and chlorine ends of the HCl molecule (see Sample Exercise 8.5). Furthermore, the distances between molecules are often larger than the distances between atoms held together by chemical bonds.

TABLE 11.2 • Melting and Boiling Points of Representative Substances			
Force Holding Particles Together	**Substance**	**Melting Point (K)**	**Boiling Point (K)**
Chemical bonds			
Covalent bonds	Diamond (C)	3800	4300
Metallic bonds	Beryllium (Be)	1560	2742
Ionic bonds	Lithium fluoride (LiF)	1118	1949
Intermolecular forces			
Dispersion force	Nitrogen (N_2)	63	77
Dipole–dipole force	Hydrogen chloride (HCl)	158	188
Hydrogen bonding force	Hydrogen fluoride (HF)	190	293

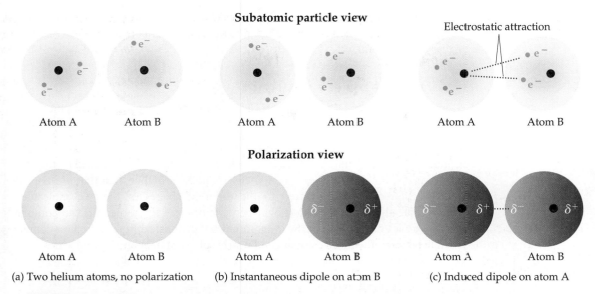

Subatomic particle view

Atom A   Atom B   Atom A   Atom B   Atom A   Atom B

Electrostatic attraction

Polarization view

Atom A   Atom B   Atom A   Atom B   Atom A   Atom B

(a) Two helium atoms, no polarization   (b) Instantaneous dipole on atom B   (c) Induced dipole on atom A

▲ **FIGURE 11.4 Dispersion forces.** "Snapshots" of the charge distribution for a pair of helium atoms at three instants.

Dispersion Forces

You might think there would be no electrostatic interactions between electrically neutral, nonpolar atoms and/or molecules. Yet some kind of attractive interactions must exist because nonpolar gases like helium, argon, and nitrogen can be liquefied. Fritz London, a German-American physicist, first proposed the origin of this attraction in 1930. London recognized that the motion of electrons in an atom or molecule can create an *instantaneous,* or momentary, dipole moment.

In a collection of helium atoms, for example, the *average* distribution of the electrons about each nucleus is spherically symmetrical, as shown in ▲ **FIGURE 11.4**(a). The atoms are nonpolar and so possess no permanent dipole moment. The *instantaneous* distribution of the electrons, however, can be different from the average distribution. If we could freeze the motion of the electrons at any given instant, both electrons could be on one side of the nucleus. At just that instant, the atom has an instantaneous dipole moment as shown in Figure 11.4(b). The motions of electrons in one atom influence the motions of electrons in its neighbors. The instantaneous dipole on one atom can induce an instantaneous dipole on an adjacent atom, causing the atoms to be attracted to each other as shown in Figure 11.4(c). This attractive interaction is called the **dispersion force** (or the *London dispersion force* in some texts). It is significant only when molecules are very close together.

The strength of the dispersion force depends on the ease with which the charge distribution in a molecule can be distorted to induce an instantaneous dipole. The ease with which the charge distribution is distorted is called the molecule's **polarizability**. We can think of the polarizability of a molecule as a measure of the "squashiness" of its electron cloud: The greater the polarizability, the more easily the electron cloud can be distorted to give an instantaneous dipole. Therefore, more polarizable molecules have larger dispersion forces.

In general, polarizability increases as the number of electrons in an atom or molecule increases. The strength of dispersion forces therefore tends to increase with increasing atomic or molecular size. Because molecular size and mass generally parallel each other, *dispersion forces tend to increase in strength with increasing molecular weight*. We can see this in the boiling points of the halogens and noble gases (▶ **FIGURE 11.5**), where dispersion forces are the only intermolecular forces at

Ne (27 K)
F₂ (85 K)
Ar (87 K)
Cl₂ (239 K)
Kr (121 K)
Br₂ (332 K)
Xe (166 K)
I₂ (458 K)

Period — 2, 3, 4, 5

Boiling point (K) — 0, 100, 200, 300, 400, 500

▲ **FIGURE 11.5 Boiling points of the halogens and noble gases.** This plot shows how the boiling points increase as the molecular weight increases due to stronger dispersion forces.

Linear molecule, larger surface area enhances intermolecular contact and increases dispersion force ·····

n-Pentane (C_5H_{12})
bp = 309.4 K

Spherical molecule, smaller surface area diminishes intermolecular contact and decreases dispersion force ·····

Neopentane (C_5H_{12})
bp = 282.7 K

▲ **FIGURE 11.6 Molecular shape affects intermolecular attraction.** Molecules of *n*-pentane make more contact with each other than do neopentane molecules. Thus, *n*-pentane has stronger intermolecular attractive forces and a higher boiling point.

work. In both families the molecular weight increases on moving down the periodic table. The higher molecular weights translate into stronger dispersion forces, which in turn lead to higher boiling points.

▲ **GIVE IT SOME THOUGHT**

List the substances CCl_4, CBr_4, and CH_4 in order of increasing boiling point.

Molecular shape also influences the magnitudes of dispersion forces. For example, *n*-pentane* and neopentane (◄ **FIGURE 11.6**) have the same molecular formula (C_5H_{12}), yet the boiling point of *n*-pentane is about 27 K higher than that of neopentane. The difference can be traced to the different shapes of the two molecules. Intermolecular attraction is greater for *n*-pentane because the molecules can come in contact over the entire length of the long, somewhat cylindrical molecules. Less contact is possible between the more compact and nearly spherical neopentane molecules.

Dipole–Dipole Forces

The presence of a permanent dipole moment in polar molecules gives rise to **dipole–dipole forces**. These forces originate from electrostatic attractions between the partially positive end of one molecule and partially negative end of a neighboring molecule. Repulsions can also occur when the positive (or negative) ends of two molecules are in close proximity. Dipole–dipole forces are effective only when molecules are very close together.

To see the effect of dipole–dipole forces, we compare the boiling points of two compounds of similar molecular weight: acetonitrile (CH_3CN, MW 41 amu, bp 355 K) and propane ($CH_3CH_2CH_3$, MW 44 amu, bp 231 K). Acetonitrile is a polar molecule, with a dipole moment of 3.9 D, so dipole–dipole forces are present. However, propane is essentially nonpolar, which means that dipole–dipole forces are absent. Because acetonitrile and propane have similar molecular weights, dispersion forces are similar for these two molecules. Therefore, the higher boiling point of acetonitrile can be attributed to dipole–dipole forces.

To better understand these forces, consider how CH_3CN molecules pack together in the solid and liquid states. In the solid [▼ **FIGURE 11.7**(a)], the molecules are arranged with the negatively charged nitrogen end of each molecule close to the positively charged —CH_3 ends of its neighbors. In the liquid [Figure 11.7(b)], the molecules are free to move with respect to one another, and their arrangement becomes more disordered. This means that, at any given instant, both attractive and repulsive dipole–dipole interactions are pres-

Attractive dipole–dipole force (red)   Repulsive dipole–dipole force (blue)

δ^-
δ^+

(a) Solid CH_3CN (b) Liquid CH_3CN

▲ **FIGURE 11.7 Dipole–dipole interactions.** The dipole–dipole interactions in (a) crystalline CH_3CN and (b) liquid CH_3CN.

*The *n* in *n*-pentane is an abbreviation for the word *normal*. A normal hydrocarbon is one in which the carbon atoms are arranged in a straight chain. ∞ (Section 2.9)

Propane
$CH_3CH_2CH_3$
MW = 44 amu
μ = 0.1 D
bp = 231 K

Dimethyl ether
CH_3OCH_3
MW = 46 amu
μ = 1.3 D
bp = 248 K

Acetaldehyde
CH_3CHO
MW = 44 amu
μ = 2.7 D
bp = 294 K

Acetonitrile
CH_3CN
MW = 41 amu
μ = 3.9 D
bp = 355 K

Increasing polarity
Increasing strength of dipole–dipole forces

◀ FIGURE 11.8 **Molecular weights, dipole moments, and boiling points of several simple organic substances.**

ent. However, not only are there more attractive interactions than repulsive ones, but also molecules that are attracting each other spend more time near each other than do molecules that are repelling each other. The overall effect is a net attraction strong enough to keep the molecules in liquid CH_3CN from moving apart to form a gas.

For molecules of approximately equal mass and size, the strength of intermolecular attractions increases with increasing polarity, a trend we see in ▲ FIGURE 11.8. Notice how the boiling point increases as the dipole moment increases.

Hydrogen Bonding

▼ FIGURE 11.9 shows the boiling points of the binary compounds that form between hydrogen and the elements in groups 4A through 7A. The boiling points of the compounds containing group 4A elements (CH_4 through SnH_4, all nonpolar) increase systematically moving down the group. This is the expected trend because polarizability and, hence, dispersion forces generally increase as molecular weight increases. The three heavier members of groups 5A, 6A, and 7A follow the same trend, but NH_3, H_2O, and HF have boiling points that

GO FIGURE

Why is the boiling point of SnH$_4$ higher than that of CH$_4$?

◀ FIGURE 11.9 **Boiling points of the covalent hydrides of the elements in groups 4A–7A as a function of molecular weight.**

GO FIGURE

To form a hydrogen bond what must the non-hydrogen atom (N, O, or F) involved in the bond possess?

Covalent bond, *intra*molecular   Hydrogen bond, *inter*molecular

$$H\!-\!\ddot{O}\!:\cdots\cdots H\!-\!\ddot{O}\!:$$
$$\quad\ \ |\qquad\qquad\ \ |$$
$$\quad\ \ H\qquad\qquad\ H$$

$$H\!-\!\ddot{\underset{..}{F}}\!:\cdots\cdots H\!-\!\ddot{\underset{..}{F}}\!:$$

$$\quad\ \ H\qquad\qquad\ H$$
$$\quad\ \ |\qquad\qquad\ \ |$$
$$H\!-\!N\!:\cdots\cdots H\!-\!N\!:$$
$$\quad\ \ |\qquad\qquad\ \ |$$
$$\quad\ \ H\qquad\qquad\ H$$

$$\quad\ \ H$$
$$\quad\ \ |$$
$$H\!-\!N\!:\cdots\cdots H\!-\!\ddot{O}\!:$$
$$\quad\ \ |\qquad\qquad\ \ |$$
$$\quad\ \ H\qquad\qquad\ H$$

$$\qquad\qquad\qquad H$$
$$\qquad\qquad\qquad |$$
$$H\!-\!\ddot{O}\!:\cdots\cdots H\!-\!N\!:$$
$$\quad\ \ |\qquad\qquad\ \ |$$
$$\quad\ \ H\qquad\qquad\ H$$

▲ **FIGURE 11.10 Hydrogen bonding.**

are much higher than expected. In fact, these three compounds also have many other characteristics that distinguish them from other substances of similar molecular weight and polarity. For example, water has a high melting point, a high specific heat, and a high heat of vaporization. Each of these properties indicates that the intermolecular forces are abnormally strong.

The strong intermolecular attractions in HF, H_2O, and NH_3 result from hydrogen bonding. **Hydrogen bonding** *is a special type of intermolecular attraction between the hydrogen atom in a polar bond (particularly H—F, H—O, and H—N) and nonbonding electron pair on a nearby small electronegative ion or atom usually F, O, or N (in another molecule).* For example, a hydrogen bond exists between the H atom in an HF molecule and the F atom of an adjacent HF molecule, as shown in ◀ FIGURE 11.10 along with several additional examples.

Hydrogen bonds can be considered a type of dipole–dipole attraction. Because N, O, and F are so electronegative, a bond between hydrogen and any of these elements is quite polar, with hydrogen at the positive end (remember the + on the right-hand side of the dipole symbol represents the positive end of the dipole):

$$\overset{\longleftarrow\!\!+}{N\!-\!H}\qquad\overset{\longleftarrow\!\!+}{O\!-\!H}\qquad\overset{\longleftarrow\!\!+}{F\!-\!H}$$

The hydrogen atom has no inner electrons. Thus, the positive side of the dipole has the concentrated charge of the nearly bare hydrogen nucleus. This positive charge is attracted to the negative charge of an electronegative atom in a nearby molecule. Because the electron-poor hydrogen is so small, it can approach an electronegative atom very closely and, thus, interact strongly with it.

| SAMPLE EXERCISE 11.1 | Identifying Substances That Can Form Hydrogen Bonds |

In which of these substances is hydrogen bonding likely to play an important role in determining physical properties: methane (CH_4), hydrazine (H_2NNH_2), methyl fluoride (CH_3F), hydrogen sulfide (H_2S)?

SOLUTION

Analyze We are given the chemical formulas of four compounds and asked to predict whether they can participate in hydrogen bonding. All the compounds contain H, but hydrogen bonding usually occurs only when the hydrogen is covalently bonded to N, O, or F.

Plan We analyze each formula to see if it contains N, O, or F directly bonded to H. There also needs to be a nonbonding pair of electrons on an electronegative atom (usually N, O, or F) in a nearby molecule, which can be revealed by drawing the Lewis structure for the molecule.

Solve The foregoing criteria eliminate CH_4 and H_2S, which do not contain H bonded to N, O, or F. They also eliminate CH_3F, whose Lewis structure shows a central C atom surrounded by three H atoms and an F atom. (Carbon always forms four bonds, whereas hydrogen and fluorine form one each.) Because the molecule contains a C—F bond and not a H—F bond, it does not form hydrogen bonds. In H_2NNH_2, however, we find N—H bonds, and the Lewis structure shows a nonbonding pair of electrons on each N atom, telling us hydrogen bonds can exist between the molecules:

$$\ddot{\underset{}{:}}N\!-\!N\!:\cdots\cdots H\!-\!N\!-\!N\!:$$

Check Although we can generally identify substances that participate in hydrogen bonding based on their containing N, O, or F covalently bonded to H, drawing the Lewis structure for the interaction provides a way to check the prediction.

PRACTICE EXERCISE

In which of these substances is significant hydrogen bonding possible: methylene chloride (CH_2Cl_2), phosphine (PH_3), hydrogen peroxide (HOOH), acetone (CH_3COCH_3)?
Answer: HOOH

The energies of hydrogen bonds vary from about 5 kJ/mol to 25 kJ/mol, although there are isolated examples of hydrogen bond energies close to 100 kJ/mol. Thus, hydrogen bonds are typically much weaker than covalent bonds, which have bond enthalpies of 150–1100 kJ/mol (see Table 8.4). Nevertheless, because hydrogen bonds are generally stronger than dipole–dipole or dispersion forces, they play important roles in many chemical systems, including those of biological significance. For example, hydrogen bonds help stabilize the structures of proteins and are also responsible for the way that DNA is able to carry genetic information.

One remarkable consequence of hydrogen bonding is seen in the densities of ice and liquid water. In most substances the molecules in the solid are more densely packed than in the liquid, making the solid phase denser than the liquid phase. By contrast, the density of ice at 0 °C (0.917 g/mL) is less than that of liquid water at 0 °C (1.00 g/mL), so ice floats on liquid water.

The lower density of ice can be understood in terms of hydrogen bonding. In ice, the H_2O molecules assume the ordered, open arrangement shown in ▼ FIGURE 11.11. This arrangement optimizes hydrogen bonding between molecules, with each H_2O molecule forming hydrogen bonds to four neighboring H_2O molecules. These hydrogen bonds, however, create the cavities seen in the middle image of Figure 11.11. When ice melts,

◢ GO FIGURE

What is the approximate H—O⋯H bond angle in ice, where H—O is the covalent bond and O⋯H is the hydrogen bond?

◀ **FIGURE 11.11 Hydrogen bonding in ice.** The empty channels in the structure of ice make water less dense as a solid than as a liquid.

▲ **FIGURE 11.12 Expansion of water upon freezing.**

the motions of the molecules cause the structure to collapse. The hydrogen bonding in the liquid is more random than in the solid but is strong enough to hold the molecules close together. Consequently, liquid water has a denser structure than ice, meaning that a given mass of water occupies a smaller volume than the same mass of ice.

The expansion of water upon freezing (◀ FIGURE 11.12) is responsible for many phenomena we take for granted. It causes icebergs to float and water pipes to burst in cold weather. The lower density of ice compared to liquid water also profoundly affects life on Earth. Because ice floats, it covers the top of the water when a lake freezes, thereby insulating the water. If ice were denser than water, ice forming at the top of a lake would sink to the bottom, and the lake could freeze solid. Most aquatic life could not survive under these conditions.

Ion–Dipole Forces

An **ion–dipole force** exists between an ion and a polar molecule (▼ FIGURE 11.13). Cations are attracted to the negative end of a dipole, and anions are attracted to the positive end. The magnitude of the attraction increases as either the ionic charge or the magnitude of the dipole moment increases. Ion–dipole forces are especially important for solutions of ionic substances in polar liquids, such as a solution of NaCl in water. ∞ (Section 4.1)

▲ **GIVE IT SOME THOUGHT**

In which mixture do you expect to find ion–dipole forces: CH_3OH in water or $Ca(NO_3)_2$ in water?

Comparing Intermolecular Forces

We can identify the intermolecular forces operative in a substance by considering its composition and structure. *Dispersion forces are found in all substances.* The strength of these attractive forces increases with increasing molecular weight and depends on molecular shapes. With polar molecules dipole–dipole forces are also operative, but these forces often make a smaller contribution to the total intermolecular attraction than dispersion forces. For example, in liquid HCl dispersion forces are estimated to account for more than 80% of the total attraction between molecules, while dipole–dipole attractions account for the rest. Hydrogen bonds, when present, make an important contribution to the total intermolecular interaction. In general, the energies associated with dispersion and dipole–dipole forces are 2–10 kJ/mol, while the energies of hydrogen bonds are 5–25 kJ/mol. Ion–dipole attractions have energies of approximately 15 kJ/mol. All these interactions are considerably weaker than covalent and ionic bonds, which have energies that are hundreds of kilojoules per mole.

▶ **FIGURE 11.13 Ion–dipole forces.**

Positive ends of polar molecules are oriented toward negatively charged anion

Negative ends of polar molecules are oriented toward positively charged cation

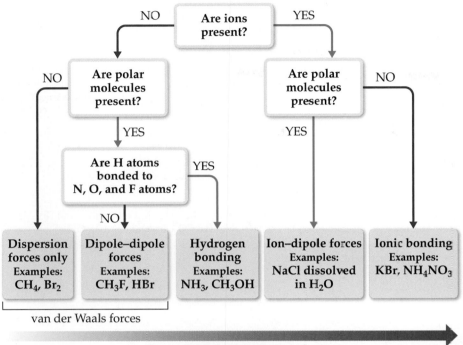

van der Waals forces

Increasing interaction strength

◀ **FIGURE 11.14 Flowchart for determining intermolecular forces.** Multiple types of intermolecular forces can be at work in a given substance or mixture. In particular, dispersion forces occur in all substances.

When comparing the relative strengths of intermolecular attractions, consider these generalizations:

1. When the molecules of two substances have comparable molecular weights and shapes, dispersion forces are approximately equal in the two substances. Differences in the magnitudes of the intermolecular forces are due to differences in the strengths of dipole–dipole attractions. The intermolecular forces get stronger as molecule polarity increases, with those molecules capable of hydrogen bonding having the strongest interactions.

2. When the molecules of two substances differ widely in molecular weights, dispersion forces tend to determine which substance has the stronger intermolecular attractions. Intermolecular attractive forces are generally higher in the substance with higher molecular weight.

▲ **FIGURE 11.14** presents a systematic way of identifying the intermolecular forces in a particular system.

It is important to realize that the effects of all these attractions are additive. For example, acetic acid, CH_3COOH, and 1-propanol, $CH_3CH_2CH_2OH$, have the same molecular weight, 60 amu, and both are capable of forming hydrogen bonds. However, a pair of acetic acid molecules can form two hydrogen bonds, whereas a pair of 1-propanol molecules can form only one (▶ **FIGURE 11.15**). Hence, the boiling point of acetic acid is higher. These effects can be important, especially for very large polar molecules such as proteins, which have multiple dipoles over their surfaces. These molecules can be held together in solution to a surprisingly high degree due to the presence of multiple dipole–dipole attractions.

Each molecule can form two hydrogen bonds with a neighbor

Acetic acid, CH_3COOH
MW = 60 amu
bp = 391 K

Each molecule can form one hydrogen bond with a neighbor

1-Propanol, $CH_3CH_2CH_2OH$
MW = 60 amu
bp = 370 K

▲ **FIGURE 11.15 Hydrogen bonding in acetic acid and 1-propanol.** The greater the number of hydrogen bonds possible, the more tightly the molecules are held together and, therefore, the higher the boiling point.

SAMPLE EXERCISE 11.2	**Predicting Types and Relative Strengths of Intermolecular Attractions**

List the substances $BaCl_2$, H_2, CO, HF, and Ne in order of increasing boiling point.

SOLUTION

Analyze We need to assess the intermolecular forces in these substances and use that information to determine the relative boiling points.

Plan The boiling point depends in part on the attractive forces in each substance. We need to order these according to the relative strengths of the different kinds of intermolecular attractions.

Solve The attractive forces are stronger for ionic substances than for molecular ones, so $BaCl_2$ should have the highest boiling point. The intermolecular forces of the remaining substances depend on molecular weight, polarity, and hydrogen bonding. The molecular weights are H_2 (2), CO (28), HF (20), and Ne (20). The boiling point of H_2 should be the lowest because it is nonpolar and has the lowest molecular weight. The molecular weights of CO, HF, and Ne are similar. Because HF can hydrogen bond, however, it should have the highest boiling point of the three. Next is CO, which is slightly polar and has the highest molecular weight. Finally, Ne, which is nonpolar, should have the lowest boiling point of these three. The predicted order of boiling points is, therefore,

$$H_2 < Ne < CO < HF < BaCl_2$$

Check The boiling points reported in the literature are H_2 (20 K), Ne (27 K), CO (83 K), HF (293 K), and $BaCl_2$ (1813 K)—in agreement with our predictions.

PRACTICE EXERCISE

(a) Identify the intermolecular attractions present in the following substances, and (b) select the substance with the highest boiling point: CH_3CH_3, CH_3OH, and CH_3CH_2OH.
Answers: (a) CH_3CH_3 has only dispersion forces, whereas the other two substances have both dispersion forces and hydrogen bonds, (b) CH_3CH_2OH

CHEMISTRY PUT TO WORK

Ionic Liquids

The strong electrostatic attractions between cations and anions are responsible for the fact that most ionic compounds are solids at room temperature, with high melting and boiling points. However, the melting point of an ionic compound can be low if the ionic charges are not too high and the cation–anion distance is sufficiently large. For example, the melting point of NH_4NO_3, where both cation and anion are larger polyatomic ions, is 170 °C. If the ammonium cation is replaced by the even larger ethylammonium cation, $CH_3CH_2NH_3^+$, the melting point drops to 12 °C, making ethylammonium nitrate a liquid at room temperature! Ethylammonium nitrate is an example of an *ionic liquid*: a salt that is a liquid at room temperature.

Not only is $CH_3CH_2NH_3^+$ larger than NH_4^+ but also it is less symmetric. In general, the larger and more irregularly shaped the ions in an ionic substance, the better the chances of forming an ionic liquid. Although many cations form ionic liquids, one of the most popular is the 1-butyl-3-methylimidazolium cation (bmim$^+$, ▼ FIGURE 11.16 and ▶ TABLE 11.3), which has two arms of different lengths coming off a five-atom central ring. This feature gives bmim$^+$ an irregular shape, which makes it difficult for the molecules to pack together in a solid.

TABLE 11.3 • Melting Point and Decomposition Temperature of Four 1-Butyl-3-methylimidazolium (bmim$^+$) Salts

Cation	Anion	Melting Point (°C)	Decomposition Temperature (°C)
bmim$^+$	Cl$^-$	41	254
bmim$^+$	I$^-$	−72	265
bmim$^+$	PF$_6^-$	10	349
bmim$^+$	BF$_4^-$	−81	403

Common anions found in ionic liquids include the PF$_6^-$, BF$_4^-$, and halide ions.

Ionic liquids have properties that are attractive for some applications. Unlike most molecular liquids, they tend to have a very low vapor pressure. Because they are nonvolatile (that is, they don't evaporate), they tend to be nonflammable and remain in the liquid state at temperatures up to 673 K. Most molecular substances are liquids only at much lower temperatures, for example, 373 K or less in many cases (see Table 11.2). Because they are good solvents for a wide range of inorganic, organic, and polymeric substances, ionic liquids can be used for a variety of reactions and separations. These properties make them attractive replacements for volatile organic solvents in many industrial processes. Relative to traditional organic solvents, ionic liquids offer the promise of reduced volumes, safer handling, and easier reuse. For these reasons and others, there is considerable excitement about the promise of ionic liquids for reducing the environmental impact of industrial chemical processes.

▲ FIGURE 11.16 **Representative ions found in ionic liquids.**

1-Butyl-3-methylimidazolium (bmim$^+$) cation

PF$_6^-$ anion

BF$_4^-$ anion

RELATED EXERCISES: 11.31, 11.32, 11.81

11.3 | SELECT PROPERTIES OF LIQUIDS

The intermolecular attractions we have just discussed can help us understand many familiar properties of liquids. In this section we examine two: viscosity and surface tension.

Viscosity

Some liquids, such as molasses and motor oil, flow very slowly; others, such as water and gasoline, flow easily. The resistance of a liquid to flow is called **viscosity.** The greater a liquid's viscosity, the more slowly it flows. Viscosity can be measured by timing how long it takes a certain amount of the liquid to flow through a thin vertical tube (▶ FIGURE 11.17). Viscosity can also be determined by measuring the rate at which steel balls fall through the liquid. The balls fall more slowly as the viscosity increases.

Viscosity is related to the ease with which the molecules of the liquid can move relative to one another. It depends on the attractive forces between molecules and on whether the shapes of the molecules are such that they tend to become entangled (for example, long molecules can become tangled like spaghetti). For a series of related compounds, viscosity increases with molecular weight, as illustrated in ▼ TABLE 11.4. The SI units for viscosity are kg/m-s. For any given substance, viscosity decreases with increasing temperature. Octane, for example, has a viscosity of 7.06×10^{-4} kg/m-s at 0 °C and 4.33×10^{-4} kg/m-s at 40 °C. At higher temperatures the greater average kinetic energy of the molecules overcomes the attractive forces between molecules.

SAE 40   SAE 10
higher number   lower number
higher viscosity lower viscosity
slower pouring faster pouring

▲ **FIGURE 11.17 Comparing viscosities.** The Society of Automotive Engineers (SAE) has established a numeric scale to indicate motor-oil viscosity.

Surface Tension

The surface of water behaves almost as if it had an elastic skin, as evidenced by the ability of certain insects to "walk" on water. This behavior is due to an imbalance of intermolecular forces at the surface of the liquid. As shown in ▶ FIGURE 11.18, molecules in the interior are attracted equally in all directions, but those at the surface experience a net inward force. This net force tends to pull surface molecules toward the interior, thereby reducing the surface area and making the molecules at the surface pack closely together.

Because spheres have the smallest surface area for their volume, water droplets assume an almost spherical shape. This explains the tendency of water to "bead up" when it contacts a surface made of nonpolar molecules, like a lotus leaf or a newly waxed car.

A measure of the net inward force that must be overcome to expand the surface area of a liquid is given by its surface tension. **Surface tension** is the energy required to increase the surface area of a liquid by a unit amount. For example, the surface tension of water at 20 °C is 7.29×10^{-2} J/m^2, which means that an energy of 7.29×10^{-2} J must be supplied to increase the surface area of a given amount of water by 1 m^2. Water has a high surface tension because of its strong hydrogen bonds. The surface tension of mercury is even higher (4.6×10^{-1} J/m^2) because of even stronger metallic bonds between the atoms of mercury.

On any surface molecule, there is no upward force to cancel the downward force, which means each surface molecule "feels" a net downward pull

On any interior molecule, each force is balanced by a force pulling in the opposite direction, which means that interior molecules "feel" no net pull in any direction

▲ **FIGURE 11.18 Molecular-level view of surface tension.** A water strider does not sink because of the high surface tension of water.

TABLE 11.4 • Viscosities of a Series of Hydrocarbons at 20 °C		
Substance	**Formula**	**Viscosity (kg/m-s)**
Hexane	$CH_3CH_2CH_2CH_2CH_2CH_3$	3.26×10^{-4}
Heptane	$CH_3CH_2CH_2CH_2CH_2CH_2CH_3$	4.09×10^{-4}
Octane	$CH_3CH_2CH_2CH_2CH_2CH_2CH_2CH_3$	5.42×10^{-4}
Nonane	$CH_3CH_2CH_2CH_2CH_2CH_2CH_2CH_2CH_3$	7.11×10^{-4}
Decane	$CH_3CH_2CH_2CH_2CH_2CH_2CH_2CH_2CH_2CH_3$	1.42×10^{-3}

GO FIGURE

If the inside surface of each tube were coated with wax, would the general shape of the water meniscus change? Would the general shape of the mercury meniscus change?

Water   Mercury

H_2O–glass adhesive forces

Hg–glass adhesive forces

H_2O–H_2O cohesive forces

Hg–Hg cohesive forces

▶ **FIGURE 11.19 Meniscus shapes for water and mercury in glass tubes.**

Because adhesive > cohesive, H_2O molecules touching glass adhere to the wall more than to each other, forming concave surface

Because cohesive > adhesive, Hg molecules touching glass adhere to the wall less than to each other, forming convex surface

GIVE IT SOME THOUGHT

How do viscosity and surface tension change
a. as temperature increases,
b. as intermolecular forces of attraction become stronger?

Intermolecular forces that bind similar molecules to one another, such as the hydrogen bonding in water, are called *cohesive forces*. Intermolecular forces that bind a substance to a surface are called *adhesive forces*. Water placed in a glass tube adheres to the glass because the adhesive forces between the water and glass are greater than the cohesive forces between water molecules. The curved surface, or *meniscus*, of the water is therefore U-shaped (▲ **FIGURE 11.19**). For mercury, however, the situation is different. Mercury atoms can form bonds with one another but not with the glass. As a result the cohesive forces are much greater than the adhesive forces and the meniscus is shaped like an inverted U.

When a small-diameter glass tube, or capillary, is placed in water, water rises in the tube. The rise of liquids up very narrow tubes is called **capillary action**. The adhesive forces between the liquid and the walls of the tube tend to increase the surface area of the liquid. The surface tension of the liquid tends to reduce the area, thereby pulling the liquid up the tube. The liquid climbs until the force of gravity on the liquid balances the adhesive and cohesive forces. Capillary action helps water and dissolved nutrients move upward through plants.

11.4 | PHASE CHANGES

Liquid water left uncovered in a glass eventually evaporates. An ice cube left in a warm room quickly melts. Solid CO_2 (sold as a product called dry ice) *sublimes* at room temperature; that is, it changes directly from solid to gas. In general, each state of matter—solid, liquid, gas—can transform into either of the other two states. ▶ FIGURE 11.20 shows the names associated with these transformations, which are called either **phase changes** or *changes of state.*

Energy Changes Accompanying Phase Changes

Every phase change is accompanied by a change in the energy of the system. In a solid, for example, the particles—either molecules, ions, or atoms—are in more or less fixed positions with respect to one another and closely arranged to minimize the energy of the system. As the temperature of the solid increases, the particles vibrate about their equilibrium positions with increasingly energetic motion. When the solid melts, the particles are freed to move relative to one another, which ordinarily means the average distance between particles increases.

Melting is called (somewhat confusingly) *fusion.* The increased freedom of motion of the particles comes at a price, measured by the **heat of fusion** or *enthalpy of fusion,* ΔH_{fus}. The heat of fusion of ice, for example, is 6.01 kJ/mol.

As the temperature of the liquid increases, the particles move about with increasing energy. One measure of this increasing energy is that the concentration of gas-phase particles above the liquid surface increases with temperature. These gas-phase particles exert a pressure called *vapor pressure.* We explore vapor pressure in Section 11.5. For now we just need to understand that vapor pressure increases with increasing temperature until it equals the external pressure above the liquid, typically atmospheric pressure. At this point the liquid boils—the particles move into the gaseous state where they are widely separated. The energy required to cause this transition is called either the **heat of vaporization** or the *enthalpy of vaporization,* ΔH_{vap}. For water, the heat of vaporization is 40.7 kJ/mol.

▼ FIGURE 11.21 shows ΔH_{fus} and ΔH_{vap} values for four substances. The values of ΔH_{vap} tend to be larger than the values of ΔH_{fus} because in the transition from liquid to gas, particles must essentially sever all their interparticle attractive interactions, whereas in the transition from solid to liquid, many of these attractive interactions remain operative.

The particles of a solid can move directly into the gaseous state. The enthalpy change required for this transition is called the **heat of sublimation**, denoted ΔH_{sub}. As illustrated in Figure 11.21, ΔH_{sub} is the sum of ΔH_{fus} and ΔH_{vap}. Thus, ΔH_{sub} for water is approximately 47 kJ/mol.

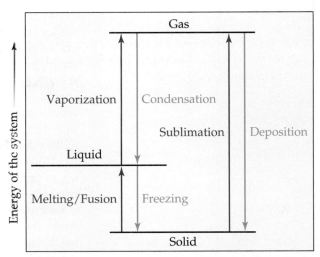

—— Endothermic process (energy added to substance)

—— Exothermic process (energy released from substance)

▲ **FIGURE 11.20   Phase changes and the names associated with them.**

GO FIGURE

Is it possible to calculate the heat of sublimation for a substance given its heats of vaporization and fusion? If so, what is the relationship?

◀ **FIGURE 11.21   Heats of fusion, vaporization, and sublimation.**

Phase changes show up in important ways in our everyday experiences. When we use ice cubes to cool a drink, for instance, the heat of fusion of the ice cools the liquid. We feel cool when we step out of a swimming pool or a warm shower because the liquid water's heat of vaporization is drawn from our bodies as the water evaporates from our skin. Our bodies use this mechanism to regulate body temperature, especially when we exercise vigorously in warm weather. A refrigerator also relies on the cooling effects of vaporization. Its mechanism contains an enclosed gas that can be liquefied under pressure. The liquid absorbs heat as it subsequently evaporates, thereby cooling the interior of the refrigerator.

What happens to the heat absorbed when the liquid refrigerant vaporizes? According to the first law of thermodynamics ∞ (Section 5.2), this absorbed heat must be released when the gas condenses to liquid. As this phase change occurs, the heat released is dissipated through cooling coils in the back of the refrigerator. Just as for a given substance the heat of condensation is equal in magnitude to the heat of vaporization and has the opposite sign, so also the *heat of deposition* for a given substance is exothermic to the same degree that the heat of sublimation is endothermic; the *heat of freezing* is exothermic to the same degree that the heat of fusion is endothermic (see Figure 11.20).

> ⚠ **GIVE IT SOME THOUGHT**
>
> What is the name of the phase change that occurs when ice left at room temperature changes to liquid water? Is this change exothermic or endothermic?

Heating Curves

When we heat an ice cube initially at −25 °C and 1 atm pressure, the temperature of the ice increases. As long as the temperature is below 0 °C, the ice cube remains in the solid state. When the temperature reaches 0 °C, the ice begins to melt. Because melting is an endothermic process, the heat we add at 0 °C is used to convert ice to liquid water, and *the temperature remains constant until all the ice has melted*. Once all the ice has melted, adding more heat causes the temperature of the liquid water to increase.

A graph of temperature versus amount of heat added is called a *heating curve*. ◄ FIGURE 11.22 shows the heating curve for transforming ice, $H_2O(s)$, initially at −25 °C to steam, $H_2O(g)$, at 125 °C. Heating the $H_2O(s)$ from −25 °C to 0 °C is represented by the line segment *AB*, and converting the $H_2O(s)$ at 0 °C to $H_2O(\ell)$ at 0 °C is the horizontal segment *BC*. Additional heat increases the temperature of the $H_2O(\ell)$ until the temperature reaches 100 °C (segment *CD*). The heat is then used to convert $H_2O(\ell)$ to $H_2O(g)$ at a constant temperature of 100 °C (segment *DE*). Once all the $H_2O(\ell)$ has been converted to $H_2O(g)$, the $H_2O(g)$ is heated to its final temperature of 125 °C (segment *EF*).

We can calculate the enthalpy change of the system for each segment of the heating curve. In segments *AB*, *CD*, and *EF* we are heating a single phase from one temperature to another. As we saw in Section 5.5, the amount of heat needed to raise the temperature of a substance is given by the product of the specific heat, mass, and temperature change (Equation 5.22). The greater the specific heat of a substance, the more heat we must add to accomplish a certain temperature increase. Because the specific heat of water is greater than that of ice, the slope of segment *CD* is less than that of segment *AB*. This lesser slope means the amount of heat we must add to a given mass of liquid water to achieve a 1 °C temperature change is greater than the amount we must add to achieve a 1 °C temperature change in the same mass of ice.

In segments *BC* and *DE* we are converting one phase to another at a constant temperature. The temperature remains constant during these phase changes because the added energy is used to overcome the attractive forces between molecules rather than to increase their average kinetic energy. For segment *BC*, the enthalpy change can be calculated by using ΔH_{fus}, and for segment *DE* we can use ΔH_{vap}.

▲ **FIGURE 11.22 Heating curve for water.** Changes that occur when 1.00 mol of H_2O is heated from $H_2O(s)$ at −25 °C to $H_2O(g)$ at 125 °C at a constant pressure of 1 atm. Heat is added over the entire temperature range, but the temperature of the system increases only when the H_2O is either all solid or all liquid or all gas (blue lines). Even though heat is being added continuously, the system temperature does not change during the two phase changes (red lines).

SAMPLE EXERCISE 11.3 Calculating ΔH for Temperature and Phase Changes

Calculate the enthalpy change upon converting 1.00 mol of ice at -25 °C to steam at 125 °C under a constant pressure of 1 atm. The specific heats of ice, liquid water, and steam are 2.03 J/g-K, 4.18 J/g-K, and 1.84 J/g-K, respectively. For H_2O, $\Delta H_{fus} = 6.01$ kJ/mol and $\Delta H_{vap} = 40.67$ kJ/mol.

SOLUTION

Analyze Our goal is to calculate the total heat required to convert 1 mol of ice at -25 °C to steam at 125 °C.

Plan We can calculate the enthalpy change for each segment and then sum them to get the total enthalpy change (Hess's law, Section 5.6).

Solve: For segment AB in Figure 11.22, we are adding enough heat to ice to increase its temperature by 25 °C. A temperature change of 25 °C is the same as a temperature change of 25 K, so we can use the specific heat of ice to calculate the enthalpy change during this process:

AB: $\Delta H = (1.00 \text{ mol})(18.0 \text{ g/mol})(2.03 \text{ J/g-K})(25 \text{ K}) = 914 \text{ J} = 0.91 \text{ kJ}$

For segment BC in Figure 11.22, in which we convert ice to water at 0 °C , we can use the molar enthalpy of fusion directly:

BC: $\Delta H = (1.00 \text{ mol})(6.01 \text{ kJ/mol}) = 6.01 \text{ kJ}$

The enthalpy changes for segments CD, DE, and EF can be calculated in similar fashion:

CD: $\Delta H = (1.00 \text{ mol})(18.0 \text{ g/mol})(4.18 \text{ J/g-K})(100 \text{ K}) = 7520 \text{ J} = 7.52 \text{ kJ}$
DE: $\Delta H = (1.00 \text{ mol})(40.67 \text{ kJ/mol}) = 40.7 \text{ kJ}$
EF: $\Delta H = (1.00 \text{ mol})(18.0 \text{ g/mol})(1.84 \text{ J/g-K})(25 \text{ K}) = 830 \text{ J} = 0.83 \text{ kJ}$

The total enthalpy change is the sum of the changes of the individual steps:

$\Delta H = 0.91 \text{ kJ} + 6.01 \text{ kJ} + 7.52 \text{ kJ} + 40.7 \text{ kJ} + 0.83 \text{ kJ} = 56.0 \text{ kJ}$

Check The components of the total energy change are reasonable relative to the horizontal lengths (heat added) of the segments in Figure 11.22. Notice that the largest component is the heat of vaporization.

PRACTICE EXERCISE

What is the enthalpy change during the process in which 100.0 g of water at 50.0 °C is cooled to ice at -30.0 °C ? (Use the specific heats and enthalpies for phase changes given in Sample Exercise 11.3.)
Answer: $-20.9 \text{ kJ} - 33.4 \text{ kJ} - 6.09 \text{ kJ} = -60.4 \text{ kJ}$

If we start with 1 mole of steam at 125 °C and cool it, we move right to left across Figure 11.22. We first lower the temperature of the $H_2O(g)$ ($F \longrightarrow E$), then condense it ($E \longrightarrow D$) to $H_2O(\ell)$, and so forth.

Sometimes as we remove heat from a liquid, we can temporarily cool it below its freezing point without forming a solid. This phenomenon, called *supercooling,* occurs when the heat is removed so rapidly that the molecules have no time to assume the ordered structure of a solid. A supercooled liquid is unstable; particles of dust entering the solution or gentle stirring is often sufficient to cause the substance to solidify quickly.

Critical Temperature and Pressure

A gas normally liquefies at some point when pressure is applied. Suppose we have a cylinder fitted with a piston, and the cylinder contains water vapor at 100 °C. If we increase the pressure on the water vapor, liquid water will form when the pressure is 760 torr. However, if the temperature is 110 °C, the liquid phase does not form until the pressure is 1075 torr. At 374 °C the liquid phase forms only at 1.655×10^5 torr (217.7 atm). Above this temperature no amount of pressure causes a distinct liquid phase to form. Instead, as pressure increases, the gas becomes steadily more compressed. The highest temperature at which a distinct liquid phase can form is called the **critical temperature.** The **critical pressure** is the pressure required to bring about liquefaction at this critical temperature.

TABLE 11.5 • Critical Temperatures and Pressures of Selected Substances

Substance	Critical Temperature (K)	Critical Pressure (atm)
Nitrogen, N_2	126.1	33.5
Argon, Ar	150.9	48.0
Oxygen, O_2	154.4	49.7
Methane, CH_4	190.0	45.4
Carbon dioxide, CO_2	304.3	73.0
Phosphine, PH_3	324.4	64.5
Propane, $CH_3CH_2CH_3$	370.0	42.0
Hydrogen sulfide, H_2S	373.5	88.9
Ammonia, NH_3	405.6	111.5
Water, H_2O	647.6	217.7

The critical temperature is the highest temperature at which a liquid can exist. Above the critical temperature, the kinetic energies of the molecules are greater than the attractive forces that lead to the liquid state regardless of how much the substance is compressed to bring the molecules closer together. The greater the intermolecular forces, the higher the critical temperature of a substance.

Several critical temperatures and pressures are listed in ▲ **TABLE 11.5**. Notice that nonpolar, low-molecular-weight substances, which have weak intermolecular attractions, have lower critical temperatures and pressures than substances that are polar or of higher molecular weight. Notice also that water and ammonia have exceptionally high critical temperatures and pressures as a consequence of strong intermolecular hydrogen-bonding forces.

Because they provide information about the conditions under which gases liquefy, critical temperatures and pressures are often of considerable importance to engineers and other people working with gases. Sometimes we want to liquefy a gas; other times we want to avoid liquefying it. It is useless to try to liquefy a gas by applying pressure if the gas is above its critical temperature. For example, O_2 has a critical temperature of 154.4 K. It must be cooled below this temperature before it can be liquefied by pressure. In contrast, ammonia has a critical temperature of 405.6 K. Thus, it can be liquefied at room temperature (approximately 295 K) by applying sufficient pressure.

When the temperature exceeds the critical temperature and the pressure exceeds the critical pressure, the liquid and gas phases are indistinguishable from each other, and the substance is in a state called a **supercritical fluid**. Like liquids, supercritical fluids can behave as solvents dissolving a wide range of substances. Using *supercritical fluid extraction,* the components of mixtures can be separated from one another. Supercritical fluid extraction has been successfully used to separate complex mixtures in the chemical, food, pharmaceutical, and energy industries. Supercritical CO_2 is a popular choice because it is relatively inexpensive and there are no problems associated with disposing of solvent, nor are there toxic residues resulting from the process.

11.5 | VAPOR PRESSURE

Molecules can escape from the surface of a liquid into the gas phase by evaporation. Suppose we place a quantity of ethanol (CH_3CH_2OH) in an evacuated, closed container, as in ▶ **FIGURE 11.23**. The ethanol quickly begins to evaporate. As a result, the pressure exerted by the vapor in the space above the liquid increases. After a short time the pressure of the vapor attains a constant value, which we call the **vapor pressure**.

At any instant, some of the ethanol molecules at the liquid surface possess sufficient kinetic energy to overcome the attractive forces of their neighbors and, therefore, escape into the gas phase. At any particular temperature, the movement of molecules from liquid phase to gas phase goes on continuously. As the number of gas-phase molecules

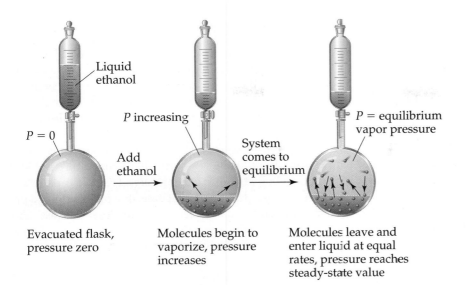

Evacuated flask, pressure zero

Molecules begin to vaporize, pressure increases

Molecules leave and enter liquid at equal rates, pressure reaches steady-state value

◀ **FIGURE 11.23 Equilibrium vapor pressure over a liquid.**

increases, however, the probability increases that a molecule in the gas phase will strike the liquid surface and be recaptured by the liquid, as shown in the flask on the right in Figure 11.23. Eventually, the rate at which molecules return to the liquid equals the rate at which they escape. The number of molecules in the gas phase then reaches a steady value, and the pressure exerted by the vapor becomes constant.

The condition in which two opposing processes occur simultaneously at equal rates is called **dynamic equilibrium** (or simply *equilibrium*). A liquid and its vapor are in dynamic equilibrium when evaporation and condensation occur at equal rates. It may appear that nothing is occurring at equilibrium because there is no net change in the system. In fact, though, a great deal is happening as molecules continuously pass from liquid state to gas state and from gas state to liquid state. *The vapor pressure of a liquid is the pressure exerted by its vapor when the liquid and vapor are in dynamic equilibrium.*

Volatility, Vapor Pressure, and Temperature

When vaporization occurs in an open container, as when water evaporates from a bowl, the vapor spreads away from the liquid. Little, if any, is recaptured at the surface of the liquid. Equilibrium never occurs, and the vapor continues to form until the liquid evaporates to dryness. Substances with high vapor pressure (such as gasoline) evaporate more quickly than substances with low vapor pressure (such as motor oil). Liquids that evaporate readily are said to be **volatile.**

Hot water evaporates more quickly than cold water because vapor pressure increases with increasing temperature. To see why this statement is true, we begin with the fact that the molecules of a liquid move at various speeds. ▶ **FIGURE 11.24** shows the distribution of kinetic energies of the molecules at the surface of a liquid at two temperatures. (The curves are like those shown for gases in Section 10.7.) As the temperature is increased, the molecules move more energetically and more of them can break free from their neighbors and enter the gas phase, increasing the vapor pressure.

▶ **FIGURE 11.25** depicts the variation in vapor pressure with temperature for four common substances that differ greatly in volatility. Note that the vapor pressure in all cases increases nonlinearly with increasing temperature. The weaker the intermolecular forces in the liquid, the more easily molecules can escape and, therefore, the higher the vapor pressure at a given temperature.

◢ **GO FIGURE**

As the temperature increases, does the rate of molecules escaping into the gas phase increase or decrease?

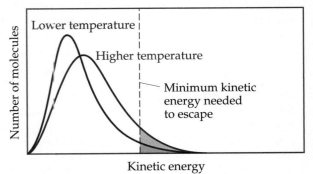

Blue area = number of molecules having enough energy to evaporate at lower temperature

Red + blue areas = number of molecules having enough energy to evaporate at higher temperature

▲ **FIGURE 11.24 The effect of temperature on the distribution of kinetic energies in a liquid.**

◢ **GIVE IT SOME THOUGHT**

Which compound do you think is more volatile at 25 °C: CCl_4 or CBr_4?

GO FIGURE

What is the vapor pressure of ethylene glycol at its normal boiling point?

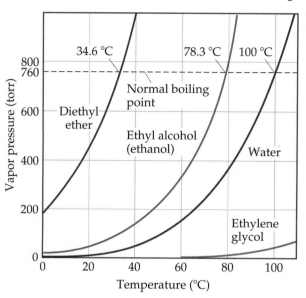

▲ FIGURE 11.25 **Vapor pressure for four liquids as a function of temperature.**

Vapor Pressure and Boiling Point

A liquid boils when its vapor pressure equals the external pressure acting on the liquid surface. At this point, bubbles of vapor form within the liquid. The temperature at which a given liquid boils increases with increasing external pressure. The boiling point of a liquid at 1 atm (760 torr) pressure is called its **normal boiling point**. From Figure 11.25 we see that the normal boiling point of water is 100 °C.

The time required to cook food in boiling water depends on the water temperature. In an open container, that temperature is 100 °C, but it is possible to boil at higher temperatures. Pressure cookers work by allowing steam to escape only when it exceeds a predetermined pressure; the pressure above the water can therefore increase above atmospheric pressure. The higher pressure causes the water to boil at a higher temperature, thereby allowing the food to get hotter and to cook more rapidly.

The effect of pressure on boiling point also explains why it takes longer to cook food at high elevations than it does at sea level. The atmospheric pressure is lower at higher altitudes, so water boils at a temperature lower than 100 °C, and foods generally take longer to cook.

A CLOSER LOOK

THE CLAUSIUS–CLAPEYRON EQUATION

You might have noticed that the plots in Figure 11.25 have a distinct shape: For each substance, the vapor pressure curves sharply upward with increasing temperature. The relationship between vapor pressure and temperature is given by the *Clausius–Clapeyron equation*:

$$\ln P = \frac{-\Delta H_{vap}}{RT} + C \qquad [11.1]$$

where P is the vapor pressure, T is the absolute temperature, R is the gas constant (8.314 J/mol-K), ΔH_{vap} is the molar enthalpy of vaporization, and C is a constant. This equation predicts that a graph of $\ln P$ versus $1/T$ should give a straight line with a slope equal to $\Delta H_{vap}/R$. Thus, we can use such a plot to determine the enthalpy of vaporization of a substance by using the relationship

$$\Delta H_{vap} = -\text{slope} \times R$$

As an example of how we use the Clausius–Clapeyron equation, the vapor-pressure data for ethanol shown in Figure 11.25 are graphed as $\ln P$ versus $1/T$ in ▶ FIGURE 11.26. The data lie on a straight line with a negative slope. We can use the slope to determine ΔH_{vap} for ethanol, 38.56 kJ/mol. We can also extrapolate the line to obtain the vapor pressure of ethanol at temperatures above and below the temperature range for which we have data.

RELATED EXERCISES: 11.83, 11.84, 11.85

▲ FIGURE 11.26 **The natural logarithm of vapor pressure versus 1/T for ethanol.**

SAMPLE EXERCISE 11.4   **Relating Boiling Point to Vapor Pressure**

Use Figure 11.25 to estimate the boiling point of diethyl ether under an external pressure of 0.80 atm.

SOLUTION

Analyze We are asked to read a graph of vapor pressure versus temperature to determine the boiling point of a substance at a particular pressure. The boiling point is the temperature at which the vapor pressure is equal to the external pressure.

Plan We need to convert 0.80 atm to torr because that is the pressure scale on the graph. We estimate the location of that pressure on the graph, move horizontally to the vapor pressure curve, and then drop vertically from the curve to estimate the temperature.

Solve The pressure equals (0.80 atm)(760 torr/atm) = 610 torr. From Figure 11.25 we see that the boiling point at this pressure is about 27 °C, which is close to room temperature.

Comment We can make a flask of diethyl ether boil at room temperature by using a vacuum pump to lower the pressure above the liquid to about 0.8 atm.

PRACTICE EXERCISE

At what external pressure will ethanol have a boiling point of 60 °C?

Answer: about 340 torr (0.45 atm)

11.6 | PHASE DIAGRAMS

The equilibrium between a liquid and its vapor is not the only dynamic equilibrium that can exist between states of matter. Under appropriate conditions, a solid can be in equilibrium with its liquid or even with its vapor. A **phase diagram** is a graphic way to summarize the conditions under which equilibria exist between the different states of matter. Such a diagram also allows us to predict which phase of a substance is present at any given temperature and pressure.

The phase diagram for any substance that can exist in all three phases of matter is shown in ▼ **FIGURE 11.27**. The diagram contains three important curves, each of which represents the temperature and pressure at which the various phases can coexist

---

◢ **GO FIGURE**

If the pressure exerted on a liquid is increased, while the temperature is held constant, what type of phase transition will eventually occur?

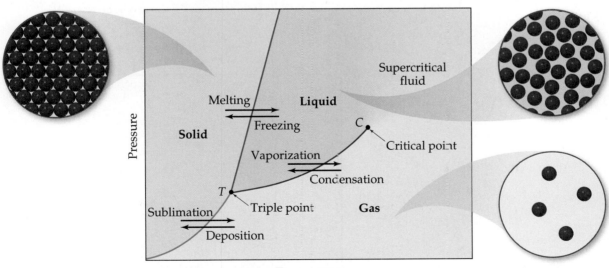

▲ **FIGURE 11.27**   **Generic phase diagram for a pure substance.** The green line is the sublimation curve, the blue line is the melting curve, and the red line is the vapor pressure curve.

at equilibrium. The only substance present in the system is the one whose phase diagram is under consideration. The pressure shown in the diagram is either the pressure applied to the system or the pressure generated by the substance. The curves may be described as follows:

1. The red curve is the *vapor-pressure curve* of the liquid, representing equilibrium between the liquid and gas phases. The point on this curve where the vapor pressure is 1 atm is the normal boiling point of the substance. The vapor-pressure curve ends at the *critical point* (*C*), which corresponds to the critical temperature and critical pressure of the substance. Beyond the critical point, the liquid and gas phases are indistinguishable from each other, and the substance is a *supercritical fluid*.

2. The green curve, the *sublimation curve,* separates the solid phase from the gas phase and represents the change in the vapor pressure of the solid as it sublimes at different temperatures.

3. The blue curve, the *melting curve,* separates the solid phase from the liquid phase and represents the change in melting point of the solid with increasing pressure. This curve usually slopes slightly to the right as pressure increases because for most substances the solid form is denser than the liquid form. An increase in pressure usually favors the more compact solid phase; thus, higher temperatures are required to melt the solid at higher pressures. The melting point at 1 atm is the **normal melting point**.

Point *T,* where the three curves intersect, is the **triple point,** and here all three phases are in equilibrium. Any other point on any of the three curves represents equilibrium between two phases. Any point on the diagram that does not fall on one of the curves corresponds to conditions under which only one phase is present. The gas phase, for example, is stable at low pressures and high temperatures, whereas the solid phase is stable at low temperatures and high pressures. Liquids are stable in the region between the other two.

The Phase Diagrams of H_2O and CO_2

▼ **FIGURE 11.28** shows the phase diagram of H_2O. Because of the large range of pressures covered in the diagram, a logarithmic scale is used to represent pressure. The melting curve (blue line) of H_2O is atypical, slanting slightly to the left with increasing pressure, indicating that for water the melting point *decreases* with increasing pressure. This unusual behavior occurs because water is among the very few substances whose liquid form is more compact than its solid form, as we learned in Section 11.2.

▶ FIGURE 11.28 **Phase diagram of H_2O.**
Note that a linear scale is used to represent temperature and a logarithmic scale to represent pressure.

If the pressure is held constant at 1 atm, it is possible to move from the solid to liquid to gaseous regions of the phase diagram by changing the temperature, as we expect from our everyday encounters with water. The triple point of H_2O falls at a relatively low pressure, 0.00603 atm. Below this pressure, liquid water is not stable and ice sublimes to water vapor on heating. This property of water is used to "freeze-dry" foods and beverages. The food or beverage is frozen to a temperature below 0 °C. Next it is placed in a low-pressure chamber (below 0.00603 atm) and then warmed so that the water sublimes, leaving behind dehydrated food or beverage.

The phase diagram for CO_2 is shown in ▼ FIGURE 11.29. The melting curve (blue line) behaves typically, slanting to the right with increasing pressure, telling us that the melting point of CO_2 increases with increasing pressure. Because the pressure at the triple point is relatively high, 5.11 atm, CO_2 does not exist as a liquid at 1 atm, which means that solid CO_2 does not melt when heated, but instead sublimes. Thus, CO_2 does not have a normal melting point; instead, it has a normal sublimation point, −78.5 °C. Because CO_2 sublimes rather than melts as it absorbs energy at ordinary pressures, this makes solid CO_2 (dry ice) a convenient coolant.

SAMPLE EXERCISE 11.5 Interpreting a Phase Diagram

Use the phase diagram for methane, CH_4, shown in ▼ FIGURE 11.30 to answer the following questions. **(a)** What are the approximate temperature and pressure of the critical point? **(b)** What are the approximate temperature and pressure of the triple point? **(c)** Is methane a solid, liquid, or gas at 1 atm and 0 °C? **(d)** If solid methane at 1 atm is heated while the pressure is held constant, will it melt or sublime? **(e)** If methane at 1 atm and 0 °C is compressed until a phase change occurs, in which state is the methane when the compression is complete?

SOLUTION

Analyze We are asked to identify key features of the phase diagram and to use it to deduce what phase changes occur when specific pressure and temperature changes take place.

Plan We must identify the triple and critical points on the diagram and also identify which phase exists at specific temperatures and pressures.

Solve
(a) The critical point is the point where the liquid, gaseous, and supercritical fluid phases coexist. It is marked point 3 in the phase diagram and located at approximately −80 °C and 50 atm.

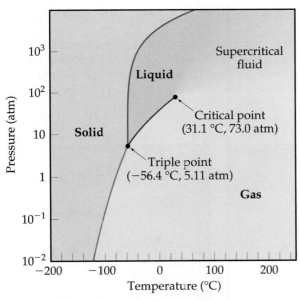

▲ **FIGURE 11.29 Phase diagram of CO_2.** Note that a linear scale is used to represent temperature and a logarithmic scale to represent pressure.

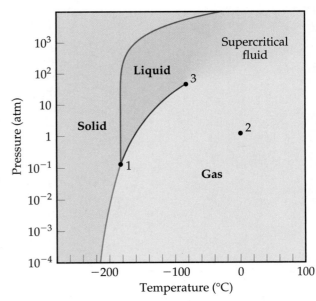

▲ **FIGURE 11.30 Phase diagram of CH_4.** Note that a linear scale is used to represent temperature and a logarithmic scale to represent pressure.

(b) The triple point is the point where the solid, liquid, and gaseous phases coexist. It is marked point 1 in the phase diagram and located at approximately $-180\,°C$ and 0.1 atm.

(c) The intersection of $0\,°C$ and 1 atm is marked point 2 in the phase diagram. It is well within the gaseous region of the phase diagram.

(d) If we start in the solid region at $P = 1$ atm and move horizontally (this means we hold the pressure constant), we cross first into the liquid region, at $T \approx -180\,°C$, and then into the gaseous region, at $T \approx -160\,°C$. Therefore, solid methane melts when the pressure is 1 atm. (In order for methane to sublime, the pressure must be below the triple point pressure.)

(e) Moving vertically up from point 2, which is 1 atm and $0\,°C$, the first phase change we come to is from gas to supercritical fluid. This phase change happens when we exceed the critical pressure ($\sim$50 atm).

Check The pressure and temperature at the critical point are higher than those at the triple point, which is expected. Methane is the principal component of natural gas. So it seems reasonable that it exists as a gas at 1 atm and $0\,°C$.

PRACTICE EXERCISE

Use the phase diagram of methane to answer the following questions. **(a)** What is the normal boiling point of methane? **(b)** Over what pressure range does solid methane sublime? **(c)** Liquid methane does not exist above what temperature?

Answers: **(a)** $-162\,°C$; **(b)** It sublimes whenever the pressure is less than 0.1 atm; **(c)** The highest temperature at which a liquid can exist is defined by the critical temperature. So we do not expect to find liquid methane when the temperature is higher than $-80\,°C$.

11.7 | LIQUID CRYSTALS

In 1888 Frederick Reinitzer, an Austrian botanist, discovered that the organic compound cholesteryl benzoate has an interesting and unusual property, shown in ▼ **FIGURE 11.31**. Solid cholesteryl benzoate melts at $145\,°C$, forming a viscous milky liquid; then at $179\,°C$ the milky liquid becomes clear and remains that way at temperatures above $179\,°C$. When cooled, the clear liquid turns viscous and milky at $179\,°C$, and the milky liquid solidifies at $145\,°C$. Reinitzer's work represents the first systematic report of what we call a **liquid crystal**, the term we use today for the viscous, milky state.

Instead of passing directly from the solid phase to the liquid phase when heated, some substances, such as cholesteryl benzoate, pass through an intermediate liquid crystalline phase that has some of the structure of solids and some of the freedom of motion of liquids. Because of the partial ordering, liquid crystals may be viscous and possess properties intermediate between those of solids and those of liquids. The region in which they exhibit these properties is marked by sharp transition temperatures, as in Reinitzer's sample.

Today liquid crystals are used as pressure and temperature sensors and as the display element in such devices as digital watches and laptop computers. They can be used for these applications because the weak intermolecular forces that hold the molecules together in the liquid crystalline phase are easily affected by changes in temperature, pressure, and electric fields.

▶ **FIGURE 11.31** **Cholesteryl benzoate in its liquid and liquid crystalline states.**

$145\,°C < T < 179\,°C$
Liquid crystalline phase

$T > 179\,°C$
Liquid phase

Liquid phase

Molecules
arranged
randomly

**Nematic liquid
crystalline phase**

Long axes of
molecules
aligned, but ends
are not aligned

**Smectic A liquid
crystalline phase**

Molecules aligned
in layers, long
axes of molecules
perpendicular to
layer planes

**Smectic C liquid
crystalline phase**

Molecules aligned
in layers, long
axes of molecules
inclined with
respect to layer
planes

◀ **FIGURE 11.32 Molecular order in
nematic and smectic liquid crystals.** In the
liquid phase of any substance, the molecules
are arranged randomly, whereas in the liquid
crystalline phases the molecules are
arranged in a partially ordered way.

Types of Liquid Crystals

Substances that form liquid crystals are often composed of rod-shaped molecules that
are somewhat rigid in the middle. In the liquid phase, these molecules are oriented randomly. In the liquid crystalline phase, by contrast, the molecules are arranged in specific
patterns as illustrated in ▲ FIGURE 11.32. Depending on the nature of the ordering,
liquid crystals are classified as nematic, smectic A, smectic C, or cholesteric.

In a **nematic liquid crystal**, the molecules are aligned so that their long axes tend to
point in the same direction but the ends are not aligned with one another. In **smectic A**
and **smectic C liquid crystals**, the molecules maintain the long-axis alignment seen in
nematic crystals, but in addition they pack into layers.

Two molecules that exhibit liquid crystalline phases are shown in ▼ FIGURE 11.33.
The lengths of these molecules are much greater than their widths. The double bonds,
including those in the benzene rings, add rigidity to the molecules, and the rings, because they are flat, help the molecules stack with one another. The polar CH_3O and
COOH groups give rise to dipole–dipole interactions and promote alignment of the
molecules. Thus, the molecules order themselves quite naturally along their long axes.
They can, however, rotate around their axes and slide parallel to one another. In smectic
liquid crystals, the intermolecular forces (dispersion forces, dipole–dipole attractions,
and hydrogen bonding) limit the ability of the molecules to slide past one another.

▲ **FIGURE 11.33 Molecular structure and liquid crystal temperature range for two
typical liquid crystalline materials.**

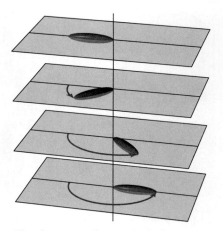

In a cholesteric liquid crystal the molecules pack into layers; the long axis of each molecule is oriented parallel to its neighbors within the same layer

The direction along which the molecules point rotates from one layer to the next, resulting in a spiraling pattern resembling the threads of a screw

▲ FIGURE 11.34 **Molecular order in a cholesteric liquid crystal.**

In a **cholesteric liquid crystal**, the molecules are arranged in layers, with their long axes parallel to the other molecules within the same layer.* Upon moving from one layer to the next, the orientation of the molecules rotates, resulting in the spiral pattern shown in ▲ FIGURE 11.34. These liquid crystals are so named because many derivatives of cholesterol adopt this structure.

The molecular arrangement in cholesteric liquid crystals produces unusual coloring patterns with visible light. Changes in temperature and pressure change the order and, hence, the color. Cholesteric liquid crystals are used to monitor temperature changes in situations where conventional methods are not feasible. For example, they can detect hot spots in microelectronic circuits, which may signal the presence of flaws. They can also be fashioned into thermometers for measuring the skin temperature of infants. Because cholesteric liquid crystal displays can be built that draw very little power, they are also being investigated for use in electronic paper (◄ FIGURE 11.35).

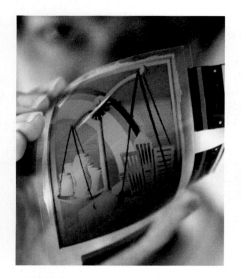

▲ FIGURE 11.35 **Electronic paper (e-paper) based on cholesteric liquid crystal technology.**

SAMPLE EXERCISE 11.6 **Properties of Liquid Crystals**

Which of these substances is most likely to exhibit liquid crystalline behavior?

$$CH_3-CH_2-\overset{\overset{\displaystyle CH_3}{|}}{\underset{\underset{\displaystyle CH_3}{|}}{C}}-CH_2-CH_3$$

(i)

$$CH_3CH_2-\bigcirc-N=N-\bigcirc-\overset{\overset{\displaystyle O}{\|}}{C}-OCH_3$$

(ii)

$$\bigcirc-CH_2-\overset{\overset{\displaystyle O}{\|}}{C}-O^-Na^+$$

(iii)

*Cholesteric liquid crystals are sometimes called chiral nematic phases because the molecules within each plane adopt an arrangement similar to a nematic liquid crystal.

SOLUTION

Analyze We have three molecules with different structures, and we are asked to determine which one is most likely to be a liquid crystalline substance.

Plan We need to identify all structural features that might induce liquid crystalline behavior.

Solve Molecule (i) is not likely to be liquid crystalline because the absence of double and/or triple bonds make this molecule flexible rather than rigid. Molecule (iii) is ionic and the generally high melting points of ionic materials make it unlikely that this substance is liquid crystalline. Molecule (ii) possesses the characteristic long axis and the kinds of structural features often seen in liquid crystals: The molecule has a rodlike shape, the double bonds and benzene rings provide rigidity, and the polar $COOCH_3$ group creates a dipole moment.

PRACTICE EXERCISE

Suggest a reason why decane

$$CH_3CH_2CH_2CH_2CH_2CH_2CH_2CH_2CH_2CH_3$$

does not exhibit liquid crystalline behavior.

Answer: Because rotation can occur about carbon–carbon single bonds, molecules whose backbone consists predominantly of C—C single bonds are too flexible; the molecules tend to coil in random ways and, thus, are not rodlike.

CHEMISTRY PUT TO WORK

Liquid Crystal Displays

Liquid crystals displays (LCDs) are widely used in electronic devices such as watches, calculators, and computer screens. These applications are possible because an applied electrical field changes the orientation of liquid crystal molecules and thus affects the optical properties of the device.

LCDs come in a variety of designs, but the structure illustrated in ▼ **FIGURE 11.36** is typical. A thin layer (5–20 μm) of liquid crystalline material is placed between electrically conducting, transparent glass electrodes. Ordinary light passes through a vertical polarizer that permits light in only the vertical plane to pass. Using a special process during fabrication, the liquid crystal molecules are oriented so that the molecules at the front electrode are oriented vertically and those at the back electrode horizontally. The orientation of the molecules in between the two electrodes varies systematically from vertical to horizontal, as shown in Figure 11.36(a). The plane of polarization of the light is turned by 90° as it passes through the liquid crystal layer and is thus in the correct orientation to pass through the horizontal polarizer. In a watch display, a mirror reflects the light back, and the light retraces its path, allowing the device to look bright. When a voltage is applied to the plates, the liquid crystalline molecules align with the voltage, as shown in Figure 11.36(b). The light rays thus are not properly oriented to pass through the horizontal polarizer, and the device appears dark. Displays of this kind are called "twisted nematic." As the name implies, materials that order as nematic liquid crystals are used for this application.

Liquid crystal displays for computer and televisions employ a light source in place of the reflector, but the principle is the same. The screen is divided into a large number of tiny cells, with the voltages at points on the screen surface controlled by transistors made from thin films of amorphous silicon. Red-green-blue color filters are employed to provide full color. The entire display is refreshed at a frequency of about 60 Hz, so the display can change rapidly with respect to the response time of the human eye. Displays of this kind are remarkable technical achievements based on a combination of basic scientific discovery and creative engineering.

RELATED EXERCISES: 11.68, 11.86

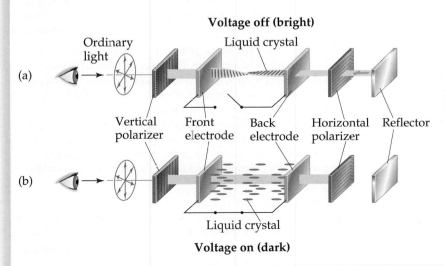

Voltage off (bright)

Voltage on (dark)

◄ **FIGURE 11.36 Schematic illustration of the operation of a twisted nematic liquid crystal display (LCD).** (a) When the voltage is off, the molecules in the liquid crystal are aligned so that they rotate the polarization of the light by 90°. This alignment allows light to pass through both the vertical and horizontal polarizers before being reflected and retracing its path to give a bright display. (b) When a voltage is applied to the electrodes, the liquid crystal molecules align parallel to the light path. In this state the light retains the vertical polarization and cannot pass through the horizontal polarizer. The area covered by the front electrode therefore appears dark.

SAMPLE INTEGRATIVE EXERCISE Putting Concepts Together

The substance CS_2 has a melting point of $-110.8\ °C$ and a boiling point of $46.3\ °C$. Its density at $20\ °C$ is $1.26\ g/cm^3$. It is highly flammable. **(a)** What is the name of this compound? **(b)** List the intermolecular forces that CS_2 molecules exert on one other. **(c)** Write a balanced equation for the combustion of this compound in air. (You will have to decide on the most likely oxidation products.) **(d)** The critical temperature and pressure for CS_2 are $552\ K$ and $78\ atm$, respectively. Compare these values with those for CO_2 (Table 11.5) and discuss the possible origins of the differences. **(e)** Would you expect the density of CS_2 at $40\ °C$ to be greater or less than at $20\ °C$? What accounts for the difference?

SOLUTION

(a) The compound is named carbon disulfide, in analogy with the naming of other binary molecular compounds such as carbon dioxide. ∞ (Section 2.8)

(b) Only dispersion forces affect CS_2; it does not have a dipole moment, based upon its molecular shape, and obviously cannot undergo hydrogen bonding.

(c) The most likely products of the combustion will be CO_2 and SO_2. ∞ (Section 3.2) Under some conditions SO_3 might be formed, but this would be the less likely outcome. Thus, we have the following equation for combustion:

$$CS_2(l) + 3\ O_2(g) \longrightarrow CO_2(g) + 2\ SO_2(g)$$

(d) The critical temperature and pressure of CS_2 ($552\ K$ and $78\ atm$) are both higher than those given for CO_2 in Table 11.5 ($304\ K$ and $73\ atm$). The difference in critical temperatures is especially notable. The higher values for CS_2 arise from the greater dispersion attractions between the CS_2 molecules compared with CO_2. These greater attractions are due to the larger size of the sulfur compared to oxygen and, therefore, its greater polarizability.

(e) The density would be lower at the higher temperature. Density decreases with increasing temperature because the molecules possess higher kinetic energies. Their more energetic movements result in larger average distances between molecules, which translate into lower densities.

CHAPTER SUMMARY AND KEY TERMS

INTRODUCTION AND SECTION 11.1 Substances that are gases or liquids at room temperature are usually composed of molecules. In gases the intermolecular attractive forces are negligible compared to the kinetic energies of the molecules; thus, the molecules are widely separated and undergo constant, chaotic motion. In liquids the **intermolecular forces** are strong enough to keep the molecules in close proximity; nevertheless, the molecules are free to move with respect to one another. In solids the intermolecular attractive forces are strong enough to restrain molecular motion and to force the particles to occupy specific locations in a three-dimensional arrangement.

SECTION 11.2 Three types of intermolecular forces exist between neutral molecules: **dispersion forces**, **dipole–dipole forces**, and **hydrogen bonding**. Dispersion forces operate between all molecules (and atoms, for atomic substances such as He, Ne, Ar, and so forth). As molecular weight increases, the **polarizability** of a molecule increases, which results in stronger dispersion forces. Molecular shape is also an important factor. Dipole–dipole forces increase in strength as the polarity of the molecule increases. Hydrogen bonding occurs in compounds containing O—H, N—H, and F—H bonds. Hydrogen bonds are generally stronger than dipole–dipole or dispersion forces. **Ion–dipole forces** are important in solutions in which ionic compounds are dissolved in polar solvents.

SECTION 11.3 The stronger the intermolecular forces, the greater is the **viscosity**, or resistance to flow, of a liquid. The surface tension of a liquid also increases as intermolecular forces increase in strength. **Surface tension** is a measure of the tendency of a liquid to maintain a minimum surface area. The adhesion of a liquid to the walls of a narrow tube and the cohesion of the liquid account for

capillary action and the formation of a meniscus at the surface of a liquid.

SECTION 11.4 A substance may exist in more than one state of matter, or phase. **Phase changes** are transformations from one phase to another. Changes of a solid to liquid (melting), solid to gas (sublimation), and liquid to gas (vaporization) are all endothermic processes. Thus, the **heat of fusion** (melting), the **heat of sublimation**, and the **heat of vaporization** are all positive quantities. The reverse processes (freezing, deposition, and condensation) are exothermic. A gas cannot be liquefied by application of pressure if the temperature is above its **critical temperature**. The pressure required to liquefy a gas at its critical temperature is called the **critical pressure**. When the temperature exceeds the critical temperature and the pressure exceeds the critical pressure, the liquid and gas phases cannot be distinguished and the substance is in a state called a **supercritical fluid**.

SECTION 11.5 The **vapor pressure** of a liquid indicates the tendency of the liquid to evaporate. The vapor pressure is the partial pressure of the vapor when it is in **dynamic equilibrium** with the liquid. At equilibrium the rate of transfer of molecules from the liquid to the vapor equals the rate of transfer from the vapor to the liquid. The higher the vapor pressure of a liquid, the more readily it evaporates and the more **volatile** it is. Vapor pressure increases nonlinearly with temperature. Boiling occurs when the vapor pressure equals the external pressure. The **normal boiling point** is the temperature at which the vapor pressure equals 1 atm.

SECTION 11.6 The equilibria between the solid, liquid, and gas phases of a substance as a function of temperature and pressure are displayed on a **phase diagram**. A line indicates equilibria between any two phases. The line through the melting point usually slopes slightly to the right as pressure increases, because the solid is usually more dense than the liquid. The melting point at 1 atm is the **normal melting point**. The point on the diagram at which all three phases co-exist in equilibrium is called the **triple point**.

SECTION 11.7   A **liquid crystal** is a substance that exhibits one or more ordered phases at a temperature above the melting point of the solid. In a **nematic liquid crystal** the molecules are aligned along a common direction, but the ends of the molecules are not lined up. In a smectic liquid crystal the ends of the molecules are lined up so that the molecules form layers. In **smectic A liquid crystals** the long axes of the molecules line up perpendicular to the layers. In **smectic C liquid crystals** the long axes of molecules are inclined with respect to the layers. A **cholesteric liquid crystal** is composed of molecules that align parallel to each other within a layer, as they do in nematic liquid crystalline phases, but the direction along which the long axes of the molecules align rotates from one layer to the next to form a helical structure. Substances that form liquid crystals are generally composed of molecules with fairly rigid, elongated shapes, as well as polar groups to help align molecules through dipole-dipole interactions.

KEY SKILLS

- Identify the intermolecular attractive interactions (dispersion, dipole–dipole, hydrogen bonding, ion–dipole) that exist between molecules or ions based on their composition and molecular structure and be able to compare the relative strengths of these intermolecular forces. (Section 11.2)
- Explain the concept of polarizability and how it relates to dispersion forces. (Section 11.2)
- Explain the concepts of viscosity and surface tension in liquids. (Section 11.3)
- Know the names of the various changes of state for a pure substance. (Section 11.4)
- Interpret heating curves and be able to calculate quantities related to temperature and enthalpies of phase changes. (Section 11.4)
- Define critical pressure, critical temperature, vapor pressure, normal boiling point, normal melting point, critical point, and triple point. (Sections 11.5 and 11.6)
- Be able to interpret and sketch phase diagrams. Explain how water's phase diagram differs from most other substances, and why. (Section 11.6)
- Understand how the molecular arrangements characteristic of nematic, smectic, and cholesteric liquid crystals differ from ordinary liquids and from each other. Be able to recognize the features of molecules that favor formation of liquid crystalline phases. (Section 11.7)

EXERCISES

VISUALIZING CONCEPTS

11.1 Does the diagram

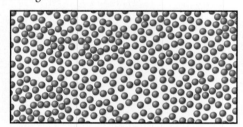

best describe a crystalline solid, a liquid, or a gas? Explain. [Section 11.1]

11.2 **(a)** Which kind of intermolecular attractive force is shown in each case here?

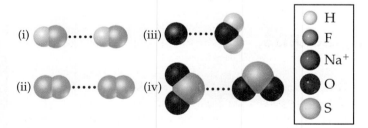

(b) Predict which of the four interactions is the weakest. [Section 11.2]

11.3 Do you expect the viscosity of glycerol, $C_3H_5(OH)_3$, to be larger or smaller than that of 1-propanol, C_3H_7OH? Explain. [Section 11.3]

(a) Glycerol   (b) 1-Propanol

11.4 If 42.0 kJ of heat is added to a 32.0-g sample of liquid methane under 1 atm of pressure at a temperature of −170 °C, what are the final state and temperature of the methane once the system equilibrates? Assume no heat is lost to the surroundings. The normal boiling point of methane is −161.5 °C. The specific heats of liquid and gaseous methane are 3.48 and 2.22 J/g-K, respectively. [Section 11.4]

$P = 1.00$ atm

42.0 kJ

32.0 g CH_4
$\Delta H_{vap} = 8.20$ kJ/mol
$T = -170$ °C

11.5 Using this graph of CS_2 data,

determine **(a)** the approximate vapor pressure of CS_2 at 30 °C, **(b)** the temperature at which the vapor pressure equals 300 torr, **(c)** the normal boiling point of CS_2. [Section 11.5]

11.6 The molecules

(a) Propanol	(b) Ethyl methyl ether
97.2 °C	10.8 °C

have the same molecular formula (C_3H_8O) but different normal boiling points, as shown. Rationalize the difference in boiling points. [Sections 11.2 and 11.5]

11.7 The phase diagram of a hypothetical substance is

(a) Estimate the normal boiling point and freezing point of the substance.

(b) What is the physical state of the substance under the following conditions: (i) $T = 150$ K, $P = 0.2$ atm, (ii) $T = 100$ K, $P = 0.8$ atm, (iii) $T = 300$ K, $P = 1.0$ atm?

(c) What is the triple point of the substance? [Section 11.6]

11.8 At three different temperatures, T_1, T_2, and T_3, the molecules in a liquid crystal align in these ways:

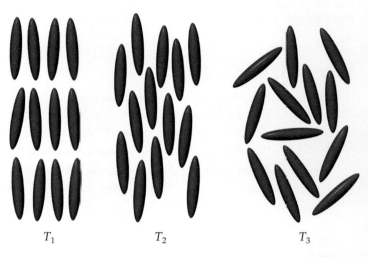

(a) At which temperature or temperatures is the substance in a liquid crystalline state? At those temperatures, which type of liquid crystalline phase is depicted?

(b) Which is the highest of the three temperatures?

MOLECULAR COMPARISONS OF GASES, LIQUIDS, AND SOLIDS (section 11.1)

11.9 List the three states of matter in order of **(a)** increasing molecular disorder and **(b)** increasing intermolecular attractions. **(c)** Which state of matter is most easily compressed?

11.10 **(a)** How does the average kinetic energy of molecules compare with the average energy of attraction between molecules in solids, liquids, and gases? **(b)** Why does increasing the temperature cause a solid substance to change in succession from a solid to a liquid to a gas? **(c)** What happens to a gas if you put it under extremely high pressure?

11.11 Arrange substances CCl_4, Si, and Ar in order of increasing boiling point.

11.12 Arrange substances Ga, Ne, and Br_2 in order of increasing boiling point.

11.13 At standard temperature and pressure the molar volume of Cl_2 and NH_3 gases are 22.06 L and 22.40 L, respectively. **(a)** Given the different molecular weights, dipole moments, and molecular shapes, why are their molar volumes nearly the same? **(b)** On cooling to 160 K, both substances form crystalline solids. Do you expect the molar volumes to decrease or increase on cooling to 160 K? **(c)** The densities of crystalline Cl_2 and NH_3 at 160 K are 2.02 g/cm^3 and 0.84 g/cm^3, respectively. Calculate their molar volumes. **(d)** Are the molar volumes in the solid state as similar as they are in the gaseous state? Explain. **(e)** Would you expect the molar volumes in the liquid state to be closer to those in the solid or gaseous state?

INTERMOLECULAR FORCES (section 11.2)

11.15 Which type of intermolecular attractive force operates between **(a)** all molecules, **(b)** polar molecules, **(c)** the hydrogen atom of a polar bond and a nearby small electronegative atom?

11.16 Based on what you have learned about intermolecular forces, would you say that matter is fundamentally attracted or repulsed by other matter?

11.17 Describe the intermolecular forces that must be overcome to convert these substances from a liquid to a gas: **(a)** SO_2, **(b)** CH_3COOH, **(c)** H_2S.

11.18 Which type of intermolecular force accounts for each of these differences: **(a)** CH_3OH boils at 65 °C; CH_3SH boils at 6 °C. **(b)** Xe is liquid at atmospheric pressure and 120 K, whereas Ar is a gas under the same conditions. **(c)** Kr, atomic weight 84, boils at 120.9 K, whereas Cl_2, molecular weight about 71, boils at 238 K. **(d)** Acetone boils at 56 °C, whereas 2-methylpropane boils at −12 °C.

Acetone   2-Methylpropane

11.19 **(a)** What is meant by the term *polarizability*? **(b)** Which of the following atoms would you expect to be most polarizable: N, P, As, Sb? Explain. **(c)** Put the following molecules in order of increasing polarizability: $GeCl_4$, CH_4, $SiCl_4$, SiH_4, and $GeBr_4$. **(d)** Predict the order of boiling points of the substances in part (c).

11.20 True or false:
(a) For molecules with similar molecular weights, the dispersion forces become stronger as the molecules become more polarizable.
(b) For the noble gases the dispersion forces decrease while the boiling points increase as you go down the column in the periodic table.
(c) In terms of the total attractive forces for a given substance dipole–dipole interactions, when present, are always larger than dispersion forces.
(d) All other factors being the same, dispersion forces between linear molecules are greater than dispersion forces between molecules whose shapes are nearly spherical.

11.21 Which member in each pair has the larger dispersion forces: **(a)** H_2O or H_2S, **(b)** CO_2 or CO, **(c)** SiH_4 or GeH_4?

11.22 Which member in each pair has the stronger intermolecular dispersion forces: **(a)** Br_2 or O_2, **(b)** $CH_3CH_2CH_2CH_2SH$ or $CH_3CH_2CH_2CH_2CH_2SH$, **(c)** $CH_3CH_2CH_2Cl$ or $(CH_3)_2CHCl$?

11.23 Butane and 2-methylpropane, whose space-filling models are shown at the top of the next column, are both nonpolar and have the same molecular formula, C_4H_{10}, yet butane has the higher boiling point (−0.5 °C compared to −11.7 °C). Explain.

11.14 Benzoic acid, C_6H_5COOH, melts at 122 °C. The density in the liquid state at 130 °C is 1.08 g/cm^3. The density of solid benzoic acid at 15 °C is 1.266 g/cm^3. **(a)** In which of these two states is the average distance between molecules greater? **(b)** Explain the difference in densities at the two temperatures in terms of the relative kinetic energies of the molecules.

(a) Butane   (b) 2-Methylpropane

11.24 Propyl alcohol ($CH_3CH_2CH_2OH$) and isopropyl alcohol [$(CH_3)_2CHOH$], whose space-filling models are shown, have boiling points of 97.2 °C and 82.5 °C, respectively. Explain why the boiling point of propyl alcohol is higher, even though both have the molecular formula C_3H_8O.

(a) Propyl alcohol   (b) Isopropyl alcohol

11.25 **(a)** What atoms must a molecule contain to participate in hydrogen bonding with other molecules of the same kind? **(b)** Which of the following molecules can form hydrogen bonds with other molecules of the same kind: CH_3F, CH_3NH_2, CH_3OH, CH_3Br?

11.26 Rationalize the difference in boiling points in each pair: **(a)** HF (20 °C) and HCl (−85 °C), **(b)** $CHCl_3$ (61 °C) and $CHBr_3$ (150 °C), **(c)** Br_2 (59 °C) and ICl (97 °C).

11.27 Ethylene glycol ($HOCH_2CH_2OH$), the major substance in antifreeze, has a normal boiling point of 198 °C. By comparison, ethyl alcohol (CH_3CH_2OH) boils at 78 °C at atmospheric pressure. Ethylene glycol dimethyl ether ($CH_3OCH_2CH_2OCH_3$) has a normal boiling point of 83 °C, and ethyl methyl ether ($CH_3CH_2CCH_3$) has a normal boiling point of 11 °C. **(a)** Explain why replacement of a hydrogen on the oxygen by a CH_3 group generally results in a lower boiling point. **(b)** What are the major factors responsible for the difference in boiling points of the two ethers?

11.28 Identify the type or types of intermolecular forces present in each substance and then select the substance in each pair that has the higher boiling point: **(a)** propane C_3H_8 or n-butane C_4H_{10}, **(b)** diethyl ether $CH_3CH_2OCH_2CH_3$ or 1-butanol $CH_3CH_2CH_2CH_2OH$, **(c)** sulfur dioxide SO_2 or sulfur trioxide SO_3, **(d)** phosgene Cl_2CO or formaldehyde H_2CO.

11.29 Look up and compare the normal boiling points and normal melting points of H_2O and H_2S. **(a)** Based on these physical properties, which substance has stronger intermolecular forces? What kind of intermolecular forces exist for each molecule? **(b)** Predict whether solid H_2S is more or less dense than liquid H_2S. How does this compare to H_2O? Explain. **(c)** Water has an unusually high specific heat. Is this related to its intermolecular forces? Explain.

11.30 The following quote about ammonia (NH_3) is from a textbook of inorganic chemistry: "It is estimated that 26% of the hydrogen bonding in NH_3 breaks down on melting, 7% on warming from the melting to the boiling point, and the final 67% on transfer to the gas phase at the boiling point." From the standpoint of the kinetic energy of the molecules, explain **(a)** why there is a decrease of hydrogen-bonding energy on melting and **(b)** why most of the loss in hydrogen bonding occurs in the transition from the liquid to the vapor state.

11.31 A number of salts containing the tetrahedral polyatomic anion, BF_4^-, are ionic liquids, whereas salts containing the somewhat larger tetrahedral ion SO_4^{2-} do not form ionic liquids. Explain this observation.

11.32 The generic structural formula for a 1-alkyl-3-methylimidazolium cation is

where R is a —$CH_2(CH_2)_nCH_3$ alkyl group. The melting points of the salts that form between the 1-alkyl-3-methylimidazolium cation and the PF_6^- anion are as follows:
R = CH_2CH_3 (m.p. = 60 °C), R = $CH_2CH_2CH_3$ (m.p. = 40 °C), R = $CH_2CH_2CH_2CH_3$ (m.p. = 10 °C) and R = $CH_2CH_2CH_2CH_2CH_3$ (m.p. = −61 °C). Why does the melting point decrease as the length of alkyl group increases?

SELECT PROPERTIES OF LIQUIDS (section 11.3)

11.33 **(a)** Explain why surface tension and viscosity decrease with increasing temperature. **(b)** Why do substances with high surface tensions also tend to have high viscosities?

11.34 **(a)** Distinguish between adhesive forces and cohesive forces. **(b)** What adhesive and cohesive forces are involved when a paper towel absorbs water? **(c)** Explain the cause for the U-shaped meniscus formed when water is in a glass tube.

11.35 Explain the following observations: **(a)** The surface tension of $CHBr_3$ is greater than that of $CHCl_3$. **(b)** As temperature increases, oil flows faster through a narrow tube. **(c)** Raindrops that collect on a waxed automobile hood take on a nearly spherical shape. **(d)** Oil droplets that collect on a waxed automobile hood take on a flat shape.

11.36 Hydrazine (H_2NNH_2), hydrogen peroxide (HOOH), and water (H_2O) all have exceptionally high surface tensions compared with other substances of comparable molecular weights. **(a)** Draw the Lewis structures for these three compounds. **(b)** What structural property do these substances have in common, and how might that account for the high surface tensions?

11.37 The boiling points, surface tensions, and viscosities of water and several alchohols are as follows:

	Boiling Point (°C)	Surface Tension (J/m^2)	Viscosity (kg/m-s)
Water, H_2O	100	7.3×10^{-2}	0.9×10^{-3}
Ethanol, CH_3CH_2OH	78	2.3×10^{-2}	1.1×10^{-3}
Propanol, $CH_3CH_2CH_2OH$	97	2.4×10^{-2}	2.2×10^{-3}
n-Butanol, $CH_3CH_2CH_2CH_2OH$	117	2.6×10^{-2}	2.6×10^{-3}
Ethylene glycol, $HOCH_2CH_2OH$	197	4.8×10^{-2}	26×10^{-3}

(a) For ethanol, propanol, and n-butanol the boiling points, surface tensions, and viscosities all increase. What is the reason for this increase? **(b)** How do you explain the fact that propanol and ethylene glycol have similar molecular weights (60 versus 62 amu), yet the viscosity of ethylene glycol is more than 10 times larger than propanol? **(c)** How do you explain the fact that water has the highest surface tension but the lowest viscosity?

11.38 **(a)** Would you expect the viscosity of n-pentane, $CH_3CH_2CH_2CH_2CH_3$, to be larger or smaller than the viscosity of n-hexane (3.26×10^{-4} kg/m-s from Table 11.4)? **(b)** If you compared their viscosities at 270 K, would you expect the viscosity of neopentane, $(CH_3)_4C$, to be smaller or larger than n-pentane? (See Figure 11.6 to see the shapes of these molecules.)

PHASE CHANGES (section 11.4)

11.39 Name the phase transition in each of the following situations and indicate whether it is exothermic or endothermic: **(a)** When ice is heated, it turns to water. **(b)** Wet clothes dry on a warm summer day. **(c)** Frost appears on a window on a cold winter day. **(d)** Droplets of water appear on a cold glass of beer.

11.40 Name the phase transition in each of the following situations and indicate whether it is exothermic or endothermic: **(a)** Bromine vapor turns to bromine liquid as it is cooled. **(b)** Crystals of iodine disappear from an evaporating dish as they stand in a fume hood. **(c)** Rubbing alcohol in an open container slowly disappears. **(d)** Molten lava from a volcano turns into solid rock.

11.41 Explain why any substance's heat of fusion is generally lower than its heat of vaporization.

11.42 Ethyl chloride (C_2H_5Cl) boils at 12 °C. When liquid C_2H_5Cl under pressure is sprayed on a room-temperature (25 °C) surface in air, the surface is cooled considerably. **(a)** What does this observation tell us about the specific heat of $C_2H_5Cl(g)$ as compared with $C_2H_5Cl(l)$? **(b)** Assume that the heat lost by the surface is gained by ethyl chloride. What enthalpies must you consider if you were to calculate the final temperature of the surface?

11.43 For many years drinking water has been cooled in hot climates by evaporating it from the surfaces of canvas bags or porous clay pots. How many grams of water can be cooled from 35 °C to 20 °C by the evaporation of 60 g of water? (The heat of vaporization of water in this temperature range is 2.4 kJ/g. The specific heat of water is 4.18 J/g-K.)

11.44 Compounds like CCl_2F_2 are known as chlorofluorocarbons, or CFCs. These compounds were once widely used as refrigerants but are now being replaced by compounds that are believed to be less harmful to the environment. The heat of vaporization of CCl_2F_2 is 289 J/g. What mass of this substance must evaporate to freeze 200 g of water initially at 15 °C? (The heat of fusion of water is 334 J/g; the specific heat of water is 4.18 J/g-K.)

11.45 Ethanol (C_2H_5OH) melts at −114 °C and boils at 78 °C. The enthalpy of fusion of ethanol is 5.02 kJ/mol, and its enthalpy of vaporization is 38.56 kJ/mol. The specific heats of solid and liquid ethanol are 0.97 J/g-K and 2.3 J/g-K, respectively. **(a)** How much heat is required to convert 42.0 g of ethanol at 35 °C to the vapor phase at 78 °C? **(b)** How much heat is required to convert the same amount of ethanol at −155 °C to the vapor phase at 78 °C?

11.46 The fluorocarbon compound $C_2Cl_3F_3$ has a normal boiling point of 47.6 °C. The specific heats of $C_2Cl_3F_3(l)$ and $C_2Cl_3F_3(g)$ are 0.91 J/g-K and 0.67 J/g-K, respectively. The heat of vaporization for the compound is 27.49 kJ/mol. Calculate the heat required to convert 35.0 g of $C_2Cl_3F_3$ from a liquid at 10.00 °C to a gas at 105.00 °C.

11.47 **(a)** What is the significance of the critical pressure of a substance? **(b)** What happens to the critical temperature of a series of compounds as the force of attraction between molecules increases? **(c)** Which of the substances listed in Table 11.5 can be liquefied at the temperature of liquid nitrogen (−196 °C)?

11.48 The critical temperatures (K) and pressures (atm) of a series of halogenated methanes are as follows:

Compound	CCl_3F	CCl_2F_2	$CClF_3$	CF_4
Critical temperature	471	385	302	227
Critical pressure	43.5	40.6	38.2	37.0

(a) List the intermolecular forces that occur for each compound. **(b)** Predict the order of increasing intermolecular attraction, from least to most, for this series of compounds. **(c)** Predict the critical temperature and pressure for CCl_4 based on the trends in this table. Look up the experimentally determined critical temperatures and pressures for CCl_4, using a source such as the *CRC Handbook of Chemistry and Physics*, and suggest a reason for any discrepancies.

VAPOR PRESSURE (section 11.5)

11.49 Explain how each of the following affects the vapor pressure of a liquid: **(a)** volume of the liquid, **(b)** surface area, **(c)** intermolecular attractive forces, **(d)** temperature, **(e)** density of the liquid.

11.50 Acetone, H_3CCOCH_3, has a boiling point of 56 °C. Based on the data given in Figure 11.25, would you expect acetone to have a higher or lower vapor pressure than ethanol at 25 °C?

11.51 **(a)** Place the following substances in order of increasing volatility: CH_4, CBr_4, CH_2Cl_2, CH_3Cl, $CHBr_3$, and CH_2Br_2. Explain. **(b)** How do the boiling points vary through this series?

11.52 True or false:
(a) CBr_4 is more volatile than CCl_4.
(b) CBr_4 has a higher boiling point than CCl_4.
(c) CBr_4 has weaker intermolecular forces than CCl_4.
(d) CBr_4 has a higher vapor pressure at the same temperature than CCl_4.

11.53 **(a)** Two pans of water are on different burners of a stove. One pan of water is boiling vigorously, while the other is boiling gently. What can be said about the temperature of the water in the two pans? **(b)** A large container of water and a small one are at the same temperature. What can be said about the relative vapor pressures of the water in the two containers?

11.54 Explain the following observations: **(a)** Water evaporates more quickly on a hot, dry day than on a hot, humid day. **(b)** It takes longer to cook an egg in boiling water at high altitudes than it does at lower altitudes.

11.55 Using the vapor-pressure curves in Figure 11.25, **(a)** estimate the boiling point of ethanol at an external pressure of 200 torr; **(b)** estimate the external pressure at which ethanol will boil at 60 °C; **(c)** estimate the boiling point of diethyl ether at 400 torr; **(d)** estimate the external pressure at which diethyl ether will boil at 40 °C.

11.56 Appendix E lists the vapor pressure of water at various external pressures.
(a) Plot the data in Appendix B, vapor pressure (torr) versus temperature (°C). From your plot, estimate the vapor pressure of water at body temperature, 37 °C.
(b) Explain the significance of the data point at 760.0 torr, 100 °C.
(c) A city at an altitude of 5000 ft above sea level has a barometric pressure of 633 torr. To what temperature would you have to heat water to boil it in this city?
(d) A city at an altitude of 500 ft below sea level would have a barometric pressure of 774 torr. To what temperature would you have to heat water to boil it in this city?
(e) For the two cities in parts (c) and (d), compare the average kinetic energies of the water molecules at their boiling points. Are the kinetic energies the same or different? Explain.

PHASE DIAGRAMS (section 11.6)

11.57 (a) What is the significance of the critical point in a phase diagram? (b) Why does the line that separates the gas and liquid phases end at the critical point?

11.58 (a) What is the significance of the triple point in a phase diagram? (b) Could you measure the triple point of water by measuring the temperature in a vessel in which water vapor, liquid water, and ice are in equilibrium under one atmosphere of air? Explain.

11.59 Referring to Figure 11.28, describe all the phase changes that would occur in each of the following cases: (a) Water vapor originally at 0.005 atm and $-0.5\ °C$ is slowly compressed at constant temperature until the final pressure is 20 atm. (b) Water originally at $100.0\ °C$ and 0.50 atm is cooled at constant pressure until the temperature is $-10\ °C$.

11.60 Referring to Figure 11.29, describe the phase changes (and the temperatures at which they occur) when CO_2 is heated from $-80\ °C$ to $-20\ °C$ at (a) a constant pressure of 3 atm, (b) a constant pressure of 6 atm.

11.61 The phase diagram for neon is

Use the phase diagram to answer the following questions. (a) What is the approximate value of the normal melting point?

(b) Over what pressure range will solid neon sublime? (c) At room temperature ($T = 25\ °C$) can neon be liquefied by compressing it?

11.62 Use the phase diagram of neon to answer the following questions. (a) What is the approximate value of the normal boiling point? (b) What can you say about the strength of the intermolecular forces in neon and argon based on the critical points of Ne and Ar? (See Table 11.5.)

11.63 The fact that water on Earth can readily be found in all three states (solid, liquid, and gas) is in part a consequence of the fact that the triple point of water ($T = 0.01\ °C$, $P = 0.006$ atm) falls within a range of temperatures and pressures found on Earth. Saturn's largest moon Titan has a considerable amount of methane in its atmosphere. The conditions on the surface of Titan are estimated to be $P = 1.6$ atm and $T = -178\ °C$. As seen from the phase diagram of methane (Figure 11.30), these conditions are not far from the triple point of methane, raising the tantalizing possibility that solid, liquid, and gaseous methane can be found on Titan. (a) What state would you expect to find methane in on the surface of Titan? (b) On moving upward through the atmosphere the pressure will decrease. If we assume that the temperature does not change, what phase change would you expect to see as we move away from the surface?

11.64 At $25\ °C$ gallium is a solid with a density of $5.91\ g/cm^3$. Its melting point, $29.8\ °C$, is low enough that you can melt it by holding it in your hand. The density of liquid gallium just above the melting point is $6.1\ g/cm^3$. Based on this information, what unusual feature would you expect to find in the phase diagram of gallium?

LIQUID CRYSTALS (section 11.7)

11.65 In terms of the arrangement and freedom of motion of the molecules, how are the nematic liquid crystalline phase and an ordinary liquid phase similar? How are they different?

11.66 What observations made by Reinitzer on cholesteryl benzoate suggested that this substance possesses a liquid crystalline phase?

11.67 The molecules shown in Figure 11.33 possess polar groups (that is, groupings of atoms that give rise to sizable dipole moments within the molecules). How might the presence of polar groups enhance the tendency toward liquid crystal formation?

11.68 One of the more effective liquid crystalline substances employed in LCDs is the molecule

$$CH_3(CH_2)_2CH{=}CH{-}\overset{\displaystyle CH_2{-}CH_2}{\underset{\displaystyle CH_2{-}CH_2}{CH}}\quad \overset{\displaystyle CH_2{-}CH_2}{\underset{\displaystyle CH_2{-}CH_2}{CH{-}CH}}\quad \overset{}{\underset{}{CH{-}C{\equiv}N}}$$

(a) How many double bonds are there in this molecule? (b) Describe the features of the molecule that make it prone to show liquid crystalline behavior.

11.69 For a given substance, the liquid crystalline phase tends to be more viscous than the liquid phase. Why?

11.70 Describe how a cholesteric liquid crystal phase differs from a nematic phase.

11.71 It often happens that a substance possessing a smectic liquid crystalline phase just above the melting point passes into a nematic liquid crystalline phase at a higher temperature. Account for this type of behavior.

11.72 The smectic liquid crystalline phase can be said to be more highly ordered than the nematic phase. In what sense is this true?

ADDITIONAL EXERCISES

11.73 As the intermolecular attractive forces between molecules increase in magnitude, do you expect each of the following to increase or decrease in magnitude? (a) vapor pressure, (b) heat of vaporization, (c) boiling point, (d) freezing point, (e) viscosity, (f) surface tension, (g) critical temperature.

11.74 Suppose you have two colorless molecular liquids, one boiling at −84 °C, the other at 34 °C, and both at atmospheric pressure. Which of the following statements is correct? For each statement that is not correct, modify the statement so that it is correct. (a) The higher-boiling liquid has greater total intermolecular forces than the lower-boiling liquid. (b) The lower-boiling liquid must consist of nonpolar molecules. (c) The lower-boiling liquid has a lower molecular weight than the higher-boiling liquid. (d) The two liquids have identical vapor pressures at their normal boiling points. (e) At −84 °C both liquids have vapor pressures of 760 mm Hg.

11.75 Two isomers of the planar compound 1,2-dichloroethylene are shown here.

cis isomer   trans isomer

(a) Which of the two isomers will have the stronger dipole–dipole forces? (b) One isomer has a boiling point of 60.3 °C and the other 47.5 °C. Which isomer has which boiling point?

11.76 In dichloromethane, $CH_2Cl_2(\mu = 1.60$ D), the dispersion force contribution to the intermolecular attractive forces is about five times larger than the dipole–dipole contribution. Compared to CH_2Cl_2, would you expect the relative importance of the dipole–dipole contribution to increase or decrease (a) in dibromomethane ($\mu = 1.43$ D), (b) in difluoromethane ($\mu = 1.93$ D)? Explain.

11.77 When an atom or group of atoms is substituted for an H atom in benzene (C_6H_6), the boiling point changes. Explain the order of the following boiling points: C_6H_6 (80 °C), C_6H_5Cl (132 °C), C_6H_5Br (156 °C), C_6H_5OH (182 °C).

11.78 The DNA double helix (Figure 24.30) at the atomic level looks like a twisted ladder, where the "rungs" of the ladder consist of molecules that are hydrogen-bonded together. Sugar and phosphate groups make up the sides of the ladder. Shown are the structures of the adenine-thymine (AT) "base pair" and the guanine-cytosine (GC) base pair:

Thymine   Adenine

Cytosine   Guanine

You can see that AT base pairs are held together by two hydrogen bonds, and the GC base pairs are held together by three hydrogen bonds. Which base pair is more stable to heating? Why?

11.79 Ethylene glycol ($HOCH_2CH_2OH$) is the major component of antifreeze. It is a slightly viscous liquid, not very volatile at room temperature, with a boiling point of 198 °C. Pentane (C_5H_{12}), which has about the same molecular weight, is a nonviscous liquid that is highly volatile at room temperature and whose boiling point is 36.1 °C. Explain the differences in the physical properties of the two substances.

11.80 Use the normal boiling points

propane, C_3H_8, −42.1 °C
butane, C_4H_{10}, −0.5 °C
pentane, C_5H_{12}, 36.1 °C
hexane, C_6H_{14}, 68.7 °C
heptane, C_7H_{16}, 98.4 °C

to estimate the normal boiling point of octane, C_8H_{18}. Explain the trend in the boiling points.

11.81 One of the attractive features of ionic liquids is their low vapor pressure, which in turn tends to make them nonflammable. Why do you think ionic liquids have lower vapor pressures than most room-temperature molecular liquids?

11.82 (a) When you exercise vigorously, you sweat. How does this help your body cool? (b) A flask of water is connected to a vacuum pump. A few moments after the pump is turned on, the water begins to boil. After a few minutes, the water begins to freeze. Explain why these processes occur.

[11.83] The following table gives the vapor pressure of hexafluorobenzene (C_6F_6) as a function of temperature:

Temperature (K)	Vapor Pressure (torr)
280.0	32.42
300.0	92.47
320.0	225.1
330.0	334.4
340.0	482.9

(a) By plotting these data in a suitable fashion, determine whether the Clausius–Clapeyron equation (Equation 11.1) is obeyed. If it is obeyed, use your plot to determine ΔH_{vap} for C_6F_6. (b) Use these data to determine the boiling point of the compound.

[11.84] Suppose the vapor pressure of a substance is measured at two different temperatures. (a) By using the Clausius–Clapeyron equation (Equation 11.1) derive the following relationship between the vapor pressures, P_1 and P_2, and the absolute temperatures at which they were measured, T_1 and T_2:

$$\ln \frac{P_1}{P_2} = -\frac{\Delta H_{vap}}{R}\left(\frac{1}{T_1} - \frac{1}{T_2}\right)$$

(b) Gasoline is a mixture of hydrocarbons, a major component of which is octane, $CH_3CH_2CH_2CH_2CH_2CH_2CH_2CH_3$. Octane has a vapor pressure of 13.95 torr at 25 °C and a vapor pressure of 144.78 torr at 75 °C. Use these data and the equation in part (a) to calculate the heat of vaporization of octane. (c) By using the equation in part (a) and the data given in part (b), calculate the normal boiling point of octane. Compare your answer to the one you obtained from Exercise 11.80. (d) Calculate the vapor pressure of octane at −30 °C.

[11.85] The following data present the temperatures at which certain vapor pressures are achieved for dichloromethane (CH_2Cl_2) and methyl iodide (CH_3I):

Vapor Pressure (torr):	10.0	40.0	100.0	400.0
T for CH_2Cl_2 (°C):	−43.3	−22.3	−6.3	24.1
T for CH_3I (°C):	−45.8	−24.2	−7.0	25.3

(a) Which of the two substances is expected to have the greater dipole–dipole forces? Which is expected to have the greater dispersion forces? Based on your answers, explain why it is difficult to predict which compound would be more volatile. **(b)** Which compound would you expect to have the higher boiling point? Check your answer in a reference book such as the *CRC Handbook of Chemistry and Physics*. **(c)** The order of volatility of these two substances changes as the temperature is increased. What quantity must be different for the two substances in order for this phenomenon to occur? **(d)** Substantiate your answer for part (c) by drawing an appropriate graph.

INTEGRATIVE EXERCISES

11.88 **(a)** At the molecular level, what factor is responsible for the steady increase in viscosity with increasing molecular weight in the hydrocarbon series shown in Table 11.4? **(b)** Although the viscosity varies over a factor of more than two in the series from hexane to nonane, the surface tension at 25 °C increases by only about 20% in the same series. How do you account for this? **(c)** *n*-Octyl alcohol, $CH_3(CH_2)_7OH$, has a viscosity of 1.01×10^{-2} kg/m-s, much higher than nonane, which has about the same molecular weight. What accounts for this difference? How does your answer relate to the difference in normal boiling points for these two substances?

11.89 Acetone, $(CH_3)_2CO$, is widely used as an industrial solvent. **(a)** Draw the Lewis structure for the acetone molecule and predict the geometry around each carbon atom. **(b)** Is the acetone molecule polar or nonpolar? **(c)** What kinds of intermolecular attractive forces exist between acetone molecules? **(d)** 1-Propanol, $CH_3CH_2CH_2OH$, has a molecular weight that is very similar to that of acetone, yet acetone boils at 56.5 °C and 1-propanol boils at 97.2 °C. Explain the difference.

11.86 A watch with a liquid crystal display (LCD) does not function properly when it is exposed to low temperatures during a trip to Antarctica. Explain why the LCD might not function well at low temperature.

[11.87] A particular liquid crystalline substance has the phase diagram shown in the figure. By analogy with the phase diagram for a non–liquid crystalline substance, identify the phase present in each area.

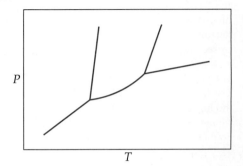

11.90 The table shown here lists the molar heats of vaporization for several organic compounds. Use specific examples from this list to illustrate how the heat of vaporization varies with **(a)** molar mass, **(b)** molecular shape, **(c)** molecular polarity, **(d)** hydrogen-bonding interactions. Explain these comparisons in terms of the nature of the intermolecular forces at work. (You may find it helpful to draw out the structural formula for each compound.)

Compound	Heat of Vaporization (kJ/mol)
$CH_3CH_2CH_3$	19.0
$CH_3CH_2CH_2CH_2CH_3$	27.6
$CH_3CHBrCH_3$	31.8
CH_3COCH_3	32.0
$CH_3CH_2CH_2Br$	33.6
$CH_3CH_2CH_2OH$	47.3

11.91 Liquid butane, C_4H_{10}, is stored in cylinders to be used as a fuel. The normal boiling point of butane is listed as $-0.5\,°C$. **(a)** Suppose the tank is standing in the sun and reaches a temperature of $35\,°C$. Would you expect the pressure in the tank to be greater or less than atmospheric pressure? How does the pressure within the tank depend on how much liquid butane is in it? **(b)** Suppose the valve to the tank is opened and a few liters of butane are allowed to escape rapidly. What do you expect would happen to the temperature of the remaining liquid butane in the tank? Explain. **(c)** How much heat must be added to vaporize 250 g of butane if its heat of vaporization is $21.3\,kJ/mol$? What volume does this much butane occupy at 755 torr and $35\,°C$?

[11.92] Using information in Appendices B and C, calculate the minimum number of grams of propane, $C_3H_8(g)$, that must be combusted to provide the energy necessary to convert 5.50 kg of ice at $-20\,°C$ to liquid water at $75\,°C$.

11.93 The vapor pressure of a volatile liquid can be determined by slowly bubbling a known volume of gas through it at a known temperature and pressure. In an experiment, 5.00 L of N_2 gas is passed through 7.2146 g of liquid benzene, C_6H_6, at $26.0\,°C$. The liquid remaining after the experiment weighs 5.1493 g. Assuming that the gas becomes saturated with benzene vapor and that the total gas volume and temperature remain constant, what is the vapor pressure of the benzene in torr?

11.94 The relative humidity of air equals the ratio of the partial pressure of water in the air to the equilibrium vapor pressure of water at the same temperature times 100%. If the relative humidity of the air is 58% and its temperature is $68\,°F$, how many molecules of water are present in a room measuring $12\,ft \times 10\,ft \times 8\,ft$?

MATHEMATICAL OPERATIONS

A.1 | EXPONENTIAL NOTATION

The numbers used in chemistry are often either extremely large or extremely small. Such numbers are conveniently expressed in the form

$$N \times 10^n$$

where N is a number between 1 and 10, and n is the exponent. Some examples of this *exponential notation*, which is also called *scientific notation*, follow.

1,200,000 is 1.2×10^6 (read "one point two times ten to the sixth power")

0.000604 is 6.04×10^{-4} (read "six point zero four times ten to the negative fourth power")

A positive exponent, as in the first example, tells us how many times a number must be multiplied by 10 to give the long form of the number:

$$1.2 \times 10^6 = 1.2 \times 10 \times 10 \times 10 \times 10 \times 10 \times 10 \quad \text{(six tens)}$$
$$= 1,200,000$$

It is also convenient to think of the *positive exponent* as the number of places the decimal point must be moved to the *left* to obtain a number greater than 1 and less than 10. For example, if we begin with 3450 and move the decimal point three places to the left, we end up with 3.45×10^3.

In a related fashion, a negative exponent tells us how many times we must divide a number by 10 to give the long form of the number.

$$6.04 \times 10^{-4} = \frac{6.04}{10 \times 10 \times 10 \times 10} = 0.000604$$

It is convenient to think of the *negative exponent* as the number of places the decimal point must be moved to the *right* to obtain a number greater than 1 but less than 10. For example, if we begin with 0.0048 and move the decimal point three places to the right, we end up with 4.8×10^{-3}.

In the system of exponential notation, with each shift of the decimal point one place to the right, the exponent *decreases* by 1:

$$4.8 \times 10^{-3} = 48 \times 10^{-4}$$

Similarly, with each shift of the decimal point one place to the left, the exponent *increases* by 1:

$$4.8 \times 10^{-3} = 0.48 \times 10^{-2}$$

Many scientific calculators have a key labeled EXP or EE, which is used to enter numbers in exponential notation. To enter the number 5.8×10^3 on such a calculator, the key sequence is

5 · 8 EXP (or EE) 3

On some calculators the display will show 5.8, then a space, followed by 03, the exponent. On other calculators, a small 10 is shown with an exponent 3.

To enter a negative exponent, use the key labeled $+/-$. For example, to enter the number 8.6×10^{-5}, the key sequence is

$$\boxed{8}\ \boxed{\cdot}\ \boxed{6}\ \boxed{\text{EXP}}\ \boxed{+/-}\ \boxed{5}$$

When entering a number in exponential notation, do not key in the 10 if you use the EXP or EE button.

In working with exponents, it is important to recall that $10^0 = 1$. The following rules are useful for carrying exponents through calculations.

1. **Addition and Subtraction** In order to add or subtract numbers expressed in exponential notation, the powers of 10 must be the same.

$$(5.22 \times 10^4) + (3.21 \times 10^2) = (522 \times 10^2) + (3.21 \times 10^2)$$
$$= 525 \times 10^2 \quad \text{(3 significant figures)}$$
$$= 5.25 \times 10^4$$
$$(6.25 \times 10^{-2}) - (5.77 \times 10^{-3}) = (6.25 \times 10^{-2}) - (0.577 \times 10^{-2})$$
$$= 5.67 \times 10^{-2} \quad \text{(3 significant figures)}$$

When you use a calculator to add or subtract, you need not be concerned with having numbers with the same exponents because the calculator automatically takes care of this matter.

2. **Multiplication and Division** When numbers expressed in exponential notation are multiplied, the exponents are added; when numbers expressed in exponential notation are divided, the exponent of the denominator is subtracted from the exponent of the numerator.

$$(5.4 \times 10^2)(2.1 \times 10^3) = (5.4)(2.1) \times 10^{2+3}$$
$$= 11 \times 10^5$$
$$= 1.1 \times 10^6$$
$$(1.2 \times 10^5)(3.22 \times 10^{-3}) = (1.2)(3.22) \times 10^{5+(-3)} = 3.9 \times 10^2$$
$$\frac{3.2 \times 10^5}{6.5 \times 10^2} = \frac{3.2}{6.5} \times 10^{5-2} = 0.49 \times 10^3 = 4.9 \times 10^2$$
$$\frac{5.7 \times 10^7}{8.5 \times 10^{-2}} = \frac{5.7}{8.5} \times 10^{7-(-2)} = 0.67 \times 10^9 = 6.7 \times 10^8$$

3. **Powers and Roots** When numbers expressed in exponential notation are raised to a power, the exponents are multiplied by the power. When the roots of numbers expressed in exponential notation are taken, the exponents are divided by the root.

$$(1.2 \times 10^5)^3 = (1.2)^3 \times 10^{5 \times 3}$$
$$= 1.7 \times 10^{15}$$
$$\sqrt[3]{2.5 \times 10^6} = \sqrt[3]{2.5} \times 10^{6/3}$$
$$= 1.3 \times 10^2$$

Scientific calculators usually have keys labeled x^2 and $\sqrt{x}$ for squaring and taking the square root of a number, respectively. To take higher powers or roots, many calculators have y^x and $\sqrt[x]{y}$ (or INV y^x) keys. For example, to perform the operation $\sqrt[3]{7.5 \times 10^{-4}}$ on such a calculator, you would key in 7.5×10^{-4}, press the $\sqrt[x]{y}$ key (or the INV and then the y^x keys), enter the root, 3, and finally press $=$. The result is 9.1×10^{-2}.

SAMPLE EXERCISE 1   **Using Exponential Notation**

Perform each of the following operations, using your calculator where possible:

(a) Write the number 0.0054 in standard exponential notation.

(b) $(5.0 \times 10^{-2}) + (4.7 \times 10^{-3})$

(c) $(5.98 \times 10^{12})(2.77 \times 10^{-5})$

(d) $\sqrt[4]{1.75 \times 10^{-12}}$

SOLUTION

(a) Because we move the decimal point three places to the right to convert 0.0054 to 5.4, the exponent is −3:

$$5.4 \times 10^{-3}$$

Scientific calculators are generally able to convert numbers to exponential notation using one or two keystrokes; frequently "SCI" for "scientific notation" will convert a number into exponential notation. Consult your instruction manual to see how this operation is accomplished on your calculator.

(b) To add these numbers longhand, we must convert them to the same exponent.

$$(5.0 \times 10^{-2}) + (0.47 \times 10^{-2}) = (5.0 + 0.47) \times 10^{-2} = 5.5 \times 10^{-2}$$

(Note that the result has only two significant figures.) To perform this operation on a calculator, we enter the first number, strike the + key, then enter the second number and strike the = key.

(c) Performing this operation longhand, we have

$$(5.98 \times 2.77) \times 10^{12-5} = 16.6 \times 10^7 = 1.66 \times 10^8$$

On a scientific calculator, we enter 5.98×10^{12}, press the × key, enter 2.77×10^{-5}, and press the = key.

(d) To perform this operation on a calculator, we enter the number, press the $\sqrt[x]{y}$ key (or the INV and y^x keys), enter 4, and press the = key. The result is 1.15×10^{-3}.

PRACTICE EXERCISE

Perform the following operations:

(a) Write 67,000 in exponential notation, showing two significant figures.

(b) $(3.378 \times 10^{-3}) - (4.97 \times 10^{-5})$

(c) $(1.84 \times 10^{15})(7.45 \times 10^{-2})$

(d) $(6.67 \times 10^{-8})^3$

Answers: **(a)** 6.7×10^4, **(b)** 3.328×10^{-3}, **(c)** 2.47×10^{16}, **(d)** 2.97×10^{-22}

A.2 | LOGARITHMS

Common Logarithms

The common, or base-10, logarithm (abbreviated log) of any number is the power to which 10 must be raised to equal the number. For example, the common logarithm of 1000 (written log 1000) is 3 because raising 10 to the third power gives 1000.

$$10^3 = 1000, \text{ therefore, log } 1000 = 3$$

Further examples are

$$\log 10^5 = 5$$
$$\log 1 = 0 \qquad \text{Remember that } 10^0 = 1$$
$$\log 10^{-2} = -2$$

In these examples the common logarithm can be obtained by inspection. However, it is not possible to obtain the logarithm of a number such as 31.25 by inspection. The logarithm of 31.25 is the number x that satisfies the following relationship:

$$10^x = 31.25$$

Most electronic calculators have a key labeled LOG that can be used to obtain logarithms. For example, on many calculators we obtain the value of log 31.25 by entering 31.25 and pressing the LOG key. We obtain the following result:

$$\log 31.25 = 1.4949$$

Notice that 31.25 is greater than 10 (10^1) and less than 100 (10^2). The value for log 31.25 is accordingly between log 10 and log 100, that is, between 1 and 2.

Significant Figures and Common Logarithms

For the common logarithm of a measured quantity, the number of digits after the decimal point equals the number of significant figures in the original number. For example, if 23.5 is a measured quantity (three significant figures), then log 23.5 = 1.371 (three significant figures after the decimal point).

Antilogarithms

The process of determining the number that corresponds to a certain logarithm is known as obtaining an *antilogarithm*. It is the reverse of taking a logarithm. For example, we saw previously that log 23.5 = 1.371. This means that the antilogarithm of 1.371 equals 23.5.

$$\log 23.5 = 1.371$$
$$\text{antilog } 1.371 = 23.5$$

The process of taking the antilog of a number is the same as raising 10 to a power equal to that number.

$$\text{antilog } 1.371 = 10^{1.371} = 23.5$$

Many calculators have a key labeled 10^x that allows you to obtain antilogs directly. On others, it will be necessary to press a key labeled INV (for *inverse*), followed by the LOG key.

Natural Logarithms

Logarithms based on the number e are called natural, or base e, logarithms (abbreviated ln). The natural log of a number is the power to which e (which has the value 2.71828...) must be raised to equal the number. For example, the natural log of 10 equals 2.303.

$$e^{2.303} = 10, \text{ therefore } \ln 10 = 2.303$$

Your calculator probably has a key labeled LN that allows you to obtain natural logarithms. For example, to obtain the natural log of 46.8, you enter 46.8 and press the LN key.

$$\ln 46.8 = 3.846$$

The natural antilog of a number is e raised to a power equal to that number. If your calculator can calculate natural logs, it will also be able to calculate natural antilogs. On some calculators there is a key labeled e^x that allows you to calculate natural antilogs directly; on others, it will be necessary to first press the INV key followed by the LN key. For example, the natural antilog of 1.679 is given by

$$\text{Natural antilog } 1.679 = e^{1.679} = 5.36$$

The relation between common and natural logarithms is as follows:

$$\ln a = 2.303 \log a$$

Notice that the factor relating the two, 2.303, is the natural log of 10, which we calculated earlier.

Mathematical Operations Using Logarithms

Because logarithms are exponents, mathematical operations involving logarithms follow the rules for the use of exponents. For example, the product of z^a and z^b (where z is any number) is given by

$$z^a \cdot z^b = z^{(a+b)}$$

Similarly, the logarithm (either common or natural) of a product equals the *sum* of the logs of the individual numbers.

$$\log ab = \log a + \log b \qquad \ln ab = \ln a + \ln b$$

For the log of a quotient,

$$\log(a/b) = \log a - \log b \qquad \ln(a/b) = \ln a - \ln b$$

Using the properties of exponents, we can also derive the rules for the logarithm of a number raised to a certain power.

$$\log a^n = n \log a \qquad \ln a^n = n \ln a$$

$$\log a^{1/n} = (1/n) \log a \qquad \ln a^{1/n} = (1/n) \ln a$$

pH Problems

One of the most frequent uses for common logarithms in general chemistry is in working pH problems. The pH is defined as $-\log[H^+]$, where $[H^+]$ is the hydrogen ion concentration of a solution. ∞ (Section 16.4) The following sample exercise illustrates this application.

SAMPLE EXERCISE 2 **Using Logarithms**

(a) What is the pH of a solution whose hydrogen ion concentration is 0.015 M?

(b) If the pH of a solution is 3.80, what is its hydrogen ion concentration?

SOLUTION

1. We are given the value of $[H^+]$. We use the LOG key of our calculator to calculate the value of $\log[H^+]$. The pH is obtained by changing the sign of the value obtained. (Be sure to change the sign *after* taking the logarithm.)

$$[H^+] = 0.015$$
$$\log[H^+] = -1.82 \qquad \text{(2 significant figures)}$$
$$pH = -(-1.82) = 1.82$$

2. To obtain the hydrogen ion concentration when given the pH, we must take the antilog of $-$pH.

$$pH = -\log[H^+] = 3.80$$
$$\log[H^+] = -3.80$$
$$[H^+] = \text{antilog}(-3.80) = 10^{-3.80} = 1.6 \times 10^{-4}\, M$$

PRACTICE EXERCISE

Perform the following operations: **(a)** $\log(2.5 \times 10^{-5})$, **(b)** $\ln 32.7$, **(c)** antilog -3.47, **(d)** $e^{-1.89}$.
Answers: **(a)** -4.60, **(b)** 3.487, **(c)** 3.4×10^{-4}, **(d)** 1.5×10^{-1}

A.3 | QUADRATIC EQUATIONS

An algebraic equation of the form $ax^2 + bx + c = 0$ is called a *quadratic equation*. The two solutions to such an equation are given by the quadratic formula:

$$x = \frac{-b \pm \sqrt{b^2 - 4ac}}{2a}$$

Many calculators today can calculate the solutions to a quadratic equation with one or two keystrokes. Most of the time, x corresponds to the concentration of a chemical species in solution. Only one of the solutions will be a positive number, and that is the one you should use; a "negative concentration" has no physical meaning.

SAMPLE EXERCISE 3 **Using the Quadratic Formula**

Find the values of x that satisfy the equation $2x^2 + 4x = 1$.

SOLUTION

To solve the given equation for x, we must first put it in the form

$$ax^2 + bx + c = 0$$

and then use the quadratic formula. If

$$2x^2 + 4x = 1$$

then

$$2x^2 + 4x - 1 = 0$$

Using the quadratic formula, where $a = 2$, $b = 4$, and $c = -1$, we have

$$x = \frac{-4 \pm \sqrt{(4)(4) - 4(2)(-1)}}{2(2)}$$

$$= \frac{-4 \pm \sqrt{16 + 8}}{4} = \frac{-4 \pm \sqrt{24}}{4} = \frac{-4 \pm 4.899}{4}$$

The two solutions are

$$x = \frac{0.899}{4} = 0.225 \quad \text{and} \quad x = \frac{-8.899}{4} = -2.225$$

If this was a problem in which x represented a concentration, we would say $x = 0.225$ (in the appropriate units), since a negative number for concentration has no physical meaning.

TABLE A.1 • Interrelation between Pressure and Temperature

Temperature (°C)	Pressure (atm)
20.0	0.120
30.0	0.124
40.0	0.128
50.0	0.132

▲ **FIGURE A.1** A graph of pressure versus temperature yields a straight line for the data.

A.4 | GRAPHS

Often the clearest way to represent the interrelationship between two variables is to graph them. Usually, the variable that is being experimentally varied, called the *independent variable*, is shown along the horizontal axis (x-axis). The variable that responds to the change in the independent variable, called the *dependent variable*, is then shown along the vertical axis (y-axis). For example, consider an experiment in which we vary the temperature of an enclosed gas and measure its pressure. The independent variable is temperature, and the dependent variable is pressure. The data shown in ◀ **TABLE A.1** can be obtained by means of this experiment. These data are shown graphically in ◀ **FIGURE A.1**. The relationship between temperature and pressure is linear. The equation for any straight-line graph has the form

$$y = mx + b$$

where m is the slope of the line and b is the intercept with the y-axis. In the case of Figure A.1, we could say that the relationship between temperature and pressure takes the form

$$P = mT + b$$

where P is pressure in atm and T is temperature in °C. As shown in Figure A.1, the slope is 4.10×10^{-4} atm/°C, and the intercept—the point where the line crosses the y-axis—is 0.112 atm. Therefore, the equation for the line is

$$P = \left(4.10 \times 10^{-4} \frac{\text{atm}}{\text{°C}}\right)T + 0.112 \text{ atm}$$

A.5 | STANDARD DEVIATION

The standard deviation from the mean, s, is a common method for describing precision in experimentally determined data. We define the standard deviation as

$$s = \sqrt{\frac{\sum_{i=1}^{N}(x_i - \bar{x})^2}{N - 1}}$$

where N is the number of measurements, $\bar{x}$ is the average (also called the mean) of the measurements, and x_i represents the individual measurements. Electronic calculators with built-in statistical functions can calculate s directly by inputting the individual measurements.

A smaller value of s indicates a higher precision, meaning that the data are more closely clustered around the average. The standard deviation has statistical significance. If a large number of measurements is made, 68% of the measured values is expected to be within one standard deviation of the average, assuming only random errors are associated with the measurements.

SAMPLE EXERCISE 4   Calculating an Average and Standard Deviation

The percent carbon in a sugar is measured four times: 42.01%, 42.28%, 41.79%, and 42.25%. Calculate (a) the average and (b) the standard deviation for these measurements.

SOLUTION

(a) The average is found by adding the quantities and dividing by the number of measurements:

$$\bar{x} = \frac{42.01 + 42.28 + 41.79 + 42.25}{4} = \frac{168.33}{4} = 42.08$$

(b) The standard deviation is found using the preceding equation:

$$s = \sqrt{\frac{\sum_{i=1}^{N}(x_i - \bar{x})^2}{N - 1}}$$

Let's tabulate the data so the calculation of $\sum_{i=1}^{N}(x_i - \bar{x})^2$ can be seen clearly.

Percent C	Difference between Measurement and Average, $(x_i - \bar{x})$	Square of Difference, $(x_i - \bar{x})^2$
42.01	$42.01 - 42.08 = -0.07$	$(-0.07)^2 = 0.005$
42.28	$42.28 - 42.08 = 0.20$	$(0.20)^2 = 0.040$
41.79	$41.79 - 42.08 = -0.29$	$(-0.29)^2 = 0.084$
42.25	$42.25 - 42.08 = 0.17$	$(0.17)^2 = 0.029$

The sum of the quantities in the last column is

$$\sum_{i=1}^{N}(x_i - \bar{x})^2 = 0.005 + 0.040 + 0.084 + 0.029 = 0.16$$

Thus, the standard deviation is

$$s = \sqrt{\frac{\sum_{i=1}^{N}(x_i - \bar{x})^2}{N - 1}} = \sqrt{\frac{0.16}{4 - 1}} = \sqrt{\frac{0.16}{3}} = \sqrt{0.053} = 0.23$$

Based on these measurements, it would be appropriate to represent the measured percent carbon as 42.08 ± 0.23.

PROPERTIES OF WATER

Density:	0.99987 g/mL at 0 °C
	1.00000 g/mL at 4 °C
	0.99707 g/mL at 25 °C
	0.95838 g/mL at 100 °C
Heat (enthalpy) of fusion:	6.008 kJ/mol at 0 °C
Heat (enthalpy) of vaporization:	44.94 kJ/mol at 0 °C
	44.02 kJ/mol at 25 °C
	40.67 kJ/mol at 100 °C
Ion-product constant, K_w:	1.14×10^{-15} at 0 °C
	1.01×10^{-14} at 25 °C
	5.47×10^{-14} at 50 °C
Specific heat:	2.092 J/g-K = 2.092 J/g $\cdot$ °C for ice at -3 °C
	4.184 J/g-K = 4.184 J/g $\cdot$ °C for water at 25 °C
	1.841 J/g-K = 1.841 J/g $\cdot$ °C for steam at 100 °C

Vapor Pressure (torr) at Different Temperatures

$T(°C)$	P	$T(°C)$	P	$T(°C)$	P	$T(°C)$	P
0	4.58	21	18.65	35	42.2	92	567.0
5	6.54	22	19.83	40	55.3	94	610.9
10	9.21	23	21.07	45	71.9	96	657.6
12	10.52	24	22.38	50	92.5	98	707.3
14	11.99	25	23.76	55	118.0	100	760.0
16	13.63	26	25.21	60	149.4	102	815.9
17	14.53	27	26.74	65	187.5	104	875.1
18	15.48	28	28.35	70	233.7	106	937.9
19	16.48	29	30.04	80	355.1	108	1004.4
20	17.54	30	31.82	90	525.8	110	1074.6

THERMODYNAMIC QUANTITIES FOR SELECTED SUBSTANCES AT 298.15 K (25 °C)

Substance	ΔH_f° (kJ/mol)	ΔG_f° (kJ/mol)	S° (J/mol-K)	Substance	ΔH_f° (kJ/mol)	ΔG_f° (kJ/mol)	S° (J/mol-K)
Aluminum				$C_2H_4(g)$	52.30	68.11	219.4
$Al(s)$	0	0	28.32	$C_2H_6(g)$	−84.68	−32.89	229.5
$AlCl_3(s)$	−705.6	−630.0	109.3	$C_3H_8(g)$	−103.85	−23.47	269.9
$Al_2O_3(s)$	−1669.8	−1576.5	51.00	$C_4H_{10}(g)$	−124.73	−15.71	310.0
				$C_4H_{10}(l)$	−147.6	−15.0	231.0
Barium				$C_6H_6(g)$	82.9	129.7	269.2
$Ba(s)$	0	0	63.2	$C_6H_6(l)$	49.0	124.5	172.8
$BaCO_3(s)$	−1216.3	−1137.6	112.1	$CH_3OH(g)$	−201.2	−161.9	237.6
$BaO(s)$	−553.5	−525.1	70.42	$CH_3OH(l)$	−238.6	−166.23	126.8
				$C_2H_5OH(g)$	−235.1	−168.5	282.7
Beryllium				$C_2H_5OH(l)$	−277.7	−174.76	160.7
$Be(s)$	0	0	9.44	$C_6H_{12}O_6(s)$	−1273.02	−910.4	212.1
$BeO(s)$	−608.4	−579.1	13.77	$CO(g)$	−110.5	−137.2	197.9
$Be(OH)_2(s)$	−905.8	−817.9	50.21	$CO_2(g)$	−393.5	−394.4	213.6
				$CH_3COOH(l)$	−487.0	−392.4	159.8
Bromine							
$Br(g)$	111.8	82.38	174.9	**Cesium**			
$Br^-(aq)$	−120.9	−102.8	80.71	$Cs(g)$	76.50	49.53	175.6
$Br_2(g)$	30.71	3.14	245.3	$Cs(l)$	2.09	0.03	92.07
$Br_2(l)$	0	0	152.3	$Cs(s)$	0	0	85.15
$HBr(g)$	−36.23	−53.22	198.49	$CsCl(s)$	−442.8	−414.4	101.2
Calcium				**Chlorine**			
$Ca(g)$	179.3	145.5	154.8	$Cl(g)$	121.7	105.7	165.2
$Ca(s)$	0	0	41.4	$Cl(aq)$	−167.2	−131.2	56.5
$CaCO_3(s, calcite)$	−1207.1	−1128.76	92.88	$Cl_2(g)$	0	0	222.96
$CaCl_2(s)$	−795.8	−748.1	104.6	$HCl(aq)$	−167.2	−131.2	56.5
$CaF_2(s)$	−1219.6	−1167.3	68.87	$HCl(g)$	−92.30	−95.27	186.69
$CaO(s)$	−635.5	−604.17	39.75				
$Ca(OH)_2(s)$	−986.2	−898.5	83.4	**Chromium**			
$CaSO_4(s)$	−1434.0	−1321.8	106.7	$Cr(g)$	397.5	352.6	174.2
				$Cr(s)$	0	0	23.6
Carbon				$Cr_2O_3(s)$	−1139.7	−1058.1	81.2
$C(g)$	718.4	672.9	158.0				
$C(s, diamond)$	1.88	2.84	2.43	**Cobalt**			
$C(s, graphite)$	0	0	5.69	$Co(g)$	439	393	179
$CCl_4(g)$	−106.7	−64.0	309.4	$Co(s)$	0	0	28.4
$CCl_4(l)$	−139.3	−68.6	214.4				
$CF_4(g)$	−679.9	−635.1	262.3	**Copper**			
$CH_4(g)$	−74.8	−50.8	186.3	$Cu(g)$	338.4	298.6	166.3
$C_2H_2(g)$	226.77	209.2	200.8	$Cu(s)$	0	0	33.30

Substance	ΔH_f° (kJ/mol)	ΔG_f° (kJ/mol)	S° (J/mol-K)	Substance	ΔH_f° (kJ/mol)	ΔG_f° (kJ/mol)	S° (J/mol-K)
$CuCl_2(s)$	−205.9	−161.7	108.1	$MgO(s)$	−601.8	−569.6	26.8
$CuO(s)$	−156.1	−128.3	42.59	$Mg(OH)_2(s)$	−924.7	−833.7	63.24
$Cu_2O(s)$	−170.7	−147.9	92.36	**Manganese**			
Fluorine				$Mn(g)$	280.7	238.5	173.6
$F(g)$	80.0	61.9	158.7	$Mn(s)$	0	0	32.0
$F(aq)$	−332.6	−278.8	−13.8	$MnO(s)$	−385.2	−362.9	59.7
$F_2(g)$	0	0	202.7	$MnO_2(s)$	−519.6	−464.8	53.14
$HF(g)$	−268.61	−270.70	173.51	$MnO_4^-(aq)$	−541.4	−447.2	191.2
Hydrogen				**Mercury**			
$H(g)$	217.94	203.26	114.60	$Hg(g)$	60.83	31.76	174.89
$H^+(aq)$	0	0	0	$Hg(l)$	0	0	77.40
$H^+(g)$	1536.2	1517.0	108.9	$HgCl_2(s)$	−230.1	−184.0	144.5
$H_2(g)$	0	0	130.58	$Hg_2Cl_2(s)$	−264.9	−210.5	192.5
Iodine				**Nickel**			
$I(g)$	106.60	70.16	180.66	$Ni(g)$	429.7	384.5	182.1
$I^-(aq)$	−55.19	−51.57	111.3	$Ni(s)$	0	0	29.9
$I_2(g)$	62.25	19.37	260.57	$NiCl_2(s)$	−305.3	−259.0	97.65
$I_2(s)$	0	0	116.73	$NiO(s)$	−239.7	−211.7	37.99
$HI(g)$	25.94	1.30	206.3	**Nitrogen**			
Iron				$N(g)$	472.7	455.5	153.3
$Fe(g)$	415.5	369.8	180.5	$N_2(g)$	0	0	191.50
$Fe(s)$	0	0	27.15	$NH_3(aq)$	−80.29	−26.50	111.3
$Fe^{2+}(aq)$	−87.86	−84.93	113.4	$NH_3(g)$	−46.19	−16.66	192.5
$Fe^{3+}(aq)$	−47.69	−10.54	293.3	$NH_4^+(aq)$	−132.5	−79.31	113.4
$FeCl_2(s)$	−341.8	−302.3	117.9	$N_2H_4(g)$	95.40	159.4	238.5
$FeCl_3(s)$	−400	−334	142.3	$NH_4CN(s)$	0.0	—	—
$FeO(s)$	−271.9	−255.2	60.75	$NH_4Cl(s)$	−314.4	−203.0	94.6
$Fe_2O_3(s)$	−822.16	−740.98	89.96	$NH_4NO_3(s)$	−365.6	−184.0	151
$Fe_3O_4(s)$	−1117.1	−1014.2	146.4	$NO(g)$	90.37	86.71	210.62
$FeS_2(s)$	−171.5	−160.1	52.92	$NO_2(g)$	33.84	51.84	240.45
Lead				$N_2O(g)$	81.6	103.59	220.0
$Pb(s)$	0	0	68.85	$N_2O_4(g)$	9.66	98.28	304.3
$PbBr_2(s)$	−277.4	−260.7	161	$NOCl(g)$	52.6	66.3	264
$PbCO_3(s)$	−699.1	−625.5	131.0	$HNO_3(aq)$	−206.6	−110.5	146
$Pb(NO_3)_2(aq)$	−421.3	−246.9	303.3	$HNO_3(g)$	−134.3	−73.94	266.4
$Pb(NO_3)_2(s)$	−451.9	—	—	**Oxygen**			
$PbO(s)$	−217.3	−187.9	68.70	$O(g)$	247.5	230.1	161.0
Lithium				$O_2(g)$	0	0	205.0
$Li(g)$	159.3	126.6	138.8	$O_3(g)$	142.3	163.4	237.6
$Li(s)$	0	0	29.09	$OH^-(aq)$	−230.0	−157.3	−10.7
$Li^+(aq)$	−278.5	−273.4	12.2	$H_2O(g)$	−241.82	−228.57	188.83
$Li^+(g)$	685.7	648.5	133.0	$H_2O(l)$	−285.83	−237.13	69.91
$LiCl(s)$	−408.3	−384.0	59.30	$H_2O_2(g)$	−136.10	−105.48	232.9
Magnesium				$H_2O_2(l)$	−187.8	−120.4	109.6
$Mg(g)$	147.1	112.5	148.6	**Phosphorus**			
$Mg(s)$	0	0	32.51	$P(g)$	316.4	280.0	163.2
$MgCl_2(s)$	−641.6	−592.1	89.6	$P_2(g)$	144.3	103.7	218.1

Substance	ΔH_f° (kJ/mol)	ΔG_f° (kJ/mol)	S° (J/mol-K)	Substance	ΔH_f° (kJ/mol)	ΔG_f° (kJ/mol)	S° (J/mol-K)
$P_4(g)$	58.9	24.4	280	$AgNO_3(s)$	-124.4	-33.41	140.9
$P_4(s, red)$	-17.46	-12.03	22.85	**Sodium**			
$P_4(s, white)$	0	0	41.08	$Na(g)$	107.7	77.3	153.7
$PCl_3(g)$	-288.07	-269.6	311.7	$Na(s)$	0	0	51.45
$PCl_3(l)$	-319.6	-272.4	217	$Na^+(aq)$	-240.1	-261.9	59.0
$PF_5(g)$	-1594.4	-1520.7	300.8	$Na^+(g)$	609.3	574.3	148.0
$PH_3(g)$	5.4	13.4	210.2	$NaBr(aq)$	-360.6	-364.7	141.00
$P_4O_6(s)$	-1640.1	—	—	$NaBr(s)$	-361.4	-349.3	86.82
$P_4O_{10}(s)$	-2940.1	-2675.2	228.9	$Na_2CO_3(s)$	-1130.9	-1047.7	136.0
$POCl_3(g)$	-542.2	-502.5	325	$NaCl(aq)$	-407.1	-393.0	115.5
$POCl_3(l)$	-597.0	-520.9	222	$NaCl(g)$	-181.4	-201.3	229.8
$H_3PO_4(aq)$	-1288.3	-1142.6	158.2	$NaCl(s)$	-410.9	-384.0	72.33
				$NaHCO_3(s)$	-947.7	-851.8	102.1
Potassium				$NaNO_3(aq)$	-446.2	-372.4	207
$K(g)$	89.99	61.17	160.2	$NaNO_3(s)$	-467.9	-367.0	116.5
$K(s)$	0	0	64.67	$NaCH(aq)$	-469.6	-419.2	49.8
$KCl(s)$	-435.9	-408.3	82.7	$NaCH(s)$	-425.6	-379.5	64.46
$KClO_3(s)$	-391.2	-289.9	143.0	$Na_2SO_4(s)$	-1387.1	-1270.2	149.6
$KClO_3(aq)$	-349.5	-284.9	265.7				
$K_2CO_3(s)$	-1150.18	-1064.58	155.44	**Strontium**			
$KNO_3(s)$	-492.70	-393.13	132.9	$SrO(s)$	-592.0	-561.9	54.9
$K_2O(s)$	-363.2	-322.1	94.14	$Sr(g)$	164.4	110.0	164.6
$KO_2(s)$	-284.5	-240.6	122.5				
$K_2O_2(s)$	-495.8	-429.8	113.0	**Sulfur**			
$KOH(s)$	-424.7	-378.9	78.91	$S(s, rhombic)$	0	0	31.88
$KOH(aq)$	-482.4	-440.5	91.6	$S_8(g)$	102.3	49.7	430.9
				$SO_2(g)$	-296.9	-300.4	248.5
Rubidium				$SO_3(g)$	-395.2	-370.4	256.2
$Rb(g)$	85.8	55.8	170.0	$SO_4^{2-}(aq)$	-909.3	-744.5	20.1
$Rb(s)$	0	0	76.78	$SOCl_2(l)$	-245.6	—	—
$RbCl(s)$	-430.5	-412.0	92	$H_2S(g)$	-20.17	-33.01	205.6
$RbClO_3(s)$	-392.4	-292.0	152	$H_2SO_4(aq)$	-909.3	-744.5	20.1
				$H_2SO_4(l)$	-814.0	-689.9	156.1
Scandium							
$Sc(g)$	377.8	336.1	174.7	**Titanium**			
$Sc(s)$	0	0	34.6	$Ti(g)$	468	422	180.3
				$Ti(s)$	0	0	30.76
Selenium				$TiCl_4(g)$	-763.2	-726.8	354.9
$H_2Se(g)$	29.7	15.9	219.0	$TiCl_4(l)$	-804.2	-728.1	221.9
				$TiC_2(s)$	-944.7	-889.4	50.29
Silicon							
$Si(g)$	368.2	323.9	167.8	**Vanadium**			
$Si(s)$	0	0	18.7	$V(g)$	514.2	453.1	182.2
$SiC(s)$	-73.22	-70.85	16.61	$V(s)$	0	0	28.9
$SiCl_4(l)$	-640.1	-572.8	239.3				
$SiO_2(s, quartz)$	-910.9	-856.5	41.84	**Zinc**			
				$Zn(g)$	130.7	95.2	160.9
Silver				$Zn(s)$	0	0	41.63
$Ag(s)$	0	0	42.55	$ZnCl_2(s)$	-415.1	-369.4	111.5
$Ag^+(aq)$	105.90	77.11	73.93	$ZnO(s)$	-348.0	-318.2	43.9
$AgCl(s)$	-127.0	-109.70	96.11				
$Ag_2O(s)$	-31.05	-11.20	121.3				

AQUEOUS EQUILIBRIUM CONSTANTS

TABLE D.1 • Dissociation Constants for Acids at 25 °C

Name	Formula	K_{a1}	K_{a2}	K_{a3}
Acetic acid	CH_3COOH (or $HC_2H_3O_2$)	1.8×10^{-5}		
Arsenic acid	H_3AsO_4	5.6×10^{-3}	1.0×10^{-7}	3.0×10^{-12}
Arsenous acid	H_3AsO_3	5.1×10^{-10}		
Ascorbic acid	$H_2C_6H_6O_6$	8.0×10^{-5}	1.6×10^{-12}	
Benzoic acid	C_6H_5COOH (or $HC_7H_5O_2$)	6.3×10^{-5}		
Boric acid	H_3BO_3	5.8×10^{-10}		
Butanoic acid	C_3H_7COOH (or $HC_4H_7O_2$)	1.5×10^{-5}		
Carbonic acid	H_2CO_3	4.3×10^{-7}	5.6×10^{-11}	
Chloroacetic acid	$CH_2ClCOOH$ (or $HC_2H_2O_2Cl$)	1.4×10^{-3}		
Chlorous acid	$HClO_2$	1.1×10^{-2}		
Citric acid	$HOOCC(OH)(CH_2COOH)_2$ (or $H_3C_6H_5O_7$)	7.4×10^{-4}	1.7×10^{-5}	4.0×10^{-7}
Cyanic acid	$HCNO$	3.5×10^{-4}		
Formic acid	$HCOOH$ (or $HCHO_2$)	1.8×10^{-4}		
Hydroazoic acid	HN_3	1.9×10^{-5}		
Hydrocyanic acid	HCN	4.9×10^{-10}		
Hydrofluoric acid	HF	6.8×10^{-4}		
Hydrogen chromate ion	$HCrO_4^-$	3.0×10^{-7}		
Hydrogen peroxide	H_2O_2	2.4×10^{-12}		
Hydrogen selenate ion	$HSeO_4^-$	2.2×10^{-2}		
Hydrogen sulfide	H_2S	9.5×10^{-8}	1×10^{-19}	
Hypobromous acid	$HBrO$	2.5×10^{-9}		
Hypochlorous acid	$HClO$	3.0×10^{-8}		
Hypoiodous acid	HIO	2.3×10^{-11}		
Iodic acid	HIO_3	1.7×10^{-1}		
Lactic acid	$CH_3CH(OH)COOH$ (or $HC_3H_5O_3$)	1.4×10^{-4}		
Malonic acid	$CH_2(COOH)_2$ (or $H_2C_3H_2O_4$)	1.5×10^{-3}	2.0×10^{-6}	
Nitrous acid	HNO_2	4.5×10^{-4}		
Oxalic acid	$(COOH)_2$ (or $H_2C_2O_4$)	5.9×10^{-2}	6.4×10^{-5}	
Paraperiodic acid	H_5IO_6	2.8×10^{-2}	5.3×10^{-9}	
Phenol	C_6H_5OH (or HC_6H_5O)	1.3×10^{-10}		
Phosphoric acid	H_3PO_4	7.5×10^{-3}	6.2×10^{-8}	4.2×10^{-13}
Propionic acid	C_2H_5COOH (or $HC_3H_5O_2$)	1.3×10^{-5}		
Pyrophosphoric acid	$H_4P_2O_7$	3.0×10^{-2}	4.4×10^{-3}	2.1×10^{-7}
Selenous acid	H_2SeO_3	2.3×10^{-3}	5.3×10^{-9}	
Sulfuric acid	H_2SO_4	Strong acid	1.2×10^{-2}	
Sulfurous acid	H_2SO_3	1.7×10^{-2}	6.4×10^{-8}	
Tartaric acid	$HOOC(CHOH)_2COOH$ (or $H_2C_4H_4O_6$)	1.0×10^{-3}		

TABLE D.2 • Dissociation Constants for Bases at 25 °C

Name	Formula	K_b
Ammonia	NH_3	1.8×10^{-5}
Aniline	$C_6H_5NH_2$	4.3×10^{-10}
Dimethylamine	$(CH_3)_2NH$	5.4×10^{-4}
Ethylamine	$C_2H_5NH_2$	6.4×10^{-4}
Hydrazine	H_2NNH_2	1.3×10^{-6}
Hydroxylamine	$HONH_2$	1.1×10^{-8}
Methylamine	CH_3NH_2	4.4×10^{-4}
Pyridine	C_5H_5N	1.7×10^{-9}
Trimethylamine	$(CH_3)_3N$	6.4×10^{-5}

TABLE D.3 • Solubility-Product Constants for Compounds at 25 °C

Name	Formula	K_{sp}	Name	Formula	K_{sp}
Barium carbonate	$BaCO_3$	5.0×10^{-9}	Lead(II) fluoride	PbF_2	3.6×10^{-8}
Barium chromate	$BaCrO_4$	2.1×10^{-10}	Lead(II) sulfate	$PbSO_4$	6.3×10^{-7}
Barium fluoride	BaF_2	1.7×10^{-6}	Lead(II) sulfide*	PbS	3×10^{-28}
Barium oxalate	BaC_2O_4	1.6×10^{-6}	Magnesium hydroxide	$Mg(OH)_2$	1.8×10^{-11}
Barium sulfate	$BaSO_4$	1.1×10^{-10}	Magnesium carbonate	$MgCO_3$	3.5×10^{-8}
Cadmium carbonate	$CdCO_3$	1.8×10^{-14}	Magnesium oxalate	MgC_2O_4	8.6×10^{-5}
Cadmium hydroxide	$Cd(OH)_2$	2.5×10^{-14}	Manganese(II) carbonate	$MnCO_3$	5.0×10^{-10}
Cadmium sulfide*	CdS	8×10^{-28}	Manganese(II) hydroxide	$Mn(OH)_2$	1.6×10^{-13}
Calcium carbonate (calcite)	$CaCO_3$	4.5×10^{-9}	Manganese(II) sulfide*	MnS	2×10^{-53}
Calcium chromate	$CaCrO_4$	4.5×10^{-9}	Mercury(I) chloride	Hg_2Cl_2	1.2×10^{-18}
Calcium fluoride	CaF_2	3.9×10^{-11}	Mercury(I) iodide	Hg_2I_2	$1.1 \times 10^{-1.1}$
Calcium hydroxide	$Ca(OH)_2$	6.5×10^{-6}	Mercury(II) sulfide*	HgS	2×10^{-53}
Calcium phosphate	$Ca_3(PO_4)_2$	2.0×10^{-29}	Nickel(II) carbonate	$NiCO_3$	1.3×10^{-7}
Calcium sulfate	$CaSO_4$	2.4×10^{-5}	Nickel(II) hydroxide	$Ni(OH)_2$	6.0×10^{-16}
Chromium(III) hydroxide	$Cr(OH)_3$	1.6×10^{-30}	Nickel(II) sulfide*	NiS	3×10^{-20}
Cobalt(II) carbonate	$CoCO_3$	1.0×10^{-10}	Silver bromate	$AgBrO_3$	5.5×10^{-13}
Cobalt(II) hydroxide	$Co(OH)_2$	1.3×10^{-15}	Silver bromide	$AgBr$	5.0×10^{-13}
Cobalt(II) sulfide*	CoS	5×10^{-22}	Silver carbonate	Ag_2CO_3	8.1×10^{-12}
Copper(I) bromide	$CuBr$	5.3×10^{-9}	Silver chloride	$AgCl$	1.8×10^{-10}
Copper(II) carbonate	$CuCO_3$	2.3×10^{-10}	Silver chromate	Ag_2CrO_4	1.2×10^{-12}
Copper(II) hydroxide	$Cu(OH)_2$	4.8×10^{-20}	Silver iodide	AgI	8.3×10^{-17}
Copper(II) sulfide*	CuS	6×10^{-37}	Silver sulfate	Ag_2SO_4	1.5×10^{-5}
Iron(II) carbonate	$FeCO_3$	2.1×10^{-11}	Silver sulfide*	Ag_2S	6×10^{-51}
Iron(II) hydroxide	$Fe(OH)_2$	7.9×10^{-16}	Strontium carbonate	$SrCO_3$	9.3×10^{-10}
Lanthanum fluoride	LaF_3	2×10^{-19}	Tin(II) sulfide*	SnS	1×10^{-26}
Lanthanum iodate	$La(IO_3)_3$	7.4×10^{-14}	Zinc carbonate	$ZnCO_3$	1.0×10^{-10}
Lead(II) carbonate	$PbCO_3$	7.4×10^{-14}	Zinc hydroxide	$Zn(OH)_2$	3.0×10^{-16}
Lead(II) chloride	$PbCl_2$	1.7×10^{-5}	Zinc oxalate	ZnC_2O_4	2.7×10^{-8}
Lead(II) chromate	$PbCrO_4$	2.8×10^{-13}	Zinc sulfide*	ZnS	2×10^{-25}

*For a solubility equilibrium of the type $MS(s) + H_2O(l) \rightleftharpoons M^{2+}(aq) + HS^-(aq) + OH^-(aq)$

STANDARD REDUCTION POTENTIALS AT 25 °C

Half-Reaction	$E°$(V)	Half-Reaction	$E°$(V)
$Ag^+(aq) + e^- \longrightarrow Ag(s)$	+0.799	$2 H_2O(l) + 2 e^- \longrightarrow H_2(g) + 2 OH^-(aq)$	−0.83
$AgBr(s) + e^- \longrightarrow Ag(s) + Br^-(aq)$	+0.095	$HO_2^-(aq) + H_2O(l) + 2 e^- \longrightarrow 3 OH^-(aq)$	+0.88
$AgCl(s) + e^- \longrightarrow Ag(s) + Cl^-(aq)$	+0.222	$H_2O_2(aq) + 2 H^+(aq) + 2 e^- \longrightarrow 2 H_2O(l)$	+1.776
$Ag(CN)_2^-(aq) + e^- \longrightarrow Ag(s) + 2 CN^-(aq)$	−0.31	$Hg_2^{2+}(aq) + 2 e^- \longrightarrow 2 Hg(l)$	+0.789
$Ag_2CrO_4(s) + 2 e^- \longrightarrow 2 Ag(s) + CrO_4^{2-}(aq)$	+0.446	$2 Hg^{2+}(aq) + 2 e^- \longrightarrow Hg_2^{2+}(aq)$	+0.920
$AgI(s) + e^- \longrightarrow Ag(s) + I^-(aq)$	−0.151	$Hg^{2+}(aq) + 2 e^- \longrightarrow Hg(l)$	+0.854
$Ag(S_2O_3)_2^{3-}(aq) + e^- \longrightarrow Ag(s) + 2 S_2O_3^{2-}(aq)$	+0.01	$I_2(s) + 2 e^- \longrightarrow 2 I^-(aq)$	+0.536
$Al^{3+}(aq) + 3 e^- \longrightarrow Al(s)$	−1.66	$2 IO_3^-(aq) + 12 H^+(aq) + 10 e^- \longrightarrow$	+1.195
$H_3AsO_4(aq) + 2 H^+(aq) + 2 e^- \longrightarrow$	+0.559	$\qquad I_2(s) + 6 H_2O(l)$	
$\qquad H_3AsO_3(aq) + H_2O(l)$		$K^+(aq) + e^- \longrightarrow K(s)$	−2.925
$Ba^{2+}(aq) + 2 e^- \longrightarrow Ba(s)$	−2.90	$Li^+(aq) + e^- \longrightarrow Li(s)$	−3.05
$BiO^+(aq) + 2 H^+(aq) + 3 e^- \longrightarrow Bi(s) + H_2O(l)$	+0.32	$Mg^{2+}(aq) + 2 e^- \longrightarrow Mg(s)$	−2.37
$Br_2(l) + 2 e^- \longrightarrow 2 Br^-(aq)$	+1.065	$Mn^{2+}(aq) + 2 e^- \longrightarrow Mn(s)$	−1.18
$2 BrO_3^-(aq) + 12 H^+(aq) + 10 e^- \longrightarrow$	+1.52	$MnO_2(s) + 4 H^+(aq) + 2 e^- \longrightarrow$	+1.23
$\qquad Br_2(l) + 6 H_2O(l)$		$\qquad Mn^{2+}(aq) + 2 H_2O(l)$	
$2 CO_2(g) + 2 H^+(aq) + 2 e^- \longrightarrow H_2C_2O_4(aq)$	−0.49	$MnO_4^-(aq) + 8 H^+(aq) + 5 e^- \longrightarrow$	+1.51
$Ca^{2+}(aq) + 2 e^- \longrightarrow Ca(s)$	−2.87	$\qquad Mn^{2+}(aq) + 4 H_2O(l)$	
$Cd^{2+}(aq) + 2 e^- \longrightarrow Cd(s)$	−0.403	$MnO_4^-(aq) + 2 H_2O(l) + 3 e^- \longrightarrow$	+0.59
$Ce^{4+}(aq) + e^- \longrightarrow Ce^{3+}(aq)$	+1.61	$\qquad MnO_2(s) + 4 OH^-(aq)$	
$Cl_2(g) + 2 e^- \longrightarrow 2 Cl^-(aq)$	+1.359	$HNO_2(aq) + H^+(aq) + e^- \longrightarrow NO(g) + H_2O(l)$	+1.00
$2 HClO(aq) + 2 H^+(aq) + 2 e^- \longrightarrow$	+1.63	$N_2(g) + 4 H_2O(l) + 4 e^- \longrightarrow 4 OH^-(aq) + N_2H_4(aq)$	−1.16
$\qquad Cl_2(g) + 2 H_2O(l)$		$N_2(g) + 5 H^+(aq) + 4 e^- \longrightarrow N_2H_5^+(aq)$	−0.23
$ClO^-(aq) + H_2O(l) + 2 e^- \longrightarrow$	+0.89	$NO_3^-(aq) + 4 H^+(aq) + 3 e^- \longrightarrow NO(g) + 2 H_2O(l)$	+0.96
$\qquad Cl^-(aq) + 2 OH^-(aq)$		$Na^+(aq) + e^- \longrightarrow Na(s)$	−2.71
$2 ClO_3^-(aq) + 12 H^+(aq) + 10 e^- \longrightarrow$	+1.47	$Ni^{2+}(aq) + 2 e^- \longrightarrow Ni(s)$	−0.28
$\qquad Cl_2(g) + 6 H_2O(l)$		$O_2(g) + 4 H^+(aq) + 4 e^- \longrightarrow 2 H_2O(l)$	+1.23
$Co^{2+}(aq) + 2 e^- \longrightarrow Co(s)$	−0.277	$O_2(g) + 2 H_2O(l) + 4 e^- \longrightarrow 4 OH^-(aq)$	+0.40
$Co^{3+}(aq) + e^- \longrightarrow Co^{2+}(aq)$	+1.842	$O_2(g) + 2 H^+(aq) + 2 e^- \longrightarrow H_2O_2(aq)$	+0.68
$Cr^{3+}(aq) + 3 e^- \longrightarrow Cr(s)$	−0.74	$O_3(g) + 2 H^+(aq) + 2 e^- \longrightarrow O_2(g) + H_2O(l)$	+2.07
$Cr^{3+}(aq) + e^- \longrightarrow Cr^{2+}(aq)$	−0.41	$Pb^{2+}(aq) + 2 e^- \longrightarrow Pb(s)$	−0.126
$CrO_7^{2-}(aq) + 14 H^+(aq) + 6 e^- \longrightarrow$	+1.33	$PbO_2(s) + HSO_4^-(aq) + 3 H^+(aq) + 2 e^- \longrightarrow$	+1.685
$\qquad 2 Cr^{3+}(aq) + 7 H_2O(l)$		$\qquad PbSO_4(s) + 2 H_2O(l)$	
$CrO_4^{2-}(aq) + 4 H_2O(l) + 3 e^- \longrightarrow$	−0.13	$PbSO_4(s) + H^+(aq) + 2 e^- \longrightarrow Pb(s) + HSO_4^-(aq)$	−0.356
$\qquad Cr(OH)_3(s) + 5 OH^-(aq)$		$PtCl_4^{2-}(aq) + 2 e^- \longrightarrow Pt(s) + 4 Cl^-(aq)$	+0.73
$Cu^{2+}(aq) + 2 e^- \longrightarrow Cu(s)$	+0.337	$S(s) + 2 H^+(aq) + 2 e^- \longrightarrow H_2S(g)$	+0.141
$Cu^{2+}(aq) + e^- \longrightarrow Cu^+(aq)$	+0.153	$H_2SO_3(aq) + 4 H^+(aq) + 4 e^- \longrightarrow S(s) + 3 H_2O(l)$	+0.45
$Cu^+(aq) + e^- \longrightarrow Cu(s)$	+0.521	$HSO_4^-(aq) + 3 H^+(aq) + 2 e^- \longrightarrow$	+0.17
$CuI(s) + e^- \longrightarrow Cu(s) + I^-(aq)$	−0.185	$\qquad H_2SO_3(aq) + H_2O(l)$	
$F_2(g) + 2 e^- \longrightarrow 2 F^-(aq)$	+2.87	$Sn^{2+}(aq) + 2 e^- \longrightarrow Sn(s)$	−0.136
$Fe^{2+}(aq) + 2 e^- \longrightarrow Fe(s)$	−0.440	$Sn^{4+}(aq) + 2 e^- \longrightarrow Sn^{2+}(aq)$	+0.154
$Fe^{3+}(aq) + e^- \longrightarrow Fe^{2+}(aq)$	+0.771	$VO_2^+(aq) + 2 H^+(aq) + e^- \longrightarrow VO^{2+}(aq) + H_2O(l)$	+1.00
$Fe(CN)_6^{3-}(aq) + e^- \longrightarrow Fe(CN)_6^{4-}(aq)$	+0.36	$Zn^{2+}(aq) + 2 e^- \longrightarrow Zn(s)$	−0.763
$2 H^+(aq) + 2 e^- \longrightarrow H_2(g)$	0.000		

CHAPTER 1

1.1 (a) Pure element: i (b) mixture of elements: v, vi (c) pure compound: iv (d) mixture of an element and a compound: ii, iii **1.3** This kind of separation based on solubility differences is called *extraction*. The insoluble grounds are then separated from the coffee solution by *filtration*. **1.5** (a) The aluminum sphere is lightest, then nickel, then silver. (b) The platinum sphere is largest, then gold, then lead. **1.7** (a) 7.5 cm; two significant figures (sig figs) (b) 72 mi/hr (inner scale, two significant figures) or 115 km/hr (outer scale, three significant figures) **1.9** Arrange the conversion factor so that the given unit cancels and the desired unit is in the correct position. **1.11** (a) Heterogeneous mixture (b) homogeneous mixture (heterogeneous if there are undissolved particles) (c) pure substance (d) pure substance. **1.13** (a) S (b) Au (c) K (d) Cl (e) Cu (f) uranium (g) nickel (h) sodium (i) aluminum (j) silicon **1.15** C is a compound; it contains both carbon and oxygen. A is a compound; it contains at least carbon and oxygen. B is not defined by the data given; it is probably also a compound because few elements exist as white solids. **1.17** Physical properties: silvery white; lustrous; melting point = 649 °C; boiling point = 1105 °C; density at 20 °C = 1.738 g/cm^3; pounded into sheets; drawn into wires; good conductor. Chemical properties: burns in air; reacts with Cl_2. **1.19** (a) Chemical (b) physical (c) physical (d) chemical (e) chemical **1.21** (a) Add water to dissolve the sugar; filter this mixture, collecting the sand on the filter paper and the sugar water in the flask. Evaporate water from the flask to recover solid sugar (b) Allow the mixture to settle so that there are two distinct layers. Carefully pour off most of the top oil layer. After the layers reform, use a dropper to remove any remaining oil. Vinegar is in the original vessel and oil is in a second container. **1.23** (a) 1×10^{-1} (b) 1×10^{-2} (c) 1×10^{-15} (d) 1×10^{-6} (e) 1×10^{6} (f) 1×10^{3} (g) 1×10^{-9} (h) 1×10^{-3} (i) 1×10^{-12} **1.25** (a) 22 °C (b) 422.1 °F (c) 506 K (d) 107 °C (e) 1644 K (f) −459.67 °F **1.27** (a) 1.62 g/mL. Tetrachloroethylene, 1.62 g/mL, is more dense than water, 1.00 g/mL; tetrachloroethylene will sink rather than float on water. (b) 11.7 g **1.29** (a) Calculated density = 0.86 g/mL. The substance is probably toluene, density = 0.866 g/mL. (b) 40.4 mL ethylene glycol (c) 1.11×10^3 g nickel **1.31** 28 Pg **1.33** Exact: (c), (d), and (f) **1.35** (a) 3 (b) 2 (c) 5 (d) 3 (e) 5 (f) 1 **1.37** (a) 1.025×10^2 (b) 6.570×10^5 (c) 8.543×10^{-3} (d) 2.579×10^{-4} (e) -3.572×10^{-2} **1.39** (a) 17.00 (b) 812.0 (c) 8.23×10^3 (d) 8.69×10^{-2} **1.41** 5 significant figures

1.43 (a) $\dfrac{1 \times 10^{-3}\,m}{1\,mm} \times \dfrac{1\,nm}{1 \times 10^{-9}\,m}$ (b) $\dfrac{1 \times 10^{-3}\,g}{1\,mg} \times \dfrac{1\,kg}{1000\,g}$

(c) $\dfrac{1000\,m}{1\,km} \times \dfrac{1\,cm}{1 \times 10^{-2}\,m} \times \dfrac{1\,in.}{2.54\,cm} \times \dfrac{1\,ft}{12\,in.}$ (d) $\dfrac{(2.54)^3\,cm^3}{1^3\,in.^3}$

1.45 (a) 54.7 km/hr (b) 1.3×10^3 gal (c) 46.0 m (d) 0.984 in/hr **1.47** (a) 4.32×10^5 s (b) 88.5 m (c) \$0.499/L (d) 46.6 km/hr (e) 1.420 L/s (f) 707.9 cm^3 **1.49** (a) 1.2×10^2 L (b) 5×10^2 mg (c) 19.9 mi/gal (2×10^1 mi/gal for 1 significant figure) (d) 26 mL/g (3×10^1 mL/g for 1 significant figure) **1.51** 64 kg air **1.53** 14-in. shoe < 57-cm string < 1.1-m pipe **1.55** 6×10^4 **1.59** 8.47 g O; the *law of constant composition* **1.62** (a) Volume (b) area (c) volume (d) density (e) time (f) length (g) temperature **1.65** (a) 1.13×10^5 quarters (b) 6.41×10^5 g (c) 2.83×10^4 (d) 4.13×10^8 stacks **1.68** The most dense liquid, Hg, will sink; the least dense, cyclohexane, will float; H_2O will be in the middle. **1.71** density of solid = 1.63 g/mL **1.74** (a) Density of peat = 0.13 g/cm^3, density of soil = 2.5 g/cm^3. It is not correct to say that peat is "lighter" than topsoil. Volumes must be specified in order to compare masses. (b) Buy 16 bags of peat (more than 15 are needed). (Results to 1 significant figure are not meaningful.) **1.77** The inner diameter of the tube is 1.13 cm. **1.79** The separation

is successful if two distinct spots are seen on the paper. To quantify the characteristics of the separation, calculate a reference value for each spot: distance traveled by spot/distance traveled by solvent. If the values for the two spots are fairly different, the separation is successful.

CHAPTER 2

2.1 (a) The path of the charged particle bends because the particle is repelled by the negatively charged plate and attracted to the positively charged plate. (b) (−) (c) increase (d) decrease **2.4** The particle is an ion. $^{32}_{16}S^{2-}$ **2.6** Formula: IF_5; name: iodine pentafluoride; the compound is molecular. **2.9** Postulate 4 of the atomic theory states that the relative number and kinds of atoms in a compound are constant, regardless of the source. Therefore, 1.0 g of pure water should always contain the same relative amounts of hydrogen and oxygen, no matter where or how the sample is obtained. **2.11** (a) 0.5711 g O/1 g N; 1.142 g O/1 g N; 2.284 g O/1 g N; 2.855 g O/1 g N (b) The numbers in part (a) obey the *law of multiple proportions*. Multiple proportions arise because atoms are the indivisible entities combining, as stated in Dalton's atomic theory. **2.13** (1) Electric and magnetic fields deflected the rays in the same way they would deflect negatively charged particles. (2) A metal plate exposed to cathode rays acquired a negative charge. **2.15** (a) Most of the volume of an atom is empty space in which electrons move. Most alpha particles passed through this space. (b) The few alpha particles that hit the massive, positively charged gold nuclei were strongly repelled and deflected back in the direction they came from. (c) Because the Be nuclei have a smaller volume and a smaller positive charge than the Au nuclei, fewer alpha particles will be scattered and fewer will be strongly back scattered. **2.17** (a) 0.135 nm; 1.35×10^2 or 135 pm (b) 3.70×10^6 Au atoms (c) 1.03×10^{-23} cm^3 **2.19** (a) Proton, neutron, electron (b) proton = 1+, neutron = 0, electron = 1− (c) The neutron is most massive. (The neutron and proton have very similar masses.) (d) The electron is least massive. **2.21** (a) Atomic number is the number of protons in the nucleus of an atom. Mass number is the total number of nuclear particles, protons plus neutrons, in an atom. (b) mass number **2.23** (a) ^{40}Ar: 18 p, 22 n, 18 e (b) ^{65}Zn: 30 p, 35 n, 30 e (c) ^{70}Ga: 31 p, 39 n, 31 e (d) ^{80}Br: 35 p, 45 n, 35 e (e) ^{184}W: 74 p, 110 n, 74 e (f) ^{243}Am: 95 p, 148 n, 95e

2.25

Symbol	^{52}Cr	^{55}Mn	^{112}Cd	^{222}Rn	^{207}Pb
Protons	24	25	48	86	82
Neutrons	28	30	64	136	125
Electrons	24	25	48	86	82
Mass no.	52	55	112	222	207

2.27 (a) $^{196}_{78}$Pt (b) $^{84}_{36}$Kr (c) $^{75}_{33}$As (d) $^{24}_{12}$Mg **2.29** (a) $^{12}_{6}$C (b) Atomic weights are average atomic masses, the sum of the mass of each naturally occurring isotope of an element times its fractional abundance. Each B atom will have the mass of one of the naturally occurring isotopes, while the "atomic weight" is an average value. **2.31** 63.55 amu **2.33** (a) In Thomson's cathode-ray experiments and in mass spectrometry, a stream of charged particles is passed through the poles of a magnet. The charged particles are deflected by the magnetic field according to their mass and charge. (b) The *x*-axis label is atomic weight, and the *y*-axis label is signal intensity. (c) Uncharged particles are not deflected in a magnetic field. The effect of the magnetic field on charged moving particles is the basis of their separation by mass. **2.35** (a) average atomic mass = 24.31 amu

(b)

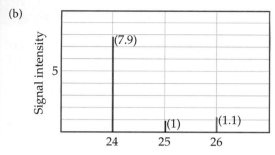

2.37 (a) Cr, 24 (metal) (b) He, 2 (nonmetal) (c) P, 15 (nonmetal) (d) Zn, 30 (metal) (e) Mg, 12 (metal) (f) Br, 35 (nonmetal) (g) As, 33 (metalloid)   **2.39** (a) K, alkali metals (metal) (b) I, halogens (nonmetal) (c) Mg, alkaline earth metals (metal) (d) Ar, noble gases (nonmetal) (e) S, chalcogens (nonmetal)   **2.41** An empirical formula shows the simplest mole ratio of elements in a compound. A molecular formula shows the exact number and kinds of atoms in a molecule. A structural formula shows which atoms are attached to which.   **2.43** (a) $AlBr_3$ (b) C_4H_5 (c) C_2H_4O (d) P_2O_5 (e) C_3H_2Cl (f) BNH_2 **2.45** (a) 6 (b) 6 (c) 12

2.47

(a) C_2H_6O,   H—C—O—C—H (with H's)

(b) C_2H_6O,   H—C—C—O—H (with H's)

(c) CH_4O,   H—C—O—H (with H's)

(d) PF_3,   F—P—F (with F)

2.49

Symbol	$^{59}Co^{3+}$	$^{80}Se^{2-}$	$^{192}Os^{2+}$	$^{200}Hg^{2+}$
Protons	27	34	76	80
Neutrons	32	46	116	120
Electrons	24	36	74	78
Net Charge	3+	2−	2+	2+

2.51 (a) Mg^{2+} (b) Al^{3+} (c) K^+ (d) S^{2-} (e) F^- **2.53** (a) GaF_3, gallium(III) fluoride (b) LiH, lithium hydride (c) AlI_3, aluminum iodide (d) K_2S, potassium sulfide   **2.55** (a) $CaBr_2$ (b) K_2CO_3 (c) $Al(CH_3COO)_3$ (d) $(NH_4)_2SO_4$ (e) $Mg_3(PO_4)_2$

2.57

Ion	K^+	NH_4^+	Mg^{2+}	Fe^{3+}
Cl^-	KCl	NH_4Cl	$MgCl_2$	$FeCl_3$
OH^-	KOH	NH_4OH	$Mg(OH)_2$	$Fe(OH)_3$
CO_3^{2-}	K_2CO_3	$(NH_4)_2CO_3$	$MgCO_3$	$Fe_2(CO_3)_3$
PO_4^{3-}	K_3PO_4	$(NH_4)_3PO_4$	$Mg_3(PO_4)_2$	$FePO_4$

2.59 Molecular: (a) B_2H_6 (b) CH_3OH (f) NOCl (g) NF_3. Ionic: (c) $LiNO_3$ (d) Sc_2O_3 (e) CsBr (h) Ag_2SO_4 **2.61** (a) ClO_2^- (b) Cl^- (c) ClO_3^- (d) ClO_4^- (e) ClO^- **2.63** (a) calcium, 2+; oxide, 2− (b) sodium, 1+; sulfate, 2− (c) potassium, 1+; perchlorate, 1− (d) iron, 2+, nitrate, 1− (e) chromium, 3+; hydroxide, 1−   **2.65** (a) lithium oxide (b) iron(III) chloride (ferric chloride) (c) sodium hypochlorite (d) calcium sulfite (e) copper(II) hydroxide (cupric hydroxide) (f) iron(II) nitrate (ferrous nitrate) (g) calcium acetate (h) chromium(III) carbonate (chromic carbonate) (i) potassium chromate (j) ammonium sulfate   **2.67** (a) $Al(OH)_3$ (b) K_2SO_4 (c) Cu_2O (d) $Zn(NO_3)_2$ (e) $HgBr_2$ (f) $Fe_2(CO_3)_3$ (g) NaBrO   **2.69** (a) Bromic acid (b) hydrobromic acid (c) phosphoric acid (d) HClO (e) HIO_3 (f) H_2SO_3 **2.71** (a) Sulfur hexafluoride (b) iodine pentafluoride (c) xenon trioxide (d) N_2O_4 (e) HCN (f) P_4S_6 **2.73** (a) $ZnCO_3$, ZnO, CO_2 (b) HF, SiO_2, SiF_4, H_2O (c) SO_2, H_2O, H_2SO_3 (d) PH_3 (e) $HClO_4$, Cd, $Cd(ClO_4)_2$ (f) VBr_3 **2.75** (a) A hydrocarbon is a compound composed of the elements hydrogen and carbon only.

(b)   H—C—C—C—C—H (with H's)

Molecular: C_4H_{10}
Empirical: C_2H_5

2.77 (a) Functional groups are groups of specific atoms that are constant from one molecule to the next. (b) —OH

(c)   H—C—C—C—C—OH (with H's)

2.79

(a, b)   H—C—C—C—Cl (with H's)

1-chloropropane

H—C—C—C—H (with H's and Cl)

2-chloropropane

2.82 (a) 2 protons, 1 neutron, 2 electrons (b) tritium, ^3H, is more massive. (c) A precision of 1×10^{-27} g would be required to differentiate between $^3H^+$ and $^3He^+$.   **2.84** Arrangement A, 4.1×10^{14} atoms/cm^2 (b) Arrangement B, 4.7×10^{14} atoms/cm^2 (c) The ratio of atoms going from arrangement B to arrangement A is 1.2 to 1. In three dimensions, arrangement B leads to a greater density for Rb metal.   **2.87** (a) $^{16}_8O$, $^{17}_8O$, $^{18}_8O$ (b) All isotopes are atoms of the same element, oxygen, with the same atomic number, 8 protons in the nucleus and 8 electrons. We expect their electron arrangements to be the same and their chemical properties to be very similar. Each has a different number of neutrons, a different mass number, and a different atomic mass.   **2.90** (a) $^{69}_{31}Ga$, 31 protons, 38 neutrons; $^{71}_{31}Ga$, 31 protons, 40 neutrons (b) $^{69}_{31}Ga$, 60.3%, $^{71}_{31}Ga$, 39.7%.   **2.93** (a) 5 significant figures (b) An electron is 0.05444% of the mass of an ^1H atom.   **2.96** Strontium is an alkaline earth metal, similar in chemical properties to calcium and magnesium. Harmful strontium closely mimics essential calcium and magnesium, then behaves badly when the body tries to use it as it uses calcium and magnesium.   **2.98** (a) Nickel(II) oxide, 2+ (b) manganese(IV) oxide, 4+ (c) chromium(III) oxide, 3+ (d) molybdenum(VI) oxide, 6+   **2.101** (a) Perbromate ion (b) selenite ion (c) AsO_4^{3-} (d) $HTeO_4^-$ **2.104** (a) Potassium nitrate (b) sodium carbonate (c) calcium oxide (d) hydrochloric acid (e) magnesium sulfate (f) magnesium hydroxide

CHAPTER 3

3.1 Equation (a) best fits the diagram.   **3.3** (a) NO_2 (b) No, because we have no way of knowing whether the empirical and molecular formulas are the same. NO_2 represents the simplest ratio of atoms in a molecule but not the only possible molecular formula.   **3.5** (a) $C_2H_5NO_2$ (b) 75.0 g/mol (c) 225 g glycine (d) Mass %N in glycine is 18.7%.

3.7

$N_2 + 3 H_2 \longrightarrow 2 NH_3$. Eight N atoms (4 N_2 molecules) require 24 H atoms (12 H_2 molecules) for complete reaction. Only 9 H_2 molecules are available, so H_2 is the limiting reactant. Nine H_2 molecules (18 H atoms) determine that 6 NH_3 molecules are produced. One N_2 molecule is in excess.   **3.9** (a) Conservation of mass (b) Subscripts in chemical formulas should not be changed when balancing equations, because changing the subscript changes the identity of the compound (*law of constant composition*). (c) $H_2O(l)$, $H_2O(g)$, $NaCl(aq)$, $NaCl(s)$

3.11 (a) $2 CO(g) + O_2(g) \longrightarrow 2 CO_2(g)$

(b) $N_2O_5(g) + H_2O(l) \longrightarrow 2 HNO_3(aq)$

(c) $CH_4(g) + 4 Cl_2(g) \longrightarrow CCl_4(l) + 4 HCl(g)$

(d) $Al_4C_3(s) + 12 H_2O(l) \longrightarrow 4 Al(OH)_3(s) + 3 CH_4(g)$

(e) $2 C_5H_{10}O_2(l) + 13 O_2(g) \longrightarrow 10 CO_2(g) + 10 H_2O(g)$

(f) $2 Fe(OH)_3(s) + 3 H_2SO_4(aq) \longrightarrow Fe_2(SO_4)_3(aq) + 6 H_2O(l)$

(g) $Mg_3N_2(s) + 4 H_2SO_4(aq) \longrightarrow 3 MgSO_4(aq) + (NH_4)_2SO_4(aq)$

3.13 (a) $CaC_2(s) + 2 H_2O(l) \longrightarrow Ca(OH)_2(aq) + C_2H_2(g)$

(b) $2 KClO_3(s) \xrightarrow{\Delta} 2 KCl(s) + 3 O_2(g)$

(c) $Zn(s) + H_2SO_4(aq) \longrightarrow ZnSO_4(aq) + H_2(g)$

(d) $PCl_3(l) + 3 H_2O(l) \longrightarrow H_3PO_3(aq) + 3 HCl(aq)$

(e) $3 H_2S(g) + 2 Fe(OH)_3(s) \longrightarrow Fe_2S_3(s) + 6 H_2O(g)$

3.15 (a) Determine the formula by balancing the positive and negative charges in the ionic product. All ionic compounds are solids. $2 Na(s) + Br_2(l) \longrightarrow 2 NaBr(s)$ (b) The second reactant is $O_2(g)$. The products are $CO_2(g)$ and $H_2O(l)$. $2 C_6H_6(l) + 15 O_2(g) \longrightarrow 12 CO_2(g) + 6 H_2O(l)$

3.17   (a) $Mg(s) + Cl_2(g) \longrightarrow MgCl_2(s)$

(b) $BaCO_3(s) \xrightarrow{\Delta} BaO(s) + CO_2(g)$

(c) $C_8H_8(l) + 10 O_2(g) \longrightarrow 8 CO_2(g) + 4 H_2O(g)$

(d) $C_2H_6O(g) + 3 O_2(g) \longrightarrow 2 CO_2(g) + 3 H_2O(l)$

3.19 (a) $2 C_3H_6(g) + 9 O_2(g) \longrightarrow 6 CO_2(g) + 6 H_2O(g)$
combustion

(b) $NH_4NO_3(s) \longrightarrow N_2O(g) + 2 H_2O(g)$ decomposition

(c) $C_5H_6O(l) + 6 O_2(g) \longrightarrow 5 CO_2(g) + 3 H_2O(g)$ combustion

(d) $N_2(g) + 3 H_2(g) \longrightarrow 2 NH_3(g)$ combination

(e) $K_2O(s) + H_2O(l) \longrightarrow 2 KOH(aq)$ combination

3.21 (a) 63.0 amu (b) 158.0 amu (c) 310.3 amu (d) 60.1 amu (e) 235.7 amu (f) 392.3 amu (g) 137.5 amu   **3.23** (a) 16.8% (b) 16.1% (c) 21.1% (d) 28.8% (e) 27.2% (f) 26.5%   **3.25** (a) 79.2% (b) 63.2%

(c) 64.6%   **3.27** (a) 6.022×10^{23} (b) The formula weight of a substance in amu has the same numerical value as the molar mass expressed in grams.   **3.29** 23 g Na contains 1 mol of atoms; 0.5 mol H_2O contains 1.5 mol atoms; 6.0×10^{23} N_2 molecules contain 2 mol of atoms.   **3.31** 4.37×10^{25} kg (assuming 160 lb has 3 significant figures). One mole of people weighs 7.31 times as much as Earth.   **3.33** (a) 35.9 g $C_{12}H_{22}O_{11}$ (b) 0.75766 mol $Zn(NO_3)_2$ (c) 6.0×10^{17} CH_3CH_2OH molecules (d) 2.47×10^{23} N atoms   **3.35** (a) 0.373 g $(NH_4)_3PO_4$ (b) 5.737×10^{-3} mol Cl^- (c) 0.248 g $C_8H_{10}N_4O_2$ (d) 387 g cholesterol/mol   **3.37** (a) Molar mass = 162.3 g (b) 3.08×10^{-5} mol allicin (c) 1.86×10^{19} allicin molecules (d) 3.71×10^{19} S atoms   **3.39** (a) 2.500×10^{21} H atoms (b) 2.083×10^{20} $C_6H_{12}O_6$ molecules (c) 3.460×10^{-4} mol $C_6H_{12}O_6$ (d) 0.06227 g $C_6H_{12}O_6$ **3.41** 3.2×10^{-8} mol C_2H_3Cl/L; 1.9×10^{16} molecules/L   **3.43** (a) C_2H_6O (b) Fe_2O_3 (c) CH_2O **3.45** (a) $CSCl_2$ (b) C_3OF_6 (c) Na_3AlF_6 **3.47** 31 g/mol   **3.49** (a) C_6H_{12} (b) NH_2Cl **3.51** (a) Empirical formula, CH; molecular formula, C_8H_8 (b) empirical formula, $C_4H_5N_2O$; molecular formula, $C_8H_{10}N_4O_2$ (c) empirical formula and molecular formula, $NaC_5H_8O_4N$ **3.53** (a) C_7H_8 (b) The empirical and molecular formulas are $C_{10}H_{20}O$.   **3.55** The molecular formula from the model is $C_8H_{16}O_2$, which corresponds to an empirical formula of C_4H_8O. The results from combustion analysis are consistent with this empirical formula.   **3.57** $x = 10$; $Na_2CO_3 \cdot 10 H_2O$ **3.59** If the equation is not balanced, the mole ratios derived from the coefficients will be incorrect and lead to erroneous calculated amounts of products.   **3.61** (a) 2.40 mol HF (b) 5.25 g NaF (c) 0.610 g Na_2SiO_3 **3.63** (a) $Al(OH)_3(s) + 3 HCl(aq) \longrightarrow AlCl_3(aq) + 3 H_2O(l)$ (b) 0.701 g HCl (c) 0.855 g $AlCl_3$; 0.347 g H_2O (d) Mass of reactants = 0.500 g + 0.701 g = 1.201 g; mass of products = 0.855 g + 0.347 g = 1.202 g. Mass is conserved, within the precision of the data.   **3.65** (a) $Al_2S_3(s) + 6 H_2O(l) \longrightarrow 2 Al(OH)_3(s) + 3 H_2S(g)$ (b) 14.7 g $Al(OH)_3$ **3.67** (a) 2.25 mol N_2 (b) 15.5 g NaN_3 (c) 548 g NaN_3 **3.69** (a) 5.50×10^{-3} mol Al (b) 1.47 g $AlBr_3$ **3.71** (a) The *limiting reactant* determines the maximum number of product moles resulting from a chemical reaction; any other reactant is an *excess reactant*. (b) The limiting reactant regulates the amount of products because it is completely used up during the reaction; no more product can be made when one of the reactants is unavailable. (c) Combining ratios are molecule and mole ratios. Since different molecules have different masses, comparing initial masses of reactants will not provide a comparison of numbers of molecules or moles.   **3.73** (a) 2255 bicycles (b) 50 frames left over, 305 wheels left over (c) the handlebars   **3.75** NaOH is the limiting reactant; 0.925 mol Na_2CO_3 can be produced; 0.075 mol CO_2 remains.   **3.77** (a) $NaHCO_3$ is the limiting reactant. (b) 0.524 g CO_2 (c) 0.238 g citric acid remains   **3.79** 0.00 g $AgNO_3$ (limiting reactant), 1.94 g Na_2CO_3, 4.06 g Ag_2CO_3, 2.50 g $NaNO_3$ **3.81** (a) The theoretical yield is 60.3 g C_6H_5Br. (b) 70.1% yield   **3.83** 28 g S_8 actual yield   **3.85** (a) $C_2H_4O_2(l) + 2 O_2(g) \longrightarrow 2 CO_2(g) + 2 H_2O(l)$ (b) $Ca(OH)_2(s) \longrightarrow CaO(s) + H_2O(g)$ (c) $Ni(s) + Cl_2(g) \longrightarrow NiCl_2(s)$ **3.89** (a) 8×10^{-20} g Si (b) 2×10^3 Si atoms (with 2 significant figures, 1700 Si atoms) (c) 1×10^3 Ge atoms (with 2 significant figures, 1500 Ge atoms)   **3.93** $C_8H_8O_3$ **3.97** (a) 1.19×10^{-5} mol NaI (b) 8.1×10^{-3} g NaI   **3.101** 7.5 mol H_2 and 4.5 mol N_2 present initially   **3.105** 6.46×10^{24} O atoms   **3.107** (a) 88 kg CO_2 (b) 4×10^2 (400) kg CO_2 **3.109** (a) $S(s) + O_2(g) \longrightarrow SO_2(g)$; $SO_2(g) + CaO(s) \longrightarrow CaSO_3(s)$ (b) 7.9×10^7 g CaO (c) 1.7×10^8 g $CaSO_3$

CHAPTER 4

4.1 Diagram (c) represents Li_2SO_4 **4.3** (a) HCOOH is a weak electrolyte. (b) HNO_3 is a strong electrolyte. (c) CH_3CH_2OH is a nonelectrolyte.   **4.5** $BaCl_2$ **4.7** (b) NO_3^- and (c) NH_4^+ will always be spectator ions.   **4.9** In a redox reaction, electrons are transferred from the oxidized substance to the reduced substance. In an acid–base reaction, protons are transferred from an acid to a base.   **4.11** No. Electrolyte solutions conduct electricity because the dissolved ions carry charge through the solution from one electrode to the other.   **4.13** Although H_2O molecules are electrically neutral, there is an unequal distribution of electrons throughout the molecule. The partially

positive ends of H_2O molecules are attracted to anions in the solid, while the partially negative ends are attracted to cations. Thus, both cations and anions in an ionic solid are surrounded and separated (dissolved) by H_2O. We do not expect ionic compounds to be soluble in molecular liquids such as $Br_2(l)$ or $Hg(l)$. There is a symmetrical charge distribution in Hg atoms and Br_2 molecules, so there are no attractive forces to stabilize the separated ions of an ionic solid.
4.15 (a) $ZnCl_2(aq) \longrightarrow Zn^{2+}(aq) + 2\,Cl^-(aq)$ (b) $HNO_3(aq) \longrightarrow$ $H^+(aq) + NO_3^-(aq)$ (c) $(NH_4)_2SO_4(aq) \longrightarrow 2\,NH_4^+(aq) +$ $SO_4^{2-}(aq)$ (d) $Ca(OH)_2(aq) \longrightarrow Ca^{2+}(aq) + 2\,OH^-(aq)$
4.17 HCOOH molecules, H^+ ions, and $HCOO^-$ ions;
$HCOOH(aq) \rightleftharpoons H^+(aq) + HCOO^-(aq)$ **4.19** (a) Soluble (b) insoluble (c) soluble (d) soluble (e) soluble **4.21** (a)$Na_2CO_3(aq) +$ $2\,AgNO_3(aq) \longrightarrow Ag_2CO_3(s) + 2\,NaNO_3(aq)$
(b) No precipitate (c) $FeSO_4(aq) + Pb(NO_3)_2(aq) \longrightarrow PbSO_4(s) +$ $Fe(NO_3)_2(aq)$ **4.23** (a) Na^+, SO_4^{2-} (b) Na^+, NO_3^- (c) NH_4^+, Cl^-
4.25 The solution contains Pb^{2+} .
4.27

Compound	$Ba(NO_3)_2$ Result	NaCl Result
$AgNO_3(aq)$	No ppt	AgCl ppt
$CaCl_2(aq)$	No ppt	No ppt
$Al_2(SO_4)_3(aq)$	$BaSO_4$ ppt	No ppt

This sequence of tests would definitely identify the bottle contents.
4.29 LiOH is a strong base, HI is a strong acid, and CH_3OH is a molecular compound and nonelectrolyte. The strong acid HI will have the greatest concentration of solvated protons. **4.31** (a) A monoprotic acid has one ionizable (acidic) H, whereas a diprotic acid has two. (b) A strong acid is completely ionized in aqueous solution, whereas only a fraction of weak acid molecules are ionized. (c) An acid is an H^+ donor, and a base is an H^+ acceptor. **4.33** When each of the strong acids in Table 4.2 dissociates, the anions formed are the same ones that normally form soluble ionic compounds (Table 4.1). The one exception is acetate, CH_3COO^-, the anion of a weak acid. **4.35** (a) Acid, mixture of ions and molecules (weak electrolyte) (b) none of the above, entirely molecules (nonelectrolyte) (c) salt, entirely ions (strong electrolyte) (d) base, entirely ions (strong electrolyte) **4.37** (a) H_2SO_3, weak electrolyte (b) C_2H_5OH, nonelectrolyte (c) NH_3, weak electrolyte (d) $KClO_3$, strong electrolyte (e) $Cu(NO_3)_2$, strong electrolyte
4.39 (a) $2\,HBr(aq) + Ca(OH)_2(aq) \longrightarrow CaBr_2(aq) + 2\,H_2O(l)$;
$H^+(aq) + OH^-(aq) \longrightarrow H_2O(l)$ (b) $Cu(OH)_2(s) + 2\,HClO_4(aq)$ $\longrightarrow Cu(ClO_4)_2(aq) + 2\,H_2O(l)$; $Cu(OH)_2(s) + 2\,H^+(aq) \longrightarrow$ $2\,H_2O(l) + Cu^{2+}(aq)$ (c) $Al(OH)_3(s) + 3\,HNO_3(aq) \longrightarrow$ $Al(NO_3)_3(aq) + 3\,H_2O(l)$; $Al(OH)_3(s) + 3\,H^+(aq) \longrightarrow 3\,H_2O(l) +$ $Al^{3+}(aq)$ **4.41** (a) $CdS(s) + H_2SO_4(aq) \longrightarrow CdSO_4(aq) + H_2S(g)$; $CdS(s) + 2\,H^+(aq) \longrightarrow H_2S(g) + Cd^{2+}(aq)$
(b) $MgCO_3(s) + 2\,HClO_4(aq) \longrightarrow Mg(ClO_4)_2(aq) + H_2O(l) + CO_2(g)$; $MgCO_3(s) + 2\,H^+(aq) \longrightarrow H_2O(l) + CO_2(g) + Mg^{2+}(aq)$
4.43 (a) $MgCO_3(s) + 2\,HCl(aq) \longrightarrow MgCl_2(aq) + H_2O(l) + CO_2(g)$; $MgCO_3(s) + 2\,H^+(aq) \longrightarrow Mg^{2+}(aq) + H_2O(l) + CO_2(g)$; $MgO(s) + 2\,HCl(aq) \longrightarrow MgCl_2(aq) + H_2O(l)$; $MgO(s) + 2\,H^+(aq) \longrightarrow Mg^{2+}(aq) + H_2O(l)$; $Mg(OH)_2(s) + 2\,HCl(aq) \longrightarrow MgCl_2(aq) + 2\,H_2O(l)$; $Mg(OH)_2(s) + 2\,H^+(aq) \longrightarrow Mg^{2+}(aq) + 2\,H_2O(l)$ (b) Yes. The reaction involving magnesium carbonate, $MgCO_3(s)$, produces $CO_2(g)$, which appears as bubbles. The other two reactions are calm. (c) If excess $HCl(aq)$ is added in each case, the identity of the ions in the clear product solution is the same. The ions are $Mg^{2+}(aq)$; $Cl^-(aq)$; and $H^+(aq)$. **4.45** (a) In terms of electron transfer, oxidation is the loss of electrons by a substance and reduction is the gain of electrons (LEO says GER). (b) Relative to oxidation numbers, when a substance is oxidized, its oxidation number increases. When a substance is reduced, its oxidation number decreases. **4.47** Metals in region A are most easily oxidized. Nonmetals in region D are least easily oxidized.

4.49 (a) $+4$ (b) $+4$ (c) $+7$ (d) $+1$ (e) 0 (f) -1
4.51 (a) $N_2 \longrightarrow 2\,NH_3$, N is reduced; $3\,H_2 \longrightarrow 2\,NH_3$, H is oxidized (b) $Fe^{2+} \longrightarrow Fe$, Fe is reduced; $Al \longrightarrow Al^{3+}$, Al is oxidized (c) $Cl_2 \longrightarrow 2\,Cl^-$, Cl is reduced; $2\,I^- \longrightarrow I_2$ I is oxidized (d) $S^{2-} \longrightarrow SO_4^{2-}$, S is oxidized; $H_2O_2 \longrightarrow H_2O$, O is reduced
4.53 (a) $Mn(s) + H_2SO_4(aq) \longrightarrow MnSO_4(aq) + H_2(g)$; $Mn(s) + 2\,H^+(aq) \longrightarrow Mn^{2+}(aq) + H_2(g)$
(b) $2\,Cr(s) + 6\,HBr(aq) \longrightarrow 2\,CrBr_3(aq) + 3\,H_2(g)$; $2\,Cr(s) + 6\,H^+(aq) \longrightarrow 2\,Cr^{3+}(aq) + 3\,H_2(g)$
(c) $Sn(s) + 2\,HCl(aq) \longrightarrow SnCl_2(aq) + H_2(g)$; $Sn(s) + 2\,H^+(aq) \longrightarrow Sn^{2+}(aq) + H_2(g)$
(d) $2\,Al(s) + 6\,HCOOH(aq) \longrightarrow 2\,Al(HCOO)_3(aq) + 3\,H_2(g)$; $2\,Al(s) + 6\,HCOOH(aq) \longrightarrow 2\,Al^{3+}(aq) + 6\,HCOO^-(aq) + 3\,H_2(g)$
4.55 (a) $Fe(s) + Cu(NO_3)_2(aq) \longrightarrow Fe(NO_3)_2(aq) + Cu(s)$
(b) NR (c) $Sn(s) + 2\,HBr(aq) \longrightarrow SnBr_2(aq) + H_2(g)$ (d) NR
(e) $2\,Al(s) + 3\,CoSO_4(aq) \longrightarrow Al_2(SO_4)_3(aq) + 3\,Co(s)$
4.57 (a) i. $Zn(s) + Cd^{2+}(aq) \longrightarrow Cd(s) + Zn^{2+}(aq)$; ii. $Cd(s) + Ni^{2+}(aq) \longrightarrow Ni(s) + Cd^{2+}(aq)$ (b) Cd is between Zn and Ni on the activity series. (c) Place an iron strip in $CdCl_2(aq)$. If $Cd(s)$ is deposited, Cd is less active than Fe; if there is no reaction, Cd is more active than Fe. Do the same test with Co if Cd is less active than Fe or with Cr if Cd is more active than Fe. **4.59** (a) Intensive; the ratio of amount of solute to total amount of solution is the same, regardless of how much solution is present. (b) The term 0.50 mol HCl defines an amount ($\sim$18 g) of the pure substance HCl. The term $0.50\,M$ HCl is a ratio; it indicates that there is 0.50 mol of HCl solute in 1.0 liter of solution. **4.61** (a) $1.17\,M$ $ZnCl_2$ (b) 0.158 mol HNO_3 (c) 54.2 mL of $6.00\,M$ NaOH **4.63** $16\,g\,Na^+(aq)$ **4.65** BAC of $0.08 = 0.02\,M$ CH_3CH_2OH (alcohol) **4.67** (a) 5.21 g KBr (b) $0.06537\,M$ $Ca(NO_3)_2$ (c) 10.2 mL of $1.50\,M$ Na_3PO_4 **4.69** (a) $0.15\,M\,K_2CrO_4$ has the highest K^+ concentration. (b) 30.0 mL of $0.15\,M$ K_2CrO_4 has more K^+ ions. **4.71** (a) $0.25\,M\,Na^+$, $0.25\,M\,NO_3^-$ (b) $1.3 \times 10^{-2}\,M\,Mg^{2+}$, $1.3 \times 10^{-2}\,M\,SO_4^{2-}$ (c) $0.0150\,M\,C_6H_{12}O_6$ (d) $0.111\,M\,Na^+$, $0.111\,M\,Cl^-$, $0.0292\,M\,NH_4^+$, $0.0146\,M\,CO_3^{2-}$
4.73 (a) 16.9 mL $14.8\,M\,NH_3$ (b) $0.296\,M\,NH_3$ **4.75** (a) Add 21.4 g $C_{12}H_{22}O_{11}$ to a 250-mL volumetric flask, dissolve in a small volume of water, and add water to the mark on the neck of the flask. Agitate thoroughly to ensure total mixing. (b) Thoroughly rinse, clean, and fill a 50-mL buret with the $1.50\,M\,C_{12}H_{22}O_{11}$. Dispense 23.3 mL of this solution into a 350-mL volumetric container, add water to the mark, and mix thoroughly. **4.77** $1.398\,M$ CH_3COOH **4.79** 0.227 g KCl **4.81** (a) 38.0 mL of $0.115\,M$ $HClO_4$ (b) 769 mL of $0.128\,M$ HCl (c) $0.408\,M$ $AgNO_3$ (d) 0.275 g KOH **4.83** 27 g $NaHCO_3$ **4.85** (a) Molar mass of metal hydroxide is 103 g/mol. (b) Rb^+ **4.87** (a) $NiSO_4(aq) + 2\,KOH(aq) \longrightarrow Ni(OH)_2(s) + K_2SO_4(aq)$ (b) $Ni(OH)_2$ (c) KOH is the limiting reactant. (d) 0.927 g $Ni(OH)_2$ (e) $0.0667\,M\,Ni^{2+}(aq)$, $0.0667\,M\,K^+(aq)$, $0.100\,M\,SO_4^{2-}(aq)$ **4.89** 91.40% $Mg(OH)_2$ **4.92** The precipitate is $CdS(s)$. $Na^+(aq)$ and $NO_3^-(aq)$ remain in solution, along with any excess reactant ions. The net ionic equation is $Cd^{2+}(aq) + S^{2-}(aq) \longrightarrow CdS(s)$. **4.94** (a, b) Expt. 1: NR; Expt. 2: $2\,Ag^+(aq) + CrO_4^{2-}(aq) \longrightarrow Ag_2CrO_4(s)$ red precipitate; Expt. 3: $2\,Ca^{2+}(aq) + CrO_4^{2-}(aq) \longrightarrow CaCrO_4(s)$ yellow precipitate; Expt. 4: $2\,Ag^+(aq) + C_2O_4^{2-}(aq) \longrightarrow Ag_2C_2O_4(s)$ white precipitate; Expt. 5: $Ca^{2+}(aq) + C_2O_4^{2-}(aq) \longrightarrow CaC_2O_4(s)$ white precipitate; Expt. 6: $Ag^+(aq) + Cl^-(aq) \longrightarrow AgCl(s)$ white precipitate. **4.96** $4\,NH_3(g) + 5\,O_2(g) \longrightarrow 4\,NO(g) + 6\,H_2O(g)$. (a) redox reaction (b) N is oxidized, O is reduced. $2\,NO(g) + O_2(g) \longrightarrow 2\,NO_2(g)$. (a) redox reaction (b) N is oxidized, O is reduced. $3\,NO_2(g) + H_2O(l) \longrightarrow HNO_3(aq) + NO(g)$. (a) redox reaction (b) N is both oxidized and reduced. **4.99** $1.42\,M$ KBr **4.100** (a) $2.2 \times 10^{-9}\,M\,Na^+$ (b) $1.3 \times 10^{12}\,Na^+$ ions **4.103** (a) $1.718\,M$ $Sr(OH)_2$ (b) $2\,HNO_3(aq) + Sr(OH)_2(s) \longrightarrow$ $Sr(NO_3)_2(aq) + 2\,H_2O(l)$ (c) $2.61\,M$ HNO_3 **4.106** (a) The molar mass of the acid is 136 g/mol. (b) The molecular formula is $C_8H_8O_2$. **4.109** (a) $Mg(OH)_2(s) + 2\,HNO_3(aq) \longrightarrow Mg(NO_3)_2(aq) +$ $2\,H_2O(l)$ (b) HNO_3 is the limiting reactant. (c) 0.0923 mol $Mg(OH)_2$, 0 mol HNO_3, and 0.00250 mol $Mg(NO_3)_2$ are present. **4.112** 1.766% Cl^- by mass **4.114** 1.5×10^{-5} g Na_3AsO_4 in 1.00 L H_2O

CHAPTER 5

5.1 (a) As the book falls, potential energy decreases and kinetic energy increases. (b) 71 J, assuming no transfer of energy as heat (c) A heavier book falling from the same shelf has greater kinetic energy when it hits the floor. **5.5** (a) No. The distance traveled to the top of a mountain depends on the path taken by the hiker. Distance is a path function, not a state function. (b) Yes. Change in elevation depends only on the location of the base camp and the height of the mountain, not on the path to the top. Change in elevation is a state function, not a path function. **5.8** (a) The sign of w is (+). (b) The internal energy of the system increases during the change; the sign of ΔE is (+). **5.11** (a) $\Delta H_A = \Delta H_B + \Delta H_C$. The diagram and equation both show that the net enthalpy change for a process is independent of path, that ΔH is a state function. (b) $\Delta H_Z = \Delta H_X + \Delta H_Y$. (c) Hess's law states that the enthalpy change for net reaction Z is the sum of the enthalpy changes for steps X and Y, regardless of whether the reaction actually occurs via this path. The diagrams are a visual statement of Hess's law. **5.13** An object can possess energy by virtue of its motion or position. Kinetic energy depends on the mass of the object and its velocity. Potential energy depends on the position of the object relative to the body with which it interacts. **5.15** (a) 1.9×10^5 J (b) 4.6×10^4 cal (c) As the automobile brakes to a stop, its speed (and hence its kinetic energy) drops to zero. The kinetic energy of the automobile is primarily transferred to friction between brakes and wheels and somewhat to deformation of the tire and friction between the tire and road. **5.17** 1 Btu = 1054 J **5.19** (a) The *system* is the well-defined part of the universe whose energy changes are being studied. (b) A *closed system* can exchange heat but not mass with its surroundings. (c) Any part of the universe not part of the system is called the surroundings. **5.21** (a) Work is a force applied over a distance. (b) The amount of work done is the magnitude of the force times the distance over which it is applied. $w = F \times d$. **5.23** (a) Gravity; work is done because the force of gravity is opposed and the pencil is lifted. (b) Mechanical force; work is done because the force of the coiled spring is opposed as the spring is compressed over a distance. **5.25** (a) In any chemical or physical change, energy can be neither created nor destroyed; energy is conserved. (b) The *internal energy (E)* of a system is the sum of all the kinetic and potential energies of the system components. (c) Internal energy of a closed system increases when work is done on the system and when heat is transferred to the system. **5.27** (a) $\Delta E = -0.077$ kJ, endothermic (b) $\Delta E = -22.1$ kJ, exothermic (c) $\Delta E = 7.25$ kJ, endothermic **5.29** (a) Since no work is done by the system in case (2), the gas will absorb most of the energy as heat; the case (2) gas will have the higher temperature. (b) In case (2) $w = 0$ and $q = 100$ J. In case (1) energy will be used to do work on the surroundings $(-w)$, but some will be absorbed as heat $(+q)$. (c) ΔE is greater for case (2) because the entire 100 J increases the internal energy of the system rather than a part of the energy doing work on the surroundings. **5.31** (a) A *state function* is a property that depends only on the physical state (pressure, temperature, etc.) of the system, not on the route used to get to the current state. (b) Internal energy is a state function; heat is not a state function. (c) Volume is a state function. The volume of a system depends only on conditions (pressure, temperature, amount of substance), not the route or method used to establish that volume. **5.33** (a) ΔH is usually easier to measure than ΔE because at constant pressure, $\Delta H = q_p$. The heat flow associated with a process at constant pressure can easily be measured as a change in temperature, while measuring ΔE requires a means to measure both q and w. (b) H is a static quantity that depends only on the specific conditions of the system. q is an energy *change* that, in the general case, does depend on how the change occurs. We can equate change in enthalpy, ΔH, with heat, q_p, only for the specific conditions of constant pressure and exclusively P-V work. (c) The process is endothermic. **5.35** At constant pressure, $\Delta E = \Delta H - P \Delta V$. The values of either P and ΔV or T and Δn must be known to calculate ΔE from ΔH. **5.37** $\Delta E = 1.47$ kJ; $\Delta H = 0.824$ kJ **5.39** (a) $C_2H_5OH(l) + 3 O_2(g) \longrightarrow 3 H_2O + 2 CO_2(g)$, $\Delta H = -1235$ kJ

(b) $C_2H_5OH(l) + 3 O_2(g)$

$\Delta H = -1235$ kJ

$3 H_2O(g) + 2 CO_2(g)$

5.41 (a) $\Delta H = -142.3$ kJ/mol $O_3(g)$ (b) $2 O_3(g)$ has the higher enthalpy. **5.43** (a) Exothermic (b) -87.9 kJ heat transferred (c) 15.7 g MgO produced (d) 602 kJ heat absorbed **5.45** (a) -29.5 kJ (b) -4.11 kJ (c) 60.6 J **5.47** (a) $\Delta H = 726.5$ kJ (b) $\Delta H = -1453$ kJ (c) The exothermic forward reaction is more likely to be thermodynamically favored. (d) Vaporization is endothermic. If the product were $H_2O(g)$, the reaction would be more endothermic and would have a less negative ΔH. **5.49** (a) J/mol-°C or J/mol-K (b) J/g-°C or J/g-K (c) To calculate heat capacity from specific heat, the mass of the particular piece of copper pipe must be known. **5.51** (a) 4.184 J/g-K (b) 75.40 J/mol-°C (c) 774 J/°C (d) 904 kJ **5.53** (a) 2.66×10^3 J (b) It will require more heat to increase the temperature of one mole of octane, $C_8H_{18}(l)$, by a certain amount than to increase the temperature of one mole of water, $H_2O(l)$, by the same amount. **5.55** $\Delta H = -44.4$ kJ/mol NaOH **5.57** $\Delta H_{rxn} = -25.5$ kJ/g $C_6H_4O_2$ or -2.75×10^3 kJ/mol $C_6H_4O_2$ **5.59** (a) Heat capacity of the complete calorimeter $= 14.4$ kJ/°C (b) 7.56 °C **5.61** Hess's law is a consequence of the fact that enthalpy is a state function. Since ΔH is independent of path, we can describe a process by any series of steps that adds up to the overall process. ΔH for the process is the sum of ΔH values for the steps. **5.63** $\Delta H = -1300.0$ kJ **5.65** $\Delta H = -2.49 \times 10^3$ kJ **5.67** (a) *Standard conditions* for enthalpy changes are $P = 1$ atm and some common temperature, usually 298 K. (b) *Enthalpy of formation* is the enthalpy change that occurs when a compound is formed from its component elements. (c) *Standard enthalpy of formation* ΔH_f° is the enthalpy change that accompanies formation of one mole of a substance from elements in their standard states. **5.69** (a) $\frac{1}{2} N_2(g) + O_2(g) \longrightarrow NO_2(g)$, $\Delta H_f^\circ = 33.84$ kJ (b) $S(s) + 3/2 O_2(g) \longrightarrow SO_3(g)$, $\Delta H_f^\circ = -395.2$ kJ (c) $Na(s) + \frac{1}{2} Br_2(l) \longrightarrow NaBr(s)$, $\Delta H_f^\circ = -361.4$ kJ (d) $Pb(s) + N_2(g) + 3 O_2(g) \longrightarrow Pb(NO_3)_2(s)$, $\Delta H_f^\circ = -451.9$ kJ **5.71** $\Delta H_{rxn}^\circ = -847.6$ kJ **5.73** (a) $\Delta H_{rxn}^\circ = -196.6$ kJ (b) $\Delta H_{rxn}^\circ = 37.1$ kJ (c) $\Delta H_{rxn}^\circ = -976.94$ kJ (d) $\Delta H_{rxn}^\circ = -68.3$ kJ **5.75** $\Delta H_f^\circ = -248$ kJ **5.77** (a) $C_8H_{18}(l) + \frac{25}{2} O_2(g) \longrightarrow 8 CO_2(g) + 9 H_2O(g)$, $\Delta H = -5064.9$ kJ (b) $8 C(s, \text{graphite}) + 9 H_2(g) \longrightarrow C_8H_{18}(l)$ (c) $\Delta H_f^\circ = -259.5$ kJ **5.79** (a) $C_2H_5OH(l) + 3 O_2(g) \longrightarrow 2 CO_2(g) + 3 H_2O(g)$ (b) $\Delta H_{rxn}^\circ = -1234.8$ kJ (c) 2.11×10^4 kJ/L heat produced (d) 0.071284 g CO_2/kJ heat emitted **5.81** (a) *Fuel value* is the amount of energy produced when 1 g of a substance (fuel) is combusted. (b) 5 g of fat (c) These products of metabolism are expelled as waste via the alimentary tract, $H_2O(l)$ primarily in urine and feces, and $CO_2(g)$ as gas. **5.83** 108 or 1×10^2 Cal/serving (b) Sodium does not contribute to the calorie content of the food because it is not metabolized by the body. **5.85** 59.7 Cal **5.87** (a) $\Delta H_{comb} = -1850$ kJ/mol C_3H_4, -1926 kJ/mol C_3H_6, -2044 kJ/mol C_3H_8 (b) $\Delta H_{comb} = -4.616 \times 10^4$ kJ/kg C_3H_4, -4.578×10^4 kJ/kg C_3H_6, -4.635×10^4 kJ/kg C_3H_8 (c) These three substances yield nearly identical quantities of heat per unit mass, but propane is marginally higher than the other two. **5.89** 1×10^{12} kg $C_6H_{12}O_6$/yr **5.91** (a) 469.4 m/s (b) 5.124×10^{-21} J (c) 3.086 kJ/mol **5.93** The spontaneous air bag reaction is probably exothermic, with $-\Delta H$ and thus $-q$. When the bag inflates, work is done by the system, so the sign of w is also negative. **5.97** $\Delta H = 38.95$ kJ; $\Delta E = 36.48$ kJ **5.102** (a) $\Delta H_{rxn}^\circ = -353.0$ kJ (b) 1.2 g Mg needed **5.106** (a) $\Delta H^\circ = -631.3$ kJ (b) 3 mol of acetylene gas has greater enthalpy. (c) Fuel values are 50 kJ/g $C_2H_2(g)$, 42 kJ/g $C_6H_6(l)$. **5.109** If all work is used to increase the man's potential energy, the stair climbing uses 58 Cal and will not compensate for the extra order of 245 Cal fries. (More than 58 Cal will be required to climb the stairs because some energy is used to move limbs and some will be lost as heat.)

5.112 (a) 1.479×10^{-18} J/molecule (b) 1×10^{-15} J/photon. The X-ray has approximately 1000 times more energy than is produced by the combustion of 1 molecule of $CH_4(g)$. **5.114** (a) $\Delta H°$ for neutralization of the acids is HNO_3, -55.8 kJ; HCl, -56.1 kJ; NH_4^+, -4.1 kJ. (b) $H^+(aq) + OH^-(aq) \longrightarrow H_2O(l)$ is the net ionic equation for the first two reactions. $NH_4^+(aq) + OH^-(aq) \longrightarrow NH_3(aq) + H_2O(l)$ (c) The $\Delta H°$ values for the first two reactions are nearly identical, -55.8 kJ and -56.1 kJ. Since spectator ions do not change during a reaction and these two reactions have the same net ionic equation, it is not surprising that they have the same $\Delta H°$. (d) Strong acids are more likely than weak acids to donate H^+. Neutralization of the two strong acids is energetically favorable, while the third reaction is barely so. NH_4^+ is likely a weak acid. **5.116** (a) $\Delta H° = -65.7$ kJ (b) $\Delta H°$ for the complete molecular equation will be the same as $\Delta H°$ for the net ionic equation. Since the overall enthalpy change is the enthalpy of products minus the enthalpy of reactants, the contributions of spectator ions cancel. (c) $\Delta H_f°$ for $AgNO_3(aq)$ is -100.4 kJ/mol.

CHAPTER 6

6.2 (a) 0.1 m or 10 cm (b) No. Visible radiation has wavelengths much shorter than 0.1 m. (c) Energy and wavelength are inversely proportional. Photons of the longer 0.1-m radiation have less energy than visible photons. (d) Radiation with $\lambda = 0.1$ m is in the low-energy portion of the microwave region. The appliance is probably a microwave oven. **6.5** (a) Increase (b) decrease (c) the light from the hydrogen discharge tube is a line spectrum, so not all visible wavelengths will be in our "hydrogen discharge rainbow." Starting on the inside, the rainbow will be violet, then blue and blue-green. After a gap, the final band will be red. **6.8** (a) 1 (b) p (c) For the $n = 4$ shell, the lobes in the contour representation would extend farther along the y-axis. **6.11** (a) Meters (b) 1/second (c) meters/second **6.13** (a) True (b) False. Ultraviolet light has shorter wavelengths than visible light. (c) False. X-rays travel at the same speed as microwaves. (d) False. Electromagnetic radiation and sound waves travel at different speeds. **6.15** Wavelength of X-rays $<$ ultraviolet $<$ green light $<$ red light $<$ infrared $<$ radio waves **6.17** (a) 3.0×10^{13} s^{-1} (b) 5.45×10^{-7} m $= 545$ nm (c) The radiation in (b) is visible; the radiation in (a) is not. (d) 1.50×10^4 m **6.19** 5.64×10^{14} s^{-1}; green. **6.21** Quantization means that energy changes can happen only in certain allowed increments. If the human growth quantum is one foot, growth occurs instantaneously in one-foot increments. The child experiences growth spurts of one foot; her height can change only by one-foot increments. **6.23** (a) 4.47×10^{-21} J (b) 6.17×10^{-19} J (c) 69.2 nm **6.25** (a) $\lambda = 3.3$ μm, $E = 6.0 \times 10^{-20}$ J; $\lambda = 0.154$ nm, $E = 1.29 \times 10^{-15}$ J (b) The 3.3-μm photon is in the infrared region and the 0.154-nm photon is in the X-ray region; the X-ray photon has the greater energy. **6.27** (a) 6.11×10^{-19} J/photon (b) 368 kJ/mol (c) 1.64×10^{15} photons (d) 368 kJ/mol **6.29** (a) The $\sim 1 \times 10^{-6}$ m radiation is in the infrared portion of the spectrum. (b) 8.1×10^{16} photons/s **6.31** (a) $E_{min} = 7.22 \times 10^{-19}$ J (b) $\lambda = 275$ nm (c) $E_{120} = 1.66 \times 10^{-18}$ J. The excess energy of the 120-nm photon is converted into the kinetic energy of the emitted electron. $E_k = 9.3 \times 10^{-19}$ J/electron. **6.33** When applied to atoms, the notion of quantized energies means that only certain values of ΔE are allowed. These are represented by the lines in the emission spectra of excited atoms. **6.35** (a) Emitted (b) absorbed (c) emitted **6.37** (a) $E_2 = -5.45 \times 10^{-19}$ J; $E_6 = -0.606 \times 10^{-19}$ J; $\Delta E = 4.84 \times 10^{-19}$ J; $\lambda = 410$ nm (b) visible, violet **6.39** (a) Only lines with $n_f = 2$ represent ΔE values and wavelengths that lie in the visible portion of the spectrum. Lines with $n_f = 1$ have shorter wavelengths and lines with $n_f > 2$ have longer wavelengths than visible radiation. (b) $n_i = 3$, $n_f = 2$; $\lambda = 6.56 \times 10^{-7}$ m; this is the red line at 656 nm. $n_i = 4$, $n_f = 2$; $\lambda = 4.86 \times 10^{-7}$ m; this is the blue-green line at 486 nm. $n_i = 5$, $n_f = 2$; $\lambda = 4.34 \times 10^{-7}$ m; this is the blue-violet line at 434 nm. **6.41** (a) Ultraviolet region (b) $n_i = 6$, $n_f = 1$ **6.43** (a) $\lambda = 5.6 \times 10^{-37}$ m (b) $\lambda = 2.65 \times 10^{-34}$ m (c) $\lambda = 2.3 \times 10^{-13}$ m (d) $\lambda = 1.51 \times 10^{-11}$ m **6.45** 4.14×10^3 m/s **6.47** (a) $\Delta x \geq 4 \times 10^{-27}$ m (b) $\Delta x \geq 3 \times 10^{-10}$ m **6.49** (a) The uncertainty principle states that there is a limit to how precisely we can simultaneously

know the position and momentum (a quantity related to energy) of an electron. The Bohr model states that electrons move about the nucleus in precisely circular orbits of known radius and energy. This violates the uncertainty principle. (b) De Broglie stated that electrons demonstrate the properties of both particles and waves and that each moving particle has a wave associated with it. A wave function is the mathematical description of the matter wave of an electron. (c) Although we cannot predict the exact location of an electron in an allowed energy state, we can determine the probability of finding an electron at a particular position. This statistical knowledge of electron location is the *probability density* and is a function of Ψ^2, the square of the wave function Ψ. **6.51** (a) $n = 4$, $l = 3, 2, 1, 0$ (b) $l = 2$, $m_l = -2, -1, 0, 1, 2$ (c) $m_l = 2$, $l \geq 2$ or $l = 2, 3$ or 4 **6.53** (a) $3p$: $n = 3$, $l = 1$ (b) $2s$: $n = 2$, $l = 0$ (c) $4f$: $n = 4$, $l = 3$ (d) $5d$: $n = 5$, $l = 2$ **6.55** (a) impossible, $1p$ (b) possible (c) possible (d) impossible, $2d$

6.57 (a)   (b)   (c)

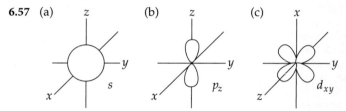

6.59 (a) The hydrogen atom $1s$ and $2s$ orbitals have the same overall spherical shape, but the $2s$ orbital has a larger radial extension and one more node than the $1s$ orbital. (b) A single $2p$ orbital is directional in that its electron density is concentrated along one of the three Cartesian axes of the atom. The $d_{x^2-y^2}$ orbital has electron density along both the x- and y-axes, while the p_x orbital has density only along the x-axis. (c) The average distance of an electron from the nucleus in a $3s$ orbital is greater than for an electron in a $2s$ orbital. (d) $1s < 2p < 3d < 4f < 6s$ **6.61** (a) In the hydrogen atom, orbitals with the same principal quantum number, n, have the same energy. (b) In a many-electron atom, for a given n value, orbital energy increases with increasing l value: $s < p < d < f$. **6.63** (a) There are two main pieces of experimental evidence for electron "spin." The Stern-Gerlach experiment shows that atoms with a single unpaired electron interact differently with an inhomogeneous magnetic field. Examination of the fine details of emission line spectra of multi-electron atoms reveals that each line is really a close pair of lines. Both observations can be rationalized if electrons have the property of spin.

(b)   (c)

6.65 (a) 6 (b) 10 (c) 2 (d) 14 **6.67** (a) "Valence electrons" are those involved in chemical bonding. They are part or all of the outer-shell electrons listed after the core. (b) "Core electrons" are inner-shell electrons that have the electron configuration of the nearest noble-gas element. (c) Each box represents an orbital. (d) Each half-arrow in an orbital diagram represents an electron. The direction of the half-arrow represents electron spin. **6.69** (a) Cs, $[Xe]6s^1$ (b) Ni, $[Ar]4s^23d^8$ (c) Se, $[Ar]4s^23d^{10}4p^4$ (d) Cd, $[Kr]5s^24d^{10}$ (e) U, $[Rn]5f^36d^17s^2$ (f) Pb, $[Xe]6s^24f^{14}5d^{10}6p^2$ **6.71** (a) Be, 0 unpaired electrons (b) O, 2 unpaired electrons (c) Cr, 6 unpaired electrons (d) Te, 2 unpaired electrons **6.73** (a) The fifth electron would fill the $2p$ subshell before the $3s$. (b) Either the core is [He], or the outer electron configuration should be $3s^23p^3$. (c) The $3p$ subshell would fill before the $3d$. **6.75** (a) $\lambda_A = 3.6 \times 10^{-8}$ m, $\lambda_B = 8.0 \times 10^{-8}$ m (b) $\nu_A = 8.4 \times 10^{15}$ s^{-1}, $\nu_B = 3.7 \times 10^{15}$ s^{-1} (c) A, ultraviolet; B, ultraviolet **6.78** 66.7 min **6.82** 1.6×10^7 photons/s, 5.1×10^{-12} J/s **6.85** (a) The Paschen series lies in the infrared. (b) $n_i = 4$, $\lambda = 1.87 \times 10^{-6}$ m; $n_i = 5$, $\lambda = 1.28 \times 10^{-6}$ m; $n_i = 6$, $\lambda = 1.09 \times 10^{-6}$ m **6.90** (a) l (b) n and l (c) m_s (d) m_l **6.92** (a) The nodal plane of the p_z orbital is the xy-plane. (b) The two nodal planes of the d_{xy} orbital are the ones where

$x = 0$ and $y = 0$. These are the yz- and xz-planes. (c) The two nodal planes of the $d_{x^2-y^2}$ orbital are the ones that bisect the x- and y-axes and contain the z-axis. **6.94** If m_s had three allowed values instead of two, each orbital would hold three electrons instead of two. Assuming that there is no change in the n, l, and m_l values, the number of elements in each of the first four rows would be 1st row, 3 elements; 2nd row, 12 elements; 3rd row, 12 elements; 4th row, 27 elements **6.97** (a) 1.7×10^{28} photons (b) 34 s **6.101** (a) Bohr's theory was based on the Rutherford nuclear model of the atom: a dense positive charge at the center and a diffuse negative charge surrounding it. Bohr's theory then specified the nature of the diffuse negative charge. The prevailing theory before the nuclear model was Thomson's plum pudding model: discrete electrons scattered about a diffuse positive charge cloud. Bohr's theory could not have been based on the Thomson model of the atom. (b) De Broglie's hypothesis is that electrons exhibit both particle and wave properties. Thomson's conclusion that electrons have mass is a particle property, while the nature of cathode rays is a wave property. De Broglie's hypothesis actually rationalizes these two seemingly contradictory observations about the properties of electrons.

CHAPTER 7

7.3 (a) The bonding atomic radius of A, r_A, is $d_1/2$; $r_x = d_2 - (d_1/2)$. (b) The length of the X—X bond is $2r_x$ or $2d_2 - d_1$. **7.6** (a) $X + 2F_2 \longrightarrow XF_4$ (b) X in the diagram has about the same bonding radius as F, so it is likely to be a nonmetal. **7.7** The number of columns in the various blocks of the periodic chart corresponds to the maximum number of electrons that can occupy the various kinds of atomic orbitals: 2 columns on the left for 2 electrons in s orbitals, 10 columns in the transition metals for 10 electrons in d orbitals, 6 columns on the right for 6 electrons in p orbitals, 14-member rows below for 14 electrons in f orbitals. The order of blocks corresponds to the filling order of atomic orbitals, and the row number corresponds to the principal quantum number of the valence electrons of elements in that row, ns, np, $(n-1)d$, $(n-2)f$. **7.9** In general, elements are discovered according to their ease of isolation in elemental form. **7.11** (a) *Effective nuclear charge*, Z_{eff}, is a representation of the average electrical field experienced by a single electron. It is the average environment created by the nucleus and the other electrons in the molecule, expressed as a net positive charge at the nucleus. (b) Going from left to right across a period, effective nuclear charge increases. **7.13** (a) For both Na and K, $Z_{eff} = 1$. (b) For both Na and K, $Z_{eff} = 2.2$. (c) Slater's rules give values closer to the detailed calculations: Na, 2.51; K, 3.49. (d) Both approximations give the same value of Z_{eff} for Na and K; neither accounts for the gradual increase in Z_{eff} moving down a group. (e) Following the trend from detailed calculations, we predict a Z_{eff} value of approximately 4.5. **7.15** The $n = 3$ electrons in Kr experience a greater effective nuclear charge and thus have a greater probability of being closer to the nucleus. **7.17** (a) Atomic radii are determined by measuring distances between atoms in various situations. (b) Bonding radii are calculated from the internuclear separation of two atoms joined by a covalent chemical bond. Nonbonding radii are calculated from the internuclear separation between two gaseous atoms that collide and move apart but do not bond. (c) For a given element, the nonbonding radius is always larger than the bonding radius. (d) If a free atom reacts to become part of a covalent molecule, its radius changes from nonbonding to bonding and the atom gets smaller. **7.19** (a) 1.37 Å (b) The distance between W atoms will decrease. **7.21** From the sum of the atomic radii, As—I = 2.52 Å. This is very close to the experimental value of 2.55 Å. **7.23** (a) Decrease (b) increase (c) O < Si < Ge < I **7.25** (a) Cs > K > Li (b) Pb > Sn > Si (c) N > O > F **7.27** (a) False (b) true (c) false **7.29** The red sphere is a metal; its size decreases on reaction, characteristic of the change in radius when a metal atom forms a cation. The blue sphere is a nonmetal; its size increases on reaction, characteristic of the change in radius when a nonmetal atom forms an anion. **7.31** (a) An isoelectronic series is a group of atoms or ions that have the same number of electrons and the same electron configuration. (b) Ga^{3+}: Ar; Zr^{4+}: Kr; Mn^{7+}: Ar; I^-: Xe; Pb^{2+}: Hg **7.33** (a) Ar (b) Ar (c) There is no neutral atom isoelectronic with Fe^{2+}. Because transition metals fill the s subshell first but

also lose s electrons first when they form ions, many transition metal ions do not have isolectronic neutral atoms. (d) No isoelectronic neutral atom; same reason as part (c). (e) No isoelectronic neutral atom; same reason as part (c). **7.35** (a) K^+ is smaller. (b) Cl^-, $Z_{eff} = 7$; K^+, $Z_{eff} = 9$ (c) Cl^-: $Z_{eff} = 5.75$; K^+, $Z_{eff} = 7.75$ (d) For isoelectronic ions, as nuclear charge (Z) increases, effective nuclear charge (Z_{eff}) increases and ionic radius decreases. **7.37** (a) Se < Se^{2-} < Te^{2-} (b) Co^{2+} < Fe^{3+} < Fe^{2+} (c) Ti^{4+} < Sc^{3+} < Ca (d) Be^{2+} < Na^+ < Ne **7.39** $Al(g) \longrightarrow Al^+(g) + 1e^-$; $Al^+(g) \longrightarrow Al^{2+}(g) + 1e^-$; $Al^{2+}(g) \longrightarrow Al^{3+}(g) + 1e^-$. The process for the first ionization energy requires the least amount of energy. **7.41** (a) False. Ionization energies are always positive quantities. (b) False. F has a greater first ionization energy than O. (c) True. **7.43** (a) The smaller the atom, the larger its first ionization energy. (b) Of the nonradioactive elements, He has the largest and Cs the smallest first ionization energy. **7.45** (a) Cl (b) Ca (c) K (d) Ge (e) Sn **7.47** (a) Fe^{2+}, $[Ar]3d^6$ (b) Hg^{2+}, $[Xe]4f^{14}5d^{10}$ (c) Mn^{2+}, $[Ar]3d^5$ (d) Pt^{2+}, $[Xe]4f^{14}5d^8$ (e) P^{3-}, $[Ne]3s^23p^6$ **7.49** Ni^{2+}, $[Ar]3d^8$; Pd^{2+}, $[Kr]4d^8$; Pt^{2+}, $[Xe]4f^{14}5d^8$ **7.51** (a) Positive, endothermic, values for ionization energy and electron affinity mean that energy is required to either remove or add electrons. Valence electrons in Ar experience the largest Z_{eff} of any element in the third row, resulting in a large, positive ionization energy. When an electron is added to Ar, the $n = 3$ electrons become core electrons that screen the extra electron so effectively that Ar^- has a higher energy than an Ar atom and a free electron. This results in a large positive electron affinity. (b) kJ/mol **7.53** Electron affinity of Br: $Br(g) + 1e^- \longrightarrow Br^-(g)$; $[Ar]4s^23d^{10}4p^5 \longrightarrow [Ar]4s^23d^{10}4p^6$; electron affinity of Kr: $Kr(g) + 1e^- \longrightarrow Kr^-(g)$; $[Ar]4s^23d^{10}4p^6 \longrightarrow [Ar]4s^23d^{10}4p^65s^1$. Br^- adopts the stable electron configuration of Kr; the added electron experiences essentially the same Z_{eff} and stabilization as the other valence electrons and electron affinity is negative. In Kr^- ion, the added electron occupies the higher energy $5s$ orbital. A $5s$ electron is farther from the nucleus, effectively shielded by the spherical Kr core and not stabilized by the nucleus; electron affinity is positive. **7.55** (a) Ionization energy (I_1) of Ne: $Ne(g) \longrightarrow Ne^+(g) + 1e^-$; $[He]2s^22p^6 \longrightarrow [He]2s^22p^5$; electron affinity ($E_1$) of F: $F(g) + 1e^- \longrightarrow F^-(g)$; $[He]2s^22p^5 \longrightarrow [He]2s^22p^6$. (b) I_1 of Ne is positive; E_1 of F is negative. (c) One process is apparently the reverse of the other, with one important difference. Ne has a greater Z and Z_{eff}, so we expect I_1 for Ne to be somewhat greater in magnitude and opposite in sign to E_1 for F. **7.57** The smaller the first ionization energy of an element, the greater the metallic character of that element. **7.59** Agree. When forming ions, all metals form cations. The only nonmetallic element that forms cations is the metalloid Sb, which is likely to have significant metallic character. **7.61** Ionic: SnO_2, Al_2O_3, Li_2O, Fe_2O_3; molecular: CO_2, H_2O. Ionic compounds are formed by combining a metal and a nonmetal; molecular compounds are formed by two or more nonmetals. **7.63** (a) An *acidic oxide* dissolved in water produces an acidic solution; a *basic oxide* dissolved in water produces a basic solution. (b) Oxides of nonmetals, such as SO_3, are acidic; oxides of metals, such as CaO, are basic. **7.65** (a) Dichlorineheptoxide (b) $2 Cl_2(g) + 7 O_2(g) \longrightarrow 2 Cl_2O_7(l)$ (c) While most nonmetal oxides we have seen, such as CO_2 or SO_2, are gases, a boiling point of 81 °C is expected for a large molecule like Cl_2O_7. (d) Cl_2O_7 is an acidic oxide, so it will be more reactive to base, OH^-. (e) The oxidation state of Cl in Cl_2O_7 is +7; the corresponding electron configuration for Cl is $[He]2s^22p^6$ or [Ne]. **7.67** (a) $BaO(s) + H_2O(l) \longrightarrow Ba(OH)_2(aq)$ (b) $FeO(s) + 2 HClO_4(aq) \longrightarrow Fe(ClO_4)_2(aq) + H_2O(l)$ (c) $SO_3(g) + H_2O(l) \longrightarrow H_2SO_4(aq)$ (d) $CO_2(g) + 2 NaOH(aq) \longrightarrow Na_2CO_3(aq) + H_2O(l)$ **7.69** Yes, the reactivity of a metal correlates with its first ionization energy. Since metals lose electrons when they form ions, the less energy required for this process, the more reactive the metal. However, we usually observe reactivity of metals in the solid state and ionization energy is a gas phase property, so there are differences between the two properties. **7.71** (a) Ca is more reactive because it has a lower ionization energy than Mg. (b) K is more reactive because it has a lower ionization energy than Ca. **7.73** (a) $2 K(s) + Cl_2(g) \longrightarrow 2 KCl(s)$ (b) $SrO(s) + H_2O(l) \longrightarrow Sr(OH)_2(aq)$ (c) $4 Li(s) + O_2(g) \longrightarrow 2 Li_2O(s)$ (d) $2 Na(s) + S(l) \longrightarrow Na_2S(s)$ **7.75** (a) Both classes of reaction are redox reactions where either hydrogen or the halogen gains electrons and is reduced. The product is an ionic solid, where either hydride ion, H^-, or a halide ion, X^-, is the anion. (b) $Ca(s) + F_2(g) \longrightarrow CaF_2(s)$; $Ca(s) + H_2(g) \longrightarrow CaH_2(s)$. Both products are ionic solids containing Ca^{2+} and the corresponding anion in a 1:2 ratio.   **7.77** (a) Br, $[Ar]4s^24p^5$; Cl, $[Ne]3s^23p^5$ (b) Br and Cl are in the same group, and both adopt a 1− ionic charge. (c) The ionization energy of Br is smaller than that of Cl, because the $4p$ valence electrons in Br are farther from to the nucleus and less tightly held than the $3p$ electrons of Cl. (d) Both react slowly with water to form $HX + HOX$. (e) The electron affinity of Br is less negative than that of Cl, because the electron added to the $4p$ orbital in Br is farther from the nucleus and less tightly held than the electron added to the $3p$ orbital of Cl. (f) The atomic radius of Br is larger than that of Cl, because the $4p$ valence electrons in Br are farther from the nucleus and less tightly held than the $3p$ electrons of Cl. **7.79** (a) The term *inert* was dropped because it no longer described all the Group 8A elements. (b) In the 1960s, scientists discovered that Xe would react with substances having a strong tendency to remove electrons, such as F_2. Thus, Xe could not be categorized as an "inert" gas. (c) The group is now called the noble gases. **7.81** (a) $2 O_3(g) \longrightarrow 3 O_2(g)$ (b) $Xe(g) + F_2(g) \longrightarrow XeF_2(g)$; $Xe(g) + 2 F_2(g) \longrightarrow XeF_4(s)$; $Xe(g) + 3 F_2(g) \longrightarrow XeF_6(s)$ (c) $S(s) +$ (d) $2 F_2(g) + 2 H_2O(l) \longrightarrow 4 HF(aq) + O_2(g)$ **7.83** Up to $Z = 82$, there are three instances where atomic weights are reversed relative to atomic numbers: Ar and K; Co and Ni; Te and I. In each case the most abundant isotope of the element with the larger atomic number has one more proton but fewer neutrons than the element with the smaller atomic number. The smaller number of neutrons causes the element with the larger Z to have a smaller than expected atomic weight.   **7.85** (a) 5+ (b) 4.8+ (c) Shielding is greater for $3p$ electrons, owing to penetration by $3s$ electrons, so Z_{eff} for $3p$ electrons is less than that for $3s$ electrons. (d) The first electron lost is a $3p$ electron because it has a smaller Z_{eff} and experiences less attraction for the nucleus than a $3s$ electron does.   **7.88** (a) The estimated distances are a bit longer than the measured distances. This probably shows a systematic bias in either the estimated radii or in the method of obtaining the measured values. (b) The principal quantum number of the outer electrons and thus the average distance of these electrons from the nucleus increase from $P(n = 3)$ to $As(n = 4)$ to $Sb(n = 5)$. This causes the systematic increase in M – H distance.   **7.92** (a) $2 Sr(s) + O_2(g) \longrightarrow 2 SrO(s)$ (b) Based on ionic radii, the length of the side of the cube is 5.16 Å. (c) There are four SrO units in the cube.

7.95 (a) O, $[He]2s^22p^4$

↑↓	↑↓ ↑ ↑	
2s	2p	

O^{2-}, $[He]2s^22p^6 = [Ne]$

↑↓	↑↓ ↑↓ ↑↓
2s	2p

(b) O^{3-}, $[Ne]3s^1$. The third electron would be added to the $3s$ orbital, which is farther from the nucleus and more strongly shielded by the [Ne] core. The overall attraction of this $3s$ electron for the oxygen nucleus is not large enough for O^{3-} to be a stable particle.   **7.98** (a) For both H and the alkali metals, the added electron will complete an ns subshell, so shielding and repulsion effects will be similar. For the halogens, the electron is added to an np subshell, so the energy change is likely to be quite different. (b) True. The electron configuration of H is $1s^1$. The single $1s$ electron experiences no repulsion from other electrons and feels the full unshielded nuclear charge. The outer electrons of all other elements that form compounds are shielded by a spherical inner core of electrons and are less strongly attracted to the nucleus, resulting in larger bonding atomic radii. (c) Both H and the halogens have large ionization energies. The relatively large effective nuclear charge experienced by np electrons of the halogens is similar to the unshielded nuclear charge experienced by the H $1s$ electron. For the alkali metals, the ns electron being removed is effectively shielded by the core electrons, so ionization energies are low. (d) ionization energy of hydride, $H^-(g) \longrightarrow H(g) + 1 e^-$ (e) electron affinity of hydrogen, $H(g) + 1 e^- \longrightarrow H^-(g)$. The value for the ionization energy of hydride is equal in magnitude but opposite in sign to the electron affinity of hydrogen.   **7.103** Electron configuration, $[Rn]7s^25f^{14}6d^{10}7p^5$; first

ionization energy, 805 kJ/mol; electron affinity, −235 kJ/mol; atomic size, 1.65 Å; common oxidation state, −1   **7.106** (a) Li, $[He]2s^1$; $Z_{eff} \approx 1+$ (b) $I_1 \approx 5.45 \times 10^{-19}$ J/mol ≈ 328 kJ/mol (c) The estimated value of 328 kJ/mol is less than the Table 7.4 value of 520 kJ/mol. Our estimate for Z_{eff} was a lower limit; the [He] core electrons do not perfectly shield the $2s$ electron from the nuclear charge. (d) Based on the experimental ionization energy, $Z_{eff} = 1.26$. This value is greater than the estimate from part (a) but agrees well with the "Slater" value of 1.3 and is consistent with the explanation in part (c). **7.108** (a) 9.8902 Å. (b) For Hg, the first ionization energy is 1007 kJ/mol, while the XPS energy of the $4f$ electron is 10,100 kJ/mol. The energy required to remove a $4f$ core electron is 10 times the energy required to remove a $6s$ valence electron. For O, the first ionization energy is 1314 kJ/mol, while the XPS energy of a $1s$ electron is 51,200 kJ/mol. The energy required to remove a $1s$ core electron is 40 times that required to remove a $2p$ valence electron. (c) Hg^{2+}, $[Xe]4f^{14}5d^{10}$; valence electrons are $5d$. O^{2-}, $[He]2s^22p^6$ or [Ne]; valence electrons are $2p$ (d) $Hg^{2+}5d$, $Z_{eff} = 18.85$; $Hg^{2+}4f$, $Z_{eff} = 43.85$; $O^{2-}4f$, $Z_{eff} = 3.85$. **7.110** (a) Mg_3N_2 (b) $Mg_3N_2(s) + 3 H_2O(l) \longrightarrow 3 MgO(s) + 2 NH_3(g)$; the driving force is the production of $NH_3(g)$. (c) 17% Mg_3N_2 (d) $3 Mg(s) + 2 NH_3(g) \longrightarrow Mg_3N_2(s) + 3 H_2(g)$. NH_3 is the limiting reactant and 0.46 g H_2 is formed. (e) $\Delta H°_{rxn} = -368.70$ kJ

CHAPTER 8

8.1 (a) Group 4A or 14 (b) Group 2A or 2 (c) Group 5A or 15 **8.4** (a) Ru (b) $[Kr]5s^24d^6$.   **8.7** (a) Moving from left to right along the molecule, the first C needs 2 H atoms, the second needs 1, the third needs none, and the fourth needs 1. (b) In order of increasing bond length: $3 < 1 < 2$ (c) In order of increasing bond enthalpy: $2 < 1 < 3$ **8.9** (a) Valence electrons are those that take part in chemical bonding. This usually means the electrons beyond the core noble-gas configuration of the atom, although it is sometimes only the outer-shell electrons. (b) A nitrogen atom has 5 valence electrons. (c) The atom (Si) has 4 valence electrons.   **8.11** Si, $1s^22s^22p^63s^23p^2$. The $n = 3$ electrons are valence electrons; the others are nonvalence electrons. Valence electrons participate in chemical bonding; the others do not.

8.13 (a) $\cdot \overset{\cdot}{Al} \cdot$ (b) $:\overset{\cdot\cdot}{\underset{\cdot\cdot}{Br}}:$ (c) $:\overset{\cdot\cdot}{\underset{\cdot\cdot}{Ar}}:$ (d) $\cdot Sr$

8.15 $\overset{\cdot\cdot}{Mg} + \cdot\overset{\cdot\cdot}{\underset{\cdot\cdot}{O}}: \longrightarrow Mg^{2+} + \left[:\overset{\cdot\cdot}{\underset{\cdot\cdot}{O}}:\right]^{2-}$

8.17 (a) AlF_3 (b) K_2S (c) Y_2O_3 (d) Mg_3N_2 **8.19** (a) Sr^{2+}, $[Ar]4s^23d^{10}4p^6 = [Kr]$, noble-gas configuration (b) Ti^{2+}, $[Ar]3d^2$ (c) Se^{2-}, $[Ar]4s^23d^{10}4p^6 = [Kr]$, noble-gas configuration (d) Ni^{2+}, $[Ar]3d^8$ (e) Br^-, $[Ar]4s^23d^{10}4p^6 = [Kr]$, noble-gas configuration (f) Mn^{3+}, $[Ar]3d^4$ **8.21** (a) *Lattice energy* is the energy required to totally separate one mole of solid ionic compound into its gaseous ions. (b) The magnitude of the lattice energy depends on the magnitudes of the charges of the two ions, their radii, and the arrangement of ions in the lattice.   **8.23** KF, 808 kJ/mol; CaO, 3414 kJ/mol; ScN, 7547 kJ/mol. The interionic distances in the three compounds are similar. For compounds with similar ionic separations, the lattice energies should be related as the product of the charges of the ions. The lattice energies above are approximately related as 1 : 4 : 9. Slight variations are due to the small differences in ionic separations. **8.25** Since the ionic charges are the same in the two compounds, the K—Br and Cs—Cl separations must be approximately equal. **8.27** The large attractive energy between oppositely charged Ca^{2+} and O^{2-} more than compensates for the energy required to form Ca^{2+} and O^{2-} from the neutral atoms.   **8.29** The lattice energy of $RbCl(s)$ is +692 kJ/mol. This value is smaller than the lattice energy for NaCl because Rb^+ has a larger ionic radius than Na^+ and therefore cannot approach Cl^- as closely as Na^+ can.   **8.31** (a) A *covalent bond* is the bond formed when two atoms share one or more pairs of electrons. (b) Any simple compound whose component atoms are nonmetals, such as H_2, SO_2, and CCl_4, are molecular and have covalent bonds between atoms. (c) Covalent, because it is a gas at room temperature and below.

8.33

8.35 (a) $\ddot{O}=\ddot{O}$ (b) A double bond is required because there are not enough electrons to satisfy the octet rule with single bonds and unshared pairs. (c) The greater the number of shared electron pairs between two atoms, the shorter the distance between the atoms. An $O=O$ double bond is shorter than an $O-O$ single bond. **8.37** (a) *Electronegativity* is the ability of an atom in a molecule to attract electrons to itself. (b) The range of electronegativities on the Pauling scale is 0.7–4.0. (c) Fluorine is the most electronegative element. (d) Cesium is the least electronegative element that is not radioactive. **8.39** (a) Mg (b) S (c) C (d) As **8.41** The bonds in (a), (c), and (d) are polar. The more electronegative element in each polar bond is (a) F (c) O (d) I. **8.43** (a) The calculated charge on H and Br is 0.12e. (b) From Sample Exercise 8.5, the calculated charge on H and Cl in HCl is 0.178e. HBr has a smaller dipole moment and longer bond length than HCl; these properties both contribute to the smaller charge separation in HBr. **8.45** (a) $SiCl_4$, molecular, silicon tetrachloride; LaF_3, ionic, lanthanum(III) fluoride (b) $FeCl_2$, ionic, iron(II) chloride; $ReCl_6$, molecular (metal in high oxidation state), rhenium hexachloride. (c) $PbCl_4$, molecular (by contrast to the distinctly ionic $RbCl$), lead tetrachloride; $RbCl$, ionic, rubidium chloride

8.47 (a) H—Si—H (with H above and below Si) (b) $:C\equiv O:$

(c) $:\ddot{F}-\ddot{S}-\ddot{F}:$ (d) $:\ddot{O}-S-\ddot{O}-H$ (with $:\ddot{O}:$ above and H below the S)

(e) $\left[:\ddot{O}-\ddot{Cl}-\ddot{O}:\right]^{-}$ (f) H—N—O—H (with H below N)

8.49 (a) *Formal charge* is the charge on each atom in a molecule, assuming all atoms have the same electronegativity. (b) Formal charges are not actual charges. They are a bookkeeping system that assumes perfect covalency, one extreme for the possible electron distribution in a molecule. (c) Oxidation numbers are a bookkeeping system that assumes the more electronegative element holds all electrons in a bond. The true electron distribution is some composite of the two extremes. **8.51** Formal charges are shown on the Lewis structures; oxidation numbers are listed below each structure.

(a) $\ddot{O}=C=\ddot{S}$
       0 0 0
   O, −2; C, +4; S, −2

(b) $0 :\ddot{Cl}-\overset{:\ddot{O}:^{-1}}{\underset{+1}{S}}-\ddot{Cl}: 0$
   S, +4; Cl, −1; O, −2

(c) $\left[-1 :\ddot{O}-\overset{:\ddot{O}:^{-1}}{\underset{+2}{Br}}-\ddot{O}:-1\right]^{1-}$
   Br, +5; O, −2

(d) $0\ H-\ddot{O}-\overset{}{\underset{0}{\ddot{Cl}}}-\ddot{O}:-1$
      0 $+1$
   Cl, +3; H, +1; O, −2

8.53 (a) $\left[\ddot{O}=\ddot{N}-\ddot{O}:\right]^{-} \longleftrightarrow \left[:\ddot{O}-\ddot{N}=\ddot{O}\right]^{-}$

(b) O_3 is isoelectronic with NO_2^{-}; both have 18 valence electrons. (c) Since each N—O bond has partial double-bond character, the N—O bond length in NO_2^{-} should be shorter than an N—O single bond. **8.55** The more electron pairs shared by two atoms, the shorter

the bond. Thus, the C—O bond lengths vary in the order $CO < CO_2 < CO_3^{2-}$. **8.57** (a) Two equally valid Lewis structures can be drawn for benzene.

(benzene resonance structures shown)

The concept of resonance dictates that the true description of bonding is some hybrid or blend of these two Lewis structures. The most obvious blend of these two resonance structures is a molecule with six equivalent C—C bonds with equal lengths. (b) This model predicts a uniform C—C bond length that is shorter than a single bond but longer than a double bond. **8.59** (a) The octet rule states that atoms will gain, lose, or share electrons until they are surrounded by eight valence electrons. (b) The octet rule applies to atoms in a covalent compound and the individual ions in an ionic compound. In the covalent compound CCl_4, the atoms share electrons in order to surround themselves with an octet. In the ionic compound $MgCl_2$, Mg loses 2 e⁻ to become Mg^{2+} with the electron configuration of Ne. Each Cl atom gains one electron to form Cl^{-} with the electron configuration of Ar. **8.61** No chlorine oxide will obey the octet rule. Chlorine has seven valence electrons, and oxygen has six. For neutral chlorine oxides, regardless of the number of oxygen atoms in the molecule, the total number of valence electrons will be an (odd + even) sum, which is always an odd number. **8.63**

(a) $\left[:\ddot{O}-\overset{:\ddot{O}:}{S}-\ddot{O}:\right]^{2-}$ (b) H—Al—H (with H below Al)

Other resonance structures that minimize formal charges but violate the octet rule can be drawn. The octet rule versus formal charge debate is ongoing. 6 electrons around Al

(c) $\left[:N\equiv N-\ddot{N}:\right]^{-} \longleftrightarrow \left[:\ddot{N}-N\equiv N:\right]^{-} \longleftrightarrow \left[:\ddot{N}=N=\ddot{N}:\right]^{-}$

(d) $:\ddot{Cl}-\overset{:\ddot{Cl}:}{C}-H$ (with H below C)

(e) $:\ddot{F}-\overset{:\ddot{F}:}{Sb}\overset{\ddot{F}:}{\underset{:\ddot{F}:}{}}$ (F atoms around Sb)
   10 electrons around Sb

8.65 (a) $:\ddot{Cl}-Be-\ddot{Cl}:$
       0   0   0
This structure violates the octet rule.

(b) $\ddot{Cl}=Be=\ddot{Cl} \longleftrightarrow :\ddot{Cl}-Be\equiv Cl \longleftrightarrow Cl\equiv Be-\ddot{Cl}:$
   +1 −2 +1   0   −2 +2   +2 −2 0
(c) Formal charges are minimized on the structure that violates the octet rule; this form is probably dominant. **8.67** Three resonance structures for HSO_3^{-} are shown here. Because the ion has a 1− charge, the sum of the formal charges of the atoms is −1.

$\left[H-\ddot{O}-\overset{+1}{S}-\ddot{O}:\right]^{1-}$ (with O below, −1) $\left[H-\ddot{O}-S=\ddot{O}\right]^{1-}$ (with O below, −1)

$\left[H-\ddot{O}-\overset{-1}{S}=\ddot{O}\right]^{1-}$ (with O below, 0)

The structure with no double bonds obeys the octet rule for all atoms, but does not lead to minimized formal charges. The structures with one and two double bonds both minimize formal charge but do not obey the octet rule. Of these two, the structure with one double bond is preferred because the formal charge is localized on the more electronegative oxygen atom. **8.69** (a) $\Delta H = -304$ kJ (b) $\Delta H = -82$ kJ (c) $\Delta H = -467$ kJ **8.71** (a) $\Delta H = -321$ kJ (b) $\Delta H = -103$ kJ (c) $\Delta H = -203$ kJ **8.73** (a) -97 kJ; exothermic (b) The ΔH calculated from bond enthalpies (-97 kJ) is slightly more exothermic (more negative) than that obtained using ΔH_f° values (-92.38 kJ). **8.75** The average Ti—Cl bond enthalpy is 430 kJ/mol. **8.77** (a) Six (nonradioactive) elements. Yes, they are in the same family, assuming H is placed with the alkali metals. The Lewis symbol represents the number of valence electrons of an element, and all elements in the same family have the same number of valence electrons. By definition of a family, all elements with the same Lewis symbol must be in the same family. **8.81** The charge on M is likely to be 3+. The range of lattice energies for ionic compounds with the general formula MX and a charge of 2+ on the metal is 3-4 × 10³ kJ/mol. The lattice energy of 6 × 10³ kJ/mol indicates that the charge on M must be greater than 2+. **8.85** (a) B—O. The most polar bond will be formed by the two elements with the greatest difference in electronegativity. (b) Te—I. These elements have the two largest covalent radii among this group. (c) TeI₂. The octet rule is be satisfied for all three atoms. (d) P₂O₃. Each P atom needs to share 3e⁻ and each O atom 2e⁻ to achieve an octet. And B₂O₃. Although this is not a purely ionic compound, it can be understood in terms of gaining and losing electrons to achieve a noble-gas configuration. If each B atom were to lose 3e⁻ and each O atom were to gain 2e⁻, charge balance and the octet rule would be satisfied. **8.90** (a) +1 (b) −1 (c) +1 (assuming the odd electron is on N) (d) 0 (e) +3 **8.95** An experimentally determined molecular structure will reveal bond lengths and angles of the B—A=B molecule. If resonance structures are important, the two B—A bond lengths will be identical. If the molecule features one single and one double bond, the lengths will be significantly different. **8.98** (a) $\Delta H = 7.85$ kJ/g nitroglycerine (b) $4 C_7H_5N_3O_6(s) \longrightarrow 6 N_2(g) + 7 CO_2(g) + 10 H_2O(g) + 21 C(s)$ **8.101** (a) Ti²⁺, [Ar]3d²; Ca, [Ar]4s². Yes. The 2 valence electrons in Ti²⁺ and Ca are in different principal quantum levels and different subshells. (b) In Ca the 4s is lower in energy than the 3d, while in Ti²⁺ the 3d is lower in energy than the 4s. (c) No. There is only one 4s orbital, so the 2 valence electrons in Ca are paired; there are 5 degenerate 3d orbitals, so the 2 valence electrons in Ti²⁺ are unpaired. **8.107** (a) Azide ion is N₃⁻. (b) Resonance structures with formal charges are shown.

$$\left[:\ddot{N}=N=\ddot{N}: \right]^- \longleftrightarrow \left[:N\equiv N-\ddot{N}: \right]^- \longleftrightarrow$$
$$\quad\ {-1} \quad {+1} \quad {-1} \qquad\qquad {0} \quad {+1} \quad {-2}$$

$$\left[:\ddot{N}-N\equiv N: \right]^-$$
$$\qquad {-2} \quad {+1} \quad {0}$$

(c) The structure with two double bonds minimizes formal charges and is probably the main contributor. (d) The N—N distances will be equal and have the approximate length of a N—N double bond, 1.24 Å. **8.112** (a) D(Br—Br)(l) = 223.6 kJ; D(Br—Br)(g) = 193 kJ (b) D(C—Cl)(l) = 336.1 kJ; D(C—Cl)(g) = 328 kJ (c) D(O—O)(l) = 192.7 kJ; D(O—O)(g) = 146 kJ (d) Breaking bonds in the liquid requires more energy than breaking bonds in the gas phase. Bond dissociation in the liquid phase can be thought of in two steps, vaporization of the liquid followed by bond dissociation in the gas phase. The greater bond dissociation enthalpy in the liquid phase is due to the contribution from the enthalpy of vaporization.

CHAPTER 9

9.1 Removing an atom from the equatorial plane of the trigonal bipyramid in Figure 9.3 creates a seesaw shape. **9.3** (a) 2 electron-domain geometries, linear and trigonal bipyramidal (b) 1 electron-domain geometry, trigonal bipyramidal (c) 1 electron-domain geometry, octahedral (c) 1 electron-domain geometry, octahedral (d) 1 electron domain geometry, octahedral (e) 1 electron domain geometry, octahedral (f) 1 electron-domain geometry, trigonal bipyramidal (This triangular pyramid is an unusual molecular geometry not listed in Table 9.3. It could occur if the equatorial substituents on the trigonal bipyramid were extremely bulky, causing the nonbonding electron pair to occupy an axial position.) **9.5** (a) Zero energy corresponds to two separate, noninteracting Cl atoms. This infinite Cl—Cl distance is beyond the right extreme of the horizontal axis on the diagram. (b) According to the valence bond model, valence orbitals on the approaching atoms overlap, allowing two electrons to mutually occupy space between the two nuclei and be stabilized by two nuclei rather than one. (c) The Cl—Cl distance at the energy minimum on the plot is the Cl—Cl bond length. (d) At interatomic separations shorter than the bond distance, the two nuclei begin to repel each other, increasing the overall energy of the system. (e) The y-coordinate of the minimum point on the plot is a good estimate of the Cl—Cl bond energy or bond strength. **9.6** SiCl₄, 109°; PF₃, 107°; SF₂, 105°. Each molecule has tetrahedral electron domain geometry, but the number of nonbonding electron pairs increases from 0 to 2, respectively. Because nonbonding electron pairs occupy more space than bonding pairs, we expect the bond angles to decrease in the series. **9.9** (a) i, Two s atomic orbitals; ii, two p atomic orbitals overlapping end to end; iii, two p atomic orbitals overlapping side to side (b) i, σ-type MO; ii, σ-type MO; iii, π-type MO (c) i, antibonding; ii, bonding; iii, antibonding (d) i, the nodal plane is between the atom centers, perpendicular to the interatomic axis and equidistant from each atom. ii, there are two nodal planes; both are perpendicular to the interatomic axis. One is left of the left atom and the second is right of the right atom. iii, there are two nodal planes; one is between the atom centers, perpendicular to the interatomic axis and equidistant from each atom. The second contains the interatomic axis and is perpendicular to the first. **9.11** (a) Yes. The stated shape defines the bond angle and the bond length tells the size. (b) No. Atom A could have 2, 3, or 4 nonbonding electron pairs. **9.13** A molecule with tetrahedral molecular geometry has an atom at each vertex of the tetrahedron. A trigonal-pyramidal molecule has one vertex of the tetrahedron occupied by a nonbonding electron pair rather than an atom. **9.15** (a) An *electron domain* is a region in a molecule where electrons are most likely to be found. (b) Like the balloons in Figure 9.5, each electron domain occupies a finite volume of space, so they also adopt an arrangement where repulsions are minimized. **9.17** (a) The number of electron domains in a molecule or ion is the number of bonds (double and triple bonds count as one domain) plus the number of nonbonding electron pairs. (b) A *bonding electron domain* is a region between two bonded atoms that contains one or more pairs of bonding electrons. A *nonbonding electron domain* is localized on a single atom and contains one pair of nonbonding electrons. **9.19** (a) No effect on molecular shape (b) 1 nonbonding pair on P influences molecular shape (c) no effect (d) no effect (e) 1 nonbonding pair on S influences molecular shape **9.21** (a) 2 (b) 1 (c) none (d) 3 **9.23** The electron-domain geometry indicated by VSEPR describes the arrangement of all bonding and nonbonding electron domains. The molecular geometry describes just the atomic positions. In H₂O there are 4 electron domains around oxygen, so the electron-domain geometry is tetrahedral. Because there are 2 bonding and 2 nonbonding domains, the molecular geometry is bent. We make this distinction because all electron domains must be considered when describing the atomic arrangement and bond angles in a molecule but the molecular geometry or shape is a description of just the atom positions. **9.25** (a) Tetrahedral, tetrahedral (b) trigonal bipyramidal, T-shaped (c) octahedral, square pyramidal (d) octahedral, square planar **9.27** (a) Linear, linear (b) tetrahedral, trigonal pyramidal (c) trigonal bipyramidal, seesaw (d) octahedral, octahedral (e) tetrahedral, tetrahedral (f) linear, linear **9.29** (a) i, trigonal planar; ii, tetrahedral; iii, trigonal bipyramidal (b) i, 0; ii, 1; iii, 2 (c) N and P (d) Cl (or Br or I). This T-shaped molecular geometry arises from a trigonal-bipyramidal electron-domain geometry with 2 nonbonding domains. Assuming each F atom has 3 nonbonding domains and forms only single bonds with A, A must have 7 valence electrons and be in or below the third row of the periodic table

to produce these electron-domain and molecular geometries. **9.31** (a) 1–109°, 2–109° (b) 3–109°, 4–109° (c) 5–180° (d) 6–120°, 7–109°, 8–109° **9.33** The two molecules with trigonal-bipyramidal electron-domain geometry, PF_5 and SF_4, have more than one F—A—F bond angle. **9.35** (a) Although both ions have 4 bonding electron domains, the 6 total domains around Br require octahedral domain geometry and square-planar molecular geometry, while the 4 total domains about B lead to tetrahedral domain and molecular geometry. (b) The less electronegative the central atom, the larger the nonbonding electron domain, and the greater the effect of repulsive forces on adjacent bonding domains. The less electronegative the central atom, the greater the deviation from ideal tetrahedral angles. The angles will vary as $H_2O > H_2S > H_2Se$. **9.37** A bond dipole is the asymmetric charge distribution between two bonded atoms with unequal electronegativities. A molecular dipole moment is the three-dimensional sum of all the bond dipoles in a molecule. **9.39** (a) Yes. The net dipole moment vector points along the Cl—S—Cl angle bisector. (b) No, $BeCl_2$ does not have a dipole moment. **9.41** (a) In Exercise 9.29, molecules (ii) and (iii) will have nonzero dipole moments. Molecule (i) has no nonbonding electron pairs on A, and the 3 A—F bond dipoles are oriented so that they cancel. Molecules (ii) and (iii) have nonbonding electron pairs on A and their bond dipoles do not cancel. (b) In Exercise 9.30, molecules (i) and (ii) have a zero dipole moment. **9.43** (a) IF (d) PCl_3 and (f) IF_5 are polar.
9.45 (a) Lewis structures

Molecular geometries

Polar   Nonpolar   Polar

(b) The middle isomer has a zero net dipole moment. (c) C_2H_3Cl has only one isomer, and it has a dipole moment. **9.47** (a) *Orbital overlap* occurs when valence atomic orbitals on two adjacent atoms share the same region of space. (b) A chemical bond is a concentration of electron density between the nuclei of two atoms. This concentration can take place because orbitals on the two atoms overlap. **9.49** (a) H—Mg—H, linear electron domain and molecular geometry (b) The linear electron-domain geometry in MgH_2 requires sp hybridization.

(c)

9.51

Molecule	Electron-Domain Geometry	Hybridization of Central Atom	Dipole Moment? Yes or No
CO_2	Linear	sp	No
NH_3	Tetrahedral	sp^3	Yes
CH_4	Tetrahedral	sp^3	No
BH_3	Trigonal planar	sp^2	No
SF_4	Trigonal bipyramidal	Not applicable	Yes
SF_6	Octahedral	Not applicable	No
H_2CO	Trigonal planar	sp^2	Yes
PF_5	Trigonal bipyramidal	Not applicable	No
XeF_2	Trigonal bipyramidal	Not applicable	No

9.53 (a) B, $[He]2s^22p^1$. One 2s electron is "promoted" to an empty 2p orbital. The 2s and two 2p orbitals that each contain one electron are

hybridized to form three equivalent hybrid orbitals in a trigonal-planar arrangement. (b) sp^2 (d) A single 2p orbital is unhybridized. It lies perpendicular to the trigonal plane of the sp^2 hybrid orbitals. **9.55** (a) sp^2 (b) sp^3 (c) sp (d) sp^3 **9.57** No hybrid orbitals discussed in this chapter form angles of 90° with each other; p atomic orbitals are perpendicular to each other. 109.5°, sp^3; 120°, sp^2
9.59 (a) (b)

(c) A σ bond is generally stronger than a π bond because there is more extensive orbital overlap. (d) No. Overlap of two s orbitals results in electron density along the internuclear axis, while a π bond has none.
9.61 (a)

(b) sp^3, sp^2, sp (c) nonplanar, planar, planar (d) 7 σ, 0 π; 5 σ, 1 π; 3 σ, 2 π (e) The Si analogs would have the same hybridization as the C compounds given in part (b). That Si is in the row below C means it has a larger bonding atomic radius and atomic orbitals than C. The close approach of Si atoms required to form strong, stable π bonds in Si_2H_4 and Si_2H_2 is not possible and these Si analogs do not readily form. **9.63** (a) 18 valence electrons (b) 16 valence electrons form σ bonds. (c) 2 valence electrons form π bonds. (d) No valence electrons are nonbonding (e) The left and central C atoms are sp^2 hybridized; the right C atom is sp^3 hybridized. **9.65** (a) ~109° about the leftmost C, sp^3; ~120° about the right-hand C, sp^2 (b) The doubly bonded O can be viewed as sp^2, and the other as sp^3; the nitrogen is sp^3 with approximately 109° bond angles. (c) nine σ bonds, one π bond **9.67** (a) In a localized π bond, the electron density is concentrated between the two atoms forming the bond. In a delocalized π bond, the electron density is spread over all the atoms that contribute p orbitals to the network. (b) The existence of more than one resonance form is a good indication that a molecule will have delocalized π bonding. (c) delocalized **9.69** (a) Linear (b) The two central C atoms each have trigonal planar geometry with ~120° bond angles about them. The C and O atoms lie in a plane with the H atoms free to rotate in and out of this plane. (c) The molecule is planar with ~120° bond angles about the two N atoms. **9.71** (a) Hybrid orbitals are mixtures of atomic orbitals from a single atom and remain localized on that atom. Molecular orbitals are combinations of atomic orbitals from two or more atoms and are delocalized over at least two atoms. (b) Each MO can hold a maximum of two electrons. (c) Antibonding molecular orbitals can have electrons in them. **9.73** (a)
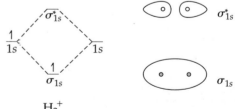

(b) There is one electron in H_2^+. (c) σ_{1s}^1 (d) BO = $\frac{1}{2}$ (e) Fall apart. If the single electron in H_2^+ is excited to the σ_{1s}^* orbital, its energy is higher than the energy of an H 1s atomic orbital and H_2^+ will decompose into a hydrogen atom and a hydrogen ion.
9.75

(a) 1 σ bond (b) 2 π bonds (c) 1 σ^* and 2 π^* **9.77** (a) When comparing the same two bonded atoms, bond order and bond energy are directly related, while bond order and bond length are inversely related. When comparing different bonded nuclei, there are no simple relationships. (b) Be_2 is not expected to exist; it has a bond order of zero and is not energetically favored over isolated Be atoms. Be_2^+ has a bond order of 0.5 and is slightly lower in energy than isolated Be atoms. It will probably exist under special experimental conditions. **9.79** (a, b) Substances with no unpaired electrons are weakly repelled by a magnetic field. This property is called *diamagnetism*. (c) O_2^{2-}, Be_2^{2+} **9.81** (a) B_2^+, $\sigma_{2s}^2\sigma_{2s}^{*2}\pi_{2p}^1$, increase (b) Li_2^+, $\sigma_{1s}^2\sigma_{1s}^{*2}\sigma_{2s}^1$, increase   (c) N_2^+, $\sigma_{2s}^2\sigma_{2s}^{*2}\pi_{2p}^4\sigma_{2p}^1$,   increase   (d) Ne_2^{2+}, $\sigma_{2s}^2\sigma_{2s}^{*2}\sigma_{2p}^2\pi_{2p}^4\pi_{2p}^{*4}$,   decrease   **9.83** CN, $\sigma_{2s}^2\sigma_{2s}^{*2}\sigma_{2p}^2\pi_{2p}^3$, bond order = 2.5; CN^+, $\sigma_{2s}^2\sigma_{2s}^{*2}\sigma_{2p}^2\pi_{2p}^2$, bond order = 2.0; CN^-, $\sigma_{2s}^2\sigma_{2s}^{*2}\sigma_{2p}^2\pi_{2p}^4$, bond order = 3.0. (a) CN^- (b) CN, CN^+ **9.85** (a) $3s$, $3p_x$, $3p_y$, $3p_z$ (b) π_{3p} (c) 2 (d) If the MO diagram for P_2 is similar to that of N_2, P_2 will have no unpaired electrons and be diamagnetic.   **9.89** SiF_4 is tetrahedral, SF_4 is seesaw, XeF_4 is square planar. The shapes are different because the number of nonbonding electron domains is different in each molecule, even though all have four bonding electron domains. Bond angles and thus molecular shape are determined by the total number of electron domains. **9.92** (a) 2σ bonds, 2π bonds (b) 3σ bonds, 4π bonds (c) 3σ bonds, 1π bond (d) 4σ bonds, 1π bond   **9.94** BF_3 is trigonal planar, the B—F bond dipoles cancel and the molecule is nonpolar. PF_3 has a tetrahedral electron-domain geometry with one position occupied by a nonbonding electron pair. The nonbonding electron pair ensures an asymmetrical electron distribution and the molecule is polar. **9.99**

(a) The molecule is nonplanar. (b) Allene has no dipole moment. (c) The bonding in allene would not be described as delocalized. The π electron clouds of the two adjacent C=C are mutually perpendicular, so there is no overlap and no delocalization of π electrons. **9.101** (a) All O atoms have sp^2 hybridization. (b) The two σ bonds are formed by overlap of sp^2 hybrid orbitals, the π bond is formed by overlap of atomic p orbitals, one nonbonded pair is in a p atomic orbital and the other five nonbonded pairs are in sp^2 hybrid orbitals. (c) unhybridized p atomic orbitals (d) four, two from the π bond and two from the nonbonded pair in the p atomic orbital   **9.104** $\sigma_{2s}^2\sigma_{2s}^{*2}\pi_{2p}^4\sigma_{2p}^1\pi_{2p}^{*1}$ (a) Paramagnetic (b) The bond order of N_2 in the ground state is 3; in the first excited state it has a bond order of 2. Owing to the reduction in bond order, N_2 in the first excited state has a weaker N—N bond. **9.110** (a) $2\,SF_4(g) + O_2(g) \longrightarrow 2\,OSF_4(g)$

(b)

(c) $\Delta H = -551$ kJ, exothermic (d) The electron-domain geometry is trigonal bipyramidal. The O atom can be either equatorial or axial. (e) Since F is more electronegative than O, the structure that minimizes 90° F—S—F angles, the one with O axial, is preferred.

CHAPTER 11

11.1 The diagram best describes a liquid. The particles are close together, mostly touching, but there is no regular arrangement or order. This rules out a gaseous sample, where the particles are far apart, and a crystalline solid, which has a regular repeating structure in all three directions.   **11.4** (a) In its final state, methane is a gas at 185 °C. **11.5** (a) 385 mm Hg (b) 22 °C (c) 47 °C   **11.6** The stronger the intermolecular forces, the higher the boiling point of a liquid. Propanol, $CH_3CH_2CH_2OH$, has hydrogen bonding and the higher boiling point.

11.7 (a) Normal boiling point, 360 K; normal freezing point, 260 K (b) (i) gas (ii) solid (iii) liquid (c) The triple point is approximately 185 K at 0.45 atm.   **11.9** (a) Solid < liquid < gas (b) gas < liquid < solid (c) Matter in the gaseous state is most easily compressed because particles are far apart and there is much empty space.   **11.11** Ar < CCl_4 < Si **11.13** (a) The molar volumes of Cl_2 and NH_3 are nearly the same because they are both gases. (b) On cooling to 160 K, both compounds condense from the gas phase to the solid-state, so we expect a significant decrease in the molar volume. (c) The molar volumes are 0.0351 L/mol Cl_2 and 0.0203 L/mol NH_3 (d) Solid-state molar volumes are not as similar as those in the gaseous state, because most of the empty space is gone and molecular characteristics determine properties. $Cl_2(s)$ is heavier, has a longer bond distance and weaker intermolecular forces, so it has a significantly larger molar volume than $NH_3(s)$. (e) There is little empty space between molecules in the liquid state, so we expect their molar volumes to be closer to those in the solid state than those in the gaseous state.   **11.15** (a) London dispersion forces (b) dipole–dipole and London dispersion forces (c) dipole–dipole forces and in certain cases hydrogen bonding **11.17** (a) SO_2, dipole–dipole and London dispersion forces (b) CH_3COOH, London dispersion, dipole–dipole, and hydrogen bonding (c) H_2Se, dipole–dipole and London dispersion forces (but not hydrogen bonding)   **11.19** (a) *Polarizability* is the ease with which the charge distribution in a molecule can be distorted to produce a transient dipole. (b) Sb is most polarizable because its valence electrons are farthest from the nucleus and least tightly held. (c) in order of increasing polarizability: CH_4 < SiH_4 < $SiCl_4$ < $GeCl_4$ < $GeBr_4$ (d) The magnitudes of London dispersion forces and thus the boiling points of molecules increase as polarizability increases. The order of increasing boiling points is the order of increasing polarizability given in (c).   **11.21** (a) H_2S (b) CO_2 (c) GeH_4 **11.23** Both rodlike butane molecules and spherical 2-methylpropane molecules experience dispersion forces. The larger contact surface between butane molecules facilitates stronger forces and produces a higher boiling point. **11.25** (a) A molecule must contain H atoms, bound to either N, O, or F atoms, in order to participate in hydrogen bonding with like molecules. (b) CH_3NH_2 and CH_3OH **11.27** (a) Replacing a hydroxyl hydrogen with a CH_3 group eliminates hydrogen bonding in that part of the molecule. This reduces the strength of intermolecular forces and leads to a lower boiling point. (b) $CH_3OCH_2CH_2OCH_3$ is a larger, more polarizable molecule with stronger London dispersion forces and thus a higher boiling point. **11.29**

Physical Property	H_2O	H_2S
Normal boiling point, °C	100.00	−60.7
Normal melting point, °C	0.00	−85.5

(a) Based on its much higher normal melting point and boiling point, H_2O has much stronger intermolecular forces. H_2O has hydrogen bonding, while H_2S has dipole–dipole forces. (b) H_2S is probably a typical compound with less empty space in the ordered solid than the liquid, so that the solid is denser than the liquid. For H_2O, maximizing the number of hydrogen bonds to each molecule in the solid requires more empty space than in the liquid, and the solid is less dense. (c) Specific heat is the energy required to raise the temperature of one gram of the substance one degree Celsius. Hydrogen bonding in water is such a strong attractive interaction that the energy required to disrupt it and increase molecular motion is large.   **11.31** SO_4^{2-} has a greater negative charge than BF_4^-, so ion–ion electrostatic attractions are greater in sulfate salts and they are less likely to form liquids. **11.33** (a) As temperature increases, the number of molecules with sufficient kinetic energy to overcome intermolecular attractive forces increases, and viscosity and surface tension decrease. (b) The same attractive forces that cause surface molecules to be difficult to separate (high surface tension) cause molecules elsewhere in the sample to resist movement relative to each other (high viscosity).   **11.35** (a) $CHBr_3$ has a higher molar mass, is more polarizable, and has stronger dispersion forces, so the surface tension is greater. (b) As temperature increases, the viscosity of the oil decreases because the average kinetic energy of the molecules increases. (c) Adhesive forces between polar water and nonpolar car wax are weak, so the large surface tension of water draws the liquid into the shape with the smallest surface area, a sphere. (d) Adhesive forces between nonpolar oil and nonpolar car wax are similar to cohesive forces in oil, so the oil drops spread out on the waxed car hood.   **11.37** (a) The three molecules have similar structures and experience the same types of intermolecular forces. As molar mass increases, the strength of dispersion forces increases and the boiling points, surface tension, and viscosities all increase. (b) Ethylene glycol has an —OH group at both ends of the molecule. This greatly increases the possibilities for hydrogen bonding; the overall intermolecular attractive forces are greater and the viscosity of ethylene glycol is much greater. (c) Water has the highest surface tension but lowest viscosity because it is the smallest molecule in the series. There is no hydrocarbon chain to inhibit their strong attraction to molecules in the interior of the drop, resulting in high surface tension. The absence of an alkyl chain also means the molecules can move around each other easily, resulting in the low viscosity.   **11.39** (a) Melting, endothermic (b) evaporation, endothermic (c) deposition, exothermic (d) condensation, exothermic   **11.41** Melting does not require separation of molecules, so the energy requirement is smaller than for vaporization, where molecules must be separated.   **11.43** 2.3×10^3 g H_2O **11.45** (a) 39.3 kJ (b) 60 kJ   **11.47** (a) The critical pressure is the pressure required to cause liquefaction at the critical temperature. (b) As the force of attraction between molecules increases, the critical temperature of the compound increases. (c) All the gases in Table 11.5 can be liquefied at the temperature of liquid nitrogen, given sufficient pressure.   **11.49** (a) No effect (b) no effect (c) Vapor pressure decreases with increasing intermolecular attractive forces because fewer molecules have sufficient kinetic energy to overcome attractive forces and escape to the vapor phase. (d) Vapor pressure increases with increasing temperature because average kinetic energies of molecules increase. (e) Vapor pressure decreases with increasing density because attractive intermolecular forces increase.   **11.51** (a) $CBr_4 < CHBr_3 < CH_2Br_2 < CH_2Cl_2 < CH_3Cl < CH_4$. The trend is dominated by dispersion forces even though four of the molecules are polar. The order of increasing volatility is the order of increasing vapor pressure, decreasing molar mass, and decreasing strength of dispersion forces. (b) Boiling point increases as the strength of intermolecular forces increases; this is the order of decreasing volatility and the reverse of the order in part (a). $CH_4 < CH_3Cl < CH_2Cl_2 < CH_2Br_2 < CHBr_3 < CBr_4$ **11.53** (a) The temperature of the water in the two pans is the same. (b) Vapor pressure does not depend on either volume or surface area of the liquid. At the same temperature, the vapor pressures of water in the two containers are the same.   **11.55** (a) Approximately 48 °C (b) approximately 340 torr (c) approximately 17 °C (d) approximately 1000 torr   **11.57** (a) The critical point is the temperature and pressure beyond which the gas and liquid phases are indistinguishable. (b) The line that separates the gas and liquid phases ends at the critical point because at conditions beyond the critical temperature and pressure, there is no distinction between gas and liquid. In experimental terms a gas cannot be liquefied at temperatures higher than the critical temperature, regardless of pressure.   **11.59** (a) $H_2O(g)$ will condense to $H_2O(s)$ at approximately 4 torr; at a higher pressure, perhaps 5 atm or so, $H_2O(s)$ will melt to form $H_2O(l)$. (b) At 100 °C and 0.50 atm, water is in the vapor phase. As it cools, water vapor condenses to the liquid at approximately 82 °C, the temperature where the vapor pressure of liquid water is 0.50 atm. Further cooling results in freezing at approximately 0 °C. The freezing point of water increases with decreasing pressure, so at 0.50 atm the freezing temperature is very slightly above 0 °C.   **11.61** (a) 24 K (b) Neon sublimes at pressures less than the triple point pressure, 0.43 atm. (c) No   **11.63** (a) Methane on the surface of Titan is likely to exist in both solid and liquid forms. (b) As

pressure decreases upon moving away from the surface of Titan, $CH_4(l)$ (at −178 °C) will vaporize to $CH_4(g)$, and $CH_4(s)$ (at temperatures below −180 °C) will sublime to $CH_4(g)$.   **11.65** In a nematic liquid crystalline phase, molecules are aligned along their long axes, but the molecular ends are not aligned. Molecules are free to translate in all dimensions, but they cannot tumble or rotate out of the molecular plane, or the order of the nematic phase is lost and the sample becomes an ordinary liquid. In an ordinary liquid, molecules are randomly oriented and free to move in any direction.   **11.67** The presence of polar groups or nonbonded electron pairs leads to relatively strong dipole–dipole interactions between molecules. These are a significant part of the orienting forces necessary for liquid crystal formation.   **11.69** Because order is maintained in at least one dimension, the molecules in a liquid-crystalline phase are not totally free to change orientation. This makes the liquid-crystalline phase more resistant to flow, more viscous, than the isotropic liquid.   **11.71** Melting provides kinetic energy sufficient to disrupt molecular alignment in one dimension in the solid, producing a smectic phase with ordering in two dimensions. Additional heating of the smectic phase provides kinetic energy sufficient to disrupt alignment in another dimension, producing a nematic phase with one-dimensional order.   **11.73** (a) Decrease (b) increase (c) increase (d) increase (e) increase (f) increase (g) increase   **11.77** When a halogen is substituted for H in benzene, molar mass, polarizability and strength of dispersion forces increase; the order of increasing molar mass is the order of increasing boiling points for the first three compounds. C_6H_5OH experiences hydrogen bonding, the strongest force between neutral molecules, so it has the highest boiling point.   **11.82** (a) Evaporation is an endothermic process. The heat required to vaporize sweat is absorbed from your body, helping to keep it cool. (b) The vacuum pump reduces the pressure of the atmosphere above the water until atmospheric pressure equals the vapor pressure of water and the water boils. Boiling is an endothermic process, and the temperature drops if the system is not able to absorb heat from the surroundings fast enough. As the temperature of the water decreases, the water freezes.   **11.86** At low Antarctic temperatures, molecules in the liquid crystalline phase have less kinetic energy due to temperature, and the applied voltage may not be sufficient to overcome orienting forces among the ends of molecules. If some or all of the molecules do not rotate when the voltage is applied, the display will not function properly.   **11.90**

(i) $\mathcal{M} = 44$ (ii) $\mathcal{M} = 72$ (iii) $\mathcal{M} = 123$ (iv) $\mathcal{M} = 58$ (v) $\mathcal{M} = 123$ (vi) $\mathcal{M} = 60$

(a) Molar mass: Compounds (i) and (ii) have similar rodlike structures. The longer chain in (ii) leads to greater molar mass, stronger London dispersion forces, and higher heat of vaporization. (b) Molecular shape: Compounds (iii) and (v) have the same chemical formula and molar mass but different molecular shapes. The more rodlike shape of (v) leads to more contact between molecules, stronger dispersion forces, and higher heat of vaporization. (c) Molecular polarity: Compound (iv) has a smaller molar mass than (ii) but a larger heat of vaporization, which must be due to the presence of dipole–dipole forces. (d) Hydrogen bonding interactions: Molecules (v) and (vi) have similar structures. Even though (v) has larger molar mass and dispersion forces, hydrogen bonding causes (vi) to have the higher heat of vaporization.   **11.93** P(benzene vapor) = 98.7 torr

CHAPTER 1

page 5 (a) 100 (b) atoms

page 10 Water is composed of two types of atoms: hydrogen and oxygen. Hydrogen is composed only of hydrogen atoms, and oxygen is composed only of oxygen atoms. Therefore, hydrogen and oxygen are elements and water is a compound.

page 13 (a) Chemical change: Carbon dioxide and water are different compounds than sugar. (b) Physical change: Water in the gas phase becomes water in the solid phase (frost). (c) Physical change: Gold in the solid state becomes liquid and then resolidifies.

page 16 pg, picogram (10^{-12} g)

page 19 2.5×10^2 m^3 is, because it has units of length to the third power.

page 21 (b) Mass of a penny

page 27 Use all digits given in the conversion factor. Conversion factors may be exact and then have "infinite" significant digits (for example, 2.54 cm = 1 inch exactly). Usually, your answer will have its number of significant digits limited by those of the quantities given in the problem.

CHAPTER 2

page 41 (a) The law of multiple proportions. (b) The second compound must contain two oxygen atoms for each carbon atom (that is, twice as many carbon atoms as the first compound).

page 44 Most α particles pass through the foil without being deflected because most of the volume of the atoms that comprise the foil is empty space.

page 45 (a) The atom has 15 electrons because atoms have equal numbers of electrons and protons. (b) The protons reside in the nucleus of the atom.

page 48 Any single atom of chromium must be one of the isotopes of that element. The isotope mentioned has a mass of 52.94 amu and is probably ^{53}Cr. The atomic weight differs from the mass of any particular atom because it is the average atomic mass of the naturally occurring isotopes of the element.

page 51 (a) Cl, (b) third period and group 7A, (c) 17, (d) nonmetal

page 54 (a) C_2H_6, (b) CH_3, (c) Probably the ball-and-stick model because the angles between the sticks indicate the angles between the atoms

page 57 We write the empirical formulas for ionic compounds. Thus, the formula is CaO.

page 60 (a) The transition metals can form more than one type of cation, and the charges of these ions are therefore indicated explicitly with Roman numerals: Chromium(II) ion is Cr^{2+}. Calcium, on the other hand, always forms the Ca^{2+} ion, so there is no need to distinguish it from other calcium ions with different charges. (b) The *–ium* ending indicates that the ion is formed from nonmetals.

page 61 An *-ide* ending usually means a monatomic anion, although there are some anions with two atoms that are also named this way. An *-ate* ending indicates an oxyanion. The most common oxyanions have the *-ate* ending. An *-ite* ending also indicates an oxyanion, but one having less O than the anion whose name ends in *-ate*.

page 62 BO_3^{3-} and SiO_4^{4-}. The borate has three O atoms, like the other oxyanions of the second period in Figure 2.27, and its charge is 3−, following the trend of increasing negative charge as you move to the left in the period. The silicate has four O atoms, as do the other oxyanions in the third period in Figure 2.25, and its charge is 4−, also following the trend of increasing charge moving to the left.

page 65 Iodic acid, by analogy to the relationship between the chlorate ion and chloric acid

page 67

CHAPTER 3

page 78 Each $Mg(OH)_2$ has 1 Mg, 2 O, and 2 H; thus, 3 $Mg(OH)_2$ represents 3 Mg, 6 O, and 6 H.

page 83 The product is an ionic compound involving Na^+ and S^{2-}, and its chemical formula is therefore Na_2S.

page 88 (a) A mole of glucose. By inspecting their chemical formulas we find that glucose has more atoms of H and O than water and in addition it also has C atoms. Thus, a molecule of glucose has a greater mass than a molecule of water. (b) They both contain the same number of molecules because a mole of each substance contains 6.02×10^{23} molecules.

page 93 The N:H ratio is 2:4 = 1:2.

page 96 There are experimental uncertainties in the measurements.

page 97 3.14 mol because 2 mol $H_2 \triangleq$ 1 mol O_2 based on the coefficients in the balanced equation

page 98 The number of grams of product formed is the sum of the masses of the two reactants, 50 g. When two substances react in a combination reaction, only one substance is formed as a product. According to the law of conservation of mass, the mass of the product must equal the masses of the two reactants.

CHAPTER 4

page 118 (a) $K^+(aq)$ and $CN^-(aq)$, (b) $Na^+(aq)$ and $ClO_4^-(aq)$

page 119 NaOH because it is the only solute that is a strong electrolyte

page 123 $Na^+(aq)$ and $NO_3^-(aq)$

page 125 Three. Each COOH group will partially ionize in water to form $H^+(aq)$.

page 126 Only soluble metal hydroxides are classified as strong bases and $Al(OH)_3$ is insoluble.

page 130 $SO_2(g)$

page 133 (a) −3, (b) +5

page 136 (a) Yes, nickel is below zinc in the activity series so $Ni^{2+}(aq)$ will oxidize $Zn(s)$ to form $Ni(s)$ and $Zn^{2+}(aq)$. (b) No reaction will occur because the $Zn^{2+}(aq)$ ions cannot be further oxidized.

page 139 The second solution is more concentrated, 2.50 *M*, than the first solution, which has a concentration of 1.00 *M*.

page 142 The concentration is halved to 0.25 *M*.

CHAPTER 5

page 162 No. The potential energy is lower at the bottom of the hill. (b) Once the bike comes to a stop, its kinetic energy is zero, just as it was at the top of the hill.

page 163 Open system. Humans exchange matter and energy with their surroundings.

page 167 Endothermic

page 169 The balance (current state) does not depend on the ways the money may have been transferred into the account or on the particular expenditures made in withdrawing money from the account. It depends only on the net total of all the transactions.

page 169 Because E, P, and V are state functions that don't depend on path, $H = E + PV$ must also be a state function.

page 170 No. If ΔV is zero, then the expression $w = -P\Delta V$ is also zero.

page 171 A thermometer to measure temperature changes

page 173 No. Because only half as much matter is involved, the value of ΔH would be $\frac{1}{2}(-483.6 \text{ kJ}) = -241.8 \text{ kJ}$.

page 176 Hg(l). Rearranging Equation 5.22 gives $\Delta T = \dfrac{q}{C_s \times m}$. When q and m are constant for a series of substances, then $\Delta T = \dfrac{\text{constant}}{C_s}$. Therefore, the element with the smallest C_s in Table 5.2 has the largest ΔT, Hg(l).

page 181 (a) The sign of ΔH changes. (b) The magnitude of ΔH doubles.

page 184 No. Because $O_3(g)$ is not the most stable form of oxygen at 25 °C, 1 atm [$O_2(g)$ is], ΔH_f° for $O_3(g)$ is not necessarily zero. In Appendix C we see that it is 142.3 kJ/mol.

page 189 Fats, because they have the largest fuel value of the three

page 191 Combustion of $H_2(g)$ produces only $H_2O(g)$. No $CO_2(g)$ or other gases that might contribute to climate change issues are produced.

CHAPTER 6

page 210 No. Both visible light and X-rays are forms of electromagnetic radiation. They therefore both travel at the speed of light, c. Their differing ability to penetrate skin is due to their different energies, which we will discuss in the next section.

page 211 $E = h\nu = (6.63 \times 10^{-34} \text{ J-s})(5 \times 10^{-3} \text{ s}^{-1}) = 3 \times 10^{-30} \text{ J}$; this radiation cannot produce a burst of 5×10^{-36} J because it can only produce energy in multiples of 3×10^{-30} J.

page 212 Ultraviolet. Figure 6.4 shows that a photon in the ultraviolet region of the electromagnetic spectrum has a higher frequency and therefore a greater energy than a photon in the infrared region.

page 214 According to the third postulate, photons of only certain allowed frequencies can be absorbed or emitted as the electron changes energy state. The lines in the spectrum correspond to the allowed frequencies.

page 215 Absorb, because it is moving from a lower-energy state ($n = 3$) to a higher-energy state ($n = 7$)

page 217 Yes, all moving objects produce matter waves, but the wavelengths associated with macroscopic objects, such as the baseball, are too small to allow for any way of observing them.

page 219 The small size and mass of subatomic particles. The term $h/4\pi$ in the uncertainty principle is a very small number that becomes important only when considering extremely small objects, such as electrons.

page 220 Bohr proposed that the electron in the hydrogen atom moves in a well-defined circular path around the nucleus (an orbit). In the quantum-mechanical model, no effort is made to describe the motion of the electron. An orbital is a wave function related to the probability of finding the electron at any point in space.

page 221 The energy of an electron in the hydrogen atom is proportional to $-1/n^2$, as seen in Equation 6.5. The difference between $-1/(2)^2$ and $-1/(1)^2$ is much greater than the difference between $-1/(3)^2$ and $-1/(2)^2$.

page 226 (a) There is one 3s orbital, three 3p orbitals, and ten 3d orbitals, for a total of 14 orbitals. (b) 3s < 3p < 3d.

page 232 The 6s orbital, which starts to hold electrons at element 55, Cs

page 237 We can't conclude anything! Each of the three elements has a different valence electron configuration for its $(n-1)d$ and ns subshells: For Ni, $3d^8 4s^2$; for Pd, $4d^{10}$; and for Pt, $5d^9 6s^1$.

CHAPTER 7

page 251 Atomic number is governed by the number of protons in the nucleus, but atomic weight is governed by both the number of protons and neutrons in the nucleus (electrons are too light to worry about). Co/Ni, Cu/Zn, and Te/I are other pairs of elements whose atomic weights are "off" compared to their atomic numbers.

page 254 The 2p electron in a Ne atom would experience a larger Z_{eff} than the 3s electron in Na, due to the better shielding by all the 2s and 2p electrons for Na's 3s electron.

page 256 These trends work against each other: Z_{eff} increasing would imply that the valence electrons are pulled tighter in to make the atom smaller, while orbital size "increasing" would imply that atomic size would also increase. The orbital size effect is larger: As you go down a column in the periodic table, atomic size generally increases.

page 259 It is harder to remove another electron from Na^+, so the process in Equation 7.3 would require more energy and, hence, shorter-wavelength light (see Sections 6.1 and 6.2).

page 260 Since Z_{eff} increases as you go from boron to carbon, we would expect that the first ionization energy would be larger for carbon. Therefore, I_2 for C is even greater.

page 262 The same

page 264 The numbers are the same; the signs are opposite.

page 265 Increasing metallic character is correlated with decreasing ionization energy.

page 268 Since the melting point is so low, we would expect a molecular rather than ionic compound. Thus, so PCl_3 is more likely than $ScCl_3$.

page 270 Its low ionization energy

page 272 In the acidic environment of the stomach, carbonate can react to give carbonic acid, which decomposes to water and carbon dioxide gas.

page 274 The longest wavelength of visible light is about 750 nm (Section 6.1). We can assume that this corresponds to the lowest energy of light (since $E = hc/\lambda$) needed to break bonds in hydrogen peroxide. If we plug in 750 nm for λ, we can calculate the energy to break one OO bond in one molecule of hydrogen peroxide, in joules. If we multiple by Avogadro's number, we can calculate how many joules it would take to break a mole of OO bonds in hydrogen peroxide (which is the number one normally finds).

page 275 The halogens all have ground-state electron configurations that are $ns^2 np^5$; sharing an electron with only one other atom makes stable compounds.

page 276 We can estimate the radius to be 1.5 Å, and the first ionization energy to be 900 kJ/mol. In fact, its bonding radius is indeed 1.5 Å, and the experimental ionization energy is 920 kJ/mol.

CHAPTER 8

page 290 No. Cl has seven valence electrons. The first and second Lewis symbols are both correct—they both show seven valence electrons, and it doesn't matter which of the four sides has the single electron. The third symbol shows only five electrons and is incorrect.

page 292 CaF_2 is an ionic compound consisting of Ca^{2+} and F^- ions. When Ca and F_2 react to form CaF_2, each Ca atom loses two electrons to form a Ca^{2+} ion and each fluorine atom in F_2 takes up an electron, forming two F^- ions. Thus, we can say that each Ca atom transfers one electron to each of two fluorine atoms.

page 292 No. Figure 7.9 shows that the alkali metal with the smallest first ionization energy is Cs with a value of $+376$ kJ/mol. Figure 7.11 shows that the halogen with the largest electron affinity is Cl with a value of -349 kJ/mol. The sum of the two energies gives a positive energy (endothermic). Therefore, all other combinations of alkali metals with halogens will also have positive values.

page 296 Rhodium, Rh

page 297 Weaker. In both H_2 and H_2^+ the two H atoms are principally held together by the electrostatic attractions between the nuclei and the electron(s) concentrated between them. H_2^+ has only one electron between the nuclei whereas H_2 has two and this results in the H—H bond in H_2 being stronger.

page 298 Triple bond. CO_2 has two C—O double bonds. Because the C—O bond in carbon monoxide is shorter, it is likely to be a triple bond.

page 299 Electron affinity measures the energy released when an isolated atom gains an electron to form a $1-$ ion. The electronegativity measures the ability of the atom to hold on to its own electrons and attract electrons from other atoms in compounds.

page 300 Polar covalent. The difference in electronegativity between S and O is $3.5 - 2.5 = 1.0$. Based on the examples of F_2, HF, and LiF, the difference in electronegativity is great enough to introduce some polarity to the bond but not sufficient to cause a complete electron transfer from one atom to the other.

page 302 IF. Because the difference in electronegativity between I and F is greater than that between Cl and F, the magnitude of Q should be greater for IF. In addition, because I has a larger atomic radius than Cl, the bond length in IF is longer than that in ClF. Thus, both Q and r are larger for IF and, therefore, $\mu = Qr$ will be larger for IF.

page 303 Smaller dipole moment for C—H. The magnitude of Q should be similar for C—H and H—I bonds because the difference in electronegativity for each bond is 0.4. The C—H bond length is 1.1 Å and the H—I bond length is 1.6 Å. Therefore $\mu = Qr$ will be greater for H—I because it has a longer bond (larger r).

page 304 OsO_4. The data suggest that the yellow substance is a molecular species with its low melting and boiling points. Os in OsO_4 has an oxidation number of $+8$ and Cr in Cr_2O_3 has an oxidation number of $+3$. In Section 8.4, we learn that a compound with a metal in a high oxidation state should show a high degree of covalence and OsO_4 fits this situation.

page 308 There is probably a better choice of Lewis structure than the one chosen. Because the formal charges must add up to 0 and the formal charge on the F atom is $+1$, there must be an atom that has a formal charge of -1. Because F is the most electronegative element, we don't expect it to carry a positive formal charge.

page 310 Yes. There are two resonance structures for ozone that each contribute equally to the overall description of the molecule. Each O—O bond is therefore an average of a single bond and a double bond, which is a "one-and-a-half" bond.

page 310 As "one-and-a-third" bonds. There are three resonance structures, and each of the three N—O bonds is single in two of those structures and double in the third. Each bond in the actual ion is an average of these: $(1 + 1 + 2)/3 = 1\frac{1}{3}$.

page 312 No, it will not have multiple resonance structures. We can't "move" the double bonds, as we did in benzene, because the positions of the hydrogen atoms dictate specific positions for the double bonds. We can't write any other reasonable Lewis structures for the molecule.

page 312 The formal charge of each atom is shown here:

$$\overset{..}{N} = \overset{..}{\underset{..}{O}} \qquad \overset{..}{\underset{..}{N}} = \overset{..}{\underset{..}{O}}$$
$$\text{F.C.} \quad 0 \qquad 0 \qquad\qquad -1 \qquad +1$$

The first structure shows each atom with a zero formal charge and therefore it is the dominant Lewis structure. The second one shows a positive formal charge for an oxygen atom, which is a highly electronegative atom, and this is not a favorable situation.

page 315 The atomization of ethane produces $2\,C(g) + 6\,H(g)$. In this process, six C—H bonds and one C—C bond are broken. We can use $6D$(C—H) to estimate the amount of enthalpy needed to break the six C—H bonds. The difference between that number and the enthalpy of atomization is an estimate of the bond enthalpy of the C—C bond, D(C—C).

page 315 H_2O_2. From Table 8.4, the bond enthalpy of the O—O single bond in H_2O_2 (146 kJ/mol) is much lower than that of the O=O bond in O_2 (495 kJ/mol). The weaker bond in H_2O_2 is expected to make it more reactive than O_2.

CHAPTER 9

page 334 Octahedral. Removing two atoms that are opposite each other leads to a square-planar geometry.

page 335 The molecule does not follow the octet rule because it has ten electrons around the central A atom. There are four electron domains around A: two single bonds, one double bond, and one nonbonding pair.

page 336 Each of the three represents a single electron domain in the VSEPR model.

page 339 Yes. Based on one resonance structure, we might expect the electron domain that is due to the double bond to "push" the domains that are due to the single bonds, leading to angles slightly different from 120°. However, we must remember that there are two other equivalent resonance structures—each of the three O atoms has a double bond to N in one of the three resonance structures (Section 8.6). Because of resonance, all three O atoms are equivalent, and they will experience the same amount of repulsion, which leads to bond angles equal to 120°.

page 339 A tetrahedral arrangement of electron domains is preferred because the bond angles are 109.5° compared to 90°. bond angles in a square-planar arrangement of electron domains. The larger bond angles result in smaller repulsions among electron domains and a more stable structure.

page 343 Yes. The C—O and C—S bond dipoles exactly oppose each other, like in CO_2, but because O and S have different electronegativities, the magnitudes of the bond dipoles will be different. As a consequence, the bond dipoles will not cancel each other and the OCS molecule has a nonzero dipole moment.

page 348 Both p orbitals are perpendicular to the Be—F bond axes.

page 348 (bottom) The unhybridized p orbital is oriented perpendicular to the plane defined by the three sp^2 hybrids (trigonal-planar array of lobes) with one lobe on each side of the plane.

page 353 The molecule should not be linear. Because there are three electron domains around each N atom, we expect sp^2 hybridization and H—N—N angles of approximately 120°. The molecule is expected to be planar; the unhybridized $2p$ orbitals on the N atoms can form a π bond only if all four atoms lie in the same plane. You might notice that there are two ways in which the H atoms can be arranged: They can be both on the same side of the N=N bond or on opposite sides of the N=N bond.

page 358 The σ bond component is formed from sp hybrid orbitals.

page 360 The molecule would fall apart. With one electron in the bonding MO and one in the antibonding MO, there is no net stabilization of the electrons relative to two separate H atoms.

page 362 Yes. In Be_2^+ there would be two electrons in the σ_{2s} MO but only one electron in the σ_{2s}^* MO; therefore, the ion is predicted to have a bond order of $\frac{1}{2}$. It should (and does) exist.

page 366 No. If the σ_{2p} MO were lower in energy than the π_{2p} MOs, we would expect the σ_{2p} MO to hold two electrons and the π_{2p} MOs to hold one electron each, with the same spin. The molecule would therefore be paramagnetic.

CHAPTER 11

page 430 $CH_4 < CCl_4 < CBr_4$. Because all three molecules are nonpolar, the strength of dispersion forces determines the relative boiling points. Polarizability increases in order of increasing molecular size and molecular weight, $CH_4 < CCl_4 < CBr_4$; hence, the dispersion forces and boiling points increase in the same order.

page 434 $Ca(NO_3)_2$ in water, because calcium nitrate is a strong electrolyte that forms ions and water is a polar molecule with a dipole moment. Ion–dipole forces cannot be present in a CH_3OH/H_2O mixture because CH_3OH does not form ions.

page 438 (a) Both viscosity and surface tension decrease with increasing temperature because of the increased molecular motion. (b) Both properties increase as the strength of intermolecular forces increases.

page 440 Melting (or fusion), endothermic

page 443 CCl_4. Both compounds are nonpolar; therefore, only dispersion forces exist between the molecules. Because dispersion forces are stronger for the larger, heavier CBr_4, it has a lower vapor pressure than CCl_4. The substance with the larger vapor pressure at a given temperature is more volatile.

CHAPTER 1

Figure 1.1 9

Figure 1.4 Vapor (gas)

Figure 1.5 Molecules of a compound are composed of more than one type of atom, and molecules of an element are composed of only one type of atom.

Figure 1.6 Earth is rich in silicon and aluminum; the human body is rich in carbon and hydrogen

Figure 1.7 They are the same; there are twice as many hydrogen molecules as oxygen molecules, and the hydrogen gas takes up twice the volume of the oxygen gas.

Figure 1.17 True

Figure 1.18 1000

Figure 1.23 The darts would be scattered widely (poor precision) but their average position would be at the center (good accuracy).

CHAPTER 2

Figure 2.3 We know the rays travel from the cathode because of the way the magnetic field diverts the path (b).

Figure 2.4 The electron beam would be deflected downward because of repulsion by the negative plate and attraction toward the positive plate.

Figure 2.8 The beta rays, whose path is diverted away from the negative plate and toward the positive plate, consist of electrons. Because the electrons are much less massive than the alpha particles, their motion is affected more strongly by the electric field.

Figure 2.10 The beam consists of alpha particles, which carry a +2 charge.

Figure 2.14 Based on the periodic trend, we expect that elements that precede a nonreactive gas, as F does, will also be reactive nonmetals. The elements fitting this pattern are H and Cl.

Figure 2.19 The ball-and-stick model more clearly shows the connections between atoms, so we can see the angles at which the atoms are attached in the molecule.

Figure 2.20 The elements are in the following groups: Ag^+ is 1B, Zn^{2+} is 2B, and Sc^{3+} is 3B. Sc^{3+} has the same number of electrons as Ar (element 18).

Figure 2.24 Removing one O atom from the perbromate ion gives the bromate ion, BrO_3^-.

CHAPTER 3

Figure 3.3 The formula CO_2 represents one molecule containing one C and two O atoms, whereas 2 CO represents two molecules, each containing one C atom and one O atom for a total of two C and two O atoms.

Figure 3.8 Both figures show combustion reactions in which the fuel is a hydrocarbon (CH_4 in Figure 3.4 and C_3H_8 in Figure 3.8). In both cases the reactants are the hydrocarbon and O_2, and the products are CO_2 and H_2O.

Figure 3.9 As shown, 18.0 g H_2O = 1 mol H_2O = 6.02 × 10^{23} molecules H_2O. Thus, 9.00 g H_2O = 0.500 mol H_2O = 3.01 × 10^{23} molecules H_2O.

Figure 3.12 (a) The molar mass of CH_4, 16.0 g CH_4/1 mol CH_4. (b) Avogadro's number, 1 mol CH_4/6.02 × 10^{23} formula units CH_4, where a formula unit in this case is a molecule.

Figure 3.13 The mole ratio is obtained by dividing the molecular weight by the empirical formula weight, Equation 3.11.

Figure 3.17 There are 7 mol O_2, and each mol O_2 yields 2 mol H_2O. Thus, 14 mol H_2O would have formed.

CHAPTER 4

Figure 4.3 NaCl(*aq*)

Figure 4.4 K^+ and NO_3^-

Figure 4.9 Two moles of hydrochloric acid are needed to react with each mole of $Mg(OH)_2$.

Figure 4.19 The volume needed to reach the end point if $Ba(OH)_2(aq)$ were used would be one-half the volume needed for titration with NaOH(*aq*).

CHAPTER 5

Figure 5.1 In the act of throwing, the pitcher transfers energy to the ball, which then becomes kinetic energy of the ball. For a given amount of energy E transferred to the ball, Equation 5.1 tells us that the speed of the ball is $v = \sqrt{2E/m}$ where m is the mass of the ball. Because a baseball has less mass than a bowling bowl, it will have a higher speed for a given amount of energy transferred.

Figure 5.2 When she starts going uphill, kinetic energy is converted to potential energy and her speed decreases.

Figure 5.3 The electrostatic potential energy of two oppositely charged particles is negative (Equation 5.2). As the particles become closer, the electrostatic potential energy becomes even more negative—that is, it decreases.

Figure 5.4 Yes, the system is still closed—matter can't escape the system to the surroundings unless the piston is pulled completely out of the cylinder.

Figure 5.5 If $E_{final} = E_{initial}$, then $\Delta E = 0$.

Figure 5.6

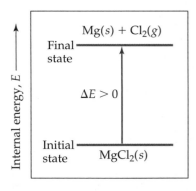

Figure 5.7 No. The sign on w is positive and the sign on q is negative. We need to know the magnitudes of q and w to determine whether $\Delta E = q + w$ is positive or negative.

Figure 5.10 The battery is doing work on the surroundings, so $w < 0$.

Figure 5.11 We need to know whether Zn(*s*) or HCl(*aq*) is the limiting reagent of the reaction. If it is Zn(*s*), then the addition of more Zn will lead to the generation of more $H_2(g)$ and more work will be done.

Figure 5.17 Endothermic—heat is being added to the system to raise the temperature of the water.

Figure 5.18 Two cups provide more thermal insulation so less heat will escape the system.

Figure 5.19 The stirrer ensures that all of the water in the bomb is at the same temperature.

Figure 5.21 The condensation of 2 $H_2O(g)$ to 2 $H_2O(l)$

Figure 5.22 Yes, ΔH_3 would remain the same as it is the enthalpy change for the process $CO(g) + \frac{1}{2}O_2(g) \longrightarrow CO_2(g)$.

Figure 5.24 Grams of fat

CHAPTER 6

Figure 6.3 The wavelength of (a) is twice that of (b) and the frequency of (a) is consequently half that of (b). Thus, the wavelength of (b) is 0.50 m and its frequency is 6.0×10^8 cycles/s.

Figure 6.4 The X-ray has a shorter wavelength and, consequently, higher frequency than the red light.

Figure 6.5 The hottest area is the white or yellowish white area in the center.

Figure 6.7 If the tube is not evacuated, the electrons that are freed from the metal surface will strike gas molecules near that surface. As a result, they will become attached to the gas molecules and never arrive at the positive terminal.

Figure 6.12 The $n = 2$ to $n = 1$ transition involves a larger energy change than the $n = 3$ to $n = 2$ transition. (Compare the space differences between the states in the figure.) If the $n = 2$ to $n = 1$ transition produces visible light, the $n = 3$ to $n = 2$ transition must produce radiation of lower energy. The infrared radiation has lower frequency and, hence, lower energy than visible light, whereas the ultraviolet has greater frequency and greater energy. Thus, the $n = 2$ to $n = 1$ transition will produce ultraviolet radiation.

Figure 6.16 The region of highest electron density is where the density of dots is highest, which is near the nucleus.

Figure 6.17 The fourth shell ($n = 4$) would contain four subshells, labeled $4s$, $4p$, $4d$, and $4f$.

Figure 6.18 There would be four maxima and three nodes.

Figure 6.22 (a) The intensity of the color indicates that the probability of finding the electron is greater at the interior of the lobes than on the edges. (b) $2p_x$.

Figure 6.24 The $4d$ and $4f$ subshells are not shown.

CHAPTER 7

Figure 7.1 Row 7—these elements are generally radioactive and not stable.

Figure 7.3 $2s$

Figure 7.6 Bottom and left

Figure 7.7 They get larger, just like the atoms do.

Figure 7.9 Ar; it has a larger Z_{eff}.

Figure 7.10 There is more electron–electron repulsion in the case of oxygen because two electrons have to occupy the same orbital.

Figure 7.11 The halogens (group 7A); it does make sense because we know that they are very stable as anions.

Figure 7.12 Ionization energy—lower ionization energy is correlated with increasing metallic character.

Figure 7.14 Anions are above the lines; cations are below the line.

Figure 7.22 Lilac

CHAPTER 8

Figure 8.1 Covalent

Figure 8.2 Yes, the same sort of reaction should occur between any of the alkali metals and any of the elemental halogens.

Figure 8.3 Cations have a smaller radius than their neutral atoms and anions have a larger radius. Because Na and Cl are in the same row of the periodic table, we would expect Na^+ to have a smaller radius than Cl^-, so we would guess that the larger green spheres represent Cl^-.

Figure 8.4 The distance between ions in KF should be larger than that in NaF and smaller than that in KCl. We would thus expect the lattice energy of KF to be between 701 and 910 kJ/mol.

Figure 8.6 The repulsions between the nuclei would decrease, the attractions between the nuclei and the electrons would decrease, and the repulsions between the electrons would be unaffected.

Figure 8.7 The electronegativity decreases with increasing atomic number.

Figure 8.9 μ will decrease

Figure 8.10 The bonds are not polar enough to cause enough excess electron density on the halogen atom to lead to a red shading.

Figure 8.12 The lengths of the bonds of the outer O atoms to the inner O atom are the same.

Figure 8.13 Yes. The electron densities on the left and right parts of the molecule are the same, indicating that resonance has made the two O—O bonds equivalent to one another.

Figure 8.14 The dashed bonds represent the "half bonds" that result when the two resonance structures are averaged.

Figure 8.15 Exothermic

Figure 8.17 As the bond gets longer, it gets weaker. We would therefore expect a plot of bond enthalpy versus bond length to have a negative slope.

CHAPTER 9

Figure 9.1 The atomic radii (Figure 7.7)

Figure 9.3 Octahedral

Figure 9.7 The electron pair in the bonding domain is attracted toward two nuclear centers, whereas the nonbonding pair is attracted toward just one.

Figure 9.8 90°

Figure 9.9 The nonbonding electron pairs exert a greater repulsive force than the bonding electron pairs.

Figure 9.10 The heads of the arrows point toward regions of highest electron density, as indicated by the red color.

Figure 9.14 As the internuclear distance decreases, nucleus–nucleus repulsion becomes a dominant component of the potential energy.

Figure 9.16 The small lobes of the sp hybrid orbitals are very much smaller in spatial extent and, therefore, provide very little overlap with the F orbitals.

Figure 9.17 Three: one s and two p orbitals

Figure 9.23 The two p orbitals that form the π bond must align, and each of them is perpendicular to the plane of the sp^2 hybrid orbitals.

Figure 9.24 Acetylene, because it has two C—C π bonds, whereas ethylene has one π bond

Figure 9.26 C—H and C—C

Figure 9.33 The σ_{1s}^*

Figure 9.34 The two electrons in the σ_{1s} MO

Figure 9.35 The $1s$ orbitals of Li are small in spatial extent because they experience a strong nuclear attraction. In addition, both the bonding and antibonding MOs formed from them are occupied, so that there is no significant net bonding.

Figure 9.36 Nodal planes between the atoms are found in antibonding MOs.

Figure 9.42 The σ_{2p} and π_{2p} orbitals. Because the σ_{2p} orbital mixes with the σ_{2s}, it is pushed to higher energy and the σ_{2s} is moved to lower energy. The σ_{2p} orbital thus rises above the π_{2p} in energy.

Figure 9.43 F_2 contains four more electrons than N_2. These electrons go into the antibonding π^*_{2p} orbitals, thus lowering the bond order.

Figure 9.45 Because N_2 has no unpaired electrons, it is diamagnetic. Therefore, it would simply flow down with no tendency to remain in the magnetic field.

Figure 9.46 11. All the electrons in the $n = 2$ level are valence-shell electrons.

CHAPTER 11

Figure 11.2 The density in a liquid is much closer to a solid than it is to a gas.

Figure 11.9 Both compounds are nonpolar and incapable of forming hydrogen bonds. Therefore, the boiling point is determined by the dispersion forces, which are stronger for the larger, heavier SnH_4.

Figure 11.10 The non-hydrogen atom must possess a nonbonding electron pair.

Figure 11.11 There are four electron pairs surrounding oxygen in a water molecule. Two of the electron pairs are used to make covalent bonds to hydrogen within the H_2O molecule, while the other two are available to make hydrogen bonds to neighboring molecules. Because the electron-pair geometry is tetrahedral (four electron domains around the central atom), the $H-O\cdots H$ bond angle is approximately 109°.

Figure 11.19 Wax is a hydrocarbon that cannot form hydrogen bonds. Therefore, coating the inside of tube with wax will dramatically decrease the adhesive forces between water and the tube and change the shape of the water meniscus to an inverted U-shape. Neither wax nor glass can form metallic bonds with mercury so the shape of the mercury meniscus will be qualitatively the same, an inverted U-shape.

Figure 11.21 Because we are dealing with a state function, the energy of going straight from a solid to a gas must be the same as going from a solid to a gas through an intermediate liquid state. Therefore, the heat of sublimation must be equal to the sum of the heat of fusion and the heat of vaporization: $\Delta H_{sub} = \Delta H_{fus} + \Delta H_{vap}$.

Figure 11.24 Increases, because the molecules have more kinetic energy as the temperature increases and can escape more easily

Figure 11.25 All liquids including ethylene glycol reach their normal boiling point when their vapor pressure is equal to atmospheric pressure, 760 torr.

Figure 11.27 Freezing, because for most substances the solid phase is denser than the liquid phase and increasing the pressure will eventually drive a phase transition from the liquid to the solid state (provided the temperature is below the critical temperature)

absolute zero The lowest attainable temperature; 0 K on the Kelvin scale and $-273.15\ ^\circ$C on the Celsius scale. (Section 1.4)

absorption spectrum A pattern of variation in the amount of light absorbed by a sample as a function of wavelength. (Section 23.5)

accuracy A measure of how closely individual measurements agree with the correct value. (Section 1.5)

acid A substance that is able to donate a H^+ ion (a proton) and, hence, increases the concentration of $H^+(aq)$ when it dissolves in water. (Section 4.3)

acid-dissociation constant (K_a) An equilibrium constant that expresses the extent to which an acid transfers a proton to solvent water. (Section 16.6)

acidic anhydride (acidic oxide) An oxide that forms an acid when added to water; soluble nonmetal oxides are acidic anhydrides. (Section 22.5)

acidic oxide (acidic anhydride) An oxide that either reacts with a base to form a salt or with water to form an acid. (Section 22.5)

acid rain Rainwater that has become excessively acidic because of absorption of pollutant oxides, notably SO_3, produced by human activities. (Section 18.2)

actinide element Element in which the $5f$ orbitals are only partially occupied. (Section 6.8)

activated complex (transition state) The particular arrangement of atoms found at the top of the potential-energy barrier as a reaction proceeds from reactants to products. (Section 14.5)

activation energy (E_a) The minimum energy needed for reaction; the height of the energy barrier to formation of products. (Section 14.5)

active site Specific site on a heterogeneous catalyst or an enzyme where catalysis occurs. (Section 14.7)

activity The decay rate of a radioactive material, generally expressed as the number of disintegrations per unit time. (Section 21.4)

activity series A list of metals in order of decreasing ease of oxidation. (Section 4.4)

addition polymerization Polymerization that occurs through coupling of monomers with one another, with no other products formed in the reaction. (Section 12.8)

addition reaction A reaction in which a reagent adds to the two carbon atoms of a carbon–carbon multiple bond. (Section 24.3)

adsorption The binding of molecules to a surface. (Section 14.7)

alcohol An organic compound obtained by substituting a hydroxyl group ($-$OH) for a hydrogen on a hydrocarbon. (Sections 2.9 and 24.4)

aldehyde An organic compound that contains a carbonyl group ($C=O$) to which at least one hydrogen atom is attached. (Section 24.4)

alkali metals Members of group 1A in the periodic table. (Section 7.7)

alkaline earth metals Members of group 2A in the periodic table. (Section 7.7)

alkanes Compounds of carbon and hydrogen containing only carbon–carbon single bonds. (Sections 2.9 and 24.2)

alkenes Hydrocarbons containing one or more carbon–carbon double bonds. (Section 24.2)

alkyl group A group that is formed by removing a hydrogen atom from an alkane. (Section 25.3)

alkynes Hydrocarbons containing one or more carbon–carbon triple bonds. (Section 24.2)

alloy A substance that has the characteristic properties of a metal and contains more than one element. Often there is one principal metallic component, with other elements present in smaller amounts. Alloys may be homogeneous or heterogeneous. (Section 12.3)

alpha decay A type of radioactive decay in which an atomic nucleus emits an alpha particle and thereby transforms (or "decays") into an atom with a mass number 4 less and atomic number 2 less. (Section 21.1)

alpha (α) helix A protein structure in which the protein is coiled in the form of a helix with hydrogen bonds between $C=O$ and $N-H$ groups on adjacent turns. (Section 24.7)

alpha particles Particles that are identical to helium-4 nuclei, consisting of two protons and two neutrons, symbol ^4_2He or $^4_2\alpha$. (Section 21.1)

amide An organic compound that has an NR_2 group attached to a carbonyl. (Section 24.4)

amine A compound that has the general formula R_3N, where R may be H or a hydrocarbon group. (Section 16.7)

amino acid A carboxylic acid that contains an amino ($-NH_2$) group attached to the carbon atom adjacent to the carboxylic acid ($-$COOH) functional group. (Section 24.7)

amorphous solid A solid whose molecular arrangement lacks the regularly repeating long-range pattern of a crystal. (Section 12.2)

amphiprotic Refers to the capacity of a substance to either add or lose a proton (H^+). (Section 16.2)

amphoteric oxides and hydroxides Oxides and hydroxides that are only slightly soluble in water but that dissolve in either acidic or basic solutions. (Section 17.5)

angstrom A common non-SI unit of length, denoted Å, that is used to measure atomic dimensions: $1\ \text{Å} = 10^{-10}$ m. (Section 2.3)

anion A negatively charged ion. (Section 2.7)

anode An electrode at which oxidation occurs. (Section 20.3)

antibonding molecular orbital A molecular orbital in which electron density is concentrated outside the region between the two nuclei of bonded atoms. Such orbitals, designated as σ^* or π^*, are less stable (of higher energy) than bonding molecular orbitals. (Section 9.7)

antiferromagnetism A form of magnetism in which unpaired electron spins on adjacent sites point in opposite directions and cancel each other's effects. (Section 23.1)

aqueous solution A solution in which water is the solvent. (Chapter 4: Introduction)

aromatic hydrocarbons Hydrocarbon compounds that contain a planar, cyclic arrangement of carbon atoms linked by both σ and delocalized π bonds. (Section 24.2)

Arrhenius equation An equation that relates the rate constant for a reaction to the frequency factor, A, the activation energy, E_a, and the temperature, T: $k = Ae^{-E_a/RT}$. In its logarithmic form it is written $\ln k = -E_a/RT + \ln A$. (Section 14.5)

atmosphere (atm) A unit of pressure equal to 760 torr; 1 atm $= 101.325$ kPa. (Section 10.2)

atom The smallest representative particle of an element. (Sections 1.1 and 2.1)

atomic mass unit (amu) A unit based on the value of exactly 12 amu for the mass of the isotope of carbon that has six protons and six neutrons in the nucleus. (Sections 2.3 and 3.3)

atomic number The number of protons in the nucleus of an atom of an element. (Section 2.3)

atomic radius An estimate of the size of an atom. See **bonding atomic radius**. (Section 7.3)

atomic weight The average mass of the atoms of an element in atomic mass units (amu); it is numerically equal to the mass in grams of one mole of the element. (Section 2.4)

autoionization The process whereby water spontaneously forms low concentrations of $H^+(aq)$ and $OH^-(aq)$ ions by proton transfer from one water molecule to another. (Section 16.3)

Avogadro's hypothesis A statement that equal volumes of gases at the same temperature and pressure contain equal numbers of molecules. (Section 10.3)

Avogadro's law A statement that the volume of a gas maintained at constant temperature and pressure is directly proportional to the number of moles of the gas. (Section 10.3)

Avogadro's number (N_A) The number of ^{12}C atoms in exactly 12 g of ^{12}C; it equals 6.022×10^{23} mol^{-1}. (Section 3.4)

band An array of closely spaced molecular orbitals occupying a discrete range of energy. (Section 12.4)

band gap The energy gap between a fully occupied band called a valence band and an empty band called the conduction band. (Section 12.7)

band structure The electronic structure of a solid, defining the allowed ranges of energy for electrons in a solid. (Section 12.7)

bar A unit of pressure equal to 10^5 Pa. (Section 10.2)

base A substance that is an H^+ acceptor; a base produces an excess of $OH^-(aq)$ ions when it dissolves in water. (Section 4.3)

base-dissociation constant (K_b) An equilibrium constant that expresses the extent to which a base reacts with solvent water, accepting a proton and forming $OH^-(aq)$. (Section 16.7)

basic anhydride (basic oxide) An oxide that forms a base when added to water; soluble metal oxides are basic anhydrides. (Section 22.5)

basic oxide (basic anhydride) An oxide that either reacts with water to form a base or reacts with an acid to form a salt and water. (Section 22.5)

battery A self-contained electrochemical power source that contains one or more voltaic cells. (Section 20.7)

becquerel The SI unit of radioactivity. It corresponds to one nuclear disintegration per second. (Section 21.4)

Beer's law The light absorbed by a substance (A) equals the product of its extinction coefficient (ε), the path length through which the light passes (b), and the molar concentration of the substance (c): $A = \varepsilon bc$. (Section 14.2)

beta emission A nuclear decay process where a beta particle is emitted from the nucleus; also called beta decay. (Section 21.1)

beta particles Energetic electrons emitted from the nucleus, symbol $_{-1}^{0}e$. (Section 21.1)

beta sheet A structural form of protein in which two strands of amino acids are hydrogen-bonded together in a zipperlike configuration. (Section 24.7)

bidentate ligand A ligand in which two linked coordinating atoms are bound to a metal. (Section 23.3)

bimolecular reaction An elementary reaction that involves two molecules. (Section 14.6)

biochemistry The study of the chemistry of living systems. (Chapter 24: Introduction)

biodegradable Organic material that bacteria are able to oxidize. (Section 18.4)

body-centered lattice A crystal lattice in which the lattice points are located at the center and corners of each unit cell. (Section 12.2)

bomb calorimeter A device for measuring the heat evolved in the combustion of a substance under constant-volume conditions. (Section 5.5)

bond angles The angles made by the lines joining the nuclei of the atoms in a molecule. (Section 9.1)

bond dipole The dipole moment that is due to unequal electron sharing between two atoms in a covalent bond. (Section 9.3)

bond enthalpy The enthalpy change, ΔH, required to break a particular bond when the substance is in the gas phase. (Section 8.8)

bonding atomic radius The radius of an atom as defined by the distances separating it from other atoms to which it is chemically bonded. (Section 7.3)

bonding molecular orbital A molecular orbital in which the electron density is concentrated in the internuclear region. The energy of a bonding molecular orbital is lower than the energy of the separate atomic orbitals from which it forms. (Section 9.7)

bonding pair In a Lewis structure a pair of electrons that is shared by two atoms. (Section 9.2)

bond length The distance between the centers of two bonded atoms. (Section 8.3)

bond order The number of bonding electron pairs shared between two atoms, minus the number of antibonding electron pairs: bond order = (number of bonding electrons − number of antibonding electrons)/2. (Section 9.7)

bond polarity A measure of the degree to which the electrons are shared unequally between two atoms in a chemical bond. (Section 8.4)

boranes Covalent hydrides of boron. (Section 22.11)

Born–Haber cycle A thermodynamic cycle based on Hess's law that relates the lattice energy of an ionic substance to its enthalpy of formation and to other measurable quantities. (Section 8.2)

Boyle's law A law stating that at constant temperature, the product of the volume and pressure of a given amount of gas is a constant. (Section 10.3)

Brønsted–Lowry acid A substance (molecule or ion) that acts as a proton donor. (Section 16.2)

Brønsted–Lowry base A substance (molecule or ion) that acts as a proton acceptor. (Section 16.2)

buffer capacity The amount of acid or base a buffer can neutralize before the pH begins to change appreciably. (Section 17.2)

buffered solution (buffer) A solution that undergoes a limited change in pH upon addition of a small amount of acid or base. (Section 17.2)

calcination The heating of an ore to bring about its decomposition and the elimination of a volatile product. For example, a carbonate ore might be calcined to drive off CO_2. (Section 23.2)

calorie A unit of energy, it is the amount of energy needed to raise the temperature of 1 g of water by 1 °C from 14.5 °C to 15.5 °C. A related unit is the joule: 1 cal = 4.184 J. (Section 5.1)

calorimeter An apparatus that measures the heat released or absorbed in a chemical or physical process. (Section 5.5)

calorimetry The experimental measurement of heat produced in chemical and physical processes. (Section 5.5)

capillary action The process by which a liquid rises in a tube because of a combination of adhesion to the walls of the tube and cohesion between liquid particles. (Section 11.3)

carbide A binary compound of carbon with a metal or metalloid. (Section 22.9)

carbohydrates A class of substances formed from polyhydroxy aldehydes or ketones. (Section 24.8)

carbon black A microcrystalline form of carbon. (Section 22.9)

carbonyl group The C=O double bond, a characteristic feature of several organic functional groups, such as ketones and aldehydes. (Section 24.4)

carboxylic acid A compound that contains the —COOH functional group. (Sections 16.10 and 24.4)

catalyst A substance that changes the speed of a chemical reaction without itself undergoing a permanent chemical change in the process. (Section 14.7)

cathode An electrode at which reduction occurs. (Section 20.3)

cathode rays Streams of electrons that are produced when a high voltage is applied to electrodes in an evacuated tube. (Section 2.2)

cathodic protection A means of protecting a metal against corrosion by making it the cathode in a voltaic cell. This can be achieved by attaching a more easily oxidized metal, which serves as an anode, to the metal to be protected. (Section 20.8)

cation A positively charged ion. (Section 2.7)

cell potential The potential difference between the cathode and anode in an electrochemical cell; it is measured in volts: 1 V = 1 J/C. Also called electromotive force. (Section 20.4)

cellulose A polysaccharide of glucose; it is the major structural element in plant matter. (Section 24.8)

Celsius scale A temperature scale on which water freezes at 0° and boils at 100° at sea level. (Section 1.4)

chain reaction A series of reactions in which one reaction initiates the next. (Section 21.7)

changes of state Transformations of matter from one state to a different one, for example, from a gas to a liquid. (Section 1.3)

charcoal A form of carbon produced when wood is heated strongly in a deficiency of air. (Section 22.9)

Charles's law A law stating that at constant pressure, the volume of a given quantity of gas is proportional to absolute temperature. (Section 10.3)

chelate effect The generally larger formation constants for polydentate ligands as compared with the corresponding *monodentate* ligands. (Section 23.3)

chelating agent A polydentate ligand that is capable of occupying two or more sites in the coordination sphere. (Section 23.3)

chemical bond A strong attractive force that exists between atoms in a molecule. (Section 8.1)

chemical changes Processes in which one or more substances are converted into other substances; also called **chemical reactions**. (Section 1.3)

chemical equation A representation of a chemical reaction using the chemical formulas of the reactants and products; a balanced chemical equation contains equal numbers of atoms of each element on both sides of the equation. (Section 3.1)

chemical equilibrium A state of dynamic balance in which the rate of formation of the products of a reaction from the reactants equals the rate of formation of the reactants from the products; at equilibrium the concentrations of the reactants and products remain constant. (Section 4.1; Chapter 15: Introduction)

chemical formula A notation that uses chemical symbols with numerical subscripts to convey the relative proportions of atoms of the different elements in a substance. (Section 2.6)

chemical kinetics The area of chemistry concerned with the speeds, or rates, at which chemical reactions occur. (Chapter 14: Introduction)

chemical nomenclature The rules used in naming substances. (Section 2.8)

chemical properties Properties that describe a substance's composition and its reactivity; how the substance reacts or changes into other substances. (Section 1.3)

chemical reactions Processes in which one or more substances are converted into other substances; also called **chemical changes**. (Section 1.3)

chemistry The scientific discipline that studies the composition, properties, and transformations of matter. (Chapter 1: Introduction)

chiral A term describing a molecule or an ion that cannot be superimposed on its mirror image. (Sections 23.4 and 24.5)

chlorofluorocarbons Compounds composed entirely of chlorine, fluorine, and carbon. (Section 18.3)

chlorophyll A plant pigment that plays a major role in conversion of solar energy to chemical energy in photosynthesis. (Section 23.3)

cholesteric liquid crystalline phase A liquid crystal formed from flat, disc-shaped molecules that align through a stacking of the molecular discs. (Section 11.7)

coal A naturally occurring solid containing hydrocarbons of high molecular weight, as well as compounds containing sulfur, oxygen, and nitrogen. (Section 5.8)

colligative property A property of a solvent (vapor-pressure lowering, freezing-point lowering, boiling-point elevation, osmotic pressure) that depends on the total concentration of solute particles present. (Section 13.5)

collision model A model of reaction rates based on the idea that molecules must collide to react; it explains the factors influencing reaction rates in terms of the frequency of collisions, the number of collisions with energies exceeding the activation energy, and the probability that the collisions occur with suitable orientations. (Section 14.5)

colloids (colloidal dispersions) Mixtures containing particles larger than normal solutes but small enough to remain suspended in the dispersing medium. (Section 13.6)

combination reaction A chemical reaction in which two or more substances combine to form a single product. (Section 3.2)

combustion reaction A chemical reaction that proceeds with evolution of heat and usually also a flame; most combustion involves reaction with oxygen, as in the burning of a match. (Section 3.2)

common-ion effect A shift of an equilibrium induced by an ion common to the equilibrium. For example, added Na_2SO_4 decreases the solubility of the slightly soluble salt $BaSO_4$, or added NaF decreases the percent ionization of HF. (Section 17.1)

complementary colors Colors that, when mixed in proper proportions, appear white or colorless. (Section 23.5)

complete ionic equation A chemical equation in which dissolved strong electrolytes (such as dissolved ionic compounds) are written as separate ions. (Section 4.2)

complex ion (complex) An assembly of a metal ion and the Lewis bases (ligands) bonded to it. (Section 17.5)

compound A substance composed of two or more elements united chemically in definite proportions. (Section 1.2)

compound semiconductor A semiconducting material formed from two or more elements. (Section 12.7)

concentration The quantity of solute present in a given quantity of solvent or solution. (Section 4.5)

concentration cell A voltaic cell containing the same electrolyte and the same electrode materials in both the anode and cathode compartments. The emf of the cell is derived from a difference in the concentrations of the same electrolyte solutions in the compartments. (Section 20.6)

condensation polymerization Polymerization in which molecules are joined together through condensation reactions. (Section 12.8)

condensation reaction A chemical reaction in which a small molecule (such as a molecule of water) is split out from between two reacting molecules. (Sections 12.6 and 22.8)

conduction band A band of molecular orbitals lying higher in energy than the occupied valence band and distinctly separated from it. (Section 12.7)

conjugate acid A substance formed by addition of a proton to a Brønsted–Lowry base. (Section 16.2)

conjugate acid–base pair An acid and a base, such as H_2O and CH^-, that differ only in the presence or absence of a proton. (Section 16.2)

conjugate base A substance formed by the loss of a proton from a Brønsted–Lowry acid. (Section 16.2)

continuous spectrum A spectrum that contains radiation distributed over all wavelengths. (Section 6.3)

conversion factor A ratio relating the same quantity in two systems of units that is used to convert the units of measurement. (Section 1.6)

coordination compound A compound containing a metal ion bonded to a group of surrounding molecules or ions that act as ligands. (Section 23.2)

coordination number The number of adjacent atoms to which an atom is directly bonded. In a complex the coordination number of the metal ion is the number of donor atoms to which it is bonded. (Sections 12.37 and 24.2)

coordination sphere The metal ion and its surrounding ligands. (Section 23.2)

coordination-sphere isomers Structural isomers of coordination compounds in which the ligands within the coordination sphere differ. (Section 23.4)

copolymer A complex polymer resulting from the polymerization of two or more chemically different monomers. (Section 12.8)

core electrons The electrons that are not in the outermost shell of an atom. (Section 6.8)

corrosion The process by which a metal is oxidized by substances in its environment. (Section 20.8)

covalent bond A bond formed between two or more atoms by a sharing of electrons. (Section 8.1)

covalent-network solids Solids in which the units that make up the three-dimensional network are joined by covalent bonds. (Section 12.1)

critical mass The amount of fissionable material necessary to maintain a nuclear chain reaction. (Section 21.7)

critical pressure The pressure at which a gas at its critical temperature is converted to a liquid state. (Section 11.4)

critical temperature The highest temperature at which it is possible to convert the gaseous form of a substance to a liquid. The critical temperature increases with an increase in the magnitude of intermolecular forces. (Section 11.4)

crystal-field theory A theory that accounts for the colors and the magnetic and other properties of transition-metal complexes in terms of the splitting of the energies of metal ion d orbitals by the electrostatic interaction with the ligands. (Section 23.6)

crystal lattice An imaginary network of points on which the repeating motif of a solid may be imagined to be laid down so that the structure of the crystal is obtained. The motif may be a single atom or a group of atoms. Each lattice point represents an identical environment in the crystal. (Section 12.2)

crystalline solid (crystal) A solid whose internal arrangement of atoms, molecules, or ions possesses a regularly repeating pattern in any direction through the solid. (Section 12.2)

crystallization The process in which molecules, ions, or atoms come together to form a crystalline solid. (Section 13.2)

cubic close packing A crystal structure where the atoms are packed together as close as possible, and the close-packed layers of atoms adopt a three-layer repeating pattern that leads to a face-centered cubic unit cell. (Section 12.3)

curie A measure of radioactivity: 1 curie = 3.7×10^{10} nuclear disintegrations per second. (Section 21.4)

cycloalkanes Saturated hydrocarbons of general formula C_nH_{2n} in which the carbon atoms form a closed ring. (Section 24.2)

Dalton's law of partial pressures A law stating that the total pressure of a mixture of gases is the sum of the pressures that each gas would exert if it were present alone. (Section 10.6)

d-d transition The transition of an electron in a transition-metal compound from a lower-energy d orbital to a higher-energy d orbital. (Section 23.6)

decomposition reaction A chemical reaction in which a single compound reacts to give two or more products. (Section 3.2)

degenerate A situation in which two or more orbitals have the same energy. (Section 6.7)

delocalized electrons Electrons that are spread over a number of atoms in a molecule or a crystal rather than localized on a single atom or a pair of atoms. (Section 9.6)

density The ratio of an object's mass to its volume. (Section 1.4)

deoxyribonucleic acid (DNA) A polynucleotide in which the sugar component is deoxyribose. (Section 24.10)

desalination The removal of salts from seawater, brine, or brackish water to make it fit for human consumption. (Section 18.4)

deuterium The isotope of hydrogen whose nucleus contains a proton and a neutron: ^2_1H. (Section 22.2)

dextrorotatory, or merely dextro or *d* A term used to label a chiral molecule that rotates the plane of polarization of plane-polarized light to the right (clockwise). (Section 23.4)

diamagnetism A type of magnetism that causes a substance with no unpaired electrons to be weakly repelled from a magnetic field. (Section 9.8)

diatomic molecule A molecule composed of only two atoms. (Section 2.6)

diffusion The spreading of one substance through a space occupied by one or more other substances. (Section 10.8)

dilution The process of preparing a less concentrated solution from a more concentrated one by adding solvent. (Section 4.5)

dimensional analysis A method of problem solving in which units are carried through all calculations. Dimensional analysis ensures that the final answer of a calculation has the desired units. (Section 1.6)

dipole A molecule with one end having a partial negative charge and the other end having a partial positive charge; a polar molecule. (Section 8.4)

dipole–dipole force A force that becomes significant when polar molecules come in close contact with one another. The force is attractive when the positive end of one polar molecule approaches the negative end of another. (Section 11.2)

dipole moment A measure of the separation and magnitude of the positive and negative charges in polar molecules. (Section 8.4)

dispersion forces Intermolecular forces resulting from attractions between induced dipoles. Also called London dispersion forces. (Section 11.2)

displacement reaction A reaction in which an element reacts with a compound, displacing an element from it. (Section 4.4)

donor atom The atom of a ligand that bonds to the metal. (Section 23.2)

doping Incorporation of a hetero atom into a solid to change its electrical properties. For example, incorporation of P into Si. (Section 12.7)

double bond A covalent bond involving two electron pairs. (Section 8.3)

double helix The structure for DNA that involves the winding of two DNA polynucleotide chains together in a helical arrangement. The two strands of the double helix are complementary in that the organic bases on the two strands are paired for optimal hydrogen bond interaction. (Section 24.10)

dynamic equilibrium A state of balance in which opposing processes occur at the same rate. (Section 11.5)

effective nuclear charge The net positive charge experienced by an electron in a many-electron atom; this charge is not the full nuclear charge because there is some shielding of the nucleus by the other electrons in the atom. (Section 7.2)

effusion The escape of a gas through an orifice or hole. (Section 10.8)

elastomer A material that can undergo a substantial change in shape via stretching, bending, or compression and return to its original shape upon release of the distorting force. (Section 12.6)

electrochemistry The branch of chemistry that deals with the relationships between electricity and chemical reactions. (Chapter 20: Introduction)

electrolysis reaction A reaction in which a nonspontaneous redox reaction is brought about by the passage of current under a sufficient external electrical potential. The devices in which electrolysis reactions occur are called electrolytic cells. (Section 20.9)

electrolyte A solute that produces ions in solution; an electrolytic solution conducts an electric current. (Section 4.1)

electrolytic cell A device in which a nonspontaneous oxidation-reduction reaction is caused to occur by passage of current under a sufficient external electrical potential. (Section 20.9)

electromagnetic radiation (radiant energy) A form of energy that has wave characteristics and that propagates through a vacuum at the characteristic speed of 3.00×10^8 m/s. (Section 6.1)

electrometallurgy The use of electrolysis to reduce or refine metals. (Section 20.9)

electromotive force (emf) A measure of the driving force, or *electrical pressure*, for the completion of an electrochemical reaction. Electromotive force is measured in volts: $1 \text{ V} = 1 \text{ J/C}$. Also called the cell potential. (Section 20.4)

electron A negatively charged subatomic particle found outside the atomic nucleus; it is a part of all atoms. An electron has a mass 1/1836 times that of a proton. (Section 2.3)

electron affinity The energy change that occurs when an electron is added to a gaseous atom or ion. (Section 7.5)

electron capture A mode of radioactive decay in which an inner-shell orbital electron is captured by the nucleus. (Section 21.1)

electron configuration The arrangement of electrons in the orbitals of an atom or molecule. (Section 6.8)

electron density The probability of finding an electron at any particular point in an atom; this probability is equal to ψ^2, the square of the wave function. Also called the probability density. (Section 6.5)

electron domain In the VSEPR model, a region about a central atom in which an electron pair is concentrated. (Section 9.2)

electron-domain geometry The three-dimensional arrangement of the electron domains around an atom according to the VSEPR model. (Section 9.2)

electronegativity A measure of the ability of an atom that is bonded to another atom to attract electrons to itself. (Section 8.4)

electronic charge The negative charge carried by an electron; it has a magnitude of 1.602×10^{-19} C. (Section 2.3)

electronic structure The arrangement of electrons in an atom or molecule. (Chapter 6: Introduction)

electron-sea model A model for the behavior of electrons in metals. (Section 12.4)

electron shell A collection of orbitals that have the same value of n. For example, the orbitals with $n = 3$ (the 3s, 3p, and 3d orbitals) comprise the third shell. (Section 6.5)

electron spin A property of the electron that makes it behave as though it were a tiny magnet. The electron behaves as if it were spinning on its axis; electron spin is quantized. (Section 6.7)

element A substance consisting of atoms of the same atomic number. Historically defined as a substance that cannot be separated into simpler substances by chemical means. (Sections 1.1 and 1.2)

elemental semiconductor A semiconducting material composed of just one element. (Section 12.7)

elementary reaction A process in a chemical reaction that occurs in a single event or step. An

overall chemical reaction consists of one or more elementary reactions or steps. (Section 14.6)

empirical formula A chemical formula that shows the kinds of atoms and their relative numbers in a substance in the smallest possible whole-number ratios. (Section 2.6)

enantiomers Two mirror-image molecules of a chiral substance. The enantiomers are nonsuperimposable. (Section 23.4)

endothermic process A process in which a system absorbs heat from its surroundings. (Section 5.2)

energy The capacity to do work or to transfer heat. (Section 5.1)

energy-level diagram A diagram that shows the energies of molecular orbitals relative to the atomic orbitals from which they are derived. Also called a **molecular-orbital diagram**. (Section 9.7)

enthalpy A quantity defined by the relationship $H = E + PV$; the enthalpy change, ΔH, for a reaction that occurs at constant pressure is the heat evolved or absorbed in the reaction: $\Delta H = q_p$. (Section 5.3)

enthalpy of formation The enthalpy change that accompanies the formation of a substance from the most stable forms of its component elements. (Section 5.7)

enthalpy of reaction The enthalpy change associated with a chemical reaction. (Section 5.4)

entropy A thermodynamic function associated with the number of different equivalent energy states or spatial arrangements in which a system may be found. It is a thermodynamic state function, which means that once we specify the conditions for a system—that is, the temperature, pressure, and so on—the entropy is defined. (Section 19.2)

enzyme A protein molecule that acts to catalyze specific biochemical reactions. (Section 14.7)

equilibrium constant The numerical value of the equilibrium-constant expression for a system at equilibrium. The equilibrium constant is most usually denoted by K_p for gas-phase systems or K_c for solution-phase systems. (Section 15.2)

equilibrium-constant expression The expression that describes the relationship among the concentrations (or partial pressures) of the substances present in a system at equilibrium. The numerator is obtained by multiplying the concentrations of the substances on the product side of the equation, each raised to a power equal to its coefficient in the chemical equation. The denominator similarly contains the concentrations of the substances on the reactant side of the equation. (Section 15.2)

equivalence point The point in a titration at which the added solute reacts completely with the solute present in the solution. (Section 4.6)

ester An organic compound that has an OR group attached to a carbonyl; it is the product of a reaction between a carboxylic acid and an alcohol. (Section 24.4)

ether A compound in which two hydrocarbon groups are bonded to one oxygen. (Section 24.4)

exchange (metathesis) reaction A reaction between compounds that when written as a molecular equation appears to involve the exchange of ions between the two reactants. (Section 4.2)

excited state A higher energy state than the ground state. (Section 6.3)

exothermic process A process in which a system releases heat to its surroundings. (Section 5.2)

extensive property A property that depends on the amount of material considered; for example, mass or volume. (Section 1.3)

face-centered lattice A crystal lattice in which the lattice points are located at the faces and corners of each unit cell. (Section 12.2)

Faraday's constant (F) The magnitude of charge of one mole of electrons: 96,500 C/mol. (Section 20.5)

f-block metals Lanthanide and actinide elements in which the $4f$ or $5f$ orbitals are partially occupied. (Section 6.9)

ferrimagnetism A form of magnetism in which unpaired electron spins on different-type ions point in opposite directions but do not fully cancel out. (Section 23.1)

ferromagnetism A form of magnetism in which unpaired electron spins align parallel to one another. (Section 23.1)

first law of thermodynamics A statement that energy is conserved in any process. One way to express the law is that the change in internal energy, ΔE, of a system in any process is equal to the heat, q, added to the system, plus the work, w, done on the system by its surroundings: $\Delta E = q + w$. (Section 5.2)

first-order reaction A reaction in which the reaction rate is proportional to the concentration of a single reactant, raised to the first power. (Section 14.4)

fission The splitting of a large nucleus into two smaller ones. (Section 21.6)

folding The process by which a protein adopts its biologically active shape. (Section 24.7)

force A push or a pull. (Section 5.1)

formal charge The number of valence electrons in an isolated atom minus the number of electrons assigned to the atom in the Lewis structure. (Section 8.5)

formation constant For a metal ion complex, the equilibrium constant for formation of the complex from the metal ion and base species present in solution. It is a measure of the tendency of the complex to form. (Section 17.5)

formula weight The mass of the collection of atoms represented by a chemical formula. For example, the formula weight of NO_2 (46.0 amu) is the sum of the masses of one nitrogen atom and two oxygen atoms. (Section 3.3)

fossil fuels Coal, oil, and natural gas, which are presently our major sources of energy. (Section 5.8)

free energy (Gibbs free energy, G) A thermodynamic state function that gives a criterion for spontaneous change in terms of enthalpy and entropy: $G = H - TS$. (Section 19.5)

free radical A substance with one or more unpaired electrons. (Section 21.9)

frequency The number of times per second that one complete wavelength passes a given point. (Section 6.1)

frequency factor (A) A term in the Arrhenius equation that is related to the frequency of collision and the probability that the collisions are favorably oriented for reaction. (Section 14.5)

fuel cell A voltaic cell that utilizes the oxidation of a conventional fuel, such as H_2 or CH_4, in the cell reaction. (Section 20.7)

fuel value The energy released when 1 g of a substance is combusted. (Section 5.8)

functional group An atom or group of atoms that imparts characteristic chemical properties to an organic compound. (Section 24.1)

fusion The joining of two light nuclei to form a more massive one. (Section 21.6)

galvanic cell See voltaic cell. (Section 20.3)

gamma radiation Energetic electromagnetic radiation emanating from the nucleus of a radioactive atom. (Section 21.1)

gas Matter that has no fixed volume or shape; it conforms to the volume and shape of its container. (Section 1.2)

gas constant (R) The constant of proportionality in the ideal-gas equation. (Section 10.4)

geometric isomerism A form of isomerism in which compounds with the same type and number of atoms and the same chemical bonds have different spatial arrangements of these atoms and bonds. (Sections 23.4 and 24.4)

Gibbs free energy A thermodynamic state function that combines enthalpy and entropy, in the form $G = H - TS$. For a change occurring at constant temperature and pressure, the change in free energy is $\Delta G = \Delta H - T\Delta S$. (Section 19.5)

glass An amorphous solid formed by fusion of SiO_2, CaO, and Na_2O. Other oxides may also be used to form glasses with differing characteristics. (Section 22.10)

glucose A polyhydroxy aldehyde whose formula is $CH_2OH(CHOH)_4CHO$; it is the most important of the monosaccharides. (Section 24.8)

glycogen The general name given to a group of polysaccharides of glucose that are synthesized in mammals and used to store energy from carbohydrates. (Section 24.7)

Graham's law A law stating that the rate of effusion of a gas is inversely proportional to the square root of its molecular weight. (Section 10.8)

gray (Gy) The SI unit for radiation dose corresponding to the absorption of 1 J of energy per kilogram of biological material; 1 Gy = 100 rads. (Section 21.9)

green chemistry Chemistry that promotes the design and application of chemical products and processes that are compatible with human health and that preserve the environment. (Section 18.5)

greenhouse gases Gases in an atmosphere that absorb and emit infrared radiation (radiant heat), "trapping" heat in the atmosphere. (Section 18.2)

ground state The lowest-energy, or most stable, state. (Section 6.3)

group Elements that are in the same column of the periodic table; elements within the same group or family exhibit similarities in their chemical behavior. (Section 2.5)

Haber process The catalyst system and conditions of temperature and pressure developed by Fritz Haber and coworkers for the formation of NH_3 from H_2 and N_2. (Section 15.2)

half-life The time required for the concentration of a reactant substance to decrease to half its initial value; the time required for half of a sample of a particular radioisotope to decay. (Sections 14.4 and 21.4)

half-reaction An equation for either an oxidation or a reduction that explicitly shows the electrons involved, for example, $Zn^{2+}(aq) + 2e^- \longrightarrow Zn(s)$. (Section 20.2)

Hall–Héroult process A process used to obtain aluminum by electrolysis of Al_2O_3 dissolved in molten cryolite, Na_3AlF_6. (Section 20.9)

halogens Members of group 7A in the periodic table. (Section 7.8)

hard water Water that contains appreciable concentrations of Ca^{2+} and Mg^{2+}; these ions react with soaps to form an insoluble material. (Section 18.4)

heat The flow of energy from a body at higher temperature to one at lower temperature when they are placed in thermal contact. (Section 5.1)

heat capacity The quantity of heat required to raise the temperature of a sample of matter by 1 °C (or 1 K). (Section 5.5)

heat of fusion The enthalpy change, ΔH, for melting a solid. (Section 11.4)

heat of sublimation The enthalpy change, ΔH, for vaporization of a solid. (Section 11.4)

heat of vaporization The enthalpy change, ΔH, for vaporization of a liquid. (Section 11.4)

Henderson–Hasselbalch equation The relationship among the pH, pK_a, and the concentrations of acid and conjugate base in an aqueous solution: $pH = pK_a + \log \dfrac{[base]}{[acid]}$. (Section 17.2)

Henry's law A law stating that the concentration of a gas in a solution, S_g, is proportional to the pressure of gas over the solution: $S_g = kP_g$. (Section 13.3)

Hess's law The heat evolved in a given process can be expressed as the sum of the heats of several processes that, when added, yield the process of interest. (Section 5.6)

heterogeneous alloy An alloy in which the components are not distributed uniformly; instead, two or more distinct phases with characteristic compositions are present. (Section 12.3)

heterogeneous catalyst A catalyst that is in a different phase from that of the reactant substances. (Section 14.7)

heterogeneous equilibrium The equilibrium established between substances in two or more different phases, for example, between a gas and a solid or between a solid and a liquid. (Section 15.4)

hexagonal close packing A crystal structure where the atoms are packed together as closely as possible. The close-packed layers adopt a two-layer repeating pattern, which leads to a primitive hexagonal unit cell. (Section 12.3)

high-spin complex A complex whose electrons populate the d orbitals to give the maximum number of unpaired electrons. (Section 23.6)

hole A vacancy in the valence band of a semiconductor, created by doping. (Section 12.7)

homogeneous catalyst A catalyst that is in the same phase as the reactant substances. (Section 14.7)

homogeneous equilibrium The equilibrium established between reactant and product substances that are all in the same phase. (Section 15.4)

Hund's rule A rule stating that electrons occupy degenerate orbitals in such a way as to maximize the number of electrons with the same spin. In other words, each orbital has one electron placed in it before pairing of electrons in orbitals occurs. (Section 6.8)

hybridization   The mixing of different types of atomic orbitals to produce a set of equivalent hybrid orbitals. (Section 9.5)

hybrid orbital   An orbital that results from the mixing of different kinds of atomic orbitals on the same atom. For example, an sp^3 hybrid results from the mixing, or hybridizing, of one s orbital and three p orbitals. (Section 9.5)

hydration   Solvation when the solvent is water. (Section 13.1)

hydride ion   An ion formed by the addition of an electron to a hydrogen atom: H^-. (Section 7.7)

hydrocarbons   Compounds composed of only carbon and hydrogen. (Section 2.9)

hydrogen bonding   Bonding that results from intermolecular attractions between molecules containing hydrogen bonded to an electronegative element. The most important examples involve OH, NH, and HF. (Section 11.2)

hydrolysis   A reaction with water. When a cation or anion reacts with water, it changes the pH. (Sections 16.9 and 24.4)

hydronium ion (H_3O^+)   The predominant form of the proton in aqueous solution. (Section 16.2)

hydrophilic   Water attracting. The term is often used to describe a type of colloid. (Section 13.6)

hydrophobic   Water repelling. The term is often used to describe a type of colloid. (Section 13.6)

hypothesis   A tentative explanation of a series of observations or of a natural law. (Section 1.3)

ideal gas   A hypothetical gas whose pressure, volume, and temperature behavior is completely described by the ideal-gas equation. (Section 10.4)

ideal-gas equation   An equation of state for gases that embodies Boyle's law, Charles's law, and Avogadro's hypothesis in the form $PV = nRT$. (Section 10.4)

ideal solution   A solution that obeys Raoult's law. (Section 13.5)

immiscible liquids   Liquids that do not dissolve in one another to a significant extent. (Section 13.3)

indicator   A substance added to a solution that changes color when the added solute has reacted with all the solute present in solution. The most common type of indicator is an acid–base indicator whose color changes as a function of pH. (Section 4.6)

instantaneous rate   The reaction rate at a particular time as opposed to the average rate over an interval of time. (Section 14.2)

intensive property   A property that is independent of the amount of material considered, for example, density. (Section 1.3)

interhalogens   Compounds formed between two different halogen elements. Examples include IBr and BrF_3. (Section 22.4)

intermediate   A substance formed in one elementary step of a multistep mechanism and consumed in another; it is neither a reactant nor an ultimate product of the overall reaction. (Section 14.6)

intermetallic compound   A homogeneous alloy with definite properties and a fixed composition. Intermetallic compounds are stoichiometric

compounds that form between metallic elements. (Section 12.3)

intermolecular forces   The short-range attractive forces operating between the particles that make up the units of a liquid or solid substance. These same forces also cause gases to liquefy or solidify at low temperatures and high pressures. (Chapter 11: Introduction)

internal energy   The total energy possessed by a system. When a system undergoes a change, the change in internal energy, ΔE, is defined as the heat, q, added to the system, plus the work, w, done on the system by its surroundings: $\Delta E = q + w$. (Section 5.2)

interstitial alloy   An alloy in which smaller atoms fit into spaces between larger atoms. The larger atoms are metallic elements and the smaller atoms are typically nonmetallic elements. (Section 12.3)

ion   Electrically charged atom or group of atoms (polyatomic ion); ions can be positively or negatively charged, depending on whether electrons are lost (positive) or gained (negative) by the atoms. (Section 2.7)

ion–dipole force   The force that exists between an ion and a neutral polar molecule that possesses a permanent dipole moment. (Section 11.2)

ion exchange   A process by which ions in solution are exchanged for other ions held on the surface of an ion-exchange resin; the exchange of a hard-water cation such as Ca^{2+} for a soft-water cation such as Na^+ is used to soften water. (Section 18.4)

ionic bond   A bond between oppositely charged ions. The ions are formed from atoms by transfer of one or more electrons. (Section 8.1)

ionic compound   A compound composed of cations and anions. (Section 2.7)

ionic hydrides   Compounds formed when hydrogen reacts with alkali metals and also the heavier alkaline earths (Ca, Sr, and Ba); these compounds contain the hydride ion, H^-. (Section 22.2)

ionic solids   Solids that are composed of ions. (Section 12.1)

ionization energy   The energy required to remove an electron from a gaseous atom when the atom is in its ground state. (Section 7.4)

ionizing radiation   Radiation that has sufficient energy to remove an electron from a molecule, thereby ionizing it. (Section 21.9)

ion-product constant   For water, K_w is the product of the aquated hydrogen ion and hydroxide ion concentrations: $[H^+][OH^-] = K_w = 1.0 \times 10^{-14}$ at 25 °C. (Section 16.3)

irreversible process   A process that cannot be reversed to restore both the system and its surroundings to their original states. Any spontaneous process is irreversible. (Section 19.1)

isoelectronic series   A series of atoms, ions, or molecules having the same number of electrons. (Section 7.3)

isomers   Compounds whose molecules have the same overall composition but different structures. (Sections 2.9 and 23.4)

isothermal process   One that occurs at constant temperature. (Section 19.1)

isotopes   Atoms of the same element containing different numbers of neutrons and therefore having different masses. (Section 2.3)

joule (J)   The SI unit of energy, $1 \text{ kg-m}^2/\text{s}^2$. A related unit is the calorie: $4.184 \text{ J} = 1 \text{ cal}$. (Section 5.1)

Kelvin scale   The absolute temperature scale; the SI unit for temperature is the kelvin. Zero on the Kelvin scale corresponds to -273.15 °C. (Section 1.4)

ketone   A compound in which the carbonyl group (C=O) occurs at the interior of a carbon chain and is therefore flanked by carbon atoms. (Section 24.4)

kinetic energy   The energy that an object possesses by virtue of its motion. (Section 5.1)

kinetic-molecular theory   A set of assumptions about the nature of gases. These assumptions, when translated into mathematical form, yield the ideal-gas equation. (Section 10.7)

lanthanide contraction   The gradual decrease in atomic and ionic radii with increasing atomic number among the lanthanide elements, atomic numbers 57 through 70. The decrease arises because of a gradual increase in effective nuclear charge through the lanthanide series. (Section 23.1)

lanthanide (rare earth) element   Element in which the $4f$ subshell is only partially occupied. (Sections 6.8 and 6.9)

lattice energy   The energy required to separate completely the ions in an ionic solid. (Section 8.2)

lattice points   Points in a crystal all of which have identical environments. (Section 12.2)

lattice vectors   The vectors a, b, and c that define a crystal lattice. The position of any lattice point in a crystal can be represented by summing integer multiples of the lattice vectors. (Section 12.2)

law of constant composition   A law that states that the elemental composition of a pure compound is always the same, regardless of its source; also called the **law of definite proportions**. (Section 1.2)

law of definite proportions   A law that states that the elemental composition of a pure substance is always the same, regardless of its source; also called the **law of constant composition**. (Section 1.2)

law of mass action   The rules by which the equilibrium constant is expressed in terms of the concentrations of reactants and products, in accordance with the balanced chemical equation for the reaction. (Section 15.2)

Le Châtelier's principle   A principle stating that when we disturb a system at chemical equilibrium, the relative concentrations of reactants and products shift so as to partially undo the effects of the disturbance. (Section 15.7)

levorotatory, or merely levo or *l*   A term used to label a chiral molecule that rotates the plane of polarization of plane-polarized light to the left (counterclockwise). (Section 24.4)

Lewis acid   An electron-pair acceptor. (Section 16.11)

Lewis base   An electron-pair donor. (Section 16.11)

Lewis structure   A representation of covalent bonding in a molecule that is drawn using Lewis symbols. Shared electron pairs are shown as lines, and unshared electron pairs are shown as pairs of dots. Only the valence-shell electrons are shown. (Section 8.3)

Lewis symbol (electron-dot symbol) The chemical symbol for an element, with a dot for each valence electron. (Section 8.1)

ligand An ion or molecule that coordinates to a metal atom or to a metal ion to form a complex. (Section 23.2)

lime-soda process A method used in large-scale water treatment to reduce water hardness by removing Mg^{2+} and Ca^{2+}. The substances added to the water are lime, CaO [or slaked lime, $Ca(OH)_2$], and soda ash, Na_2CO_3, in amounts determined by the concentrations of the undesired ions. (Section 18.4)

limiting reactant (limiting reagent) The reactant present in the smallest stoichiometric quantity in a mixture of reactants; the amount of product that can form is limited by the complete consumption of the limiting reactant. (Section 3.7)

line spectrum A spectrum that contains radiation at only certain specific wavelengths. (Section 6.3)

linkage isomers Structural isomers of coordination compounds in which a ligand differs in its mode of attachment to a metal ion. (Section 23.4)

lipid A nonpolar molecule derived from glycerol and fatty acids that is used by organisms for long-term energy storage. (Section 24.9)

liquid Matter that has a distinct volume but no specific shape. (Section 1.2)

liquid crystal A substance that exhibits one or more partially ordered liquid phases above the melting point of the solid form. By contrast, in nonliquid crystalline substances the liquid phase that forms upon melting is completely unordered. (Section 11.7)

lock-and-key model A model of enzyme action in which the substrate molecule is pictured as fitting rather specifically into the active site on the enzyme. It is assumed that in being bound to the active site, the substrate is somehow activated for reaction. (Section 14.7)

low-spin complex A metal complex in which the electrons are paired in lower-energy orbitals. (Section 23.6)

magic numbers Numbers of protons and neutrons that result in very stable nuclei. (Section 21.2)

main-group elements Elements in the s and p blocks of the periodic table. (Section 6.9)

mass A measure of the amount of material in an object. It measures the resistance of an object to being moved. In SI units, mass is measured in kilograms. (Section 1.4)

mass defect The difference between the mass of a nucleus and the total masses of the individual nucleons that it contains. (Section 21.6)

mass number The sum of the number of protons and neutrons in the nucleus of a particular atom. (Section 2.3)

mass percentage The number of grams of solute in each 100 g of solution. (Section 13.4)

mass spectrometer An instrument used to measure the precise masses and relative amounts of atomic and molecular ions. (Section 2.4)

matter Anything that occupies space and has mass; the physical material of the universe. (Section 1.1)

matter waves The term used to describe the wave characteristics of a moving particle. (Section 6.4)

mean free path The average distance traveled by a gas molecule between collisions. (Section 10.8)

metal complex An assembly of a metal ion and the Lewis bases bonded to it. (Section 23.2)

metallic bond Bonding, usually in solid metals, in which the bonding electrons are relatively free to move throughout the three-dimensional structure. (Section 8.1)

metallic character The extent to which an element exhibits the physical and chemical properties characteristic of metals, for example, luster, malleability, ductility, and good thermal and electrical conductivity. (Section 7.6)

metallic elements (metals) Elements that are usually solids at room temperature, exhibit high electrical and heat conductivity, and appear lustrous. Most of the elements in the periodic table are metals. (Sections 2.5 and 12.1)

metallic hydrides Compounds formed when hydrogen reacts with transition metals; these compounds contain the hydride ion, H^-. (Section 22.2)

metallic solids Solids that are composed of metal atoms. (Section 12.1)

metalloids Elements that lie along the diagonal line separating the metals from the nonmetals in the periodic table; the properties of metalloids are intermediate between those of metals and nonmetals. (Section 2.5)

metallurgy The science of extracting metals from their natural sources by a combination of chemical and physical processes. It is also concerned with the properties and structures of metals and alloys. (Section 23.1)

metathesis (exchange) reaction A reaction in which two substances react through an exchange of their component ions: AX + BY $\longrightarrow$ AY + BX. Precipitation and acid–base neutralization reactions are examples of metathesis reactions. (Section 4.2)

metric system A system of measurement used in science and in most countries. The meter and the gram are examples of metric units. (Section 1.4)

microstate The state of a system at a particular instant; one of many possible energetically equivalent ways to arrange the components of a system to achieve a particular state. (Section 19.3)

mineral A solid, inorganic substance occurring in nature, such as calcium carbonate, which occurs as calcite. (Section 23.1)

miscible liquids Liquids that mix in all proportions. (Section 13.3)

mixture A combination of two or more substances in which each substance retains its own chemical identity. (Section 1.2)

molal boiling-point-elevation constant (K_b) A constant characteristic of a particular solvent that gives the increase in boiling point as a function of solution molality: $\Delta T_b = K_b m$. (Section 13.5)

molal freezing-point-depression constant (K_f) A constant characteristic of a particular solvent that gives the decrease in freezing point as a function of solution molality: $\Delta T_f = K_f m$. (Section 13.5)

molality The concentration of a solution expressed as moles of solute per kilogram of solvent; abbreviated m. (Section 13.4)

molar heat capacity The heat required to raise the temperature of one mole of a substance by 1 °C. (Section 5.5)

molarity The concentration of a solution expressed as moles of solute per liter of solution; abbreviated M. (Section 4.5)

molar mass The mass of one mole of a substance in grams; it is numerically equal to the formula weight in atomic mass units. (Section 3.4)

mole A collection of Avogadro's number (6.022×10^{23}) of objects; for example, a mole of H_2O is 6.022×10^{23} H_2O molecules. (Section 3.4)

molecular compound A compound that consists of molecules. (Section 2.6)

molecular equation A chemical equation in which the formula for each substance is written without regard for whether it is an electrolyte or a nonelectrolyte. (Section 4.2)

molecular formula A chemical formula that indicates the actual number of atoms of each element in one molecule of a substance. (Section 2.6)

molecular geometry The arrangement in space of the atoms of a molecule. (Section 9.2)

molecular hydrides Compounds formed when hydrogen reacts with nonmetals and metalloids. (Section 22.2)

molecularity The number of molecules that participate as reactants in an elementary reaction. (Section 14.6)

molecular orbital (MO) An allowed state for an electron in a molecule. According to molecular-orbital theory, a molecular orbital is entirely analogous to an atomic orbital, which is an allowed state for an electron in an atom. Most bonding molecular orbitals can be classified as σ or π, depending on the disposition of electron density with respect to the internuclear axis. (Section 9.7)

molecular-orbital diagram A diagram that shows the energies of molecular orbitals relative to the atomic orbitals from which they are derived; also called an **energy-level diagram**. (Section 9.7)

molecular-orbital theory A theory that accounts for the allowed states for electrons in molecules. (Section 9.7)

molecular solids Solids that are composed of molecules. (Sections 12.1 and 12.6)

molecular weight The mass of the collection of atoms represented by the chemical formula for a molecule. (Section 3.3)

molecule A chemical combination of two or more atoms. (Sections 1.1 and 2.6)

mole fraction The ratio of the number of moles of one component of a mixture to the total moles of all components; abbreviated X, with a subscript to identify the component. (Section 10.6)

momentum The product of the mass, m, and velocity, v, of an object. (Section 6.4)

monodentate ligand A ligand that binds to the metal ion via a single donor atom. It occupies one position in the coordination sphere. (Section 23.3)

monomers Molecules with low molecular weights, which can be joined together (polymerized) to form a polymer. (Section 12.8)

monosaccharide A simple sugar, most commonly containing six carbon atoms. The joining together of monosaccharide units by condensation reactions results in formation of polysaccharides. (Section 24.8)

nanomaterial A solid whose dimensions range from 1 to 100 nm and whose properties differ from those of a bulk material with the same composition. (Section 12.1)

natural gas A naturally occurring mixture of gaseous hydrocarbon compounds composed of hydrogen and carbon. (Section 5.8)

nematic liquid crystalline phase A liquid crystal in which the molecules are aligned in the same general direction, along their long axes, but in which the ends of the molecules are not aligned. (Section 11.7)

Nernst equation An equation that relates the cell emf, E, to the standard emf, $E°$, and the reaction quotient, Q: $E = E° - (RT/nF) \ln Q$. (Section 20.6)

net ionic equation A chemical equation for a solution reaction in which soluble strong electrolytes are written as ions and spectator ions are omitted. (Section 4.2)

neutralization reaction A reaction in which an acid and a base react in stoichiometrically equivalent amounts; the neutralization reaction between an acid and a metal hydroxide produces water and a salt. (Section 4.3)

neutron An electrically neutral particle found in the nucleus of an atom; it has approximately the same mass as a proton. (Section 2.3)

noble gases Members of group 8A in the periodic table. (Section 7.8)

node Points in an atom at which the electron density is zero. For example, the node in a $2s$ orbital is a spherical surface. (Section 6.6)

nonbonding pair In a Lewis structure a pair of electrons assigned completely to one atom; also called a lone pair. (Section 9.2)

nonelectrolyte A substance that does not ionize in water and consequently gives a nonconducting solution. (Section 4.1)

nonionizing radiation Radiation that does not have sufficient energy to remove an electron from a molecule. (Section 21.9)

nonmetallic elements (nonmetals) Elements in the upper right corner of the periodic table; nonmetals differ from metals in their physical and chemical properties. (Section 2.5)

nonpolar covalent bond A covalent bond in which the electrons are shared equally. (Section 8.4)

normal boiling point The boiling point at 1 atm pressure. (Section 11.5)

normal melting point The melting point at 1 atm pressure. (Section 11.6)

nuclear binding energy The energy required to decompose an atomic nucleus into its component protons and neutrons. (Section 21.6)

nuclear disintegration series A series of nuclear reactions that begins with an unstable nucleus and terminates with a stable one; also called a **radioactive series**. (Section 21.2)

nuclear model Model of the atom with a nucleus containing protons and neutrons and with electrons in the space outside the nucleus. (Section 2.2)

nuclear transmutation A conversion of one kind of nucleus to another. (Section 21.3)

nucleic acids Polymers of high molecular weight that carry genetic information and control protein synthesis. (Section 24.10)

nucleon A particle found in the nucleus of an atom. (Section 21.1)

nucleotide Compounds formed from a molecule of phosphoric acid, a sugar molecule, and an organic nitrogen base. Nucleotides form linear polymers called DNA and RNA, which are involved in protein synthesis and cell reproduction. (Section 24.10)

nucleus The very small, very dense, positively charged portion of an atom; it is composed of protons and neutrons. (Section 2.2)

octet rule A rule stating that bonded atoms tend to possess or share a total of eight valence-shell electrons. (Section 8.1)

optical isomerism A form of isomerism in which the two forms of a compound (stereoisomers) are nonsuperimposable mirror images. (Section 23.4)

optically active Possessing the ability to rotate the plane of polarized light. (Section 23.4)

orbital An allowed energy state of an electron in the quantum mechanical model of the atom; the term *orbital* is also used to describe the spatial distribution of the electron. An orbital is defined by the values of three quantum numbers: n, l, and m_l (Section 6.5)

organic chemistry The study of carbon-containing compounds, typically containing carbon–carbon bonds. (Section 2.9; Chapter 24: Introduction)

osmosis The net movement of solvent through a semipermeable membrane toward the solution with greater solute concentration. (Section 13.5)

osmotic pressure The pressure that must be applied to a solution to stop osmosis from pure solvent into the solution. (Section 13.5)

Ostwald process An industrial process used to make nitric acid from ammonia. The NH_3 is catalytically oxidized by O_2 to form NO; NO in air is oxidized to NO_2; HNO_3 is formed in a disproportionation reaction when NO_2 dissolves in water. (Section 22.7)

overall reaction order The sum of the reaction orders of all the reactants appearing in the rate expression when the rate can be expressed as rate $= k[A]^a[B]^b \ldots$ (Section 14.3)

overlap The extent to which atomic orbitals on different atoms share the same region of space. When the overlap between two orbitals is large, a strong bond may be formed. (Section 9.4)

oxidation A process in which a substance loses one or more electrons. (Section 4.4)

oxidation number (oxidation state) A positive or negative whole number assigned to an element in a molecule or ion on the basis of a set of formal rules; to some degree it reflects the positive or negative character of that atom. (Section 4.4)

oxidation-reduction (redox) reaction A chemical reaction in which the oxidation states of certain atoms change. (Section 4.4; Chapter 20: Introduction)

oxidizing agent, or oxidant The substance that is reduced and thereby causes the oxidation of some other substance in an oxidation-reduction reaction. (Section 20.1)

oxyacid A compound in which one or more OH groups, and possibly additional oxygen atoms, are bonded to a central atom. (Section 16.10)

oxyanion A polyatomic anion that contains one or more oxygen atoms. (Section 2.8)

ozone The name given to O_3, an allotrope of oxygen. (Section 7.8)

paramagnetism A property that a substance possesses if it contains one or more unpaired electrons. A paramagnetic substance is drawn into a magnetic field. (Section 9.8)

partial pressure The pressure exerted by a particular gas in a mixture. (Section 10.6)

particle accelerator A device that uses strong magnetic and electrostatic fields to accelerate charged particles. (Section 21.3)

parts per billion (ppb) The concentration of a solution in grams of solute per 10^9 (billion) grams of solution; equals micrograms of solute per liter of solution for aqueous solutions. (Section 13.4)

parts per million (ppm) The concentration of a solution in grams of solute per 10^6 (million) grams of solution; equals milligrams of solute per liter of solution for aqueous solutions. (Section 13.4)

pascal (Pa) The SI unit of pressure: 1 Pa = 1 N/m^2. (Section 10.2)

Pauli exclusion principle A rule stating that no two electrons in an atom may have the same four quantum numbers (n, l, m_l, and m_s). As a reflection of this principle, there can be no more than two electrons in any one atomic orbital. (Section 6.7)

peptide bond A bond formed between two amino acids. (Section 24.7)

percent ionization The percent of a substance that undergoes ionization on dissolution in water. The term applies to solutions of weak acids and bases. (Section 16.6)

percent yield The ratio of the actual (experimental) yield of a product to its theoretical (calculated) yield, multiplied by 100. (Section 3.7)

period The row of elements that lie in a horizontal row in the periodic table. (Section 2.5)

periodic table The arrangement of elements in order of increasing atomic number, with elements having similar properties placed in vertical columns. (Section 2.5)

petroleum A naturally occurring combustible liquid composed of hundreds of hydrocarbons and other organic compounds. (Section 5.8)

pH The negative log in base 10 of the aquated hydrogen ion concentration: $pH = -\log[H^+]$. (Section 16.4)

pH titration curve A graph of pH as a function of added titrant. (Section 17.3)

phase change The conversion of a substance from one state of matter to another. The phase changes we consider are melting and freezing (solid $\rightleftharpoons$ liquid), sublimation and deposition, and vaporization and condensation (liquid $\rightleftharpoons$ gas). (Section 11.4)

phase diagram A graphic representation of the equilibria among the solid, liquid, and gaseous phases of a substance as a function of temperature and pressure. (Section 11.6)

phospholipid A form of lipid molecule that contains charged phosphate groups. (Section 24.9)

photochemical smog A complex mixture of undesirable substances produced by the action of sunlight on an urban atmosphere polluted with automobile emissions. The major starting ingredients are nitrogen oxides and organic substances, notably olefins and aldehydes. (Section 18.2)

photodissociation The breaking of a molecule into two or more neutral fragments as a result of absorption of light. (Section 18.2)

photoelectric effect The emission of electrons from a metal surface induced by light. (Section 6.2)

photoionization The removal of an electron from an atom or molecule by absorption of light. (Section 18.2)

photon The smallest increment (a quantum) of radiant energy; a photon of light with frequency ν has an energy equal to $h\nu$. (Section 6.2)

photosynthesis The process that occurs in plant leaves by which light energy is used to convert carbon dioxide and water to carbohydrates and oxygen. (Section 23.3)

physical changes Changes (such as a phase change) that occur with no change in chemical composition. (Section 1.3)

physical properties Properties that can be measured without changing the composition of a substance, for example, color and freezing point. (Section 1.3)

pi (π) bond A covalent bond in which electron density is concentrated above and below the internuclear axis. (Section 9.6)

pi (π) molecular orbital A molecular orbital that concentrates the electron density on opposite sides of an imaginary line that passes through the nuclei. (Section 9.8)

Planck's constant (h) The constant that relates the energy and frequency of a photon, $E = h\nu$. Its value is 6.626×10^{-34} J-s. (Section 6.2)

plastic A material that can be formed into particular shapes by application of heat and pressure. (Section 12.8)

polar covalent bond A covalent bond in which the electrons are not shared equally. (Section 8.4)

polarizability The ease with which the electron cloud of an atom or a molecule is distorted by an outside influence, thereby inducing a dipole moment. (Section 11.2)

polar molecule A molecule that possesses a nonzero dipole moment. (Section 8.4)

polyatomic ion An electrically charged group of two or more atoms. (Section 2.7)

polydentate ligand A ligand in which two or more donor atoms can coordinate to the same metal ion. (Section 23.3)

polymer A large molecule of high molecular mass, formed by the joining together, or polymerization, of a large number of molecules of low molecular mass. The individual molecules forming the polymer are called monomers. (Sections 12.1 and 12.8)

polypeptide A polymer of amino acids that has a molecular weight of less than 10,000. (Section 24.7)

polyprotic acid A substance capable of dissociating more than one proton in water; H_2SO_4 is an example. (Section 16.6)

polysaccharide A substance made up of many monosaccharide units joined together. (Section 24.8)

porphyrin A complex derived from the porphine molecule. (Section 23.3)

positron emission A nuclear decay process where a positron, a particle with the same mass as an electron but with a positive charge, symbol $_1^0e$, is emitted from the nucleus. (Section 21.1)

potential energy The energy that an object possesses as a result of its composition or its position with respect to another object. (Section 5.1)

precipitate An insoluble substance that forms in, and separates from, a solution. (Section 4.2)

precipitation reaction A reaction that occurs between substances in solution in which one of the products is insoluble. (Section 4.2)

precision The closeness of agreement among several measurements of the same quantity; the reproducibility of a measurement. (Section 1.5)

pressure A measure of the force exerted on a unit area. In chemistry, pressure is often expressed in units of atmospheres (atm) or torr: 760 torr = 1 atm; in SI units pressure is expressed in pascals (Pa). (Section 10.2)

pressure–volume (PV) work Work performed by expansion of a gas against a resisting pressure. (Section 5.3)

primary structure The sequence of amino acids along a protein chain. (Section 24.7)

primitive lattice A crystal lattice in which the lattice points are located only at the corners of each unit cell. (Section 12.2)

probability density (ψ^2) A value that represents the probability that an electron will be found at a given point in space. Also called **electron density**. (Section 6.5)

product A substance produced in a chemical reaction; it appears to the right of the arrow in a chemical equation. (Section 3.1)

property A characteristic that gives a sample of matter its unique identity. (Section 1.1)

protein A biopolymer formed from amino acids. (Section 24.7)

protium The most common isotope of hydrogen. (Section 22.2)

proton A positively charged subatomic particle found in the nucleus of an atom. (Section 2.3)

pure substance Matter that has a fixed composition and distinct properties. (Section 1.2)

pyrometallurgy A process in which heat converts a mineral in an ore from one chemical form to another and eventually to the free metal. (Section 23.2)

qualitative analysis The determination of the presence or absence of a particular substance in a mixture. (Section 17.7)

quantitative analysis The determination of the amount of a given substance that is present in a sample. (Section 17.7)

quantum The smallest increment of radiant energy that may be absorbed or emitted; the magnitude of radiant energy is $h\nu$. (Section 6.2)

quaternary structure The structure of a protein resulting from the clustering of several individual protein chains into a final specific shape. (Section 24.7)

racemic mixture A mixture of equal amounts of the dextrorotatory and levorotatory forms of a chiral molecule. A racemic mixture will not rotate the plane of polarized light. (Section 23.4)

rad A measure of the energy absorbed from radiation by tissue or other biological material; 1 rad = transfer of 1×10^{-2} J of energy per kilogram of material. (Section 21.9)

radial probability function The probability that the electron will be found at a certain distance from the nucleus. (Section 6.6)

radioactive Possessing **radioactivity**, the spontaneous disintegration of an unstable atomic nucleus with accompanying emission of radiation. (Section 2.2; Chapter 21: Introduction)

radioactive series A series of nuclear reactions that begins with an unstable nucleus and terminates with a stable one. Also called **nuclear disintegration series**. (Section 21.2)

radioisotope An isotope that is radioactive; that is, it is undergoing nuclear changes with emission of radiation. (Section 21.1)

radionuclide A radioactive nuclide. (Section 21.1)

radiotracer A radioisotope that can be used to trace the path of an element in a chemical system. (Section 21.5)

Raoult's law A law stating that the partial pressure of a solvent over a solution, $P_{solution}$, is given by the vapor pressure of the pure solvent, $P^\circ_{solvent}$, times the mole fraction of a solvent in the solution, $X_{solvent}$: $P_{solution} = X_{solvent}P^\circ_{solvent}$. (Section 13.5)

rare earth element See **lanthanide element**. (Sections 6.8 and 6.9)

rate constant A constant of proportionality between the reaction rate and the concentrations of reactants that appear in the rate law. (Section 14.3)

rate-determining step The slowest elementary step in a reaction mechanism. (Section 14.6)

rate law An equation that relates the reaction rate to the concentrations of reactants (and sometimes of products also). (Section 14.3)

reactant A starting substance in a chemical reaction; it appears to the left of the arrow in a chemical equation. (Section 3.1)

reaction mechanism A detailed picture, or model, of how the reaction occurs; that is, the order in which bonds are broken and formed and the changes in relative positions of the atoms as the reaction proceeds. (Section 14.6)

reaction order The power to which the concentration of a reactant is raised in a rate law. (Section 14.3)

reaction quotient (Q) The value that is obtained when concentrations of reactants and products are inserted into the equilibrium expression. If the concentrations are equilibrium concentrations, $Q = K$; otherwise, $Q \neq K$. (Section 15.6)

reaction rate A measure of the decrease in concentration of a reactant or the increase in concentration of a product with time. (Section 14.2)

redox (oxidation-reduction) reaction A reaction in which certain atoms undergo changes in oxidation states. The substance increasing in oxidation state is oxidized; the substance decreasing in oxidation state is reduced. (Section 4.4; Chapter 20: Introduction)

reducing agent, or reductant The substance that is oxidized and thereby causes the reduction of some other substance in an oxidation-reduction reaction. (Section 20.1)

reduction A process in which a substance gains one or more electrons. (Section 4.4)

rem A measure of the biological damage caused by radiation; rems = rads × RBE. (Section 21.9)

renewable energy sources Energy such as solar energy, wind energy, and hydroelectric energy derived from essentially inexhaustible sources. (Section 5.8)

representative (main-group) element An element from within the *s* and *p* blocks of the periodic table (Figure 6.29). (Section 6.9)

resonance structures (resonance forms) Individual Lewis structures in cases where two or more Lewis structures are equally good descriptions of a single molecule. The resonance structures in such an instance are "averaged" to give a more accurate description of the real molecule. (Section 8.6)

reverse osmosis The process by which water molecules move under high pressure through a semipermeable membrane from the more concentrated to the less concentrated solution. (Section 18.4)

reversible process A process that can go back and forth between states along exactly the same path; a system at equilibrium is reversible if equilibrium can be shifted by an infinitesimal modification of a variable such as temperature. (Section 19.1)

ribonucleic acid (RNA) A polynucleotide in which ribose is the sugar component. (Section 24.10)

root-mean-square (rms) speed (μ) The square root of the average of the squared speeds of the gas molecules in a gas sample. (Section 10.7)

rotational motion Movement of a molecule as though it is spinning like a top. (Section 19.3)

salinity A measure of the salt content of seawater, brine, or brackish water. It is equal to the mass in grams of dissolved salts present in 1 kg of seawater. (Section 18.3)

salt An ionic compound formed by replacing one or more hydrogens of an acid by other cations. (Section 4.3)

saponification Hydrolysis of an ester in the presence of a base. (Section 24.4)

saturated solution A solution in which undissolved solute and dissolved solute are in equilibrium. (Section 13.2)

scientific law A concise verbal statement or a mathematical equation that summarizes a wide range of observations and experiences. (Section 1.3)

scientific method The general process of advancing scientific knowledge by making experimental observations and by formulating hypotheses, theories, and laws. (Section 1.3)

secondary structure The manner in which a protein is coiled or stretched. (Section 24.7)

second law of thermodynamics A statement of our experience that there is a direction to the way events occur in nature. When a process occurs spontaneously in one direction, it is nonspontaneous in the reverse direction. It is possible to state the second law in many different forms, but they all relate back to the same idea about spontaneity. One of the most common statements found in chemical contexts is that in any spontaneous process the entropy of the universe increases. (Section 19.2)

second-order reaction A reaction in which the overall reaction order (the sum of the concentration-term exponents) in the rate law is 2. (Section 14.4)

sigma (σ) bond A covalent bond in which electron density is concentrated along the internuclear axis. (Section 9.6)

sigma (σ) molecular orbital A molecular orbital that centers the electron density about an imaginary line passing through two nuclei. (Section 9.7)

significant figures The digits that indicate the precision with which a measurement is made; all digits of a measured quantity are significant, including the last digit, which is uncertain. (Section 1.5)

silica Common name for silicon dioxide. (Section 22.4)

silicates Compounds containing silicon and oxygen, structurally based on SiO_4 tetrahedra. (Section 22.10)

single bond A covalent bond involving one electron pair. (Section 8.3)

SI units The preferred metric units for use in science. (Section 1.4)

smectic liquid crystalline phase A liquid crystal in which the molecules are aligned along their long axes and arranged in sheets, with the ends of the molecules aligned. There are several different kinds of smectic phases. (Section 12.8)

solid Matter that has both a definite shape and a definite volume. (Section 1.2)

solubility The amount of a substance that dissolves in a given quantity of solvent at a given temperature to form a saturated solution. (Sections 4.2 and 13.2)

solubility-product constant (solubility product) (K_{sp}) An equilibrium constant related to the equilibrium between a solid salt and its ions in solution. It provides a quantitative measure of the solubility of a slightly soluble salt. (Section 17.4)

solute A substance dissolved in a solvent to form a solution; it is normally the component of a solution present in the smaller amount. (Section 4.1)

solution A mixture of substances that has a uniform composition; a homogeneous mixture. (Section 1.2)

solution alloy A homogeneous alloy, where two or more elements are distributed randomly and uniformly throughout the solid. (Section 12.3)

solvation The clustering of solvent molecules around a solute particle. (Section 13.1)

solvent The dissolving medium of a solution; it is normally the component of a solution present in the greater amount. (Section 4.1)

specific heat (C_s) The heat capacity of 1 g of a substance; the heat required to raise the temperature of 1 g of a substance by 1 °C. (Section 5.5)

spectator ions Ions that go through a reaction unchanged and that appear on both sides of the complete ionic equation. (Section 4.2)

spectrochemical series A list of ligands arranged in order of their abilities to split the *d*-orbital energies (using the terminology of the crystal-field model). (Section 23.6)

spectrum The distribution among various wavelengths of the radiant energy emitted or absorbed by an object. (Section 6.3)

spin magnetic quantum number (m_s) A quantum number associated with the electron spin; it may have values of $+\frac{1}{2}$ or $-\frac{1}{2}$. (Section 6.7)

spin-pairing energy The energy required to pair an electron with another electron occupying an orbital. (Section 23.6)

spontaneous process A process that is capable of proceeding in a given direction, as written or described, without needing to be driven by an outside source of energy. A process may be spontaneous even though it is very slow. (Section 19.1)

standard atmospheric pressure Defined as 760 torr or, in SI units, 101.325 kPa. (Section 10.2)

standard emf, also called the standard cell potential ($E°$) The emf of a cell when all reagents are at standard conditions. (Section 20.4)

standard enthalpy change ($\Delta H°$) The change in enthalpy in a process when all reactants and products are in their stable forms at 1 atm pressure and a specified temperature, commonly 25 °C. (Section 5.7)

standard enthalpy of formation ($\Delta H_f°$) The change in enthalpy that accompanies the formation of one mole of a substance from its elements, with all substances in their standard states. (Section 5.7)

standard free energy of formation ($\Delta G_f°$) The change in free energy associated with the formation of a substance from its elements under standard conditions. (Section 19.5)

standard hydrogen electrode (SHE) An electrode based on the half-reaction $2 H^+(1 M) + 2 e^- \longrightarrow H_2(1 atm)$. The standard electrode potential of the standard hydrogen electrode is defined as 0 V. (Section 20.4)

standard molar entropy ($S°$) The entropy value for a mole of a substance in its standard state. (Section 19.4)

standard reduction potential ($E°_{red}$) The potential of a reduction half-reaction under standard conditions, measured relative to the standard hydrogen electrode. A standard reduction potential is also called a **standard electrode potential**. (Section 20.4)

standard solution A solution of known concentration. (Section 4.6)

standard temperature and pressure (STP) Defined as 0 °C and 1 atm pressure; frequently used as reference conditions for a gas. (Section 10.4)

starch The general name given to a group of polysaccharides that acts as energy-storage substances in plants. (Section 24.8)

state function A property of a system that is determined by its state or condition and not by how it got to that state; its value is fixed when temperature, pressure, composition, and physical form are specified; *P, V, T, E,* and *H* are state functions. (Section 5.2)

states of matter The three forms that matter can assume: solid, liquid, and gas. (Section 1.2)

stereoisomers Compounds possessing the same formula and bonding arrangement but differing in the spatial arrangements of the atoms. (Section 23.4)

stoichiometry The relationships among the quantities of reactants and products involved in chemical reactions. (Chapter 3: Introduction)

stratosphere The region of the atmosphere directly above the troposphere. (Section 18.1)

strong acid An acid that ionizes completely in water. (Section 4.3)

strong base A base that ionizes completely in water. (Section 4.3)

strong electrolyte A substance (strong acids, strong bases, and most salts) that is completely ionized in solution. (Section 4.1)

structural formula A formula that shows not only the number and kinds of atoms in the molecule but also the arrangement (connections) of the atoms. (Section 2.6)

structural isomers Compounds possessing the same formula but differing in the bonding arrangements of the atoms. (Sections 23.4 and 24.2)

subatomic particles Particles such as protons, neutrons, and electrons that are smaller than an atom. (Section 2.2)

subshell One or more orbitals with the same set of quantum numbers n and l. For example, we speak of the $2p$ subshell ($n = 2$, $l = 1$), which is composed of three orbitals ($2p_x$, $2p_y$, and $2p_z$). (Section 6.5)

substitutional alloy A homogeneous (solution) alloy in which atoms of different elements randomly occupy sites in the lattice. (Section 23.6)

substitution reactions Reactions in which one atom (or group of atoms) replaces another atom (or group) within a molecule; substitution reactions are typical for alkanes and aromatic hydrocarbons. (Section 24.3)

substrate A substance that undergoes a reaction at the active site in an enzyme. (Section 14.7)

supercritical mass An amount of fissionable material larger than the critical mass. (Section 21.7)

supersaturated solution A solution containing more solute than an equivalent saturated solution. (Section 13.2)

surface tension The intermolecular, cohesive attraction that causes a liquid to minimize its surface area. (Section 11.3)

surroundings In thermodynamics, everything that lies outside the system that we study. (Section 5.1)

system In thermodynamics, the portion of the universe that we single out for study. We must be careful to state exactly what the system contains and what transfers of energy it may have with its surroundings. (Section 5.1)

termolecular reaction An elementary reaction that involves three molecules. Termolecular reactions are rare. (Section 14.6)

tertiary structure The overall shape of a large protein, specifically, the manner in which sections of the protein fold back upon themselves or intertwine. (Section 24.7)

theoretical yield The quantity of product that is calculated to form when all of the limiting reagent reacts. (Section 3.7)

theory A tested model or explanation that satisfactorily accounts for a certain set of phenomena. (Section 1.3)

thermochemistry The relationship between chemical reactions and energy changes. (Chapter 5: Introduction)

thermodynamics The study of energy and its transformation. (Chapter 5: Introduction)

thermonuclear reaction Another name for fusion reactions; reactions in which two light nuclei are joined to form a more massive one. (Section 21.8)

thermoplastic A polymeric material that can be readily reshaped by application of heat and pressure. (Section 12.8)

thermosetting plastic A plastic that, once formed in a particular mold, is not readily reshaped by application of heat and pressure. (Section 12.8)

third law of thermodynamics A law stating that the entropy of a pure, crystalline solid at absolute zero temperature is zero: $S(0 \text{ K}) = 0$. (Section 19.3)

titration The process of reacting a solution of unknown concentration with one of known concentration (a standard solution). (Section 4.6)

torr A unit of pressure (1 torr = 1 mm Hg). (Section 10.2)

transition elements (transition metals) Elements in which the d orbitals are partially occupied. (Section 6.8)

transition state (activated complex) The particular arrangement of reactant and product molecules at the point of maximum energy in the rate-determining step of a reaction. (Section 14.5)

translational motion Movement in which an entire molecule moves in a definite direction. (Section 19.3)

transuranium elements Elements that follow uranium in the periodic table. (Section 21.3)

triple bond A covalent bond involving three electron pairs. (Section 8.3)

triple point The temperature at which solid, liquid, and gas phases coexist in equilibrium. (Section 11.6)

tritium The isotope of hydrogen whose nucleus contains a proton and two neutrons. (Section 22.2)

troposphere The region of Earth's atmosphere extending from the surface to about 12 km altitude. (Section 18.1)

Tyndall effect The scattering of a beam of visible light by the particles in a colloidal dispersion. (Section 13.6)

uncertainty principle A principle stating there is an inherent uncertainty in the precision with which we can simultaneously specify the position and momentum of a particle. This uncertainty is significant only for particles of extremely small mass, such as electrons. (Section 6.4)

unimolecular reaction An elementary reaction that involves a single molecule. (Section 14.6)

unit cell The smallest portion of a crystal that reproduces the structure of the entire crystal when repeated in different directions in space. It is the repeating unit or building block of the crystal lattice. (Section 12.2)

unsaturated solution A solution containing less solute than a saturated solution. (Section 13.2)

valence band A band of closely spaced molecular orbitals that is essentially fully occupied by electrons. (Section 12.7)

valence-bond theory A model of chemical bonding in which an electron-pair bond is formed between two atoms by the overlap of orbitals on the two atoms. (Section 9.4)

valence electrons The outermost electrons of an atom; those that occupy orbitals not occupied in the nearest noble-gas element of lower atomic number. The valence electrons are the ones the atom uses in bonding. (Section 6.8)

valence orbitals Orbitals that contain the outer-shell electrons of an atom. (Chapter 7: Introduction)

valence-shell electron-pair repulsion (VSEPR) model A model that accounts for the geometric arrangements of shared and unshared electron pairs around a central atom in terms of the repulsions between electron pairs. (Section 9.2)

van der Waals equation An equation of state for nonideal gases that is based on adding corrections to the ideal-gas equation. The correction terms account for intermolecular forces of attraction and for the volumes occupied by the gas molecules themselves. (Section 10.9)

vapor Gaseous state of any substance that normally exists as a liquid or solid. (Section 10.1)

vapor pressure The pressure exerted by a vapor in equilibrium with its liquid or solid phase. (Section 11.5)

vibrational motion Movement of the atoms within a molecule in which they move periodically toward and away from one another. (Section 19.3)

viscosity A measure of the resistance of fluids to flow. (Section 11.3)

volatile Tending to evaporate readily. (Section 11.5)

voltaic (galvanic) cell A device in which a spontaneous oxidation-reduction reaction occurs with the passage of electrons through an external circuit. (Section 20.3)

vulcanization The process of cross-linking polymer chains in rubber. (Section 12.6)

watt A unit of power; 1 W = 1 J/s. (Section 20.5)

wave function A mathematical description of an allowed energy state (an orbital) for an electron in the quantum mechanical model of the atom; it is usually symbolized by the Greek letter ψ. (Section 6.5)

wavelength The distance between identical points on successive waves. (Section 6.1)

weak acid An acid that only partly ionizes in water. (Section 4.3)

weak base A base that only partly ionizes in water. (Section 4.3)

weak electrolyte A substance that only partly ionizes in solution. (Section 4.1)

work The movement of an object against some force. (Section 5.1)

7

WRITING LABORATORY REPORTS

Laboratory instruction should give students hands-on experience with chemistry, the self-confidence and competence to keep legible and complete experimental records, and to communicate effectively through oral and written reports.

COMMITTEE ON PROFESSIONAL TRAINING,
AMERICAN CHEMICAL SOCIETY

THE ROLE OF LABORATORY INSTRUCTION

All laboratory instruction requires that students write regular laboratory reports and submit them for grading. The laboratory reports that you write as an undergraduate are models of the writing that professional chemists and other scientists do as an integral part of their jobs. Professionals in most career fields find that the ability to write reports that communicate concisely and unambiguously is a key to advancement and promotion.

As we are sure you realize by now, communicating research findings to other members of the chemistry community is a fundamental feature of the way that chemistry develops. Chemists publish new findings to those working in their own areas in the form of a journal article, which, as discussed in Chapter 2, is something you must know how to read. There are other forms of written research reports that are important in chemistry, and we discuss these in Chapter 10. As a student, however, writing laboratory reports presents you with an opportunity to practice and develop your skills at a writing task that is essential to success in a scientific career.

Reports of experimental work—lab reports and journal articles— are mostly put together in the same way: according to an established, time-honored format with particular components, each of which has specific objectives and conventions. Learning how to write a report of experimental work goes something like this:

a. Your instructor explains how to write the report and shows you some examples.
b. You try to do it yourself for a situation in which you won't do much damage if you don't get it quite right.
c. Your instructor gives you critical feedback, which you internalize.
d. You try again.
e. You repeat steps (b), (c), and (d) until you are competent.

Although writing a lab report may not seem to be a task that would require skill and practice (it's not like playing the violin), many students find it a quite difficult task to master. It does require skill, and like any skill—take, for example, swimming—you don't learn to do it well by watching someone else do it or by reading or hearing a lecture about it. You learn to swim by getting into the water and practicing doing it. The more you practice, the better you get. If you have the benefit of a coach, an instructor who provides you with feedback, you will improve that much faster.

We offer the following advice.

• Approach writing lab reports as learning a basic skill, analogous to typing, which once mastered, will save you many hours during your career both as an undergraduate and beyond. Exploit the opportunities to hone your skills in this regard.
• Recognize that thinking and writing are intimately intertwined and that writing the lab report represents an opportunity not only to learn to write but also to write to learn.
• Pay attention to the differences between what your instructors in, say, organic chemistry want, and what your analytical chemistry instructors ask for. Not all branches of chemistry employ identical formats.

As we emphasized in Chapter 1, the ability to communicate effectively and accurately is essential to a successful career in any field. Make the most of the opportunities presented by your chemistry lab classes to learn to write well.

WRITING REPORTS OF TEACHING-LABORATORY EXPERIMENTS

There is considerable variation among instructors in regard to what they expect from you in terms of a lab report. There may also be variations during any particular course: some reports may only be "partial" reports; others are "full" reports. Study the information from your instructor carefully and ask for clarification if needed. Instructors are often reluctant to give you examples of model reports for your particular lab course because they feel that students may be tempted to copy the model and not generate their own original report. Before writing your first report for a particular course, look at a few short papers published in relevant chemistry journals, such as the *Journal of the American Chemical Society* or *The Journal of Organic Chemistry*. Your instructor may provide you with a few especially good models. Reading these journal articles for content is unnecessary; you do not need to understand the topic of a paper to appreciate how the article is constructed. Note the way the Introduction is constructed, the amount of detail included in the Experimental section, and the format of figures and tables in the Results section. You should note that, for some synthetic laboratory courses, the convention may be to put the Experimental section after the Results and Discussion section. Just as in journal articles, each section of your report should be written in complete sentences.

For reports of syntheses, you will almost certainly be required to draw chemical formulas and, possibly, suggest mechanisms, which requires access to chemical-drawing software. You may be able to obtain such software free. Ask your instructor for advice, and check the course or department Web site for links to "useful" sites.

COMPOSITION OF THE REPORT

The various sections of a research report are as follows:

Title

Authors

Abstract

Introduction

Experimental Details or Theoretical Analysis

Results

Discussion

Conclusions and Summary

Acknowledgments

References

We suggest that you write the **Experimental Section** first, then the **Results Section**, then the **Discussion Section**, and, only after you have written all these components, write the **Introduction**. Then and only then can you write an **Abstract** that distills it down to its essence. We will examine the sections in this order and will discuss the specific details required in a teaching-laboratory report. As a general rule, **never write anything in your report that you do not understand**.

TITLE AND AUTHORS

Give the title as it appears in the laboratory handout, or, if this was a more open-ended, project-type experiment, create an appropriate title, such as "Investigation of the chloride content of calcium chloride," rather than "Report on calcium chloride project." Give the names of all your group members (if this was a group effort) and, assuming that each member of the group writes an individual report, indicate that this is your individual report. Also give the date(s) on which the experimental work was performed. Write the month in letters to avoid any ambiguities.

EXPERIMENTAL SECTION

One educational goal of a lab class is to teach students how to design the experiments themselves. To this end, you will probably find that as you advance from first year to senior classes, the instructions in the lab manual or handout become less detailed, because your instructors expect you to know or work out what you need to do. By writing a complete experimental section in your report, you show that you were able to decide on the course of action appropriate for the experiment.

Another educational goal for this activity is for you to practice writing about standard laboratory procedures in the concise language and voice used by chemists. Report what you did in sufficient detail so that another student could repeat your work. Often the difficulty in writing this section of a lab report is in selecting the right level of detail; it is hard to hit it just right, but keeping your fellow students in mind as your audience will help.

Ten Guidelines for Writing the Experimental Section

1. *Use subheadings.* In general, an experimental section has several subsections; therefore, consider creating subheadings that are relevant to your particular lab experiment. For example, in the determination of the hardness of water experiment, you might have subheadings such as "Preparation of EDTA standard solution," "Standardization of EDTA," "Analysis of water samples," and "Statistical evaluation of results."

2. *Give specific details.* Provide details of operations that are variable, such as the length of time the reaction mixture was heated under reflux, but omit details of standard procedures, such as weighing, using a buret, or measuring a melting point.

3. *Write in the past tense and passive voice.* For example, you would write,

> The reaction mixture was heated under reflux for 20 min, cooled and transferred to a 100-mL separatory funnel. Hexane (25 mL) was added and the flask shaken for 30 s. After separation, the UV-vis absorption spectrum (190–800 nm) of the hexane layer was measured.

You would not write,

> You reflux the mixture as per the lab manual, and then we extracted some of the stuff we made into hexane and ran the UV-vis.

4. *Use formal language.* In addition to problems with voice and tone, the negative example above illustrates some other common problems. Scientists, including your instructors, are bilingual when it comes to communicating science. They will speak in an informal language in the teaching lab and lecture classroom, but they will speak in a formal language at a conference and will certainly write about their science in formal language. In writing your lab report, you must adopt the formal language. Words like "stuff" are not appropriate. Nor is it acceptable to use the name of a technique as shorthand for making a measurement with an instrument. Although your instructor may say, "OK, now run the IR and see if there's a carbonyl stretch," in your report you will write, "The product was examined by IR absorption spectrometry" or "The IR absorption spectrum of the isolated product was obtained." Watch out for similar issues with gas chromatography (GC), nuclear magnetic resonance spectrometry (NMR), and mass spectrometry (MS). Ask for guidance from your instructor regarding abbreviations. It is acceptable to use some abbreviations such as GC and NMR without defining them since they are so widely recognized (see Chapter 5). Other abbreviations are context dependent: "FIA" could stand for either "flow injection analysis" or "fluorescence immunoassay."

5. *Avoid ambiguity with formulas, phases, and formulations.* If you were to write "CH_3OH (50 mmol) was added," there is no doubt that about 2 mL of methanol was added; however, if you were to write "NaOH (50 mmol) was added," it is not clear how this was done: was the additive solid sodium hydroxide or was it a solution of sodium hydroxide? To remove this ambiguity, write either "Sodium hydroxide (2.0 g) was added," or "Sodium hydroxide solution [20.0 mL, 10.0% (m/v)] was added." For reports of syntheses, you may be asked to include the number of moles in addition to the mass of the chemical added. Most instructors will discourage the use of abbreviations such as EtOH for ethanol and similar nonstandard abbreviations or shorthand.

6. *Avoid ambiguity with numbers.* The numbers of digits you include is important. If you write, "The mixture was refluxed for 22.5 min," there is no doubt, to the nearest 0.1 of a minute, about the length of time involved. However, if you write, "The mixture was refluxed for 100 min," does this mean any time between 95 and 105 minutes or any time between 99.5 and 100.5 minutes? We are talking about significant digits here (all the digits known with certainty plus the first uncertain digit), and you should not be ambiguous about how many digits are significant. To remove this kind of ambiguity, write numbers in standard format. For example, if three digits were significant, write the number as 1.00×10^2. Don't forget to include zeros at the end of the number if they are significant. A mass of 25.00 g is known with much greater certainty than one of 25 g. Remember that you a creating a document that, in principle, would allow someone else to repeat the work.

7. *Pay attention to chemist's style.* Note that the numbers are written as numerals and not as words, but it is considered unacceptably poor style to start a sentence with numerals. So you would *not* write,

 25 mL of hexane were added.

You would write,

 Hexane (25 mL) was added.

Note the change from the plural to singular form of the verb, and note that there is a space between a number and its unit (see page 89).

8. *Avoid relying heavily on the verb* to use. This construction results in dull and tedious writing, as in the following example illustrates.

 A top-loading balance **was used** to obtain approximate weights, then a four-place analytical balance **was used** to determine the precise weight of the potassium hydrogenphthalate. Bulb pipets **were used** to transfer aliquots of the sample. A hot plate **was used**

to heat all ten sample solutions simultaneously. Watch glasses **were used** to cover the beakers while heating. A 50-mL buret **was used** for the titration.

In place of the monotonous *a ____ was used to ____* formula, you might, by identifying the action and substituting more specific verbs, write instead,

 Approximate weights of potassium hydrogenphthalate were **obtained** with a top-loading balance followed by precise weighing, to four decimal places, on an analytical balance. Solutions were **transferred** with bulb pipets and titrations were **performed** with a 50- mL buret. All 10 samples, in beakers covered with watch glasses, were simultaneously **heated** on a hot plate.

The present participle, *using,* can get you into trouble. If you write, "The precipitate was clearly seen using a microscope," you would elicit a wry smile from your reader who might conjure up some image of a crystal trying to manipulate a microscope to examine something more closely. You could avoid this kind of problem by writing "The precipitate was clearly observed with the aid of a microscope."

9. *Include information about computation.* You should describe any mathematical treatment of quantitative data, and, if you performed statistical analysis with the help of a computer, you should provide information about the identity of both the software and the statistical technique(s).

10. *Remember to note the make and model of any instruments.*

RESULTS SECTION

For the purposes of a lab report, it is probably a good idea to **deal with the results and the discussion as separate sections, but be guided by the instructions for your particular course.** You should write an account of the results in a way that guides the reader and does not just present a series of tables and figures with no explanatory narrative. You will also need to establish the level of detail your instructor wants to see in your report. Does he or she wish to see the individual weighings or just the information that so many grams of disodium EDTA were weighed out? Do you need to include the initial and final buret readings or just give the average value together with some indication of the spread of the results such as the standard deviation? Remember, of course, that all these details will be in your laboratory notebook. If you obtained an IR absorption spectrum as part of the process of confirming the identity of the product, should the spectrum be included as part of the report? If it is, then you need to give it a figure number and refer to it in the text. For example, you would write, "The IR absorption spectrum of the product is shown in Figure 2" and not "See the attached IR spectrum." **Charts, graphs, diagrams, spectra, and pictures are all called "figures" in the context of a report of work in a chemical laboratory**.

The figures and tables are numbered and presented in numerical order; the first ones you present are called Figure 1 and Table 1, respectively. Figures and tables are called out, that is, **refer to them by number and not as "the table below."** Avoid trying to insert the tables or figures into the text so that you do not have to refer to them. You should draw the reader's attention directly to the figure or table and point out the feature(s) of interest. You would not write,

The fluoride concentrations were all below the detection limit of 0.1 mg L^{-1} (Table 1).

The writer of this example puts the work on the reader. An effective writer guides the reader to the table, to what is there, and to what is important. For example,

As can be seen from Table 1, the concentration of fluoride in all samples was below the detection limit of 0.1 mg L^{-1}.

Note that when you refer to a specific table or figure, the words *Table* and *Figure*, as well as the abbreviation *Fig.*, begin with a capital letter.

If the goal of the experiment was to investigate the trend in chloride concentrations in soil as a function of distance from a highway, you need to consider whether a graph of chloride concentration as a function of distance is needed. The decision about how to display results is a judgment call for you (unless the lab handout specifically tells you to plot the data). If there are only three data points—for example, 0 m 100 mg L^{-1}, 10 m 50 mg L^{-1}, and 25 m 10 mg L^{-1}—a plot is not necessary; a table will do very nicely. On the other hand, if you sampled 20 locations, it will be difficult to visualize the profile unless you create a plot. In a lab report, you will also need to show any instrumental calibration plots. In this case, assuming that ion chromatography was the technique involved, you

Table 3. Concentration of Arsenic Species (μg g^{-1} as elemental arsenic) in Soil Spiked with As(III) Sequentially Extracted with 100 mmol L^{-1} H$_3$PO$_4$ and 100 mmol L^{-1} NaOH.

Species	H$_3$PO$_4$ extract[a]	NaOH extract[a]	total[b]
As(III)	3.0 ± 0.2	2.6 ± 0.2	5.6 ± 0.3
DMA	ND[c]	ND	ND
MMA	ND	ND	ND
As(V)	12.7 ± 0.9	2 ± 2	15 ± 2
Total[b]	15.6 ± 0.9	5 ± 2	21 ± 2

[a]mean $\pm$ standard deviation (n = 3), [b]$\pm$ term is square root of sum of squares, [c]not detected

should include a plot of detector response as a function of chloride concentration. In a lab report, it is quite acceptable to include both a table and a plot of the same data, but this is something for which your instructor will provide guidance.

Tables

Pay close attention to the numbers of digits that you quote in a table, especially if you have copied the table from a spreadsheet. Present information about units the minimum number of times and use footnotes to provide additional information (such as what the $\pm$ term means and the number of replicate measurements in the calculation). An example is given in Table 3. The numbers presented in the table are given to the number of significant digits as specified by the value of the $\pm$ terms that indicate which digit is the first uncertain digit. In calculating the numbers in the "Total" column, more digits will have been carried in the calculation, and then the result would have been rounded appropriately. The format of this table is a close approximation to that which you would see in an American Chemical Society journal.

If the entries in a table do not all have the same units, label the top of the column appropriately [for example, density (g mL^{-1})]. When writing about these results, it is helpful to match up items with their values by using a convention in which the units are given only once followed by "a comma and the word *respectively*." For example,

 The concentrations of As(III) and As(V) found by extracting with phosphoric acid were 3.0 ± 0.2 and 12.7 ± 0.9 μg g^{-1}, **respectively**.

Figures

Avoid having multiple figures when several similar graphs could be included in the same plot. Be sure that you have the axes in the correct orientation. The x-axis (the horizontal axis or abscissa) is assigned to the independent variable, whereas the y-axis (the vertical axis or ordinate) is assigned to the dependent variable (the one you measure in your experiment). Usually this also means that the values on the x-axis are known with (much) greater certainty than are the y-axis values. Assigning the axes in this way is important, because to fit a mathematical function to your data you will, almost certainly, use a procedure that assumes that that the x-direction error is negligible compared to the y-direction error. Do not subtract the instrument response to the blank (the solution with no analyte) before processing the data, and even if the response is 0.00, still include this (0, 0) point in the data set to which the best line is fitted. Be sure that you can enter the appropriate number of significant digits into the cells in your spreadsheet or other program. A detailed discussion of the statistics behind fitting mathematical functions to data points is beyond the scope of our book. For further explanation, we suggest that you consult "Statistics for Analytical Chemistry" by J. C. and J. N. Miller. This text also explains why the "correlation coefficient" value (calculated by the software you used) doesn't really tell you very much about whether the underlying relationship is a straight line or not.

Dealing With Spreadsheet Software Output

When copying and pasting figures from a spreadsheet program such as Excel, you will need to edit the figure so that it conforms to the appropriate format. Look at the figures in a relevant journal article. An example of a figure that the spreadsheet software typically produces is given in Figure 9, together with commentary on how to modify this output so that the figure appears as shown in Figure 10. Bear in mind that **there are differences between the different branches of chemistry regarding the formatting of figures, and be guided by your instructor**.

You will notice that the student who produced this graph has used µ for micro (and not u) and has found a way to make the -1 a superscript. One way to fix the limitations of the formatting of text in the spreadsheet program is to create a text box in the word-processing program and overwrite the label after the plot has been copied into the word-processing document.

For the situation described in Figure 10, it is appropriate to fit a trend line because the underlying relationship between the two variables is expected to be linear, but this is not always the case. Consider the experiment mentioned earlier in which the concentration of chloride was

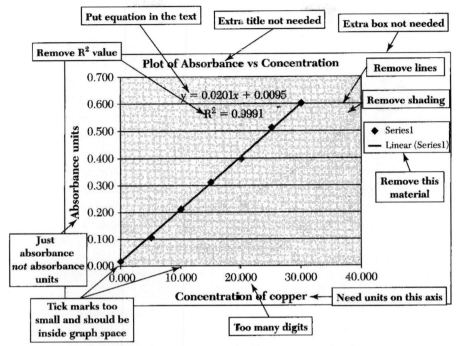

Figure 9. Typical plot from a spreadsheet program with comments about what needs fixing.

Figure 1. Flame atomic absorption calibration for copper. The line, which is the best fit by least squares regression, is $y = 0.0201x + 0.0095$, where y is absorbance and x is concentration in μg ml^{-1}, with correlation coefficient 0.9996.

Figure 10. Figure showing the result of fixing the problems shown in Figure 9.

Figure 11. Chloride concentration in soil as a function of the distance from the highway. The trend line is the best exponential fit to the data points.

Figure 12. Chloride concentration in soil as a function of the distance from the highway.

monitored as a function of the distance from the highway. The results of this experiment are shown in Figure 11.

As there is no reason to expect that the relationship between the chloride concentration and the distance from the road is exponential, some instructors will consider that it is not appropriate to give the impression that this is the case by including this trend line on the plot. In a case such as this, the graph space should simply display the points, or you should create some simple visual aid, such as joining the points by straight lines, as shown in Figure 12.

Other instructors may disagree. If you are not sure which format is acceptable, ask your instructor.

DISCUSSION AND CONCLUSIONS SECTION

Most instructors will ask that in a teaching-lab report you include your conclusions in the discussion section. In this section of the report, you must interpret your results in the context of the specific goals of the experiment and in the light of any specific questions that you were asked in the lab handout. Make sure that you know what these are; otherwise, if you do not answer all of them, you will not receive full credit for your report. In general, you should consider the following issues:

1. What did you expect to find and why?
2. How did your results compare with those expected? If you set out to test specific hypotheses, do your data support one hypothesis more than another or allow you to eliminate one or more of them? Explain your logic.
3. How might you explain any unexpected results?
4. Based on your results, what question or questions might you logically want to ask next?
5. How can your conclusions be generalized to other systems/reactions?
6. Did you answer all the questions posed by the instructor?

You should assume that the discussion is the one place in the report where you can show that

- You have understood why you did what you did (in the context of the goals of the experiment)
- You understand the reason for what you observed in terms of the behavior of the atoms and molecules of the materials involved
- You understand how your results compare with what is already known
- You have thought about and understand any discrepancies in your data (either internally or with respect to what is already known)
- You have suggestions for further interesting experiments that would resolve some of the problems you encountered
- You can make some comments about the broader implications of your results.

In other words, **you can show that you have been thinking like a chemist**.

In discussing your results, you should start from the premise that most teaching-laboratory experiments are based on reproducible phenomena that have been studied and reported previously. Therefore, there is relevant material in the literature about your topic. It may well be in the textbook for your course, or it may be in the original primary literature. You should make an effort to find some further information to include in your report. As we have said elsewhere (see page 35), Internet sources are acceptable places to start your search, but any citations you include in your report should be to validated sources, such as articles in research journals.

Errors in Chemistry Experiments

There are three sorts of error: **random errors, systematic errors**, and **blunders**. **Random errors** are unavoidable; they are consequences of the natural uncertainties of operations, and they are just as likely to be positive as negative. A **systematic error**, on the other hand, causes a unidirectional bias in your experiment, and, if it can be identified, it can be compensated for or corrected. Systematic error is always present, but it may be insignificant. For example, the purity of any chemicals used to make standards will be less than 100%. On the other hand, a systematic error may be significant: for example, the additional amount of titrant needed to cause a detectable change in color of the indicator. In this case, you can determine this volume experimentally by titrating a solution containing no analyte and correct all of your values by this amount. A **blunder** is a mistake (such as spilling some of the chemical you have just weighed out while transferring it to a beaker for dissolution) that causes your results to be inaccurate. For experiments that result in the calculation of a numerical value, you should estimate the overall ± term based on the propagation of errors throughout the procedure. If you know the true value, you can comment on the accuracy of your result. If your value is significantly different from the true value, based on some appropriate statistical test, then you should discuss possible reasons for this. Go easy on the blunder-type explanation as this does not gain you many points with whoever is grading your work. Everybody makes mistakes, but you should not be offering this type of error as the explanation for every result that is not in agreement with what you expect.

Now for some comments about chemical reactions: although reactions used in teaching experiments may be **reproducible**, they may not be **robust**, meaning that the course of the reaction is sensitive to small changes in the conditions. You should recognize that many reactions do not go to 100% completion with the formation of just one product, and therefore yields may well be less than the theoretical value and that your target compound may be contaminated with the products of side reactions and unreacted starting materials. Not all reactions are instantaneous and are therefore subject to a variety of kinetic effects. Small concentrations of catalysts (or inhibitors) can have quite dramatic effects on reaction rates, as can changes in temperature. Also small variations in starting conditions can lead to variations in the relative amounts of products of the primary reaction and the side reactions.

You should also recognize that when instruments are being used near the limit of their performance, the ± terms will be quite large. This does not necessarily mean that you are dealing with very low concentrations. It may be, for example, that for the wavelength at which you are measuring, very little light intensity is reaching the detector.

Here are some extracts from the discussion and conclusions sections of a report of an experiment involving the measurement of chloride as a function of the distance from the highway. Note that the writers have used *we*, as this was a joint report on behalf of all of the group members. If you are solely responsible for the report, it is quite permissible (we think) to write in the first person singular (*I*) in this section; however, not all instructors agree with us and you should ask for clarification from yours. These extracts do not make a complete discussion section, but they are meant to illustrate the kind of material you should include, as we described on page 123.

1. The writers show that they understand why they did what they did.

1.1 The writers show that they understand how quantitative information is obtained from a calibration curve.

As can be seen from Fig. 4, the peak-area calibration for chloride was linear over the range 0.1 to 80 ppm, but the response to the 100 ppm standard was 8% lower than would be expected on the basis of the sensitivity established by the lower concentration standards. This part of the calibration is still useful, but would require additional standards to establish the curvature beyond 80 ppm.

1.2. The writers show that they understand the concept of detection limit, and they show that they know that a further experiment could be performed.

The detection limit, that is the concentration that would give a signal-to-noise ratio of 3, is estimated based on the expanded scale trace shown in Figure 5, to be 0.06 ppm. Not enough replicate measurements were made to estimate the detection limit based on the IUPAC definition (the concentration giving a signal equal to three times the standard deviation of the responses to a blank), as sufficient time was not available. We conclude that ion chromatography is a suitable technique for incorporation in an instrumental method for the determination of chloride in soil extracts, as the instrumental detection limit is considerably lower than values typically encountered in real samples.

1.3. The writers show that they understand the idea of method validation by spike recovery measurements, and that they are aware of what is already known about this aspect of the experiment.

 The results of our attempts to validate the procedure by adding a known amount of chloride to a soil sample prior to analysis (a spike and recovery study) showed that we may not be extracting all the chloride, as the recovery values varied from 85 to 105% with an average of 92%. This is within the acceptable range of 80–110% specified by the International Soil Contamination Society [4].

2. The writers show that they have looked for the results of other similar experiments with which to compare their results. They discuss the differences.

 If road salt were the source of the chloride contamination, then it might be expected that the concentration would decrease with distance from the roadway. We did observe this general trend, though the roughly linear decrease is not in agreement with the findings of Sparrow and Thrush [7], who found that the chloride concentration first increased with distance and then decreased. They explained their results as due to the ejection of liquid and solid particles by vehicle tires and snowplow activity. The profile at our site is probably influenced by the drainage ditch, which is approximately 15 m from the road.

3. The writers make some critical evaluative comments about the technique they used, showing that they are aware of some limitations, such as interference effects and time needed.

3.1. The writers show that they understand a possible interference effect (that is, a source of systematic error).

 Of the common inorganic anions that might also occur in soil samples, only sulfate is a possible interference as the peak is not fully resolved from that of chloride in the chromatogram. This partial overlap was not a problem in the analyses reported here, but for samples with a high sulfate concentration, some further chromatographic method development would be needed. A good starting point for such experiments would be the conditions reported by Hawk et al. [6] who showed that with an IONSEP column, good resolution between sulfate and chloride could be obtained.

3.2 The writers show that they have made an effort to discover if anything can be done to overcome another limitation, and that they understand the implications of switching to another measurement technique.

 Another limitation of the overall procedure is the time taken for each analysis. One chromatographic run takes 20 min and thus, even if the instrument could be run 24 h per day, the throughput would only be 72 analyses per day. If chloride were the only analyte of interest, for large numbers of samples an alternate procedure such as flow-injection spectrophotometry would be preferable. Ruzicka and Hansen showed [8] that such a system could process up to 30 samples per hour. Under these circumstances, the extraction of the analyte from the sample would be the rate-limiting step and investigations of the possibilities of accelerated extraction procedures would be warranted.

INTRODUCTION

The introduction should follow this structure: first "big picture," then "small picture," then "reason for doing the work" (i.e., the goal of the experiment). Writing the introduction is an opportunity for you to learn about the subject of the experiment. You may be able to base your introduction entirely on your own lecture notes, but more likely you will want to use both the course textbook and other sources. You may be directed to some literature sources by your instructor. The material you find will also be useful for your discussion. Make sure that any citations conform to the conventions for chemistry (numbers, not names and dates). The first citation should be number 1, the next number 2 and so on. **You should use the present tense for writing about the reasons for doing the work** (for example, "the goal of this experiment is to synthesize bromobutane"). **This section is best written after the results and discussion sections have been written**.

You should define specialized terminology. Your instructor probably knows the meaning of the terms you will use, but by defining them in your own words in your report, you can convince the instructor that you also know what these words mean. **Write to illuminate, not to impress**. Even though your instructor is grading the report, write for an audience of your peers. Here are two examples of extracts from introductions that illustrate this rule.

Alkyl halides may be prepared from the corresponding primary alcohol by reaction with a hydrogen halide HX, where X is Cl, Br, or I. The reaction, which is reversible, is an example of an SN_2, i.e., a bimolecular nucleophilic substitution, reaction. In this case, the nucleophile is the bromide ion, Br^-, and the leaving group is water, the first step in the reaction being the protonation of the hydroxyl group of the alcohol.

 Metals in aqueous solution may be determined at concentrations of a few tens of mg L^{-1} by flame atomic absorption spectrometry (FAAS). Atoms are formed in an air-acetylene flame when the aerosol, produced by a nebulizer and spray chamber, is introduced in the premixed gases. The radiation from a special light source, the hollow-cathode lamp, characteristic of the element to be determined passes through the cloud of atoms in the flame. The decrease in intensity is converted to absorbance by the instrument signal-processing electronics.

Never set out to prove, verify, or demonstrate the truth of something. Rather, set out to **synthesize, analyze, determine, measure, test**, or **describe**. In chemistry and other sciences, truth is elusive, and one experiment will never prove anything conclusively; it will add further evidence that the phenomena you are observing are well understood. It is not uncommon to repeat someone else's experiment and obtain a different result. But one such experiment does not necessarily overturn current thinking. There are many uncontrolled factors that may be capable of changing the outcome of an experiment. You want to show that you understood this when you did your experiment, so you would *not* write,

 The goal of our experiment was to prove that hydrogen halides react with alcohols to form alkyl halides.

or

 For this experiment, our aim was to verify that calcium can be measured in orange juice by flame atomic absorption spectrometry.

or

 This experiment was designed to show that the ionization constant of a weak acid can be obtained from conductivity measurements.

The first example, which contains a grandiose and unwarranted generalization, might be modified to read,

The goal of our experiment is to synthesize bromobutane from the reaction between 1-butanol and bromide ion in concentrated sulfuric acid solution.

Note that the writer uses the present tense.

Be brief. Although every sentence should be designed to prepare the reader for the statement about the goal of the experiment that will appear at the end of the introduction, you should explain the wider context of the chemistry that you are studying. If, for example, your study was undertaken to determine the calcium content of tap water by titration with EDTA, you should explain why the "hardness" of water is an issue. Or, if you set out to measure the rate constant for the basic hydrolysis (saponification) of ethyl acetate, you might mention the use of saponification in the manufacturing of soap or the use of ethyl acetate for flavoring.

A Sample Introduction

 When coal is burned, any sulfur it contains is converted to sulfur dioxide. If this is released into the atmosphere, it can be further oxidized to sulfuric acid [1]. Rain containing sulfuric acid is harmful to plants and can leach toxic elements, such as aluminum, from soil into surface waters endangering aquatic life [2]. It is important, therefore, to know the sulfur content of the coal used for the generation of electricity. The goal of this experiment is to determine the sulfur content of coal. The procedure involved the conversion of sulfur to sulfate by heating the powdered coal with sodium carbonate and magnesium nitrate. After dissolution in water, the sulfate was determined by high-performance ion-exchange chromatography.

Note that in this introduction, the material progressed from a rather general statement, "burning coal releases sulfur dioxide," to more specific statements, "acid rain can mobilize aluminum from soils," and finally to the specific objectives of the experiment, "to measure the sulfur content of coal." You will see the same progression in the Introduction sections of most published reports. Your instructor should also see it in yours.

ABSTRACT

An abstract is a summary of the report that includes the quantitative results. Leave writing the abstract until last. Include your quantitative results together with a statement about errors and whether the results are in agreement with what you expected. If they are not, then you need to include a statement as to why this might be the case. Here is an example from a report of an experiment in which students investigated the determination of copper in tap water by the technique of flame atomic absorption spectrometry.

 Copper was determined in aqueous solutions by atomic absorption spectrometry with an air-acetylene flame atomizer, following optimization of the instrument parameters (fuel oxidant ratio and burner position) for the highest absorbance for a 10 mg L^{-1} solution. Data for calibration of the instrument over the range 0 to 20 mg L^{-1} were obtained. Unknown solution number 5 was analyzed, after a 10-fold dilution, against this calibration and found to contain 1.4×10^2 mg L^{-1} copper, but when analyzed by the method of standard additions, the concentration found was 1.0×10^2 mg L^{-1}. In a separate experiment, it was found that the presence of ethanol (50% v/v) caused the absorbance value to increase by about 40% compared with that for a pure aqueous solution. This enhancement is attributed to the greater number density of ground state atoms formed when ethanol is sprayed into the flame due to the increase in flame temperature and more favorable aerosol formation and transport. It is concluded that unknown 5 contains a matrix component that increases the atom number density. The instrumental detection limit, determined on the basis of spraying solutions containing 1.0, 0.1, and 0.01 mg L^{-1} of copper, was estimated to be 0.1 mg L^{-1}. As was expected, all of the samples of Gordon Bennett residence tap water examined contained less than 0.1 mg L^{-1} copper. To determine copper at this concentration by flame atomic absorption spectrometry, sample solutions would need to be preconcentrated.

Note also that **the sample abstract is informative**. The writer does not simply say that "copper was measured by atomic absorption spectrometry." Rather the writer provides a specific summary of the results and what they mean. Be sure that your abstract is equally informative. Clearly, this section of your report will be easier to write if you save it for last.

ACKNOWLEDGMENTS AND REFERENCES

For a teaching-lab report there will, most likely, be no need for any acknowledgements, and your references should be collected in numerical order in the appropriate style. For a discussion of the formatting of references see Chapter 3.

CHECKLIST FOR A LABORATORY REPORT

❏ Conforms to the general guidelines provided by the instructor.

❏ Conforms to the specific instructions for this experiment.

❏ Anticipates the needs of an audience of peers.

Title

❏ Gives specific indication of what the experiment was about.

❏ Consists of no more than 20 words, ideally fewer.

Abstract

❏ Briefly (in one or two sentences) summarizes background.

❏ Clearly, succinctly states the question addressed and the hypothesis tested.

❏ Concisely reports major finding.

❏ Includes quantitative results (numerical values).

❏ Consists of a single paragraph of 200–500 words.

Introduction

❏ Offers a clear statement of the specific issue or question addressed in the present tense.

❏ Clearly describes the big picture, then the small picture, then aim of experiment.

❏ Articulates clearly why the question is being addressed or the purpose of the experiment.

Experimental Section

❏ Is divided into subsections relevant to the particular experiment.

❏ Provides a continuous narrative in the passive voice, in the past tense (*the beaker was swirled*).

❏ Includes details of chemicals, instrument(s), and software.

❏ Mentions all factors likely to have influenced the outcome.

❏ Provides sufficient detail to enable someone else to repeat the work.

❏ Does not contain any results or discussion.

Results Section

❑ Provides a continuous narrative.

❑ Summarizes important findings in the data; does not simply repeat raw data.

❑ Presents results in the past tense and in active voice whenever possible.

❑ Includes tables and figures that are properly formatted, numbered, and called out (referred to by number in the text).

❑ Includes data that have been subjected to statistical analyses and ± terms calculated.

Discussion and Conclusion Section

❑ Contains answers to all the questions posed by the instructor.

❑ Shows understanding of molecular-level behavior.

❑ Offers interpretation of statistical analysis.

❑ Compares results obtained with expected results and discusses differences.

❑ Offers evaluative comments and addresses broader implications.

❑ Cites and discusses other relevant work in the literature.

References Section

❑ Cites references in ACS (or other appropriate) format.

Useful Conversion Factors and Relationships

Length

SI unit: meter (m)

$$1 \text{ km} = 0.62137 \text{ mi}$$
$$1 \text{ mi} = 5280 \text{ ft}$$
$$= 1.6093 \text{ km}$$
$$1 \text{ m} = 1.0936 \text{ yd}$$
$$1 \text{ in.} = 2.54 \text{ cm (exactly)}$$
$$1 \text{ cm} = 0.39370 \text{ in.}$$
$$1 \text{ Å} = 10^{-10} \text{ m}$$

Mass

SI unit: kilogram (kg)

$$1 \text{ kg} = 2.2046 \text{ lb}$$
$$1 \text{ lb} = 453.59 \text{ g}$$
$$= 16 \text{ oz}$$
$$1 \text{ amu} = 1.660538782 \times 10^{-24} \text{ g}$$

Temperature

SI unit: Kelvin (K)

$$0 \text{ K} = -273.15 \text{ °C}$$
$$= -459.67 \text{ °F}$$
$$\text{K} = \text{°C} + 273.15$$
$$\text{°C} = \tfrac{5}{9}(\text{°F} - 32°)$$
$$\text{°F} = \tfrac{9}{5}\text{°C} + 32°$$

Energy (derived)

SI unit: Joule (J)

$$1 \text{ J} = 1 \text{ kg-m}^2/\text{s}^2$$
$$= 0.2390 \text{ cal}$$
$$= 1 \text{ C-V}$$
$$1 \text{ cal} = 4.184 \text{ J}$$
$$1 \text{ eV} = 1.602 \times 10^{-19} \text{ J}$$

Pressure (derived)

SI unit: Pascal (Pa)

$$1 \text{ Pa} = 1 \text{ N/m}^2$$
$$= 1 \text{ kg/m-s}^2$$
$$1 \text{ atm} = 1.01325 \times 10^5 \text{ Pa}$$
$$= 760 \text{ torr}$$
$$= 14.70 \text{ lb/in}^2$$
$$1 \text{ bar} = 10^5 \text{ Pa}$$
$$1 \text{ torr} = 1 \text{ mm Hg}$$

Volume (derived)

SI unit: cubic meter (m³)

$$1 \text{ L} = 10^{-3} \text{ m}^3$$
$$= 1 \text{ dm}^3$$
$$= 10^3 \text{ cm}^3$$
$$= 1.0567 \text{ qt}$$
$$1 \text{ gal} = 4 \text{ qt}$$
$$= 3.7854 \text{ L}$$
$$1 \text{ cm}^3 = 1 \text{ mL}$$
$$1 \text{ in}^3 = 16.4 \text{ cm}^3$$

Color Chart for Common Elements

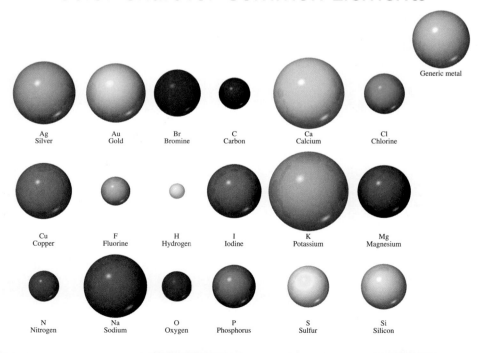